MY MOTHER / MY SELF
The Daughter's Search for Identity

By Nancy Friday

MY SECRET GARDEN
FORBIDDEN FLOWERS
MY MOTHER / MY SELF

MY MOTHER/ MY SELF

Nancy Friday

DELACORTE PRESS/NEW YORK

Published by
Delacorte Press
1 Dag Hammarskjold Plaza
New York, New York 10017

Grateful acknowledgment is made for permission to reprint the following material:

Excerpt from PENTIMENTO: *A Book of Portraits* by Lillian Hellman: used by permission of Little, Brown and Company.

Excerpt from LETTERS HOME BY SYLVIA PLATH: used by permission of Harper & Row, Publishers, Inc.

Lines from "Effort at Speech Between Two People" by Muriel Rukeyser: reprinted from WATERLILY FIRE by Muriel Rukeyser by permission of Monica McCall, ICM. Copyright © 1962 by Muriel Rukeyser.

Lines from "The Double Image" by Anne Sexton: reprinted from TO BEDLAM AND PART WAY BACK by Anne Sexton by permission of Houghton Mifflin Company.

An excerpt from this work first appeared in *Good Housekeeping* magazine.

When I stopped seeing my mother with the eyes of a child, I saw the woman who helped me give birth to myself. This book is for Jane Colbert Friday Scott.

CONTENTS

AUTHOR'S
ACKNOWLEDGMENTS

In 1973, I picked up a book which correlated women's orgasmic potential with the degree of security they once had with their fathers. I can remember the day, where I was sitting, the weight of the volume in my hands, and my instantaneous reaction: *what about mother?*

I had just written a book on women's sexual fantasies. It left no doubt in my mind where repression or sexual acceptance begins. Who first takes our hand away from our genitals, who implants pleasure or inhibition about our bodies, who lays down The Rules and with her own life, gives us an indelible model? That week I wrote an outline for a book entitled, "Mothers and Daughters: The First Lie."

I thought myself a good candidate for this subject because although I would have told you I loved my mother, I also felt sufficient psychological space between us, a separation that would allow me to be fair and objective. As if any woman could. It took two years of research to get beyond the anger in that first title. Even to recognize how angry I was.

My intention was to do a series of interviews with mothers and daughters within a family, and where possible, with grandmothers too. In these last four years, I interviewed more than two hundred women across the United States. Most were mothers. All were daughters. On the most meaningful level, they were experts. But I quickly learned that a book of interviews would not be enough.

I had hoped to avoid the subjective through finding patterns that would hold for most women. By tracing these patterns through the generations, we could see the conscious and unconscious repetitions, correct for the best in our maternal inheritance, and get rid of the rest. If women's lives are going to change, we must have access to the formative strength of that relationship. We must get past the anger at lies told us "for our own good," find what real love exists between mother and daughter—or be freed from the illusion of a love that never existed at all. I was looking for clarification. I discovered Rashomon. Mother: "I very carefully prepared my daughter for menstruation." Daughter: "My mother told me nothing." Two versions of the same story, different and yet the same. Neither woman thinks she is lying.

To understand contradictions like these I talked to psychiatrists, educators, doctors, lawyers, sociologists. I did not want textbook answers alone: of the twenty-one professional women quoted in this book, sixteen are mothers of daughters themselves. No woman gave more generously of her wit, wisdom, professional knowledge and personal life than Dr. Leah Schaefer; I will always be in her debt. What is most poignant to me is how often these highly trained people confess difficulties in applying what they intellectually knew to their own lives.

One of my earliest discards was the notion that I could learn all I needed from women. We can hop instead of walk, but why not use two legs? When Dr. Sirgay Sanger telephoned in answer to my request to interview a certain eminent child psychiatrist—a woman— he informed me she was out of town. She had asked him to take my call. Rather impolitely, I said that since I believed women understood women best, I would wait for his female colleague to return. I am grateful to this day he did not hang up on me. Some of the possibilities of conduct and insights into behavior which I feel most rare and exhilarating in these pages, come from him and other men. They have daughters too.

I first talked to Dr. Richard Robertiello on an afternoon like any other. It was one of the shaping events of my career, and began a series of conversations over the years without which this book would have been immeasurably poorer. As the reader follows the development of the argument, I hope it becomes clear that before I could explain the mother-daughter relationship to anyone else, I had to understand my own. Without Dr. Robertiello's awesome knowledge, powers of analysis, original mind, and personal involvement (he is the father of three daughters), I would have given up long ago.

The authorities whose names appear below shared not just their learning but time and concern too. As I could not list their credentials within the text, I do so here with all my thanks:

Pauline B. Bart: associate professor of sociology in psychiatry, College of Medicine, University of Illinois; author of *The Student Sociologist's Handbook.*

Jessie Bernard: sociologist/scholar-in-residence at the U.S. Commission on Civil Rights; author of *Women, Wives, Mothers: Values and Options, The Future of Motherhood,* and *The Future of Marriage.*

Mary S. Calderone, M.D.: director of Sex Information and Education Council of the United States; author of *Release from Sexual Tensions.*

Sidney Q. Cohlan, M.D.: professor of pediatrics; associate director of pediatrics, University Hospital New York University Medical Center.

Helene Deutsch, M.D.: psychoanalyst; author of *The Psychology of Women.*

Lilly Engler, M.D.: psychiatrist in private practice in New York City, consultant to various institutions here and abroad.

Cynthia Fuchs Epstein: professor of sociology, Queens College, City University of New York; project director, Bureau of Applied Research, Columbia University; author of *Woman's Place: Options and Limits in Professional Careers* and co-author, *The Other Half: Roads to Women's Equality.*

Aaron H. Esman, M.D.: chief psychiatrist of the Jewish Board of Guardians; member of the faculty of the New York Psychoanalytic Institute; author of *New Frontiers in Child Guidance* and *The Psychology of Adolescence: Essential Readings.*

Mio Fredland, M.D.: assistant clinical professor of psychiatry, Cornell University Medical School.

Sonya Friedman: psychologist; marriage and divorce counselor; co-author of *I've Had It, You've Had It!* Advice on divorce from a lawyer and a psychologist.

Emily Jane Goodman: attorney; co-author of *Women, Money and Power.*

Amy R. Hanan: personnel director, AT&T General Departments.

Elizabeth Hoppin Hauser: psychotherapist on the staff of the Long Island Consultation Center in Forest Hills.

Helen Kaplan, M.D.: psychoanalyst and sex therapist; associate clinical professor of psychiatry, Cornell University Medical College; associate attending psychiatrist of the Payne Whitney Clinic of New York Hospital; author of *The New Sex Therapy*.

Sherwin A. Kaufman, M.D.: associate attending gynecologist and obstetrician, Lenox Hill Hospital, New York City; author of *Intimate Questions Women Ask, New Hope for the Childless Couple,* and *The Ageless Woman*.

Jeanne McFarland: professor, Economics Department, Smith College.

Gladys McKenney: teacher of marriage and family classes in a suburban high school in Michigan.

George L. Peabody, Ph.D.: applied behavioral science.

Vera Plaskon: family planning coordinator, Roosevelt Hospital, New York; clinical specialist in parent/child nursing.

Virginia E. Pomeranz, M.D.: associate clinical professor of pediatrics at Cornell University Medical College and associate attending pediatrician at The New York Hospital; author of *The First Five Years: A Relaxed Approach to Child Care* and co-author of *The Mothers' and Fathers' Medical Encyclopedia*.

Wardell B. Pomeroy, Ph.D.: sex researcher, Kinsey reports, *Sexual Behavior in the Human Male* and *Sexual Behavior in the Human Female;* author of *Boys and Sex* and *Girls and Sex*.

Jessie Potter: faculty member of human sexuality program, Northwestern University, School of Medicine; director of the National Institute for Human Relationships.

Helen Prentiss: professor of child psychology at a midwestern university. Her name is a pseudonym since she asks to remain anonymous.

Ira L. Reiss: professor of sociology, University of Minnesota.

Richard C. Robertiello, M.D.: senior training consultant at the Long Island Institute for Mental Health; member of the executive board of the Society for the Scientific Study of Sex; supervising psychiatrist for the Community Guidance Service; author of *Hold Them Very Close, Then Let Them Go* and co-author of *Big You, Little You*.

Sirgay Sanger, M.D.: director, parent-child program, St. Luke's Hospital; instructor, Columbia College of Physicians and Surgeons; author, *Emotional Care, Hospitalized Children*.

Leah Cahan Schaefer: psychotherapist; staff member of Community

Guidance Service, New York City; executive board, Society for the Scientific Study of Sex; author of *Women and Sex*.

Joan Shapiro; professor of social work, Smith College.

Marcia Storch, M.D.: head of adolescent gynecology and family planning clinic, child and youth division, Roosevelt Hospital; assistant clinical professor of obstetrics and gynecology, Columbia University College of Physicians and Surgeons, Roosevelt Hospital, New York City.

Betty L. Thompson: psychoanalyst in private practice.

Lionel Tiger: professor of anthropology at Rutgers University; author of *Men in Groups, The Imperial Animal,* and *Women in the Kibbutz.*

To those women whose names do not appear—both mothers and daughters who gave me all they could, even if anonymously—my special thanks. They will recognize their words. I hope they will feel some of the added life I now have, knowing what this book, their lives and my own have taught me.

Ideas on women's identity had been roiling in my mind for years. But I was a travel writer until I married. There are certain questions we do not dare to ask without the support of another person. In this book, as in my life, that person has been Bill Manville.

—N.F.
New York City
April 1977

MY MOTHER / MY SELF
The Daughter's Search for Identity

Chapter 1

MOTHER LOVE

I have always lied to my mother. And she to me. How young was I when I learned her language, to call things by other names? Five, four—younger? Her denial of whatever she could not tell me, that her mother could not tell her, and about which society enjoined us both to keep silent, distorts our relationship still.

Sometimes I try to imagine a little scene that could have helped us both. In her kind, warm, shy, and self-deprecating way, mother calls me into the bedroom where she sleeps alone. She is no more than twenty-five. I am perhaps six. Putting her hands (which her father told her always to keep hidden because they were "large and unattractive") on my shoulders, she looks me right through my steel-rimmed spectacles: "Nancy, you know I'm not really good at this mothering business," she says. "You're a lovely child, the fault is not with you. But motherhood doesn't come easily to me. So when I don't seem like other people's mothers, try to understand that it isn't because I don't love you. I do. But I'm confused myself. There are some things I know about. I'll teach them to you. The other stuff—sex and all that—well, I just can't discuss them with you because I'm not sure where they fit into my own life. We'll try to find other people, other women who can talk to you and fill the gaps. You can't expect me to be all the mother you need. I feel closer to your age in some ways than I do my mother's. I don't feel that serene, divine, earth-mother certainty you're supposed to that she felt. I am unsure how to raise you. But you are intelligent and so am I. Your aunt loves you, your teachers already feel the need in you. With their help, with what I can give, we'll see that you get the whole mother package—all the love in the world. It's just that you can't expect to get it all from me."

A scene that could never have taken place.

For as long as I can remember, I did not want the kind of life my mother felt she could show me. Sometimes I think she did not want it either. The older I get, the further away she gets from my childhood, from her ironclad role as my mother—the more interesting woman she becomes. Perhaps she should never have been a mother; certainly she was one too soon. I look at her today, and with all the love and anger in the world, I wish she had had a chance to live another life, mine perhaps. But hers was not an age in which women felt they had a choice.

I have no idea when I began to perceive with the monstrous selfishness that dependency lends to a child's eyes that my mother was not perfect: I was not her whole life. Was it at the same age that I began to make the terrible judgment that she was not the woman I wanted to be? It seems I have always known both. It accounts for my guilt at leaving her, and my anger that she let me go. But I am sure that she has always known, on a level her indoctrinated attitudes toward motherhood would never let her admit, that my sister and I were not enough. We had not brought the certification of womanhood that *her* mother had promised. That, once in her life, sex and a man had been more important than motherhood.

A more dutiful daughter than I, my mother wanted to accept the view of reality my grandmother taught her. She lied with the rest. She subverted herself, her genuine feelings, those burgeoning intimations of life's hope and adventure which she found in my father, and which induced her to elope with him against her family's wishes—all lost, in the name of being a good mother. Her mother's rules had the authority of the entire culture behind them. There was no such thing as a "bad mother"; there were only bad women: they were the explicitly sexual ones, who lived out the notion that what went on between themselves and their husbands had at least as much right to life as their children. They had little "maternal instinct."

We are raised to believe that mother love is different from other kinds of love. It is not open to error, doubt, or to the ambivalence of ordinary affections. This is an illusion.

Mothers may love their children, but they sometimes do not like them. The same woman who may be willing to put her body between her child and a runaway truck will often resent the day-by-day sacrifice the child unknowingly demands of her time, sexuality and self-development.

In our perception of our mother's inauthenticity—her own anxiety and lack of belief in over-idealized notions of womanhood/mother-hood she is trying to teach us—anxieties about our own sexuality are born. There is the beginning of doubt that we will succeed as people with identities of our own, separate from her, established in ourselves as women before we are mothers. We try for autonomy, try for sexuality, but the unconscious, deepest feelings we have picked up from her will not rest: we will only feel at peace, sure of ourselves, when we have fulfilled the glorified "instinct" we have been trained, through the image of her life, to repeat: you are not a full woman until you are a mother.

It is too late to ask my mother to go back and examine evasions she made as silently as any mother and to which I agreed for so long —if only because she doesn't want to. I am the one who wants to change certain dead-end patterns in my life. Patterns which, the older I get, seem all the more familiar: I've been here before.

The love between my mother and me is not so sacrosanct it cannot be questioned: if I live with an illusion as to what is between us, I will have no firm resting place on which to build myself.

In my years of interviewing, how many women have repeatedly said to me, "No, I can't think of anything significant I've inherited from my mother. We're completely different women . . ." This is usually said with an air of triumph—as if the speaker is acknowl-edging the enormous pull to model herself on her mother, but believes she has resisted. But in my interview with her daughter, she smiles ruefully. "I'm always telling mom she treats me just the way she said grandma treated her . . . ways she didn't like!" In yet another inter-view, her husband says, "The longer we're married, the more like her mother she becomes."

To be fair, if my interviewees and I talked long enough, they them-selves began to see the similarities with their mothers' lives. First the superficial, outward differences had to be worked through. Mother lived in a house, the woman I was talking to lived in an apartment.

Mother never worked a day in her life, the daughter held down a job. We cling to these "facts" as proof that we have created our own lives, different from hers. We overlook the more basic truth that we have taken on her anxieties, fears, angers; the way we weave the web of emotion between ourselves and others is patterned on what we had with her.

Whether we want our mother's life or not, we never escape the image of how she was. Nowhere is this more true than in our sexual lives. Without our own sexual identity, one we can put our full weight upon with as much certainty as once we enjoyed being "mother's girl," we are unsure. We have spurts of sexual confidence, activity, exploration, but at the first rejection, hint of loss, of sexual censure or humiliation, we fall back on the safe and familiar: sex is bad. It was always a problem between mother and ourselves. When men seem bright and alluring, we momentarily ally with them against mother's antisexual rules. But men cannot be trusted. We say the fault is our own: we go from mother to men, with no self in between. Marriage, instead of ending our childish alliance with her, ironically becomes the biggest reunion of our lives. Once we wanted to be "nice girls." Now we are "nice married ladies"—just like mother. Those quarrels with her over men are ended at last. The hardest thing to face in mother is her sexuality. She found it hardest to face in us.

Two women, each hiding from the other exactly that which defines her as a woman.

Unless we separate mother's love from her fear of sex, we will always see love and sex as opposites. The dichotomy will be passed on to our daughters. "Mother *was* right," we say, and the fervor with which we deny our daughter access to her own body is fired with all the anger, confusion, and self-abnegation we have experienced in giving up on our own sexuality.

"Believe that I love you, no matter what I say or do to you," is the message behind the madonna. "No one will ever love you as I do. Mother loves you best in all the world and I will always be there for you." Many mothers offer this kind of impossible love because they are lonely and want to bind their daughters to them forever. All mothers imply it because they are in a trap too: to suggest less is to be "a bad mother." The real love she may have for us does not have the binding power of the idealized and perfect love we both need to believe in. It is a bargain none of us can refuse.

"If the mother has a genuine sexual relationship with her hus-

✱ band," says psychotherapist Leah Schaefer, "but pretends to her daughter that in some way all erotic life must be tied up with motherhood, the girl senses this. She gets the feeling she cannot trust her mother. In my psychoanalytic practice, *I have found again and again this is the basic lie.* Parents tell their kids, 'No, no, you mustn't'—but the little girl senses that the mother herself is doing the forbidden. It makes a certain aspect of the mother's life and personality a big secret to the girl—and yet the mother always wants to know everything about the daughter. She pries into the girl's psyche, she's always telling her daughter they are friends, they must tell each other everything —but once more the girl knows mother is keeping one big secret from her, one part of herself is out of bounds. It is a one-way relationship, supposedly based on trust, but which the girl experiences as manipulative. She resents it.

"What makes the situation more difficult for the girl is when the mother is not conscious of telling this lie. She rationalizes: 'How can you tell a child *that?*' You may choose to withhold certain information, but this is not the right to tell your daughter a lie. Some women work their own minds around to where they themselves believe the only purpose of sex is motherhood. So they don't think they're lying at all. They think they are safeguarding the girl's 'morals.' What they're doing is setting up a lifelong distrust on the girl's part, and also a feeling of isolation, of helplessness. Sex is very confusing to the daughter, but if she gets the feeling that her mother is lying about it— whom can the girl ever trust? And trust of yourself and the other person is the basis of life, marriage, and of sexual orgasm."

Mother's difficulty is not necessarily that she is a liar or hypocrite. She says one thing, does another, and yet communicates on a profound level that she really feels something totally different. Most of us have learned to live with this tripartite split in the people we know and take each other as a whole. As daughters, however, we are so focused on our mothers, that we take them literally and try to integrate all three warring aspects they present to us. Since this confusion permeates the mother-daughter relationship and will be seen again and again throughout this book, let me clearly separate the three ideas here:

1. *Attitude.* This is what we say, the outward impression we give people, and is the quickest aspect of ourselves to change. It is often a reflection of public opinion, books we've read, what our peers believe, etc. An example is the mother who decides that her daughter

will not grow up in sexual ignorance, as she did; she buys the girl a copy of the latest book on sex education—like *Show Me.*[1]

How she acts when the girl puts the book's precepts into use is the difference between attitude and:

2. *Behavior.* Mother finds her daughter touching and exploring her vagina, just like the photographs in the book. She grimaces and pushes the girl's hand away.

Behavior has changed greatly in recent years, but it is a mistake to believe how we act always correlates with our up-to-the-minute attitudes. Dr. Wardell Pomeroy, Kinsey's foremost researcher, tells me that changes in behavior usually lag at least a generation behind changes in attitude. This conservatism is strongly influenced, if not determined, by our:

3. *Deepest (often unconscious) feelings.* These buried, basic forces or motivations are usually learned from our parents. They are the most rigid aspects of ourselves, carry-overs from the past which often nullify the other two. They may be denied or "forgotten" but will nevertheless often express themselves in irrational or distorted behavior. A mother tells (attitude) her daughter that sex is beautiful. In her behavior, she carefully does not "know" that the girl has gone off for the weekend with a man. But her deepest feelings are betrayed when the daughter comes home on Monday to find mother resentful, worried, and angry for no reason she can name out loud.

Saying one thing about sex and motherhood, feeling contrary emotions about both at the same time, mother presents an enigmatic picture to her daughter. The first lie—the denial that a woman's sexuality may be in conflict with her role as a mother—is so upsetting to traditional ideas of femininity that it cannot be talked about. The girl is left with perception of a gap between what mother says, what mother does . . . and what the girl detects mother feels beneath it all. Nothing mother really feels ever escapes us. Our problem is that because we try to live out all parts of the split message she sent us, our behavior and lives all too often represent a jangled compromise. We don't know what to do. We unbutton the top button on our dress and then button it back up again. That is a joke. But when we are in bed and feel the promise of orgasm, our unconscious and divided feelings assert their primacy, depriving us of satisfaction. That is no joke.

Our efforts to see mother clearly are frustrated by a kind of denial. It is one of our most primitive mechanisms of defense. Early on, children begin to avoid knowledge that mother is anything less than the "good mother" she pretends to be. Very often this is done by splitting the idea of mother into *good* and *bad*. The bad mother is the other one, not the real one. She is the one who is cruel, has headaches, does not like us. She is temporary. Only the good one is real. We will wait for her return for years, always convinced that the woman before us, who makes us feel guilty, inadequate, and angry, is *not* mother. How many of us who live away from home, periodically go back to mother, perhaps at Christmas or on a birthday, hoping that this time "Everything will be different"? Grown women ourselves, we are still looking for, still tied to the illusion of the all-loving, good mother.

Children think their parents are perfect, and if anything is wrong it's their fault. We have to think our parents are perfect because as children we are so totally dependent. We can't afford to hate mother, so what we do is turn our anger against ourselves. Instead of saying she is hateful, we say, "I am hateful." Mother *has* to be all wise and kind.

The most extreme example of our need to believe in the all-loving mother is found with battered children. Take a severely abused and physically mistreated child and put it with a loving foster mother. Again and again it is found that the child will prefer to go back to the original cruel mother. Stronger than the desire for cessation of beating and abuse, stronger than life itself, the child wants to perpetuate her illusion that she has a good mother.

The truth is that while the child *wants* to believe her mother loves her unequivocally, she can live with disappointment at finding out it is not so. What is most necessary is that the child feel her mother is for real, *authentic*. It is better to learn as early as possible that while mother loves us, it is not to the exclusion of everything and everyone else. If the child is encouraged to enter into collusion with mother, to pretend that the maternal instinct conquers all, both will be stuck ever after with mechanisms of denial and defense which cut them off from the reality of their mutual feelings; gone is any hope of a true relationship between them. The daughter will repeat this relationship with men and other women. The idea of mother and daughter lying to maintain a pastel-pretty fiction between them may sound touching. The reality is that the price paid for maintaining the lie is enormous. The cost to the battered little girl is to be beaten black and blue. Is that touching?

Little girls playing with their dolls give us an almost laboratory example of how the illusion of perfect maternal love is maintained. In his book *Playing and Reality,* the English child psychoanalyst D. W. Winnicott notes that children's play expresses a form of wish fulfillment. A little girl playing with her dolls acts in the way she hopes her mother will act toward her. The very act of playing this game out gives the illusion a form of substance.[2]

Where did the child of even a nonmaternal woman get this idea of perfect mother love? From what her mother says, if not from what mother does. Mother always presents herself as totally loving. Her verbal formulas tell the girl that there is no question of the ideal way she feels. The reason mother is so angry or upset or cold right now is that father has been awful, the groceries didn't arrive, there is little money in the house, or the girl herself has been bad. In the end, the child comes to understand that whatever it is, it is because *she* has been naughty. It is her fault the groceries are late, Daddy is awful, there is no money, etc., etc.

Primitive cavemen drew pictures of antelopes on the walls before the hunt to make the animals come forth. In the same magical way, little girls play the perfect mother with their dolls, hoping the incantation will bring forth the ideal mother hidden in the less-than-perfect woman who promises so much and delivers so little.

Playing with dolls, the little girl perpetuates the illusion. "See how loving I am with my doll? It's so easy, it's so close, so near. Why aren't you like this with me?" It's been many years since I last played with dolls, but the hardest part of writing this book will be giving up the illusion that if I myself had just said or done or drawn the right magical thing, the illusion of perfect love between my mother and me would have been made real.

There *is* real love between most mothers and daughters. There is real love between my mother and me. But it is not that kind of love she always led me to believe she felt, which society told me she felt, and about which I have always been angry and guilty. Angry because I never really felt it, guilty because I thought the fault lay in me. If I were a better daughter I would be able to take in this nourishing love she had always told me was there. I have recently found I could get angry with my mother and that it would not destroy her or me. The anger that separated me from her also put me in touch with the real love I have for her. Anger broke the pane of glass between us.

I have heard daughters say that they do not love their mothers. I have *never* heard a mother say she does not love her daughter. Psychoanalysts have told me that a woman patient would rather consider herself "crazy" than admit that she simply does not like her daughter. She can be honest about anything else, but the myth that mothers always love their children is so controlling that even the daughter who can admit disliking her mother, when her own time comes, will deny all but positive emotions toward her children.

Difficulties begin with the word *love* itself. Literature and daily human intercourse might have been better off if the word were never used. It is too ambiguous; we recognize this in our most intense relationships when we become aware of the mystery that always surrounds its meaning. But we cherish it for its very ambiguity, which allows it to say anything we want. No wonder so many people say they don't know what it means.

"I love you, it's for your own good," mother says when she forbids us to play with a friend. "If I didn't love you so much, I wouldn't fuss so about you wearing galoshes." "Of course I love you, but that's why I want you to go to camp. I want you with me always, but it's better for you to enjoy a summer of fresh air." All these explanations seem reasonable on the surface. We want to believe that love is the motivation for everything mother does. Often it is not love, but, respectively, possessiveness, anxiety, and outright rejection that is being expressed in sentences like these. We cannot afford to believe this on a cognitive level. Way down deep we feel it.

To take mother's words about love at face value is to distort the rest of our lives in an effort to find again this ideal relationship. "Love is not an indivisible emotion," says psychoanalyst Richard Robertiello. "Our job as adults is to separate out the elements in this big package we got from mother which she called love, and to take in what she did give us, and to look in the real world for those other aspects we did not get from her."

We learn our deepest ways of intimacy with mother; automatically we repeat the pattern with everyone else with whom we become close. Either we play out the role of the child we were with mother, and make the other person into the mother figure, or we reverse: playing mother to the other person's "child." "All too often," says Leah Schaefer, "what we play out with this other person has little to do with them or who we are today." This is why arguments or frictions between some people can never be resolved: they are not reacting to what is going on between them, but to old, unhealed hurts and rejections suffered in the past.

Intimacy is just an old record we replay. "First," says Richard Robertiello, "we *introject*—take into ourselves—mother's tangled-up notion of what love is. Then we *project* it upon our lovers, husbands, and our own daughter."

Perhaps mother was very possessive and tried to live through us, but at the same time did give us a lot of cuddling, satisfying physical contact and affection. It is all too easy for us forever afterward to buy the whole package—clutching dependency and physical warmth are both tied into an inextricable knot and labeled *love*. Our husband may be physically affectionate, but unless he is possessive too, we decide he doesn't "really" love us, something is missing from the perfect love he is supposed to feel for us.

Another example is the mother who tells her daughter she loves her, but is always sending her away to stay with grandmother, leaving her in the care of nurses, or packing her off to boarding school. Is it surprising that a girl like this will often grow up convinced that the only people who love her are the ones who don't want her around? Rejection and affection have become inextricably mixed.

Sometimes we are so hurt by mother's ambivalences that we reject the entire package—throwing out the good, positive aspects mother presented to us, along with the painful ones. It is not useful to merely say, "Mama never loved me, she didn't do this or that for me!" This is to refuse, in our childish anger, to acknowledge what love there was.

Says Dr. Robertiello: "What we must do is break down the specific components of mother's love—analyze exactly the ways she did not love us, but also the ways in which she did. Did mother give you a kind of basic security—a structure of stability, shelter, nurturing? Did she give you admiration—a genuine feeling that you were worth plenty in your own right? Did she give you warmth and physical affection, cuddle, hold and kiss you? Did she really care what happened to you and accept you—my daughter right or wrong? These are some of the components of real love."

No mother can score 100 in all of them. Perhaps your mother was good about admiring and praising you, giving you a feeling of value—but what she also called love was her need for someone to mother *her*. If so, you may have few problems of self-esteem, but often feel you cannot get enough closeness, intimacy with others. People always let you down. Here is just such a woman, twenty-seven years old, and on the ladder of a career.

"My mother always told me," she says, "'Aim high! Dare to be different!' She was the rare kind of wonderful mother you can talk to about your sex life, but since I was six or seven, I've felt very protective of her. I knew I was stronger than she. She used to confide in me about her troubles with my domineering father. Even when I was growing up, I'd stand up to him for her, as if she were a child. My mother's emotional support helped me a lot. I've made myself up. But I don't trust men. They can't understand what a woman needs. They won't support you emotionally, but want it for themselves instead. I need a man who's as self-confident as I am, a man I can lean on. That's why I don't sleep with any of the men I know nowadays. There's not much a man can do for me other than give me enormous emotional or financial support, but I haven't found the strong partner who can, or is willing, to do that. Everything else, I can do for myself, but I know that a one-to-one relationship with a man is the most important thing in my life." She tries to make up for the maternal protection and solicitude she didn't get from her mother by extracting it from men. Her emotional politics are that men must take care of her as if she were a child, while she withholds the sexuality they expect from a woman.

I've heard many a grown woman still lament the fact that mother wasn't home when she returned from school in the afternoon. Forget that mother may have been a terrific role model as a professional working woman—the role model the daughter may have patterned her own career upon. Until she accepts that mother didn't have to be perfect, her childish anger will inhibit the full use of the admirable traits her mother did have. Very often for women like these, their very success in work will bring with it associations of the "bad" mother they do not wish to grow into. They marry suddenly, giving up their career with a sigh of relief. But the marriage doesn't work out either: the wife tries to turn her husband into the all-caring, protective mother she never had.

Mother may have felt she had to present an image of perfect love. As adults we have to accept that we can live without it. We must give up our resentment that she wasn't ideal so that we can take in what she was good at; it will enhance our lives.

Spontaneous and honest love admits errors, hesitations, and human failings; it can be tested and repaired. Idealized love ties us because we already intuit that it is unreal and are afraid to face this truth.

"I only tell my mother what she wants to hear," women say. The inference is that the lie is an outgrowth of love; the daughter is merely translating into action her desire to protect her mother. The fact is we become our mother's protectors not because we are such good daughters but to protect ourselves. In some part of our psyche we are still children who are afraid to risk losing mother's unbroken love even for the short space in time of an argument. Telling the truth is a test; it lays bare what in fact goes on between two people.

"I have a wonderful relationship with my mother," a thirty-eight-year-old woman says, "but why do I start climbing the walls if I'm around her for more than a few hours? The awful thing is I can see my daughter is already becoming that way with me." Fantasies of perfect understanding are hard to maintain when you are face to face with reality. It is easier to do when you are apart.

Our mutual refusal to show our true selves, good and bad, to each other does not allow either woman to explore her separate life, her own identity. The unspoken fear is that if one partner leaves, if either questions the perfection of mother-daughter love by being "different," we are both destroyed. How many grown women dread the idea of living alone, being alone? There is only one thing in this world that approaches the pain of letting go of our mothers, more wrenching than giving up the illusion that she loves us unambivalently. It is separating from—letting go of—our daughters.

"I needed and loved my mother so intensely at times," says a young mother of a five-year-old daughter, "that I remember saying to her when I was eight, 'I will never love my child as much as you love me.' Now I know that I meant *smother,* not love. So many harmful ideas are hidden by the word love. My mother seemed so selfless, so giving. I remember dreading the thought of my mother dying. But I didn't want her to live for me. It piled too much guilt on me. And yet, I didn't dare ask for any space. It would have made me guilty. When I was seventeen I couldn't wait to get away from home. When I married and had a daughter of my own, I became just as possessive of her as my mother was of me. I was a working mother, and thought that meant I was giving my daughter the space I never had. But I used to telephone home all the time from work, and when I got home, guiltily made up for being away by smothering her. Just like my mother, I called every possessive, overprotective thing I did 'love.'"

The maternal instinct says we are all born mothers, that once we are mothers we will automatically and naturally love our children and always do what is best for them. If you believe in the maternal instinct and fail at mother love, you fail as a woman. It is a controlling idea that holds us in an iron grip.

I propose to use "maternal instinct" as it is emotionally experienced by most women. For us it does not necessarily have the same meaning as it does for biologists, ethologists, or sociologists. The concept has as many meanings as there are scientists, and many will tell you the maternal instinct doesn't exist at all. Anthropologist Lionel Tiger advised me to avoid using the phrase even in quotes. He felt no matter how I qualified the term, I would be jumped on. It is outside the purpose of this book to prove or disprove the reality of the maternal instinct. But I don't think any woman interested in the forces or choices that shape her life can avoid thinking about what these words mean, not genetically, but imaginatively.

Whether you call it "instinct" or not, most women enjoy having children, want to, and do. For this majority, the trouble begins not with being mothers, but with the emotional propositions contained in the notion of maternal instinct—that being a good mother is as natural and undifferentiated to humans as it is to a she-wolf with her cubs.

Those who like to make this argument from nature forget that while a she-wolf does care for her cubs instinctively, guards them with her life and teaches them to hunt, the same instinct leads her to abandon them without a backward glance as soon as they are able to fend for themselves. Other instincts may well lead her to mate, in season, with her son.

Nor does mother love in humans spontaneously well up the moment a child is born. "I tell mothers on the first day," says pediatrician Dr. Sidney Q. Cohlan, "it's not having the baby that makes the relationship, it's the day by day living and caring for the infant that makes the relationship. You can't love your baby twenty-four hours a day, seven days a week. Taking care of a baby in the first few months can be hard work and at times a monumental bore. The rewards begin to come after the mother and infant have lived through a period of adjustment and responsiveness to each other's needs. But she has read all the poetry in the magazines and expects 'instant motherhood,' and thinks there is something wrong with her if she doesn't respond at first sight to her new baby in picture-book fashion. Maybe she doesn't deserve to be a mother? How can she explain even a fleeting negative emotion? Her society won't allow her to verbalize this—so there is a good deal of lying that goes on subconsciously when you ask a new mother about her feelings of fulfillment. They often tell you what they want to believe themselves."

Says psychiatrist Mio Fredland, who is the mother of a three-year-old daughter: "I've seen many mothers who were rapturous at the birth of their child, and others who were profoundly depressed. This implies they were in love with a fantasy. In fact mothers often feel extremely guilty and depressed because they don't love their babies at first. The baby looks like a stranger. Yes, we build up some Gerber baby-food fantasy, the great American myth that all mothers love their babies. I've heard women say it can take them two or three weeks before they really begin to 'care' for the child. There is that moment of shock when you first see your baby. You don't love her automatically at all."

This is the tyranny of the notion of maternal instinct. It idealizes motherhood beyond human capacity. A dangerous gap is set up. Mother *feels* the mixture of love and resentment, affection and anger she has for her child, but she cannot afford to *know* it.

The split between what mother says, the way she behaves with her baby—*and what she unconsciously feels on the deepest level*—leaves her unsure of herself. Says Dr. Robertiello: "Women walk around feeling they have something to hide, that they are secretly 'unnatural' or 'bad mothers.' The act of giving birth does not set up an ability in you to be a mother, you will not necessarily feel this marvelous 'maternal instinct' welling up in you, telling you what to do with your baby at every moment. Women must have this myth taken off their backs. It puts them at the mercy of a male chauvinistic society. Men are 'sure' that women are meant to be mothers. But each woman in her heart, when she has a baby, is not so 'sure.' She becomes paralyzed, looking to other people to tell her what to do. Male supremacy uses the myth of the maternal instinct to reinforce its power position."

If we are going to give women emotionally—on the deepest level— all the alternatives and options of contemporary life, we must enable both sexes to believe that some of us, male and female, have the desire to take care of small creatures like babies, *and that this has nothing to do with one's sexual identity.* Nor need it be instinctual. We may or may not be born with the reflex to pick up and comfort a crying baby, but we can be taught. "A lot of people, and this includes men," says Leah Schaefer, "do like to take care of small, dependent people. In my clinical practice, I've come to believe what is ordinarily called 'the maternal instinct' is just this simple liking to 'take care of' smaller creatures. Some human beings do not like it at all. It is not some great biological imperative, which if frustrated will ruin or impoverish a woman's life. Mother love may once have been an instinct in humans," continues Dr. Schaefer, who is the mother of a teen-age girl, "but civilization bred it out of us. I doubt that any woman is born more 'maternal' than any other. I wouldn't be surprised if men were born with about the same capacity as women to care for and nurture children—except for the obvious biological differences."

A human baby's needs are greater than an infant wolf's. The skills we must learn are too complex to be left to animal instinct alone. Human childhood goes on far longer than any other creature's. And so while we may say, if we like, that maternal instinct plays a role in mothering a human child, it is clear that instinct alone could never do the whole job. It has had to be supplemented by skills, arts, emotions, and desires humans have learned from other humans. Professionals who work in children's shelters find that mothers who themselves never received adequate mothering when little do not know how to mother, and show little interest in learning. "The battered-child pattern usually runs in families," says Dr. Lionel Tiger. "There's a very strong correlation between battering your baby, and having been one yourself."

"My mother didn't know how to give love," says a forty-year-old lawyer, "so when I had a daughter, I didn't know how to do it either. Where was I going to learn how to give love? I'd never known it as a child myself. You can't learn it from books. You cannot grow up in a home where there is hostility and not reflect it later. Maybe I shouldn't have been a mother. . . . No, I take that back. I should have been a parent because I want to and can give everything a child needs. But my daughter turns away from my efforts to give her love. Maybe I'm doing it wrong. I should have been taught, there should be some form of education, how to convey love to children. I didn't know how to get love as a child so I don't know how to give it . . . beginning with giving it to myself."

Says child psychologist Dr. Aaron Esman: "To give good mothering, you have to have received it."

It is commonplace that the notion of "the teen-ager" did not exist before the present century. Similarly, the idealization of motherhood, of infancy and childhood, is also an invention of modern times. Recent books suggest that only when the desperate struggle for existence had been won on a broad enough scale could society afford to apportion sufficient amounts of time, emotion and money to the care of babies. "Maternal infanticide was 'the most common crime in Western Europe from the Middle Ages down to the end of the eighteenth century,'" writes Adrienne Rich.[3] Says Edward Shorter, ". . . traditional mothers were not monsters. . . . If they lacked an articulate sense of maternal love, it was because they were forced by material circumstances and community attitudes to subordinate infant welfare to other objectives, such as keeping the farm going or helping their husbands weave cloth. . . . Good mothering is an invention of modernization."[4]

"Why do so many women rush into motherhood?" says Dr. Esman. "It surely isn't out of 'maternal instinct.' Not if they are hoping to get a lot of the experience out of identification with their own children that they didn't get themselves. Or if the reason they have a child is to hang on to their husband, to save the marriage—that's a terrible reason. People say, 'Well, maybe we should have a child,' when a marriage is going badly, which is the worst advice. Again and again I see women whose own childhoods were deprived, who have the fantasy that they are going to do for their baby what their mother didn't do for them. They are going to relive their childhood through their baby, and that baby is going to be given all the things they didn't get. . . . Or else. Maternal instinct? We have no evidence of it. Women want to become mothers for lots of reasons; it's part of their biological condition, having the equipment for it, one of the things being a woman is about, but I wouldn't call this 'instinct,' not in the terms in which I define the word. Also there are social expectations; all her life a woman has been expected to grow up, marry and have babies, it's been drummed into her all along, so that her whole orientation is geared toward these expectations from others. But this is not 'maternal instinct.' Reasonably healthy women want to have children because of what I would describe as wanting to nurture somebody, to get pleasure out of feeding and caring for a child, to do for somebody else what was done to them by their mother, and to share a particular type of experience with their husband. This is a growth, developmental experience."

The first thing it can be said a mother honestly feels in relation to her child is a kind of self-love. The child is essentially a narcissistic extension of herself. The child used to be a part of her, inside her. It is now external but is still closely connected with her own body. Whatever investment she has in her body is continued in the child. If the infant is all she hoped it would be, she may more easily live up to society's injunction that she love the child more than herself. But if there is something about the baby—if it's a boy instead of a girl, too fat, too thin, too lethargic—that makes her feel less than the exaltation she has been led to expect, she must deny it. Any wound to her narcissism—that tidal basin out of which all maternal emotions flow—must go unacknowledged, repressed, unfelt. I suspect that when post-partum depression enters, it begins in the silence she must maintain if her child does not fulfill her fantasy of perfect maternal bliss.

The glorification of motherhood demands that when her child is born, autonomy over her own emotions must end. Like those unnatural madonnas in early Christian art, she is supposed to focus only on the infant. Little emblazoned letters follow the golden beam from her one eye to the child: love. The four letters cancel her emotional past, command her to unlearn a whole life's way of thinking and feeling about people. She must ignore her own subjectivity, her real pleasure in physical beauty if her child is not pretty, her boredom with stupidity if the child is slow. Above all, she must not let the sex of her child make any difference to her. She must shut her eyes to the very first item of information we take in about any new person we meet, and which colors every single transaction we have with them thereafter. The day the baby's pram is bought, we decorate it in pink or blue, signaling to the outside world what it wants to know. Only to the mother is it not supposed to matter if her child has a penis or a vagina.

And yet the truth is that when one woman gives birth to another, to someone who is like her, they are linked together for life in a very special way. Mother is the prime love object, the first attachment for both male and female infants. But it is their sex, their sameness that distinguishes what a mother has with her daughter. No two people have such an opportunity for support and identification, and yet no human relationship is so mutually limiting. If a mother suggests to her daughter that motherhood was not the glorious culmination she had been promised, that life had not opened out for her but been somehow diminished instead, this is saying to the girl: I should not have had you.

A woman without a daughter may try to explore life's infinite possibilities. Her own mother left out so much. But when a daughter is born, fears she thought she had conquered long ago are re-aroused. Now there is another person, not simply dependent on her, but *like* her, and therefore subject to all the dangers she has fought all her life. The mother's progress into a larger sexuality is halted. Ground gained that she could have held alone is abandoned. She retreats and entrenches herself in the cramped female stance of security and defense. The position is fondly hailed as mother protector. It is the position of fear. She may be only half alive but she is safe, and so is her daughter. She now defines herself not as a woman but primarily as a mother. Sex is left out, hidden from the girl who must never think of her mother in danger: in sex. It is only with the greatest effort that the girl will be able to think of herself that way.

"I think what frightens me most is my daughter's vulnerability," says a mother of a six-year-old. "It's my own fear that I would be exploited sexually. I know I overprotect her. But I'm so afraid she'll be hurt, taken advantage of. She's so naturally unguarded." How is she going to protect this pitifully vulnerable female infant until she reaches the safe haven of marriage? The mother just doesn't know. What she does know is that for a little girl—as opposed to a little boy—sex is a danger. It must be denied, suppressed. Her daughter will not be raised a sexy hussy, but "a lady." No erotic stimuli must intrude into the little girl's consciousness, no dirty jokes, no daring clothes, no indication that the mother's own body responds sexually. If mother doesn't mention it or think about it or respond to anything herself, it will go away. In order to keep the child's attention from turning to the anxious-making topic of sex, the mother goes the final step and desexualizes herself.

"A couple of months after my daughter was born," says a twenty-eight-year-old woman, "I had lunch with a man I'd known for years. 'Well,' he said, 'how does it feel not to be a sexy woman any longer?'" Society gives mother all the unsolicited help she needs in her desexualization. The week before Mother's Day recently, this banner headline ran in a full-page newspaper ad for a famous designer's seductive at-home wear for women: ". . . before she was a mother, she was a woman."

From the girl's earliest years, her emergent sexuality will be a cause of anxiety, seeming to make her not more like her mother, but unlike her. If mother denies her own sexuality, and reacts to mine with such shame or fright, how big an asset is it? How difficult it is to be a woman! Better to remain a child, a good little girl.

By trying to protect her daughter from sexual hazards which, imagined or not, lie far in the future, the mother begins, from the daughter's birth, to withhold the model of herself as a woman who takes pleasure and pride in sexuality. The daughter is deprived of the identification she needs most. Every effort on the daughter's part to feel good about herself as a woman will be an uphill struggle—if not betrayal—against this sexless image of her mother. The lifelong puzzle between mother and daughter has begun. Is it any wonder that mothers and daughters scan each other like unfinished murder mysteries, unable to let one another go?

When I was an art history student at college, I used to yawn over the great masters' efforts to explain the greatest miracle of them all: The Virgin Birth. I blamed my boredom on an aesthetic ennui with all that sweetness and symmetry beloved of the Renaissance. I know now that what we call boredom is often a defense against anxiety, and what was making me anxious was the Mystery embodied by the Immaculate Conception: how to have sex and remain a virgin at the same time? Eventually I lost my virginity, but I never learned how Mary did not. Any girl who ever uncrossed her legs and prayed may be interested in one explanation I recently heard. Mary and Joseph *did* have sexual intercourse. What kept Mary chaste was that she wasn't thinking about it. She was pure of mind and with God. Therefore, it didn't count.

Sometimes I wonder what kind of model Mary makes for our daughters, but it can't be far from how we perceive the sexual image of our mothers: certainly she did it with our father, but from what we know of her, we can't imagine for a minute that she enjoyed it.

"Close your eyes and think of England," Victorian mothers told their daughters on their wedding night. Today we laugh at the joke. But one of the growth industries in our culture is the sex clinics whose job with women is to put them in touch with their sex, to get them to think about the unthinkable, and push past the sexless image of their mothers.

When women's lives were more predictable, we could more easily afford this enigmatic picture of womanhood. When we had no alternative but to repeat our mother's life, our mistakes and disappointments were pretty much confined to her space, her margin of error and unhappiness. I do believe our grandmothers, even our mothers, were happier; not knowing as much as we do and not having our options, there was less to be unhappy about. A woman might give up her sexuality, hate being a housewife, not like children, but if every other woman was doing it, how could she articulate her frustration? She could feel it certainly, but you can't want what you don't know about. Television, for instance, gave them no sense of thwarted expectations. Today women's lives are changing at a rate and by a necessity we couldn't control if we wanted to; we need all the energy that suppression consumes. If we are going to fill more than women's traditional role, we can't afford the exhaustion that goes with constant emotional denial. There are pressures on women other than the "maternal instinct." They are the new economic and social demands. Even if we decide to lead our mothers' lives, the fact is that our daughter may not. We may continue, through denial and repression, to keep alive the idealization of motherhood for another generation, but where will that leave her?

If women are going to be lawyers as well as mothers, they must differentiate between the two, and then differentiate once again about their sexuality. That is the third—and *not* mutually exclusive—option. As the world changes, and women's place in it, mothers must consciously present this choice to their daughters. A woman may incorporate all three choices within herself—and even more—but at any given moment she must be able to say to herself and her daughter, "I chose to have you because I wanted to be a mother. I chose to work —to have a career, to be in politics, to play the piano—because that gives me a different feeling of value about myself, a value that is not greater nor lesser than motherhood, only different. Whether you choose to work or not, to be a mother or not, it will have nothing to do with your sexuality. Sexuality is the third option—as meaningful as either of the other two."

"If a mother has a life of her own," says Dr. Robertiello, "the daughter will love her more, will want to be around her more. She must not define herself as 'a mother,' she's got to see herself as a person, a person with work to do, a sexual person, a woman. It isn't necessary to have a profession. She doesn't have to have a high IQ or be president of the PTA to have this added life. So long as she isn't just sitting home, chauffeuring the kids and baking cookies, giving her children and herself the feeling that their life is hers. Of course the best thing the mother can do is try to have her main connection with her husband instead of her daughter."

The truth is that the woman and the mother are often at war with one another—in the same body. Dr. Helene Deutsch, in *The Psychology of Women,* takes the classical Freudian view on the "passivity" of women, one in which many analysts today do not join (nor do I myself), but I think she gives us an important clue here: "The origin of this longing in primitive, unsublimated instinctual drives," she says, "manifests itself in various ways. Ardent wishes to be desired, strong aspirations to exclusive egoistic possession, a normally completely passive attitude with regard to the first attack . . . are characteristic attributes of feminine sexuality. They are so fundamentally different from the emotional manifestations of motherhood that we are compelled to accept the opposition of sexuality and eroticism on one hand and reproduction instinct and motherhood on the other."[5]

Like so many women since the world began, my mother could not believe in this opposition of the two desires. Tradition, society, her parents, religion itself told her that there was no conflict; that motherhood was the logical and natural end product of sex. Instead of believing what every woman's body tells every woman's mind, that as Dr. Deutsch states, sexuality and eroticism are a "fundamentally different" and "opposite" drive to motherhood, my mother accepted the lie. She took as her act of faith the proposition that if she were a real woman, she would be a good mother and I would grow up the same. If I repeated her path and pattern of motherhood, it would show I did not blame her for her choice. It would justify and place the final stamp of value on what she had done. It would say her attitude, behavior, and deepest feelings were not split, but were in fact in harmony, a woman in unison with nature.

Some women do make this choice gladly. They may be the majority, but my mother was not one of them. As I am not—her daughter in this too. Even in a good marriage, many women resent the matronly, nonsexual role their children force them to play. My mother didn't even have a good marriage; she was a young widow.

Frightened as she was, as much in need of my father as my sister and I were of her, mother had no choice but to pretend that my sister and I were the most important part of her life; that neither fear, youth and inexperience, loss, loneliness or her own needs could shake the unqualified and invincible love she felt for us. My mother had no body of woman-to-woman honesty and shared experience to use in her fight against the folk wisdom that said just being a woman carried all the inherent wisdom needed to be a mother—that it was either "natural" to her, or she was a failure as a woman.

In all the years we lived together, it is a shame we never talked honestly about our feelings. What neither of us knew then was that I could have stood honesty, no matter how frightening. Her angers, disillusionments, fears of failure, rage—emotions I seldom saw—I could have come to terms with them if she had been able to speak to me. I would have grown used to the idea that while mother loved me, at times other emotions impaired that love, and developed trust that in time her love for me would always return. Instead, I was left trying to believe in some perfect love she said she had for me, but in which I could not believe. I did not understand why I couldn't feel it no matter what her words said. I grew to believe that love itself, from her or anybody else, was a will-o'-the-wisp, coming or going for reasons I could not control. Never knowing when or why I was loved, I grew afraid to depend on it.

The older I get, the more of my mother I see in myself. The more opposite my life and my thinking grow from hers, the more of her I hear in my voice, see in my facial expression, feel in the emotional re-actions I have come to recognize as my own. It is almost as if in ex-tending myself, the circle closes in to completion. She was my first and most lasting model. To say her image is not still a touchstone in my life—and mine in hers—would be another lie. I am tired of lies. They have stood in the way of my understanding myself all my life. I have always known that what my husband loves most in me is that I have my own life. I have always felt that I had partially deceived him in this; I am very clever at pretense. My work, my marriage, and my new relationships with other women are beginning to make his as-sumptions about me true—that I am an independent, separate individ-ual. They have allowed me to respect myself, and admire my own sex. What still stands between me and the person I would like to be is this illusion of perfect love between my mother and me. It is a lie I can no longer afford.

Chapter 2

A TIME
TO BE CLOSE

I grew up in a house of women. It's a different way to begin life, but I
didn't allow myself to feel the loss of the father everyone else had. I
would later theorize that perhaps my kind of childhood had its advantages: not having seen a man diminished by women's impossible
demands on him, I grew up believing all things were possible between
a man and a woman. Of course I missed him.

In our house there were always four women: my mother, my older
sister Susie, and myself; at first, the other woman was my nurse
Anna. I loved Anna so much I let her slip out of my life as painlessly
as my father. The day she left I told myself I felt nothing. I had
learned everything about love and separation in the first years of my
life.

Anna was fearless, and she loved me in a way I can still feel. She
was as tough and dependable as my mother was timid and out of her
depth. "My poor mother"; why do I think of her that way even
today, with my stepfather and a world of friends around her? I suppose in the same way that she still sees me as a child, I still see her at
twenty, a widow with two baby girls. But what did I feel then? With
the terrible injustice of children who know that to be fair can cost
them their lives, I always wanted her complete and unswerving love
and attention; all she had to offer was her vulnerability and sadness.

In the space between what I demanded and she could give, I lived. From there it was not a far step for a child to decide my demands were what made her unhappy. That in some way I was the cause of her unhappiness. It's why I hated her to braid my hair: I could hear her sighing behind me. Her sadness was my guilt. Whenever she talks about her own mother, whom I never knew, that look comes over her face. It's worse when she talks about my father. She only does when I ask, and I was twenty-two before I dared. Can you stand your mother's sadness? We believe that if we had been better children, or even right now could do or say the right thing, we could make it go away. I cannot bear to be in the same room when my mother's face changes from the look I love to that maddening unhappiness. My intellect tells me the guilt I feel whenever I say good-bye to her has nothing to do with what I did or didn't do. My mother is a reasonably happy woman, other people would say. I've been a reasonably good daughter, my mother would say. But until I understand my guilt, I will not be free of her.

"Oh, Nancy," she'll begin, "I wish you had known Mama. She was such a wonderful woman. . . ." and her voice will drift away to some distant image which she sees beyond me, and we'll talk about something else. I'd like to see that image, to share anything that may tell me more about my grandmother—and so about my mother, and so about me. But the stories my mother tells about her mother, lovely as they are, much as I like to hear them again and again, are as diffused with sentiment as the faded, misty Bachrach photos in the leather volumes at my grandfather's house that I have pored over every summer of my life, looking . . . for what? My mother is the oldest child, but in all the photos even the sister eleven years younger looks more self-assured than she. How dizzying it must have been to be picked at seventeen by my handsome father, she the thorn among the roses in her father's stern eyes. She eloped with him against that father's wishes, though sometimes I wonder if even her elopement itself didn't express her silent dutifulness as a daughter: if she did not find favor in her father's eyes, she was prepared to go away. How unprepared she must have been for motherhood a year later, and two years after that for my father's death. So much loss for a person who never had a sense of self.

As we both grow older I see how suited she was to be a wife, how gracefully she moves now that she has a second chance and my sister and I are grown, leaving her role as our mother almost negligible beside her life as a woman. I am sure much of her talent as a wife comes from her mother, as does mine; again and again she tells me what a strong influence her mother was on all her children—this woman who has taken on almost mythic magnitude in my imagination. But my grandmother died suddenly and mysteriously of an incurable disease called sleeping sickness when my mother was sixteen. *Sleeping sickness.* All my life it has seemed the appropriate and romantic end for this fairy-tale woman. "I can remember coming home from school, running into the house and calling, 'Mama, Mama,'" my mother says, "and then realizing she wasn't there any more."

As much as I want my mother to go beyond the pretty pictures of her mother ("so beautiful, so kind"), and of my father ("so handsome, so charming"), I have come to realize she needs her own protection against loss and pain. She will see in those early years only what she can afford to live with.

Nowadays my mother and I talk more than we used to. It began with my marriage, an alliance that has always seemed to have strengthened her as well as me. It has been gradual, this unraveling of the unspoken between us, but I think she is as eager as I now to talk. Suppression eats up her energy too. I am not the only one who is guilty. Several years ago my husband, Bill, and I were visiting her and my stepfather, Scotty. We'd just come down to the library for our welcome-home martini when she handed me a faded letter. It was almost as if she'd been waiting to give it to me, unable to take it in until I too had read it.

It was a letter written to her when she was fourteen by her mother. My grandmother had just left my grandfather, and gone to Florida with the youngest of their five children. It was a stunning thing to do in that era. I've often stared at her self-portrait that now hangs in my living room and wondered, angry as she was with my grandfather, how she could have left her children—none of whom to this day can speak of her without a kind of adoration and longing. But then, given my grandfather, I would probably have married and left him too. In the portraits of him which she painted, he looks like the young F. Scott Fitzgerald. He was easily twice as difficult. They met at an amateur theatrical, and she flatly refused to play opposite a man with red hair. She had red hair herself. They did the play, and though I'm told he never loved any woman as he loved her, they never stopped arguing.

My grandfather made his fortune in steel alloys in Pittsburgh, lost it in the Depression and made it all back again. He loved power, horses, trophies, and beautiful women. He never forgave my mother for not being one. She grew into beauty too late. As a little girl I would stand in the room with the silver cups, the red and blue ribbons, the stuffed swordfish, the photos of yachts and fox hunts, and I would imagine myself beautiful and winning them all for him. On those evenings when my grandfather dined out with the Mellons and the Carnegies, I'm told my grandmother cooked spaghetti for her arty friends in her studio at the top of the house.

My mother, her three sisters, and brother loved and feared my grandfather until his death a few years ago. Their feelings about their mother are totally unambivalent. I have seen each of them turn at different moments to one of us grandchildren and say, "For a moment there, you looked just like Mama. . . ." It has always been the highest compliment. It promised more than beauty, some inner secret that would make people love you forever as they did her. From their stories I have a picture of a woman who was every child's dream, a beauty with large eyes and dark hair who wrote plays for her children, who dressed up with them and was as capable of entering their world as she was of taking care of them. She was as romantic and sensitive to life as my grandfather was ambitious and incapable of demonstrating the love he felt for his children. The reason I love the paintings that fill my house is that she painted them.

When my grandmother wrote this letter, I doubt that she intended to return to my grandfather. I don't think her leaving him was a false gesture, but a desperate last alternative. She saw only separation ahead and clearly wanted to give her eldest daughter something to help fill the void. Of all the memorabilia that came out of my grandfather's files after his death, this is what my mother wanted me to see. It was a message to her from her mother, of course, but I think it was also her own silent way of saying something to me:

My darling Jane:

When you read this I want you to do it with an open heart. Forget the things that have been said—the thoughts you may have had, and try to remember only the better, more beautiful phase of life. When I am not there with you, it is going to be your task to try to help the little ones to see things. Try to guide them in the right way. This is your work and your duty.

To me motherhood has been the most beautiful thing in my life. The wonder of it never ceases for me—to see you all developing from tiny helpless babies into big strong girls and boys, to see your minds changing with your years and to remember that some day you will be grown men and women. It is overwhelming.

All my life as a child I looked forward to the time when I would have children of my own—and in spite of my so-called talents or urges toward other things, underneath was that spark which had to burst into flame sometime. And when I held you, Jane—my first baby—in my arms, I had the greatest thrill I have ever experienced. I felt almost saintly, as if I had really entered heaven, and now I know that every time a mother receives a new baby she really does enter heaven. There is nothing else in life like it. And anyone who receives such a blessing should be eternally grateful.

I am telling you this, Jane, just so you will understand my love and feeling for you. Always remember this and as you grow older, think of me sometime and try to understand what I am trying to convey to you.

My heart is full, but I could not write the things I feel in a thousand years. Love each other and be good to daddy and he will take care of you. This is the hardest, bitterest moment of my life, leaving you, but I cannot do anything else. I cannot see through my tears. God bless you all,

Mama

I believe my grandmother did feel close to heaven when she first held my mother, but I feel that what makes this letter most valuable to my mother is that her mother could feel other emotions too. My mother doesn't remember reading the letter when she was fourteen. Perhaps her father kept it from her. But however he explained his wife's departure, her leaving could only be felt as loss, the kind of intolerable pain no one can admit to. Perhaps this letter confirmed for my mother what she always wanted to feel, not so much that her mother deeply loved her, but that her mother's act of leaving my grandfather when she felt his imperiousness too denigrating was proof that while she was a mother, she was a woman first. She would not go through all her short life celebrating only self-abnegation and the maternal emotions. She loved other ideas and people besides her children. She was their mother, but would not be their martyr—which is one reason they loved her so. I have never heard one word from my mother, aunts or uncle of any guilt she ever made them feel. If they have idealized her to disguise the pain and anger they felt at the loss of her, surely this letter confirmed, at least for my mother, what she needed to know, not just as her mother's child, but as a parent with children of her own. In showing it to me she was saying, "See, if I wasn't as present, as close, maternal and mothering as other mothers were to their children, it wasn't because I didn't love you. My mother loved me, but she was absent too."

My mother's life doesn't look like her mother's, but the emotions beneath the surface are hauntingly familiar. My mother too chose a man who could not give her the emotional security she desperately needed. She too found that her life as a woman created demands opposed to her role as a mother; she abandoned that role as her mother did, separated herself from her children emotionally because without my father, in the midst of bitter deprivation of her own, she had little left to give my sister and me. In her letter, my grandmother tried to face her children's inevitable anger and loss by speaking to them of the perfect love felt for them by the part of herself which was their mother. Unable to speak to me herself, but resonating in her depths to my sense that I too had somehow been deserted when I was little just as she had been, my mother used her adored mother's own words to tell me she recognized my anger, to say that she had always loved me even if imperfectly, and to ask me to forgive her, just as she had forgiven her mother.

We are the loving sex; people count on us for comfort, nurturing warmth. We hold the world together with the constant availability of our love when men would tear it apart with their needs for power. We feel incomplete alone, inadequate without a man, devalued outside marriage, defensive without children. We are raised for love, but when love comes to us, sweet as it is, somehow it is not as ultimately satisfying as we dreamed. We are being loved for being a part of a relationship, for our function—not for ourselves.

He asks us out for dinner, and even as we hang up the phone, hot with pleasure, we wonder who else he asked before us. As he holds us in his arms, we are already half afraid he will forget us tomorrow.

On the day he marries us, we ask him yet another time: "Do you really love me?"

Men don't say to us, "Climb the highest mountain, catch me a star, prove you love me so I can believe it." If we are so loving, why are we not lovable in ourselves? When our children are born we believe at last in love, our own and theirs too. These people, our children, will never stop loving us, ever. Love. It's all we know, but we do not trust it.

The seed of our disbelief goes back to our first love, a time we can't remember. The lessons learned from mother in the way she loved us and the way she loved herself stay with us for life.

All my life I've resented the tyranny of infancy, the notion that my adult behavior was determined by a stage of life that I couldn't remember, that was past, and therefore beyond change, regret, or control. Sentences filled with psychiatric rhetoric of "oral rage," "infantile omnipotence," and "penis envy" irritated me almost to anger. What did all that mumbo jumbo have to do with my life? I believed in learning from experience, that we could make ourselves up out of whatever material had been handed us; that we could change our lives if we were strong enough. Didn't I know my own fears and anxieties? Hadn't I learned to keep them in check? I was proud of my self-discipline, resentful of the very idea of a doctor rummaging around in my neat emotional closets.

Strong—the very word has always been glamorous but mystifying to me. Surely if it means anything, it is the ability to be effective, do something by and for one's self, using one's own inner resources and leaning on no one? The puzzle has always been then—why did one person have this inner strength and someone else not? To say someone is "strong" is only to give that person a name or adjective; it is merely labeling. It gives no clue to where strength comes from.

If I am "strong," why is there so much anxiety in my life? Why am I so haunted by fear that my work isn't good enough? Yesterday's triumphs have little meaning; tomorrow "reality" will take over again and I will fail or be found out. Above all, why can't I enjoy what my husband and friends tell me—that they love me? Why do I dream at night and worry by day about the loss of others? Ever since I can remember, I have been, outwardly at least, a winner—good in school, good at sports, people liked me, I did accomplished work. Why then do I still feel insecure?

How often I've heard my own rationalizations and defenses in the voices of other women I have interviewed. How stubbornly most of us resist what now seems to me to be common sense; over the years the "mumbo jumbo" of the psychiatrists whose names fill this book took on a power I could no longer deny: in our beginnings is our essence.

We get our courage, our sense of self, the ability to believe we have value even when alone, to do our work, to love others and to feel ourselves lovable from the "strength" of mother's love for us when we were infants—just as every single dyne of energy on earth originally came from the sun.

Most of you will never be psychoanalyzed. I have not been myself. Like me, you may have a built-in resistance to going back to where lack of belief in yourself began. First impressions of life cut the deepest. They form the grooves of character through which experience comes to us; and if this or that groove becomes distorted, this or that emotion becomes blocked or twisted. We can understand it intellectually. We can never "take it in." Certain patterns that come heavy-laden with ambivalence, rejection, and humiliation from the past have us in their grip. The maturation process demands that we understand our history before the energy bound up in repression can be released. Self-deception begins with boredom or cleverness: "Oh, I know all about my mother and me," you may say. "All that business with my mother was over years ago." You don't and it wasn't.

There is a great deal of data that says an unresolved relationship with her mother sets a woman's mind in certain nonautonomous patterns, encloses her in fear of certain experiences, often stops her from going after what she wants in life, or, when she finds what she wants, keeps her from taking from it the gratification she needs.

If as a tiny child we didn't get the kind of satisfying closeness and love that gives an infant the strength to grow on, we do not evolve emotionally. We become older but a part of us remains infants, looking for this nurturing closeness, never believing that we have it, or that if we do, soon it will be taken away.

Freud, Horney, Bowlby, Erikson, Sullivan, Winnicott, Mahler—the great interpreters of human behavior—may disagree profoundly in some ways but are as one about beginnings: you cannot leave home, cannot grow up whole, separate and self-reliant, unless someone loved you enough to give you a self first, and then let you go. It begins with our mother's touch, our mother's smile and eye: there is someone out there whom she likes to touch, there is someone out there she likes to see. That's me. And I'm OK!

It used to be thought that if you loved a child too much, you would spoil her. We know now you cannot be loved too much—not in the first years of life. In the depths of that first closeness to our mothers is built the bedrock of self-esteem on which we will erect our good feelings about ourselves for the rest of our lives. An infant needs an almost suffocating kind of closeness to the body whose womb it so recently and reluctantly left. The technical word for this closeness is *symbiosis*.

It is especially important for women to understand the meaning of this word because for so many of us, it becomes our lifelong way of relating. Very early on, the young boy is trained to make it on his own. To be independent. As young girls, we are trained to see our value in the partnerships we form. To symbiose.

At the beginning of life, symbiosis is of prime, positive importance to both sexes. It begins as a growth process, freeing the infant of the fear of being vulnerable and alone, giving her the courage to develop. If we get enough symbiosis in the beginning, we will later remember its pleasures and be able to look for it in others; to accept and immerse ourselves in it when we find it, and *move out of it again* when we are sated, knowing that we will always be able to re-establish it. We will trust and enjoy love, take it as part of life's feast—not feel we must devour every crumb because it may never come again. If we do not experience this first symbiosis, we look for it the rest of our lives, but even if we do find it, we will not trust it—hanging on so desperately that we will suffocate the other person, boring him to death with our cries of, "You don't love me!" until, in fact, we have made it come true.

The first meaning of symbiosis is found in botany, where it means two organisms, a host and parasite, who cannot live without each other. In the animal world, it often means a slightly different relationship, one of mutual help; the bird that wins its food by obligingly picking the hippopotamus's teeth clean is a partner in symbiosis. In human terms, the meaning shifts a little once again. The most classical symbiosis is the fetus in the womb. Here we have an illustration of two different kinds of symbiosis.

The fetus is in *physical* symbiosis with the mother; literally, it cannot live without her. The mother (most of the time) is in *psychological* symbiosis with the unborn baby. She can live without it, but pregnancy gives her the feeling of more abundant life. In this way, the fetus nourishes her. In our earliest symbiosis with mother, both partners win.

At birth we don't know there is anything outside of ourselves. Our unfocused eyes cannot differentiate shapes, we don't know where mother ends and we begin. When we reach out our hand, she is there to touch. When we cry, we are fed or picked up. We rule the world! No wonder we are so reluctant to give up mother; she sustains this wonderful feeling of total power, "infantile omnipotence." In a sense we continue to be physically connected to her, just as mother psychologically still experiences us as almost a part of her body, her own narcissistic extension. The symbiosis is mutual, complete, and satisfying.

Gradually, our eyes begin to be able to focus. Things, people, are near or far. We become aware that another person is there—mother— but she is so close that we still see her as merged with us, not separate. She is different from anybody else, anything else. She is still us, we are her.

In this early stage of symbiosis, the good mother sees her needs as entirely secondary to her infant's. This is to mutual advantage: the infant is enabled with gradual comfort to get used to the idea of powerlessness; nor is it presented as very terrible anyway: mother is always near to fix things. As for the mother, knowing what the child wants, feeling with her baby's skin, sensing with her tiny daughter's eyes or ears or stomach, gives her an almost mystic feeling of union and being needed. It is an experience of transcendence.

In the next stage, we may begin to distinguish our body from mother's, but can't separate our thoughts from hers. When we are wet, she changes us. Hungry? She knows it almost as quickly as we do, and food arrives. But now anxiety begins to enter. When mother is not around, the blanket isn't pulled up, the breast or bottle isn't offered. Our power has begun to erode. Anxiously we keep watch for her. If she's around, everything is OK. If she's not, we can die. When mother's love is steady and uninterrupted, we gradually come to be able to do without having her around for longer and longer periods of time. Trust is being born.

Instead of clutching at mother in fear that she will leave, the infant lets her go, secure in the knowledge that she always comes back when needed; meanwhile, there are these colored toys to play with. But if the fear should ever strike that mother may not come back, that she may be inattentive to our needs, that she does not care about us, growth stops. Interest in bright lights or playing with crib toys disappears. The self has been swallowed by fear. The baby can think of nothing else in the world but that mother must never go away again. We must not be left alone. The foundations of a lifetime of uncertainty have been laid.

The word for the next stage of development is *separation*. The child, more or less secure in the symbiotic love of her mother, begins to feel she can do with a bit less of it. She wants to venture out into a larger world. As important as it was for the mother to symbiose with her infant when that was all baby could understand, it is equally important now for her to begin to let her child go, to let the daughter proceed into her own life according to her inner, psychic timetable. The long march toward individuality and self-reliance has begun.

Symbiosis and the early beginnings of separation do not proceed on one long, smooth, upwardly inclined plane. There are ups and downs, of course. Nor does any single absence of mother when we want her mean that traumatic damage will inevitably result. *Mother doesn't have to be perfect.* She merely has to be a "good enough mother," in words of the English psychoanalyst, D. W. Winnicott,[1] to give the growing child a feeling of "basic trust"[2]—that on the whole people and things, life itself, are more to be trusted than not. We all know how quickly children recover from this or that emotional upset, if the upsetting event doesn't go on too long, or occur too frequently.

In the normal course of events, a sense of self begins to emerge at about three months; the child shows she is reacting to specific events or faces: she smiles. Around eight months, the child can tell the difference between mother and a stranger. At the age of one and a half (give or take), the growth process away from mother picks up momentum. We start to separate from her more and more, *to want to separate.* It's a beautiful, exciting world, and there are so many things other than mother to bite, touch, taste, see. The self is becoming more and more conscious.

The fascinating process of growing away from mother and becoming your own person is crucial between eighteen months and three years—a period of life to which Dr. Margaret Mahler has given the name "Separation-Individuation."[3] By age three or three and a half, if we are lucky and mother has been loving, we emerge with a sense of ourselves as separate people—still loved by mother, but with a life of our own that is not hers. All those hours and hours of attention she has paid us, the sacrifice of her sleep and most of her waking hours, have become part of us. Memory has developed, and we can feel her tender concern follow us around like a supporting arm on our shoulders.

"The first demonstration of social trust in the baby," says Erik Erikson in *Childhood and Society,* "is the ease of his feeling, the depth of his sleep, the relaxation of his bowels."[4] The child has begun to trust his mother, to relax; he doesn't have to keep awake or sleep with one ear open for fear she will go away. "The infant's first social achievement, then," Dr. Erikson goes on, "is his willingness to let the mother out of sight without undue anxiety or rage, because she has become an inner certainty. . . ."[5]

This need to feel a basic trust of life is essential for both males and females. But because of the inevitable modeling relationship between mother and daughter, we are not just stuck for life with the sense of basic trust she did or didn't give us. We are also stuck with the image of her as a woman, *her* sense of basic trust that *her* mother gave her. A boy will grow up, and following his father's lead, leave home, support himself, start a family. He may or may not be successful. Much of his success will depend upon the basic sense of trust his mother gave him; but he will not identify with his mother. He will not base all his relationships on what he had with her (unless he is a certain kind of homosexual).

But a girl who did not get this sense of basic trust, though she may leave her mother's house, get a job, marry and have children, will never really feel comfortable on her own, in control of her own life. Part of her is still anxiously tied to her mother. She doesn't trust herself and others. She cannot believe there is another way to be because this is how her mother was. It is also how most other women are. If our mothers are not separate people themselves, we cannot help but take in their anxiety and fear, their need to be symbiosed with someone. If we do not see them involved in their own work, or enjoying something just for themselves, we too do not believe in accomplishment or pleasure outside of a partnership. We denigrate anything that we alone experience; we say, "It's more fun when there's someone else along." The fact is we're afraid to go any place alone. How many adult women have you heard joke, "I haven't decided what I'm going to be when I grow up. . . ."? How many women call their husbands Daddy or Pappa, and think of their children as *"my* daughter," instead of Betsy or Jane?

Emotionally unseparated from mother, just as afraid as she was, we repeat the process with our own daughter. An unfortunate history, a way of growing up female that our society has amazingly left unchallenged. Being cute and helpless, clinging, clutching, holding on for dear life, becomes our method for survival—and ultimate defeat.

It is important to understand it is not the mere number of hours that mother spends that assures the child of those early, satisfying, symbiotic feelings of warmth and life assurance she needs. "It is better," says Dr. Robertiello, "that the child doesn't get her mother's full attention than a charade of a mother who would rather be at her office or out having lunch with her friends. Inauthentic behavior, especially when it comes disguised as love, creates the worst problems." A lifetime pattern is set up in which the person feels that love is faked, easily distracted or at best, grudgingly given.

It is the *quality* of attention we get from mother that counts. If we, as infants, are cold or hungry and she doesn't notice; if when she looks at us she is thinking of something else and so we do not see on her face a smile of love, we are deprived. A shadow on the sun. "I was always thinking about so many things, I had so many ideas and ambitions when my child was little," Dr. Helene Deutsch told me, "that when my little son was with me, he would take hold of my chin with his hands and focus my attention on him. He knew I was thinking about something else."

Incomplete, unsatisfying, or interrupted symbiosis stamps a woman for life. We missed something from our mothers; despaired; grew guarded—and learned early a cramped line of defense: not to expect too much from the world. Even as our lovers hold us we cannot believe they will not leave. Our husband complains that we are suffocating him: "What more do you want of me?" he cries. We cannot give it a name but we feel a distance is there. As mothers, we turn and cling to our own daughter. "Call me when you get there, no matter what time it is."

Life for the woman who did not get enough symbiotic closeness as a child becomes a problem of juggling security *v.* satisfaction. We marry the first man who asks, afraid we may not be asked again; we take a safe civil service job instead of braving the risks of an independent career. "Unless the little girl has had a successful symbiotic period with her mother," says Dr. Robertiello, "she is still fixed on that warmth she missed. In babies we see this in the fact that they don't have the energy available over and beyond this craving to explore the sound and meaning of the words mother speaks, or the amount of new space she gives the infant to crawl in. In grown people, unsatisfied symbiosis is often expressed in terms of low energy too. They are too tired for this, not interested in that, never believe in themselves enough to try all out for any of the fascinating and novel aspects of life that present themselves. But if they are able to attain separation through therapy, we see a dramatic difference. There is a sudden burst of energy, of creativity. We see this in their lives, their work, their sexuality."

Each of us knows people, on the other hand, who obviously were emotionally deprived in their first years, but who are successful enough in their adult lives. All is not lost if we missed out on early symbiosis. But it is unlikely—most psychiatrists would say impossible —for these people to enjoy fully their success or be emotionally secure in what success brings. These are people who say, "I have all this or I have accomplished all that, but what does it all mean?" Emotionally impoverished as infants, they are emotionally impoverished still amid all their worldly success.

Society plays us a dirty trick by calling us the loving sex. The flattery is meant to make us proud of our weakness, our inability to be independent, our imperative need to belong to someone. We are limited to need and nurture, leaving erotic love to men. A "lovesick" man makes people uncomfortable because the condition weakens him, jeopardizes his manhood, cuts down his productivity. But a woman who can't think clearly, who dreams over her law books, loses weight and walks into brick walls arouses warm feelings in everybody. Men and women both know how good it feels to be knocked out by love, but someone has to mind the store. Since women haven't got anywhere to go anyway, and a needy woman makes a man work harder in order to provide for two, romance itself becomes fuel for the economic mill.

He will make love to us in the moonlight to the sound of violins, but in the morning he will shower, shave, put on his clothes, and go to the office in pursuit of his "real" interests. In almost every novel you read or film you see, love is a disaster for the female protagonist, depriving her of initiative, courage, or sense of order, sending her down into masochism and loss of self.

Modern corporations, hiring Ph.D.'s in psychology to set employment policies, take advantage of female fears as standard business practice. Often mistakenly called "paternal" organizations because they are run by men, they are psychologically much more like giant mothers, havens of symbiosis which await us: secretaries, clerks, office managers, assistants, women who will work loyally, part of the "great corporate family" for twenty-five years in dull, safe, routine jobs—willing victims of shrewd personnel people who know we would rather have the cozy joys of the Widget Division Glee Club, and going on the Annual Company Picnic, than striking out alone (leaving mother) to get higher pay. Thousands, millions of women never leave the boss who "needs" them, and happily work overtime for him because they symbiotically feel his career is theirs, they are part of him. Nevertheless when his raise comes, it is not divided into two shares. In sex or in business, the cost of symbiosis comes high.

A good mother finds it very hard to let her baby fall on its face the first time it takes a few steps, but she knows that is the way you learn. A little boy will crawl away, try to maneuver the stairs, even push his mama away when she interferes because the impulse to grow is so strong. She is afraid for him but knows she must train him in courage. Before they have left for kindergarten little boys have learned to push away little girls who want a kiss. Mom has already begun to teach him not to cling to her, much as they both may still want it. "Don't baby him," her husband says. "Let him go," the culture warns. The boy is emerging from symbiosis into the pleasures of separation. The world opens before him. Through experience, practice, and repetition the boy learns that accidents happen but are not fatal, rejections are lived through, the self goes on.

Little girls, on the other hand, get the opposite training. The great, crippling imperative is Nothing Must Ever Hurt My Little Girl. She is denied any but the most wrapped-in-cellophane experiences. When a little girl ventures into the backyard and hurts herself, mother doesn't encourage her daughter to try again, as she would her son. She holds the girl tighter, fearing for them both because she's been there; she has been hurt, anxious, and afraid much of her life. "I knew this would happen," mother says, repeating to her daughter a lifelong warning to herself, implanting the notion that women are tender, fragile, easily and irremediably hurt by life.

Other elements of the mother-daughter relationship inhibit the little girl's sense of adventure: she seeks kisses but expects rejection. In mother's earliest and usually unconscious efforts to handle feelings of competition with her daughter, she teaches the little girl not to expect too much physical attention from daddy. "Come away. Daddy has important papers to go over." Mother is teaching us that men don't have "our" need for love.

The message to the little girl is clear: there is only one person who will never leave her, who always has time for her. Even if there should be an absence of mother's kisses, it is not due to mother's lack of love. If only the little girl were more obedient, if only mother had more time, if, if, if. . . .

We forget the faulty performance. The promise that love will be available next time has seduced us. Brothers, sisters, friends—they are all unreliable. Only mother will be ever constant.

"You can see why a little girl may cling to her mother through fear of the threatening outside world," says Dr. Robertiello, "but what must be realized is that mother isn't an ogre, keeping the girl locked up for spite. Mother has real fears and needs too, which seem to be met by symbiosis with her daughter. Too often, the mother never separated from *her* mother, and as the grandmother gets older and mama begins to feel the loss of that secure tie, she substitutes a bond to her daughter. She fears more than anything that she may end up alone, with no one to tell her what to do. She wants to be 'a prisoner of love.'

"Because of this primary, unconscious tie to her own mother, the wife/mother was never free to give her first loyalty to anyone new, including her husband. Oh, she may have had a sudden spurt of separation on getting married, a fine new flush of sexuality for a while. But all too often, when her daughter was born, she settled back into that less exciting, but known-and-safe feeling she had with her mother . . . only doing it this time with her daughter. She cuts off her independence, diminishes her sexuality, her intellect; she is no longer a young woman but a 'matron' instead; a mother. Now she's safe forever. She's got a guarantee against ever being alone again for the rest of her life because her daughter is going to outlive her."

No wonder partings between mothers and daughters at airports and railroad stations are so packed with guilt.

To explain separation, how we build an identity, we must go back once more to symbiosis, just as the tiny child who is learning to be on her own keeps going back to mother. The urge that brings baby, in panic at being alone, suddenly crawling back, to see that mother is "there," that "everything is all right," is as inevitable as the Second Law of Thermodynamics.

Technically, this is called "the rapprochement stage," but I prefer a more familiar term child psychologists use: "refueling." Having touched base with mommy, thus refueled, the child is confident and ready to venture out again. The good mother understands the frightened return, but does not use it as a warning not to leave again; in fact, once she sees the child is refueled, she encourages it to go off again. The clinging mother magnifies the child's fears: "Ah, poor baby. It's so scary out there. Don't ever go out again unless I come with you."

A mother like this is so unseparated from her daughter that she cannot figure out if the anxiety is her own or her child's. In the end, it doesn't matter: the girl will pick up the mother's fear and make it her own. The outside world comes to seem threatening, forbidding. When she grows up and is away from home, she worries that the gas was left on, that somebody is sick or dying. Above all, she does not like to do anything alone. She wants to feel *connected* at all times, at any cost.

There is a phrase a woman I once knew used to use at the end of an evening. She had been a Martha Graham dancer and had had a successful life of her own. By the time I met her, she was married and the mother of two. "Gee, it's been a great night," someone would say. "Let's find a place to have ham and eggs and Irish Coffee." My friend would always demur. "Well," she would say to her husband, "we've been all around Robin Hood's barn, it's time to touch home base." They would leave. Childhood phrases, childhood emotions. I think this story is a metaphor for her whole life—beginning with her decision, made years before, to give up dancing because the road trips made her "too nervous." Her need to touch home base—not to be separated from some idealized notion of security—always brought her running home when most people would have gone on.

In explaining how a daughter's sense of adventurousness can be nipped in the bud, Dr. Robertiello speaks of the mother's anxiety: "She is the first one afraid when she realizes *she* is alone, without her child. So she decides her child needs her, or is in danger. She goes running after the little girl. The daughter may be sitting safe in the backyard playing with the daisies, but here is mother, alarmed, worried, calling her home, retrieving the little girl *before* the girl feels the need to return, to refuel. So the daughter develops a sense that even if you are having a good time, something may be going wrong back home."

However, every action has an equal and opposite reaction. Beginning around fourteen to eighteen months and continuing to about the third year, the child begins to experiment with resistance to mother's demands on her. This try at self-assertion is marked by the almost constant use of the word *NO*.

This is a very important experience for the child, separating out what she wants to do—even if it is not to make up her mind yet—and what mother wants her to do. *"We* want to go to the park, don't *we?"* says mother, using the symbiotic pronoun as imperiously as any queen. "No," says the little boy, asserting an early step toward individuality and separation. *"I* don't want it." Everyone who hears him applauds—even mother. "What a little man he is! He knows his own mind, just like his father." Girls get the opposite treatment.

Says child psychiatrist Sirgay Sanger: "Boys have an easier time in this period because mother thinks, 'Well, I don't know enough about boys. I'd better leave him alone.' There is also a cultural bias against mothers who keep their sons tied to them. But if her child is a girl? Well, she knows all about girls. She's the expert. So she gives her daughter less latitude, less chance for growth. She rides like a steamroller over her girl's individuality. 'Come on,' mother will say to the little girl. 'You always like to go shopping with me, so we're going to do that now.' Right away the little girl becomes less assertive. She loses a lot of her gumption. This starts as early as the time between the first and second year."

Separation, outgrowing the need for degrees of symbiosis inappropriate to the present stage of development, is not a case of black or white. Theoretically, separation from mother should be completed by age three or three and a half, "but I think it goes on as long as we live," says Dr. Robertiello. "I've never met anyone yet for whom it has ended, man or woman. We are all very much connected to our mothers or some substitute. I think it's especially acute with women because the girl has that constant image of her mother from which she never escapes." Vital as it is in our first years of life, the only way to describe symbiosis between mother and daughter after age three is unhealthy. It is a sticky issue because our culture confuses symbiosis and love; *but when we are grown, symbiosis and real love are mutually exclusive.* Love implies a separation. "I love you" can only have meaning if there is an "I" to love "you."

In a symbiotic relationship, there is no real concern for the other person. There is just a need, a craving to be connected, no matter how destructive. Marriage is often seen as releasing the daughter from her symbiotic tie to her mother. In fact, it may be merely a switch to her husband. Now he must support her, supply her with life, make her feel good about herself. Unless we have separated from mother long before marriage, it is almost impossible to set up a healthy relationship with a man.

The best definition of love I know is psychoanalyst Harry Stack Sullivan's: love means you care almost as much about the other person's safety, security, and satisfaction as you do about your own. I feel this is a realistic definition; you *can't* love somebody else more than yourself. The truly loving mother is one whose interest and happiness is in seeing her daughter as a person, not just a possession. It is a process of being so generous and loving that she will forgo some of her own pleasure and security to add to her daughter's development. If she does this in a genuine way, she really does end up with that Love Insurance Policy. The mother will have someone who cares about her forever—not a guilty, resentful love, but a daughter who gives her love freely.

"Genuine mother-daughter love?" said psychiatrist Mio Fredland when I first interviewed her in April 1974. "I think it implies a recognition on the part of each of the separateness of the other, and a respect for the other. In the case of the daughter, she has to first love her mother so that she can love herself as a woman; then she can love her mother back when she is more mature. But she must first 'take in' the good mother while she is still an infant; then she will emerge from infancy as a separate person.

"How do I feel about my daughter? I think she's heavenly. I was just waiting for her. In fact, I had dreams about her when I was pregnant, and she's just exactly the way she was in my dreams. I wanted a daughter for many reasons. One of them was that I wanted to make up in my relationship with my daughter, for what I had missed in my relationship with my own mother. My mother wasn't really there. She loved me and did her best to be a good mother, but she was so frightened of so many things. My daughter is exactly what I wanted all my life."

It is interesting to note how Dr. Fredland's feelings about her daughter had changed by the time I interviewed her again, one year later in April 1975:

"How do I avoid seeing my daughter as a narcissistic extension? My training helps me to see her objectively, of course, but I also think my attitude has changed since we talked last year. As she has become older and more her own person, I feel more detached from her, which doesn't mean I love her less . . . but I love her in a different way. I see her as quite separate from myself. I see what her talents are, what her interests are, and what her shortcomings are. If you allow the child to detach herself from you, *she* will draw the limits, *she* will tell you what she insists on for her living space."

I like these two statements by Mio Fredland. They show real growth in mother-daughter love. Dr. Fredland's first comments were made at a time when she still felt her daughter to be a kind of narcissistic extension of herself. One year later, the mother's focus has turned outward upon the girl, *her* separation and growth.

Most of the time it is too difficult to examine what we really have with mother because there is not enough distance between us. Is she a "bad mother"? Are we "bad daughters"? Either proposition is so emotionally loaded, so *hot,* that we cannot reply sensibly. I would also suggest that another reason they are so difficult is that they are put as moralistic propositions. We are asking the wrong questions. The real question is, Have the two of us loved each other in the early years and separated in the later so that we allow each other room enough, air enough, freedom enough to continue that love?

Those telephone calls to mother, are they done out of real love or a need to maintain symbiosis? If we call her happily, voluntarily, because we get a lift out of talking to her—that is love. If we move to the phone—though it be daily—with a heavy feeling of constraint and duty, with an anxious need that these calls never seem to fill, if they leave us in tears, angry, defensive, or guilty, then, though the culture may call ours a loving mother-daughter relationship if only for the sheer size of our telephone bill, I would not.

Another place to look for clues as to whether we may still be overly tied to mother is in our relationship to men, to other women, and in our approach to work. The need to cling, fear of loss, the inability to push forward and/or compete—these are not patterns of behavior picked up after we got on that plane and left home. They are patterns of action and reaction learned at home during our formative years with mother.

I have known women whose mothers loved them for themselves

and then let them go. Their hallmark is a consistency of behavior; they do not play the chameleon, changing to suit every new personality or situation they encounter. When they talk to their mothers they remain grown women—and do not relapse into childish voices, querulous tones, and evasive answers. When asked what they think, they give a straight answer. They are not afraid the other person will become angry at their candor. Faced with a difficult emotional situation, they may not be able to resolve it right away, but their first impulse is not to try to spy out the response expected of them by others. The question they ask is, What do I want, how do I feel about this? They have a certainty about themselves.

On the other hand, uncertain people often make their fears come true. A woman tells me: "Right from the start, I knew it wouldn't last. You know what he said when he walked out on me? 'I'm sick and tired of you asking if I love you and then not believing it when I say I do.'" Insecurity often masks itself as its opposite. It does not surprise us, for instance, that the macho stud often has doubts about his virility. In the same way, women are accused of being vain, of being caught up in self-admiration. The truth is we have no certainty at all about the way we look.

A woman friend with a beautiful figure constantly complains about her "huge" hips. She tells me how lucky I am not to have to worry about such things. She is my height. Finally I ask what her hips measure. I tell her mine are two inches bigger. "But they can't be!" she cries. "You have a great figure, your hips can't be bigger than mine!" We refuse the facts today because the image was set at a time we can no longer remember by someone who knew everything. We do not spend all those hours in front of the mirror because of vanity, because we are in love with ourselves. It is because of anxiety. Something is wrong with our basic narcissism.

Until recently, narcissism was thought to be a kind of pathological development—a dirty word to the psychiatrist and general public alike. Freud thought of it as regression, a withdrawal of interest from other people and reality, a morbid concentration of the libido (energy) on the self. Today, we make a sharp distinction between this faulty sense of self, which is called "secondary narcissism," and healthy, primary narcissism.[6]

Secondary narcissism is pathological because it attempts to fill the void in the healthy self-image with an intense preoccupation with the self. This can be expressed through an excessive focus on appearance, or physical and emotional symptoms (hypochondria). A person like this is trying to make up for a lack of attention in childhood—most especially in the first year of life—by paying the same kind of exaggerated attention to herself that she needed from her mother but did not get at that stage of development. Secondary narcissism is marked by anxious repetition; since it is an ineffective substitute, we can never let it rest. The irony is that these are the women who are usually called vain because they can never stop praising themselves, never cease trying to attract attention or get compliments.

They are a splendid example—if only in reverse—of how not too much but too little admiration "spoils" children. All the praise in the world cannot help them, nourish them, once they've missed out at the appropriate time. Compliments fly right past as though meant for someone standing behind them.

Usually it is easy for mother to gratify our narcissistic needs when we are first born. In the early stages of symbiosis, we are still so meshed, so undifferentiated from her, that to love us is to love her-self. But as we grow away from her, it takes an informed, mature kind of selfless love for her to accept that baby's needs are not always her needs. Mother must grow herself, to give the child room and space to gratify its desires even if they are in conflict with, outrage or disappoint, hers. In early stages of toilet training, for instance, the baby may be proud of her first productions, pick them up and offer them to mother as tokens of love. If this conflicts with mother's image of us as nice little girls made of pink ribbons, serious trouble can ensue. She must let us be separate enough from her so that we can develop at our own pace, not hers. She must love us for what we do and need, not just when we coincide with her fantasy image of the perfect baby.

"The first time I saw my newborn daughter, Katie," says Dr. Leah Schaefer, "she was immense—edemic, water-logged. 'Oh, God,' I thought, 'don't tell me she is going to be one of those fat kids?' I had this sudden fantasy of me as this trim, chic, *Ladies' Home Journal* mother dragging this eight-year-old into Best and Company, hoping against hope I'd be able to find something to cover all that fat. On the third day, I was combing my hair in a mirror and it occurred to me: maybe she isn't going to like having a mother who is older than her friends' mothers. Maybe she's going to want a park mother in-stead of a professional mother. *Maybe she won't like me!* Just to have said that to myself was the most freeing thing I could have done for her. Just as I had given myself freedom to think it was possible she wouldn't be the child of my dreams, I had also given her the freedom not to have to approve of me. It was an extraordinary experience, fundamental to everything in our relationship."

What mother hasn't dreamed that her baby will be some ideal creature? Side by side, intertwined with, and the very first cause of mother's symbiotic love for us is her own self love. She begins by loving us because we are her own body and spirit made flesh—a narcissistic extension of herself. We are going to be everything she wanted out of life.

"But the dream doesn't last more than a few months," says Dr. Sanger. "The baby can't give what mother wants—she is asking that it make *her* dreams come true. Reality quickly steps in. The baby lets mother know it is not going to fulfill her every fantasy. It is colicky. It cries and vomits. It lets mother know that it has a real life of its own." It is a first hint of separation; some mothers become displeased at these signs of the child's self struggling to be born. They are hurt or disappointed. The adoration turns off. When the baby looks into mother's face, she no longer sees herself in a loving, kind mirror; no longer is the little girl "the fairest of them all." "Mother's adoring looks may stop," continues Dr. Sanger, "because she feels the baby is not responding to her enough. She takes this as an accusation. She has a very strong and self-reverent ideal of how baby should be toward her and it is not being satisfied. Very simply, once more the mother turns off." Mother's inability to allow her baby an authentic, separate life of its own has disrupted the relationship between them right from the start.

Healthy, primary narcissism is rooted in infancy. Mother is the first "objective" voice we hear; her face is our first mirror. When we are born, she cannot hear enough wonderful things being said about us. She absolutely absorbs the praise of friends and relatives as they coo and gurgle about our beauty, size, and amazing agility. She transfers it to us like heat. At this stage she is rightly so tied to us that she doesn't know where praise for us leaves off and admiration for her giving birth to such a miraculous baby begins. We feed her narcissism and she feeds ours. It is the height of symbiosis at its best, primary narcissism functioning as it should. Our ego is being born.

All this is grist for the mill of identity. Out of this experience will come a person who is going to have a good image of herself. Someone who will be able to walk into rooms without undue shyness, believe that other people like her, accept praise for her work as her due, and smile at the nice reflection of herself in other people's eyes just as she smiles back at what she sees in the mirror. When a man says, "I love you," she is pleased, not gripped by disbelief and fear.

Does this describe you, or women you know? What happened? What becomes twisted, even when life begins with strong primary narcissistic gratification? Why do we either not continue to seek it in later life, or, if we do, cannot enjoy it—take no nourishment from it to feed our self-esteem?

"Five years ago," says Dr. Robertiello, "we didn't know what narcissism was all about. Now we know that healthy narcissism is a normal and necessary part of growth. Today we try to get people in touch with their needs. For instance, in group therapy, I'll have people stand up, show off, give a speech about themselves as though they've just died and have to give a eulogy. Even with this explicit permission—even an order—to say something nice about themselves, this is the hardest thing in the world for people to do. They'd rather take their clothes off.

"The reason they are so upset at seeking praise, getting a good feeling about themselves from others, is that as infants they didn't get enough adulation from their mothers. This kind of mother is usually someone who is very condemnatory of being 'conceited.' So that when the child, in a normal, healthy way, does make some attempt to get this, the mother not only squashes her but humiliates her too for showing off. Eventually babies like this grow into people who either can't seek praise or are unable to believe it when they do get it. Today we are trying to get people past this feeling of being ashamed of their needs. We encourage them to go out and find people to give them the praise they need in a very open, direct way."

Take this as a familiar enough occurrence: a mother who could not hear enough praise for her infant, suddenly begins to say to admiring friends when the girl is three or four, "Now, that's enough. She gets enough praise from her daddy. We don't want a conceited little girl on our hands." Primary narcissistic gratification stops.

What has happened to turn mother off praise and begin to make the little girl self-conscious about getting it—and unable to take it in when she does—is that the mother has begun to project upon the child her own fear of seeming irrationally conceited. Now that we are no longer infants—little mute, passive, adorable receptacles for admiration—but have become active people instead, mother identifies with us. She knows how she would feel if she were getting this extravagant praise. *She projects herself into our minds because she is not separate*—and brings with her *her* own damaged narcissism, *her* inability to believe compliments, *her* fear that if she let herself think they might be true for one moment, *she* would get a swelled head. When we were infants, she shared the warm praise we got. Now that we are people—her own image—she projects her shame onto us. This is the way in which *her* mother began to undermine and make her feel embarrassed about her own healthy narcissism. Now she is doing it to us.

This is the essence of the chain of low self-esteem and ego-abnegation that binds women through the generations: unless the mother can grant her child her own identity, *unless she is separated,* she will not be able to contain her anxiety at the compliments being showered on a child. Have you ever watched an untalented friend get up and sing at a party? Remember how your skin crawled in embarrassment for her? You felt in yourself her naked hunger for attention and approbation; you felt in yourself in advance the humiliation she would feel when she did not get it. In this experience you have identified yourself with your friend. How much more deeply a mother feels for her daughter, when the little girl, with the trusting, naïve innocence of children, hurries forward to a stranger, seeking a rewarding smile; mother blushes, embarrassed, and snatches the baby from its path.

The seed has been planted: if we do not learn to reject these compliments ourselves, we are not good little girls. We are bad daughters, unlike mother. Mother must be aware of flaws in us we do not suspect and which the stranger will detect in a moment. We blush at our stupidity in thinking we were so lovable.

Mother's shame for us is the expression of her effort to protect us. Picking up her anxiety, we reject the stranger's smile—the approval of the outside world—and turn in toward mother. Mutual lack of separation is reinforced. The very thing—admiration and praise from others—that would give us the courage to grow into ourselves, to fix a clear line between activities that might embarrass mother but have a totally different and positive effect on us, has been erased.

Giving a baby too much praise, love, or adoration is impossible—*just as long as it begins to be accompanied by separation.* If mother didn't let me go, doesn't let me be myself, if she and I continue to be merged in symbiosis, then all the praise in the world isn't going to help—because there isn't any me. There isn't any self-image. There is only "we," and anything good said about me merely because I am an extension of her will make me uncomfortable. It says I am praise-worthy only as part of her; by myself, I barely exist at all.

How many mothers have you heard say to their daughters (of any age), "You look absolutely wonderful!"—without any howevers, buts, or qualifiers like, "—but must you wear so much eye shadow?" When did your mother last say to you, "You did that perfectly, darling!" with the absolute certainty of one individual admiring another?

Says Dr. Sanger: "Almost from birth, we see mothers conveying to their daughters that they aren't good enough as is. Mom doesn't fuss much with her son, but she is constantly adjusting, fixing, trying to perfect this little female picture of herself in the same way she fiddles with her own never-perfect appearance. She can't keep her nagging hands off the girl. We even hear it as the mother hangs over the cra-dle. 'Now, let's fix this little piece of hair. . . .' In time the daughter learns that this kind of attention is a knock. She thought she looked OK, but the instant her mother lays eyes on her, she knows she was wrong."

In time the daughter may learn to shrink from her mother's nag-ging eye or hands. She may go so far away geographically that mother can't reach her. Or she may become tied to mother in a sul-len, half-shrinking, half-dependent relationship, constantly looking and hoping for her mother's promised—but never *felt*—unqualified love. Either way, the mother who never gave us her total approval binds us to her forever. We keep trying for mother's praise because we never outgrow the child's belief that maybe, just once, if we do it right, she will admire us totally in that pure, unqualified way we al-ways wanted.

But mother cannot do it. Since she does not feel separated from us, every tiny failure of ours is *her* failure. When something goes wrong, she says, "How could you do this to me? What will the neighbors say?" Our desires, feelings, actions—even our failures—are not our own.

If a mother experiences herself as unattractive or unsuccessful, she may easily project these negative feelings onto her daughter and make her feel she is a failure too. She may feel competitive with the daughter or push the girl to be the beautiful person she would like to be herself. The combinations and permutations are endless: two peo-ple with two sets of physical, intellectual, emotional and temperamental histories, constantly interacting. A mother can say about a boy, "My son, the doctor." He may be annoyed, but he is not an extension of her. Psychiatrists call this "child wearing"—mother wears the child like an ornament.

A twenty-eight-year-old woman tells me: "When my child was born and the doctor held it up, I started to scream. I thought I saw a penis. Then, thank God, I realized it was a girl." Does the intensity of this mother's wish for a female child fill you with high hopes for the girl's future? I feel a certain foreboding. A mother who wants a daughter that much has such expectations that her girl may never live up to them—never get away from the mother for whom she is such a pleasure-giving service. As long as she is mother's little girl, the praise will not stop. If she tries to grow up and grow away, the approval, which has come to mean life itself, will stop. *Narcissistic gratification without separation is a trap.* Praise for yourself alone is lovely. Praise because what you do makes me look good—that denies you count for yourself at all.

Daughters with mothers like this often grow up in a paradox: "My mother loves me, she has given me everything. She is concerned for me, is interested in everything I do. We write often, we talk often, we visit often, and if I ever need someone to talk to, I know I can count on her . . . but why do I feel something is missing in my life?" Daughters who have tried to live out their mothers' dreams end up with a diminished self. Little is ever felt—success, beauty, marriage, wealth—because the daughter has always been her mother's extension and not her own person.

To one degree or another this describes most of us. We go through life wondering after the fact: why didn't I let myself love that terrific man, grab that opportunity, do that exciting thing? We didn't because mother wouldn't have. We cut the self-actualizing, individuating things out of our lives because that's what she would have done, though *to have done them anyway, in spite of her, would have strengthened our separation.*

"The cause of most of the indignities that are labeled 'female' usually begins at birth," says Dr. Sanger, citing mother/infant studies going on now at St. Luke's Hospital in New York. "The subtle deprivation of physical demonstrations of affection that little girls often suffer from their mothers makes women more vulnerable to fear and the loss of attachment; they were never sure of it to begin with. It makes women greedy to hold on even to men who treat them badly, more possessive and competitive for whatever crumbs of love may be available to them.

"This deprivation that little girls suffer begins very early, and there need not be any conscious prejudice or bias on the mother's part. If a little boy does something cute or winning, he will be rewarded by mother with a fond pat, a touch, a physical expression of approval he cannot misunderstand. On the other hand, if a little girl infant performs the same action, we notice that she will often be rewarded only with a smile on her mother's lips, or a verbal compliment. Neither baby of course is capable of making any comparison; both children would be said to have an approving, accepting mother. But in the strong feeling of physical approval he is getting from his mother, the boy unconsciously—even before he is able to speak—begins to build his bank account of lifelong self-acceptance. For the girl, the absence of physicality—which is the most direct communication of security and approval a mother can give an infant—means she will not be nearly as rich in autonomy and self-esteem."

Dr. Sanger concludes: "In time, the little girl may come to feel that mother doesn't fondle her enough because she isn't good enough, not valuable enough. Very often, what makes things worse is that the kind of touching she does get from mother—primping, adjusting, fiddling, fixing—is a negative kind. It tells the girl there *is* something about her that is not right, missing, not good enough."

Though Dr. Sanger's studies are documented with filmed, objective evidence, most mothers with whom I've discussed these findings deny any degree of difference in the physicality they show their daughters as opposed to that they show their sons. The idea is deeply threatening. A woman will smile fondly at the old saw about mothers being fond of their sons while fathers prefer daughters; but when you try to translate the idea into personal terms—that maybe she kissed and hugged her son more than she did her daughter—she is offended. But no great psychological mystery is being presented here. Simple common sense and experience tell us that women kiss, touch, and find it more "natural" to hug men than women.

Great consequences follow for the psychological life of women from this everyday fact. "It's like the sapling," says Dr. Robertiello. "If you make a small scratch on its bark, when it grows into a big tree, it will have a big cut in it. The earlier something happens, the bigger the impact. These things aren't irreversible, but they are time-specific. If you didn't have that mother who absolutely adored you and whose face and whole body manner showed it during that first year, a mother who loved you enough for yourself to let you go by the end of the third year, it's awfully hard, no matter what happens from then on, to make up for it later."

In fact, after the child is eighteen months old or so, it is usually destructive to try to make up for the kind of closeness that should have been there from birth. Here's how one thirty-seven-year-old remembers what happened when her mother tried to give her the kind of love as a little girl that she had really needed as an infant:

"I have a photo of me being held up in my christening dress by two enormous nursemaids. Years later I asked my mother why she wasn't in the picture. 'Oh,' she said, 'I was out antiquing.' Before I was three, I was sent to nursery school. I remember not liking it, but my mother said I went off with a bottle under one arm, some extra diapers under the other, and I waved the bottle and said, 'Hi, kids.' She thought that was a wonderful adjustment. Then my younger sister died—I was five—and that changed everything. My mother became tremendously possessive of me. Of course I responded to all that love she offered—I was a very needy little five-year-old—but it crippled me for years. I may have been insecure, but I had worked out ways of dealing with that situation. When my mother moved in with all that suffocating love, it just took away all the security I'd won on my own. I can remember that my fears and insecurities really began about that age. I'd have been better off if she'd continued to just let me alone."

The primary rule is always that a mother can't go wrong, *ever,* by encouraging her child after age one and a half to be as individuated and separated as possible. If she was not as good a mother before as she would like to have been, she must get over her guilty desires to overcompensate, and place herself on the side of the child's developing ego. The symbiotic train has left.

In the name of fairness, and reality too, let me add an important postscript which is true not only for this chapter but of this whole book: looking over our shoulder at what mother may or may not have done so many years ago locks us into the past. "She did it. There is nothing I can do about it." *Blaming mother keeps us passive, tied to her.* It helps us avoid taking responsibility for ourselves.

All any mother can do is her best. She doesn't have to be perfect—just a "good enough" mother. Unfortunately, children are more single-minded than adults in their standards. "Children are so dependent on their parents," says Dr. Sanger, "that any flaw or imperfection seems to the child to threaten her/his existence. 'If mother is forgetful or careless about this little matter, maybe next time she won't be able to take care of me at all.' It is directly tied with the nurturance, the sustenance of life."

Perhaps it is too much to ask of children that they appreciate complexities, but is it too much to ask now that we are grown? Mother seems so godlike to children that they forget she too is subject to the vicissitudes of life. Perhaps the family was poor. Maybe father drank or ran after other women. Perhaps the child herself brought certain temperamental traits into life which made her develop in a manner no mother could have helped.

"One of the major resistances in analytic work," says child psychiatrist Aaron Esman, "is the notion, 'It was my mother's fault.' Patients don't want to see their own responsibility, so they blame mother. In our post-Freudian world, it's very fashionable, but to blame mother means one doesn't have to examine one's self, to face one's own problems. Parent-baiting, mother-baiting uses up energy that might better go into examining the wrong choices one has made oneself." Brooding over past injustices, we have little emotion left over to create a better future.

Those of us who had rejecting mothers are often drawn to men with the same cold temperaments. We try to manipulate warmth from them. This is merely to repeat the past. We would be better off giving up the sour comfort of recriminations and finding someone who doesn't have to be cajoled but gives warmth easily and gladly. Our job as adults is to understand the past, learn its lessons, and then let it go. Blaming mother is just a negative way of clinging to her still.

Chapter 3

A TIME
TO LET GO

Over the years I've collected from family attics a sepia-toned history of my mother's youth. My grandfather photographed everything. The pictures hang in their original ornate frames in a hallway in my house where guests invariably stop. "Who's this?" They point to a young woman bent low over the neck of a horse in midair. "My mother at the Pittsburgh Steeplechase," I say. "And these people?" they ask. I tell them that the woman seated at the grand piano is my mother once again, and the others are her sisters and brother. Most of my friends don't know my mother's family, of course; but they stare as though they did. Old family photos, even other people's, fascinate—we're all looking for clues.

The expression on my mother's face is always the same: concern. Whether at the peak of a six-foot hurdle or seated placidly at the piano, hands in her lap, the anxious face seems to be waiting for her father to tell her—what? To hide her unattractive hands? But how do you play the piano and hide your hands? And how did my mother, who today will not drive a car over forty miles per hour, jump those horses? I remember as a small child asking her, "Can't I see you jump a horse like in those pictures?" "Oh, Nancy," she would say with a nervous laugh, "that was years ago." At most it had been only six or seven, but I could see even then that all the tea in China wouldn't get my mother back on a horse now that she had left her father's house. I've never seen her ride.

Several years later, in my perpetual attic rummaging, I came across steamer trunks filled with all the riding and hunting regalia of the photos I so loved. I put on my mother's boots, but my feet were already bigger than hers. The heavy riding habits were too uncomfortable even for an eight-year-old in search of a way to be. Luckily I'd had another model of courage from the day I was born. They tell me I was put in my nurse Anna's arms the day I was brought home from the hospital.

Anna lived on Camel cigarettes and murder mysteries. Like me, she preferred horror films and Westerns to the romantic movies my sister, Susie, begged to see. She preferred me to my sister. I don't know why Anna favored me; perhaps she saw the bond between my mother and sister; maybe it was our similar temperament, but no doubt about it, I was Anna's girl. I grew strong on the toast dunked in her coffee and milk. My home was her kitchen, my security her lap, my days began with her rough hands that braided my hair. She made the best meatloaf in the world, and would give it to me raw, seasoned with onions and green peppers, from the bowl. When it was time for the State Fair she made sandwiches out of ground ham and pickle and I remember the aroma and Anna talking of the joys of the roller coaster, as we drove to the fair grounds. I was four and I loved the roller coaster because she was beside me.

When Susie heard footsteps coming and tried to hide the forbidden candle behind the window shade, thus setting the bedroom on fire, it was Anna who pushed aside the other squealing women and extinguished the blaze. Before I went to kindergarten Anna and I made a pact: when I grew up she and I would go West and put Dale Evans out of the horse business. Meanwhile, we settled for protecting the home front, meaning my mother. Mostly, this amounted to avoidance.

From my earliest years I learned from Anna not to tell my mother anything that would cause her anxiety. I don't remember much of my mother from those years. I never got on with my sister when we were little. It seems I was always angry with Susie, ready for a fight. Even as a little girl she was sweet-natured. I considered her "soft," a loser at all the games we played. "Leave me alone," I'd tell her when she tried to cuddle me, "I don't like all that mushy stuff." I didn't mind it with Anna. With her I was allied to a winner, and the first time I left the earth in a plane, along with the thrill of speed and power, I felt *the safety* I'd known when I was four and Anna took me on the roller coaster.

And yet I am my mother's daughter still. In her life I see an eerie and yet comforting precursor of my own. She jumped her father's horses at fourteen, daredevil enough to win silver cups—yet it took my marriage in Rome to get her into an airplane. That reckless physical courage I had as a child—no tree too high or dangerous to climb—has diminished now that I am grown. I will take the cable car to the highest mountain, but I will ski down carefully, always in control. Today I prefer trains and boats to flying. The fear in the house in which I grew up left me when I left that house, but it did not go away. It seemed to have waited its time and I sometimes feel it stirring within me now that I have a house of my own. I wonder how much more of my mother's anxiety I would feel if I had a daughter. If I close my eyes and imagine me with a little girl in my arms, I know the answer too well: too much.

Anna had a boyfriend named Shorty. He used to drive his beat-up Chevrolet behind the house where Anna had taught me to dig to China—my earliest effort to leave home. Shorty would stand just inside the screen door of our linoleum-floored kitchen, as if he wasn't sure Anna was going to let him stay or throw him out. After dinner, the two of them would smoke countless Camel cigarettes that stained their fingers the same brown and yellow as the Camel pack itself.

My mother smoked Chesterfields from a cool gold and white pack, and her fingers were never stained at all. I knew the man who brought her the delicious chocolate butter creams loved her more than she loved him. Sunday evenings he would take us to a restaurant where they played Jack Benny on the radio and served a children's ice cream dessert surrounded by marching animal crackers. The ice cream made us shiver when we went outside and he would wrap us in soft blankets in the back seat of his big car. I didn't know what love meant, but I felt sorry for him; he gave the most beautifully wrapped presents I'd ever seen.

Once Shorty drove Anna, my sister, and me to visit some people in the country. I don't know if they were Anna's or Shorty's friends, but they were different from us. Their whole house was covered in linoleum. And all the children were bathed in a big metal tub in the middle of the kitchen. I'd never seen so many naked people. I don't remember any shame. I can still see the steam and feel the thrill of being part of all that good-humored nakedness. At home we may have been a house of women; that didn't mean you left the bathroom door open. I undress without hesitation among friends, but to this day I am modest around my mother. I worry if other people's bathroom doors don't lock properly, even if I've only gone in to comb my hair. I imagine their embarrassment at walking in on me. But I have the clearest recollection of Anna on the toilet, smoking cigarettes and reading *The Return of the Grave Snatchers*.

There was no worrying about doors during that visit with Anna's friends. There were no doors. There were no bathrooms. On the landing at the top of the stairs there was a bucket, a communal chamber pot in which everyone peed in the night. I don't know where we went during the day, but in my memory the time is night and that bucket is full to the brim, with a puddle around it on the linoleum floor. A nasty place to have to tiptoe in the dark. It is a persistent memory filled with chords of fear and excitement. What made it all OK was that Anna took me there.

I recently told this story to a psychiatrist I was interviewing. "You were probably lucky to have had someone like Anna," he said. "Because she was 'lower class' and physical, it helped you accept your sexuality." It sounds so simplistic, but the minute he told me I knew he was right. I have always known that I owed Anna. I don't like his words "lower class" applied to someone I loved, but I know that sex is different from love, and if I am able to enjoy them both today it is because of Anna, who loved me and let me go. Of one thing I am positive: we never told my mother about those Breughel baths in the kitchen or the bucket of pee. I am her daughter and Anna's too; I carefully wipe out the wash basin with a Kleenex when I have finished my make-up, but I can stand up and pee without wetting my shoes as neatly today as when I was five.

This first trip away from home gave me a taste for other people's houses. I knew our neighbors' homes as well as my own and the sidewalks of Pittsburgh lay before me like an invitation. I wasn't yet in school when I picked up my first nice old couple. They were walking their dog, and when I followed them home they served me cream of tomato soup and peanut butter sandwiches. I learned the traveler's wisdom that things taste better in other people's houses. I also learned that there was always another place at the table for a kid who knew how to turn on the charm. Eventually Anna stopped calling the police because I always came home. I had to. I didn't know how to braid my hair.

Four years later I still hadn't learned and was puzzled, even embarrassed because I couldn't, nor could I answer my mother when she asked why I didn't want Anna to teach me. A big girl like me who wasn't afraid of anything? But Anna knew: every morning I'd go to her with my comb and every night she would take off the rubber bands without pulling my hair while we sat on her bed and listened to "The Lone Ranger." I don't think I ever did learn to braid my hair.

When I was five we moved from Pittsburgh to Charleston, South Carolina. Anna came with us, but she didn't like the South. Maybe she missed Shorty. When I was nine, she left us to go back up north. I don't remember saying good-bye, cannot even recall my last image of her, but I do remember the night, remember the anxiety of the others surrounding me like a protective circle. I was put to bed in my mother's room, something that had never happened before. But I didn't cry. I don't even remember missing Anna in the days that followed. There's such an absence of feeling around her departure that I must have done what children automatically do when the pain is too unbearable: I blanked out everything, Anna and her love, along with her leaving.

There were some Bobbsey Twins books that arrived on later birthdays, but strict as my mother was about thank-you notes, I don't think I wrote Anna back. Many years later an aunt told me she thought she had seen Anna scrubbing floors in the Pittsburgh railroad station. I changed the subject. I could no more accept the guilt that somehow I'd abandoned her to scrubbing floors than I'd been able to accept the rejection of her leaving me. Until I married, I could only think about winning love, prizes, silver cups—winning, winning, *winning*—winning something the world did not easily give.

It was only at night when I closed my eyes that the old separation and guilts came to haunt me. They still do.

In an interview with a young mother in Detroit which lasts five hours, she smiles and talks easily about how she is raising her daughter to be "an individual person." She never uses the word *separation*, and I am not sure if she understands what I mean, or if she is simply light years ahead of me in acceptance of the idea. "You don't think then that mothers have problems separating from their daughters?" I ask as we are parting. She laughs nervously: "When you first said that word, I felt goose flesh up and down my arms." Separation—the word sounds so final, fraught with loss, abandonment, and guilt that mothers don't want to talk about it.

Nor can we as daughters easily contemplate an act so desperate *vis-a-vis* our mothers. We sidestep the issue, taking the word not in its emotional sense but in a cooler, more pragmatic way: separation is so simple *we* don't have the problem at all. "Oh, I've been separated from my mother ever since I left home and came to Chicago five years ago," a woman tells me. No need to face the emotional turbulence of the issue. The problem is solved with an airplane ticket.

It's not us; mother is the one with the problem. "I love my mother," a young woman says, "but she can't seem to understand I'm an adult. She still treats me as if I were twelve." The slightest hint that this kind of attention is not wholly unwelcome, that it still carries ambivalent notions of security and connection, is denied. To buttress the argument that we have outgrown the need for mother, many of us smile and say we have reversed the roles—mother is now the "child" in the relationship. *This ignores the fact that the tie, the link through dependency, is still there.* Just because we're now mother's protector doesn't mean we're separate. Until research for this book forced me beyond superficial meanings of the idea, I would have told you I was well and truly separated from my mother. I have since learned that my ties to my mother permeate every aspect of my life as a woman in ways as numerous and mysterious as the ways of love.

"Letting go" is perhaps a friendlier way to put it. It implies generosity, a talent a good mother needs in abundance. Separation is not loss, it is not cutting yourself off from someone you love. It is giving freedom to the other person to be herself before she becomes resentful, stunted, and suffocated by being tied too close. Separation is not the end of love. It creates love.

It is hard for women to let go. We are born collectors. We live in the treasured bits and pieces of past life. Mothers collect the memorabilia of their children's past, shoes from the time they possessed baby most totally. Grown women collect match covers and menus from nights when a man held us close, when we felt most possessed, and we count the hours dead until he calls and brings us back to life. A woman and a man exchange Valentine cards; he opens his, smiles,

kisses her and then throws the card away. "You're not going to keep
it?" she cries. She's saved every card since she was thirteen. But
men don't need our collections; their future may be uncertain, but
they feel they have a hand in its creation. They are not dependent on
the past. When we cut our hair, mother cries, "You've changed!" It
is not a compliment to growth but a fear of disloyalty and separation:
"You're leaving me!"

When a mother refuses to let her daughter grow up, she is retarding her own growth as well; in overlong symbiosis, both partners
suffer. Speaking of various disguises symbiosis can take, Dr. Fredland
names what has been traditionally called "school phobia." "The child
isn't phobic to school," she says, "the little girl is phobic to leaving
the side of her mother." She has been conditioned to think leaving
mother is to leave love. "I don't want to go to school today," the
child says. "I have a cold," or, "the other children play too rough."
The mother who is lonely, who fears separation as much as her
daughter, takes these excuses at face value. By ignoring reality and
going along with her daughter's fictions, she turns the child into a
jailer. Being a "good mother" is her excuse for not doing anything
with her own life.

Motherhood is also a good excuse for giving up sex. Mother has
"more important" things to worry about than the ambivalent emotion
which has tempted but troubled her all her life long; she stops thinking of herself as a sexual woman. "This is usually unconscious," says
educator Jessie Potter, married thirty-four years and mother of two
daughters. "She may in fact have been an interesting sexual partner
until her child was born, but now she is too tired, too busy, she says
the children take up too much of her attention. It's all culturally induced, but the result is that she goes underground sexually until the
kids are grown. As for the daughter, she grows up seeing a mother
who has no sexual life at all."

Little wonder that physical love comes to seem frightening to
young girls. "If mother has given up on a sexual life," says Dr.
Fredland, "she will send the little girl bad vibrations. When the
daughter asks questions, as four- and five-year-olds do, the mother
will denigrate the subject or communicate her embarrassment. The
daughter soon comes to think her own sexual feelings and fantasies
are bad."

Nobody knows a mother like her daughter. Mother says sex is
beautiful. When her words go in one direction, but the music is going

in another, the daughter listens to the music. "It is extremely important," says Wardell Pomeroy, "that the five-year-old girl be enabled to recognize that mother has something very warm and special with daddy. Studies show that teen-agers overwhelmingly complain, not that their parents did not give them the technical facts but that they never presented their children with an image of physical affection between mother and father." The girl develops an image of sex, not as something to grow up to and hope for but as something to fear.

When mother's silent and threatening disapproval adds dark colors to the girl's emergent sexuality, this fear becomes eroticized in such strange forms as masochism, love of the brute, rape fantasies—the thrill of whatever is most forbidden. But it is not the rapist, not the man who will impregnate us and run away whom we fear—though in our efforts to give flesh to our dread fantasies we may say it is. In reality we can learn to protect ourselves against men like these, but even after years of psychoanalysis, doctors find that women cannot or dare not mention the real root of their sexual anxiety. To name her would be to have to face our anger at her, and to lose her—the mother who first planted fear in us.

The emergence of our sexuality arouses in mother all the pride she ever felt about her body and her sex . . . but all the shame, fear, guilt, disgust, dirtiness, and rejection too. Grown women, we ask ourselves why instead of our putting his hand on our vagina or guiding his mouth there, we feel an almost instantaneous reflex of rigidity when he touches us. We want to enjoy sex; our mind tells us we are free to. We examine and re-examine our anxieties, wondering if the inhibition is in us, in him—is the fault in our social system that sets the sexes at war with each other? The truth is you cannot be sexual with another person until you accept yourself. Another person doesn't make you sexual. Often with the best intentions in the world —to protect us—mother denies our sexuality, loading sex with a fear that makes us want to cling to her all the more. Only in partnerships, in mergers, in marriages like hers—runs the silent message—can we be safe. Masochism? Rape? Like sex itself, the beginnings and fascination of these ideas lie more between the ears than between the legs.

"When I look at my daughter, I feel all the fears and anxieties that have dogged me all my life," says a mother of five-year-old twins, a boy and a girl. "I treat my son as I would a man, and my daughter as I would a woman. No—as I would treat myself. I know I do this; I have since her birth. For instance, I'll let him go to the corner store alone, but I wouldn't trust her for a minute. She'd get lost or forget what she went for. I treat them this way in all things even while I realize I'm projecting all my fears onto her." Raising a daughter to be an autonomous person with a sexual identity is a job for which few women are equipped because they never succeeded in doing it in their own lives; it is why the business between a mother and daughter is never finished. "Now there's a real woman," a man says, and every woman in earshot turns to glean what a "real" woman is.

Sexuality is one of the first forces to forge our identity. At four, five, six, children go through a big spurt of sexual growth and separation. "But they're practically babes in arms!" is the outcry. There is an unconscious logic to the adult denial of the sexual component of these oedipal years: intuitively we know that without separation there is no true sexuality.

"A kind of inborn timetable," says Dr. Aaron Esman, "brings children to a sexual polarization around five or six. Little boys talk about wanting to marry mother. Little girls can become extremely feminine and seductive with their fathers." But while mother may fondly recognize and even enjoy her son's "romance" with her, she will deny the little girl's open flirtation with her father. The denial may take the form of, "Stop bothering your daddy!" Other mothers practice avoidance, ignoring what the little girl is doing even as she parades naked in front of daddy, dances for him, or falls into the flirtatious poses she's picked up from watching TV or mommy herself.

This early interest in daddy is a childish but meaningful rehearsal; it is practice opposite the one man who loves us enough to applaud what we are becoming. That's all we want at this stage; we may come on as if to steal him away from mommy, but we'll happily settle for his smile, his fond kiss, his lighthearted acknowledgment that we're just about the prettiest little girl he's ever seen. But if he ignores our gleeful dance-of-the-seven-veils, or worse yet, dismisses us with embarrassment, the rehearsal ends prematurely. The show never opens. A fearful, frigid personality is being born. "This kind of woman often marries early," says Dr. Sanger. "Having been oedipally rejected by her father, she is afraid to take risks. She marries the first man who asks."

It is important that the daughter feel there is room for privacy from her mother by the time the oedipal stage is reached. The little girl needs a psychic place of her own to get used to the turbulent desires, fantasies, fears and unaccustomed body signals welling up from within. But while she wants to feel she can shut the door on mother, she also has the seemingly contradictory wish that from the other side of that closed door mother approves. She doesn't want any detailed talk with mother right now; she hasn't sorted out her emotions yet. To have to put them into words makes them too real, too concrete and frightening. This is why children so often "forget" answers to sexual questions they have asked.

The girl wants to feel that mother acknowledges and approves whatever signs of sexuality she may show. If she can react to her experience, life, and body without guilt, she can learn to enjoy and be proud of her sexual self. But the symbiotically tied girl picks up on her mother's fear or dislike of sex. She is afraid to enjoy these new feelings; they would mark her as *different* from mother, separating her from the only source of love she has been taught she can depend on.

Afraid of losing mother by seeming to prefer expression of the burgeoning new feelings she has for daddy, many a little girl ignores him instead. Even if there is no man in the house—mother may be divorced or widowed—there are still a hundred ways a daughter will try to get acceptance and acknowledgment of her sexuality. If mother ignores or calls it by other names, the girl retreats. A pact is set up: "It's you and me against the world, mummy darling!"

It is a triumph of the human spirit that in spite of all our fears we don't give up on sex. It is as if nature, knowing how seductive and powerful is the pull of symbiosis, creates in sex a counterforce more powerful still.

Ever since we were four months old we knew there was a wonderful sensation if we rubbed ourselves between the legs. When mother changes her baby's diaper and inadvertently touches its genitals, the infant, male or female, feels pleasure. The tiny hand naturally goes to the source of that pleasure; mother automatically pushes the hand away. She does this whether the baby is male or female, but the way she does it—her deepest, perhaps unconscious feelings behind the gesture—will already be different depending on the sex of the child.

Four years later her boy's sexual awareness may worry or frighten her, but what does she know about male sexuality? She is reluctant to meddle in male business, maybe to set up inhibitions in him as a grown man. In her hesitation, she gives him space. She may even feel an unacknowledged thrill, sensing the emergence of the man who is so unlike her, but is the product of her body. Unconsciously sensed by the little boy, this adds to an early basis of his pride in being male.

She feels no such hesitation conveying her feelings to her daughter. Without mother having said a word, by the time we are four we know that touching ourselves makes her angry. "Women say to me, 'But I never masturbated,'" says Dr. Fredland. "We know from clinical experience that a child's natural impulse *is* to masturbate. 'Can you remember why you didn't?' I ask. 'Were you told not to or were you punished for it?' The standard response is, 'Oh, nothing was ever said to me.'

"Of course it *was,*" says Dr. Fredland, "but it has been repressed. Maybe something as mild as, 'Ladies don't do that,' which is quite enough, if they're afraid of losing their mother's love—enough for them to feel humiliated, frightened."

I hear this story at a Parent/Teacher workshop: A mother takes her baby to the pediatrician. The baby is only six or seven months old and the mother holds him on her lap. When the baby begins to play with his penis, the mother takes the child's hand and holds it for the rest of the interview. At the end of the interview the doctor says, "And what do you do when your baby plays with himself?" The mother looks him in the eye and says, "My baby never plays with himself, Doctor." All the mothers in the room smile nervously at the story; their own children are anywhere from five to eight years. They begin tentatively to discuss problems of masturbation they have with their own sons. *Daughters are never mentioned.*

"Mothers' expectations of boys," the teacher who is leading the group explains to me, "are quite different from girls. Girls are expected to be neater, quieter, better behaved, do better scholastically. They are good, and good little girls don't masturbate. These expectations are almost wish fulfilling."

Little girls can be furtive about masturbation; we soon learn to be furtive about everything sexual. A little girl can rock back and forth in her chair watching TV, masturbating under everybody's nose. While she gets away with it, it is a small triumph. Her sexuality comes to seem too unimportant to notice. The problem, like our anatomy, is buried. What nature has begun—hiding our clitoris so well that many of us never find it—repression finishes.

"Whether she did or did not masturbate," says Dr. Schaefer, "everyone in my study on women and sex was anxious about the subject.

Some women masturbated but didn't know that is what they were doing. When they heard the word for it, they stopped."[1]

Where does guilt come from? We aren't born with it. Guilt is the result of introjection, the taking in of the critical parent we can't afford to leave "out there," to hate, be angry with, and possibly lose. Instead, we introject the critical mother inside ourselves and carry her around in the form of her restrictive rules, for the rest of our lives. We turn the anger at her against our self. It no longer is mother who denies us this, says no to that. We do it to ourselves, and if we break any of her rules, even if she does not know it, our overly strict conscience punishes us for her with feelings of guilt.

The mother of a six-year-old tells me how determined she is to raise her daughter without these overwhelming feelings of guilt so recognizable in women. "It frightens me," she says, "the power I have over my daughter." Several hours later in the interview, she tells me that the previous summer her daughter had one of her little friends sleeping over. Around midnight the mother had gone into the room to see that everything was all right. "I found both girls with their pajama bottoms off, under the covers," she says. "I was too tired and irritated to act the way the books tell you. I just said, 'OK, put your pants on and get into your own beds.' I made them sleep in different rooms, though I didn't say they had done anything dirty. And now in the past year, when I call my daughter, she comes running out of her room with this frightened, guilty look as if she *knows* I'm going to scream at her. It makes me cry that she thinks of me this way."

In her own mind, this mother has never said anything to her daughter to make her feel guilty about sex. She's never called it dirty. But the girl has read her mother's emotional message anyway—one that fills her with fear, that makes her come guiltily rushing out of her room as if mother could know what she was doing in there. Of course mother cannot. "But the girl has introjected her no-saying mother," explains Dr. Robertiello. "The antisexual mother *is* in the room, in the girl's conscience; so she does know what the girl is doing or thinking of doing. This mother must have been angry at *her* mother for being sexually repressive. Instead of overtly experiencing the anger, she took her critical mother into herself, as a part of her conscience. Now she is playing the same model to her own daughter." From the daughter's guilty reactions where there was no realistic way for anyone to know what she was doing or thinking, it is clear that the girl has dutifully introjected her mother's guilt too. Is there any doubt that she will probably pass it on in time to her daughter?

"The taboo against looking at and touching yourself," says Dr. Schaefer, "is directly associated with the taboo on masturbation, on self-pleasure. Young girls are taught that pleasure for pleasure's sake is bad. When you masturbate you can't elaborate or embroider what you're doing into an idea that you love somebody madly, or that you're doing this because you want to be a good wife or mother. You have to face it: you are doing it for yourself, with no other goal but your own pleasure. Most people can't face it. Do you know that until I was twenty-seven I didn't know women *could* masturbate?"

Because sex is so visible today, so talked about, we tend to assume "everything is different." We confuse our new liberal attitudes with our deepest, often unconscious feelings. National surveys indicate people today are far more liberal in their sexual attitudes than they used to be. Liberal about *other* people. "The most interesting thing I've learned," says Dr. Schaefer, "is that people's attitudes about sex *outside* the family are exceptions to what they feel about sex within the family."

A mother can read a book and intellectually accept masturbation, but when her own little girl locks the bedroom door, mother is in agony as to what's happening on the other side. We think it very sweet to watch romance bloom between an older couple in a film, but when it's our own seventy-five-year-old mother, we are dismayed. "Imagine, at their age!" People aren't even necessarily aware that they have these two sets of attitudes.

Mother has an uncanny way of thinking that if she doesn't tell us about something we will never find out, that she is our only source of knowledge. The extension of this crippling, symbiotic way of thinking is the older woman's assumption that *her* feelings of shame and embarrassment are what we feel. It is a self-fulfilling prophecy: the daughter who goes against her mother and does the forbidden, does so with her mother's anxious feelings. When I masturbate today, my fantasies deal with the thrill of the forbidden, of being discovered, an anxiety my mother didn't have to voice. Psychiatrists have told me that one of the common fantasies women have while they masturbate is of their mother walking in on them.

Sexual self-discovery is the only self-discovery that is not celebrated in infancy and childhood. The day the child learns to eat with a spoon, everyone says, "Isn't she wonderful? Isn't that great? Someone get the Polaroid!" But the day she discovers her vagina, nobody says, "It's six months earlier than it should have been, isn't she the precocious darling!"

In her research Dr. Schaefer found that even mothers who masturbated, who enjoyed it and said they wanted their daughters to enjoy it too—sexually oriented, college-educated women—nevertheless could not discuss the subject with their girls. "How can you talk to a child about such a thing?" they say. "How can you not?" replies Dr. Schaefer, who is the mother of a thirteen-year-old girl. It is as though there are two kinds of honesty: one for adults, the other for children.

"There used to be a widely held theory among psychoanalysts," says Dr. Sanger, "that during the Latency Period—from about eight to ten—a child's sexual impulses disappeared to reappear again only in adolescence. In the last twenty years, we've come to realize that the sexual impulse goes up, up, up all the way along. What happens is that by the time a little girl is seven or eight, she has become socialized enough to learn to keep it quiet, to be afraid of it and not let mother know because it would upset her."

To grow into a sexual woman we must fight the person closest to us. A blade of grass will crack through cement to reach the sun. We too must go on blind, uninstructed energy. Even when we make it, and emerge sexual women at last, how many of us are not crippled by the struggle?

When you teach a girl not to touch herself, you make her passive, someone who will look to others not just to arouse her but also to take care of her. By keeping us ignorant (the usual word is "innocent"), we are kept from learning sexual responsibility. We resist an intelligent understanding of how we are built, we keep the truth of our vagina a dirty secret. We do not contracept and become pregnant. We learn duplicity with ourselves long before it becomes our standard behavior with men—to say No when we mean Yes, to feign what we don't feel, to fake orgasm, to tease him and ourselves, not because we don't want it but because we don't know what it is we want.

When we get a scratchy feeling in our throat, the most natural thing in the world is to drink water. When a boy is sexually aroused— even if his mind does not know that is what it is—his body gives him a signal as real as the thirsty person's scratchy throat: an erection. And so sexual excitement comes to him as "natural." He didn't do it.

It just happened to him. He moves to satisfy this new desire his body has informed him of.

A young girl's anatomy doesn't tell her she has a sexual life. When she reads a book, has a fantasy, sees an exciting movie or a picture of a naked man, there is no physical signal by which she can connect the inchoate feelings in her mind to the life of her body. "Oh, it's so romantic," she says, having no words for it, no sign of her desire, wanting to keep what is happening to her safely in the mind, cordoned off from the body she has been taught to keep her hands off.

The idea that she might stimulate herself, give physical expression to her inner feelings, is too threatening. Mother would never do a thing like that. Sex becomes not the "natural" expression of her body's life but a statement of her will. If she wants to connect what is in her mind to her sexuality, she must perform the action, overcome the safety of passivity, take responsibility, give up the great childhood excuse, "It's not my fault, I didn't do it!" It is too much for us. We make up a set of yearning fantasies instead. They express what we expect of men, and what we think they want of us; the erotic becomes so connected with the forbidden that sex, fear, and protection are merged together and fused.

During adolescence when sex with a partner—intercourse—enters our lives, the picture becomes more muddled than ever. Men are not raised with our fears. Sex does not present them with the idea of losing mother. When we are in his arms, he feels no need to stop. We must put on the brakes not for us only but for him too. So there we are: young boys applauded for their sexual adventurousness, young girls filled with the romantic fluff they've been taught by magazines and films to feel is somehow "better," more refined—certainly more acceptable to mother—than sex.

Had we learned the ABC's of masturbation before boys entered our lives, we might have explored our sexuality and our fantasies, and gotten used to this erotic new world. We might have learned there are different things you can have with men, some of them sexual, some of them romantic, some warm and friendly, etc. We might have learned to trust and follow our feelings so that we knew when it was sex we wanted—to be fucked—or when it was romance and loving comfort—to be held. There is a difference between love and sex; it is nice when they are combined, but they needn't be. You can have and enjoy one without the other.

Nor is our command over reality, our feelings of sexual identity, strengthened by the ambiguous code language in which we are trained to speak about sex or emotions. We lose power over our lives when we can't call things by their real names. (No wonder we have been the silent sex for so long.) If you cannot call a vagina a vagina, you are in trouble with your own body. We find that menstruation is called the curse, passivity is lauded as feminine while autonomy is masculine; competition, possessiveness, and anger are called signs of love, and lust is pronounced romance. Is it any wonder we have not been able to answer Freud's, "What do women want?"

We ask mother, "Can I go out?" "No," she says. We are made to feel that it is for our own good, while in fact her real reason for not letting us go is that she is lonely, afraid, irritated at father. No is easier than Yes. "Why?" we ask, when she tells us that certain words aren't "nice" to use. If she tells us what she wants us to believe and not what she really feels, we too learn to give people double messages. "Don't," we say when a boy touches us; we mean "Do," but he is meant to make it happen against our will or in spite of us, and we lose faith in him when he doesn't understand our code.

"A lady never talks about money," mother says. How do you do *that?* one part of us questions, but the part tied to her dutifully suppresses any hint that cash concerns us. We twist our minds to please her. From this, how far a step it is to learn to twist others? These misnomers and crosscurrents of mother's anxiety leave us uncertain of a foothold in any reality but hers. "But *why* do you love me?" we ask her as children. We need a specific answer to help us know who we are. Says Leah Schaefer: "When I say in a burst of feeling to my daughter, 'Katie, I just love you!' she always asks me why, just like she asks why I'm angry. I don't think it's enough to say, 'I love you because you're my daughter.' It says no one else can love you but your mother. But if I say I love you because you're bright or fun to be with and we had a terrific afternoon, then she *knows*. It is a kind of power. She knows she can be that way to someone else and arouse love in them . . . she's an effective person at getting love and it's not only because she's my daughter. I don't ever remember asking my mother why she loved me or why she was angry. It was some mysterious gift my mother could give or withdraw."

To protect us against real dangers, and the imaginary ones she fears even more, mother makes it understood that she knows everything. "The maddening thing is that everything seems out of your control," a mother tells me. "There is the fear always: can I cope or can't I?" Since she cannot control the world so that nothing bad happens to her little girl, mother manipulates the girl into the only security she knows: the false security of symbiosis. The bargain is, if we stay close and listen to her, do as she says, she will love us always. It is a very attractive bargain because her love is what we want more than anything. More than love, more than control, this is manipulation.

"Right from the start," says Dr. Sanger, "mothers teach daughters to be followers, good dancing partners. They tell her, 'I know the kind of girl I want you to be. I'm going to show you, just leave your arms there and I'll move them.' Like a puppet on a string. Mother feels entitled to manipulate her daughter because she, the mother, is a woman. She knows the way. She's the expert on women. The daughter only has to do what she is told. When the girl grows up, she turns to a man and says, 'Now move my arms, tell me what I should do, how to be.'" It's a transference expectation on to men that started when mother was only too willing to give us a total map.

"What irony!" says Dr. Sanger. "That the woman asks a man to show her how to be a woman, and after marriage resents his not being able to do this. This may explain the attraction for older men, who may be better instructors, or at least favor the child in the woman. If he can't make her feel like a woman, at least she feels like a pampered child."

Mother's manipulative love doesn't give us the security we need. It keeps us anxious and drives the real self down deeper into shadows and secrecy. If she knew our "secret selves," our fantasies, desires, the things we do, think, and hide from her, she would no longer love us. The ironic lesson is that to keep mother's love, we learn to manipulate her.

The lesson is carried on throughout life. Through manipulation, we may get our way this time, win mother, keep the friendship, get the job, fascinate the man. But we can't be sure of tomorrow. The victory doesn't warm us. Are we really the femme fatale in the slinky black dress we put on because we heard that's the type he likes? What will we do tomorrow when he finds out that's not really us? Play the helpless little cuddly thing and hope that'll hold him for a while? What if he sees us without our false eyelashes, our fall, our bra . . . should we undress in the dark? We don't know what he loves us for because we have no idea who we are.

We manipulate to keep him with us through guilt, if nothing else—convinced we would die on our own. Just as mother convinced us she would die if we left her. If in the end he does go, it hurts, but we are not surprised: knowing we tricked and duped him into loving some persona that is not ourselves, how can we believe his love would last?

Sometimes at the great crises of our lives, when these manipulative methods for getting what we want have not worked out, we look back to mother in anger and in tears. "My daughter is suddenly bringing up all this business from the past," a mother exclaims. "The last time we met, she practically accused me, 'But why did you and daddy go to Europe when I was four?' Imagine! Why, she's thirty-eight."

Sometimes we make the journey back over thousands of miles, and a lifetime of physical separation. "I telephoned my mother in Wisconsin last night," a woman tells me. She is the mother of three daughters and we are sitting in an outdoor restaurant in southern Florida. "Why did you call her?" I ask, surprised. She has repeatedly told me how she never got along with her mother. From the day she was fourteen and lost her virginity, she'd made it a point to get as far away as possible. "Because—" begins this fifty-three-year-old woman who prides herself on having "fucked" while her mother only had sexual intercourse, "because I wanted her to tell me what this goddamn womanhood business was all about!"

While these journeys back to mother are often disastrous, the instinct is correct. Before we can understand the fears that plague us today, we have to find where they began for us as children. We must distinguish which of our fears are real, and which are only carry-overs of mother's long-ago fear for her vulnerable little girl.

In the beginning, a mother cannot but fear for her child. The girl is a projection of herself, she loves her as she loves herself. And so she sees all her own fears magnified in her daughter. It follows therefore that the quality of a mother's protection will be determined by the value she puts on what she is protecting. In the end, for any woman, this is her sexuality.

This opens something of a paradox, a double bind. We have been raised to think sex is wrong, dangerous, and dirty, but also that it is our prime bargaining exchange. We protect what is between our legs but keep our own distance from it, we don't like it, we don't have an easy, affectionate name for it; and yet "everything" depends on it. It is a mysterious, poisoned jewel but the game is on: we must get men to believe "it" is life's golden chalice. We can't bear to touch it but must pretend to him its possession is worth his giving up other women and working his ass off in our lifelong support. Sex is offered on condition. Manipulation again.

We offer men our bodies if they will marry us; afterward, we are mystified because we are less interested in sex now he is "ours." What we wanted all along wasn't sex, but closeness. *Mother most rewarded us with symbiotic love when we denied our sexuality.* Sex, even with its infinite pleasures, becomes merely a means to an end; nothing is sweeter than symbiosis. Grown women, we find we have manipulated ourselves out of our own sexuality.

Besides the awakening of sexual identity in the oedipal years, there is also an increase in all kinds of across-the-board assertiveness; great progress in separation and individuation. We want to know about sex and where babies come from, but also want to explore the world in general. The exhibitionism and seductiveness of a four-year-old is as much an assertion of self—"Here I am, world!"—as it is a come-on with daddy.

Overworked, anxious, fearful herself, mother sees too much life in her children, coupled with too little caution; little wonder vitality is seen as dangerous. A mother may accept an overactive little boy. "That's how boys are." But girls are different. "Even before the little girl is old enough to know what is being done to her," says Dr. Sanger, "her mother begins to put the brakes on. She limits the girl: 'Don't get too excited, don't get too full, don't run so fast, don't overdo it, don't get too tired!' What I would prefer to see is a mother who encourages her girl to feel that accomplishment can lead to even greater levels of energy. It is marvelous for a girl when her mother can be seen as someone who gets turned on, who says, 'Now that I've sent out all the Christmas cards I really feel good. Now I'm going to do something I enjoy. Let's go ice skating in the park!' Just because a certain level of satisfaction is reached, it doesn't mean you have to relax and recover—you can go on to even greater excitement. I like mothers to show their daughters that they are exhausted with excitement, not to just talk about doing something, but *do it,* right then and there. So what if there's school tomorrow? Once in a while it's not going to kill the girl to lose an hour of sleep."

Another factor works to make women more docile and compliant than men. As Dr. Sanger's studies at St. Luke's Hospital show, boy babies more often get direct, physical expression of love and approval from their mothers, while girl babies get it in words and smiles. The important gulf that opens here is that a physical caress needs no interpretation, and carries no conditions. It is spontaneously offered, spontaneously accepted, almost without going through the cognitive centers of the brain. But a smile, a kind word has to be interpreted . . . thought about. Verbal signals and facial expressions carry under- and over-tones, perhaps shades of ambivalence. From her earliest days, the little girl thus learns she must interpret what somebody else wants of her before she gets approval—and even that approval cannot be accepted at immediate face value. This is her first lesson in compliance. "The physical thing with a little boy is easier, more natural than with my daughter," a mother tells me. "In a way, I'm closer to my daughter, but I'm not as physical with her."

In kindergarten, teacher knows the best way to handle an excited little boy. "A touch calms them down," says Dr. Sanger. But while the little girl next to that excited boy may be as starved for touching, holding, and hugging as he is, she has already learned to respond to other, more verbal signals. And that's what she gets. Ironically, it is because of this deprivation little girls go through that they are so often better students than little boys. "Their distance perceptors," says Dr. Sanger, "—eyes, ears—have been better exercised. Little girls aren't born 'brighter' and more verbal than little boys, any more than they are born more passive." We have been socialized that way at a certain psychic cost.

In nursery school, the first structures little girls build are enclosures, and the boys' first are towers. You may interpret these along strictly Freudian lines, but it is not necessary to do so to understand what is being expressed. An enclosure stands for something safe, cozy, protective. A tower assaults the heavens, and stands for effort and adventure. In a free, nonsexist society, one might expect that since both these ideas are legitimate to children, there would be some little girls who might build towers, some little boys who construct low houses. But the normative pressures in our society are so terrific that the rigid demarcation along sexual lines continues. It isn't just mommy who praises us for staying with enclosures, for playing quietly with dolls, who lets us see she is displeased if we imitate fire engines or make raucous noises: "Now, dear, don't do that with your mouth." "What's my little snooksie-poopsie doing?" says daddy. "Playing like a rough Indian?"

Passivity isn't always a mask, hiding a more active—often angry—and assertive person. Questions of temperament enter. Quietness, passivity may be genetic for some. Many little girls are simply born with lethargic dispositions. "There is nothing wrong," says Dr. Sanger. "The girl is just relaxed and nonassertive. But there are so many others who, underneath that passivity, are just seething. There's a beautiful person just waiting to come out, but she won't emerge. She's waiting, always waiting to be spoken to before speaking, waiting to be asked, waiting for the ice cream to be passed to her, waiting, waiting, waiting. If the waiter forgets her portion of ice cream, she just doesn't get it." A little girl goes to school and sits quietly, like a little robot. Nobody thinks it matters because at least she isn't throwing bricks through the window like the little boy. But her inner disturbance can be just as great, the problem underlying the behavior may be the same.

"There's a crucial growth period from five to ten," says Dr. Sanger, "when little girls' passivity and underachievement is too often accepted as normal. They are losing essential technical knowledge because these years are vital to developing life patterns. I see ten boys professionally for every girl in this age group. Little girls aren't less troubled than little boys, but mothers are more willing to admit they have a problem, maybe made a mistake, with a boy than a girl. The most 'aggressive' behavior little girls show at this age is they become very bitchy, competitive with other little girls. With everyone else, they behave in a passive manner."

The term "passive" has been used as such an all-embracing label for women that it has become almost a definition for femininity itself. And yet the meaning is always at least slightly pejorative. The problem is compounded further by the fact that it is not always easy to separate what is active from what is passive.

In sexual terms, for instance, it is usually thought the woman is passive because the man is on top, with most of the "doing" left to him. But even in the missionary position, the woman may be far from motionless. She can be even more active than he. Many women have told me that far from finding any truth in the *Playboy* joke that the big male turn-on is the "nymphomaniac whose father owns a liquor store," they have found a more seductive image to be the woman half asleep. The man stays up late, ostensibly to do some work. When he comes to bed, he finds her passive, drowsy, not asking/expecting anything. Thus he feels safe in expressing his sexual needs. Indeed, he feels aroused because she seems less active, less powerful, unthreatening. The contact of their bodies helps, but equally important is her pose of symbolic passivity.

The sexual act may then take place. But who is the active partner? Who is the passive? Who has initiated it? Or let us say that we ask him to perform certain sexual acts. While we may lie back and enjoy them, we are not the passive partner. We have initiated the event.

This is not just playing with terms. If you and I use different words to describe the same thing, we will place different values on what is happening. For instance, mother says to us, "I want you to grow up to be a woman with a personality of your own, to know what you want and take care of yourself." But when we try to be that way with her, she criticizes us for being willful. We tell our lover, "I want you to be very aggressive sexually," but at the same time say, "I get scared when men come on to me." This puts him in a double bind, just as mother did with us. Two contradictory and mutually exclusive demands are being made simultaneously, paralyzing him. He is the one who must decide what to do. But it is we who have determined the quality of the relationship.

In even this simple analysis, we can see that the words *active* and *passive* are overly rigid and emotionally loaded. In our society, men need us to seem passive if they are to assert their "manhood." If we want to change these traditionally limiting ideas of masculinity and femininity, we must give up the ambiguous advantages of passivity. Says Dr. Sanger: "Women have to learn to say, 'I really like this part of my body, and, god damn it, I'm going to get it taken care of. I like my clitoris, I like my breasts to be played with. I really want it, and now it's your turn to do it!' If she finds her partner won't, she should find someone who will."

There are men who like sexually active, autonomous women. Women tend to say such men are hard to find. We have to ask ourselves if the fault is not half in us. We ask him to let us get on top, to fondle our breasts, adore our clitoris—*taking the initiative*—but still holding on to the image of ourselves as people who need others to take care of us, who are vulnerable, little, perishable, and passive. Confused, the man turns away, to seek a more traditional, even if more inhibited, partner. Both sexes have lost, the crippling game of role-playing perpetuated.

The girl of four or five is facing two rough separations. She's physically leaving home for the first time—going to school. She is also facing the difficult need to psychologically separate from her mother, to work out her oedipal rivalries and compromises; mother can't help her in this.

Nor does she get much help or encouragement from daddy. "Most men in our culture," says Dr. Robertiello, "may be flattered by their little girl's attention, but they have such an incest taboo built into them that they ignore the little girl's sexuality."

The daughter is left with feelings of unfinished competition with mother. But right along with her wishes to replace her is the accompanying anxiety about retribution from mommy for having these jealous feelings. None of this gets expressed, most of it is unconscious. How can the little girl get angry if mother is pretending that nothing has happened? But somewhere in her soul, the little girl has shifted; mother has become the enemy, and all that tamping down, all mother's pacification are now seen differently by the girl. Under the aegis of the competitive oedipal situation, the former relationship with mother is now seen to have been something less than perfect sweetness and light.

When someone teaches us to sit on our hands, modulate our voice, control our temper, check our enthusiasm, bite our tongue, control, control, control every spark of spontaneity—unless we are born that way, unless we are temperamentally, constitutionally, genetically a quiet, compliant person—we are going to be angry at the inhibitor. Even though we cannot afford to show that anger out of fear of loss, even if the anger is denied, it is still there. One of the earliest ways a child may handle her anger against the dominating mother is to develop certain romantic fantasies. When we meet other little girls' less manipulative mothers, we decide, I was not born to my mother, there was this changeling thing that went on in the incubator. *I don't want this mother,* the daughter is saying, she is just a baby-sitter who stole me from my real mother.

Rage is a human emotion. Male or female, we all have known it, felt it first as infants when we realized we could not control mother, that she was *not* us, but in fact could go away and leave us. The pioneering work of child psychiatrists like John Bowlby[2] and Margaret Mahler[3] tells us that these first signs of anger occur around age eight months and are a normal part of development no matter how well loved we are.

It is the fear of loss that makes babies bite and pull mother's hair.

This fear is "normal," even a part of growth. Unless mother raises us to feel secure in ourselves, to have an identity and feeling of value separate from her, we will always be terrified of anger at her. It means we might lose her, and we need her still.

And yet it is only by learning we can show mother our anger, and that she will not stop loving us, that we can begin to accept our furies enough to handle them. It is a noble role that mother must play here —the target of all our storms, but one strong enough not to storm back. If she cannot allow us to go through this process, if the loving contact with her is not there, if the formation of our separate identity doesn't take place, then we are forever left in the position of frightened infants, never secure, always open to rage that shakes us with unexpected furies.

Frightened by these rages against a mother we cannot afford to lose, we enter what is usually called *latency,* hiding our oedipal competition from mother and ourselves. Often we root out our old baby dolls at this period, throwing ourselves back to a simpler time, calling a truce to the sexual wars, becoming close to mother again. But this denial of our bodies, desires, and independence is not based on love for mother. It is a reaction formation, in which we disguise what we really feel and act out its opposite. It is a form of "protesting too much": "Oh, no, I'm not mad at mommy for keeping daddy away from me, and telling me there's something wrong and dangerous about what I feel in my body. In fact, mother is the one I want to be close to all my life long." Competition and anger have not been resolved, only denied and repressed.

Very often this state—at age seven or eight—is marked by a passing focus on the little boy who sits next to us in school. But we quickly learn that this arouses antagonism in the other little girls; they have given up their own oedipal strivings and want to present a united front, solidarity with mother—with men left out. So out of fear of retribution from the other girls—ostracism—we give up on little Johnny too.

Our anger at being kept compliant, at not being able to express our anger, may never come out. "When my friends criticize my mother for being so strict," says an eight-year-old, "I won't listen to them. When they want to go somewhere, and I know my mother won't let me go, I don't say my mother won't let me. I say that I'm the one who doesn't want to go. I can't bear it when anyone says anything against my mother." *Reaction formation again:* hearing any negative remarks about her stern mother arouses such guilt in this girl that she won't let them be spoken. In her depths she realizes they name out loud the angers she herself feels but is afraid to let flare up.

Hidden angers may boil like Vesuvius just under the surface, or pop up in distorted, disguised forms. A year ago a woman called me from California; I had interviewed her for this book six months earlier. She is twenty-seven, one of the sweetest-natured women I've ever met, with a responsible position in a bank. "Ever since you and I talked," she said, "I've been thinking about your question: How was I like my mother, what had I learned from her? Six months ago, I told you I couldn't think of any way I was like her. And that seemed strange to me too. But recently I developed stomach pains, and my doctor said it was an ulcer. He asked if I was aware of bottling up any of my angers. Trying to answer his question made me aware that what I had learned from my mother is that you don't ever express negative emotions. You are polite, never angry. I never saw my mother angry at my father. She played the martyr, and I grew up believing my father was an ogre. Now I've come to see this blameless-victim role she played—that's what made him seem to me to be such a difficult man. Thinking about this brought back another memory whose importance I never realized before. I must have been five, because my mother and I were in the grocery store around the corner from where we lived. They had those big old-fashioned glass cookie jars, and the counterman offered me a cookie. My mother said, 'No,' and I hit her. I've remembered that all my life and felt guilty about it. It was the only time I've ever struck out at my mother . . . or anyone."

These unspeakable furies are the source of countless physical and psychological problems women have. "Often, part of the anger a little girl of eight or nine feels is a realization that all the criticism, the manipulation, the intrusion from mother wasn't because she loved me for my *self*," says Dr. Sanger, "it's because she loves me to be a little mommy, an image of her. 'Boy, I'm going to let her have it!' may be the girl's reaction. There is the fight, a postponed individuality struggle. It is the same fight between them twenty years later. Angry as the daughter is, she keeps going back, though all they ever do is argue. She's still looking for those crumbs of mother's affection."

The oedipal stage, adolescence, love affairs, our first job, marriage, the birth of our own children . . . these are rites of passage, marking important stages of our lives. Why are they so often accompanied by fear, anxiety, or depression—women's disguise for anger? The moments are incomplete, we find ourselves unable to live up to them because something is missing: a feeling of self with emotions we can trust. "It was my birthday . . . and I was told to be happy," are lines from a poem by Muriel Rukeyser.[4] I do not believe it is an accident that this poem about the alienation of a child's emotions, the injunction to pretend to be happy when she's not, was written by a woman.

In his book *The Female Orgasm*, psychologist Seymour Fisher states he finds orgasmic difficulties in women correlate with the fear of desertion by the man. Little importance is attached to erotic technique. The woman's ability to "let go" can be traced back to her feelings about her father. If she "trusted" him not to leave her, she will be able to trust the man in bed with her and have an orgasm.[5]

Without doubt the relationship with father is enormously important. He was our first model of what to expect of men. If he was accepting, happy to see us—we expect other men to be. If he ignored our sexuality—we became insecure about it ourselves. But who put on the sexual brakes to begin with? Who pushed away the tiny hand long before we became oedipally interested in daddy, who invaded our privacy? Above all, who, with her own body, in what she said and didn't say, provided our most enduring image of how to be a woman? Who says, "Nice girls don't"? I agree with Dr. Fisher that trust is the basis for letting go, for orgasm, for love and life itself, but who, more than father, earlier than anyone else, inhibits our ability to trust ourselves?

"Why are you so critical?" we ask, and mother's reply is that we wear too much lipstick.

Chapter 4

BODY IMAGE
AND MENSTRUATION

It was a decision of Daddy Colbert's (he was young and didn't like to be called grandfather) that my mother should move from Pittsburgh south to Charleston, where he was building a steel alloys plant on the banks of the Ashley River. He was a patriarch and liked his family near him; he also thought it would be a good place for my mother to raise my sister and me. He was right.

Our house was tall and pink with pale blue shutters and a wrought-iron balcony. I remember my first walk, and the stillness of those narrow streets. Had I turned left, I would have come to the bay and seen Fort Sumter. I turned right instead and eventually found what I was looking for—a grocery store where I bought a box of Mallomars with coins taken from the pocket of a coat in the hall closet. The shabby grocery was on the corner of what Gershwin had named Catfish Row, and a few years later I was to get my first job there, paying $2.50 a week. Mother only found out about it when one of her friends saw me sweeping the doorstep in my Girl Scout uniform. I never told her about that first walk either, or that I'd got lost and frightened. I was five, but I knew the mother-daughter bargain: if you don't stay close, it's no fair running back for consolation.

I'd had only two near misses with danger. Both had happened in Pittsburgh. I remember a man and woman in a car calling to me from

across the street to come ride with them; then there was the newspaper boy who unzipped his fly and showed me the most amazing
thing. Each time I'd run like crazy. But Charleston was safe for all of
us. I'm sure my mother found a kind of haven there after the unhappy years in Pittsburgh.

The people in my dreams are the people with whom I grew up in
Charleston. The houses there were four-storied, and had their elegant
shoulders to the street; the verandas ran back at right angles. All my
life I've judged the beauty of other cities by Charleston, where you
cannot see the gardens from the street. You have to be invited in.

Our own house leaned slightly to the right. When you sat in the
drawing room, your head automatically tilted in line with the sloping
walls. There were metal poles running just under the ceiling. "In case
of late summer hurricanes," someone told me. But nothing ever fell
down in Charleston. And nobody ever left. I grew up surrounded by
permanence, a world that was warm and generous and promised to
go on forever.

I wanted desperately to belong to that world. Society was defined
very strictly. It meant living "below Broad Street," having a deep
Southern accent and generations of kinfolk just around the corner.
Our address was right, I learned to say mirruh instead of mirror, but
neither my grandfather's money nor the private girls' school I attended could change the fact we were Yankees. There wasn't a house
in which I was not welcome, not a time when I didn't feel loved by
the extra mothers I found all over town; but I knew we didn't belong.
Even my name—Friday—was different. Later I grew to love its uniqueness just as I grew to love being tall, but when I was ten and people asked my name I would slouch and say, Nancy.

Had I not grown up at this tiny angle of divergence from the
inbred security of Charleston and the strict rules that such closed
societies lay down, I'm sure I would be different today. Perhaps I
would never have married Bill or written books on women's sexuality. My life would have been a straight, strengthening line, one solid
note; the life of a woman who never questioned her convictions. But
I wasn't cut out for a straight line anyway, or I would not have taken
so many walks. I would have stayed forever below Broad Street. I
would rather live with my old anxiety about feeling left out than to
have been merged so completely that I never left Charleston at all.
But I know that my ability to live different lives today, to deal with
abstractions, to change and accept consequences, rests on what I

found in Charleston. As I place one foot forward into the unknown, I have one foot in the secure past.

Today my mother lives a thousand miles away from Charleston, where she has roots and friendships as deep as the old ones. She puzzles at my distinterest in "settling down," but we share a deep nostalgia for those years when we almost could believe we belonged to a community that held to the preservation of anything beautiful—old houses, eighteenth-century hymns, and, above all, family. I don't have to know where I will be next year, but I have my own need for permanence. I find it in people, not houses. What luck I have finding it comes from a basic trust I learned in Charleston: that if I expose my need for love, I may find it in others. It's only in my dreams that they still reject me.

There was a girl named Sophie who moved onto our street when I was ten. Her family came from "above Broad Street," which made her more foreign than a Yankee. It wasn't because she was a year older that I became her slave. Until Sophie, I'd been used to taking the lead. When a friend slept over, it was I who insisted we have a string between the twin beds, tied to each of our big toes, so that any movement during the night would be sure to awaken us. Quietly, we would get up, dress, and slip down the three flights of stairs past my sleeping mother and out onto the dark streets of Charleston. It was I who insisted we play in the forbidden warehouses on the waterfront, sneak aboard the ships in the harbor, and ride with the black delivery men on the horsedrawn ice wagons that still serviced that part of town. But I never questioned Sophie's leadership.

She had the mysteriousness of someone from the moon. She had lived the déclassé life "above Broad," which fascinated me almost as much as the Saint Cecilia Society, for which I would never be eligible due to my Yankee birth. It was Sophie who told me where babies came from; never mind that she was incorrect. I'd never even known one could have such a conversation. There was, in fact, an amazing level of sexual ignorance in my "group" that stayed with us throughout our teens. In all those years of heated dreams and steamed-over car windows, no one talked of sex. We spoke of love.

Even Sophie's house was different. Charleston homes were kept immaculate by maids who had been with the family forever; the disarray at Sophie's said there were more important things in life than the genteel hush of beautiful rooms. Ashtrays spilled onto the carpet, the morning coffee cups glued to the slopped-over coffee, still on the table at noon, the heavy, awkwardly placed furniture—all were exciting, half-revealing, half-concealing clues to another, secret, and exuberant sense of life more enticing to Sophie's family than neatness.

There were no scheduled meals at Sophie's, no time to be home, no rules; when a grownup entered the room I was the only one who shot to her feet. Upstairs deepened the mystery. There three sisters shared a vast room that was like a female factory. Face powder hung in the air, and Sophie's older sisters sat in their slips at dressing tables applying layers of blood-red lipstick. One day they rouged my face. They looked at the results, sighed, and told me not to worry; I had a "good personality." Every evening Citadel cadets arrived to carry Sophie's sisters off into the night like prizes they had won. One night Sophie and I hid behind a sofa while her sister said goodnight to her date. Sophie got so excited she wet the floor.

Sophie taught me how to dance. I loved the shag, the fast music. Learning how to move my body was almost as exciting as climbing walls or chasing boys. (Other girls weren't interested in running and climbing.) One favorite game was to hide under the veranda of Pete's or Henry's house until they came home. Lying in the dirt, listening to their conversation when they didn't know we were there, was excruciating. But the best part was being discovered and chased, over the roofs, through the alleys, up and down Charleston's cobblestone streets. One day when the boys caught us they kissed Sophie. It was then I realized it mattered to Sophie whom she danced with or was chased by. More significant, neither Pete nor Henry kissed me. It filled me with anxiety. I was involved in a game in which I couldn't win.

One night when I was sleeping over at Sophie's she took my hand and placed it on her breast. She instructed me to suck her nipples. I would have followed Sophie into fire. When she moved down in the bed and put her mouth between my legs, I learned a pleasure I'd never dreamed possible. But when she instructed me to do the same, I cheated. I used my thumb instead.

Overnight Sophie was into dresses while I remained in blue jeans. During our last confusing days of play together, I tried desperately to follow her, not to lose her. On my way to her house, I would stop my bicycle just outside our big iron gate, lean over my handlebars with my head hidden in the bicycle basket, and slash a streak of color on my lips. My blue-jean pockets bulged with the accessories of my two lives, lipsticks and jackknives. I was prepared for anything.

But nothing could prepare me for Sophie's rejection. I tagged behind her and her new friends, girls her own age. When she applied for Kanuga Camp's Senior Division, I lied about my age; frantically I followed her up into the mountains, to spend the worst three weeks of my life, stuffing my latex aquamarine bathing suit with falsies—which promptly showed when it got wet. Evenings I sat alone under the trees and watched couples disappear into the woods. One morning the Junior Division walked by on their way to the lake, among them the girls I'd grown up with, my best friends until Sophie had appeared. I would have given anything to be with them.

How many months, years, later was it that I tried to re-create that night at Sophie's? A friend was sleeping over and I rolled on top of her, rubbing up and down. But nothing happened. It wasn't shameful, it just wasn't fun. We gave it up and went to torment my older sister instead. Susie had her bedroom door locked but we could hear Frank Sinatra singing "Night and Day." "Oh, Frankie," we screamed, rattling the doorknob, laughing hysterically.

My mother is very good about not throwing out my trunks of childhood memorabilia that clutter her attic. Recently I came across a tarnished identification bracelet. They were the rage when I was growing up. Boys gave them to their girls, with their names on either side. On mine "Nancy" was engraved on one side and on the other, two names, "Pete" and "Henry." I had bought it for myself that terrible summer when I was ten.

The day I began to menstruate it was raining. A paralyzing Saturday, smothered in heat and the indecision of whether the rain would cancel my riding lesson. The odor of the magnolia tree outside my bedroom window held me down, reminding me all the while that if I didn't get up and move my bicycle, which was parked under the tree, the seat would soak up so much water I'd have to stand up and pedal all the way to school on Monday. Another niggling worry was the discomfort in my lower stomach. Once before I'd talked my mother out of the need to have my appendix removed; it would have meant missing basketball season. Now the entire summer was threatened. When I saw the little brown spots on my pants, I breathed a sigh of relief. So that's all it was. The rain stopped. I could go riding. The summer was mine.

My friends and I knew all about those blue and white Kotex boxes in our mothers' bathrooms. We knew they were our future. When we'd moved from the big pink house, my friend Joanne and I had gagged with laughter when a moving man held up a loose Tampax from a bathroom cupboard and asked, "Shall I pack these candles?" Many's the time I'd stuffed a Kotex into my pants and walked about, enjoying what would one day be mine. We were very knowing girls, who knew absolutely nothing.

There was no one but mother to instruct me how to put on a Kotex. My sister was away at boarding school. If my horse wasn't waiting, I might have lain in bed and bled to death rather than go to her for such intimate help. She had been busy all morning with a workman, who was installing a siren outside her bedroom window; Charleston was in alarm over a burglar whom the newspapers had named Amorous—a name that accurately reflected Charleston's condescending assurance that even burglars knew their place. Amorous got into bed with female victims, but never dared go further. My mother was having the On-Off switch installed within easy reach of her pillow when I came in. I mumbled something and she followed me back to my room. I still remember the unmentionable discomfort between us of that moment.

She got me a pink elastic belt and showed me how to hook the ends through the metal hooks. I sucked in my stomach away from her fingers and rushed her through her patient explanation. "All right, all right, I understand, I can do it." I couldn't wait to get out of the house. Beginning menstruation meant two things to me: relief that it wasn't appendicitis, and deep embarrassment at having to go through the initiation rites with my mother. I didn't tell her about my stomach ache, and she didn't cancel my riding lesson. I was used to telling my mother as little as possible and getting my way. Years later I was to accuse her of indifference. Mothers cannot win.

Driving me to a friend's house the next day, she caught me off guard with a new voice: "Well, how does it feel to be a woman?" I hated the friendliness those strained words offered. I leaned far out the car window, my pigtails flying behind. My answer was appropriately lost in the wind. They were the last words my mother was to utter on the subject.

I didn't mind menstruation. I'd expected it, but probably not so soon. It was ironic that I was the first of my group to begin; many of my friends were into bras while I was quite flat and hairless. I don't think I brought up the subject until one of the other girls mentioned she'd begun. "Oh, that," I said. "I began ages ago." But I didn't want to talk to my mother, ever, about "those kinds of things." And I couldn't care less about being a woman. I was eleven.

I am still working on her question about how it feels to be a woman. But I never have understood the secrecy about menstruation.

Women live in an isolation that belies the picture we show the world. We kaffee-klatch and gossip, turning our lives inside out for one another, exposing our feelings with a compulsion we ourselves don't understand, telling each other things we hide from our lovers. The world nods, agreeing not to notice even our early experiments in homosexuality. "That's how girls are."

Close, loving, tender, and intimate as we may be, we would rather have these ties with men; we will betray one another when a man offers them to us. Men are disappointing; they do not have our need for intense relationships. They cannot convince us that they love us. The leitmotif of our lives is that we will fail with men and bind ourselves to other women. The bond is not one of loving friends. It is the bond of mutual jailors, keepers of the unmentionable secret—which is our sexuality.

"Those women who boast most fulsomely of their love for their own sex (apart from lesbians, who must invent their own ideal of love)," says Germaine Greer in *The Female Eunuch,* "usually have curious relations with it, intimate to the most extraordinary degree but disloyal, unreliable and tension-ridden, however close and long-standing they may be. . . . Of the love of fellows they know nothing. They cannot love each other in this easy, innocent, spontaneous way because they cannot love themselves."[1]

When we were little we knew mother had a secret. As close as we felt to her, as much as she knew about us and said we must tell each other all, we knew she was hiding something. She denied there was "more" to her life than what we saw and imitated, but we knew better. We bided our time. We gladly forfeited the things boys did— though we envied their mobility, speed, and daring; hadn't mother too given up these things? Didn't she acquiesce in daddy's being the one who left the house to work, who went out at night alone and handled the money? There was clearly some wonderful reward up ahead in being a woman like mommy. It had a lot to do with what went on between her and daddy when they were alone. They aroused emotions in each other, tensions, angers, joys that touched chords in our own bodies; deep resonances that made us fear and envy and anticipate mother's secret. It was only a matter of time, of waiting, before all would be revealed to us.

And we were used to waiting.

Have you ever known something was going on, yet everyone denied it? Part of you really doesn't want to know, so you ignore it. Then suddenly you find out what it is, and realize you knew it all along—and wish you'd never found out. That is women and sexuality.

When we are still little, we get our most important lesson about our body from the person who holds, feeds, and disciplines us. Mother may spank our brother when she catches him playing doctor games. He may feel guilty, but he gets his attitudes about his body, his sex, from other boys and men. "No," says mother when we touch our vagina. "No," she says again when we chase boys, "wait till you're older." "Don't bother daddy," she says when we discover how much we like the feel of his lap. We obey. Later we may masturbate and lust after men, but what do we feel? Long before the lectures, the book left on our bedside table, the film at school, we have learned about our sexuality from mother's denials, avoidance, and her relationship to her own body.

"There may be a critical period for learning the art of mothering," says anthropologist Lionel Tiger. "If you don't learn it then, you are not likely to pick it up. For example, Benjamin Spock thought that girls learned to be mothers between three and six, when they played with dolls and watched mommy make chocolate-chip cookies. They put away all this information for a while and then at twenty, or when they marry, they retrieve the cookie utensils." Then he added an associated but different idea: "There is also reason," Dr. Tiger said, "to believe we learn our sex roles very early."

Not a world-shattering statement until we examine the distinction made between the mothering role and the sexual one. (The fact that they are both being learned at the same time compounds the confusion.) We love the first part, admitting easily and with grateful affection that we got our terrific skills in housekeeping from mother. We remember watching her in the kitchen, how good she was at taking care of people. We love her for it. More important, we *want* to love her. The slightest twinge of anger or dislike fills us with gnawing unease. It is for this reason we don't like to think the same mother who taught us to be good mothers also taught us to be lousy sex partners. We never "see" her as the model from whom we learned our fear of our bodies as naturally as we learned to prize clean hair; we do not connect our anxiety when he tries to touch us "there" with the same anxiety she felt when we, as babies, did it ourselves. We go home to her to visit, filled with good intentions of expressing our love and gratitude, needing to reinforce our bond with her, but all too often there is tension in the air, and when we kiss her good-bye, we are guilty.

Why? What goes wrong? Even women who say, "I just don't get along with mother," do not cite sexual tensions as a problem between them. We cannot face the fact that our sexual anxieties today are inherited from mother.

It is a pediatric commonplace that children have a self-protective way of learning about sex. We take in only as much information as we can handle at any one time. "I thought I'd told my daughters very well how babies got in and out," says a mother of two girls, seven and nine, "until we were watching a Dick Van Dyke show. A little girl said that the way babies were born is the mommy and daddy wish upon a star and then go into the garden and if they see a blue cabbage, it's a boy, and if it's a pink one, it's a baby girl. So I said to my oldest girl, 'We know better than that, right?' And she said, 'Of course, everybody knows that it's a pink rose, not a cabbage.'"

This story reassures mothers. On one level it says their little girls don't want to know about sex anyway. Mother is right, therefore, to postpone the talk about sex and menstruation another year or two. It also reinforces the feeling that mother can control what happens to her daughter: my little girl will only know what I tell her.

"It's a common kind of wishful thinking mothers have about their daughters," says Dr. Schaefer, "a prime example of the unreality of symbiotic thought patterns. They don't know where they leave off and their daughter begins. If you see your daughter as your extension, you cannot imagine that she has thoughts and feelings different from yours. A mother assumes, 'If I'm embarrassed and uncomfortable about sex, my child is too.'" It is another self-fulfilling prophecy.

Women who have outstripped their own mothers' limited lives, who act in a sexually liberated way and consider themselves open-minded, are bewildered when their daughters haven't "heard" their brave new message. "It's as though I hadn't told her a thing," a mother of a sixteen-year-old says. "Why didn't she use a diaphragm? It's as though she's been listening not to me but to my own guilt-ridden mother." There is a clue here to the conservative backlash so often found in children of women who proclaim themselves sexually liberated: the daughter does not so much take in her mother's brisk new chatter about freedom as she is conforming to the deep, often unconscious feelings about sex mother learned as a little girl herself. It takes more than a generation to change the lessons we learn from our mothers.

"Personally, I think the more a girl is intimate with her mother, the more natural will be the daughter's feelings about her body," says Dr. Fredland, who feels that her own attitudes have changed enough so that she can communicate a message different from the one she got from her mother. "My four-year-old daughter loves to look at her vagina. Sometimes when I'm getting out of the shower, she'll come and lie down on my bathroom rug and just stare up at me and say, 'I like to see what your vagina looks like and what your rectum looks like,' and I say, 'OK, have a good look.' When my daughter was younger, she liked me to hold her up to the mirror and look and locate which places were for what. This kind of ease about the body *can* be set up through a real intimacy with the mother."

The idea of my lying on my mother's bathroom rug, smiling up at her vagina, is too awful to imagine; more to the point, it was too awful for my mother, and probably yours too. It sounds like a utopian way to raise a child, Dr. Fredland's ease and naturalness with her little girl. But Dr. Fredland is an M.D. and psychiatrist; she has been analyzed and has thought more about this issue, both professionally and personally, than any other mother I've interviewed. She would be the first to dissuade you from imitating her *unless you believe in your bones you are as accepting of your sexuality as you tell your daughter you are.*

Nothing confuses us more about sex than the double message. If a naturalness hasn't been there since birth, sex cannot be communicated "naturally." After six or ten years of silence, if mother plucks up all her courage, takes a deep breath, and suddenly announces like the J. Arthur Rank man banging a gong that Sex Is the Most Natural Thing in the World—she fills us with contradictions. "The mother has read all the books," says educator Jessie Potter, "and knows what she is supposed to say. But the girl has lived in that house all her life and knows that sex is not a happy part of her parents' life."

Mrs. Potter goes on: "My experience in school and in talking to hundreds of parents tells me that some rare and special people—parents or teachers—have been raised to have a comfortable feeling about sex. Most have not. So while they think they are merely telling children the facts, their own discomfort is what the child learns."

"Except for telling us that if we masturbated we wouldn't be interested in men," says a twenty-two-year-old woman, "my only other memory of sex education was how rigid and prissy the teacher was."

Mother doesn't have to be perfect, just consistent. If she is herself, then we can feel secure enough either to identify with her, go to the right of her or to the left. She is giving us a known position to start from. She has held out the model of her honesty to us. She has freed us. We can accept her timidity or embarrassment about sex because that is how we have always perceived her. But mother's double message makes us grow anxious about our perceptions of reality.

"Never do anything you don't feel good about," advises Dr. Fredland. "If a mother is uncomfortable, she should find someone who feels easy about sexual subjects to talk to her daughter." That too is a frank avowal of mother's feelings—that we must get the facts from a stranger rather than from her. It may distance us a bit; it may hurt. But telling us one thing while she in her gut feels something else hurts more. In fact, many women readily acknowledge that the best thing their mothers did was not to try to talk to them at all about sex.

"My mother never said anything was good or bad," a thirty-year-old woman says. "This is usually thought to be unhealthy, but I often think it somehow worked for me. I had no preconceptions. I found out about sex from other girls. I didn't masturbate until my late twenties—or have an orgasm until my second marriage—but at the same time I always had a nice feeling about sex. I always felt free to ask for what I wanted—even though I usually learned it later than other people. I think the real lesson about sex was one my mother never could put into words, but I got it anyway: she and my father always had a nice, warm relationship."

It is a commonplace among psychiatrists and educators that children—even when we're grown—don't want to think our daddies and mommies "do it." But the lesson that transcends all the words and books is summed up in this woman's last statement: "Because my parents really liked each other and we kids knew it, I got the idea that whatever went on between men and women was OK."

When we despair of getting the truth from mother, we turn to other little girls. They promise the kind of intimacy we still need but cannot afford with mother. Sleeping over at one another's house, our whispers confirm what we suspect: mother never experienced what we are going through. That is why she never told us, not because she didn't love us. If she ever did feel as we do, it was long ago, long before she was a mother, in some other, overly moralistic, prediluvian time. We must protect ourselves—and her prudery—by keeping what we know from her. In choosing to act without her approval—in secret from her—we not only lose her help in discovering our "forbidden" sexuality, we also assume responsibility for her. Sex frightens mother. We protect her with our own silence. And yet, love her as we may, there is a feeling of betrayal: if she loved us, why didn't she say there was more to being a woman than being a mother?

We try to set up with other girls the best of what we had with mother, a warm pool of closeness wherein we can tell and share "everything." By revealing our deepest secrets, we hope to bind our best friend to us forever, but mother's invisible hand pursues us. "My sister and I were as close as two girls could be," a woman says. "We talked about everything—except intimate things. I guess that was mother's influence."

Long after we have left mother's house, even after her death, she remains embodied in the feminine "moral" system she taught us; it was the special territory we shared with her, from which our father and brothers were excluded. To get rid of the prudery we took over from her, to free ourselves of the fear that she inculcated into us as a form of protection, takes more than mouthing a slogan or reading a new book. Good or bad, her anxieties are our maternal inheritance, our solidarity with her. To kill her unceasing vigilance, her sexual distrust, is to kill the part of her that lives on in us as the maternal conscience. That is why it is so hard to do, even when our minds say *yes, yes.* It means to go it alone.

Even when we were little girls, we had already begun to project this feminine superego onto our friends. It is why we cannot trust other girls. We will fondle one another in a tryst of gentleness, aching to think up new secrets to share—but we hold one back. "Have you ever touched yourself down there?" we venture, already afraid of having gone too far. "No!" she exclaims, confirming our fears. "Have you?" "Oh, no!" we agree, denying everything for fear she will not love us. The acme of our desire is to be—to *make* ourselves—just like every other girl.

We will never be as comfortable thinking of ourselves as sexual as we will when thinking of ourselves as mothers; the word sex never rings as true as love. Silence is preferable to any name given our genitals, and much as we may enjoy him touching us "down there," we will never believe he likes it. The role-playing we learned with our dolls has come full circle and we are only twelve. We may have wondered why there was no daddy for our dolls when we were three, but by the time we learn where babies come from, we are more comfortable without men. Didn't mommy give up sex for us?

Our need for acceptance by women is already stronger than any sexual need we will have of men. Jailed or jailer, it is one and the same in women's prison. Our sexuality will always seem to be in defiance of other women. Marriage, rather than a go-ahead to sex without guilt, soon becomes a stroll down memory lane, mom and dad all over again. By the time we become mothers, it is second nature to protect our daughters by denying our own sexuality. We edge out our husband, just as mother did dad, when we were three and baby dolls and cookie-making were what love was all about. At best, sex is an anxious business. Now that we're married, the center of life shifts from the troublesome vagina, out there to home, church, family. Life is pleasant. Why do we feel there is a void at its heart?

That so many women give up on men after pursuing them all our lives, cannot just be that men fail us. Perhaps we are as bloody minded as they. We say they fuck us and leave us. But once we've gotten them to father our children, don't we lose interest in the penis that has served what we see as its prime function?

"If we can repress and police a young girl enough about her genitals," says Jessie Potter, "she'll never find them. Even if she does, she is going to have had so many negative messages, she will have been anesthetized from knees to belly button. After we've taught her that part of her body is so awful you can't even call it by name, that it smells bad and she'd better not even look at it, then we tell her she must save it for the man she loves. Women must be pardoned for being less than enthusiastic about such a gift."

A little boy comes to grips with his sex very early, literally every time he urinates. When he is excited, his erection appears "naturally." At camp, the fire is extinguished by a group pee. Seeing who can shoot his sperm the farthest is like long-distance peeing: a test of mastery and control, a confirmation of OK maleness.

But females are so cunningly made it is as if mother had a hand in the design of the vagina. We do not see ourselves when we urinate. We cannot control the stream. The only time we are allowed to touch ourselves is when it is unavoidable: when we wipe ourselves clean. Toilet training is mother's first big hurdle in raising us. Her role as a "good mother" is at stake, and she will judge herself by how early she can report success to her friends and neighbors. When we fail her, it is, "How can you do this to me?"—a refrain we will hear all our lives. Even when we shit in our pants it is her disgrace.

"One thing mothers tend to do," says pioneer sex educator Dr. Mary S. Calderone, "is to get between their child's body and the child's self. They insert themselves in there because they apparently feel they own the child's body. They demand from it, first: feces, at a given time and in a given way: 'I want you to do it this way. I want you to give me a beautiful bowel movement. You're a good girl if you give it to me here in this pot.' Then they begin to demand urine in the same way. Next, they get between the child and its desire to suck its thumb. Eventually they get between the child and her desire to touch and enjoy her genitals. We interpose ourselves: we forget that we don't own that child's body. *She* owns her body and our efforts should be limited to helping *her* socialize her own control of it. Early, rigid training lays the groundwork for later feeling that sexuality is wrong, enjoyment of the body is wrong, masturbation is wrong, intercourse is wrong!"

After such denigration of the vagina, is it surprising that so many little girls look at their brothers enviously? He has something in that area we do not. "My little girl called me in the other night," a mother tells me. "She said she couldn't sleep. 'I keep thinking about penises,' she said. 'I want one. Oh, I want to be a girl but I'd just like to have a penis so I can hold it in my hand and make it go this way or that.'" Then the mother added, "My daughter is the kind of child who likes to be in control of things."

Who doesn't want control of her own body? To a little girl who has had trouble pleasing her strict mother during toilet training, how useful the penis must appear! "The boy seems to have the answer to getting mommy's praise," says Dr. Robertiello. "He has a handle, something he can control, as familiar, simple and easy to understand as a kitchen faucet—you just turn it on or off. And it is clean. It stands away from his body, so the little boy doesn't have to wipe himself off after he pees. Of course a little girl would like a handle like that, to control, to be clean, to please mother. But to extrapolate from this simple desire and declare that therefore the girl would rather be a boy is to leap into mythology."

Toilet training focuses our whole relationship with mother onto the vastly important area between our legs. Because we are like her, mother transfers feelings about her own genitals onto us, much more than onto our brother. Remembering her own difficulties and humiliations, her defense is to instill into her daughter the notion of fastidiousness. Is it surprising that the little girl wonders, at some deep level, What is so shameful about her that such iron control must guard against? A ground of anxiety has been laid, and we are only two.

I grew up without a father or brother, but by the time I was four I was already trying to pee standing up, to control that all-important function. You might ask where I got that idea—there was no male in the house to see, let alone envy. Does that mean I never saw the neighbor's little boy peeing confidently behind a tree? Penis envy is born, not from the specific desire to be male, but to solve the problem of control, of mother's anxiety and shame, and our own.

In 1943, psychiatrist Clara Thompson wrote "Penis Envy in Women"—a paper that significantly changed the course of psychoanalytic thinking. Dr. Thompson's findings were that penis envy is primarily symbolic—a rationalization for women's feelings of inadequacy in a patriarchal society. ". . . Cultural factors," she wrote, "can explain the tendency of women to feel inferior about their sex and their consequent tendency to envy men. . . . The attitude called Penis Envy is similar to the attitude of any underprivileged group toward those in power."[2]

In a male-dominated society, the penis is seen as the symbol of the more privileged sex. In a matriarchal culture the symbol of power might be the breast or pregnant abdomen. A Boer child raised in an African tribe would wish her skin were black. In our own lives, we may envy our friend Louise's beautiful curly hair, *but we do not want to be Louise*. Similarly, we may envy the penis—the obvious "extra" boys have—without wanting to be men ourselves. Penis envy is merely what the words say, before Freud overweighted the phrase: it is *anatomical* envy, not *gender* envy.

"Unfortunately," says Dr. Schaefer, "the phrase still holds anxiety for many women. Despite all our denials, we are afraid it might be true, bringing with it all the horrid notions of 'the castrating woman' —even though today only the most rigid of Freudians still take the idea literally. We know now that women's feelings of being 'less' are due to society in general, and mother in particular, not putting the same value on a girl's sex as they do her brother's. The constellation of self-depreciation called penis envy is not biologically imbued but is a learned piece of social behavior."

While I believe Clara Thompson is right to think penis envy is in part due to the male's greater cultural status, in my gut I feel the problem begins earlier and closer to home—with the little girl's perception that her anatomy causes problems with mother that little boys do not have. In the end, however, it does not matter. Both ideas work together to produce low self-esteem in women.

In context, penis envy can be seen as part of the little girl's exploration of the idea of herself and reality. "It's not so much a problem of envy," says Dr. Sanger, "as of perfectionism. The little girl wants a penis, but she also wants a vagina, she wants to smoke a pipe like daddy and wants a tail like Black Beauty in the movies."

When a little girl looks at her parents, she doesn't have mother's breasts or other easily visible signs of adult sexuality. Mother's promise that we will grow into these things is difficult to imagine. For the boy, the promise is less abstract. He looks at his father and thinks, "Well, at least I have a start. Even if mine is smaller, it will grow, just as I am growing." Says Dr. Sanger: "It's like being given the key to the car, and told actual possession will come in twenty years. At least you have the key, a tangible promise to grow on."

On the other hand, the little girl has only her mother's promise that a penis is not more enviable than a vagina, that when she grows up, she will be glad to have a vagina. This assurance is one of the most important things a mother can give her girl; but it must be based on the girl's perception that her mother is telling her what she really feels. The little girl wants to believe mother, and so if penis envy is no problem to mother, it is soon forgotten by the daughter.

"When my daughter was two and one half," says Dr. Fredland, "she became interested in penises. She would say she wanted to stand up to make wee-wee like the boys—which is universal. I told her penises are very nice, but that she had a beautiful vagina. 'Do I? OK, let me see it,' she would say. So I would hold her up in front of the mirror. That satisfied her but the next thing she wanted was a baby.

At three and one half she recognized she couldn't, so she said I should have the baby and I should give it to her. At first, she said she would nurse the baby from the breast, but then she said she'd feed it from the bottle. 'Why are you going to feed it from the bottle instead of nursing it at your breast?' I said. She looked at me very angrily and scornfully and said, 'You know perfectly well that I don't have any breasts.' She was very hurt. The next thing she wanted, of course, were breasts. One phase succeeded another."

Today, Dr. Fredland's daughter wants hair on her vagina. Tomorrow, who knows? A little girl should keep wanting things until she's tried enough to know what she does want. After penises, breasts, hair on her vagina, with luck she'll shift her attention outward; she'll go on to envy people who have self-esteem and courage, who are aviators or philosophers. If her childhood training has not left her feeling vulnerable from within, and if her problems of controlling her body are resolved, she will have just that much more energy to face what reality offers.

In the end, mother must and does win the battle of the chamber pot. Our loss is that all too often we have come to think that the source of our pleasure and our waste are one and the same. Mother's confusing instructions have set up a kind of Lady Macbeth phobia: we will never be able to wash away the taint (to the joy of makers of vaginal sprays and the blue chemicals we flush through our toilet bowls).

I'd hate to tell you how old I was before I learned that the Tampax I'd been inserting for years didn't enter the same passage through which I urinated. I'd always wondered why the Tampax didn't block the urine—*but not enough to ask.*

There is in fact a name for this kind of thinking, and it describes women like me who long resisted trying to locate our holes and to understand their functions. It is called "the cloaca concept." Like the word "symbiosis," it resonated within me with multilevel meanings the first time I heard it. It was an emotional summing up of years of untalked-about experience, an explanation of the cultural put-down of the "cloacal" vagina, compared to the cleaner, more estimable penis.

The cloaca is the one opening in the body of simple, lower animals such as earthworms. It serves both excretory and sexual functions. Many little girls have this unthought-out idea—a "feeling"—that they urinate and defecate out of the one place, and that babies are perhaps born out of it too. Later, this confusion spreads to include the notion that sex itself is connected with this one opening—which leads us to think our sexual organs are dirty, not-to-be-mentioned, in the same way that we learned during toilet training to feel no great pride in the function of the anus. "Many mothers are terribly confused about their anatomy," says Dr. Robertiello. "By the time she's given birth, a woman will usually have learned the difference between her urethra, vagina, and anus, but there is a split between intellectual grasp and emotional belief. During toilet training she may pass on to her daughter the confusion that these three areas are all lumped together in one idea, 'down there,' or 'your bottom.'"

"When I was little," says a thirty-five-year-old woman who was valedictorian of her graduating class, "some girl said that babies come out of where you wee-wee. I just rejected that out of hand, because any fool can see if you look at a navel that it's a drawstring. When the time came you just opened up the drawstring, took out the baby, and pulled the drawstring back. I really didn't learn about sex until my sophomore year at college. But I've never liked a man to touch me down there, never."

Men too have problems with bad body images: they grow up under the shadow of the Marlboro Man. Eventually, though, they find more important things to worry about. It is their lot in life to be judged by their accomplishments. They may worry that they are too tall or thin, but even the ugliest man can find women, if he's successful enough. But our culture's heavy emphasis on the need for beauty in women, all by itself, does not explain why even the loveliest women are unable to believe they are beautiful. It's almost a joke: compliment a woman on her face or legs and she will sigh and say, "But if only my breasts were bigger." Nothing is ever perfect, something always needs changing.

We don't understand it ourselves. We show our best friend a photo of the two of us taken last summer; she is lean and beautiful in her bikini. "What a terrible picture!" she cries, and tears it up. "I'm going on a diet!" Nothing we say can persuade her that she is already svelte and slim. Women's magazines know there is one never-fail cover story: Elizabeth Taylor Does Not Believe She Is Beautiful! Impossible as that idea seems to be, we buy the magazine because we know it's true; after all, Elizabeth Taylor is a woman, isn't she?

We all have something to hide. Why else would society build us stalls and cubicles with locks to undress and urinate in, when men are left to get on with it in large, communal, open locker rooms? And in these locker rooms, men shower together whether they are fat or skinny or bowlegged; they wrestle and snap towels, their bodies touch or not, they stand in front of adjoining urinals, holding their penises in their hands while they urinate and talk about sex. They may lie, but on the whole they are easy with each other, unself-conscious. Why are women different about this?

"I don't think I've ever met a woman whose mother said anything positive to her about her genitals," reports Dr. Fredland. "On the contrary, they were all warned against promiscuity at the least, and threatened at the worst if they masturbated or got too interested in boys. Most women can't touch themselves and can't imagine anyone else getting any pleasure touching them there. It's what an analyst friend of mine wryly calls 'lack of vaginal self-respect.' "

By the time the high school teacher rolls down the anatomical charts in the classroom and runs the sex education film, we are beyond seeing the separation of the urethra and vagina; an invisible veil of embarrassment glazes our vision, as real as the sheet we will later clutch in front of our bodies when we visit the gynecologist. By then, we are so trained in myopia that we can't "see" the plaster cast on the desk. I ask Vera Plaskon, who is twenty-eight and teaches sex education to teen-agers at New York's Roosevelt Hospital, if this idea gibed with her experience. "Have I run into it?" she laughs. "I went through it myself! That couldn't be me! I thought. Those plaster casts are so inhuman-looking. Women know they have arms and legs, hands, a tongue . . . but they have disassociated themselves from their genitals, particularly their internal organs. Don't look, don't touch. Everything down there is dirty. In our work here at Roosevelt, we try to give young girls information. But more important, a feeling that their body is a good body. By six or eight, we have such poor body images."

"Women's ignorance about their bodies is learned behavior," says gynecologist Marcia Storch. "Little girls are taught to be frightened and insecure where their bodies are concerned. At the opposite end of the pole we have The Great Sex Queen Person, who is held up to be very, very special. Since you cannot attain that position, you are ashamed of the body you are given. So young girls get it from both directions, forced to aspire to something they know they will never be."

Why are we never satisfied? Why the incredible importance taken on by our fat thighs and small breasts, why can we think only of our faults and so rarely take pleasure in what is fine or beautiful about us? Why the displacement of attention from our *selves* to our bodies —as if that is all we are?

Because these nagging worries are displacements indeed!

We never get over our worries about our waists and weight because they are not the real, unmentionable, and unthinkable root of our concern. Complaining about our skin, our calves, distracts our attention from that other area mother would never mention, that had no name, that made her face distort with disgust if it got dirty. We say it is our breasts, our thighs, that are ugly; we fear it is our vagina.

When we do give our sexuality expression, we do it blindly. We close our eyes when we masturbate. We get drunk so that the next morning we can feign ignorance and not take responsibility for our pleasure. "I don't remember a thing I did." When a loving man kisses us between our legs, we have a fantasy of a stranger we need never see again rather than the man who is actually doing it. We fear that he won't be expert enough to find our secret clitoris, and pray that if he does, he will fight his boredom and dislike long enough to get us past our own learned repugnance. Was there ever any man more adored than he who finally gets through to us that he knows our secret and loves it?

The fashion and cosmetic industries didn't create women's dissatisfaction with our bodies. Commerce merely preys upon an already learned insecurity, putting a dollar sign in front of the hope that someday we may find something that makes us smell, taste, and feel good about ourselves. Those who would encourage women to reject "meaningless" preoccupation with beauty and get on with the real business of being equal—without first explaining the very significant fear underlying this preoccupation—are merely offering women another piece of uncertain ground. Self-acceptance cannot be built on blind denial. Why do we spend too much money on clothes, too many hours over facials? Because we can't believe anyone would want us as we are. Convince a woman that her vagina is beautiful, and you have the makings of an "equal" person. I believe this with all my heart.

Our attitude toward menstruation is a vivid example of the power of emotion over intellect. My mother wanted to give me the information she had. I needed that information. I am certain she tried, but our crossed emotions got in the way. As I think back to that crucial moment in our lives, I feel we were enacting a universal mother-daughter drama. She could not give me the facts in a way I could hear; because listening was hard for me, she became even more inhibited herself. For most of us the results are the same: grown women of twenty-five or forty-five, we are not easy about a function which more than any other sums up what we've subliminally been taught to feel about that part of our bodies: it is not nice.

In my entire research on the mother-daughter relationship, I have found no aspect more ruled by contradiction, loss of memory, confusion, and denial than menstruation. There is no behavior about which we express such cool certainty, but over which we have less control.

To be fair to mothers in general, and my own in particular: "Often there's no way you can tell a child about something in advance," says Dr. Sanger. "People often talk about everything but what really is important. The same is true of listening. There is a general anxiety about facing something new. The case of the student who can't open a book until the night before the exam is similar to the inability to listen to your mother's description of menstruation before it begins."

Long before we are eleven or twelve we have been aware that mother bleeds once a month—something that is difficult not to learn in any household. (If by some extraordinary arrangement, mother has kept us from knowing it, that speaks perhaps loudest of all.) By the time we reach puberty, we already know how mother feels about *anything* connected with sex. If she likes her own body, takes care of it, is proud of it, we too may feel pride in becoming a woman. If she enjoys men, if she doesn't become someone we don't recognize when she's around them—then, when she takes us to lunch and tells us that we are beginning "the most beautiful part of a woman's life," we may believe her.

"I get such mixed emotions about her growing up, going to high school," says a mother of a premenstrual twelve-year-old. "I'm proud of her, but I know that she's going to be leaving me. It's very ambivalent, these feelings when your daughter begins to menstruate and goes into a new, grown-up phase of life. I see my own life changing."

Gynecologist Marcia Storch tells me of an eleven-year-old who had just begun menstruating but refused to wear Kotex, or anything. Then she saw the mother, an intelligent, politically active woman; the deeper implications of the problem came out. The mother was upset that her "baby" had started menstruating. "The basic message the mother was sending the girl was anxiety," says Dr. Storch. "So the daughter was trying to hide what had provoked her mother's fears. The story is not uncommon. A lot of girls pretend they haven't really begun because of the negative emotion it arouses in their mothers."

Says psychiatrist Dr. Lilly Engler: "Many mothers don't want to face their daughter's menstruation because it means the girl is now sexual. If there's another woman in the house, it makes her the 'older' woman. I've known mothers who really want to prepare a daughter and even think they *have* done it . . . but have not. We don't like to admit this, but it often has to do with jealousy."

On the other side of the oedipal door, "menstruation reminds a young girl that her mother is sexual in a way she cannot deny," says Dr. Schaefer. "A girl of fourteen came to see me. She could not understand her own reluctance to discuss menstruation with her mother. She said she 'hated' it, that suddenly her mother was 'connected with the whole business.' She was worried, guilty that she no longer felt as close to her mother."

Until we begin to menstruate, we have some distance from mother. We identify with her, but we are not like her. It is a kind of freedom. The gulf allows us to ignore the facts of her life we don't yet want to face. We ask questions, open doors, but when we bump into facts we aren't ready for, we close the door, forget what we just saw or heard, and go back to our childish games. But once we begin to menstruate, we can't look away. Her life is ours. Having to understand what the periodic cycle means to mother makes us unable to avoid any longer recognizing that mom is not merely the kindly, "pure," and totally unsexual being we had always assumed, but is as irrationally taken by the same erotic desires as we. She feels our emotions and knows the same excitements as we do within our own bodies. It is disturbing. Obscure oedipal conflicts are stirred up. She is not only our mother, she is a woman too. And a rival.

Two years ago I interviewed an eleven-year-old girl. She was very much looking forward to menstruation. "It's funny," she said, "how the older girls who've started don't like to talk about it, but my friends and I, we've decided to throw a party for the first one of us who begins. I hope it's me!" Times have changed, I thought. Six months later, I saw her again. "Did you get that party?" I asked. "Oh, that." She shrugged off the subject, not embarrassed, just uninterested. When I interviewed the girl's mother she said, "The day she began, I suggested that we all go out to dinner to celebrate, but my daughter said, 'Oh, no, please don't tell daddy!' "

The excitement of becoming "one of the girls" quickly disappears. Becoming a woman isn't a rite of passage into a new and exciting world; it's more of the same, more waiting to be asked before you can go anywhere, do anything, more dependence on others. More tension with mother too; she watches us with a new anxiety. Being a woman means being "less." The little girl who used to strut about with one of her mother's Kotex between her legs feels no excitement now when she puts it on to do its real job. Whatever feelings of achievement and sexual identity menstruation brings with it are soon diminished by old, rearoused memories of feeling unclean in "that place."

The truth is that menstruation poses for every woman a Janus-faced problem. It points us inexorably forward into womanhood. At the same time it turns us back, regressing us in its own unheeding manner to that earlier time when we were unable to control our bodies. Suddenly we are back in touch with emotions we haven't felt in years, the primitive shame that went with wetting our bed, bad odors, soiling our clothes. The humiliation of involuntary or untimely excretion has been so pounded into us by years of zealous toilet training that to avoid it we have learned absolute control, iron control, control so rigid that neither our bladder nor sphincter dare to let go even while we are asleep. Abruptly, we are back in the middle of all that.

The enemy steals upon us in the night. We wake with the sick feeling that there is no way to hide the evidence. So humiliating is the return of these old emotions that we hide from them, repress them, determined not to think about menstruation in any but the most commonsense manner. Is it any wonder that, later, the repression has worked only too well, and we forget to discuss this "dirty" side of menstruation with our daughters? Of course not—we are still ashamed ourselves.

Every woman remembers her first day: "I was wearing my sister's pajamas, and when I saw the blood. . . ." "My mother had given me a book, it was blue and beige. . . ." "We were on our way to Europe, on the *Queen Elizabeth*. I thought the blood was from being seasick. . . ." "My mother made me stay home from school and go to bed, which puzzled me. . . ." These details are stenciled on our brains, like a screen behind which we can hide everything else associated with menstruation. "The book had a cow and her calf on the cover," a woman says twenty-five years later, but when you ask her what her mother told her, she says, "She told me nothing." When you ask the mother, she says, "I told her everything." Rashomon.

"And what do you feel today about menstruation?" I ask the same woman. "What is there to feel?" she smiles. Nothing.

"My mother slapped my face when I showed her my bloody clothes," is how a twice-divorced woman, who is a lawyer and a grandmother, remembers her first menstruation. Her voice is still indignant. I share this anger until, months later, someone tells me it is a customary Jewish rite for the mother to slap the daughter's face at this time. The lawyer had wanted me to share her resentment rather than understand the custom. Did this woman's mother indeed use the ritual slap as an excuse for her own anger at being faced with a sexual situation she felt unable to handle? Or is her anger the emotion she needs to displace onto her mother to express the disappointment she has found in her own sexuality? Throughout our interview, anger is her dominant emotion about her sex, about her mother, about men, about her own daughter, and what it is to be a woman.

In contrast, here is a story another woman tells me: "I was so happy when I began. I was eleven. Up till then I had felt like an oddball. I was two years ahead of myself at school. Everyone else was thirteen. They'd all begun long before. I knew these intimate things made my mother uncomfortable, so I went to my closest friends. It was thrilling. For the first time in my life, I was like every other girl."

How we remember the onset of menstruation is largely determined by how we feel about our sexuality today. If we are easy about sex in our grown lives, we will remember any embarrassment, shame, or fear attending that first time with a rueful smile, maybe a laugh. If sex is a problem now, *that* was one of the first signs of trauma. It was clear to me in this interview that this woman likes her sexuality. She wants to like her mother. That her mother was shy, and did not prepare her, is not so important as that her mother was consistent. By not lying to her daughter, not pretending a false confidence, she freed the girl to turn to people who could help. That's how mother was. How we get through menstruation, loss of virginity, marriage, childbirth . . . it is all of a piece.

There may be mothers who feel they have failed in preparing their daughters for menstruation. I have rarely met one. At the very least they say, "I didn't have to tell her. She knows more than I do. They pick it up from their friends." But I could count on one hand the women who feel they themselves were prepared—not with equipment, but with an intelligent, accepting and emotional understanding of their bodies. I agree with gynecologist Marcia Storch that a girl's peers are probably her best teachers in sex and menstruation; most mothers are still too emotionally indoctrinated in their own generation's inhibited attitudes to avoid giving the girl a double message. But the fact remains: whether we get the information in school or from our friends, we are still stuck with the sexual attitudes of the woman who raised us. "The parents do the primary and longer-lasting sexual education of the child," says Dr. Mary Calderone, "whether they know it or not: good or bad, positive or negative, inevitably *they do it.*"

Dr. Fredland makes an important point: "There is a kind of regression that goes on in the mother-daughter relationship. The mother tends either to repeat what her parents have done or to undo it—to do exactly the opposite—which is sometimes just as bad. Usually, of course, it is an uncertain oscillation between the two. For instance, if a woman had a very inhibited mother herself, who told her nothing about menstruation, she may be determined to prepare her daughter better. But what does she do? She leaves a book on the girl's bedside table. *This is so much more than her mother did for her,* that she feels she has told her daughter 'all about it.'"

Menstruation is the elimination of a waste product. We all go through it. Why then should it not be something we share, a common experience that ties women together? "If men menstruated, they would probably find a way to brag about it," writes a male reviewer of a recent book on menstruation. "Most likely they [men] would regard it as spontaneous ejaculation, an excess of vital spirits. Their cup runneth over, their sexuality supererogates. They would see themselves as 'spending' blood in a plenitude of conspicuous waste. Blood, after all, is generally considered a good. 'Blood sports' used to be the true test of manhood and at the successful conclusion of a boy's first hunt, he used to be 'blooded.' All that is turned around when it is the woman who bleeds. Bleeding is interpreted as a sign of infirmity, inferiority, uncleanliness, and irrationality."[8]

"One of the first things I found out in working with women and health," says Paula Weideger, author of *Menstruation and Menopause,* "is that absolutely every woman, no matter what she looks like, thinks something about her is ugly. In my view, that is closely related to thinking there is something *centrally* wrong with you—and that thing is menstruation."

"My daughter has become so modest, I haven't seen her undressed in over a year now," says a mother of a thirteen-year-old. "She's always worrying about herself, always bathing, always washing her hair. Suddenly all she wants to do is diet. She has a beautiful little figure, but she's never satisfied with it." Everything seems to happen at once in puberty. How can anything feel right? Of course, we want our privacy. Then, simultaneous with pubic hair, the lift of a breast, the curve of a thigh, comes menstruation. We cannot face the real source of our discomfort. Instead, we begin our life pattern of dieting and unhappiness about our bodies, but we cannot diet away our vagina nor wash it clean. We cannot face the idea that dissatisfaction with our bodies begins with what we have been taught to feel about our genitals.

We pretend disinterest in a function that begins on an hour and day of its own choosing, that may make us irritable, that can cause pain, public embarrassment, that makes us reject our men sexually or feel rejected by them. Again and again I warn my husband about my evil temper prior to my period; again and again I am aware of how true it is—after the fact, after my period has begun, after the quarrel. When I was seventeen, my best friend—like many other brides—planned her wedding around her menstrual cycle. Inexorably, it began as she was, literally, stepping into her wedding dress. We bridesmaids stood about her in horror.

Medical research shows that the brain affects our menstrual cycle; it may even control it. We also know that what goes on hormonally at the time of menstruation feeds back into the brain. But no doctor can tell you exactly how or why. The amount of control menstruation has over our lives is indeed so profound emotionally and physically that we can only deal with it in silence and denial. We douse ourselves with perfume—*against what smell?* We make a fetish of clean, clean, clean underwear—*against what soiling?* After telling me the story of her first day—a memory still alive with anger, pride, accomplishment, whatever—every woman I interviewed, including women doctors, then says, "What's there to discuss? It's like fingernails, hair—they grow. It's just a fact of life. What's there to feel?" Different as our individual stories may be about the onset of menstruation, we're all agreed without words that there is nothing more to talk about—which means it doesn't have to be talked about at all. "A whole book about menstruation?" women said to Paula Weideger when she began her research. "How do you find enough to say about that?"

Dismissed: a function that has been the subject of myth, speculation, mystery, and taboo since the world began, a function that is
unique in every woman's life and that ends one day just as it began:
unannounced. We prefer superstition to knowledge. Says Jessie Potter: "My experience has been that seventy-five percent of women in
this country (and that's a modest estimate), couldn't give an explanation of menstrual periods to a sixth grader. They don't know how it
happens, have little or no idea of what does go on in their bodies."

"Not many other people thought menstruation worth a course on
its own," says Paula Weideger about her experience teaching
women's health. "The attitude was you just give women the nuts and
bolts stuff about the egg and the uterus and that's it." Her book, published in 1976, was the *first* on menstruation ever brought out by a
major publishing house with intent to reach a large popular audience.
Nevertheless, when she began to publicize her book, TV talk shows
invariably focused the discussion less on menstruation than on menopause. They said it was because their audiences were "health
oriented." What does that say? That they found menstruation unhealthy?

"One media woman who interviewed me," continues Ms. Weideger, "said she knew all she needed about menstruation. 'Therefore,'
she told me, 'your book is useless to me.' But as we continued to talk,
she kept coming back to one subject. 'Maybe you can tell me why I
sometimes feel so ashamed when I go to buy tampons?' I explained
to her the primitive notions of shame, feeling dirty, et cetera, that are
so often attached to menstruation in our society. 'Oh, no,' she said. 'I
don't feel like that at all. But why am I ashamed to buy tampons?' "

A woman recently told me of an event she still finds almost unbearable to speak about, though it happened twelve years ago. She
had been in love with a handsome man, who at last asked her out. In
time they went to bed, but to her horror when she woke up before
him in the morning, she discovered her period had started. "I knew
just what I had to do," she said with only half a smile. "I got up like
a thief, put on my clothes and sneaked out of his apartment. I would
never go out with him again, even though he phoned and phoned to
ask." Her humiliation was so great she could not face the man even
though she was in love with him. (Or because she was in love with
him?)

To prepare for writing this chapter, I play back a taped interview
with Dr. Sanger; I hear myself break up with laughter when he says,

"It's a shame more women can't see the beauty of their menstrual cycles. How can a woman not want to learn what's going on in her
body? The beauty of the ovaries, the fantastic performance of the
Fallopian tube. . . ." On the tape, my voice interrupts, changing the
subject. Do you too find his comments nervously funny? What does
that say about us as women?

We are so embarrassed about menstruation that we cannot abide
to hear it spoken about even if in a complimentary manner. We believe the words must be merely empty flattery, and only fools are
taken in by flattery.

Men have always been willing to play the clown. A little boy will
fart in class. It is thought to be embarrassing perhaps, but essentially
funny. It is no laughing matter when a little girl farts. It is dreadful.

When men go through a humiliating experience, they may get mad,
curse, or fight. Then they have a drink, make a joke about the whole
thing, and laugh it off. "You know those terrible roast programs they
have on TV, where all the men make fun of the star?" a woman says
to me. "Well, last week they had a woman as guest of honor. When
they began knocking her for being ugly, about her shape and her
funny hair, I got terribly uncomfortable." When a woman is insulted,
made fun of, if she gets drunk or stains her clothes, we look away. It
is so painful, it hurts. Low self-esteem, rooted in notions that there is
something wrong with our body, makes us more the prey to feelings
of humiliation than men. There is no space for light-hearted kidding.

Humiliation is perhaps the most persistent of all emotions. In time
we forget feelings of passion, the faces of people we've loved. We
laugh at old angers and rages, time heals the memory of even physical pain. But old humiliations stay with us for life. They wake us out
of the deepest sleep and flush our face with shame and anger even
when we are alone. "Patients with problems of humiliation," says Dr.
Robertiello, "are the most difficult to treat." Humiliation is so powerful it can make us wish for our own annihilation: our very ego
shrinks and wills itself for the moment no longer to exist. "I felt as if
I wanted the ground to open up and swallow me." The strongest feelings of humiliation, according to all the psychotherapists I have consulted, are those associated with soiling ourselves in public, with loss
of body control. In the end this is perhaps the most difficult barrier to
accepting menstruation: we have no control over this new body function. What is worse, nobody has warned us about this aspect of it.

Perhaps, too overcome by the excitement of the awaited event, we don't feel shame the first day we bleed. Eventually it surfaces. In all the talk about beauty and being a woman, why has nobody warned us, for instance, about the smell? And if nobody has mentioned it, it must be the most terrible smell of all. The surprise of it, the silence in which we experience it, our isolation in feeling we alone are fouling the air of everyone near us—all double the shame.

What I myself liked about the pill was that you always knew when you would menstruate, the flow was less and so were the cramps. Psychologist Karen Page finds a direct relationship between heaviness of flow and high menstrual tension. In her studies,[4] the women who were less anxious and moody during menstruation, who tended to ignore the old taboos against sex, swimming, etc., tended to bleed less. Dr. Page traces anxiety about menstruation to cultural taboos: the menstruating woman is unclean. Psychoanalytic authorities tend to give more importance to early childhood experiences—overly rigid toilet training, and consequent shame over loss of body control. My own feeling is that it is a question of emphasis—both factors undoubtedly enter. The important fact is that no matter what the reason, the humiliation is there.

"But," you say, "*I* feel no shame about menstruation!"

"Emotions as painful to handle as humiliation about a body function," says Dr. Robertiello, "tend to be repressed. We 'forget' them."

Psychiatrists say that when we are little, we think everyone else shits ice cream. Only we make a foul mess. If no one, especially mother, mentions the embarrassment that goes with loss of body control in menstruation, it must be that other women don't bleed like us: they merely bedew themselves with the attar of roses. We are the only ones whose dark, often clotted blood flows from the heart of mystery. What have we to do with those beautiful women, gowned by Givenchy, stepping out of the limousine in the Modess Because advertisements?

And yet with infernal cleverness, the Modess Because ads go right to the root of our unease. Giant market research companies know that during her period a woman feels unattractive and nervous about what she is wearing, so they associate their product with the most beautiful—and most beautifully dressed—women they can find. They are saying to us that what they sell is the antidote to our feelings of wounded narcissism; but perhaps they will forgive me if, while I salute their diagnosis, I do not buy their cure.

The best protection against feelings of humiliation associated with menstruation is to have a mother who believed in positive narcissistic training in our earliest years, who rewarded us with love and praise for learning control of our body functions. Rather than feeling disgusted and shamed when we didn't perform for her, we would have emerged with a sense of mastery and self-achievement. A mother like this would probably have been trained in the same way by her mother, since the most difficult ideas to change late in life are those of low self-esteem. If she didn't feel as good about her body and ours as she said she did, we would have gotten the old double message: "Don't feel as I do, but as I say."

Menstruation—the great fact of life which mother and daughter share—becomes the dirty secret that pushes us apart. "In my practice," says Dr. Robertiello, "I've known people with delusions. They can never form relationships because to be with them, the friend or lover has to believe the delusion too. The sheer lack of reality causes too much strain, and the relationship breaks up." Mother says menstruation is beautiful but the daughter knows in mother's life that is a lie.

Menstruation is beginning younger and younger. We may like the idea of sexual liberation—"I wish things had been this free when I was a kid!"—but we don't like to think that gynecologists are now seeing nine-year-olds. "There isn't a decent book available, no good information for girls in the eight to twelve bracket," says gynecologist Marcia Storch.

"The first reason mothers give me for not wanting their daughters to use tampons," says Jessie Potter, "is that it will break the hymen. But what it really is, is an inability to encourage the girl to bend over, look for the vagina, put something in it, take something out, touch herself. Even physicians, who should know better, still imply it's better to wait until you are more grown up to use them. We still want to deny a girl access to her genitals, to put distance between her and her body. We could teach women who are reluctant to have sex during menstruation that they can put a diaphragm up there to hold back the blood, but we don't—as simple a piece of information as that is."

Kids will tell you that things are different now, that "menstruation isn't a big deal like it used to be." When Paula Weideger was talking to twelve- and fourteen-year-olds, she did find them less embarrassed than her own generation, "but they would gleefully tell me how they could get a male teacher to let them off homework by hinting they had cramps. They *use* menstruation." When Ms. Weideger asked if they ever mentioned menstruation to boys, "Oh, no!" was the universal chorus.

One of the most self-proclaimed liberated women I have interviewed, a well-known writer of twenty-seven, laughingly talks about a man whose summer house she visits. "I don't want to fuck him," she says, "so each time I go out there I say I can't because I'm having my period. He must think it's the longest one in history." If you use menstruation effectively enough as a barrier—against sex, work, or anything else—pretty soon you will believe it too.

Contrary to the fable this writer foisted off on her summer host, there is evidence that for many women sex relieves cramps. Sex, especially before and during menstruation, keeps the muscles limber— the opposite of cramped. How much more pleasurable than a bottle of Midol and a heating pad. You would think every gynecologist in the country would suggest at least we try it. But sex therapists tell me that many gynecologists are too shy to discuss sex with their patients. I myself have found that sex when I am bleeding, when my body is at its most "unattractive," is often the best. It makes me believe myself loved as can no mere verbal protestations of "I love you."

Men offer one of our great opportunities to dissolve the maternal inheritance of negative feelings about our body. How they feel about menstruation is therefore significant. "Men get their attitudes about menstruation from women," says Dr. Robertiello when I ask his opinion on this subject. "That it is something secret, not to be discussed, to be avoided as much as possible. Women can be insane about not wanting men to know they are menstruating. The analytic explanation is that they make the man into the parent who is going to judge them as being 'dirty children.' Even without menstruation women see the man's organ as being cleaner than their own. For instance, a menstruating woman may try to conceal the evidence of her 'waste.' She will wrap her sanitary napkin in layers of paper, and carry it outside to his garbage can rather than leave it in his nice clean wastebasket. It is also why most women don't want to have sex with men at this time. In a woman's eyes, since he doesn't share this dirtiness with her, he will look down upon her with tremendous contempt. The woman projects onto a man this demandingly 'clean' parent, unconsciously left over from the toilet-training period, who is going to see her as dirty, disgusting, not acceptable."

When I went home and thought about this, I felt that as far as he went, Dr. Robertiello sounded right. But I felt there must be something more. I called him. "Couldn't men's difficulty about menstruation," I asked, "be due not only to their picking up on the woman's embarrassment, but to some emotion of their own they bring to the subject?"

What I like best about Richard Robertiello is that he is always willing to rethink any idea, no matter how long he has held it, nor how grounded it may be in conventional psychoanalytic theory. He heard me out and then said, "You know, I remember as a boy thinking how mysterious menstruation seemed to me. And what you don't understand tends to frighten you. Today, even though I have an M.D.'s knowledge of the physical facts, and a psychoanalyst's knowledge of the psychology of menstruation, I still find it mysterious."

He went on: "Yes, there must be an anxiety in men about menstruation that women sense. What creates men's anxiety is not only that it is a mystery connected with female anatomy. It is also a reminder of another feminine mystery—allied, but not the same. It is the power to reproduce. Men don't have this power, so it makes them edgy. And finally, women's mysterious powers rearouse another unconscious anxiety in men: at one time, a woman was all-powerful in every man's life . . . when he was a baby. Her sex once gave her power over him, and now that he's grown up, do you think those humiliations are all forgotten? Not in the unconscious, they're not. Also, if her sex gave her power over him then, might it not happen again? Men's safest bet was never to give women a chance to have power again. And they went right to the heart of any person's strongest feelings of identity—the power of total sexual acceptance and freedom."

As recently as our great-grandmother's day, women's power was thought to rest in her voracious sexuality. Certain male surgeons in the mid-nineteenth century won immense prestige for inventing instruments and operations that would remove women's clitorises, the source of their "dark sexual appetites." The same woman who was deified as the creator of character and the custodian of familial and even national morality was feared as the potential ruination of every strong man. These surgical excisions were performed for the sake of the power balance. A male fear and injustice, yes—but it is women who keep guard over women, mother who cuts us off, not only from our clitoris but from our vagina. What women feel they must protect and deny through fear, women can learn to release.

Menstruation has never kept me from anything, from that first horseback ride to sex today. But as I began to write this chapter, my period began (a week early) and I had my first and worst cramps in years. Every beginning I wrote seemed superficial. Something was missing, nothing I wrote resonated with the deep, inner conviction—*That's right, that's how it is!* I had to get up from my typewriter twice, almost shaken by anxiety, to walk across Central Park in the April sunshine to resume a conversation with Dr. Robertiello.

When he had stressed the emotions of shame and humiliation buried beneath women's matter-of-fact attitudes toward menstruation, I had shrugged him off. I had decided his opinions were overly colored by experience with women who came to him for help. I had identified myself more strongly with Dr. Schaefer and the majority of women who say they have no particular feelings about menstruation: it happens, that's all. But in the face of some unexplainable resistance, I now realized I had no easy reply to Dr. Robertiello's question during our last talk: "OK, then, Nancy, you tell me why you are having such a difficult time writing what you say is just a straightforward chapter on one of the simple facts of life?"

It is troublesome to have cramps, humiliating to stain your clothes, to be caught somewhere bleeding and unprepared. But I would rather bleed than not. I remember how disturbed I was when I was on the pill and would miss a period entirely. Doctors told me not to worry, that it was "normal." But I did worry. I wanted it, blood and all. I wanted that reminder. When I read of primitive tribes who were in religious awe that women could bleed once a month and not die, something in me resonates to their emotions. "No, I don't feel any strong personal emotions about menstruation," says Dr. Schaefer. "But I am glad I still do." She is in her early fifties. Although she more than any woman I know realizes the falsity in the myth that sex ends with the end of menstruation, I am sure she will feel "something" when she reaches menopause.

Menstruation alone does not explain women's problems with humiliation—no more than my difficulty with this chapter has to do only with unconscious anxieties. Our feelings about menstruation are the image of what it is to be a woman in this culture. While menstruation and the fear of revealing evidence of loss of body control bear possibilities of humiliation for women of which men are not aware, it is humiliating too to be that sex whose voice and presence carry less significance. It is humiliating to speak the same words as a man and have his heard, and not yours. It is humiliating to feel invisible when God gave you a body as solid as his. It is humiliating that women are accorded little dignity unless they are married. We twist these humiliations around, of course, and say it is glorious to have a man fight our battles for us, put us on a pedestal, take care of us. It is, if you enjoy being dependent on someone else.

There are other emotions as secretive as the shame that surrounds menstruation. They are the feelings that remind us of life, that we can give life, and that we are still alive, young—sexually capable of reproducing ourselves. It is difficult to tell an eleven-year-old daughter about these inchoate and complex stirrings of sexuality, life, and death which are hers to live with. How do you describe the awe that has always surrounded reproduction, the mystery and emotion that such a gift (the power to reproduce) and such a curse (to bleed once a month) must arouse in those who do not share them?

How do you not?

Chapter 5

COMPETITION

Although I didn't realize it at the time, my mother was getting prettier. My sister was a beauty. My adolescence was the time of our greatest estrangement.

I have a photo of the three of us when I was twelve: my mother, my sister, Susie, and I, on a big chintz sofa, each on a separate cushion, leaning away from one another with big spaces in between. I grew up fired with a sense of family spirit, which I loved and needed, with aunts and uncles and cousins under the omnipotent umbrella of my grandfather. "All for one and one for all," he would say at summer reunions, and no one took it more seriously than I. I would have gone to war for any one of them, and believed they would do the same for me. But within our own little nucleus, the three of us didn't touch much.

Now, when I ask her why, my mother sighs and says she supposes it was because that was how she was raised. I remember shrinking from her Elizabeth Arden night-cream kiss, mumbling from under the blanket that yes, I had brushed my teeth. I had not. I had wet the toothbrush in case she felt it, feeling that would get even with her. For what? The further we all get from childhood, the more physically affectionate we try to be with one another. But we are still shy after all these years.

I was a late bloomer, like my mother. But my mother bloomed so late, or had such a penetrating early frost, that she believed it even less than I would in my turn. When she was a freckled sixteen and sitting shyly on her unfortunate hands, her younger sister was already a famous beauty. That is still the relationship between them. Grandmothers both, in their eyes my aunt is still the sleek-haired belle of the ball, immaculately handsome on a horse. My mother's successes do not count. They will argue at 2:00 A.M. over whether one of my aunt's many beaux ever asked my mother out. My mother could never make up a flattering story about herself. I doubt that she so much as heard the nice things men told her once she had grown into the fine-looking woman who smiles at me in family photos. But she always gives in to my aunt, much as I'm sure as she gave in to the old self-image after my father died. He—that one splendidly handsome man—may have picked her out from all the rest, but his death just a few years later must have felt like some punishment for having dared to believe for a moment that her father was wrong: who could possibly want her? She still blushes at a compliment.

I think she was at her prettiest in her early thirties. I was twelve and at my nadir. Her hair had gone a delicate auburn red and she wore it brushed back from her face in soft curls. Seated beside her and Susie, who inherited a raven version of her beautiful hair, I look like an adopted person. But I had already defended myself against my looks. They were unimportant. There was a distance between me and the mirror commensurate with the growing distance between me and my mother and sister. My success with my made-up persona was proof: I didn't need them. My titles at school, my awards and achievements, so bolstered my image of myself that until writing this book I genuinely believed that I grew up feeling sorry for my sister. What chance had she alongside The Great Achiever and Most Popular Girl in the World? I even worked up some guilt about outshining her. Pure survival instinct! My dazzling smile would divert the most critical observer from comparing me to the cute, petite girls with whom I grew up. I switched the contest: don't look at my lank hair, my 5'10", don't notice that my right eye wanders bizarrely (though the eye doctor said it was useless to keep me in glasses); watch me tap dance, watch me win the game, let me make you happy! When I describe myself in those days my mother laughs. "Oh, Nancy, you were such a darling little girl." But I wasn't little any more.

I think my sister, Susie, was born beautiful, a fact that affected my mother and me deeply, though in different ways. I don't think it mattered so much until Susie's adolescence. She turned so lush one ached to look at her. Pictures of Susie then remind me of the young Elizabeth Taylor in *A Place in the Sun*. One has to almost look away from so much beauty. It scared my mother to death. Whatever had gone on between them before came to a head and has never stopped. Their constant friction determined me to get away from this house of women, to be free of women's petty competitions, to live on a bigger scale. I left home eventually but I've never gotten away from feeling how wonderful to be so beautiful your mother can't take her eyes off you, even if only to nag.

I remember an amazing lack of any feeling about my only sibling, with whom I shared a room for years, whose clothes were identical to mine until I was ten. Except for feelings of irritation when she tried to cuddle me when I was four, bursts of anger that erupted into fist fights which I started and won at ten, and after that, indifference, a calculated unawareness that has resulted in a terrible and sad absence of my sister in my life.

My husband says his sister was the only child his father ever paid any attention to; "You have done to Susie what I did to my sister," he says. "You made her invisible." Me, jealous of Susie, who never won a single trophy or had as many friends as I? I must have been insanely jealous.

I only allowed myself to face it twice. Both times happened in that twelfth year, when my usual defenses couldn't take the emotional crosscurrents of adolescence. When I did slash out it wasn't very glorious, no well-chosen words or contest on the tennis courts. I did it like a thief in the night. Nobody ever guessed it was I who poured the red nail polish down the front of Susie's new white eyelet evening dress the day of her first yacht club dance. When I stole her summer savings and threw her wallet down the sewer, mother blamed Susie for being so careless. I watched my sister accept the criticism with her mother's own resignation, and I felt some relief from the angry emotions that had hold of me.

When Susie went away to boarding school, I made jokes about how glad I was to be rid of her. It was our first separation. Conflicting urges, angers, and envies were coming at me from every direction; I had nothing left over to handle my terrible feelings of loss at her going. It was the summer I was plagued by what I called "my thoughts."

I read every book in the house as a talisman against thinking. I was afraid that if my brain were left idle for even one minute, these "thoughts" would take over. Perhaps I feared they already had. Was my sister's going away the fulfillment of my own murderous wishes against her? I wrote in my first and only diary: "Susie, come home, please come home!!!!!!! I'm sorry, I'm sorry!!!!!!!"

When I outgrew the Nancy Drew books for perfect attendance at Sunday School, and the Girl Scout badges for such merits as selling the most rat poison door to door, I graduated to prizes at the community theater. I won a plastic wake-up radio for the I Speak for Democracy Contest. I was captain of the athletic association, president of the student government, and had the lead in the class play, all in the same year. In fact, I wrote the class play. It might have been embarrassing, but no one else wanted these prizes. Scoring home runs and getting straight A's weren't high on the list of priorities among my friends. (The South takes all prizes for raising noncompetitive women.) In the few cases where anyone did give me a run for the money, I had an unbeatable incentive: my grandfather's applause. It was he for whom I ran.

I can't remember ever hearing my grandfather say to my mother, "Well done, Jane." I can't remember my mother ever saying to my sister, "Well done, Susie." And I never gave my mother the chance to say it to me. She was the last to hear of my achievements, and when she did, it was not from me but from her friends. Did she really notice so little that I was leaving her out? Was she so hurt that she pretended not to care? My classmates who won second prize or even no prize at all asked their families to attend the award ceremonies. I, who won first prize, always, did so to the applause of no kin at all. Was I spiting her? I know I was spiting myself. Nothing would have made me happier than to have her there; nothing would induce me to invite her. It is a game I later played with men: "Leave!" I would cry, and when they did, "How could you hurt me so?" I'd implore.

If I deprived her of the chance to praise me, she never criticized me. Criticism was the vehicle by which she could articulate her relationship to my sister. No matter what it was, Susie could never get it right—in my mother's eyes. It continues that way to this day. Difficult as it is to think of my mother as competitive with anyone, how else could she have felt about her beautiful, ripe fourteen-year-old daughter? My mother was coming into her own mature, full bloom but perhaps that only made her more sensitive to the fact that Susie was simultaneously experiencing the same sexual flush. A year later, my mother remarried. Today, only the geography has changed: the argument begins as soon as they enter the same room. But they are often in the same room. They have never been closer.

How often the dinner table becomes the family battleground. When I met Bill he had no table you could sit around in his vast bachelor apartment. The dinner table was where his father waged war; it was the one time the family was together. In Charleston, dinner was served at 2:00. I have this picture of our midday meals: Susie on my right, mother on my left, and me feeling that our cook, Ruth, had set this beautiful table for me alone.

No one else seemed to care about the golden squash, the crisp chicken, the big silver pitcher of iced tea. While I proceeded to eat my way from one end of the table to the other, Susie and mother would begin: "Susie, that lipstick is too dark. . . . Must you pluck your eyebrows? . . . Why did you buy high-heeled, open-toe shoes when I told you to get loafers? . . . Those pointy bras make you look like a, like a—" But my mother couldn't say the word. At this point one of them would leave the table in tears, while the other shuddered in despair at the sound of the slammed bedroom door. Meanwhile, I pondered my problem of whose house to play at that afternoon. I would finish both their desserts and be gone before Ruth had cleared the table. Am I exaggerating? Did it only happen once a week? Does it matter?

I was lucky to have escaped those devastating battles. "I never had to worry about Nancy," my mother has always said. "She could always take care of herself." It became true. Only my husband has been allowed to see the extent of my needs. But the competitive drive that made me so self-sufficient was fired by more than jealousy of my sister. If my mother wasn't going to acknowledge me, her father would. If she couldn't succeed in his eyes, I would. It's my best explanation for all those years of trophies and presidencies, for my ability to "reach" my grandfather as my mother never could. I not only won what she had wanted all her life—his praise—I learned with the canniness of the young that this great towering man loved to be loved, to be touched. He couldn't allow himself to reach out first to those he loved most, but he couldn't resist an overture of affection.

I greeted his visits with embraces, took the kisses I had won and sat at his feet like one of his Dalmatians, while my sister stood shyly in the background and my mother waited for his criticism. But I was no more aware of competing with my mother than of being jealous of my sister. Two generations of women in my family have struggled for my grandfather's praise. Perhaps I became his favorite because he sensed I needed it most. The price I paid was that I had to beat my mother and my sister. I am still guilty for that.

In the stereotyping of the sexes, men are granted all the competitive drives, women none. The idea of competitive women evokes disturbing images—the darker, dykey side of femininity, or cartoons of "ladies" in high heels, flailing at each other ineffectively with their handbags. An important step has been left out of our socialization: mother raises us to win people's love. She gives us no training in the emotions of rivalry that would lose it for us. With no practical experience in the rules that make competition safe, we fear its ferocity. Never having been taught to win, we do not know how to lose. Women are not raised to compete like gentlemen.

The young girl does not begin by thinking of it as competition at all. The adolescent merely wants what mother has. And she has so much! Food from her plate has always tasted better. Putting on her clothes has always been more thrilling than our own. Hasn't she said a thousand times, as she's scolded, bathed, clothed, and taught us, that she does it all because she loves us? Well, then, why doesn't she just step aside and give us daddy, and let us succeed her as the woman of the house? It has nothing to do with wanting to hurt her. Our biology is our logic. Competition only enters when mother resists.

Freud defined the Oedipus complex as the sexual feelings of the four-, five-, or six-year-old child, directed toward the parent of the opposite sex, accompanied by competitive urges against the parent of the same sex. But contemporary psychoanalytic theory believes the contest between mother and daughter isn't only for daddy. It is the girl's struggle for recognition, for the limelight, for her place in the world, with or without daddy's presence.

Alas, the entire literature and folklore of the oedipal conflict is written from the child's point of view. Nobody tells mother what she should feel. Nobody gives her sanction for what she *is* feeling. All she knows is she is supposed to have only nice, storybook, motherly emotions. There is no place here for jealousy of a young girl, resentment at finding your place as the only woman who matters undercut, anger that the person who always obeyed you, *and whom you love,* now demands to do things her way, and makes you feel old.

Mother recognizes these feelings with anger and shame: they are a rearousal of her old, buried, oedipal competitive wishes against her own mother. She is not evil; how can she admit to feeling these evil things? "It is not easy for a mother to admit competition with her daughter," says Dr. Helene Deutsch. "She has these sincere motherly wishes for the girl. They cover her own competitive urges." Out of this conflict, rationalizations are born. After all, mother is a grown woman—it is undignified, unrealistic, to feel this way about her little girl. Mother wants to make things nice. Her denial makes them worse. Our desires are so bad, she won't even name them.

We've been afraid of this all along! To the savage, untamed id, competition knows no bounds or civilized rules. From the Freudian point of view, the oedipal struggle is experienced as a kind of death wish. We never solved it at five. In adolescence the ego is still threatened by these dread impulses. The rivalry goes underground, becomes intense and deadly.

We have no lived-out experience that competition can be anything but this frightening, murderous urge the unconscious says it is. We never fully expressed our rivalry with mother, she never acknowledged that we had these feelings with a smile and a kiss that told us they are not so bad after all. And yet, self-respect demands we continue to try to win our place, fulfill our needs, posit our identity. Sex itself is not ours but seems to be something that must be won from somebody else.

Once upon a time our emerging sexuality almost made us lose the most important person in our lives. We gave in to her then, denying our desires; had we not, her anger could have meant abandonment at an age when we could not live without her. We go through life denying we are competitive, while feeling other women's gains somehow bar us from life's feast.

"Competitive? *Me?* I'm not competitive!" we hotly deny as if we've been accused of murder—even as we blindly race against the only people who count: other women. The exercise is to win the prize, but perhaps more urgently, to test once again the limits of the contradictory reality which hems us in: can you beat out the other woman and still have her love?

"I adored my father," says a twenty-year-old woman, "but more than anything I think I've always wanted my mother's approval. I'm still very much aware of my need to have women like or admire me. I'll spend more time getting dressed for lunch with a group of women than I do for a date. When I go to a party alone, I love it when men turn to look. But when there are just women in the room, I hate coming late. When they turn to look, I feel they are making a judgment against me. This makes no sense, but that's what I feel." Little girls or grown-up women, our greatest source of love as well as our toughest competition are one and the same. How can we not be confused?

Mother denies any rivalry on her side, and acts instead on the emotions that surround and protect her from competition. It is irritation, motherly concern, and exasperation she feels at our adolescent behavior. We are her "little girl," not her rival. When we grow up and another woman gets a dazzling new job, we aren't as comfortable around her. We say she "irritates" us. She is our best friend; we didn't want the job anyway. What is irritating is that her promotion threatens to make us conscious of our competition with her.

In a similar manner, to avoid acknowledgment of competition, we declare it no contest and put ourselves down before anyone else can pass judgment. When our husband talks too long to another woman, we say, "I know I'm not as interesting as she. . . ." Feelings of inferiority are a classic defense. We feel diminished by her, frightened, we could kill her. Or him. But we do not feel competitive. Do you understand? *We are not competitive!*

Even women psychoanalysts, who smile ruefully and say that feelings of competition between mother and daughter may be denied but are universal, are unaware of any discontinuity in their thinking when later—often in the same interview—they tell me that they have never felt any competition with their daughters. "My daughter is a very beautiful little girl," one such woman analyst says to me. "She is twelve, and just developing. I don't know what will happen when she starts looking better in a bathing suit than I do." She laughs. "For instance, I work one night a week in a clinic, and my husband told me that she said to him, 'You know, Daddy, when mother is away, there are a lot of things I can do for you, just like she does.'" I ask if her daughter's beauty and open flirtations with her father make the mother feel competitive with the girl. "Oh, I don't think so . . . they are both much nicer people than I am." Competition first, a charming denial second. I recognize these disarming techniques. They were my own for a long time.

When we were infants, it was appropriate that we should get the feeling of narcissistic enhancement so essential to growth from mother. Now we are young women ourselves and want it from a man. How father responds to his daughter's adolescence can determine which way we go: toward men and our own identity, or back to mother and the symbiotic tie. If father can make us feel we are the most glorious young girl in the world, we will gain confidence to move forward. Says a young woman: "My father was a very warm, loving person. I think that is where I get my terrific interest in sex, my good feelings about my body. Not that I ever saw him being demonstrative with my mother, but he was with me, when I was young. He made me feel wonderful. I would love to have known my mother before she became a mother. I think motherhood did her in sexually. She must have been more sexual before we kids were born, because *he* is so physical. My whole feeling that sex is forbidden comes from my mother."

There is much a father has to offer a daughter at adolescence. But what a tightrope he must walk! He must give attention to the needs of both wife and daughter, while being careful not to set one jealously against the other. "My husband is crazy about our daughter," says psychologist Liz Hauser, "but initially he didn't realize what he was setting up. For instance, if she and I were having a quarrel, he would come in and give her a little sign: don't worry about what mommy is saying, I'll fix it up. That wasn't good, he realized. The child doesn't know where her loyalties should be." It arouses mother's jealousy, but may also instill in the child the doomed desire to win out over her mother permanently.

Very often, father's reaction to his daughter's adolescence is determined by his wife. If the mother has laid claim to the girl, if they have this tight thing between them, a father is going to be wary of responding to his daughter's blooming sexuality. The mother who has tried to avoid competition with her daughter by playing down sex with her husband isn't going to want the girl to have him either. She may not want him, but still has a certain ego involvement: she doesn't want any other woman to have him, not even her daughter.

Many mothers try to keep their daughter and husband apart by denigrating the father. Says Dr. Robertiello, "It's their way of competing with the girl while keeping both the daughter and father for themselves. Divide and conquer." "You know your father can never handle that kind of problem," says mother. "Why didn't you come to me in the first place?" Mother remains the friend of both sides, always firmly in the middle.

It is a destructive situation, leaving room for all sorts of oedipal fantasies to enter. If mother doesn't want him, if she doesn't understand him, maybe the girl can win him after all. But even if mother is a bitch, the girl can't afford to lose her primary alliance. Father may be the spice of life, but mother is the bread and butter. The relationship to mother was formed earlier, and runs deeper, than anything the daughter has with her father.

Here is a poignant story from a thirty-five-year-old woman and mother of three daughters whose own marriage ended recently. When I heard it I couldn't help wondering how many fathers are like hers: "It wasn't until I got married myself and geographically far away from my parents that I began to see their relationship realistically. I had always thought of my father as a tyrant who had to be lied to and manipulated. My mother and I had always been very close. She was very much the martyr in the marriage. But when I began to examine my own marriage recently, I began to see that my father had a pretty raw deal, which made me feel different toward him. A year ago I gathered up all my courage and telephoned home, and after I talked with my mother I asked to speak to daddy; when he got on the phone I said, heart in mouth—I don't know what I was afraid of—'I wanted to tell you that I love you.' There was this silence and then my mother came on anxiously exclaiming, 'What did you say to your father?' I told her, 'I told him that I love him, which is something I've never said, and I thought he might like to know.' She said, 'He's sitting over there sobbing.' She called me back in several days and said, 'Your father and I've been talking'—which is not something they frequently do—'and he told me that all these years he thought you hated him.'"

For mother and daughter the problem becomes not so much winning the man as sorting out their own relationship: controlling their jealousy, denying anger, finding other words for their guilt. Years after he is gone, divorced or even dead, the struggle between the two women remains: how to maintain the truce, the pact, the symbiosis?

"Once a year my mother and I take a vacation together," a fifty-five-year-old woman tells me. Her mother is eighty; they are both widows. "What infuriates me is that whenever anyone approaches us, man or woman, my mother just takes them over. Just as she did when I was a girl." I don't ask why she continues to vacation with her mother. In symbiosis, you would rather stay with your partner—competition, defeat and all—than break the tie.

"If the mother doesn't have a good relationship with the father," says Helene Deutsch, "she will be jealous of the girl. This arouses competitive feelings in the mother which inhibit the daughter." On the other hand, if father is absent, preoccupied when at home, if he tries to sidestep the competitive issue between mother and us by ignoring our needs for recognition, we will take in mother's negative sexual message, wait passively for men, not believing in them if and when they do come along, and remain dependent on women for our deepest emotional needs.

Many women can only fall in love with married men. They say they want the man to leave his wife—just as they wanted father to leave mother for them. But when the man is ready to divorce his wife, the woman loses interest. She didn't really want her father to leave her mother, it was just a wish. If mother and father should get divorced, and the daughter goes to live with daddy, she is guilty. She didn't want the wish to come true. *"Some oedipal wishes are very ardent but are not meant to be fulfilled,"* says Dr. Deutsch.

Father has his own oedipal feelings to contend with. When we were five, he may or may not have felt nervous about our sexual overtures. "Little girls can be terribly seductive," says Dr. Esman. "At least, fathers can experience it as such." But when we are thirteen, there is no way he can dismiss our advances as the games of a little girl. Nor do we want him to. We press up against him as daddy, the one person who loves us so well we can try behavior with him we wouldn't dare with boys our age. We expect him to run the show, to be able to know the difference between actions that say, "Treat me as a woman," and our continuing need to be loved as a daughter. We expect the world of him since he's daddy. Therefore, we are terribly hurt if he is threatened, if he precipitously withdraws and says, "Get off my lap, you're a big girl now." We are thrown back onto mother. The healthy sexual thrust of adolescence toward men has been dammed up or even reversed; the major movement of our lives remains focused on women.

"It is not so much that he is sexually aroused by the girl," says Dr. Sanger. "It is the idea that something uncontrollable may happen that bothers a father. I think it is essential that a girl feels her father finds her attractive. Unfortunately, too many fathers—and mothers—can't put into words what they feel. It would be nice to grow up feeling that your body was loved by your parents, who knew how to kiss it, hold it and verbally let you know you are lovely."

In tracing the line of the adolescent girl's psychosexual development, sociologist Jessie Bernard warned me against putting too much weight on any one variable, including mother. "It oversimplifies the problem," she said. "Things are coming at the daughter from all sides." I agree; mother is not the only determining factor in the girl's life. But whatever else happens to us in relationships to father, peers, teachers—the tie to mother is the one constant, a kind of lens through which all that follows is seen.

Games are paradigms for life, in which children can learn about losing and winning on a scale they can take in. How often do you see a mother and daughter pitted against each other in deadly earnest on the tennis court or in a game of cards? Today, a young girl may learn competition in Little League baseball. Her mother never did. Losing anything to another woman is not "just a game" to mom. It rearouses deeper feelings of loss and anger that were never resolved with her own mother. The girl gets the message that open competition is OK merely in marginal matters like baseball. In matters with mother or other women, to compete and to win means risking the loss of a prime connection.

"The problem is not so much that the daughter pushes the mother aside to get to her father," says Helene Deutsch, "but that the daughter sticks to the mother. That is the explanation of the anxiety. The daughter is troubled because she is *dependent* on mother even while she wants to be *free* of mother."

Father is not the only man who arouses oedipal competitions. "There was a man, my father's best friend," says a woman of thirty-five. "We called him Uncle Steve. Years later I was to find out that my mother was very attracted to him. But to her dying day my mother patted herself on the back for never having had the slightest affair with this man. I was fourteen when this incident happened. We were out on the terrace. I was lying alongside Uncle Steve on a redwood chaise. He was a very affectionate man. The whole family was there . . . my brother, father, my sister and mother. Out of a clear sky my mother said, 'Helen, you're a bit too old for that now.' I remember going scarlet. I instinctively knew there was something between my mother and him. She was jealous. I was utterly embarrassed, but nothing further was said."

Later in our interview, this woman tells me that when she and her husband were living together before they were married, she always dreaded that her mother would telephone while he was there. "I was afraid she would know he was in my apartment, in my bed. I just didn't want her to." How could her mother know? Because her mother lived on in her head. Love for the man she was to marry was pushed aside by fear of her competitive, No-saying mother.

The dictionary gives this ecological definition of competition: "The struggle among organisms, both of the same and of different species, for food, space, and other factors of existence."[1] What two organisms share as close physical and psychological space as mother and daughter? What better force to make each seek her own place than the sexual drive? We could even accept losing to mother, if she would just acknowledge what is going on between us. The hard but necessary lesson to the loser in the oedipal competition is that she just can't continue to hang out around her rival's house forever. She has to grow up and get out if she is ever to find her own man. But mother dismisses our efforts at sexuality as silly, brushes off our independence as foolhardy, and denies our growing ability to want and feel what she does. She says it is for our own good, but we are not so sure.

The family that was once felt to be lovingly close, now seems claustrophobic and boring. We want to get out, to get away. We are often drawn to people and activities mother doesn't like. With her grudging permission, or behind her back, we do them anyway. *An identity is being formed*—but we feel it is in the teeth of her opposition. Guilt piles upon anger, we twist and double back on her. How can you hate your own mother? It is a Laocoon struggle, endlessly unresolved.

The oedipal situation is less complicated for boys. They need the same early symbiotic tie to mother that girls do, but there is another figure in the house, against whom they can afford to express self-assertive notions of competition because in no way does it threaten what they have with mother. This figure, of course, is dad. A second, related reason boys don't find adolescence as painful or unsettling is that they don't go through the love-object shift that girls do. The boy's primary, straightline involvement is always with women. First his mother, then girl friends, later his wife, etc. Girls must make this extremely complicated shift to the male sex—away from mother to father.

Almost from the beginning, long before they are ready to begin the work of cutting the symbiotic tie to mom, little boys are learning how to separate, establishing themselves in their own identities through competition—first against the male parent, later against other little boys. At four or five, they begin to vie with dad, often at his urging. They wrestle and race with him, beating him at Monopoly or Ping-Pong. By the time he is an adolescent, the boy will have become accustomed to all sorts of structured situations in which competition is allowable, encouraged, and even fun because it is protected from the dark and murderous underside of the competitive urge by the rules of the game: the limits are clearly defined.

Psychoanalyst Dr. Reuben Fine, who is also a chess master, writes of this struggle dominated by powerful Kings and Queens—perhaps the most nakedly oedipal game of all—that the enduring fascination it holds is that while the King is captured, he is never destroyed.[2] In the same way, boys learn through the strict rules and structures of sports that if you beat the other guy in baseball, it will not kill him, and he will not hate you forever. Besides, there will be another game tomorrow, and maybe he will win then. Through these social situations that men share, the latent hostility in competitiveness that is in us all is brought into the open and given expression as play. The lesson is taught to the boy without words: feeling competitive, acting competitively, *winning* is not betrayal. *It's natural.* And as long as it is kept within rules, it can even lead to deeper friendships. Counselors at boys' summer camps have long known that if you take two little boys who dislike each other, put them in a ring with strict rules and heavily padded gloves, they will more often than not emerge after even the toughest fight as the best of friends.

Fathers are so unthreatened by their son's competition that at the beginning they can allow the boy to win. They want him to "stand up for himself," "to fight his own battles," "be his own man"—to separate. The son who stays tied to his mother is no tribute to his father. Eventually the younger man may honestly beat his father. The older man may not like it. But he is so at home with feelings of competition that he can even let his son see he is momentarily annoyed at being beaten. This only gives the boy greater feelings of independence and pride. Griping at each other's prowess at the game, father and son advance in their relationship. They may grow closer, they may not; but the airing of competitive feelings has given the son experience in handling these emotions in a highly charged situation.

Women watch men walking off tennis courts, leaving football stadiums in tight, amiable groups of two and four, and we feel the lack of something they have. I used to think it was an open sharing of feelings. I now know that men's camaraderie is not about honest communication. What they do have is a learned communal release of pressure, a way of letting off steam, hostility, competition; it allows them to be easier with one another. Men learn to play to win, to stretch their competitive limits and be proud of it. Some men overdo it, but all men learn the vital lesson: "A young boy," says Dr. Robertiello, "can't get through adolescence without learning how to take defeat." He has lost, but it has not destroyed him. Therefore he feels he can win in his own turn, without destroying his opponent. Men do not feel their happiness or sexual success comes at the expense of crippling someone else.

"It's very healthy to let your body act out, thrash out, your competitive feelings," says Dr. Robertiello. "I often tell women they would look better if they could just let it out, verbally and physically. If they don't, they acquire that strained, tight mask, they become anxious-looking people." Tact calls for us to contain our feelings, but if it is too rigid, there is often a psychosomatic price to pay.

"The development of adolescent girls is probably the most complicated process in human growth," says Dr. Esman (himself the father of three daughters). "They have to cope with the complexities of their reactivated oedipal conflict over desires for their father, the resulting rivalries with their mother, and the hostility it engenders in both women. At the same time, they must learn to accept themselves as women. In a society like ours, which values the male more than the female, this can be a very tough, even reluctant acceptance."

It is a dilemma; we are between worlds. We have not yet arrived at the safe harbor of discovering we can love men, and that they will love us back—and that in this new, exciting (but still frightening) kind of sexual love, we will find feelings of warmth, intensity, arousal, and power that in their different way are as rewarding as what we had with mother. We look to boys for the confirmation of the burgeoning sexuality mother doesn't like, and the reinforcement which daddy would not give us. But the acceptance we get from boys never holds the deep reassurance we had with mother. Boys are so strange. Often, we ask too much: who can live up to the glamour of being the forbidden, unattainable object—once he is attained? Men have drives and needs of their own. From their side of the sexual fence, they resent our demands or feel insufficient to meet them. They hurt us and depart. Unlike the promise mother makes, their love is conditional. They have been raised to see us as appendages, symbols of their success, sex objects. They want us for something we don't wholly believe in.

We went looking for love, but somehow sex came with the package. Sex *is* exciting, but it's scary and dangerous too. The whole business becomes problematic, tinged with anxiety. Wouldn't it be wiser to retreat? If we go back, become "good" again, mother's girl, mother would stop being angry. These endless arguments about whether she doesn't like this boy or that would end. We would have her love forever. There would be no competition.

Instead of asserting our individuality, our needs and desires, we become more like mother; join in her protest that sex isn't important to us after all. Pretty soon, the sexual drive is tamed, symbiosis wins. We grow up, we marry and have children, but never really left home.

On a realistic level, mother is not afraid we are going to steal daddy away from her. But there is a difference between a six-year-old who can fit into a man's lap, and a thirteen-year-old who fits perfectly into your clothes, who vies for the only man in the house and elicits from male visitors the kind of smiles you haven't seen in years—all the while, making plans of her own for a future you will never see again. Perhaps mother has come to terms with her fantasies of motherhood—but nobody ever mentioned treating her daughter as another woman. Certainly her own mother never treated her as one. Another wife, another mother, yes. But another *woman?* Never.

If we are our mother's claim to immortality, we are also a reminder of her years. How can we be going out with boys? Mother was just fourteen herself. "Adolescence is classically the time when mothers begin to relive their own lives through their daughters," says Dr. Schaefer. "It can happen with bewildering suddenness. With my adolescent daughter, I can practically name the day when she began to change, last September."

Mother helps us come to a healthy resolution more by example than by lecture. At best, she is comfortable in her own role of a woman—*however she defines it.* She may have a career, or be a traditional wife and mother, but a daughter needs the day-by-day perception that mother has chosen her role, and is not constantly embittered or bored by being consigned to what she feels is an inferior place. "It is also very important," says Dr. Esman, "for the girl to sense that her mother has a reasonably satisfying sexual life, so she can see that the relationship between a man and a woman is rewarding. She sees something exciting up ahead toward which to grow."

A daughter's adolescence brings into high relief whatever problems or conflicts sex may still hold for mother. How can you explain the difference between romantic and sexual love if neither is present in your own life? Can you talk about the promise of womanhood, a career, motherhood—and not want a bit of that promise again if you yourself feel stifled?

Some women have always felt overwhelmed by their more glamorous friends, that other women were more sexual. Now their daughter too is more beautiful, and younger. They withdraw from the competition by letting themselves go, becoming even more of a mom. Other mothers become so sexual that the daughter doesn't dare compete: "My mother flirts with men outrageously," says a fifteen-year-old. "She is what's called a cock-teaser. She tells my father all about it when different men proposition her at the country club. I think dad likes it, it boosts his ego. But I think her behavior is ridiculous." This young girl is twenty pounds overweight; she admits, "I can't beat my mother at her own game. I've given up trying to compete with her."

Says psychoanalyst Betty Thompson: "People tend to keep on being whoever they are. Becoming a mother doesn't change that. So a woman who is more concerned with her own feelings than anyone else's can be unreasonably competitive with her daughter. I've known mothers who forget they are twenty years older than the girl the minute their daughter starts bringing boys home. They compete as if the man were their own age. It's habit. Any time a man comes in the room, they have to feel attractive."

"I've been wondering if I should get Penny a bra," a mother who is thirty-four says to me. Her daughter is thirteen. "No, she hasn't asked for one, but I've noticed that people are beginning to look." What kind of people—men, women? What kind of look? I don't ask. But what is this pretty young mother feeling? Fran is a good mother who sees her work as caring for children and husband. Feelings of envy, competition, would be out of the question. At the dinner table that night, the daughter scolds the father: "Daddy, do you know how many calories there are in that dessert?" It is her mother's voice. She starts to take the dessert away from him, playing the stern mother (wife), but her father draws the line. "Sit down, Penny," he says. He is smiling. Fran watches from across the table. It is difficult to read the expression on her face. Where does she fit into this? The challenge comes on all levels, from the girl she loves, but also from everyone and everything that would take the girl or her husband away from her. Psychiatrists say we should air these feelings, maybe joke about them. But Fran's mother didn't joke with her about feelings of jealousy, competition. So Fran too is silent. The husband says privately to me, "My wife and daughter argue about everything and anything. I don't think they even know what it's about. I find it kind of amusing because I know it's about me. It's nice to have two women fighting over you, though they'd deny it to the death." Meanwhile, Fran sighs and confides to me, "I must find some exercises for Penny, she's getting round-shouldered."

I remember being round-shouldered, not because I needed a bra, but because I didn't. I hated the nasty pink one my mother finally bought me after kindly pointing out that I didn't need one. Seeing my humiliation, she'd tried to cover it up by telling me how lucky I was: I wouldn't have strap marks on my shoulders when I was her age. *I wanted strap marks!* The battle of the bra is an adolescent classic.

Why should something as trivial as a bra bring such storms into the mother-daughter relationship? Perhaps it is answered by this fifteen-year-old: "Before I even kissed a guy, I had a bad reputation. I don't know where it came from. I think it's because I had breasts before anyone else did."

Mother knows what breasts mean in our culture. If she likes hers, if she allows us the peculiarly female rite of passage of the first bra when we want it, and not when she does, we too may grow to like our breasts. If not, our round shoulders try to hide the inadmissable truth: at one time in our lives, our breasts were the focal point of anxiety about the new sexuality we wanted to be proud of, but which mother feared and shamed us into hiding. The perfect symbol of this unresolved conflict is the fifteen-year-old of the liberated '70s who goes braless under her tight T-shirt, and stands with her arms crossed, hiding her chest. "The classic mistake mothers make with adolescent girls," says Dr. Fredland, "is that they won't let them become women."

Skills and abilities that once gave us recognition and self-esteem now also betray us. "Up to the age of puberty," says Jessie Bernard, "the young girl does all right, but now she traditionally begins to fall behind in school." We used to raise our hand enthusiastically for teacher's attention, to speak out loudly and clearly when we knew the answer. Now we hide our intelligence and bite our tongue. We want to attract boys, we want to be "feminine," and lo and behold, the way you do this is the same way mother taught us to keep her love: submission and passivity. For every sociological study I see that shows this is changing—that girls now stay on the honor roll right through high school—there is another study indicating that while boys tend to prefer high prestige occupations the more they get into adolescence, the reverse is true for teen-age girls.[3]

"Because adolescent boys are anxious of their ability to perform," says Dr. Sanger, "an assertive girl will scare them off." Often the little, simpering itsy-bitsy girl will be most popular because she is less threatening. In her book *Letters Home,* Sylvia Plath's mother recounts an incident that speaks poignantly to any woman who knows what it is to be torn between being bright and being popular at school: "By the time [Sylvia] was a senior in high school, she had learned to hide behind a façade of light-hearted wit when in a mixed group and, after a triple date, was exultant as she reported to me, 'Rod asked me what grades I got. I said airily, "All A's, of course." "Yeah," he replied, grinning, as he led me out to the dance floor. "You *look* like a greasy grind!" Oh, Mummy, they didn't believe me; they didn't believe me!' "[4]

Girls are raised for partnerships, boys to perform. If we are now beginning to raise our girls to achieve, that doesn't mean we aren't still raising them for partnerships. We instill in them what psychiatrists call a "hidden agenda." We say, Go to college, succeed, be self-sufficient, but we also give them this message: if you don't succeed as a wife and mother, you have failed. The message need not be spoken. A mother's own life is experienced by a daughter as a standard of achievement. No one tells us that it is difficult, painful, maybe even impossible for many women to be a success in a career and a good mother as well. Nor does anyone prepare us for the fact that to be a success you must be competitive, and that most men in our culture still feel the competitive woman to be a threat.

"We will not make men's mistakes," say feminists. "We will not be competitive with our sisters." This is hailed as an advance. It is childish to think denying something will make it go away. "Be sexual, fulfill yourself," women today are encouraged. Why do so many of us still hold back? On some level we know we are being encouraged to reach this goal using only a child's make-believe tools. A world in which you are told competition can be eliminated does not exist. I am not holding out as an ideal for women the lunatic degree of passion men bring to their drive to "win" at any price. That doesn't mean competition doesn't have a rightful, necessary place in women's lives.

"I grew up in Georgia," says a twenty-eight-year-old woman, "and in the South, women are supposed to have some kind of magical power. But it's really manipulation, the women hanging in together to run the men. A good example is in my family, where my mother was Big Betty and I was Little Betty. Being just like your mother, even sharing her name, says you have this power to manipulate men just like she does. You and she are a team, so there can't be any competition between you. You both want the same thing. If women ever stuck up for their individual rights, they'd lose their solidarity; the men could pit one against the other and do what they want. The hitch is of course that southern women are terrifically competitive over men, looks, who has the prettiest children. Smothering that competitiveness, denying it, eats up all the energy that women might use to win themselves a real position of power, if only over their own lives."

The speaker, who teaches high school, continues: "There are dozens of girls in my classes who are loath to compete. They blush if they get high marks. Last week, a class of seniors staged a debate and the girls automatically elected boys to lead both debate teams . . . even though several of the girls were smarter and better debaters. I was horrified. By the third day of the debate things were in a shambles. Some of the girls got up their nerve and put the best people—themselves—in charge. But they didn't feel good doing it. They were afraid the boys would think them aggressive. I think they minded even more that the other girls would be angry because these smart girls had shown themselves to be superior.

"It reminded me of when I was young—Little Betty. It was understood that part of the magic of being half of Little Betty–Big Betty, was that we had fixed places. I would never beat out, never outgrow Big Betty. We were always close—still are. But it gets rougher every time I go home. I'm successful on my own now, and it's hard to maintain the childhood tie. How can I? It's based on the assumption that she is bigger than me. But I don't want to give it up. There's a strength there. Big Betty and Little Betty—it sounds awful, but it's home."

Billie Jean King and Bella Abzug may be the wave of the future but they are still marginal figures in a world where young women are not taught how to express competitive feelings within approved structures, nor given rules with which safely to express rivalry. The girl who strikes out with the bases loaded at the picnic is still thought to be adorable. She may have lost the game but has succeeded in something more important: reinforced the sexual status quo. By rising above merely masculine notions of winning and losing, she gives living evidence to the rule that women are noncompetitive, and all the more lovable for it.

"What makes women afraid to compete with other women," says Dr. Robertiello, "is a fear that if they show they want to beat out the other person, but don't totally succeed, the unconscious talion law will exact revenge. To the unconscious, competition is to the death. People are afraid to compete because they are afraid of the powerful, unseparated mother. She would kill *them*."

"How can a mother help her daughter to separate?" reflects Dr. Deutsch. "You cannot make a rule, personality enters into it. A mother who has already separated from *her* mother is more likely to be able to help her daughter do the same. It also helps if the mother has a life of her own, other things she does and is interested in besides taking care of the daughter. But then that too can create a problem for the girl. Maybe the mother has more talents than she. Then the girl has to handle not only the oedipal jealousy but the thought that the mother is more gifted than she. It arouses feelings of competition, analogous to the sons of famous or successful fathers. But it is better for the child if the mother has something else. Yet, often when the mothers do work, children wish their mothers were like other mothers, always at home. It is ironic."

Should mother try to do better by her daughter than her own mother did by her—give the girl a greater measure of self-confidence— is it any wonder she may occasionally feel an irrational anger at her own efforts? Nobody ever did it for her! "I didn't want my daughter to grow up as I did," a mother tells me. "My mother was an anxious woman and tried to hold on to me all my life. I try to separate my own subjective fears from what may be realistically dangerous for my daughter. For instance, I have a terrific fear of deep water. I didn't want her to have it, so I made sure the first times she went into the water she was with people who *enjoyed* swimming, who felt safe in the water, and not with me. When she was nine she wanted to take the public bus to school. I used to send her on private buses. At first I thought: Oh, dear, the idea of going all that way on a public bus in the middle of the city. Then I thought: it's me who is nervous about it. She wants to try it. The bus picked her up right in front of our house. It was safe and made her feel terrific. Her world had grown. On the other hand, when I am certain that the danger is real and not involved with my own personal fears, then I insist she do it my way. I don't want to deprive my daughter of an experience that enlarges her, that gives her a growing sense of mastery over herself and the outside world just because I'm anxious."

How does this woman's fourteen-year-old daughter describe the relationship? "I used to be closer to my mother. It changed when I started going out with boys. I don't know why she thinks the parties I go to are so wild. She's practically waiting at the door when I get home, and she asks a lot of questions. Who was there, what did you do, what was this person like? She asks the same questions before I go. I get the idea she's kind of anxious. I sometimes think she's jealous of my friends."

When a mother tries to make up in her daughter's life for the mistakes experienced in her own, it often works fine until adolescence. When sex enters, mother cannot intellectualize away the feelings of competition and anger if they were never resolved with her own mother. The ugly thought that she doesn't really want her daughter to outstrip her makes her feel guilty. While she pushes for the girl's success, she brakes for her safety. There are always three generations of women's voices in a house.

The daughter tries to act out her mother's double message: "Be sexual and popular as I would have liked to have been," but also, "Don't, because that is bad." The girl often resolves the conflict by putting both halves of her mother's message into action serially: first she stops, then she goes. The classic story that psychiatrists tell is of the mother who repeatedly warns her fourteen-year-old daughter not to get pregnant; but the very strength of her injunction signals the girl of the intensity of forbidden delight by which pregnancy is achieved. First the girl acts on the spoken *Don't* part of her mother's ambivalent words. Then, in a rebellious moment, she acts on the unspoken *Do*. She becomes pregnant.

Adolescence is a tempestuous time, filled with rivalries, crushes, rages, disappointments, and unreal, giddy exultations of new relationships. It is the time for up-till-then undemonstrated problems to come to a head. An ego structure that was adequate to handle the conflicts and tasks until the time of puberty "is no longer adequate to handle this tidal wave of increased sexual drive that takes place now," says Dr. Fredland. "It's like a house built on stilts; it's fine until a wave comes along that is too strong for the stilts. Then the house comes down. Angers and anxieties that could be suppressed earlier can no longer be held back. You suddenly have all these new feelings to cope with—hormonal and psychological—but with the old apparatus."

At adolescence we go through what psychoanalysts call "the pregenital tug." With every step forward, away from mother, we want to run back for reassurance. "One minute my daughter wants to choose and do everything by herself," a mother tells me, "and the next minute she's having a temper tantrum and acting like a baby, wanting to crawl into my lap." I would hate to tell you how many of the mothers I interview have read their daughters' diaries. "I was so worried about her," they excuse their behavior. "She has become so withdrawn, I just had to find out."

We know our privacy is being violated; it undermines our halfhearted efforts to break away. "No, you can't stay out till midnight," mother says. "No, you can't go out with that girl, that boy." Her answers seem to come ironclad in the same wisdom and certainty with which she has always run our lives, but our anger has new weight. She is proud when a teacher says we think for ourselves; when we try to assert our independence at home and lock our bedroom door, she doesn't like it. Says pediatrician Virginia E. Pomeranz: "When we find out that our parents' values are irrational, untrue or phony, that's when we turn."

We talk of adolescent rebellion. Applied to women, the word is a farce. "My mother and I have become like total strangers," a fourteen-year-old says. "She doesn't like this guy I'm going out with. We get into terrible fights. I'll slam my door, turn the record player on full blast, and just sit in there fuming. Or when she tells me to be home at a certain time, and I can see that the time is coming near—I have a watch on—I'll just stay where I am, two more hours maybe, and then I'll go home and she'll be hysterical. I'll tell her I'd completely lost track of time."

We slam doors, stay out late, go out and get pregnant, or rush into early marriage—but it is stasis. We have done nothing for ourselves, only something in reaction to her. Rebellion implies a break. Dr. Sanger defines it as self-differentiation and self-definition. "It is a way of saying, 'The family is great, I love the family, but I have to do it on my own, leave me alone.' With some people you have to rebel in order to get them to listen."

When we rebel against mother, it has no teeth in it. No more than when we later tell our husbands we are leaving. We pack our suitcase as he sets out for the office, but when he comes home at the end of the day, we are there. Says Dr. Sanger: "A girl can't say, 'I've got this fight with my mother and I know I'm right. I'm going to go out and make something of myself.' Instead, it all dwindles down to this endless arguing and reconciliations. 'Hey, break it up!' I say to women. 'What on earth do you keep hoping for from your mother? The few crumbs you're going to get from her at the end of this argument aren't worth it. Find a way to argue and not to look for crumbs.'"

In adolescence we want rules, if only to assert ourselves by breaking them. The girl who complains about her mother's strictness is disturbed by her friend whose mother doesn't lay down any rules at all. "This friend of mine tries to pretend she has the best deal," a thirteen-year-old says. "She's always going on about don't I wish my mother was like hers, but I don't think she's really happy. She's like a lost soul."

"I hated only having the backs of cars, dark hallways," one mother says. To give her daughter the privacy she missed, this mother goes out when her girl has a date. "I don't want her to think I'm playing the heavy chaperone, spying on her." Privately, the girl tells me that when she has a date, she always spends the night at a girl friend's house. "They are a big family, there's always someone at home." The daughter wants her mother around in case she needs the control, in case she wants to tell the guy, "We can't do that, my mother's home." The irony is that the mother never asked if the girl wanted her there. She didn't consider that her daughter's needs might be different from hers. *She made the assumption that the daughter wanted what she wanted.*

The girl who is ready to break the rules, will. The girl who is not can use them to buttress her lonely position in a society where everyone seems to be "doing it." "I love you, Johnny, but I've been raised so strictly." It is not she who is putting him off. It is her stern mother. A situation that helps both her ego and Johnny's.

"There is a cliché which I tell mothers of girls of this age," says Dr. Esman. "You have to resign yourself to the fact that between the time your daughter is twelve and fifteen, whatever you do will be wrong. It is my effort to give them a sense of humor about the situation to help them—the mothers—survive." A mother who finds she must play the square for her daughter's own good, even while her daughter protests, needs a certain appreciation of irony.

"Kids today," says Dr. Sanger, "often find themselves in the difficult position of having to set their own rules because mothers mistakenly believe the new freedoms should be applied to young as well as older women. A girl of thirteen needs enough rules to feel she can regulate her growing sexual experience. She needs to be protected from taunts of, 'What kind of girl are you if you don't put out on the first date?' Well, why should she? She just doesn't know enough about human beings to be able to posit sufficiently strong answers to such questions. Not that much has changed. The needs are still there, the kids want rules. The years between seven and eight, and thirteen and fourteen are very valuable years, scholastically, socially, athletically. Things you learn in those years last the whole of your life. To have those years loaded down by excessive sexual worries hampers the consolidation of those skills."

We may bitch at mother's rules but we will accept them if something at the back of our mind tells us they are sensible, consistent, and in accord with reality. But if we perceive her decisions as arbitrary and/or phony, we will resent her and them: they come out of that inauthentic gray area we cannot define but don't like. We fight to win ground for ourselves but she shifts the argument from the content of our request to the tone of our voice: we are rude and unladylike. We want to be popular and have our own friends, separate from her; she says certain girls aren't good enough and are just taking advantage of us. She feels left out of our decisions, rejected, and becomes punitive about the high cost of the telephone calls we make. We want a string bikini, but the argument becomes one about the clutter in our room. Years later when we fly home to visit, her first words at the airport are, "Oh, darling, what a short skirt!"

What is confusing is that part of mother does worry about our well-being. Half of us knows that is so. When this is genuinely the case, the criticism is not so unceasing; sometimes there is none at all, just pleasure in seeing us again. But if time after time, the first words we are met with make us feel like naughty little girls, the pattern is clear: more than our welfare or beauty, mother wants to put us in our place.

In adolescence the sexual drive is an explosion of energy that tries to break through, once and for all, the sticky, little-girl ties that bind us to mother. Sex is an expression of our own individual needs and desires. "I am a woman who likes this, does that, and goes for the other kind of man." It says who you are—and takes no account of mother at all.

If mother's fear of sexual self-assertion has made us reluctant to assert our own, our growth will stop. To deny that we are in sexual competition with her, we will say we are not sexual at all. The girl comes up to the threshold, but the full woman never does emerge. The processes of separation and individuation slow or cease; we merge with mother instead and become what Mio Fredland calls one of the "latency girls."

These are the women whose lives express a certain safe, nonsexual quality. It is as if they are living still in that period—between eight and ten—that is characterized by palships with other girls and not too great interest in boys. "There are millions of women," says Dr. Fredland, "who are very successful at jobs and careers, even as wives and mothers, but who never really got into adolescence. They are well organized, get along fine with other women, not too competitive on a 'female' level. Psychosexually they are still back in their latency years. They are easy to identify. They have a different 'feel,' a kind of Girl Scout quality."

Many mothers do not see this kind of behavior as arrested development but as a process that has produced exactly the kind of daughter they want. A "nice girl," pal to girls and boys alike, who will dutifully get good grades at school and never be seen by mother as any kind of sexual competitor. She won't be heavily involved with men until it is time to marry, and then she will choose an equally "nice" boy who himself will carry none of the anxiety provoking overtones that mother distrusts. "In this way," says Dr. Fredland, "the mother avoids feeling competitive or threatened. The daughter never makes her feel she herself may have missed out on the possible erotic richness of life. Very often, these mothers themselves are latency girls who never became women. They are the wreckers of daughters."

We all know women of thirty and forty who are still referred to in their family as "the baby," or "the kid." It is not uncommon to run into daughters who phone their mothers two and three times a day, or whose mothers call them. "It's one thing to think along the lines of the extended family," continues Dr. Fredland, "where there seemed to be space enough under one roof for everyone. But I'm talking about the 'little girl' who never grows up. She leaves home physically, but never psychologically. *From the very beginning, the mother has to encourage the daughter to be her own person, not just let her go but encourage her!"*

Unless we learn the rewards of being our own women now, we will ever need to merge with a man as we did with mother, rather than expand his life and our own by joining in a union of two separate individuals. It may look like sex, but it will be symbiosis. Never mind that it is taking place with a man; it is modeled on what we had with mother during latency.

True sex, continuing sexual excitement, can exist only between two separate people, each aware of herself/himself as individual entities and therefore of the alien magnetism of the other. It is then we feel the lightning bolt of sex, that electric charge that connects two bodies: we orgasmically "have" one another—and separate again. There is no passion in symbiosis.

Can it be exciting when—as the saying goes—the right hand caresses the left? Symbiotic partners may struggle for orgasmic sexuality but are defeated before they begin by this presexual need to belong and blend into someone, to be so close that his head (as mother's once was) will be inside ours telling us how we feel, who we are, what we like and don't like—giving us an identity we never established on our own. We love the people in our families; we feel sexual desire for strangers.

"Do you remember the lookalike clothes that mothers and daughters used to wear?" says psychologist Liz Hauser. "I can remember thinking when I was a little girl how wonderful that would be. When my daughter Liza was little, she loved to look at them in Altman's catalogs. Before I understood the problem of separation, I thought those clothes would be wonderful for her and me too. It's a terribly symbiotic way of relating. It's thought to be cute in our society, but it tells both mother and daughter that they get extra applause for being tied together as tightly as possible. If they are on their own—separated—they are somehow diminished. Today, Liza has three pairs of jeans that fit her like skin; the old unseparated me would have tried to make her wear what I wanted her to wear. If she doesn't want to give them up, that's fine with me. Mothers who want their daughters to dress for them should realize this is what we accuse men of doing when we say they are chauvinistic and want their women to look pretty because it reflects on them."

When we were little, we loved to romp in mother's oversize dresses. When we are thirteen, her clothes fit us. We are older. So is mother. We approach one another's wardrobe with the desire to "take on" something the other possesses. "Hey, you stole my favorite blouse!" says mother when we walk into the room. She would give her life for us. Seeing us in her clothes makes her proud of the daughter she has produced. But what have we "stolen" from her in the process?

The rare mother who can believe that there is enough sexuality to go around, that her daughter's doesn't threaten her own, says, "You look better in it than I do." We heave a great sigh of relief. We love her more. The wish to outstrip her, to take away her crown, has been experienced safely, symbolically. Mother recognizes our sexuality, concedes we may even be a more beautiful (if only because a younger) woman—but does not hate us for it! She still loves us!

What if mother wears our clothes too well? We hear her boast to her friends she could take even a smaller size than we. At a time when we have little but youth to give us an edge in the race with her, if she can "get away with" wearing the same clothes we do, she has won. The victory may seem pleasant to her, a small triumph over her years. To us it can be shattering. We have not had so many victories as women to be able to afford this defeat.

Little wonder that young girls adopt clothing so outlandish that mother would never want to put it on. "Mother doesn't like it," says Dr. Schaefer, "when the daughter ignores her ideas of good taste and is totally guided by her peer group's standards of what to wear, what is in, what is out, and ugly. It is a competition for control. A lot of it has to do with how much of an independent person the mother feels herself to be. If your children are your reason for living, then you need your children to be a certain way to satisfy you. If I have a life where I get other satisfactions and am not dependent on the satisfaction I get from being Katie's mother, I can tolerate the difference growing between us."

The reason so many women do not let go of their daughters is that they have little else in their lives, nothing of their own. Or else they have been so frustrated in their relationships with their own mothers that they try to make up for it in symbiosis with their daughters. "Many girls," says Dr. Fredland, "have mothers who are trying to fill up the empty hole inside left by their own absent, cold or distant mother. Usually the mothers aren't aware of it because if they were they would have to let the girl go. It recalls the pain of loss of their own mother. These mothers insist their daughters tell them everything about their lives, their friends; the girl has no private corner for her thoughts or activities."

"My mother tells me the same thing over and over," says a thirteen-year-old. It's always in this whiny tone that drives me nuts: 'Call me when you get there. Call me when you get there. . . .' Then when I complain about one of her rules I don't think is fair, she says *I'm* whining." Because we cannot afford to hate mother, *we become like her*. We take on her whiny tone, her anxiety, her "nice girl" rules and fear of sex. We are only thirteen.

"I know from my own personal experience," says Dr. Deutsch, "that sometimes a woman will say, 'There is a certain expression I get which I hate.' When she stops to think about it, very often it is an expression her mother wore, which she disliked. It is true of me. We don't want to be like our mother, to be reminded of her in ourselves, because in the first great oedipal competition, she was the victor."

Before you know it, we are thirty-three and whining at our own husband and daughter. Rather than become angry with mother—which would force the issue of separation—we take on her voice and those expressions we liked least. Married or not, "we" are still not sure sex is nice. We blame our husband for not making sex more enjoyable, for not making us feel like "a real woman." Our husband wonders what became of the sexual woman he married. He cannot compete with our first ally. Who is also our first censor.

Women of forty or fifty with grown daughters of their own tell me that they are not able to see men except as husbands, fathers, and brothers. Divorced women who want a sexual life react to men in the old childhood ways, hemmed in by adolescent rules. "I tried to fantasize about sex with this man," a forty-eight-year-old divorcée tells me, "but it only got as far as the motel. I couldn't imagine myself going through that door with him, and taking off my clothes. And that was only a fantasy!" This woman is "disgusted" with herself for her inhibitions, but she remains a little girl, angry at her mother's rules, and protected by them too—inappropriately.

Our pre-oedipal alliance with mother sets up patterns we can never understand. Without her encouragement to leave and find a larger world, something always holds us back. Our intellect and ambition want to try for a better job, but an older voice says, "Don't take chances." Without mother's acknowledgment of our sexuality, the move toward men always seems tinged with a sense of betrayal. We go out with boys, we grow to want them sexually, but feel an inhibition: our deepest emotions remain with her. Eventually we may choose men who are diametrically opposed to the kind "we" approve of—sexually exciting men, whom mother cannot control. We may even marry one of them, but the battle is not over. "Not tonight, Tom," the woman says, knowing that even as she rejects him, she is rejecting her own pleasure. She knows she likes sex. What is holding her back? It is puzzling because it is not her body which is saying no. It is the old recorded message in her head which continues to tell "us" what "we" feel.

We develop migraines and ulcers. We would rather live with the pain of suppressed rage than lose the illusion of a love that is eating up any real love we may feel for her. We go home to visit, but are relieved when it's over. We know there is love between us, but can't touch it.

"Women have these endless fights with their mothers," says Dr. Sanger, "and then they feel guilty. The mothers feel guilty too. There's a tremendous reconciliation until the next big fight. It's endless and it gets nowhere. It looks as though something is happening or going to happen, to change, but nothing happens, nothing changes. It's a series of fights and reconciliations and guilt . . . no progression."

We want both to separate from mother and not to separate. As long as we stay attached to her, we remain her little girl—*safe*—but immature. What keeps us attached? "Guilt!" says Dr. Schaefer. "Mother feels the only way to continue to be needed is to keep us dependent. She cries at our birthdays. 'How big you've grown!' The girl wants to break away but that is mixed up with 'breaking mother's heart,' and she's guilty about that. The idea has been instilled never to leave mother, never to go out on your own. Who will love you like mother? We are frightened at the idea of separating. And so even if we are unsuccessful at it—as most women are—we are still guilty for having wanted to."

Guilt eats up our lives, but we don't want to be cured. To be free of guilt would mean to be free of mother herself. When I ask Dr. Fredland why mother's prohibitions against masturbation stay with us long after we outgrow so many of her other *don'ts*, she speaks of the unconscious fantasies that so often accompany masturbation. "It isn't just the act that's forbidden—the fantasies are forbidden too. There are fantasies that are oedipally tinged, so there's the incest taboo but also the terrific fear of oedipal competition." Masturbatory fantasies in which, in some half-understood manner, we set ourselves up as rivals to mother are so threatening that we give up the pleasure of masturbation when we are four or five, or younger. Eventually, we may give up sex too. All we are really guilty of—is wanting to be women ourselves.

In the end, however, I wonder if *guilt* is not a euphemism for something else—for the dread we feel must be the consequence of an ambivalent action. The fear is that if we do this wrong thing, the other person will become so angry she will go away. Guilt is merely the first step, which we name with tears and regret, but the *consequence* is so awful that even in our own minds we cannot speak it: loss. It is too embarrassing to admit to childhood emotions like that.

When I first began to ponder these ideas, I went to see a woman psychoanalyst whose work I've admired for years. She spoke of her two daughters, now in their late twenties and thirties: "Where did I go wrong?" she cried out to me. "They say now they had so many battles with me as children, of which I wasn't aware. And yet I nursed them all! I enjoyed it. I *did* take care of them, and loved reading to them. I was always there when they left for school and always there when they got home. I didn't go to work until the youngest was six and I was forty-five, but their memory of me was that I was always away. Something was wrong with me . . . to have thought I was *present,* available to them, and for them to have felt I was not there at all."

This conversation took place early in my research. I had not yet realized that to end any discussion of "Where did I go wrong?" with vague explanations of "guilt" is not enough. The next question must be, "And what dreadful event does your guilt make you fear will happen?" Loss is unspeakable.

I came to this after talking to Jessie Bernard. "Guilt is the biggest thing for mothers," she said. "Guilt is built into the role. You don't have all that much power and yet you assume the responsibility if anything goes wrong. When I talk to people about the future of motherhood, they aren't interested. Mothers are the most put-down people you can imagine. What young women want is babies, someone to hold and cuddle. They don't want sons and daughters like themselves, who are going to grow up, shake their fists at them, the way they did at their parents."

Angry sons and daughters, furious over the restraints and frustrations of family life, threaten mother they will leave her forever. A baby in your arms cannot.

A mother who did not give her baby a bottle of the right temperature, who wasn't home when her daughter got the flu, may feel guilty —but it is in proportion to the "wrong" act she has committed. It is not a fear of unimaginable consequences, that terrible malaise that hangs in the air like thunder. That is left for mothers who have children old enough to utter the dread sentence mother has been afraid of all along: "That's the last straw. I hate you. I'm never going to see you again."

Daughters fear they will anger their mother so much that mother will desert them. Mothers fear they will anger their daughters so much that daughters will desert them. Both women call it guilt. Every woman speaks of it. It is not guilt. It is terror. The terror of losing each other. It makes them cling even harder, tightens the claustrophobia between them even more. In the end, the ironic truth is that if you have the courage to let each other go, you may be friends for life.

I've been thinking about these problems for three years and still they elude me. Last night I dreamed about them, this morning as I lay in bed I understood them, but by the time I get to my desk, I find I am chasing shadows in my head. It takes all my force of concentration to get over the resistance to knowing what I *do* know—and even while I write this, I can hear my husband in the next room, typing away toward the finish of his novel. "Look what chapter you're writing!" my friend Richard Robertiello says. "You're afraid that if you do this book well, if you succeed, your mother and Bill will be jealous, they'll hate you. The fact is, it doesn't matter to them."

Why do I think my success and/or failure are so murderously important to everybody else?

Competitive urges will always be frightening because they stand for our desire to be sexual and separate. They are associated with feelings of being left, reprisals, etc. *They were never aired and found to be simply childish fears!* And so, at thirty-five, we still feel as we did at fifteen: that competition with other women must be denied because of our need to be loved and accepted by them too. We are left in anxious stasis: the only way to kill competition, it seems, is to kill in ourselves the desire for life.

I have always thought my emotional highs and lows were with

men. It was men who peopled my days and nights. Today I know it is not that I don't need women, it is that I need them too much and my need of them precedes my need of men. I have long despaired of ever finding with women what I want, and I fear the retribution I would wreak on them for not giving me the love I need. I would have told you before I researched this book that, yes, of course I love my mother but that we are two different people living in different ways in different cities. I know today that I am tied to my mother more deeply than I dreamed, to the point where I have always avoided competition, not just with her but with every other woman.

—*Which does not say I am not competitive.* I am; so strongly that I cannot admit it.

"It is much easier to get a woman to accept that a man is treating her badly," says Dr. Robertiello, "than to make her see that her best woman friend is doing her in. Another woman will steal her man, talk behind her back, but women refuse to give one another up." The story of a thirty-year-old woman's best friend making off with her husband is a cliché, but from mother after mother I hear about the same thing among twelve- and fourteen-year-olds: "I tell my daughter, if that girl is after your boy friend, she's no friend of yours. But my daughter won't give her up."

A fourteen-year-old girl tells me a story that she says has nothing to do with competition. "It's about how girls hurt each other," she says with resignation. "They are not honest with one another." It will be a self-fulfilling prophecy in her life.

The events on which she bases her conclusion began one afternoon when her girl friend lost her virginity. "Then that night, the boy turned around and had sex with her best friend!" My interviewee became the confidante of the injured girl—and of the boy too. In fact, she and the boy "happened" to become very close. "He needed someone to lean on." She quickly explained to me that she was not a sexual competitor with either of the other two girls because she was still a virgin. She and the boy "only kissed and touched."

I asked if the friend minded her seeing this boy to whom she had given her virginity, and who had then deserted her. "I don't know how my friend feels. She's not a very honest person, so I don't know her real feelings. I don't feel guilty, though. He didn't leave her for me. If she were nicer to him, and if she were a good enough person, he'd want to be involved with her again. I didn't tell the other girls, though. They wouldn't understand why I was seeing him. There's nobody that I really trust at all, except him. He has something that I never have found among my girl friends. I know he would never betray me to anybody. No matter what I do, or what I tell him, he will always like me. Boys don't turn on you the way girls do."

That interview was a year ago. Today the girl is fifteen and there is a different boy. She looks to him too for those things she cannot find with women—like trust. Given her unresolved and denied contest with women, what are her chances with men? In some mysterious way, they will always seem to fail her. And if she gives up on men, and falls back on the company of women—relieved to be rid of the competitive struggle—how long before she finds she is irritated and angry at women once more, hurt by them and hurting them herself? Getting rid of men doesn't rid our lives of competition. Men may be the sexual prize, but long before they came along, the struggle with women was going on for life itself.

When we were little, we had to live by mother's rules. It was her house, her man. Now there are enough men to go around, and the rules are up to us. If we lose one job to another woman, there is another good one around the corner. Fear of competition is nurtured by notions of living in a psychic economy of scarcity. Grown-up life is an economy of abundance.

---Chapter 6---

THE
OTHER GIRLS

When I was nine I went to a private summer camp, a beautiful plantation home on an island hung with Spanish moss. I had my first cases of homesickness, impetigo, and rejection by a best friend. Her name was Topsy and she came from Atlanta. We slept together, we ate together, we jumped hand-in-hand off the diving board on the big oak pier together, and we made a pact to do everything together, especially to be best friends, forever. One day a mother arrived and left her little girl at the big house. She was put into our room. Topsy and I eyed her during lunch, conspicuously leaving her out with our giggles, as we left out everyone from our secret world. By supper time I was the one on the outside. They whispered when they looked at me, sharing secrets you would think they'd shared for years. Their friendship was born on the strength of my exclusion. That night I lay in my bed and sang "Onward, Christian Soldiers" to myself to keep from crying. My head ached, trying to know what I had done.

One afternoon when I was eleven, Mary Stonewall and I were playing at Betty Anne's house. Betty Anne was my best friend. We paid her brother a quarter to let us see one of his dirty comic books. The three of us retreated under Betty Anne's canopied bed to read it. *What was this?* "Oh, no!" we cried, straining for a better look. Our heads bumped. "Let me see!" we cried, but it was too terrible to look at, too thrilling to bear. The space under the bed was suffocating. We rolled away from one another in hot-faced shame and an excitement we did not know how to share. Laughing hysterically we ran from the bedroom, bumping headlong into three workmen who were painting the backstairs landing. Men! They might as well have been brandishing ten-foot penises as paintbrushes. The three of us flew in all directions, screaming. Ten minutes later we convened on the veranda, damped down by thick sandwiches of chopped olive and Hellman's mayonnaise on Pepperidge Farm bread.

What to do next? It was a hard act to follow. Boredom worked on us like an itch. "How do you spell brassiere?" I asked, and Mary giggled. She had been Betty Anne's best friend before I even knew Betty Anne, who now tightened and blushed. She was the first in our group to wear one and she had secretly told me how much she hated it. Mary took up my chant, "Brassiere, brassiere," and the funny word that one minute earlier had left flat-chested Mary Stonewall and me out of its portentous, exciting meaning, now became the ugly thing no one wanted part of. Betty Anne squeezed her shoulders together to hide her breasts and tears. At last the afternoon had a name: leave out Betty Anne. Within minutes the front door slammed, and two little girls had left one little girl behind.

Every Friday night when we were thirteen we went to Madame Larka's dance class at the South Carolina Hall on Meeting Street. At a resounding chord on Madame Larka's piano, we girls would rise and stand in front of our chairs, waiting on our side of the room as the boys approached to make their selection, one by one, until there were none—but the unpicked girls. If I danced it was usually with Gordy Benson. My Aunt Kate couldn't understand why I didn't like Gordy; wasn't he taller than I? I told her that Gordy Benson smelled of Cream of Wheat.

Certain girls were always asked to dance and they were my best friends. I have always preferred good-looking friends; until I grew into my own looks, not being picked for the dance didn't hurt so much as being grouped with the losers. What had I in common with them but this unfair rejection by men? My feelings about myself as every bit equal to any other girl were jangled by this new role in which winning had nothing to do with ability, initiative, daring, and action. I got through dancing class with an optimism that each time it would be different.

After dancing class there was always a party at someone's house, to which we would race in a fleet of cars borrowed from worried parents. South Carolinian adolescents can drive at fourteen and we girls, still half-bludgeoned by Madame Larka's lesson in passivity, would half run, half saunter in slow motion to reach our favorite boy's car before our opponents. It was a deadly sort of ballet we did down those graceful swooping stairs of the South Carolina Hall, pacing each other out of the corners of our eyes while we pretended animated interest in anything but what was really going on. Did the boys know how totally our lives were focused on them, how we could have gladly betrayed one another for their favors? I doubt it. Their ignorance, their disinterest—*maddening!* While we died in closed rooms to the sound of recorded music, they roamed the streets, played football, lived quite easily without us.

Their cars were our one chance to get close to them. As they "gave us a ride" for a few blocks, we girls would giggle and invent endless airy chat to camouflage our deadly intent to get close to an arm, a leg, a pair of trousers that went with a particular song or passage on the violin. "Touch me," we would pray, "just let him touch me." Meanwhile we would smile at our best friend, who had out-maneuvered us and was sitting next to him. No malice was ever exchanged, the desperate strategies for position and counterposition mutually ignored. But when we were planning the last party of the season, I blackballed Patty Hanson. I can't remember how I did it, but I made sure she wasn't invited—a girl as much a part of our group as I. Nobody stood up for her. Had they, I would have lied a thousand lies rather than admit I simply couldn't bear the possibility that once again, because of something I couldn't control, Patty would get to sit beside the boy who filled my dreams. The night of the party, Patty sat home and never knew why.

I grew up with Helen. I learned to smoke in her kitchen, we studied together for exams all through high school, and when the right Sunday came along, we put on our first garter belts and stockings and walked into St. Philip's Church together. When I had finished my own dinner at home, I would often go to Helen's to help them finish theirs. It had gone on for so long that her mother never bothered to ask, "Nancy, would you like to join us?" A place would be set for me and the maid would make her rounds again. More than the food, I liked having a man at the table, being part of a family with all the roles accounted for.

Once a month in history or math class I would get terrible menstrual cramps. The school infirmary offered nothing more than a heating pad. Home was too far away to go for the shot of gin that eased the pain like nothing else, so I would usually go to Helen's house across the street. Once, when her mother wasn't home, I climbed in the kitchen window to help myself to the gin. It never crossed my mind that Helen's mother would object to my entering her house this way. She loved me like a daughter, a love I took gladly. And once repaid badly.

It was a Sunday night and we were leaving the church parish house after a party. We girls were standing in the vestibule, putting on our coats, when someone saw something outside through the distorting stained-glass window; she announced it to be Helen and Tommy Boldon, kissing.

Helen and Tommy hadn't even had a first date. Judgment was passed instantly. The next day Helen was snubbed in the halls at school, given "the treatment." Not too coincidentally, Helen was the most voluptuous girl in our crowd; the older boys were already paying attention to her. No one was sure if the crime had been committed, but our gnawing envy told us it must have been. Ostracizing Helen released us from jealousy. Her exclusion fed into the group a cohesive strength we hadn't felt in some time.

"Why?" Helen's mother asked me, when I could no longer avoid going to see her. "What did Helen do, Nancy? She is so unhappy. You are her best friend." How could I tell her the truth? The truth was a lie. Helen had done nothing. I could not answer Helen's mother because the things women do to one another, in cruel anger and even crueler silence, do not bear talking about. It is the work of bitches.

Instead, I told my best friend's mother I would make things right. I did, but I know Helen never forgot. Neither have I. I blush that I might still be capable of that kind of cruelty, that I could feel deprived by my friends' successes, and not adult enough to live in my own accomplishments.

After mother and before we are ready for men, there are the other girls. At five and six, they appeared in our lives like life rafts, bright welcoming alliances to carry us away into a new identity. We could never have left mother on our own. Father had failed us. Little boys weren't interested in our overtures—but little girls! They are our great chance to separate. They have all the safety and familiarity of home: they are female and needy, just like us. All of us are eager to find something more than mother, to embrace life, but the prospect is frightening. We rush into one another's arms the first day at school. Those arms close round us as tightly as the pair we just left at home. We don't struggle. We went looking for freedom, but found something too good to resist: tightness and closeness. We think we've left home. We have only changed partners. Symbiosis with a new face.

What human relationship contains as much ambiguity and ambivalence as women with women? We have so much to offer one another, but our history is one of mutual inhibition. The bond that ties us to other women parallels what we had with mother. She too began in our life as a loving friend. She became a no-sayer and a rival. Her very success in helping us grow through the difficult early stages of development brought us to the threshold of sex. Dad was the first man we saw. Mother was in the way. All her goodness and patience did not help. Within the family, there is only one prize. She had him. We wanted him. In one way, our desire was as natural as a river finding the shortest way to the sea; in another, guilt was the inevitable result. The irony is, the better mother she was, the greater the guilt. It is one of the inexorable, situational tragedies of human nature.

"What happens next," says Dr. Robertiello, "varies within different family constellations. Generally, the girl develops a negative oedipus complex. Her feelings of guilt, and the attendant fear of losing mother, make the girl deny the wish for her father. She bonds herself to mother and the female sex. With most girls, this drive leads to the tight, intense friendships which are such a famous feature of the latency period."

The fear of competing against mother and the guilt at wanting to beat her out anyway spreads to the entire female sex. We like the little boy who sits next to us in class and want to win him away from Sally. But to go after him might incur Sally's anger, so we defend against wanting him at all. Instead of being jealous of Sally, we telephone her to come spend the night. In these misdirected circumstances, is there any wonder there is often overt homosexual behavior?

Clinically, this is called reaction formation. It is a way of denying an unconscious impulse; the act comes masked as its opposite. Men who are afraid they are ninety-five-pound weaklings in their soul, go in for muscle building and parade on the beach as Mr. Universe. Censors read and see more pornographic works than anyone else. They say that because they hate it so, they must see everything dirty in order to know what to ban. The reaction formation against wanting to be filthy is to be compulsively clean. Instead of expressing our anger and competition toward women, we join with them and express love.

Now we are fourteen and fifteen. The boys who five years ago wouldn't give us the time of day want us. Our own bodies are stirred by mysterious desires and passions. The most natural thing in the world would be to respond. It is not so much sex we want, but to feel something that cannot be denied as easily as when we were six years old. We want recognition of whatever degree of sensuality we possess and whose expression we feel is life itself. But what we have with other women is already more important than anything we might have with boys.

Three little girls cannot play together. When we were seven we had one best friend. "If you have more than two, you have trouble," says a mother. "When my daughter used to ask for more than one girl to come play, I always said no. I couldn't stand the fights. At that age, they have terrific jealousies, whisperings, and secrets. 'She's *my* friend.' They just cannot share someone with another girl. My daughter is fourteen now and travels in huge groups, gangs of girls. But they still say vicious things about one another."

In an interview with this mother's daughter, she speaks of love and hostility in the same breath. "My best friend is always trying to get the boy I like," she says. "It's not just a malicious thing pointed at me, but a general idea she has. She always says she can get any boy to be interested in her. She's not unique, though. Girls just do mean things to each other. For instance, whenever a girl talks behind your back, the person she confides in will immediately turn around and tell you the mean things she said about you."

Boys do not develop girls' reaction formation, our denial of competition with mother. *Unlike us, they do not compete with mother*. This means the boy can still hang on to her as the nurturing figure, while expressing his competitive feelings against the dominant male. He suffers of course from sexual taboos placed on his feelings for the mother, but he is not in the position of the little girl: in competing with mother, we are in the impossible position of one who wants to bite the hand that feeds her.

"Girls can be merciless," says Dr. Sanger, "organizing vendettas against other girls, suddenly turning on each other. A girl needs all the help her family can give her. The tears I have lived through with my own daughter and the young girls who come to see me . . . what they go through is terrible. Boys do it, but it doesn't have that personal, poignant cruelty. Boys have defeats to deal with too, but they don't have this sense of violation, betrayal: 'This morning, I thought she was my friend, and this afternoon I found out what she was doing to me.'"

With no outlets for feelings of envy, competition, or jealousy, our emotions become compressed, escaping like steam through cracks in our nice-girl veneer. Before we know it, we have dealt the stab in the back, said the unkind word. We don't want to be bitches. Where did we learn it? Even as she separated us from our own body mother smiled and said she loved us. Blending love and anger, smiles and deceit, she taught us that our only rejoinder was to love her back no matter what she denied us—daddy, independence, sexuality—or we could suffer even worse loss.

"Of course you learned to play mother's game," says Dr. Robertiello. "You still needed at least the illusion of perfect love with her. You didn't have anything to replace it with."

One of the characteristics of childhood is singleness of mind. The baby likes this, is overjoyed by that, hates the third thing. As we grow older, as we take in more of the crosscurrents of life, conflict comes to sit in the heart. The intense friendships with other girls may be an experiment in replacing the closeness we once had with mother, but we are no longer innocent dwellers in Eden. Our competitive feelings have not magically gone away. They have merely found safer targets, been transferred onto these girls who, like mother, are both friends and rivals at the same time. All that love and affection between little girls masks the turbulence within—which is why we hurt each other so often. Our love for our friend to whom we talk for two hours on the phone every night and swear eternal devotion is not unmixed. It is not the same we felt toward daddy or Johnny, the little boy next door. It is born of détente, on mutual avoidance of anger. "But underneath, you are just plain mad at women," says Dr. Robertiello. "When you see a chance to get more love from someone else by turning on your friend, all that old anger is there to justify what

you're doing." The anger left over from the unresolved oedipal situation just breaks through. Mother won daddy's love by excluding us.
Now we're doing it to our best friend.

"I think adolescent girls' rules are almost biologically determined,"
continues Dr. Sanger. "They are there to be relied on when you can't
think of any other way to protect yourself." Dr. Sanger was referring
specifically to rules on conduct, the need for curfews, times to be
home when things are getting out of hand with a boy. But aren't the
rules for dress, for instance, when we are twelve, also biologically determined? They camouflage us against a sexuality we are not supposed to feel. "When we're going somewhere after school," says a
twelve-year-old, "we call each other up and say, 'Everybody wear
football shirts,' or, 'Everybody wear shirts with the alligators.' All seventh graders do nutty things, my teacher says, like we'll all wear
different-colored socks. My teacher is in love with a man who teaches
at our school. His name is Ken, and we wrote all over the door one
day, 'Ken my love.'" We ache with love at twelve. It doesn't hurt so
much if everyone is wearing different-colored socks on each foot.

When our world was small, one friend was all we needed. In this
narrow focus, she came to stand for life itself, and our demands on
her became ironclad. We live on the edge of bliss with our best
friend, just as we once did with mother; just as we did with mother, if
she falters or grows disinterested, we despair. We want more life but
we want absolute security too. We are not above leaving our best
friend if more love should beckon elsewhere, but we could not bear it
if she left us.

Adolescence faces us with more complex problems. Boys are everywhere, moving with mobility and freedom, tempting and frightening. We are caught in too many gusts of emotion; the world, alluring,
dangerous, huge and glittering is upon us. We need greater numbers
to hold our own. The single, one-to-one relationship we used to prize
with one best friend is too narrow. We want to be free to join in the
swim of life. We need more varied relationships, larger groups of girls
to help us handle the experiences rushing in from all sides. Our gang
of girls becomes a microcosm of the universe, big and complex, shifting, changing, but nevertheless understandable and ordered. The
group is power and fun but it is based on control. Its laws are arbitrary, cruel, capricious, dictatorial. That doesn't matter. It offers the
great recompense: the law of symbiosis. No one will be alone.

People together, people in crowds, feel emotions, have a heightened sense of life and daring (for good and bad) that individuals rarely achieve. In the end, the group does not merely substitute for mother, it takes us over totally. It supplies us with love, friendship, protection, strength, precisely defined outlets for emotion, a source of approval and a promise against the loneliness of being thirteen. The group may be a prison with a code of iron, but as a member, we have the biggest identity in town.

Our adolescent ties with the other girls could provide the balance and self-confidence we need now so desperately. We know there are more pitfalls for us in sex than there are for men. Boys are stronger. They don't have to worry about their reputations. Only we can become pregnant. If anything goes wrong, it is always the girl's fault. Within our friendships with women, a larger and freer framework than the stultifying one at home, we might explore ourselves with people who are subject to our own anxieties, curiosity, and joys. We want confirmation that it is all right to go, to separate, to seek our identity on our own and with men. We ask one another for encouragement, for community and a boost up out of childhood. We want the other girls to tell us that it's OK, that they too feel what we feel. What we get instead are The Rules.

The Rules institutionalize the anger in our reaction formation. I've never met a woman of any age who could tell me when they were drawn up. It seems at fourteen they were always there. There were certain things no "nice girl" ever did. No woman I interview can list them, but The Rules run our lives at thirty-five as they did at fifteen. They make us push men away, edit our opinions, dress like everyone else. More than anything, The Rules make us choose: which do we want—sexuality or the love of other women?

The group's job is to find outlets for those pressures society does not yet want to see in us. Slumber parties, romantic gossip, covert and overt sexual relationships with other girls substitute for sex with boys. *The group must keep the woman a girl for a few more years.* An increasingly difficult job when you consider that on the average, girls today are ready to bear children a full six years earlier than a century ago.[1] If you agree that early motherhood is often disastrous, it can be said that the group performs a valuable function here. The price, however, is that many women never really outgrow The Rules.

We never make rules of our own that we believe in more wholeheartedly than we do those of our fourteenth year. "When I began to go out with men again after my divorce," says a forty-five-year-old woman, "I would sit in the car and wonder at the end of the evening, should I let him kiss me, say good-night with a handshake, or go to bed with him? It was like being a kid with all those rules all over again."

Like some ten commandments of the flesh, The Rules are a list of Thou Shalt Nots: no kissing, no touching, no sexual expression, except to the degree the group allows. "The rules are made so none of the girls can outdistance any of the others sexually," says Dr. Schaefer. "It is a truce, an attempt to contain the violence of the competition of all against all for the small amounts of male attention we are allowed. Instead of sex being something that women eagerly join together to get more of, we join together to protect ourselves against it . . . and to make sure that someone isn't getting more than any other girl of that dreadfully dangerous but even more dreadfully exciting stuff." Those who break The Rules, walk around like pariahs —living examples of the punishment for making us jealous, bringing our competitiveness to consciousness. "I was fourteen when I started going out with boys," a woman tells me. "The rules were unspoken. But there was a pair of twins at school. Everyone speculated about whether they went all the way. We thought one did not, so we were friends with her. Nobody spoke to the other one." To be excluded from her love was one of the worst punishments mother could dole out. Exclusion is the sentence girls mete out to rule breakers now.

In contrast, boys don't hate the other guy who has sex. They may envy him, but they identify with his success. For a young boy, another's triumph is not a diminishment but a goal, something he can go after. "When I was sixteen or seventeen," says Dr. Robertiello, "listening to some other guy talking about what happened in bed with this girl the night before, I admired him. It didn't matter if he was lying, because we wanted to hear those stories. Men are tremendously reinforced by sexual talk. This kind of first-hand data helps get us over our insecurities. Whereas women are silent. So when they get to their first man, or tenth man, they are just as insecure about their performance and sexuality as when they were born. Talks with the other guys gave us a handle on how to act, what boys were supposed to do. Maybe it wasn't the best advice on how to be with a girl but at least when you were sixteen and crawled into bed with a girl for the first time, you remembered what the guys said. That sex is OK. That what is bad is *not* to be sexual. For girls, it's like going into the water without a swimming lesson. No, it's like being told that if you go in the water, you'll drown."

When the mysterious tides turn in the group and one girl is suddenly left out, she cannot retaliate. She is alone, while those on the inside are bonded even tighter by the fact of her exclusion. The process is merciless and the kindest little girls, the nicest grown women, understand it: the girl who is out at the moment must wait, bottle up her anger and pain. In *Pentimento,* Lillian Hellman describes a young woman: "Anna-Marie was an intelligent girl, flirtatious, good-mannered with that kind of outward early-learned passive quality that in women so often hides anger."² No trace of it can be allowed to show.

"I'm president of the class," says a fourteen-year-old. "But this other girl, who's vice-president, is always running the meetings, which is my job. I never say anything, even though it gets on my nerves. She's one of my best friends. I never show anger because if I'm angry, and I tell my other friends, it always gets back to her. You just can't afford to be angry with your friends. A few of the girls will show their anger, but they aren't popular." Once more, we are acting out a parallel to the lesson mother began to teach us almost from the day we were born: nice little girls don't get angry.

And yet, anger is one of the dynamics of life. It lingers and rankles; years later it may explode, safely disguised as defense of our own adolescent daughter. "I could kill those little girls," a mother says. "Yesterday, my daughter was *un*invited to a party by this girl Laura, one of her friends! I remember how that can hurt. I tell you I'm furious with those little bitches!"

What does her daughter feel at being excluded? Exactly what her mother felt when *she* was thirteen, and suffered these same hurts. "I hope Laura changes her mind and invites me again," she says. "When she first invited me, my mother changed my dentist appointment so I could go. The next day, I found Laura had taken me off the list. Then a few days later, she said, 'Oh, by the way, you're invited to the party.' But I found out yesterday I wasn't invited again. Am I angry? Oh, no, I really don't care."

I really don't care. Is there any reader who believes these four familiar, sad words? Is there any woman who does not recognize herself in this passive reaction?

We pool our (mis)information and aspirations, changing any opinion that is too personal or individual, until everything we say or think boils down to the group attitude. Wanting more, we settle for the lowest common denominator. "I had to really work to get into the In group," says a mother of thirty-four. "All the girls in that group married by the time they were twenty-one, and began popping babies like crazy. They thought I was strange to want to travel, to have a career. I live three thousand miles away now, but I still keep up with them. Whenever my husband and I go to Paris or Rome, I send them a picture postcard. I'm that wild glamorous person to them, and I'm delighted to have them think that. I have a feeling that for most girls who were super-popular as adolescents, life ever after is downhill. I think my keeping up with those girls is a way of verifying that I have succeeded."

We may never see the girls again whom we knew at fourteen. We never forget their standard of success. If the group's goal was marriage and two babies by twenty-two, even if we succeed in our own self-chosen goals, something is missing at the heart of our achievement. Alternative success never seems so sweet as when it is seen in the group's eyes.

Mother raised us on the principle of *two*. "It's the *two* of us against the world. Mother may scold but no one loves you more." It is her defense against the anxiety of our future separation. If she had raised us to feel we could have her love and that of others too, we would embrace our new friends, two, three, and four of them. Abundance would be exciting instead of laced with duplicity and the watering down of the bond. We have been raised as if we were shut-ins, but when we go to school, we are tall enough to see out the windows. Mother's silence about that exciting world out there, her evasions and lack of encouragement for us to go out and explore, makes us evasive and silent too. Our new friend is part of that "out there" that mother distrusts. We rush home, clutching the idea of her to ourselves like secret treasure. "Leaving my daughter at camp that first day was devastating," says a mother. "I felt I was leaving a part of myself, that I might never see her again. When summer was over, when she came home, she was very secretive. She didn't even want to tell me her new friends' names."

Says Dr. Fredland: "Children go away to camp for a month, to school for a day, and they come home changed . . . *if* parents can accept these changes and not move in with the old arguments."

How mother reacts to our new alliances determines not just the wholeheartedness with which we form them but what we come to expect from these new friendships. If mother is afraid for us, controlling, prying, telling us who we can or cannot see, we will try to control our friend, unable to expect more from her than we get at home. If mother is jealous, we will be jealous too—fearful of other people taking our friend away. "My mother resented one of my friends," says Dr. Liz Hauser. " 'Why do you spend so much time with her?' she'd say. 'You're always over there, you even eat there.' I was a very insecure little girl. I was always afraid something would happen to my mother, that I would lose her as well as anyone else I got close to. Sure enough, as a mother myself, I used to interfere with my daughter Liza's friends too. Just like my mother, I was constantly overprotecting. Often I thought that the other girl was taking advantage of Liza. But I was wrong. In effect, what I was saying was: You can only trust, be honest and open with mommy. Making Liza dependent on me, just as my mother had made me dependent on her. When Liza was born they weren't teaching about symbiosis and separation in my psychology courses at Columbia. Liza was six when I began to try to undo what I had done. It was late but I tried to encourage her to enlarge her world, see more friends, to spend the night out. I want her to get close to a lot of people so that the world seems a welcoming place. Not some place that's only safe if I'm there."

If mother had said, "I love you but I want you to love other people too, to have relationships with them as rich as you can make them, and to try other lives than the way I live," our discovery of life's variety would not seem a betrayal of her. Mother never said we could have this wonderful identification with anyone but her. We are deceiving her . . . or did she deceive us? The very plenty of what is suddenly being offered is bewildering. Richness comes mixed with guilt. Why do women feel they cannot love more than one person at one time? Why does the thought—that the person we love may also love someone else—terrify us? Loving in two directions threatens us with the loss of whomever we are not facing at the moment; there seems to be a minus to every plus in life. "Promise me that I will be your only friend, your best friend, and that you will leave everybody else out," we say to another girl. We want the same thing of men ten years later. We cannot ask it of our husband because that would be childish, but when he turns his full attention on others, we feel deprived, hurt. Behind every new love is the fear of loss. We never learned there is enough to go around, enough success, enough friends, enough love.

We lead double lives. We learn to take off our new selves before we get home, before mother's anxiety and control start setting the old limits: "Don't get so excited, Don't dress that way, Don't talk so loud." We are aware of her immense influence. Before walking in the door, we tamp down the excitement of being seen by others as the secret selves we've always been, at finding intimates, confidantes, twin people just as hidden and "misunderstood" as we. We whisper on the phone, though it's only that day's math problems we're comparing. "She's so quiet nowadays," a mother says. "It's not like her. I held her diary in my hand one day, but I knew I couldn't face myself if I read it."

I interview this woman's fourteen-year-old daughter: "When I was thirteen," she says, "I was with another girl and we smoked a cigarette. Afterward I felt very guilty. I came home and told mom about it. I thought I was going to be forgiven, that I'd have a clean slate and she'd say, 'That's all right, just never do it again.' But she got angry and yelled at me. I was very hurt, and I think that had a lot to do with my turning away from her. It disappointed me. Up to that age, I'd just assumed if I told the truth I wouldn't be punished. It made me lose trust in her. The same thing happened when I went out with the first boy who kissed me. I didn't tell my mother because I knew she'd be worried about what else had gone on. Nothing else happened, but she'd never believe that. I can't tell her things any more because if I did, she wouldn't believe me."

Mother "betrays" us because the old bargain no longer works. She cannot trust us because she does not trust sex and we have suddenly become sexual. Men will deceive us, just as they deceived her. How can she hope we will fare better than she? She says that we cannot learn to drive, though our brother learned when he was a year younger than we. She says we cannot have our own key to the apartment because we are too "irresponsible and scatter-brained." We know that is not the real reason. Behind mother's anxiety to guard us against all sorts of dangers which we sense are not very important is the one that *is* important. It is sex, but she will not name that.

Nor can we expect more from the girls in our crowd. "My friends and I tell each other everything," says a fourteen-year-old, "but we have certain understandings. Definite lines. When we go out with boys, we tell each other what we did and didn't do. But if you go past the line of 'feeling'—I only mean touching breasts—you don't say anything about it. There's one girl in our crowd who's had sex. There's so much talk about her behind her back that you get paranoid about being talked about that way too if you break the rules. At a slumber party last night, one of the girls left to go to the bathroom. When she returned, she was sure we'd said something horrible about her behind her back."

Fear of exclusion from the group is a stronger glue than love. It makes us angry even as it holds us together. We feel the group's limits throttle us back, as once we also were by mother's double check of love and control. Reinforced by the group, we dare to break mother's rules: "One of our favorite expressions is 'freaking out,'" says a thirteen-year-old. "My mother hates it. And cursing is in. Everything, especially fuck." Similarly, when the opportunity comes along—one we are sure no one of our sisters could resist either—we betray the group and break its rules too: "When I was fifteen and a boy put his hand on my breast," a woman recalls, "I thought it was terrible. No nice girl ever did that. But he'd been voted the handsomest boy at Fishburn Military Academy, so I let him."

Knowing mother's criteria for "nice girls"—the kind she likes us to be with—it is almost inevitable that we will be drawn to the kind of girl she doesn't like. "When my daughter started doing more things away from home I was delighted," a mother says. "I have a lot going on in my own life. I don't expect her to spend so much time at home, but I don't like some of her friends. One girl I dislike is Sally. She sleeps with boys. That isn't why I dislike her, but she's a disloyal friend. Any time my daughter likes a boy, Sally goes after him. I asked her, if Sally does this, why do you still see her? 'I think I'll just not confide in Sally when I like a boy,' my daughter said."

When I interview this woman's daughter she says, "I like to go around with Sally because she's so different. You sort of feel that you're doing something out of the ordinary by being with her. She's very exhibitionistic, and all the boys talk about her. My mother hates her, absolutely hates her."

Mother is inhibition; things and people she doesn't like have come to represent life and excitement. In fact, much of what we do with other girls is thrilling only because we know mother would disapprove. In time, when we break the group's rules, the exploit will be all the more thrilling for being forbidden. When we are grown, how often the best sex, the most exciting, will be that which mother and other women wouldn't approve. Stolen sex with the wrong kind of man, in the wrong kind of place, all the more electric because he's married or we're flying home tomorrow. What kind of grown-up sexual people are we when our greatest moments are in ratio to their disobedience to The Rules? The bottom line is that when we marry, when we have the kind of sex mother would approve, sex goes stale. Our true excitement was not purely erotic. Underneath was the greater adolescent kick of rebelling against mom and other women too.

If it were really sex we wanted, if it were our strongest drive, we would break the adolescent rules and join with men in a sexuality that reinforced us. If it was a realistic fear of sex and its consequences (such as pregnancy) that held us back, we would be more intelligent about the use of contraceptives. But it is not sex we want most, nor sex we fear. It is the loss of our place in the society of women.

A woman at a cocktail party tells me she wants to be a writer. She is twenty-five and has a responsible job. She'd had an idea for a story that grew out of a dream. "It was about a woman on a desert island with a man and another woman," she says. "I was one of the women and I was terribly attracted to this man. But I never finished the story. Every time I tried to write what seemed so evocative and powerful to me, I would come up with this same dull ending: this other woman and I just walking off together." I ask her if she thinks it has to do with competition, that the story says she would do anything rather than compete with a woman. The idea fascinates her and she calls me in a few days to say she finally finished writing the story—*by awarding the man to the other woman.* "You know," she says, "I'll argue with a man. I'll even compete with him for a job. But I hate arguing with women."

Sociologists speak of a cult of domesticity that once existed, a special "woman's sphere." "It was a secure place," says Jessie Bernard, "in which women had warm ties with one another. It was a woman's world, and they loved it." Sociologist Pauline Bart feels this area in which women were by right and by birth preeminent disappeared when male professionals like gynecologists began to take over. "Women used to help each other with their own special problems," she says. "My great-grandmother used to have herbal recipes for sickness and burns. These were the accumulated bits of female wisdom women shared with one another and passed on to their daughters."

Perhaps the woman's sphere of our grandmother's day belongs to a time we will see no more. That does not mean a community of women cannot be formed today which would be relevant to contemporary life. "Men always have had their old-boys' network," a woman tells me, "which gives each man within it a feeling of place and identity. In this way, they don't have to see someone younger as a terrifying rival, but as someone it is a pleasure to help out. Since I've become successful in my work, I've gone out of my way to help younger women. It's a great satisfaction. It makes me feel close to women, close to life, part of something larger than my own narrow ambitions. I've always wondered why I had women friends, but felt isolated from them anyway. It was that I always felt I had to protect what I had from them. I'm beginning to feel now that there can be a continuity of 'helping' among women, that I can belong to some kind of network myself."

Jessie Bernard moves me strongly when she says, "Women have been left sort of bereaved—psychologically high and dry. Women give emotional support to their husbands twice as much as husbands give it back. It leads to severe emotional deprivation, especially in housewives, whose mental health I regard as the Number One public health problem in this country."

I do not think that the passing of the old "woman's sphere" alone explains why we are such emotionally hungry people. Our problems of emotional deprivation go back too early in both our collective history as women, and in our individual biographies as daughters. The difficulty is that we have no healthy reserve of narcissism, no trust in our feelings of value built up in the first years of life and then strongly reinforced in adolescence. Perhaps our grandmothers felt this emotional deprivation less because theirs was a time when women lived through others—when independence and sexuality were not so highly prized, and therefore ties to other women were not threatened by anyone's individual success. Another woman might have a bigger house, a more successful husband or children, but these "achievements" did not threaten. A name, a home, wealth, sexuality— all were given. No woman achieved them for herself; the competition was muted.

The woman's sphere was secure precisely because it was so small. Today a woman's world is as large as she can make it—but that means she has larger yardsticks by which to measure herself. It is from this sense of competition and potential loss that our anachronistic, adolescent fears come back to haunt us.

"You don't get dropped by your group if you have sex," teen-agers today tell me. "We are more liberal than our mothers. What gets you into trouble with the group is when you have sex with more than one guy." Superficially, The Rules seem to be new. Factually, if one girl gets more than anyone else, she threatens the cohesion of the group. The need for symbiotic bonding above all else remains the same. How can there be any meaningful new "woman's sphere" if girls are still raised to feel another woman's gain somehow and mysteriously diminishes them?

How grand is our success when we know other women would love us more if we were less—less beautiful, sexual, successful? We give up our will and initiative. We say to the man, Here I am, defenseless, vulnerable, take care of me. More than sex, we have always wanted symbiosis. We think men will reward and love us forever for giving ourselves over to them. Instead, when we get pregnant, they leave us. If we marry, they get bored with our suffocating clinging and look for more adventurous partners. Hurt, we regress to the only real protection we could ever trust: other women.

The Rules pursue us to the end of life. Winston Churchill's mother outlived his father by a quarter of a century filled with numerous affairs and two marriages to men much younger than herself. On her pain-filled deathbed, she asked herself, "Is this the punishment for living life the way I wanted and not the way others wanted me to?"

Chapter 7

SURROGATES
AND MODELS

On a day that began like any other, my dentist removed my braces. Losing those wires marked my entry into puberty more significantly than menstruation. What had my vagina ever done for me? We were not even on touching terms. It was my mouth that carried the full potential for excitement: I had recently discovered kissing when my friend Daisy's older brother—who had nothing better to do that evening—put his tongue in my mouth. Fearful that my braces would tear it to shreds, I curled my tongue protectively around the barbed wires. I knew no more about kissing than fucking, but that kiss gave my life direction. It told me how I wanted to spend it. Stripped of my braces, I was ready. If only someone would try again.

I left my dentist's ante-bellum mansion on Broad Street like a prisoner unexpectedly released for good behavior. Grinning and astonished, I moved my lips over my naked teeth and ran all the way to the Memminger Auditorium, where we were rehearsing *The Wizard of Oz*. My Aunt Kate was the Cowardly Lion and I was the Tin Woodsman. She took one look and wrapped her arms around me.

Aunt Kate was the only woman, after my nurse Anna, whose embraces I welcomed, whose breast I allowed myself to lie on. I knew her perfume and the smell of her skin and when the world threatened to be too much in those years, her voice, her presence, the mere idea of her was something to hold on to. "You're just going through adolescence," she said to me once, and because she had a name for it, I believed it would end. She was the way I wanted to be when I grew up.

Kate was my mother's youngest sister. She had come to visit us after graduating from Cornell and had stayed on to live in our house. I don't remember her arrival. My memories begin with an overwhelming need for her, which she filled with a generosity and love I can never repay. She saved my life. If that sounds overly dramatic, understand that it wasn't just the pain of adolescence that she got me through. She also gave me my present life. She got me ready for my husband and my work. The idea of her life, the picture of her, how she was physically and mentally, were my motivation and goal for years when I wanted everything and didn't know what it was I wanted. Long after adolescence, things she had told me, ideas she believed in, ways I observed her to be, were my guideposts. We are very different women today, but I am her child. My whole family knew that, including my mother.

Aunt Kate was different from anyone I had ever known or seen. All my years in Charleston I had wanted nothing more than to blend, to melt into "the group" and be like everyone else. She had a style, a self-assurance, a truly original spirit that made being "different" a glorious prize. She didn't try to control me, didn't argue with the southern girl mold I was trying to squeeze into. Her opinions and knowledge fell about me like gifts, waiting until I was ready to open them. One by one they were incorporated into the self I was forming. Even as I stuffed falsies into my bra and made myself shorter by dancing with my knees bent under the conveniently long skirts of the New Look, I was beginning to take pride in being smart, to question whether there might be more to life than chasing boys. I wanted boys too, desperately; I wanted to be popular and to kiss in parked cars until the music station went off the air and my white panties with the lace trim were soaked through. But I wanted more than the standard conclusion of this southern dream—to wear graduation- and wedding-white on the same day. I wanted to act, to write, to travel, to be Kate.

She was my height and had my mother's beautiful auburn red hair. There was nothing in grown women's usual clothes that I coveted; they were a boring sea of shirtwaist dresses and spectator pumps. Kate wore ballet slippers. Her dirndl skirts were cinched at the waist with wide belts, and a gold Egyptian coin dangled from her wrist. Hers could never be called a peasant look; to this day I think of her as the most elegant creature I could imagine. During the day she wrote copy at the radio station and in the evenings she went to the Dock Street Theatre. She didn't just act in plays, she wrote them as well. And she painted. "Painter or not," my mother said with caution, "no one in Charleston has a loft, Kate." A grand piano, easels, old velvet couches and candles filled the loft Kate rented on the waterfront. I would go there alone and sit for hours, inhaling the turpentine like a promise.

Once Kate brought home one of her big colorful nudes and hung the canvas in the drawing room. My mother didn't notice until guests had arrived for cocktails: "Oh, Kate, how could you!" she blushed. The red-headed nude in the painting had my mother's face. Everyone laughed and embraced my shy mother and said, "Jane, you are funny, Jane." Kate put her arm around my mother and it was all right.

Though I was possessive of my aunt, and distant with my mother, I liked it that they were such good friends. One night when Kate had ingeniously wrapped her bosom in a halter made of two large silken scarves, mother's voice drew the line once more: "Kate, you can't go to the yacht club like that. People just don't dress like that down here!" My mother has never been able to stop anyone from doing anything—except my sister. When I visit her today and she says, "Nancy, people don't dress like that here!" I know her anxiety will pass if I am not affected by it. I have often thought that behind my mother's exclamations and disclaimers at what the rest of us do, is an envy, perhaps even some pride, that we are able to carry off a style she would never dare try.

It was the summer after Kate had come to live with us that I dropped out. I stayed home, refused to see my friends, followed Kate around like a shadow. My sister was away at boarding school that year; a time that was to be a grievous experience for her too. I felt abandoned, but more to the point, I felt I was going crazy. I shrank from my mother, rejecting her touch, answering in monosyllables. I would stand at the bathroom basin with the iodine bottle in my hand, fully aware of my overdramatization but also of my fear. I read everything in the house to stave off my impending lunacy. Reading was the only way of marking time until Kate came home for two o'clock dinner. I could rest in her.

Kate didn't just tolerate me, she included me. I followed her everywhere, to her studio, to the theater, out to dinner. In vain, I sought a way of being hired at the radio station so that I could be near her when she worked. And if I wasn't jealous of her friends, it was because they accepted me too. One by one they came from Cornell to visit; some even stayed. It seemed to me they were all tall and beautiful. The men were architects, poets, and actors, people they didn't breed in Charleston. They took me with them to the beach, and when they sat around drinking chilled white wine in the evenings and reading plays together aloud, I was given a part. One night, as we were getting into a car, one of the men said to me in passing, "You know, you remind me of Kate." I would gladly have given him my life.

Kate drew up book lists for me. She introduced me to Willa Cather, Conrad, and Henry James. She bought me water colors, and on weekends we would sit in St. Philip's graveyard with our sketchbooks on our knees. While she typed her first play on the card table in her bedroom, I wrote my first story about a girl and a horse. She did not mind my interruptions when I asked how to spell a word—interruptions I can see now must have been maddening. When she read my story, she suggested I put in a description of the girl. I did and she said it was good. When her own play was finished, I was given a small part.

It was a big success. I still remember the male lead's line to the heroine, played by Kate's roommate from Cornell: "You move like a panther, like a tawny panther." I wanted someone to say that to me when I grew up. I walked like a crippled person, shoulders hunched, knees bent, anything to be shorter. When Kate and I walked up Meeting Street past the Old Slave Market where I had once delivered a paper on General Wade Hampton to The Daughters of The Confederacy, Kate would slap me on the back and say, "Stand up straight, the Goldwyn Girls are the tallest and most beautiful girls in the world."

That time in my life when I stayed home to read to avoid my "thoughts" and clung to Kate as to life itself ended as quickly as it began. Summer was over, school began, and once again I only came home to eat and sleep. As I was on my way out the door one day to meet a friend, Kate called after me, "Hey, how about a chocolate sundae?" I was late, but I must have heard something in her voice that reminded me of myself: she missed me. We walked to Byer's Drug Store like we used to when I couldn't live without her. During the next years I would run into her on my way out to chase boys, to meet boys, to talk about boys, and I would avoid her eyes. I didn't need her anymore. She never said a critical word.

When I went to my first formal dance, I stood frozen to the wall the entire evening. Not one boy asked me to dance. Kate was waiting when I got home. She had seen the tiny size of the boy who had been sent to escort me. She sat on the edge of the bed stroking my hair while I cried, and told me the story of Lancelot and Guinevere. Once again the promise of her life covered me like a blanket. It wasn't just her words that said my life would become more than I could dream; it was the way she was.

How simple it was when we were three, or even nine and ten. Whatever else we wanted, we wanted "to grow up like my mother and have children." Says Jessie Bernard: "Our society makes a much greater effort to masculinize boys than to feminize girls. It is not necessary for girls. The model each girl lives with is female." But adolescence and the advent of sexuality change our ideas. Even if we want to be mothers, we don't want to get there her way. In our eyes, mother is not sexual.

For the girl who genuinely wants to re-create her mother's life, the repetition comes with a sense of peace and fulfillment. It feels *right*. Her path goes straight through girlhood, early marriage, pregnancy, with mother's smile and society's approval every step of the way. The daughter who wants something different has a harder time; the idea goes against her mother's model.

Either way, most of us repeat our mother's emotional life. We may not like the idea, but it is a fact. When we are young and energy flows in the veins like wine, we have no intention of giving up vitality, humor, adventurousness. It is unthinkable that we will ever be as anxious and conservative as mother. Then one day we hear ourselves telling our husband not to drive so fast, nagging our children to clean up their rooms, and we know we've heard that voice before. The degree to which we can forge our own emotional selves depends greatly on the help we get from other people who love us, people whose lives offer a pattern we can follow. People whose great virtue is the paradoxical one that they are not mother.

When we meet an old friend of mother's, who recounts how daring and exciting mother was before she married, it is riveting as a fairy tale. It has the power of truth in a framework of the mythic. We both want to believe and don't. "My mother finally took the mirrors out of my bedroom because she thought I looked in them too much," a woman of forty-five says. "And yet my father tells me she was very vivacious before they married, that she loved dancing and laughed a great deal. Now he is the one with the sense of humor. I suppose as he became more lively, she felt someone had to keep the balance in the family. In a way, I can understand that. I used to be more lively . . . before I was married, before I had children."

During family reunions when I was growing up, I loved my aunts to tell stories about my mother as a young woman. My mother—with different men, making conquests! I still pore over old photos of her jumping horses in dangerous steeplechases. It is thrilling to think of her taking chances. By the time I came along, she had changed.

If she could have offered herself to me as a model of daring, independence, and sexuality, would it have availed? I've known so many admirable women whose daughters reject their lives. Other women's daughters may emulate them, but the girl under their own roof will look elsewhere, *outside* the immediate family, for someone who stands for a different, roomier world, simply because mother is not in it. What I did learn from my mother was her other side: overcaution, anxiety, fear. I have tried to hide these traits behind the more daring qualities I learned from others. I know the world sees me as independent. I know myself as my mother's daughter. Mother is love and life itself, and we want to hold on to that, but a model for sexuality and independence is a bridge toward separation. Mother cannot be that for us.

Taking our mother as a model opens the door to problems of competition. Many of the women therapists I have interviewed are very much aware of why their daughters have turned to totally opposite fields of achievement. "My daughter is a first-class musician, a superb cook," one psychiatrist says. "I've got a tin ear and I couldn't be less interested in cooking. She has a tough job, coming after me. I can understand why she doesn't even want to dabble in those areas where I'm so proficient."

I do not mention the word competition to this woman's fifteen-year-old daughter. She brings it up herself, but denies any competition at all between mother and herself. "People don't understand how my mother can have her family and a full career too. Why should she be home taking care of me twenty-four hours a day? I get a lot of talk from my friends and their mothers, 'She must be hard to compete with,' they say. Why should I be jealous of her? She's given me the knowledge I can do what she's done, but there is no competition. I don't want her life. She is not my model. I'm a different kind of person than she is. My mother's more competitive than me. I just hate that feeling. I dropped out of the school orchestra because I didn't like fighting for chairs. I want to get ahead for my own pleasure, not because I want to knock someone down on the way up."

This young woman recently broke with a longstanding boy friend when he objected to her plans to become a lawyer and continue a career after marriage. She says she does not want to emulate her mother's life, but she rejects a man who will not play her father's role —he actively did encourage his wife to combine marriage and a career. If she finds such a man, if she succeeds in her desire to become a lawyer, her life will have paralleled her mother's. And yet she denies the repetition. It is not so much the emulation of her mother's life this young woman wants to avoid as knowledge that to set her goals as high as her mother's, necessarily brings with it a kind of psychic competition. She doesn't want to "knock down" or be "knocked down" by her mother. In any contest, her mother starts with all the aces.

"Getting unstuck from even a 'good enough' mother," says Dr. Robertiello, "is best accomplished if you can form an alliance with someone else, someone close, like your grandmother or father. To separate, you have to ally yourself with a person you feel knows the way, who is stronger, wiser or more independent than you." These people give us a source of power and strength outside of mother. They need not physically take care of us, but in a sense psychologically stand *in loco parentis*. They have many names in the technical vocabularies, least awkward among which are identification figures or role models. They are the dreams for us to grow on.

Childhood is marked by dependency; mother's tutelage means we are "done to": instructed, told to do this, wear that, go there and eat our spinach. Role models open the door to the concept of choice and activity. They see us as bigger people than mother did and show us that there are self-directed people who make their own decisions, go out and do it, taking the credit or blame for their lives. Obviously, it is possible to get through childhood without identification figures, but our need for them is intense during adolescence. It is a stormy period because all the problems that weren't resolved in our first three or five years now come up again. Life gives us a second chance here, but without help, new images, hope in the form of other people, it often doesn't turn out any better than the first time around. We give in. We stay attached.

"Oh, God, yes! Alternatives to mother!" says Dr. Sanger. "Mother is so absolute. She knows how she wants her daughter to be. 'Be like this, be like that, be like me!' If the girl has an aunt, an older friend, a grandmother, a teacher, a great lady like Eleanor Roosevelt who's impressive as a woman—that's terrific. Even knowing men who like women to be independent can be helpful too. It doesn't have to be direct, it can be indirect and still be useful."

"I can't think of any woman I admire, that I want to be like," says a fourteen-year-old whose mother is one of the most admirable women I know. "Except this older friend of mine. She's seventeen. She's very creative. I think she's wonderful. She's got her own opinions, which doesn't mean she doesn't hear other people out. But she doesn't let them make her go against herself." A couple of days after our interview, this girl telephones me long distance to tell me she has remembered another woman who is "sort of a heroine of mine." It is Katharine Hepburn.

Katharine Hepburn. She was one of my models too. Unmarried, childless, flat-chested—she is the antithesis of what mother and society want for us. And yet my mother adores her, and men too seem to sense something heroic in her. She transcends looks, style, or whatever particular circumstances the scriptwriter places her in; through force of character, by making it on her own, by never giving up and keeping her integrity intact, she wins us all. She is an image of the separate person.

Our model may be someone we meet one day or night, and never see again. She can be just a glimpse of an idea that we will fill in later, the way we imagine her and want to be ourselves. "There was a woman who came to lecture one day when I was in the eighth grade," says a thirty-four-year-old mother of two girls, who runs her own industrial design company. "She showed slides, and I remember she gave a little talk on Barnard. She was an alumna, and I guess she was drumming up business, but I never got over her. She was young, pretty, so cool and intelligent and unlike all the nice mom-like moms in the little town where I grew up. I fastened on her and that college like a signal from heaven. I don't remember what she said, but that was it, the other side of the rainbow. I was going there, by God!"

We don't need an ongoing relationship with her so much as an image we can hold ever before us. She need not even be alive. The women we read about as young girls, the Nancy Drews, the Diana Riggses of television, or the more contemporary Isadora Wings, spark our imaginations and give us something to live for, to grow toward when our emotional bags are packed and we have no definite place to go, no identity to travel in. "Very often," says Dr. Robertiello, "we analysts tend to say someone's personality is formed by the time they are seven. But some of us are beginning to get away from that dogmatic notion. I strongly feel that somebody you run into at twelve or fourteen can change your life enormously—the people you take in and identify with at that age can have tremendous influence on the rest of your life. Think of how many lives have been changed, for instance, by a child meeting a certain teacher.

"Most analysts—I am guilty too—focus on the idea of mother being the central figure, but in the course of a psychoanalysis we often uncover other, forgotten people who turn out to be crucial in the person's development. Mother and father may have nowhere near the impact of a childhood nurse. Whatever matrix has been developed from your good and bad experiences can be greatly changed through identification figures even after childhood is over."

Often we don't know what it is we want. We have abilities, talents, the potential to go long distances, but until somebody *sees* us, recognizes our secret selves, we will go the short distance and remain the safe, unexplored person. "When I went to college," recalls a twenty-five-year-old woman, "I expected by the third day for everyone to see through my facile ways and say, 'I don't know how you got here, but if you're going to stay, you're going to have to buckle down and use that brain of yours.' I had the feeling up till then that I had fooled everyone at school. It wasn't until my senior year that I met this teacher who was head of the English Department. She gave me the first C I ever got in my life. I'd always got straight A's without trying. I went to her and said, 'Miss James, yours is the only class in this college I've worked hard for. Why did I get a C?' She smiled diabolically and said, 'Because you've been doing B work, and if you tried harder you could do A work. I wanted to shake you up.' I was hers. I was her slave. Somebody had seen through me at last, *had seen me*. I've never forgotten her."

Even images of how *not* to be can be crucial to our development. Many women choose life-styles as much unlike their mother's as they can. "I am not convinced you have to like the people who are your models," says sociologist Cynthia Fuchs Epstein. "Men have traditionally tried to be like their fathers—whom they may have despised. Nobody has really paid too much attention to these processes in studies, but the impact of role models can be subtle and unacknowledged." Women may not have liked the fact that their mothers worked when they were little; they may still be angry that when they came home after school, mother was at the office or taking a postgraduate degree. Later, when these same daughters end up with interesting work and careers of their own, where do you think they got the idea?

The negative models perhaps most often objected to when we are young are overly strict or puritanical parents. One usual course is for the child outwardly to act against the harsh strictures the parents lay down, but to introject their values nevertheless. That is, we will break our parents' rules, but feel we are a rat, a bad daughter, for doing so. "An extremely important kind of identification figure," says Dr. Betty Thompson, "is someone who can relieve the girl of this guilt, of her mother's introjected superego. This new figure can allow the daughter to develop a better opinion of herself. The girl can recognize there is more than one set of standards in the world that she can opt for. If someone you admire lets you feel you don't have to be all that perfect for her to like you, it's very satisfying, very relaxing. There are usually many people around for an adolescent to identify with, and they can fulfill many different functions. A healthy person will tend to pick out the best available model in her environment." If a girl with a mother who doesn't want to let her go finds a strong role model—a teacher, for instance, or an aunt—the new figure can give her insight into why mother didn't want her to grow up. "You might find out what your rights are as a human being," Dr. Thompson continues, "rights which you may have been afraid to exercise until you saw the model of someone else to whom these freedoms were as matter-of-fact as air."

Before Leah Schaefer became a psychotherapist she was a jazz singer. "I think I got my idea for this kind of life from the movies I saw as an adolescent. I lived in the movies. I remember my adolescence as miserable. I didn't feel that boys liked me, or that my mother understood what I was feeling. We had always been close—until then. Now I felt cut off from her. But I wanted to be sexy and glamorous and wear terrific clothes and have all the boys fall down dead over me. All of which I wasn't about to have. There was no one to help me have even a part of it. So I felt terribly alone. Except for these wonderful people in the movies. After college I became a singer. When I was successful, my mother loved it. But when I was out of work she wanted no part of me. When I was doing what she would have liked to have done—to be a winner at something—she was the most helpful person in the world. When I decided to go back to graduate school and become a therapist, she loved it. Her daughter the doctor.

"I used to get angry and depressed when she disapproved of me. But now I can see that if she was unfair to me, she was unfair to herself. She treated me exactly as she treated herself. I figured out that it wasn't me, Leah, she disapproved of. What she didn't like was when she saw something in me of herself that she didn't like. You see, I was her narcissistic extension. When I wasn't a winner, she saw herself as a loser.

"From my side, I felt that if my mother didn't give me what I wanted—her approval and love—there must be something wrong with me. I was leading a very different life from hers, but I was still emotionally tied to her. As children we assume that if our omniscient, omnipotent parents don't give us what we want, there is something wrong with *us*. My mother led me to believe in her great powers from the beginning. She knew everything. She could do anything. Not even my life as a singer—just about as far from her life as I could get—convinced me that I could live in my own identity. Powerful as those images were that I had grown up on, those successful, glamorous people in the movies, magnetic as they had been in helping me get away from home, they could not contend with this even stronger pull I had to remain attached to my mother. Once I stopped demanding that she be the perfect mother, the kind of mother I wanted, we got along fine. But I was forty-two before I came around to that way of thinking."

Until recently, the women to whom young girls turned for role models during adolescence were almost stock figures. There were so few areas in which women were, by the nature of their work, assertive and self-affirming, that school teachers and camp counselors appear with the regularity of family friends. Today, my woman editor, my woman literary agent, or any of the dozens of admirable women you and I know if only on television, are available models. Pediatrician Dr. Virginia E. Pomeranz tells me that many of her women patients "are eager for their daughters to go to both women pediatricians and women gynecologists, so that they can see a good role model, a woman who is a wife and a professional success. For the same reason," she smiles, "they bring their sons here too."

As yet, the women with whom an adolescent is most likely to come into contact, to get a real feel of, remain the tried and true favorites. A gym teacher embodies the idea of aggression in the best sense, of being very connected with selfhood: if you play tennis with style and can throw a basketball well, that is a self-affirming kind of activity. Drama teachers are attractive because they direct people; in fact, anyone "in charge" is helpful, people who put things together and furnish direction but leave room for you to bring your own talents to the role. They allow autonomy to grow because they do not do the whole job for us; they let us stand or fall on our own. It is wonderful when your heroine returns your affection and respect, but you don't want her living through you the way mother did. Ideally, she is there when you need her, but she doesn't cry Betrayal when you walk away. She has her own life, and allows you to have yours.

"I've always had my dreams," says a seventeen-year-old freshman from a small coed college in the Midwest. "I wanted to take a premed course, but I got so much hassle I dropped the idea. Then I got to know the woman who is dean of students here. I admired her liberation, her feelings that all the doors are open to women nowadays. I know now there is no way I'm going to be like most women on this campus . . . the homecoming queen type going out with a jock. What is depressing is that so many girls only come here for husbands. Maybe the guys encourage it, but if I hadn't met this woman, I don't know where I'd be. Watching her, seeing the things she has done, I know I can do the same. She's full, she's complete. She's not married, but she's perfectly happy with her life."

If we cannot find models who will safely help us separate and become our own women, we may just give up and retreat back to where we started. A return to mother at this stage of development is a significant defeat, sapping our self-confidence and undermining our will to try again. People like this carry a feeling of resignation through life, never trying too hard for anything; they are convinced of failure before they begin. They are the eternal victims, repetitiously falling into masochistic relationships with dominating and selfish men whom they are unable to leave. Whatever significant models of self-affirmation may have come along in their formative years, just never "took." As they reached out toward people who represented autonomy, their need for security pulled them back to the person who never wanted them to go in the first place. They wake one day and find themselves in a spot they never intended to be, and don't know how they got there. In their lives—especially when they become mothers—they recognize an all too familiar pattern of behavior in which they feel trapped.

I am not saying that women would be better off not to marry, nor that it is a defeat to become like your mother. What matters is whether your life is your choice. If you have won independence first, so the decision to follow your mother's life comes of your own volition, and not out of a sense of passive inevitability, duty, or fear, that is a victory. It is a self-affirmative life, as valid as anyone else's.

The discussion here is about another kind of woman, one who did not want her mother's life, but finds she is repeating it anyway. Alternatives may have come along, were tried out, but always held too great an element of danger. They were exhilarating for a month or two, all right for a few years after college, but could not be counted upon for a lifetime. These young women may have geographically left home, experimented with sex, dabbled at love, work, men, but were never fully engaged in what they were doing. "I have always thought there was a boarding school side of me, representing my conservative mother," a young woman says, "and a hippy side, which represents the people I lived among for the first years after I left home. But I don't feel I belong to either. When I'm on the top floor of a high building, I sometimes think I'm just going to drift away." The usual solution for women like this is marriage. Sally Smith doesn't sound like much—largely because she has always been Mrs. Smith's daughter. But Mrs. John Jones—*that's* an identity.

Or is it?

In all fairness, it must be said that our view of mother makes it almost impossible for her life to aid our separation. An independent woman is one who has a totally different relationship to life, to men, to work, and to herself than we were ever willing to perceive in mother. If she has an existence independent from us, we dislike it, discredit it. *She is our mother!* She should be *there,* attached, waiting for us when we got home from school or from a fight with our friends. It is our privilege to leave her, not hers to leave us. The lament is almost universal among the daughters of successful women I've interviewed. I am guilty myself: I've said that I used to be thrilled by photos taken before I was born, of my mother as an intrepid horsewoman; but I also remember—with greater emotional intensity—my silent recriminations that she was often out for the evening, was younger than the mothers of my friends, that she didn't wear an apron and have gray hair.

We insist that mother be homey, unglamorous, "Like everybody else's mother." Then with the unfairness of children, once we have safely imprisoned her in the stereotype, we reject her as lacking excitement and jaunt off looking for someone else—someone who will be different, who will give us an idea on how to leave home, an arm to lean on while we try on our shaky new identities.

What makes the mother-daughter relationship so poignant is its bewildering reciprocity. What one person does, feels, inevitably affects the other. "Even with all my professional training," says Dr. Schaefer, "I can't help getting these feelings of rejection and abandonment about my adolescent daughter. Katie had always loved going everywhere with Thomas and me, to the theater, to friends' houses. She was wonderful company and we loved to include her. Suddenly, she didn't want to go anywhere with us. The phone rang endlessly for her, and she only had time for her friends. A friend would come to visit, they'd immediately go up to Katie's room, the door would close, and that would be that. Of course I was happy for her to be growing up, but it took terrific objectivity on my part plus Thomas's repeated assurance that she was just going through a phase, and that she hadn't rejected me; I could just feel the surge of retaliation in me, the desire to be punitive about the telephone or to set strict hours in which she could see her friends. If you have been close with your daughter, it is very, very hard when she turns to other people for what she almost exclusively used to find in you."

An important ethical point arises. If it is mother's duty to let us go, the responsibility for our going rests with us. I agree with Mio Fredland that "a mother should be a good loving consultant," but among the first signs of maturity is to know the difference between what your mother should be told about your experiments in new life-styles, and what should be kept to yourself. If we tell her everything, more than she's asked to know, it is a sure sign we are not serious about our efforts to be independent. We are like adulteresses who lay their sins on the conjugal bed in a childish plea for forgiveness.

"All my friends communicate better with their mothers than I do," says a fifteen-year-old. "A lot of things I'd like to tell her, but she just wouldn't understand. She thinks I'm not mature and responsible enough to handle things. She just wouldn't believe the things I do and think." In simple justice, if mother must show almost superhuman generosity by giving her teen-age girl a boost out of the house, then surely there has to be a commensurate obligation on the daughter. Says Mio Fredland: "Mother usually doesn't expect too much back from her child. She regards what is best for her daughter as paramount in the relationship. But the girl will always be more concerned for herself than for her mother."

So be it. But all too often the complaint, "I wish I could talk to my mother," really means, "Why can't I tell her I'm smoking dope or drinking in bars and get her approval for it?" One of the harsh laws of growth is that adolescents are going to make dangerous explorations of life. It may be necessary; I think it is. One of the great crimes against young girls is parents' passion to wrap the darlings in so much crippling cotton wool that we never run a moment's risk of unhappiness. Young girls are not made to understand you can't have it both ways. We want to imitate the exciting, perhaps dangerous people we meet, but to do so with mother's full approval. This kind of protectionism leads to the feeling there are no consequences to our actions which our parents cannot fix. It is a distortion of reality, retarding maturation and prolonging symbiosis.

Just as we understand when a racing driver's wife prefers not to go out to the track to watch him in his risky occupation, by adolescence we should understand that maybe mother might prefer not to know we are having sex with a man of twenty-five—and should not be asked for her sanction. If we are not old enough to take the responsibility, we should not do it.

The wonder is not that so many of us fail, but that so many succeed—that we aren't all walk-around, wind-up children, sexual pygmies for life. When you think about it, how do we get through all that denial? The areas of conflict with mother that we've learned to avoid—our bodies, anger, masturbation, aggression, sexuality, competition—read like a program for retardation. And yet there we are: me writing this book, you raising your children, working—most women on the whole making a pretty satisfactory job of their lives. We may resonate with terror at the anonymous telephone call in the night, at the stranger in the street who whispers *fuck* into our ear, but we don't retreat. We don't go into a room and barricade ourselves against life forever. We try again.

Where do we get all that bravery?

"That's something I don't understand myself," says sociologist Pauline Bart. "All these theories say if you don't have good childhood experiences, you won't have a good sex life. I had the worst early experiences: double messages from my mother—which I feel are worse than no messages—consistent abuse from my father during adolescence, and then a bad early marriage. And yet—here I am!"

Why indeed is Pauline Bart one of the most vital and lively women I have met, while others, who seem to have had better psychological starts in life, strike me as dull and timid, living under wraps? We cannot forget that our genetic inheritance is not democratic.

Among my own friends, the most interesting people had difficult parents and stormy adolescences. Basic temperament and other mysteries of the personality cannot be dismissed in trying to explain the paradox of transcendence—that so many of us *do* move against all the odds to find a larger world. And while I believe that role models make up a great part of the answer, it is fascinating to wonder why we choose some people to serve as this bridge toward growth and ignore others—who, to the outside eye, would seem to be very glamorous indeed. In my research, for instance, I have found that people like Gloria Steinem and Jane Fonda don't "take" the imagination of most women. We may admire them, but I've never heard a woman say she wanted to be like them. They are the revolutionaries; we are still our mothers' daughters. We may intellectually admire or respect the ethos that extreme feminists project, but on the deeper, gut levels where we live, we have not yet introjected these values and made them our own: they seem anti-male, or so "unfeminine" they make us uncomfortable. It may take another generation or two for women to begin to differentiate between a kind of generalized antipaternalistic anger directed against society as a whole, and our own individual furies. Meanwhile, the Jane Fondas and Gloria Steinems are models of assertiveness and independence that do not totally convince us. At fourteen we are shopping for a picture of sex we can accept—and hip, emotionless movie-star sex, or the feminist-separatist notion of no sex at all, is not it.

Our model of self-individuation is not always our sexual model. In a society that denigrates explicit female sexuality, we will be lucky to find any sexually defined woman at all. Little wonder that the people we look to for sexual models are often the "bad" girls our own age. Their spirit is just too much to resist. By being "bad" they are dem-

onstrating what we long to achieve: separation. Even if we ourselves
are not yet ready to "go all the way," we want to know there are people who do. They are our future.

During my interviews, I met a woman with marked nonphysical,
even asexual demeanor, but whose twenty-one-year-old daughter
broadcasts just the opposite notion of sensuality. I wonder where the
girl gets the freedom to see that sexuality is allowable for women, and
ask for an interview. I questioned her about the first time she consciously realized some people had sexual ideas different from her
mother's. "When I was fourteen," she says, "there was a really beautiful girl in the small town where we spent our summers. Whatever I
had that she didn't—intelligence, kind parents—they didn't seem as
important as her suntan, her amazing figure, and popularity with the
boys. She made an agreement with her boy friend. If he would stop
smoking, she would not wear a brassiere. I've always remembered
that. I never dreamed you could have such a daring agreement with a
boy. I was fascinated by her, and a bit repelled too, but I have always
remembered her."

Adolescent boys have an easier time finding sexual models than we
do. They may not think of their fathers as Don Juans, but at least
they see them responding to women, turning to look at a pretty girl in
the street, talking about sex. We may not like this, it may be done in
bad taste, but it gives the boy a sense that it is OK to be sexual. But
when did you last hear a mother remark to her daughter about the
sexual appeal of a good-looking man? Oh, we talk about his hands,
his eyes, the cut of his suit, but what about the seductive line of his
hip or shoulder? How does mother react to an off-color joke? No
wonder women have no background, no role models, for response to
blue movies. We have no sexual camaraderie.

I remember how puzzled I was the first trip to the beach when
nobody talked about those fascinating bulges in men's bathing suits. I
sat with my little shovel, staring at my first man in a latex Jantzen
and learned women's silence.

Today men have begun to dress to be looked at. In part, this is due
to the perception that women are no longer as responsive to the
undifferentiated male role as they used to be. If most women used to
set their sights so modestly that "anything in pants" was good
enough, the gray-flannel suit would do. As women come to value
themselves more, and thus feel they have greater latitudes of choice,
men have begun to compete for the eyes of women.

Women may not yet be aroused by the nude male centerfolds in magazines. Psychologists report we are not as sexually stimulated visually as men. The implication is that this is biological, that we are born nonvoyeurs. My own feeling is that it is learned behavior. Once women are given an unprejudiced start as sexual people, we will know at last if the eye alone can turn women on. We will also know *what* turns us on, and instead of men's ideas of what women want, we will produce our own erotic imagery. Meanwhile, young girls today still turn reverentially West, to Hollywood, for an image of sexuality.

At least, films fill the aching void. At worst, they give us an idea of woman and sex so overly romanticized that when it does come at last, we wonder why it doesn't feel the way it did when Robert Redford held Ann-Margret in his arms. We confuse sex with romance because we never see a sexual woman from a woman's point of view. Says film critic Molly Haskell: "What we get instead are men's fantasies of women, that a woman is either a virgin or a whore. We used to get the pure girl next door—Debbie Reynolds, Doris Day, Grace Kelly. In the late '60s they tried to give us sexual women—Carrie Snodgress in *Diary of a Mad Housewife* and Jane Fonda in *Klute*. But these women were not a source of energy and imagination for women. They projected a kind of enervated, used-up feeling." They were not the way we wanted to be.

Molly Haskell's general remarks are given poignant, individual meaning in an interview with a thirty-year-old woman. "I used to go to the movies three times a day," she tells me. "I didn't have any sex activity in my early life at all, no sex play, never masturbated, no sex games with other kids, but I did have tremendous amounts of fantasy, based on what I saw in the movies. I used to get a tremendous amount of sexual feelings through watching them make love in the movies—though of course I didn't know then that was what I was feeling. Nobody had told me anything about my body. I just thought my crushes and movie nostalgia were romantic fantasies that adolescents were supposed to have. I had no idea that I was reacting not romantically to the people on the screen but sexually. I didn't know what to name these feelings, and since I'd never touched myself, and I never looked at myself—had in fact been discouraged to look at myself "there"—I was just terrifically curious and confused about sex and romance most of my life. I resisted getting married. I was always afraid that if you lived with someone day to day, the "mystery" would go. He would see me as I really was, and not as the romantic sex queen I'd made myself after all those stars of the silver screen."

Between mother's great No to sex and the false sexuality we see in the commercial world we live in, little wonder that one of the biggest jobs we have in adolescence is to establish that core of self which psychiatrists call "gender identity." It is a fascinating concept.

Gender identity can be defined as the way we see ourselves as either male or female—subjectively, not anatomically. And one of the measures of our lives is the degree of certainty we feel in this identity. Until recently, how a woman felt about her femaleness didn't matter. If her anatomical identity said she was female, there was a rigid set of personality and character traits she was expected to have, and they corresponded exactly with how others reacted to her. Today we are beginning to see that by strictly defining emotional or behavioral patterns as *masculine* or *feminine,* we put straitjackets on both sexes.

When I was fifteen and read Stendhal's *The Red and the Black,* I think I identified not with the Duchess but with the daring and courage of Julien Sorel, the hero who leaves home to seek fame and fortune (which is the storytelling way of saying goes off on the quest for identity). But my identification was a secret one. Twenty years ago it was unladylike to even think of acting "like a man." Because my identification was hidden and shameful to me, it was only partially nourishing. When instead of marrying like the girls I grew up with, I left home to go north, my allegiance to my role was only tentative. Because I could not be open about who and how I wanted to be, I was only half responsible for myself. I worked as ambitiously as Julien, but unlike him, when I succeeded and the top jobs were offered to me, I made excuses to turn them down. I slept with the men I wanted, but feared rejection constantly. My heroes, my models, the people who had attracted me in books and in real life were men. It was too confusing. I wanted to be a woman but I didn't want to be like other women. I had no models.

"Everyone has the potential to have the qualities we think of as masculine or feminine," says Jessie Bernard. "I would like to see both sexes have them—sons who are gentle and tender, daughters who can be strong and assertive. Perhaps with men becoming involved with the raising of children today we will see this happen." The contemporary idea of gender definition is more complex and richer for women than it has ever been. Given a modicum of ease about her gender identity, a young girl in the process of formation will try to strengthen those feelings about herself she likes best, borrowing character traits from the most admirable female and male figures around her. She may choose to be a girl-girl, as pop lyrics put it, an old-fashioned, clinging creature; or she may take on the characteristics of a woman so contemporary she has not yet been given a pop-tune name—someone sexually giving, who possesses what used to be called masculine assertiveness. Or any mixture of the two. When I was nineteen, my authoritarian grandfather turned on me when I argued with him. "Where did you learn to speak back like that?" he demanded. "From you," I told him. If we are secure in our gender identity, it never occurs to us to feel we are "wrong" to be the way we are. "Since I am a woman," a friend said to me recently, "anything I do is womanly."

But let me add an important caveat here. While I do believe notions of gender identity are changing to allow all of us to take in more of life's complexity, that change has not yet become a universal gut feeling. We live an almost schizoid sense of values. Right along with our assent to the latest manifesto on sexual freedom, says Dr. Robertiello, "we find that a woman's idea of her gender identity, her subjective feeling about herself as a woman, is much more connected with her concept of herself as a mother than it is with her concept of herself as a sexual person.

"For instance, say a woman is divorced and has a number of lovers. She still isn't going to be able to think of herself as an adequate woman if she isn't fulfilling her mothering functions with her child. Can you have good sex if you think of yourself as a bad woman? You might have a good time in bed, but you would put a pejorative connotation on it. Instead of saying, 'Aren't I an exciting, sexual woman?' you would say, 'I'm a bad person. I should be home taking care of my daughter.'"

I would go even further than Dr. Robertiello. We do not even have to be mothers to see our gender identity more connected with motherhood than sexuality. So long as we have not repeated the model of our mother's life, most of us will live with a suspicion of failure, of being incomplete.

For instance, I would have told you that I was totally committed to my decision not to have children; and yet when I was writing the first chapter in this book, my argument against the maternal instinct was so strong and out of proportion that I was almost unable to get past it. I could not give it logical emphasis—no more, no less—because

I was defending myself. All the intellectualizing in the world hasn't yet convinced me that in going against my training I have not abandoned my true gender identity, true femininity.

Women I have interviewed who are fifteen years younger than I say it is easier for their generation to choose whatever life they want. To whatever degree this is true, I am sure it has to do with the models of other women's lives. Young women today have an unmistakable advantage over previous generations, and as they consolidate the gains made by the women who came before, they too will become models for those yet to come. When a woman can have sex with her husband or lover and feel as sure of herself in that role as when she holds a baby in her arms—that is a time worth working for.

In a fascinating study, sociologist Pauline Bart documents the damage done to the psyche when a woman substitutes *motherhood*—which is one possible element in gender identity—for *femaleness,* which is the whole. The study was based on hospital records of 550 depressed women in Los Angeles, in the age bracket forty to fifty-nine. "I also did twenty interviews," says Dr. Bart. "When I asked the women about sex, they would sort of avoid it. If I asked them to rank sex roles in order of importance—one of which was 'Being a Sexual Partner to My Husband'—that was never chosen first or second, and only rarely did it even come in third."

In another part of this test, Dr. Bart showed women twelve simple but evocative pictures and asked the subjects to make up a story about the life of the women in the pictures—a well-tested and standard projective technique. In one of the pictures, the woman is seen in bed wearing a black lace nightgown, and with one leg raised. "It was a very sexy picture," Dr. Bart says, "but the subjects rejected the picture. If they did choose it, they denied the sexual content. They'd say something like, 'This is a picture of a woman who has just put the baby down for a rest, and she's tired herself.'" The threatening idea of sex was immediately replaced with the safe association of motherhood. When Dr. Bart asked why the picture was omitted, the reply she often got was, "Oh, that picture is about a woman with not very good morals."

"These women," Dr. Bart concludes, "just could not deal with sex. They were very, very conventional, good, traditional, well-scripted women who followed the rules a hundred and fifty percent, and part of the script is that a woman is not sexual." Can we doubt that the inability to connect femininity and sexuality is in part responsible for the depression suffered not only by the women interviewed by Dr. Bart but by the female race as a whole?

While role models and identification figures help us separate from mother, surrogates play a different role in our lives. Child psychologists usually limit the meaning of the word "surrogate" to those early substitutes for mother—often dimly remembered but almost mythically important people who fed us emotionally as well as physically. They were the nurses, housekeepers, grandmothers and older sisters who gave us warmth and intimacy when mother was physically or psychologically not available to us for any of a variety of reasons. In that dependent time of life, before we were ready to separate, and closeness to someone was all, surrogates taught us many of the emotional and personality traits we carry through life.

Theirs were the smiles we wanted and it was in their eyes we looked for the love and approval we needed. "They are our psychological mothers," says Betty Thompson, "the ones who teach us our emotions. Many women who have unemotional, nondemonstrative biological mothers nevertheless grow up with the spontaneity, vitality, eye behavior or warm voice cadence of the surrogates who held them and responded to their needs when they were babies."

"I actually call the woman who nursed me for six years 'mother'," says Joan Shapiro, professor of social work at Smith College. "I have her sense of humor, her gestures, her love of music, dancing and out-of-doors. When my daughter went to visit her, she saw so much of me in her that she immediately called her 'grandmother.' My nurse's feelings about me as her oldest child are even now so strong that her own grown children are jealous."

Given the developmental imperatives of adolescence, in which we need to experiment with freedom while never wanting to lose our bond to mother, the need for surrogates arises again. At twelve and fourteen we go through a replay of the *rapprochement—or refueling— phase,* experienced first at two or three. In adolescence, the person we find to substitute for mother in this experimentation with getting away is often a girl of our own age. We hold on to each other for safety even as we plan for the adventures ahead. These ardent crushes, even when there is homosexual activity, are usefully understood as a need for refuge and mutual mothering more than a desire for explicit sex. "The first love one has," says Betty Thompson, "is usually a re-creation of the emotional relationship of Eden—the one that once existed between your mother and yourself." Falling in love means falling in love either with a memory of that relationship, or with a fantasy of how you wish it had been. "Even in those suffocating affairs," adds Dr. Thompson, "where the girl cannot bear to be away from the boy for one moment—that's a re-creation of the infantile relationship. It is easy to see that the boy friend is playing the role of surrogate mother."

Fortunate is the adolescent who has a relationship with someone she can admire, but who also loves her back. This other person combines the role of both surrogate and role model. It can be a girl's first taste of resolving the seeming contradictions of wanting freedom from mother but wanting to be close to someone too. One of the great advantages is that the surrogate is not so fearful for us, nor so locked on. The emotional intensity of the relationship is not so burning. Equally important, our fears of re-engulfment by mother are eased. With a surrogate, we have the old mothering security at our back, giving us the freedom to face into the future. If we are lucky, we will find this feeling with someone else once again later in life. This marvelous balancing act between two people can be a rehearsal for marriage.

"In my work, as well as in my own personal life," says Professor Shapiro, "I've found that when you have a good experience with an early mother surrogate, you tend to develop a nose for finding others along the way. You develop an appealing 'needy' quality that potential surrogates pick up on. There are those who need mothering. There are those who enjoy giving it."

There is a big difference between the surrogates of childhood and those we find during adolescence. It is choice—ours. Our nurses and older sisters who comforted and held us when we were babies did so by their choice. The surrogates of adolescence, the people whose bodies, approval, touch, and esteem become so vital to our continued growth, are chosen by us. *We pick them.* We are old enough by now, formed enough to have some notions of what we want. Our needs are more psychological than to be fed, held, and bathed. And yet both early and later surrogates often share a similar fate in the end: oblivion. We tend to forget them, to play down their importance.

"I had this nurse when I was little," recalls a fifteen-year-old. "I remember folding laundry with her. I loved that. I called her grandma, though she wasn't my grandmother. I still love folding laundry." She also loves being close to someone and has an ability for intimacy her cool, unemotional mother doesn't understand. "My daughter has this intense thing with her boy friend," says the mother. "I never went through that sort of thing. She's far more affectionate than I. I can't imagine where she gets it." No one remembers where the girl learned her emotional behavior. A fondness for folding laundry is as close as the young woman allows herself to come to admitting her inheritance.

Another woman I interview speaks of the influence of a teacher in her life, but says she felt compelled to hide it. "My English teacher when I was fourteen changed my life," she says. "She taught me to read and to value being intelligent. She was not pretty, which was what all the girls in my crowd prized. I am ashamed to say that I never told anybody how much I admired her. I just took what I wanted and ran. I never thanked her, never, and I've always been sorry about that."

This odd ingratitude has nothing to do with intelligence or age. "It was only recently, in my own group analysis," says Dr. Robertiello, "that I rediscovered this very important uncle of mine. He was nineteen when I was five, and was perhaps the most important man in my childhood. Even with all my years of psychoanalysis, he's just never before appeared on the scene in my conscious mind. Here I am today, fifty-one, and he's been completely repressed all these years."

These are just three examples; again and again in researching this chapter, I come upon evidence of this denial. Even when directly asked if there isn't someone who mothered them, or with whom they identified while growing up, most people will pause, shrug and say no, there was nobody. No surrogate, no heroine, no model: "There wasn't anybody who mothered me (besides mother), or anyone I wanted to grow up to be like." Are these women lying to me?

I don't think so. There is no anger or defensive heat in their dismissal of the subject. They are puzzled themselves—especially if they feel they have transcended the image their mother presented to them. How did they do it? "I guess I just made myself up," they shrug.

"I think this kind of forgetting," says Dr. Robertiello, "may be a feeling it is disloyal to our parents to recognize how important these other people were. If only unconsciously, we realize that we owe the role models of our youth too much, and turn away. This is a kind of defense of our old notions of omnipotence. We may acknowledge that our parents were formative to us. After all, that's normal. But that we needed other people too? Oh, no!"

To admit even to ourselves that we once preferred someone else to our mother opens us to the awful self-accusation of being cold, selfish, and terrible people. We "forget" because we are too guilty to remember. "It is often the case," says Dr. Helene Deutsch, "that if a woman cannot remember how important a nurse or housekeeper was to her emotional development as a child, it was because of guilt toward the mother, that she allowed herself to have these feelings of love toward another woman."

It is a guilt born of symbiosis. To people who are attached, admitting there is someone else opens them to fear of the symbiotic partner's anger, retribution, and possible abandonment. We can no longer afford to live in this squeeze. Today, when mothers are involved in more than one job, children need more than one mother. Not just someone who sits with them as coldly as a television set, but a person to whom they feel free to turn, who will be there for them, and from whom they can openly take in warmth without feeling they are making mother jealous. Young women, particularly, are going through great changes in manners, mores, and expectancies; they need all the love they can find from as many different people as possible; they need access to a variety of role models other than mother.

But mother first must give up her illusory gains from symbiosis carried on too long. Perhaps the easiest person to whom she can cede at least part of mothering is her husband. Says Mio Fredland: "It really doesn't matter what the gender of the mothering person is." Some men are maternal. Some women are not. To the child, it does not matter where the warmth comes from. "Motherhood is too important to leave to women," says Jessie Bernard. "It's got to be shared."

There is no doubt however that most fathers have not yet learned to accept responsibility for children to the same degree as women. "When I'm at work, I can't help worrying about whether he's given Susie her lunch," one woman tells me. "I know that when we're both at home and the baby cries, he sleeps on. It's me who hears it. How can I rely on him?"

How can she not? The fault is not entirely with men. So long as a mother feels her main value derives from being the only one who can be counted on to raise a child, she will never accept that anyone else can take care of and understand her daughter as she does. Never given full responsibility, father soon takes less than his half.

"In the modern family," says Dr. Betty Thompson, "the mother-daughter relationship is going to be seriously altered. There is going to be more than one mothering person. Some men make marvelous mothers. If you have a father pinch-hitting for a mother, you have a surrogate relationship right there." This idea is reinforced by Dr. Fredland: "I don't know what makes a woman maternal. I know women who have had terrible mothering from their biological mother but are very maternal anyway. Other women who had adequate mothering, aren't maternal at all. I think what it is, is that *somebody* has been very maternal to them. I don't think it has to be the mother, or even a woman. It could have been the father, or an uncle."

Day-care centers and flexible work hours are not the subject of this book, but any scheme involving surrogate care will be undercut if mothers do not learn to give up some of the responsibility for what happens to everyone in the family. They cannot be total mother, total wage earner, total wife. Daughters of women like these pick up their mothers' anxieties and jealousies. Even if part of the surrogate is taken in, the gift will be poisoned by fear that the gain is a betrayal of mother's symbiotic emotions. The daughter gets the worst of two worlds. She suffers from her mother's absence, and struggles with her ambivalence at allowing herself to be warmed by the substitute.

"Freud said that very often life itself is the great healer," says Dr. Fredland. "Certain experiences, people you come into contact with— they can undo early damage. A child is very plastic. Neurosis sets that plastic into a hard, distorted form. But if the child is lucky and has happy life experiences, for instance with a surrogate, the neurosis may be at least partially repaired, and the basic emotional structure given a chance to reset in healthier form."

If in her heart mother knows she was as good a mother as she could be in the circumstances, she may come to terms with her daughter's need for other models in her life. "But if she knows she was not a good mother," says Dr. Sanger, "her guilt will make her furious. She will show terrific hostility to the very people who could have helped her daughter the most. How can she admit she was not all the mother society and her own mother taught she must be? Her own womanhood is at stake."

Social workers report case after case where mothers want their freedom, but still want their child to be primarily tied to them. "The worst mothers I've seen," says Mio Fredland, "the minute the child gets attached to a nurse or another person, they get rid of that person. They hate the child, they hate their role, they hate everything about it, but they can't stand that the child should be emotionally attached to somebody else.' "

One mother will resent surrogates because she is symbiotically tied to her daughter and fears the break. Another resents surrogates because she doesn't really like her child, but fears that a surrogate reveals her lack of love. Either way, the daughter is the loser. When she becomes a mother herself, she will remember her mother's anxiety that to give a child over to someone else for love and care is to be a "bad mother." It will never feel right for her to do it with her own child—even if economic circumstances dictate that she must go out and find a job.

While many women today have to take on all the risks, fatigues, and drudgery of what used to be the male workaday world, they cannot give up any of the risks, fatigues, and drudgery of being a mother too. Says Jessie Bernard: "A three-year-old boy will say, 'I want to be an astronaut, a fireman and a soldier.' We accept that as he grows up he will see that he can't be all those things, and that he will narrow his sights. But little girls are raised to live by a hidden agenda. On the surface we say, Yes, you have as much right as a boy to have a career, to be a doctor, a lawyer, but there is a hidden message: first, you are going to be a mother too. So the girl says, Yes, I'm going to be a lawyer, but I'm also going to have a family. No recognition is given to the fact that in our society it is structurally very difficult to be a mother and a lawyer too. It is like the little boy saying, 'I'm going to be a fireman *and* an astronaut.' "

Some women can combine full-time careers with being full-time mothers, but they are the superhumans among us, and you cannot base a rational society on all women being superpeople. It is too much to ask, and when we fail, we are in a rage—*but don't know why*. Other young women recognize they can combine marriage and a career, but decide they can't be mothers too. Says Professor Jean McFarland: "I feel it's only fair to warn women that having a career and being a mother is worth the effort, but don't think for a second it is easy. Some of our best women are choosing not to become mothers, not because they don't want to, but because they recognize they can't do both jobs well. It's a tragic choice for women to have to make, and society will be sorry."

During an interview, I ask a prominent sociologist if there were any important identification figures in her life. She pauses, then says, "My mother admired Margaret Sanger and had a book about her that

I read. On one level, my mother was just wonderful. I thought women social reformers were wonderful. I wanted to go out and change the world like them, to do good. I came from a very political family, but I didn't really have an identification figure. Maybe my aunt, she was a doctor. I'm furious at my family now. I was never presented with any alternative to marriage. Their plan was that I'd go to college to have something to fall back on, but I was never presented with the possibility of having a serious career. And we had a woman doctor in the family! They left me with the feeling I had to marry, so when that schmuck came along, I married him. I really got married to get out of the house, to get away. It was idiotic."

This woman is divorced now. Her story opens up with Margaret Sanger's name, her M.D. aunt is mentioned, but her remarks close on the denial of any identification figures and a great deal of anger. One might think she could say today: "It was because of Margaret Sanger and my aunt that I had courage and incentive to become a sociologist." But instead of emphasizing the positive force these women may have been in her life, she dwells on her anger at her family, including her "wonderful" mother. Isn't her real anger at the hidden agenda— the understanding conveyed to her by mother that Yes, she could have a career, but had to be a wife and have children first?

How destructive that anger at mother should take up so much of our adult lives. We may say, "I'm not angry at my mother!"—but why do we go into such a rage when our daughter doesn't clean up her room, or our husband is late? The fury is not appropriate. It has been displaced from mother onto someone "safer." This is unfair and bewildering, leading to arguments that cannot be resolved because the real target for our furies is never named or even made conscious; to examine our unresolved angers even now would mean to reawaken those infantile emotions of loss and retribution we never outgrew.

The truth is that once faced, we could live with that anger today. Unfaced, it contaminates any real love we may have for our mother. As the models and images of independence and life we once found so attractive slip through our fingers, we find ourselves becoming more like the anxious, critical, sexually frightened woman we never intended to be. Anger at the person who inhibited our trust in any model but herself works on us in the disguise of passivity, conservatism, and resignation.

Says Dr. Betty Thompson: "Passivity in women can be humiliation, fear, lack of ego strength, terror that you're going to be found wanting. All too often it is anger." Unlike men, who get points for being tough and hot-headed, women have their anger termed unlady-like. We start to get angry, but feel guilty about it, and tamp it down. The passive-aggressive personality is the result: someone who expresses her anger in a seemingly civilized disguise. "Where do you want to go tonight, honey?" the husband says, not so much wanting to get the name of a restaurant from his wife, but wanting to hear in her emotional tone that she is pleased to be going out with him. "Anyplace you want," his wife says, depriving him of the real answer he hoped for but disguising her desire to frustrate and annoy him by seeming to comply with the overt question put to her. "The passive-aggressive personality," says Dr. Thompson, "is like a parked car that only backs up." Such a person is the two-year-old who won't do what anybody wants. It makes her feel strong to say No. To withhold is reinforcing to her sense of self—even if she is merely being asked to go forward into growth. The natural desire is for life, and a child feels thwarted when growth is denied, no matter if she is doing it to herself.

Anger is negative, but still it is a tie. It retards separation because as long as we are angry at mother, she is uppermost in our thoughts, and we are still her daughter. "OK, so you're angry, let it go," a ther-apist might say. "Let *her* go." But no, we would rather have the anger than nothing.

One day when I was talking to Dr. Robertiello, he said as an after-thought, "Nancy, why can't you accept the fact that your mother doesn't love you?"

For a moment, I thought I was going to hit him. Instead, I went through one of those instantaneous, self-protective reflexes, and changed the subject. But his sentence thundered around in my head. For the first time in my professional discussions with Richard Rober-tiello, a subject had come up that I did not want to discuss.

For weeks I would think about it, wince, retreat, and then return to it again. How could he have said such a thing? It became a famil-iar pain, until one day, like a weight lifted, I felt relief. Of course she didn't love me! Not in the perfect, idealized way I'd wanted all my life, since I was a baby.

I couldn't wait to tell Dr. Robertiello of the feeling of freedom that had come out of this understanding of his disturbing statement. "But, Nancy," he said, "you've twisted my words. I didn't say your mother didn't love you 'perfectly.' From all you've told me about your relationship, I said she didn't love you, period."

Every mother-daughter story has two versions, and Dr. Robertiello knows only what I've told him. For the first time in writing this book, it has occurred to me that my version of my relationship with my mother is not just distorted by the absence of her voice, but by my own unfaced emotions.

Perhaps the reason I have always felt free to acknowledge the importance in my life of my nurse and my aunt was that my mother so easily accepted them. She has never hesitated to give them credit for what they gave me, never made any reluctant show of her gratitude to them. How many times have I heard her tell other people how much she owes them, how glad she is for me that I found them. Isn't this love?

The lunatic other side of the coin is that I am angry at her for not giving me herself what I found in them. It is the case of the woman with the too-liberal lover. She is grateful that he takes her back after he learns of the other man, but why didn't he throw her out? Did he value her so little?

I have never wanted to confront my mother with my anger. It would be to little avail. She wouldn't understand, and if she did, what could she do now? It is too late for nursery angers, but I will be left with them for all my life if I do not accept that they are there, and why. Otherwise I will be in the position of those people who, as Dr. Sanger puts it, "endlessly try to shake love out of their mothers by the lapel."

The possibility that mothers may come not to resent but to welcome the necessity for role models and surrogates in their daughters' lives is a thrilling idea for the future. Equally remedial in raising the mother-daughter relationship to an adult level is to see our own lives become a model for mother. Says a twenty-eight-year-old divorcée: "My mother is fifty-three. The last time I was home, she said to me, 'I never in my life thought what it would be like to sleep with another man than your father . . . until I heard about your life.' "

The reversal of roles in which the child teaches the parent seems to release both women from the fixed demands of anger and symbiosis. Even if we have outgrown her, we can forge a new and loving tie by becoming *her* role model. "My mother worked from the time I was fourteen," says a twenty-nine-year-old woman. "Whatever my mother achieved was subordinated to make my father happy and seem successful. I married when I was a sophomore in college. I wanted a family, I expected to be a traditional wife, like my mother. The stereotype didn't work out that way. The man I married never found a career—he was just like my father. I followed my mother's model and did everything so this man could be successful. I got a part-time job, I went to graduate school, I wanted to be as strong as my mother in helping my father. Eventually I couldn't take it. I left him.

"I was glad to be out of a bad marriage. I found a good job, everything should have been rosy, but I felt this terrible anger in me. I thought it was at him. I soon realized how much of it was at my mother. I had been a good daughter, I had done everything she had trained me to do, and it hadn't worked. In a sense, she had lied to me about what life was all about.

"I'll tell you something that has helped relieve the anger. I have recently come to see how much my life has influenced my mother. She makes choices now she never could have before, without me. Like saying to my father, after thirty-three years of marriage, 'You can do as you like, but I'm not going to turn down promotions because you'd feel like a failure. I'm going to go as far as I can in this career.' She couldn't have said that without having watched what I've been through. I am proud of my mother when I see her growing and doing things she should have done years ago. It gives all those years she spent raising me significance and meaning. I am prouder of this than anything, that my life has given mother a second chance."

If mother can believe in our new identity enough to trust her own weight on it, we can believe in it too. We have not lost her. The debt is paid.

Chapter 8

MEN
THE MYSTERY

To this day I make M's. When I scribble while on the telephone or write in the sand, it's always M's. M stands for Morgan, and Morgan stood for Man Incarnate, Man the Mystery, Man Unobtainable. From the beginning—around age thirteen—I focused on Morgan. I never took my eyes off him, though he never put his hands on me. Except to punch me. Whenever one of us girls teased him, pushed him too far, trying to get something (what?) out of him, he would haul off and give her a swift rabbit punch in the arm. He did it dispassionately and without words, as if she were a fly. It was a badge of honor to carry one of Morgan's bruises. We had been touched.

Morgan belonged to the crowd of boys our own age, the ones we girls started on. We went to dancing class together, and theirs were the photos we carried in our Genuine Leather wallets, along with the eighth-grade graduation head shots of one another autographed, Love ya', Mary Beth. Within a couple of years we would outgrow the local boys and graduate to the cadets at the Citadel—a military college for men in name, but in fact a repository for southern boys. But throughout all those years and beyond, I remained faithful to Morgan in fantasy. He stood for an idea of manliness, the person who would stand opposite me and make a woman of me. He was the promise of my sexuality, the white heat of my glandular fever, the ache I loved living with while I waited. I grew to love the waiting too, and was so in love with love that something in me still waits for Morgan. My husband knows I dream of Morgan at night, and smiles at what he calls my "persistence of emotion." How can I expect him to understand? He grew up in New York, that very unadolescent city, safe from the sexual heat of small southern towns, the drive-ins and drugstores, matriarchy and male supremacy. Besides, he is a man. Only women understand waiting, how years of it train you to dream, to never expect it *will* happen, or to recognize it if it should.

Occasionally I wonder what sort of man Morgan grew into; I imagine myself sitting opposite him, me grown splendid and sexual, Morgan now the one suffering from the white heat in the groin. But in this fantasy, we are not in some smart bar but in Schwettman's Drug Store, and while I look like one of those women in a vodka ad, Morgan is still fourteen. On those infrequent trips back to Charleston, I never seek him out. I do not choose to confront the old fantasy, to ruin it. How can you update a god? To me Morgan will always be slouched behind the wheel of his black Chevrolet, wearing a maroon windbreaker with the sleeves rolled up, and a tough look. Morgan never smiled.

When he chose one of my best friends as his girl, I kept right on dreaming about him. Nothing could touch what he stood for. It was about the time my mother quietly announced at the dinner table that she was going to remarry. I had no words for my anger. I left the table. It was my Aunt Kate who walked me to the Battery and sat with me on a park bench beside the cannon balls while I sulked and stared at Fort Sumter. She talked about her days at college and once again, in the light of her life, everything seemed possible.

I can't help wondering how relevant to my mother's decision to remarry was the emergence of all the women in our house into a time of sexuality. It would have been an unconscious pressure, of course, but timing is so much. There we were, four women: my mother, Aunt Kate, my sister, and I, each needing her own man, her own identity. My aunt married within a year of my mother. My reaction to the news of my mother's remarriage was childish but much less important than my own need to solve the mystery of men. In the end, I took the arrival of a man in our house as no more disturbing than Morgan's choice of another girl. My time would come. When I thought of Morgan, I simply x'd her out.

To be near Morgan I went out with his fat friend, a football player painfully shorter than I and from the wrong side of town. (Morgan had a taste for thugs.) I was sure Morgan realized my sacrifice and silently approved. I settled for Friday nights at the drive-ins with lesser mortals, all the while making M's on the cover of my blue loose-leaf notebook and up and down the spines of Homer's *Iliad, Ivanhoe,* and *Basic Geometry.* I wrote other boys' names too but only to obscure the intensity of my desire, the portent that leapt out at me each time I faced that sea of names and saw only one. Other boys held me, and eventually, in their arms, I reached that weightless state that enough kissing could arouse in me, but when I closed the library doors at home and put on my favorite records, the longing and the dying I willed to well up inside me was for Morgan.

Nothing really happened in those fantasies; Morgan didn't even have to materialize in them for me to reach the feeling I was after. But pushed to humanize these desires, to put a name to my wish on the first star at night, it was his. It wasn't sex, or life in a vine-covered cottage that I wanted with Morgan. It was to have his eyes on me, for him to see me, to make me whole, to want me so that all those desires that made moonlight painful could be consummated in one great crescendo of Tony Bennett's "There's No Tomorrow."

After we girls had cut our teeth on the mating grounds of Madame Larka's dancing class, we were ready for the more sophisticated sexual posturing that was traditional every Friday afternoon at the Citadel Parade Grounds. Like generations of young Charleston women before us, we instinctively knew it was our turn to move in the ritual procession of cars to the four o'clock dress parade. With neither instruction nor invitation, we lined up our cars along the edge of the parade grounds, bumpers to barracks, car hoods (with us perched prettily atop) aimed at the sea of blue that drilled smartly past for our inspection. Was it here I developed my keen eye for a well-turned ass, the poignant stab of pleasure at the sight of what I later learned in art history to call the classic S curve? Certainly no one said a word about the unnervingly tight zip-front jackets the cadets wore, or the heartbreak reversed parentheses of the two dark lines down the back, tracing the curve of shoulder, waist, and hip. Nor did we even think about the real reason we came to these parades: to be on display ourselves. We were the ones who needed to be looked at, to have a man's eye on us; a very genteel southern meat rack, if you will. Somewhere in that army of men there was someone who would make us a pair, give us stature, significance, mobility. "A woman alone is nothing."

It is a message mothers give their daughters still. If my own didn't say it, I knew it well. I had not been trained to dream of a future without men, myself flourishing alone. Though I had no idea who a man was, I knew one was necessary. After the parade, it was dancing class all over again; gone were the drums and the bugles, the dreaming and watching. Here came reality, as hundreds of men broke rank and moved toward us, the waiting women, all of our future, our importance in their hands. How effortlessly they chose us, singling this one out, rejecting that one, most of them, I am sure, unaware of the very real power they had over us. For those girls who wore their men's company insignia on their cashmere sweaters, there was no tension; somebody wanted them. The rest of us sat and smiled as though it were the most inconsequential thing in the world whether or not a uniform would stand opposite us and give us life.

In time, I too had my share of cadets, loved one after another, went to Christmas hops and homecoming games, collected white dress gloves and other pieces of oversized male garments. In fact, I cannot remember not being in love. I could catalogue the past twenty years of loves by the take-me, make-me songs to which I loved them, each man to his own music. In time I would have jobs, wonderful work, but my emotional sustenance, the air I needed, came from what men breathed into me. If I owed my life to my aunt, I was my mother's daughter.

Being in love was a habit. Though I never wanted to marry, I had to believe each love was forever. I didn't want a husband, I didn't think of men as the fathers of my children. It was the promise of men, that around each corner there was yet another man, more wonderful than the last, that sustained me. You see, I had men confused with life. Since you couldn't count absolutely that one would never leave you, I loved each man of the moment with a kind of madness. His not telephoning reduced me to a zero. His presence, my sureness that he cared for me, enabled me to charm the world and even be nice to my sister. It was a religion of a god who gave and took away life, bringing peace so that I could go to school, sit at meals with my family, and not appear to the outside world like the deranged person I was inside. You can't get what I wanted from a man, not in this life. Morgan was and always will be unobtainable.

Growing up in the South is different. But only by degrees. The hu-

midity simply reinforces the cultural priority: men first. When I went
north to college, the first thing I wanted to share with my new roommate was my collection of pictures of Sam. By him she would know
me. I talked of my summer in the sun with Sam, and showed her his
class ring. She talked about her summer job. Oh, she talked about
her man too, but I realized there were other things in her life. No one
I knew ever had a summer job. What we did best in the heat was lie
on the beach and hypnotize the boys with the sheen of our oiled bodies. Something in me responded like a drum to what I found in the
North. I wanted men in my life, but I wanted to be free of my fear of
their rejection. Intuitively and instinctively I knew that finding alternative sources of life, satisfactions in addition to those I knew with
men, would free me—like a hypnotic freed from the spell.

Mine, however, is not one of those stories of the beauty and power
of nature, the blade of grass growing through stone to reach the sun.
Getting past those years of training in romantic delirium and need for
men was like going against nature. It still is.

One night before I left for college, I found myself in the back seat
of a car with Morgan. Emboldened by our steps away from the boys
of our youth, my friend Kathy and I had telephoned Morgan and his
friend Steve. The four of us went to a drive-in movie and suddenly
there I was, lying across the back seat in Morgan's arms. He kissed
me, and I began to give myself to what I believed would be as close
to heaven as I would ever get. Now, I thought, would begin the evening of rapture, hours and hours of window steaming, holding and
kissing. He put his hand between my legs. I pushed his hand away,
burying my head in his chest and prayed against hope that like every
other boy I had ever dated, he would agree to my rules. But Morgan
was a god, and had not become one by acceding to women's rules.

"You see, Nancy, it wouldn't work with us. That's what I want
and you don't." He said it in the kindest way, with a man's certainty.

Until I met Bill, I never knew a man whose rules I respected as
much as my own, who had absolute certainty about himself. I will
probably make M's for the rest of my life, but at least now I know
why.

Sexuality is the great field of battle between biology and society. It
is born long before we are deemed adult enough to play with its
magnificent fire. Mother is the first regiment pressed into battle. The

job comes with surprising suddenness. She is still young, not yet ready to limit her own sexuality in order to chaperone ours. No matter what the sacrifice costs her, whether she does it well or badly, angrily or gladly, we resent her for it. Do we thank our jailers?

When, as infants, we touch our genitals, her job begins. She takes our hand away. "No," she says. It is one of the crucial experiences in life, and starts mother's lifelong role as the eternal no-sayer in her daughter's eyes. Conversely, men are set up as her opposite, yea-sayers to sex, daring, and freedom. Men are not prim and proper prudes like mother. They are lusty rogues, sexy devils, and we yearn for our time with them to come. But we wait with mother's watchful eye upon us.

When mother takes our hand away from between our legs, when, as we grow older, she lets us know by look, tone of voice, attitude and gesture, that it isn't nice, she is being what society considers a good mother. *The effect is to cut us off from our own bodies.* "In our culture," says Dr. Robertiello, "women are trained to expect that in some magical way, men will make them sexual people. They can't do it to themselves." Little wonder then that men seem mysterious to us. Who can understand such powerful creatures that they can command sexuality itself? "Invariably," says Dr. Schaefer, "the way women put it is, 'He gave me an orgasm.' I tell them, 'Someone doesn't give you an orgasm. You give yourself an orgasm.' " Usually, words like these are treated as if they were merely semantic tricks, not to be taken seriously. A woman thinks she needs a man to bring her to life. Passivity is indoctrinated and reinforced.

"When a mother hinders or arrests a daughter's sexual activity, she is fulfilling a normal function whose lines are laid down by events in [her own] childhood, which has powerful, unconscious motives, and has received the sanction of society," wrote Freud in 1915. "It is the daughter's business to emancipate herself from this influence and to decide for herself on broad and rational grounds what her share of enjoyment or denial of sexual pleasure will be."[1]

Freud's dictum seems to be fair enough. It lays the responsibility for our sexuality where it belongs—with us. But he is talking about the years when we are old enough to decide "on broad and rational grounds" how much sexuality we should allow ourselves.

For most of us in our teens, that time is not yet. Mother's inhibition of our sexuality re-creates in each of us the myth of Sleeping Beauty, and a complementary myth becomes our future: some day my prince will come, the knight in shining armor who will awaken my dormant sexuality. Our parents smile at our teen-age acned Lancelots, but in our eyes, they arrive trailing clouds of glory. We become pinned to them, braceleted, chained and enslaved to how we feel when they hold us in their arms. They release us for a time from prison, from waiting, sleep, and passivity. When not in their arms, we live on fantasies, until they hold and release us once more. I am not talking of the release of orgasm, but of the release from tension—the fear that no man will want us as much as we need him. Of course this tension is sexualized, is itself part of the rhythmic build to orgasm, but we learn to satisfy it without the forbidden climax. We come to find more release in the certainty that he will never leave us than in having him inside us. *That certainty becomes more important than orgasm ever can be.*

The real thing, the penis inside, for many women never does live up to that early substitute: security. And tight security—control—is the antithesis of orgasm—letting go. After hours of fondling and kissing, young girls go to their rooms with their pretty panties soaked through, but do not lie awake in sexual frustration. We sleep sound in our virginal beds because we have lain in his arms long enough to believe again, at least for tonight, that "everything will be all right, I'll never leave you, I'll love you forever." Who he is, what he wants—*sex itself*—is never so important as the fantasy of permanent security he gives us. Is it any wonder that after a year or two of marriage, so many women wake up with a stranger? "Why did I ever marry him?"

"I was an only child growing up in a house full of women," says actress Elizabeth Ashley, "so men were always mysterious to me. My mother had been damaged, but, like so many women of her generation, she felt impelled to hide her scars. To show pain would have been a fall from dignity. She was really an early and very private feminist, strong, idealistic and brave. Her mission was to raise me to be independent. And she succeeded in that, but those mysterious men still had this huge power.

"In a way, men to us were like drugs are to this generation. The kids are told, 'If you take them, you'll be addicted forever.' Men were our 'reefer madness.' They became inbued with this mystical, dangerous, irresistible romance. And romance is, of course, the cornerstone of any addiction."[2]

Young women today tend to have friendships with men where ten or twenty years ago there could only have been romantic love. It is a significant change. However, when sex does enter, the pregnancy and abortion rates among teen-agers are frightening. Young girls still expect something wonderful, magical, mystical, and dreamy from their sexual partners. As much as any generation before them, they think love will make the lyrics to the songs come true. It is a hard-nosed axiom in the rock music business that for every girl singer who makes it, there are at least a dozen male superstars: girls dream to music, boys do not.

In a recent study, educator Patricia Schiller found that adolescent girls tended not to read pornographic books, nor were they aroused by the sight of men nude or in tight trousers. The major sexual stimulant among young girls of every socioeconomic group, she found, was music—especially the words to the songs.[3] It is not sex young girls dream of. It is this unknown and mysterious fulfillment that men will bring. For instance, a major manufacturer of vibrators tells me that when he advertises in college newspapers, the response is nil. Adult women may buy his product from adult magazines, but young girls yearn for the satisfaction of mysteries no vibrator can touch.

"Our lives as women," says Dr. Schaefer, "are filled with fantasies. You have the fantasy of what you think your father is, and the fantasy of what your mother says he is. You have the fantasy of the kind of man you think you should marry and the fantasy of the kind of man you actually do marry. You have a fantasy of what life is going to be like. A lot of us end up not being able to cope with the reality we live because we always have that fantasy in our mind of what it should have been." The cliché is that the wish is the father to the thought. Perhaps it would be more accurate to say the wish is mother of the thought.

"How will I know if it's really love?" a girl asks her mother. "You'll know when it comes along," mother says. And then one day, astoundingly, it turns out to be true. Being held in our lover's arms creates a feeling of warmth, love, and happiness we have never felt before—or have we? The odd thing is that it is almost familiar. We are pervaded by an eerie sense of having been here before. We have always known this feeling existed, and have merely been waiting for it to come along again. *It feels right.*

"The reason the feeling of love at these moments is so satisfying," says Dr. Robertiello, "is that in a perfectly acceptable, heterosexual situation, the woman has re-created the intensity of satisfaction she once felt at being held like this. It was when she was a baby in her mother's arms." Since this thought is vaguely unpleasant, somewhat threatening to our gender identity as women, it is repressed. For all their masculinity, men can give us moments in which they remind us so much of the love we once had with mother that we are afraid to recognize it. We cloud the feeling in mystery.

But they give us sex too! It is easy to be unconscious of the fact that the feelings of tenderness we find with men are rooted in our earliest experiences with mother, when our present, and equally real feelings of sexual excitement are rooted very much in the now—*this man, this* moment, *his* arms and body. The difference between the two ideas is important. It helps explain women's lives.

When both elements are present—the nurturing plus the explicitly sexual—the marriage or affair is said to be serious, and continues for some time. If the unconscious nurturing we learned to expect from mother is missing from a relationship, we say it is "merely sexual," and it soon ends. The ultimate richness of life depends, in my experience, more often on satisfying our unconscious needs than meeting the demands of the physical.

"The whole emphasis in psychoanalytic thought in the past ten years," says Dr. Schaefer, "is to move to an earlier time than the years of the oedipal triangle. We used to be so focused on that; now we're beginning to concentrate on the earlier, mother-child dyad." Whether we like it or not, in the vast majority of American families the major figure for the child—male or female—is the mother. Our entire pattern of relating to others is set up first with her. "Whatever mother is," says Dr. Robertiello, "that is what we learn. She is our first model on how to be a person. We not only learn how to deal with reality through her, but we also use her as a model of the kind of person we will want to be close to."

Women who perceive that their mothers didn't like men in general or their father in particular suffer a devastating effect. "If the girl does like her father," says Dr. Schaefer, "mother's negativism sets up conflict in her. She doesn't feel free to like him if mother doesn't, if mother is always finding fault, nagging him. She may ally with her father, but it will be a guilty alliance. Her relationships with men often repeat the way her mother was with her father: nagging. Father didn't make enough money, he wasn't as smart as other people—that is how the daughter remembers family life."

Dr. Schaefer continues: "Often we find that men rebel against these nagging wives. They act like naughty, contrary children. Although they are capable of doing better, they don't—just to spite the wife. A daughter in a family like this grows up seeing men not as strong people you can depend on but as irresponsible children up in arms against women."

The reverse of this kind of daughter would seem to be those who call themselves *daddy's girl*. These women are adamant about denying any ties or similarities to mother. "I was always closest to my father. He was stricter than my mother but never as petty."

Of course not! He'd given over all the nasty, necessary jobs—including the titanic-even-if-forgotten struggle over toilet training—to mother. She got the shitty end of the stick—all puns intended.

Daddy is godlike, not just because he's distant and has this attractive sexual quality, but because like executives who let underlings deliver the bad news while they themselves announce promotions and raises, mother has had to do the day-by-day discipline, withholding allowances and pleasures when we are naughty, forcing us to eat and do things we don't like. When dad comes home from work, we may be at the end of our rope with mother. He enters with a clean slate. We are a bit of dessert at the end of his day. We argue less with him when he tells us to come home early because we don't have this long-standing battle with him over a hundred other things. "I never talked to my mother when I was young," a thirty-five-year-old woman says. "It was my father who gave me my most important feelings about myself. With him, I felt this wonderful security. As soon as he left the room, that feeling went away." I asked this woman if she spent a lot of time with her father. She tells me that he was away in the war until she was five. The most significant moment with him she can remember was, "when he drove me to the train when I left home at sixteen. He said, 'You must remember that not everyone is going to be as kind as they are at home.' I think that was his way of referring to sex." This oblique reference is her most significant memory of sex education and of what she calls her deep and significant relationship to her father.

"Women like these," says Dr. Robertiello, "have the illusion of being closer to father than mother. Maybe they got more of the pure unadulterated loving stuff with him but there is no way they could have been closer to him. Ask any man, the fondest father, just how much time do you spend in direct communication with your daughter? It boils down to maybe ten minutes a week. A one-to-one, up-and-back system of intimate, meaningful, close communication between father and daughter? Very, very rare." No wonder that in his silence, absence, and mystery, we can make dad the most wonderful man in the world. The absence of real data about him makes him the stuff of dreams.

The popular superstition is that daddy's girls get along better with men when they are grown. They are "a man's kind of woman," have affinities with the male sex that the rest of us are sorely lacking. The reality is that these women often have the hardest time finding a man who can live up to the idealized image of manhood they got from their father. Even if by some magic of time travel they could meet their father as he was twenty-five years ago, *he would not do*. He would not measure up to the fantasy.

All our real, nitty-gritty, personal interactions are with mother. It is with her that we work through the important issues on which our character and personality are based. Mother is the hammer, we are the anvil, and in our arguments and agreements on getting fed, being held and loved, getting toilet trained, getting disciplined, facing competition and reality, learning separation—our souls are forged.

If father is the ice cream of life, mother is the daily meat and potatoes. It is an issue of semantics: we may *like* him more, but we are *closer* to her. Mother doesn't have his glamour, but with her we know where we are. She is more familiar than anybody else we will ever meet. Later, when we run into anyone—man or woman—who arouses in us some of the feelings we once had with her, we will be attracted. Even if they are not nice people, even if they treat us badly, we will dismiss other people's injunctions against them and declare we find them "simpatico," taking the woman as a friend, the man as a lover. The illusion is that we are coming home.

"I meet a lot of women," says Dr. Robertiello, "who will tell you how mad they were about their fathers, and that they even married men who looked like him. But when you get to know them better, you very often find that whatever he looks like, *inside* the husband has the personality of her mother. A girl whose mother was cold and narcissistic, but still gave her enough so that the girl has some positive feelings about her—she will often marry a man who is also cold and narcissistic. Just as she learned to have a high tolerance for these character traits, she will tolerate them in her husband also. She has unconscious ideas and fantasies that he cares about her in the same stupid, nutty way that she had fantasies of her mother caring for her behind that coldness and narcissism. Man or woman, our first marriage is often to someone with the personality of our mother. If your mother wasn't a nice person, you're in trouble."

"What kind of man was my first husband?" a woman says. "He was as cold as my mother. To this day my daughter calls her father The Machine. I had no reason to be allergic to this kind of man. My mother was my model so I was used to it. Like living in a part of the country where the soil is poor—you don't think about it because it's all you know."

This kind of unconscious, usually self-defeating, behavior goes on even among women who think they dislike aspects of their mothers so much that they take her as a negative model . . . the way *not* to be. For instance, here is a twenty-seven-year-old woman who consciously laughs at her mother's disagreeable "little sergeant" character, and therefore chooses to think she is more like her father. Even though she senses that her life and actions contradict this wishful thought, she is unable to grasp the full degree to which her mother's pattern still dominates her relations to other people:

"No, I'm not like my mother. I'm more like my father. All my friends look upon my parents as a model because they have such a solid marriage, but I know my mother is a bitch. We call her the little sergeant. She is fussy, and my father is patience itself. I can remember laughing at my mother's irritability because it was so irrational. But I have been the same irrational person with my oldest daughter—over a bobby pin. And I see my daughter calmly saying, 'Really, mother,' when I fly in all directions."

This woman thinks of her one identification with her mother's way of reacting as a kind of aberration, an isolated "funny" bit of business which really has nothing to do with the way she leads her life as a whole. But people like this repress a larger part of their models than they are aware. "She will probably act like her mother in larger, more subtle patterns, but never be able to see it," says Dr. Robertiello. "Her whole story is out-and-out repression. She practically comes right out and says she acts like her mother, whereas she consciously thinks she is like her father. Women don't want to think of themselves as those parts of their mother they hated most, but those are the very parts they take in. It's awful to think that everything you hated in your mother, you've become. But that is how it works. That is one of the biggest shocks in therapy."

Since nagging is so abhorrent, but so many women find we do it anyway, let me once again try to illustrate its genesis. This time the story is about a young woman of sixteen, but the mechanism of repression works as powerfully in her as in any of the previous illustrations of wives or mothers. "I hope I won't nag my husband the way mom nags dad," she says. "I used to hear myself doing it with my boy friend. Even though it was what I hated most in the relationship between my parents, I couldn't stop. My boy friend used to tell me, 'You nag me just like your mother nags your father.' It frightened me when he said that. My father and I are very close. He's far more supportive than my mother. One day he said to me that he hoped I would break the tradition of nagging women in our family."

This is a classic story. The young woman says she is closer to her father, but the way she acts is like her mother. She's unable to stop nagging even though she says she hates it. Proximity, sexual identity, need for mother's protection—all kinds of forces work to make mother, not father, her model. She takes in both what she likes and what she does not.

Professionally successful women often consciously think they have modeled their lives on their adored successful fathers. They give as evidence of their closeness to him the fact of their success itself. A life in his footsteps. They are right to a point.

In Margaret Hennig's Harvard doctoral study of twenty-five high-level women executives, she found that every one indeed had had a strong attachment to and identification with her success-oriented father. Their mothers were usually conventional, noncompetitive women with no great involvement in matters outside the home, and never loomed in the girls' lives as a giant figure who might cut them down in the rivalry for father's attention. Father had been theirs from the start.

These women were never seen as substitute sons; their fathers did not believe in sexual role-playing (at least as far as their daughters were concerned), and so their daughters did not confuse feminine gender identity with masculine notions that striving and achievement were for men only.[4]

And yet in my research, I have met one executive woman after another who, no matter how cool and competent she was in the office (like father), experienced a deep emotional change when she married or became seriously involved with a man. Often, the change was not apparent except in hindsight.

"I was always my dad's girl," says a thirty-five-year-old professional woman. "I thought he was the handsomest, smartest man in the world. When he was home I hung on him, and when he left the house, I was always two steps behind, waiting for an invitation to come along. He used to talk to me, not like a kid, but like an adult—stories about Don Quixote or how the Mormons settled Utah. I don't remember my mother having any opinion at all about my closeness to my dad. Her stand about the whole thing was kind of like we were invisible. She was a nice warm loving mom, but I didn't want to grow up to have her life. I got my good grades for my dad. Because I was more adventurous and wanted more than most of the girls I grew up with, I gave myself the phrase 'my dad's girl.' It was a way to think about myself, an acceptable category I could fit into. After college I continued my studies because I wanted a career, to teach like my dad. I always planned to get married. When I did five years ago everything began to change. I didn't notice because I was still working. Outwardly, everything looked the same, but on some level, my work had begun to take a back seat to my role as a wife. As the marriage progressed, I tended to slip into a position where my feelings about myself as a success, as a person, were far more attached to my role as a wife. I think a lot of it had to do with how my mother had been with my father.

"All my life I'd denied I was like her, but when I married, it was uncanny. For the first time in my life, the big thing with my father didn't come in handy. He couldn't be my model of how to be a wife. If you've always had a pretty clear idea of who you are and how you operate, it's startling to see how marriage changes you, how you suddenly find yourself slipping into the one role you said you'd never be in—the way your mother was with your father. This accelerates when you become a mother yourself. I'll tell you a funny thing that happened after my daughter was born. The bank called and asked why was I suddenly signing my checks Mrs. Philip Henderson. I'd always signed them Sheila Henderson. It took me a long time to understand that when I became a mother, I had stopped being *me* and had become Karen's mother, my husband's wife, *Mrs. Philip Henderson.*"

The different roles our parents played in our earliest life furnish a clue to why even successful, career-oriented women so often slip back into regressive roles when they marry: mother began to teach us how to be a woman and a wife long before dad came along to teach us how to be a success in the office. The way we are in our jobs and careers relates to patterns of behavior and feelings learned relatively late. These ideas are more conscious, can be handled more rationally, than needs picked up in our earliest relationship with mother. "Father may be the model for how to behave in an office," says Dr. Robertiello, "but how to behave with a man, at home, on a date, in the bedroom, anywhere basic emotions rule—the structure of that relationship is based on mother. Women take mother's life as the model of how to be with men in terms of how they perceived she was with father. *Or with them*—which was usually not so different."

If mother was mousy and masochistic, we may be a tiger at work; in our intimate relationships we will suffer a man we would never hire at the office, or even give the time of day. If our mothers were domineering and/or symbiotic, then we are that way with men. "You see it again and again," says Dr. Robertiello. "A woman will tell you she identifies with and is looking for a man like her father. Then she marries someone who puts her in the same unconscious bind mother used to."

This is an illustration of what Freud called the "repetition compulsion." It is a reluctance to let go of infantile omnipotence. Says Dr. Robertiello: "It centers around the unconscious conviction that you can go back and take a bad mother like the one you had and make her a good one today. The repetition is due to inability to accept that we failed with our mother . . . that she didn't love us enough, or the way we wanted. This time, it's going to be different."

This mechanism explains the magnetic power of Mr. Rat, those dreadful men who pretend to love us but do not. The nice guy who just plain loves us out and out—why does he seem so insignificant, his love so meaningless beside the chance to win the heart of Mr. Wrong? Because the model of love our "bad" mother once held out to us is reincarnated in Mr. Wrong. With Mr. Wrong, we get our second chance to win the love of our life—the one we failed to get the first time around. The love of that nice boy next door? It holds none of the glamour of a chance to succeed where once we failed.

Just who daddy is, is never quite so clear as what he does for mother . . . and by extension, for us. He is this mysterious outside force, he "brings home the bacon," showers the family like Santa Claus with the goodies of life—the house, the car, the washing machine, summer vacations, money for that special pretty dress for a dreamed-of occasion. Even in those families where mother also works, she usually contributes less than he to the income. It is a feeling that she reinforces for her own reasons: most women need to feel that their husbands are the major providers, and this is the feeling they pass on to their daughters.

On the other hand, mother sits at the gate of all this wealth. She is the day-by-day administrator, giving us our allowance or withholding it. If we are "good girls" we get extras—a form of behavior we have seen her practice on father. For us too, the reward of money conferred by a man soon has greater significance than any we earn on our own. "I get my allowance from my husband," says a woman who makes six figures annually. "Money is sexy."

Father is the source of generosity; mother is niggling over pennies. Mother scans the shopping pages of the newspaper to find the cornflakes sale so she can save three cents a box. When we want to go to an expensive summer camp, it is father who says the meaningful Yes. If we see a film in which Steve McQueen, when the waiter presents the check, carelessly puts some bills on the table and does not wait for the change, we respond with a sexual warmth. That's how men are, moving in a world so large nobody quibbles over the bill; when we have lunch with our girl friends, the pettiness is notorious: "You had the extra cole slaw, and Sally had the glass of wine . . ."

Little wonder then that long before the question has arisen of how/whether mother should prepare us for the sexual experience of men, she has given us a picture of life in which they are indispensable. Like those photos in fashion magazines where the men are either out of focus, characterless, or homosexuals, *who* they are is never so important as what they give the women in the picture: stronger definition. The dress costs $200, but without a man, whole gaggles of men lolling at her feet or helping her out of the car, the image of the woman in that dress would be far less significant *to other women*.

The thrust of our development today is away from this; and yet the notion that men are absolutely vital to any value we may have is so woven into feminine reality that most women think to reject it would be like trying to reject the law of gravity. When I say women still need men "to take care of us," the idea sounds dated and old-fashioned. It is too easy to dismiss if taken only at its superficial meaning. Women do not need men to pay our bills or repel marauders. We need men to take care of us because we don't believe we are visible, that we exist, without one . . . much as we felt lost,

abandoned, near death as infants if mother did not appear when we
became frightened at being alone.

"No, I insist. I'll pay for myself," says a young woman who has
joined my husband and me at a restaurant table. But when she
reaches into her wallet, she doesn't have enough money. If he can, a
man usually goes out in the evening with more money than he thinks
he will need. He knows emergencies may arise, and he wants to be
prepared to cope. Women are trained to carry only "mad money"—
just enough for a taxi ride home. In her mind, this young woman who
was offering to pay for herself was willing to be a contemporary and
responsible person. Something deeper, inculcated into her since childhood, made sure she could not.

What makes this inability to take care of ourselves so maddening is
that women are beginning to realize that the free ride men supposedly
offer is not free at all. "My boy friend doesn't have much money,"
says a sixteen-year-old. "I've told him I don't mind paying for myself,
but he only likes that to a point. He's always going out with the boys
—which admittedly doesn't cost much. But when he does, he expects
me to stay home. Why can't he use the little money going out with
the boys costs, and add my dutch treat money, and go out with me?
No, I'm supposed to stay home when he's not in the mood to see me
—because that's what it really means when he says he's broke. If I go
out alone, or to a party without him, he's furious." If the man only
"lets" you share expenses when it suits him, the independence that
money offers is as false as the quality of the relationship.

By turning men into Father Christmas, mother deals an enormous
blow to the problem of competition between us. Daddy isn't this sexual person, this attractive man we both want. He's really a nice, big,
warm provider, as comfortable and nonerotic as a hot-water heater.
What could be sexual about a person who works his way to an early
heart attack, who comes home so tired and grumpy he barely has the
strength to peck a kiss on Mommy's cheek? Mother further cements
the alliance between us: Daddy is not the competitive prize we both
want but a fuddy-duddy opponent whom we league together to fool:
"We'll tell him the dress only cost twenty-five dollars, not forty-five."

There is an enigma in this nice, safe, domestic picture she is presenting. Here she is, telling us what a nice man daddy is, how hard he
works for us, how much he loves her, what an ideal marriage they
have. But why is she always up to these sly little manipulative tricks
that make him look like an oaf? Doesn't she remember they just had

that frightening quarrel last week? Doesn't father usually seem bored with her, spending more time than she likes away at the office or bowling with his friends? When she talks of the rewards of marriage (as opposed to the dangers of sex), we feel a loss of reality. Part of us does want to get married, but her own marriage turns us off. Something is missing. Sex is problematic, she's always telling us; brutish boys are only out for one thing. We may be young but we already know that life is not worth living without the excitement boys give us. How can we buy mother's promises? She presents boys in such a dangerously attractive light that sex becomes the one thing we are always thinking about too.

We accommodate ourselves to this fact of life by deciding that mother is good and we are bad. Little wonder then that daughters become puzzled and resentful if mother divorces and begins to bring home different men. These aren't nice, comfortable, rent-paying daddies: Can it really be that it is sex she wants—after spending all those years telling us it is bad, unnecessary, dangerous and that it must never come between us? She has broken the symbiotic bond: she is more attached to this new person than she is to us. "I'm not competitive with my mother," says a fifteen-year-old whose mother has brought her lover to live in the house. "I'm competitive with him— when she pays more attention to him than me. When I grow up, I'd rather be married to someone, not just live with him. I don't want my mother's life." In this girl's circle of friends, she has the reputation of being naïve and antisexual.

Marriage and divorce counselor Dr. Sonya Friedman speaks of a case where a live-in lover brought about an opposite reaction. "When her thirty-five-year-old mother brought this man to live with them, the daughter was so embarrassed that she wouldn't invite her friends in. They would ask, 'Who is that man? He's not your father. Why is he sleeping in your mother's bedroom?' The daughter couldn't stand that. Children have a very narrowly defined sense of morality, of right and wrong. I was not surprised when it turned out that the daughter soon entered into some pretty wild sexual experimentation of her own."

When mother reveals that her interest in men is not merely cozy and domestic, as she had always promised us, she robs men of their mystery. They are sexual, and we want what she has. The flood gates of competition suddenly open. Daughter's anger is often expressed by finding as explicitly sexual a man as she can to flaunt at mother, to get back at her.

Mother did not deliberately lie. She wishes us to repeat her life because thus she is validated herself. She keeps life a mystery because if we knew the little she knew, we might not repeat the cycle; if we reject her choices, she would feel anxious and guilty. "Where did I go wrong?"

Once again, the wish is mother to the thought. As Dr. Schaefer says, mother actually does have the fantasy that her marriage is, if not perfect, well, then, better than most. If it isn't, why has she sacrificed so much for it? Says Gladys McKenney, who teaches in a high school in suburban Michigan:

"Daughters are only too aware of the inconsistencies going on in many marriages—mother saying one thing about the beauty of marriage, and all the while living this unhappy relationship. It's hard to admit to a child, 'Dad and I haven't always been too happy together.' In the families I see of above-average socioeconomic status—which means most families in the place where I teach—there is a great deal of anger between husband and wife that doesn't get expressed. The kids are aware of it, but it is hidden, suppressed." A double message is being sent out: sometimes we hate each other but it is better to call it love.

The mystery grows.

Says Dr. Schaefer: "The only way for a mother to prepare her daughter for the reality of living with a man is by being honest about her life with her husband. If you try to tell your daughter one thing, but you are living something else, the split creates the biggest hardship. It is what I like to call The Big Lie—to be caught between what our parents say and what our parents really feel." We want to believe life with father is as nice as mother says, but in our heart we know it just isn't so. We are left with her rosy picture of him, but with no idea of how to reach this ideal goal. All we know in the meantime is that any man who does not make us feel this idealized emotion is not Mr. Right. That is how we will recognize him when he comes along at last. He will transport us into this magical place that mother is always talking about.

Mothers raise their daughters as fools because they believe in the divinity of innocence. Sexually, all mothers are Catholic. They pray for their daughters' innocence while simultaneously praying for a man for their untutored, unblemished girls. The keepers of the vestal virgins guarded their purity, knowing sex would be their doom. Our mothers keep us pure and dumb, knowing that even if sex is our future, it will also be our doom. In the light of such inevitability, rational, intelligent thinking fails. A pious belief that the innocent shall be spared prevails. In case after case where I have interviewed both mother and daughter, the mother will say, "Oh, my daughter knows it all, she picks it up at school, from her friends, in the street. I don't have to tell her." But when I interview the fourteen-, fifteen-, sixteen-year-old daughter, her knowledge is piecemeal. What she doesn't want to know—the whole truth about her body, contraception—is frightening. Where does she get her reluctance to know about herself in a world that has never before had so much sexual information available?

Our difficulty begins with mother's ambivalence. If it is hard for her to say, it is impossible for us to listen. "Nobody tells you about the feelings you will have when you get close to someone," says Dr. Schaefer. "In fairness to mother, how can anybody prepare you for the enormity of orgasm? Many women are so unprepared they don't want it. They resist it. It is not that they can't reach orgasm, they just can't handle all those feelings."

Dr. Schaefer continues: "Take the problem facing a mother if she tries to get specific with her daughter. Just because the older woman can accept certain sexual ideas—even welcome them—doesn't mean they don't frighten the hell out of her when she thinks of them in connection with her daughter. Now the boy friend has come around to pick up the daughter in a car. The mother knows that they'll park sooner or later tonight. She knows her daughter's fantasies are about the good feelings she gets from kissing. But she also knows that the boy's fantasies are about the girl touching his cock. How does she explain that to her girl if she is still guilty about sex herself?"

"A lot of women are objective about a man until they go to bed with him," says Sonya Friedman. "Then they literally get all screwed up. They become inappropriately bonded to him. He assumes an emotional importance out of all proportion. Here is this woman, so calm and rational yesterday, agreeing with the man that it is just a little flirtation, a roll in the hay, a limited affair . . . and today she's crying, 'I want him, I want him, I'll die without him!' I hope this kind of thinking is dying out. It was awful in my generation where we had a little hanky panky, a lot of guilt and/or the terrific 'want' of him.

Above all, the imperative notion that if you wanted him sexually you had to marry him.

"One of the things that happens as you mature," continues Dr. Friedman, "is that you gain the ego strength to remain intact. You can enjoy someone physically and emotionally without becoming bonded to him, sitting beside the telephone waiting for it to ring. This is what I hope my daughter is learning, that if she has some significant skills, a good opinion of herself as someone all by herself, she won't have to trade that off for a relationship dominated by the notion that she can't live without him."

We expect marriage to liberate us from this sexual guilt. The contradiction is that while the wife wants the man to be strongly erotic and magically male, to awaken us sexually, we want him to do this within the emotional framework of warmth, nurturing, cuddling, affection. "No, don't touch me there!" we exclaim when something he does threatens to take all tenderness out of the erotic. The man is bewildered: if she doesn't think that's sexy, what the hell does she want? We have kept our hands off our body for the past twenty years. How can we tell him what we want, when we have never been allowed to explore the idea ourselves?

What is puzzling and frightening is when mother says in one breath that men are bad, they aren't trustworthy, they're children who will selfishly let you down—and then in the next breath tells us of the marvelous future we will have married to one of them! In our culture, a good mother never, never admits to her daughter that she may not marry, or that it may not be the best idea in the world. The fear and distrust of men that some mothers lay on their daughters is later projected on each man in the girl's life as he comes along. The love affair, the marriage is doomed before it starts. The girl is often angry at all men for what one man did to her mother, or what mother *said* he did.

Women justifiably make the complaint about Don Juans that the specific girl doesn't count: "He'll go to bed with anyone." Men return the compliment when they say about a woman, "She'll marry anyone in pants." We wake up like sleepwalkers and say, "I didn't make a choice. It was simply part of the picture. You got married, and had two children, and then you got the dog and the summer house. . . ."

At fifteen we of course are no less a mystery to boys. But they are edgy, only too aware of how close to female dominance and entanglement they still are: mother is always around. And although young men may want closeness and love as much as we do, they don't want all that other business females (mother) stand for: rules, dependence, and control. Both boy and girl see in each other an escape from mother—an alliance that will separate us for good from her —but in mutual ignorance of any relationship between men and women except the symbiotic one we have seen at home, we proceed to set up the same thing between ourselves. "Going steady" gives both boy and girl what they feel is security. More often it is like two drowning swimmers, clutching each other by the throat. Men are usually the ones who break the death grip first. Their major advantage is that they have alternatives, experience in walking away: they don't need to "buy" a relationship at any price. Their cry of suffocation— just before they slam out the door—is famous. What is little commented upon in these situations is that the woman too must have felt suffocated. But she would have paid that price—anything to keep the relationship going.

When the romance and fantasy fade, when we see men defrocked and their great mystery turns out to be that they are merely human like us, we grow angry. When we were fifteen, mother seemed archaic; we were sexual heroines, breaking ground that would have terrified her had she known. What happened? Suddenly, the glow has left our lives and we realize we have gone no further than she did. *We are just like her!*

This explains the inappropriate anger we feel when our men say, "You're just like your mother." We may feel it is disloyal to take that as an accusation, but even stronger is our fear that he means we are as asexual as we perceive her to be. "How does it feel to be a woman?" my mother asked the day my first period started. A conventional enough question, but I was embarrassed. I didn't feel like a woman, and any discussion of womanliness/sexuality between women made me feel awkward. It would be men—not menstruation, not my mother, not other women—who would define and help me understand my womanliness. Writing this book has confirmed something my body and soul understood long before I did: to play the passive spectator to the life of our own body is a choice we make or not. Women are beginning to see that sexuality cannot be conferred by anyone else. If men remain a mystery it is because of their intrinsic "differences," not because of some magical power they have over us. Women today are mysterious to our mothers because we have become active agents in our own sexuality.

—— *Chapter 9* ——

THE LOSS
OF VIRGINITY

My Aunt Kate was expecting her first child the summer of my freshman year at college, and because my family had moved north that winter, I was staying with her in Charleston. We were painting the new nursery, and talking about my best friend's wedding in which I was to be a bridesmaid, when she casually remarked she had been a virgin when she married. Given this atmosphere—my aunt's pregnancy, the wedding, my mother being far away—you might think a discussion of sex and contraception would follow. It did not.

I asked no question, not thinking of myself as sexual; she had given me as much as she was able, comfortably, to say on the subject. Except that she did add how much her virginity had meant to her husband. The conversation was easy and nonmoralistic, parenthetically slipped in between pale pink brush strokes—my aunt's loving way of giving me something meaningful from her life. Her comment meshed easily with my romantic visions of what lay ahead and I promptly "forgot" it. Looking back now, I can see her message etched itself on my brain.

If, unlike my aunt, I wasn't a virgin when I married, it doesn't lessen my indebtedness to her. I had gone north to college, like her; and was to become an actress and then a writer, like her. These were things I wanted to do but I had taken over the idea of them from her.

Without the model of her life to help me out of that warm southern bath I'd grown up in, I might have married as young as all my friends. The way she was, the picture of her, allowed me to become sexual in my own time and without guilt. This is what I owe her . . . not a rule or command that held me back but a model of restraint I could use while I needed it. The best our heroines can do is give us a hand up and then let us go; the way we thank them is to grow into ourselves—not them. Whenever I drew the seventh virginal veil in my current lover's face—after helping him part the first six—it wasn't because I heard my aunt's words thundering like doomsday: *save it!* I simply wasn't ready. The example of her life was all the reason I needed. My body had experienced everything but the final penetration; in my mind I remained a virgin. The night I did lose my virginity was as meaningful and memorable as the ritual nuptials of any maiden raised by nuns.

One sunny afternoon during my junior year at college, I happened to open a medical textbook left on a table by a friend's date. A paragraph informed that you can get pregnant without penetration. It said that highly active sperm can wiggle up a warm moist vagina on their own even if you were only doing what Steve and I had been doing in his car the night before. While I read, I was counting on my fingers the days since my last period. I knew the next one would not come.

It was destiny that that book fell open to that page, one of those accidental bulletins that were to mark my life. I searched the text for reassurance but quickly ran into a sea of medical jargon. The Great Curtain had briefly parted to give me a message and, as quickly, closed again. I was pregnant. I was certain of it, and that there was no one to whom I could turn. I'd never known a girl who'd become pregnant. I had never heard abortion discussed. I was madly in love with Steve but marriage was out of the question. I had too many things to do. Unable to face either alternative, I was left with panic.

It never occurred to me to call my mother. Mother was someone to whom I went when I was on top of the world. I couldn't bear to see anxiety in my mother; my remedy was for her never to see it in me. I circled the college infirmary on the hill, desperate to know the truth, but unable even to form the sentence in my head: "I think I'm pregnant, help!" Me?—president of my freshman class, secretary of student government? What would people say when I was revealed as a split personality, a person who wanted to spend her life with a man's cock between her legs, who would take it anywhere, in cars, on sandy beaches, any dark secluded place out of sight (but just barely) of others? I would be expelled, shunned; I was immobilized.

I telephoned Steve but his reassurances weakened as the days passed and my own anxieties increased. The chances of impregnation were a million to one, he told me. I was the one millionth. I was six days late. On the seventh day I woke to find a beautiful red spot on the sheet and I shared a religious moment with my God: "Dear God, thank you, thank you, I will never do it again."

That Friday I signed out for a weekend, and Saturday morning Steve and I were naked in each other's arms in his roommate's sister's canopied bed on Beacon Hill, his cock moving between my legs, my vagina hot and moist as the intrepid sperm once again tried for that one chance in a million. Is there anyone as stupid as an eighteen-year-old virgin?

Recently I had lunch with a man I hadn't seen since I was nineteen. He had read one of my books and when I heard his voice on the telephone, I smiled, remembering those days in the big feather bed in Kitzbühl, the wine, the après-ski massages we gave each other, the days we never skied at all. I had loved him madly, but when he talked of marriage and slipped me a copy of St. Thomas Aquinas our last night (he was Catholic), I let him carve his initials in my arm instead. I still could not think of marriage: I was just beginning. But I wanted to give him something, and so I gave him my arm. We were in bed, drunk on wine and good-byes, and where we got the idea of his autographing me midway between elbow and wrist, I don't know. It is what I remember most of Kitzbühl and him—the act was so unlike me.

What he remembered, he told me at lunch, was that, "I almost took your virginity. You are what we used to call a *professional virgin*," he said over our Bloody Marys. "Don't you remember that last night? I almost had it in. If I hadn't said, 'Nancy, do you realize what you are doing . . . ?'"

"But you didn't put it in," I said. "It takes two to keep a virgin. You are what we virgins called a professional virgin-keeper."

My mother came to visit me before I flew down to San Juan, Puerto Rico, to begin my first job on an English-language newspaper. She came with my stepfather and two friends to the summer playhouse on Cape Cod where I had been an apprentice my last three summers at college. I had reserved them the best rooms at the best hotel, the best table at the best restaurant and had, of course, gotten them the best seats in the house for that night's performance. I was proud of my mother. She was pretty, young, and she never criticized me.

"You know," she said, admiring my summer setup, my friends, my perfect life, "Susie would love to be doing something like this. But she's so irresponsible." My older sister was still living at home. My mother's preoccupation with the difficulties of my sister's life faded as she turned to me. "Oh, Nancy," she smiled, putting a hand on my shoulder, "you've always been able to take care of yourself. I've never had to worry about you."

I don't know when my mother and I had agreed on that bargain. It seems it had always been that way. I never took the bad news home. Certainly, by the time I was twenty, my mother and I had further refined the deal: since she did not worry, she wouldn't interfere either. I would take care of myself. That night at dinner I brought along another of the men I was always madly in love with, this time a bad actor. I mentioned that he was driving me to New York, where we would have a night before my flight to San Juan. My mother never asked where I would be staying in New York, whether I had enough money for my ticket, or what I was doing with such a disreputable fellow, one who obviously had neither the background nor manners for the country club. Instead, she smiled shyly at him, and gave me a neatly folded check for twenty-five dollars.

"Now let me know if there's anything you need," she said, knowing I would not. Suddenly, at the last minute, her face collapsed into that sad wistful look she always had when we parted. "Oh, Nance," she began, and reached for me tentatively. I returned her embrace with less warmth than I would have liked, hating myself for not being able to give my mother what she wanted. Why did these good-byes always fill me with such guilt? I waved them out of sight, then drove to New York with my actor. My grandfather had told me I could use his suite at the Plaza. Never a word of caution, even from him. The sign around my neck told the world: Nancy can take care of herself. That night, the actor and I did everything but.

I shared an apartment in San Juan with two other girls, virgins all. The night of our housewarming party, someone brought us a palm tree from which hung three hollowed eggs, symbols of fertility. We laughed and planted ivy in the bidet.

By the end of that year, each had lost her virginity, each in her own time. Not a word about contraception. Not a diaphragm in the house. I had been awakened one night by noise on the terrace and had sat up in bed to see my one roommate making love to a man I had never seen before, and she would never see again. My turn came soon afterward. Riding down Ponce de Leon Avenue on the bus the next morning, I remember my surprise that the freckles on my sun-tanned arm were still there. I hadn't changed.

From the primitive to the most sophisticated cultures, the uncon-scious wisdom of the race has seen the need for young men to be confirmed in the assumption of manhood through puberty rites, Bar Mitzvahs, hunting ordeals, etc. Today you are a man. In complex civ-ilizations, sex may still be delayed a few years. Nevertheless the youngster has been signaled: it is time for you to put away childish ways and begin to separate from your family. He has looked forward to this ceremony of separation for so long that when it comes he has no doubt of its value. His mother weeps for joy, his father is proud, he himself knows he has reached life's next lofty step. When sex comes, it is the inevitable outgrowth of the rest.

There is almost nothing comparable for girls. There is no ritual, no step-by-step training for womanhood. No celebration of our sexual-ity. Our one symbolic act is loss of virginity, which is done in secret and without applause. Should we wait until we are married, the act of sex like marriage itself is meant to accomplish what should take years of process and preparation. What should be an act of separation be-comes but another form of symbiosis: now that he's "taken" our vir-ginity, will he love us forever, call us tomorrow, leave us for another woman? Instead of making us free, curious, experimental about the future, sex fills us with regressive, postcoital anxiety. "Hold me, love only me as I will love only you, forever. Promise."

Everyone remembers the first time. What we were wearing, the lighting fixture in the ceiling, the feel of the car upholstery. It is set apart in an airtight compartment of memory. The initiation rite has been experienced. One act that says we are children no more, and have pushed aside mother's rules. We are adult, grownup, sexual—synonyms for separate. Except we are not.

More than in any other area of our lives we expect sex to grow us up. Much as mother may not have wanted us to leave home or take a career, she forbade nothing so much as she did sex. We are right to think of it as a step away from her, but it cannot do the job alone. "Because women have no other formal preparation for sexuality," says Dr. Robertiello, "the act of losing your virginity comes to bear an impossible load. It just cannot accomplish what people think it will. Separation is not a physical act, like breaking the hymen. It is an emotional one. It must begin during the first years of life and be progressively strengthened all during development. It's no wonder so many women grow disappointed and lose interest in sex. They have feared it so long and then expected it to do so much in one fell swoop. Nothing makes you independent all at once." Separation is not something that "happens" to you one night in the back seat of a car or is given to you by a husband in a honeymoon suite.

What a blessing if women could be relieved of their virginity at birth. One simple act to get rid of a label which more than anything else confounds our thinking about sexuality; the marketplace for virgin brides wiped out once and for all, mothers relieved of an anxiety that has nothing to do with their daughters' essential heart, soul and character. Instead of cops, they could function more easily as loving nurturers. Instead of thinking that in one night we "lose" some mysterious treasure between our legs, we might come to understand that our sexuality lies between our ears and is won by us alone.

Every free act, every victory over fear and inhibition, leaves an increment of courage, making it easier to try again the next time. Therefore, let's imagine an area of development in which a young person *could* practice her sexuality and learn to feel separate from her mother. Ideally, it should be safe, cheap, quiet, private and hurt nobody's feelings. It should be self-motivated and self-performed—a self-satisfying pleasure with no possible consequences to anyone but yourself: masturbation. Nature is cunning.

And yet, Kinsey reported in the early '50s that "No other type of sexual activity has worried so many women as masturbation."[1] In 1964 Dr. Schaefer found every woman in her study on female sexuality—which included some who were professionally trained psychotherapists—felt anxiety about masturbation.[2] Nor did the sexual revolution of the last decade profoundly change our ideas. According to Robert Sorenson's 1974 research, women today may masturbate more, but still describe what they feel as "defensiveness and discomfort."³

The topic itself continues to be anxiety-laden, whether women do or do not masturbate. Why? Says Dr. Schaefer: "The anxiety is connected to an unwillingness to be responsible for one's own pleasure—one's own fantasies—even to be responsible for one's own orgasms."

If we do not understand why we do not masturbate, we cannot understand why we do not ask for what we want in bed. If we do not feel free to touch ourselves, how can we open ourselves to pleasure with another person? When mother began to take our hand away from between our legs when we were infants, we didn't persist because we were symbiotic with her; whatever she wanted, we wanted.

"When I was six," says an eighteen-year-old college sophomore, "I never connected masturbation or childhood sex games with intercourse. I remember lying on my stomach, spreading my legs and wiggling until what I called 'the good feelings' came. I felt no guilt about it and even tried to turn my friends onto it. The guilt only started when my mother caught me and I was scolded. I didn't connect the pleasure I gave myself with sex. I thought sex was a very fast maneuver when you wanted a child. I'm still too tense to use Tampax. Last year I fell in love with a smooth talker who finally talked me into going to bed with him. My God, but it hurt! The only thing I enjoyed was being close to him. He went into the army and I never heard from him again. I haven't let myself get close to anyone since."

This young woman enjoyed masturbation until her mother connected it with sex and told her it was bad. She continued to masturbate but she feels so uneasy about that part of her body that she can't even use tampons. If she doesn't like to touch herself, how can she believe anyone else enjoys it? What chance did she have of actively choosing a partner for sex? He chose her, he smooth-talked her into it, he hurt her, he deserted her. A "good girl" to the end, she sounds as if she were hardly there at all. "The only thing I enjoyed was being close to him." Symbiosis.

"I can't live without him!" cries the abandoned wife. Is that the cry of a woman or baby? Is it lack of sex she is dying of, or lack of someone to be dependent upon?

Little wonder then that most women do not think of entering into sexuality as a break with the symbiotic patterns of childhood; it becomes instead a search for that old togetherness, even if in a new, sexual mode. "I'm glad I saved myself for Steven," a young woman says. "My first time was wonderful. It made me feel part of him." These are beautiful sentiments, sincerely felt. But there is a confusion of two important ideas here. Closeness and sex are not synonymous. As long as we mesh one with the other, we jeopardize our chance of having the best of either.

I believe that sex is an absolute, an end in itself. If "making love" does that for you, it is a bonus, not the *raison d'être* of sex. Sex with love is marvelous, but sex can be exciting without love or closeness. If we enter into it only to heighten the symbiotic union, we soon find we have been using sex for a function it cannot perform well. Sex gets its energy from connecting two people; the spark needs a gap to jump. If it is used as a kind of treacle syrup to hold together two people already meshed like a layer cake, you may stay together, but the sex is smothered in sweetness.

In spite of our training, many of us do feel at least a momentary thrill of separation. "I had a great feeling of power after that first night," one woman says. "I felt exhilarated, relieved of a burden," says another. "It was wonderful!" says a third. "I'd arrived; I was a woman at last!" Despite the commonplace phrases, these words have terrific emotion; they give us the sense of people living in their authentic selves if only for the moment, doing what they wanted, walking into the den of fear they had been warned against and finding it instead a fountain of pleasure. They were living in their own experience, not mother's.

But this sudden confirmation of self is unsettling. The experience of reveling in this body, this skin, these breasts, my vagina—an awareness of an inner life that is ours alone—is joyous but scary too. Nothing says you can make it on your own more clearly than a shot of sexuality. Good as it feels, we retreat instinctively. It is too foreign to the only identity we have been taught is acceptable for women: I am a nice girl, not really sexual at all.

"After I lost my virginity, I felt free," says a twenty-eight-year-old woman. "I felt more attractive, but it didn't change my sexual pattern. I went out with the next man for nine months before I went to bed with him. I still didn't think sex was nice. In my head, I was still a virgin. I'd had sex with one man but that didn't mean you shouldn't wait until you were married."

If you've smiled with recognition at what this woman says, you will understand the rest. Part of her had agreed to go to bed with a man, but a more important part had not. She still wanted to be nice, to obey mother's rules, to be loved for not entering sexuality. We want to be women. We want to remain daughters too. In this split we live. Sex has failed to do its magic thing.

The world sees us as women; we have the sexual experience of the female race. Why don't we feel it? Why aren't we the sexually mature people we dreamed of becoming when we were still virgins, saving ourselves for this glorious event? We hasten to confirm the legitimacy of our title of woman. Props are hauled in, a stage production is being born. Who are you? Are you that little girl you fear you still are? No, I am the woman everyone envies for having that wonderful man, this fantastic house, those tickets-around-the-world, six lovers, sixteen Halston gowns, a Christmas card family. Some of us use men and sex like props too, piling up numbers to bolster our subjective fears that we are a sham. Is there anything missing from your sex life? No, I am the woman who had four orgasms last night and seventeen different men in the past month. And yet late at night—even though we lie beside a beloved man and count our blessings and tell ourselves we have everything a woman could ask for—the doubts go on. Is this all? We decide that sex is overrated. We do not realize that by trying to make it function as a form of symbiosis we never gave sex a chance.

The beginning of menstruation and the loss of virginity are doors into the adult world. "Menstruation," says Dr. Schaefer, "is stepping into it biologically, while loss of virginity should be the emotional step into adulthood." Menstruation is something over which we have no control. Sex, when it happens, where, with whom and whether we take responsibility—these are things we can choose to control. Most of us do not.

I am not saying that outwardly we do not say yes, nor that the man rapes us. On an overt level, we do consent, but a distinction must be made between consent that is the signal of active choice, and consent that is hesitant, passive or no choice at all: "I don't know what I want, do with me what you will." To the camera eye, the woman chooses the man, decides to uncross her legs. Subjectively, from the inside, we don't look at it that way: we want to feel carried away. Do we want him to touch our breasts? Not a word is breathed. Do we wish he would move more rapidly or slowly? More silence. We communicate with our lover by hope and by prayer. Would we like him to kiss us between the legs? The thought is so unsettling we aren't sure we do want it. Better to let the moment take us where it will, let him push our body here, put our legs there. He did it, not me.

"If women could subjectively say, 'I choose to do it, and this is what I want'—and mean it—they would make a developmental jump," says Dr. Robertiello. "But this would increase their separation, and that is frightening." When we were mother's little girl and living under her roof, it was appropriate to be aware of her strictures. How appropriate is it for a woman old enough to be in bed with a man still to be bound by rules to the point where she hesitates to do and ask for what she wants?

The next morning we question the mirror: Am I now a woman? We go over that first time like an unsolved mystery: what was missing? It was our sense of choice. We did not choose to enter sex. The experience was not *ours*. We just let it happen.

"What a letdown after all those years of waiting," a woman recalls. "I'd been expecting an earthquake. I didn't even get a tremor." After years of saying No, we decide to go! In one jump we go—but stop too. It's like being shot from a cannon and falling down a foot or two from the cannon's mouth. A big decision to go nowhere.

Who are the men we choose for this momentous occasion? We choose a nice boy. A boy who has a familiar feel; who is, in fact, like us, not too experienced. Should we by some chance choose a sexy devil, you can be sure that either he or we are just passing through town: he won't be around tomorrow to remind us of our secret indiscretion, to suggest to our friends, or mother, that we are anything less than good girls.

Ostensibly what we want is a sexual experience, but we choose men who are good at relationships, good providers, men who are serious about their work, who will take care of us. These are reasons perhaps for liking someone, loving him, marrying him, if that is what you want. But they cannot be said to be criteria for a sexual partner. These are men mother would approve of. In fact, they are often male versions of mother. No wonder they are so popular with her. They do not arouse in her the dangerous ideas of sex she warned us about and would prefer not to think about herself. Women proudly say, "Of all the women in the world, he chose me." We close our eyes to the fact that we had certain reasons of our own for choosing him.

"You always hear about men who are out for only one thing," says a thirty-five-year-old woman. "I never met them. I must have had a sign around my neck. They knew I was untouched and untouchable, so they never even tried. Even after college, men still didn't try to get me into bed. I was always the one they wanted to marry. I guess I was the only full-fledged virgin they'd ever run into."

Certainly there are men who want virgins, just as there are men who don't. But this woman makes it sound as if it were only pure luck that sent her the first kind, never the second. She takes a passive stance—these nonsexual, marrying-type men merely happened to be attracted to her; she didn't actively choose them. The truth is that she chose to "see" only them. She sent out signals by the way she dressed, the people she moved among, her body poses, clothes, language, attitudes. If ever a scoundrel of the other kind approached, you may be sure her choice became less passive and more active: "No!" she would say if he asked her out. All of this is forgotten now. But her story takes an interesting turn as she continues:

"In the end, I began to get a bit curious. I *wanted* sex. Finally, I met Pete. But I didn't have an orgasm. You know what that bastard called me? He said I was frigid! What a rat!" When she finally chose a man, she picked one who called her asexual. She may call him a bastard today, but he gave her a satisfaction so deep she cannot acknowledge it: he told her that she maintained her psychological virginity so deeply, he had been unable to touch it.

"If only somebody had told me what I intend to tell my daughters," this woman goes on. "I'm going to tell them to pretend orgasm. Yes, it perpetuates dishonesty for women, but it would have made my marriage very different. I'm going to say, 'Look, if he's the kind of man to whom it is terribly important that you come, learn to fake it.'" Never a word about learning to tell a man what you like so that you might actually reach orgasm instead of lying about it; certainly not even a suspicion of the truth that your sexuality, your orgasm, is your responsibility, not his. It is a chilling story from a very well meaning mother who has learned nothing in the past twenty years.

We decide to let a man touch our breasts. For years we have felt ashamed of our bodies. We have been taught to cover them up. Our breasts aren't right, too big, too small. We expect that his hand will now give us a magically different feeling about them than we ever had. Stupidity. A man enters our vagina, the battleground of our emotional lives; we expect what we feel to have nothing to do with toilet training, masturbation, menstruation. Arrogance. Seductive as is its promise of pleasure, our vagina has also been the source of our greatest humiliations and anxiety. It is over this very part of our body that we almost lost mother. Fear of that loss made us introject her notions that the vagina, far from being a source of pleasure, is indeed a source of anxiety and unpleasantness. It was a painful victory over ourselves but it won us her love. It cost us so much, how can we choose to give it all away now? We try to compromise: we will let him touch our vagina, but we won't enjoy it.

We will go to bed with him, but won't come.

A moment's introspection tells us that his reality has begun to blur. We are turning him into a shadowy figure, a projection. He is more "mother" than lover. We are afraid that if we showed him we had those "dirty" sexual appetites and desires mother disliked, he would reject us. Mother did—until we hid them from her.

We explain all this to ourselves as "guilt"—that catchall word that merely gives a negative name to what we feel but explains nothing. "What is important," says Dr. Robertiello, "is the feeling behind the 'guilt.' The real anxiety is the woman's fear that the sexual act has made her separate, on her own, cut off from her upbringing and so having to take responsibility for the course of her life. To do the traditional thing is always easiest. To strike out on a new road, to try to be independent, is difficult. To most people, facing the fact that they are still tied to their baby needs is the most shameful thing in the world. So the word 'guilt' is brought in. It gives a serious, grown-up sound to the childish anxiety."

It is not guilt we feel, but fear—fear of having made the break from the girl that mother wanted us to be. Fear that if she finds out, she will angrily widen the break, and we will not be able to go back. Fear of separation.

For instance, when you secretly had sex or went too far and felt "guilty," didn't you feel better when you got home and found mother washing the dishes as if nothing had happened? The turmoil was due to your unseparated self being *sure* mother would know. How could she? When you were a baby, she knew when you were hungry, when you were wet—she was so tuned in to you that she could "read" your mind. The unseparated self fears she still can.

To continue: when you had sex a second and third time didn't the "guilt" diminish? The first time, sex gave us a feeling of separation from mother. We lived through it. We got used to it. It wasn't so bad. In fact, the pleasures of sex were so nice that it was worth it. When we have sex a second and third time it doesn't increase our degree of separation. We are simply repeating at the same level, and so we don't feel so guilty.

But let's say we introduce a new element, and conduct two affairs at the same time. Once again we feel that old stab of "guilt." Once again we are relieved when we get home and find that our lover/husband is sitting there reading the paper as if nothing has happened. Our degree of separation has been stepped up by having sex of a more "forbidden" nature than before; once again we are reassured when we find the world has not come to an end. It is not postcoital guilt from which we suffer, but postcoital anxiety. Sex has cut us off from being the nice girl mother once loved. Because the fear is free-floating, we may not associate it with the loss of the early, all-approving mother. In fact we will most likely connect it with fear of loss of the man, loss of self-respect, loss of our women friends or roommate (should we have been too sexually explicit) . . . but it's loss, loss, loss.

What is being discussed here is not the morality of sex or even the wisdom of conducting two affairs at the same time. That is private business. What is common to most of us is fear of loss of the beloved because of the notion that in some uncanny way what we are up to is no secret. True guilt resides in the conscience, and you feel it whether or not anyone else knows what you've done. Nonseparated anxiety means you are afraid that your partner *knows*. "He'll see it in my eyes." You are afraid you'll lose him.

In a study conducted by sociologist Ira Reiss from the University of Minnesota, a nineteen-year-old woman says, "I'm not doing as much as I would intellectually allow myself, and yet I feel guilty anyway. I believe in my head that it's OK to have intercourse before marriage, but I haven't done it yet. I get these guilt feelings even when I pet."[4] In another study at the University of Minnesota, Dr. Reiss found fascinating similarities between the approach to premarital and extramarital sex: "You would think you'd get technical virgins only in the premarital affair—females who say, 'I'll do anything *but*' and still consider themselves virgins. But we find we're getting the same thing in extramarital groups, where women say, 'Yes, I pet and kiss extramaritally, but I don't have intercourse.' We even find women who say, 'I have oral sex but I'm faithful to my husband because I haven't had intercourse.' "[5]

Even now, in the final quarter of the twentieth century, the act of intercourse remains a very powerful symbol. It puts you in a new category. It implies a break, loss, separation. That is its thrill and its fear.

When we were learning to walk, mother helped us practice, and her confidence in our success encouraged us to keep trying. When it came to sex, her emotions became communicated to us too; this time what we learned from her was anxiety and failure. Our practice in masturbating, sexual fantasy, pleasure in our body became secret, repressed. Since mother had always denied there could be competition between us, we have not learned through experience that we can win ground that she did not want to yield to us, and that the battle will not destroy her or us.

A nineteen-year-old is talking about her mother. They are very close, but like most of us she cannot put her finger on what is wrong between them. "When I was eleven," she says, "I wanted a bra. All my friends had one, but mother wouldn't let me. One night we were having dinner with friends and she started saying in front of all those people how ridiculous it was that someone my age should want a bra. I was so ashamed." Later in the same interview, she says, "My mother is the kind of person who talks a great deal. In a group, she is always the center of attention. When I bring a guy home who is older than me, for instance, she'll just take over. I can't get a word in. It really disturbs me."

In the daughter's mind there is no link between these incidents that happened eight years apart. The idea of competition between her and mother is unthinkable. It has never occurred to her that her burgeoning sexuality may make mother feel older. The mother would not like to think that she becomes seductive when her daughter's date comes in the room—a man twenty years younger than she! If you told this mother she was acting competitively with her daughter, she would deny it. Her major criticism of her daughter's behavior is, "She is not responsible enough."

How could she be? Every time the young woman has tried to be separate, to be sexual, her mother has interfered—all the while denying interference. With no practice in seeing herself as a woman, in finding she can be sexual and still keep her mother's love, the girl avoids competition by being irresponsible. She tells me that when she lost her virginity, she did not use any contraceptive. "See, mother," this kind of act says, "I don't understand about all that. I may be entering sex, but only timidly. I don't have your expertise. Don't be mad at me. I'm still a little girl."

The authentic self is not born. It is won. Regression into fear ever beckons. If you let some childhood limit keep you from doing something you know is your right, you are diminished. Our old infantile needs for symbiosis creep up again and again like jungle underbrush; you have to fight to keep clear what you won last week, last month, last year. Sex does not make a woman of you. It is your reward for having made a woman of yourself first.

And yet, some people who do not have sex are marked by that very fact as autonomous. "If a girl feels she is still too young to handle sex," says Dr. Robertiello, "and says no—that is very self-confirming. She is more separated than her friends who get into sex because everyone else is." If we choose to remain a virgin until marriage, not because mother or society wouldn't approve but because chastity until marriage is one of the principles of our inner value system, that is an act of independence—much more so than is the case with girls who leap into bed for fear of losing the man.

Autonomy enables a girl to say *No* as meaningfully as *Yes.* "Very often," says Gladys McKenney, "the girls who don't have sex in high school are the ones who have well thought-out goals, like going to college. They're not ready for sex yet, and they resist all peer pressures to get into it because everyone else is doing it. They will look at the other girls and maybe they wonder what these girls are doing, but they don't condemn it. You don't get the feeling they are holding back from sex because they are frightened of it. They just don't want it for themselves yet."

To ask, "What will he think of me tomorrow?" is to put the power into someone else's hands. The right question is, What will I think of myself tomorrow? Autonomy is making up our mind, not accepting the values or timetables of other people.

We tend to think that girl friends, the men in our lives, our school, college, or job are paths away from mother, alternatives and sources of support for our independence. Sometimes they are. Often they are not. Society, other people, and institutions reinforce what mother taught, adding their pressures to the unconscious residue of her we carry in our minds, making our tries for selfhood that much more difficult.

My emphasis has been on mother as the dominant force in the daughter's behavior but mother's rules would not have their heavy weight without public sanction. In fact, she is the prime agent charged by society for acculturating us to its norms. When we leave home and try to establish a moral framework of our own, the boss, the corporation, people at the office, our girl friends and lovers often compound our conflicts. They seem to be saying: here is your job, your apartment, here is friendship, here is sex; it is nobody else's business what you do. What is confusing is that behind it all we hear the old familiar double message.

Take men, for instance. We think they are as different from mother as possible. Haven't they always been talking us into sex, encouraging us to break mother's rules? And yet what are *their* rules? "The boys know how far girls will go," says a sixteen-year-old. "You have to know when to say stop. Otherwise, a guy may suddenly say, 'I love you, but I can't see you any more.' The girl can't understand why. She's done what he's been begging her to do, but instead of committing himself to her more, suddenly he's backing off."

The pattern is familiar enough. It might be said the boy needs more time to study, to pursue his career. He may talk about being suffocated, tied down by the relationship. We know he means something else, and we have already condemned ourselves. He has told us, *I love you but you have broken one of my secret rules so I'm not going to love you any more*. We went too far.

Despite all he said, what he really wanted was someone who was less threatening to his socially indoctrinated role, a nice girl. "When I was single and men were always trying to get me into bed," says one woman who speaks for hundreds, "no matter how much a guy pleaded and persisted, I would refuse. I always knew that if he and I became a serious item, he would end up protecting and loving that virginity of mine more than I. What if I'd given in? I can't help wondering. What do men really want, a virgin, or a good lay?"

By putting us into double binds like these, just as mother did, men hinder our efforts to find our own direction at a time when we are experimenting with sexuality, and, hence, most vulnerable.

In a campus survey at the University of Iowa, Dr. Reiss found that a third of the girls interviewed said they intellectually accepted the idea of sex before marriage but had not yet put this notion into practice. The boys they met and liked were too double standard. Says Dr. Reiss: "These girls thought that if the man had sex, he could not do it without prejudice. He would think less of her and they would break up."[6] If we intuit this about our boy friend, little wonder we postpone sex.

Most sociologists I interview agree that young men today are more

amenable than their fathers to women being independent and assertive—traits once deemed for men only. This is an important change.
But it does not follow that these same young men are prepared to
grant equality in sexual experience to their women. In her recent
study of college men, *Dilemmas of Masculinity,* Professor Mirra Komarovsky found most men still felt more comfortable when they were
the more experienced partner. "Making love to someone more experienced frightens the hell out of me . . ." said one of her respondents. Another student reported "he'd feel funny, less masculine,
making love to a more experienced girl." Professor Komarovsky
sums up: "The great majority would not demand virginity in their future mates, though they would reject 'promiscuous' girls."[7]

The definition of promiscuous, nevertheless, continues to run along
lines of the old double standard: "While you're dating," says a nineteen-year-old woman, "men tell you they don't care if you're a virgin
or not. But when they find the girl they want, then it's important to
them. Most guys could tolerate it if you weren't a virgin, but they'd
rather pretend that they were *the* one."

The media message goes out to women: "It's a great big, free, sexual world out there!" The real one is: "But you better not believe it."
Says a very attractive divorcée of thirty-three:

"I met this man and he told me at dinner how much he liked my
style, my independence. When we got back to his apartment, I
thought, well, this is today, not the Victorian era. So what if it's the
first date? I let him know I was willing to go to bed with him. After
all, he'd admiringly called me 'an upfront woman.' As soon as we
were in bed, I knew I'd done the wrong thing. It was awful."

I asked several sex therapists if this story was uncommon. "I'm always floored when this kind of thing comes up in a group therapy,"
says Dr. Schaefer. "A man will relate the kind of experience you just
mentioned. 'What kind of woman is it,' he asks, 'who carries her diaphragm around in her purse just in case?' He's half embarrassed but
he means it, and the other men nod sympathetically. 'We don't ask
that she be a virgin,' they explain, *'but . . .'* "

Society too sits in for mother. Gladys McKenney is not allowed by
Michigan law to teach birth control in her high school Marriage and
Family classes. "I can only answer their questions," she says. "The
kids know the law is outmoded and that way of offering information
is a kind of hypocrisy."

Despite the youth explosion, things are not all that much better on college campuses. "There was no gynecologist or birth control clinic on campus and none in town," says a young woman who goes to college in a western state. "A friend and I went to the administration and asked that a gynecologist be appointed. The trustees finally agreed to hire one part-time, but stipulated that no contraceptives could be prescribed." This kind of story was repeated to me in several variations, in a dozen states.

Young women can't even get full support from their peers. They are as divided as anyone by parental and cultural norms. "I'm on the Commission on the Status of Women at my college," says a nineteen-year-old. "There is no birth control clinic on campus and you have to be twenty-one or have a note from your parents to go to a gynecologist in town. I get calls from girls who say, 'I have this problem, but I can't tell you what it is.' As for venereal disease, they can't even bring themselves to say the words. I wanted my girl friend to come work with me in the clinic but she said, 'Oh, I can't! Everyone would know I'm on the pill!'"

Is it any wonder that even when we "choose" to have sex our lifelong internalized *No* is still with us? We can make our bodies do this or that, but our minds and emotional consent lag behind. And so there is this absolutely uncanny, almost suicidally foolish manner in which women enter sex. What it says is that the solution to our problem is not to have to face it at all. It is the great Swept Away phenomenon.

"You don't want to be ready for it," says an eighteen-year-old. "You just want it to take over and happen, especially the first time. You want it to be spontaneous. You want to get carried away. There's a free clinic in town, where you can get advice and your first contraceptive free, but if you plan—that takes all the romance out of it."

Swept Away: it is not merely a phenomenon of the very young. Women of all ages give it—unblinkingly!—as rationalization. "I couldn't help myself," they smile, as if you must agree that they have satisfactorily explained everything. You're a woman too, aren't you? "Of course I didn't want to get pregnant," explains a thirty-five-year-old divorced mother who recently had an abortion. "Look, it was so great, this guy was so fantastic, I just didn't want to think about it. Besides, I was safe. How could it have happened? My period had ended four days before." When I told her she had probably been entering her most fertile period, she said, "I thought you began counting from the end of your period."

There are songs for women like this: "You Made Me Love You, (I Didn't Want to Do It)" . . . "I Got Lost in His Arms" . . . "Don't Blame Me." . . . The underlying message is always the same: I don't usually do that kind of thing. I'm not that kind of girl. I had no choice. I was just carried away.

Even our daydreams—the safest possible playground to toy with new ideas—are written along symbiotic lines. In over seven years of research on women's sexual fantasies, the most prevalent themes I found were rape, domination, and force. Good girls to the end, we make the other person *do it* to us.

I want to say this emphatically: not a single woman I ever talked to said she did want to be raped in actuality. What is wanted is something only in the imagination, release from the responsibility of sex. Only the terrible force of the brute can free us from the fear of wanting the sexuality he represents. "Women are almost as strong as men," says Dr. Sonya Friedman, "or at least, they could be. But they like to make the disparity seem enormous. Their feeling of almost total helplessness is used to keep themselves children, not responsible, needing to be taken care of." It wasn't our fault. If we hadn't drunk so much, if things hadn't gotten out of hand, if the moonlight hadn't been so bright. . . . *He made me do it!*

How many women lose their virginity or have their most abandoned moments with a stranger, the steward on the cruise ship, the handsome translator in Rome? "These women are compartmentalized," says Dr. Schaefer. "They go to Europe and have all sorts of adventures, and then they come back home and are back to being good little girls. They may not have sex again for months. They've said, Europe is not reality, it's fairyland, it doesn't count. What counts is when I'm home in my mother's domain, and here I am a 'nice girl.' Yes, they've done better than the ones who never have sex, but they've only allowed it because it was in a place that let them keep the all-important tie to mother."

Young women today are more likely to have their first sex with someone they are emotionally involved with. Vera Plaskon works with teen-agers in the Family Planning and Gynecological Clinic at Roosevelt Hospital. She is twenty-nine but remembers only too well how girls lost their virginity when she was growing up. It was usually "on vacation," she says, "with some stranger, rather than with the boy back home. Today, kids have sex within the important relationship. There is more caring with sex. That doesn't mean however that they are more responsible. The feelings don't get translated into actions. It's so rare that I will get a young woman who will say to me, 'I'm planning to have sex, tell me what to use.' They prefer to let it come without thinking about it in advance, to be swept off their feet."

Even the scientific organization SIECUS (Sex Information and Education Council of the U.S.) cites the Swept Away phenomenon as a seemingly valid reason so many reject using a diaphragm or the pill. ". . . they cannot conceive of themselves as being prepared for coitus all the time. They must be emotionally carried away for coitus to occur."[8]

Incredible! Never before in the history of the world has so much contraceptive information been available to young women. And yet the rate of premarital pregnancies is higher today than twenty-five years ago. In the '50s, Kinsey found that 20 percent of the women who had sex before marriage became pregnant. In more recent studies a full generation later, Zelnik and Kantner found 30 percent of such women got pregnant.[9] That is a full 50 percent increase in rate of unwanted pregnancies!

"Every woman knows about contraception, or could if she wanted to," says anthropologist Lionel Tiger. "In our book *The Imperial Animal,* Robin Fox and I compared the drugstore cosmetic counter with the contraceptive counter. Young women seem perfectly capable of understanding the 25,000 different items on the cosmetic counter, which can be used in millions of permutations and combinations on many different parts of their bodies. But they very often appear not to know how to—or be willing to—manage the contraceptive counter, though it involves a quite simple business. When one looks at this behavior, one must say there is something strong driving these people to do what is often far removed from their rational plans."

There are many explanations, of course. Each one a logical, seemingly sufficient reason for a young woman's lack of decision or skill in using contraception. "If you are raised to be a passive partner," says educator Jessie Potter, "you do not get fitted for a diaphragm. If you raise girls not to touch themselves, they make rotten contraceptors. If you teach them to think sex is beautiful only when the right man comes along and does it to you, then you are raising them to wait, to avoid taking responsibility for themselves." Other explanations for not using contraception include rebellion, religion, getting pregnant in order to get the man to marry you, or to prove to yourself that you are capable of getting pregnant. Boys promise girls that they can control it, withdraw in time. Many women have a phobic avoidance of contraceptives. Dr. Helen Kaplan, a psychiatrist at the Payne Whitney Clinic, says women have a deep, unconscious wish to be impregnated by a man they care about. The list grows with every authority I interview. The fact is that all these explanations fit right into, and work along with, the need to be Swept Away—a need every professional worker in sexuality mentioned in addition to any other specific reason he/she gave.

"To sum up the terrific power and longing that being Swept Away holds for women," says Dr. Robertiello, "you have to understand that it is *a method for avoiding separation.* If the woman feels there are forces which took her over, she is confirmed in her role of dependency. If she had no power, then it isn't her fault that mother's rules were broken; therefore mother should still love her. Swept Away is an escape from freedom. It tells the girl that even if she did have sex, it wasn't her fault. She didn't want to go against mother. She had no choice."

From the day we are born there is a bit of what society calls *male* in all of us. It is our lust. Mother did her best to keep it in check. As we grew older she passed the job on to us. To be sexual was to be "out of control," like an animal, like a man. Badgered to be "feminine," we grew up afraid of our lust. We learned control instead, iron control—of ourselves, of him, of the situation.

It is hard for men to understand women's problems with control. A young boy is baffled by a girl's fear of being touched, her reluctance to touch him back. "Girls in the sixth grade are horrified that a boy wants to finger-fuck," says Jessie Potter. "I try to explain to the boy, 'Look, she hasn't even allowed *herself* to put her finger there.' He can't understand that because he's touched his penis every time he pees and a lot of other times besides. Boys masturbate in front of each other, but there is no 'show-and-tell' for girls. He expects her to be as eager to touch him as he is to touch her. I say to her that she must understand that his desires don't say anything judgmental about her or him, he is not 'gross' to have these wishes. Because he wants to do it to her, she isn't any less the nice girl she wants to be. They meet like two strange people from different planets. When he wants to touch her breasts, he has no way of understanding her feeling about this encroachment on the body she has been taught to keep so private. So he perceives himself as being rejected and unlovable. In self-defense, to gain back some of his lost ego, he decides she must be frigid. She, not understanding how she was taught to withhold, frequently sees herself as unloving."

Many young women have a tremendous fear that if we allow ourselves to become sexual, we will become promiscuous, whores. Why else would society/mother put on these ten-ton chains if sex weren't so titanically strong and dangerous? If we once let the barrier down, we will become sex addicts. "We have a whole cultural fix," says Dr. Robertiello, "about how sexuality is such a powerful urge that it overcomes all other forces. Men aren't afraid of this sexual force or of loss of control; they get points for being sexual. Women do not."

A controlling relationship is what we know best. We may say we want the man to be stronger, brighter, taller, and that we want to be dominated in bed. That doesn't mean we don't want to control him. What we know about intimacy, how to gain and keep it, is how mother was with father—and with us. Mother's control proved she cared. Some men don't mind our moving in with ideas of eternal togetherness, others jump like rabbits. To be fair to both sexes, many women aren't aware of the manipulation involved in control. It comes disguised as love. "If you really cared for me," we say . . . Guiltily, he does what we ask.

Perhaps mother was a quiet, retiring person. She may have claimed to know nothing about money, leaving it all to dad. But we knew she had a way of getting what she wanted and getting him to do what she wanted too. It had to do with the very fact of her seeming lack of power, her womanliness. *Already we know that as long as we are virgins, we have a form of control and power ourselves.*

"I was afraid of having sex," says a college senior. "Afraid that once I went all the way, that I would have no more leverage with him. If I couldn't hold out on him any more, I'd have no more control. Once you have sex, you never know if it's you or the conquest that was important; when you're growing up, ninety percent of the time it's the conquest."

Increased experience does not lessen our fear of the overwhelming power of sex. "Oh, no, the adolescent rules didn't affect my later sexual life," says a woman of twenty-eight. "When I started I really started. But I've always been monogamous. It is a kind of self-protection. The only way you can protect yourself is to mind your behavior . . . or it just slips away."

As we move out of mother's area of control, and the man is gradually allowed to enter our vagina in the one-step-at-a-time ritual loss of virginity, we make a trade. We construct with him the kind of bargain we had with her: if I allow you to touch me there, promise you will never leave me. If I reject mother's laws for your sake, and give up my once-in-a-lifetime power as a virgin, promise nothing bad will happen and that you will take care of me as she did.

The man is being made to assume the protective stance of the absent mother. Symbiosis is continued. Forbidden sex, the source of anger for as long as we can remember, need not destroy us after all! We thought men were so powerful, so self-sufficient, but we can use sex to control them. "Withholding sex," says Sonya Friedman, "is women's greatest source of power."

"My first lover stayed with me for a year and a half," says a thirty-year-old woman. "I didn't want to marry him, but I didn't want him to leave me. Sex gave me the power to keep him. I'd always felt so powerless before. Now, with sex, here was something that I was good at. Maybe not good at, but that didn't matter. I had it. Men stay with you because of it."

The price to the woman is high. To preserve our bargaining position, we must control our own desire first, hoarding lust like a miser, never spending it on pleasure. "When I'm with a guy for the weekend," says a twenty-seven-year-old woman, "it's heaven while I'm there, while we're in bed. But Monday morning when I go to work, the good feeling fades and I get this funny idea I've lost something. I'm in a weaker position with him, and I can't help myself . . . I begin these maneuvers about when am I going to see him again. I hate myself for it, but I have to do it." The bitter irony is that having got rid of mother's control, we are unhappy without it. We long to set it up with the man. Under these circumstances, we are not taking on a lover. We just switch mothers.

My own sexual ideas are different from what they were ten or fifteen years ago, and so I expected to find dramatic changes in behavior and attitudes toward virginity in young women today. Even my mother's attitude—unswerving for all of my life—has been affected by what she has seen and read, and perhaps most of all, by her neighbors' attitudes—those whose children have come of sexual age in the sixties. "When your child runs away to San Francisco," says Dr. Sidney Q. Cohlan, "or becomes pregnant, or marries a hippy or goes on drugs, you must accept some of the changes in the life-style of her generation if you want to keep a relationship with her. You may not like these changes, but it is easier for you to accept them nowadays because you find your neighbors are accepting them too."

Surely if I lost my virginity today, instead of in the sex-taboo fifties, I'd do it differently. "In 1963, only twenty percent of adults said it was OK to have intercourse in some circumstances before marriage," Dr. Ira Reiss tells me. "That was a national sample. By 1970, it had jumped to fifty percent. If we took a new national sample today, I'm sure we'd get more than half the parents saying it was OK under some circumstances."

Therefore I am not surprised when gynecologist Sherwin A. Kaufman tells me that the mothers who consult him today are not so concerned with their daughter's loss of virginity as they are afraid of her becoming pregnant. "They have come to accept that a girl who goes off to college," he says, "may not graduate without sexual experience. It's an idea they didn't want to think about ten years ago." And though Dr. Kaufman is quick to add that the New York women who consult him are a special subculture, I wonder if these liberal mothers aren't in tune with what college girls in their teens and early twenties are feeling all across America. They are a special subculture too.

"What *has* changed are attitudes," says Wardell Pomeroy. "The real change is more in approach than practice. A lot of people talk a bigger game than they play. From this big change in attitude will come later changes in behavior, in what people do (and not what they say they do). But it really hasn't shown up yet with statistical significance. People just don't change that rapidly. They develop certain norms and ideas, but it takes more than a film or book to change their behavior. It is a gradual process. Change usually comes between generations, not within one."

Statistics must be read in context. There are over 200 million people in the U.S. today, double the number fifty years ago. When twice as many people do something, we are prone to believe "everybody" is doing it, that something new is going on. It is merely more visible. We are changing, but not all that rapidly. There is more talk and general acceptance of sex today. Nonvirgins used to keep it a secret. Today, they go on TV talk shows. "Everything is different nowadays," we tell each other.

Gladys McKenney recalls that not too many years ago a high school girl would never admit she had lost her virginity. "Of course some had, but they would tell me privately," she says. "They couldn't be honest in class. They didn't want the judgment of their peers on them. It's almost a reverse of that in the higher grades now. Last semester I had a class in which there was a group talking very openly about how they enjoyed sex and wouldn't consider marrying a boy they hadn't slept with. But there was another group of girls who I know hadn't even dated much. They didn't say a word because they didn't want to reveal their inexperience. What has changed, you see, is the openness of those who have sex. There is no longer a stigma attached to losing your virginity. But that doesn't mean it is not still a very important event."

"What is important about losing your virginity," says a nineteen-year-old, "is that you keep it important. That you don't have sex casually."

We want so badly to be easier about sex. As mothers, we don't want our children to grow up with our sexual inhibitions. We change *our* attitudes and think that will change *their* lives. We look at them behaving far more guiltlessly than we'd have dreamed ten years ago, and identify more with their generation than the one we grew up in. We talk of multiorgasms and bisexuality and glibly think something as primary and emotive as loss of virginity is old-fashioned, tame stuff. But for all our new attitudes, the liberated poses we strike, our children don't believe us. They are still uncomfortable when we bring up sex. We are hurt. Haven't we made enormous efforts to understand their world? Haven't we met them more than halfway?

A parent who asks these questions is being as sincere as she knows, but once again is confusing the difference between attitude and gut feeling. Children may listen to mother's words; what they really take in is how mother feels on the deepest level. Our ideas about our bodies, our eroticism, our sexual limits, are so much a basic part of us that we may not be aware how they determine the things we *say* to our daughters. We got them from our mother; she got them from hers. When we talk to our daughters about sex, or when we have sex —what we feel is a mixture of the old and new, of what our mothers felt about it, and what we would like to feel.

In a study on parent-child perception and behavior at Illinois State University, low correlation was found between what parents said were their sex attitudes and what their children said they were. But there was a high correlation between how the children *perceived* their parents, and how the children behaved. For instance, if a seventeen-year-old girl said, "My parents are very low on permissiveness," she was often wrong, but the girl herself was more likely to be low on permissiveness. And if an eighteen-year-old said, "My parents are very high on permissiveness," again, she might be wrong, but she was more likely to be high on permissiveness herself. The conclusion was that the *perception* of one's parents' permissiveness is more important in predicting the child's behavior than are the actual words of the parents.[10] Clearly, if a daughter thinks her mother—no matter what she says—is permissive about premarital sex, the daughter is more likely to be permissive herself.

If mother has sincerely tried to change her attitude, it gives the daughter a certain freedom to experiment, to see just how much mother really does mean what she says. If the girl is courageous, lucky, and gets enough societal and peer approval, she can make a start on discarding the old sexual inhibitions. In time, reality will come to reinforce her new ideas: it's easier, happier to live this way. Then whatever ground is gained can be passed on to the daughter's children. This is the work done "between generations" that Dr. Pomeroy mentions.

Some mothers can do it. For most it is not easy. When we take the lag Pomeroy speaks of—the distance at which *behavior* follows *talk* of sexual freedom—and then add the even greater lag in our gut about whether what we are doing is *right*—it is evident that very few mothers are so integrated on all three levels that they can send their daughter a message behind which the girl will not hear older, more familiar overtones of anxiety: if these ideas make my mother nervous, where may I put my full weight? On what she says, or on what she feels? For instance:

Two girls both know about the pill. One takes it methodically, in advance of sex. When, sooner or later, she enters the bedroom, it will be with the fear of pregnancy (at least) diminished. The other girl doesn't take it, or does so sporadically. Statistics say neither is a virgin, and that both are members of the liberated seventies. But the quality of their sexual experience is totally different. Why? Because the first girl's attitude toward sex, her behavior and gut feelings, acted together. Faced with no conflicting double message, she felt free to choose the pill. All too often girls in therapeutic counseling sessions for unwed mothers know about the pill but do not use it or use it incorrectly. They have one attitude in their head about sex. In their gut, they are entirely different, much more judgmental.

"In their hearts, the parents of girls who come to the Family Planning Clinic," says Vera Plaskon, "are against early sexual activity. At the same time, they are middle class, they want to be IN. So these mothers rerun their own fantasies of what they would have liked to have done—or what they would do if they were their daughters today. They push these fantasies onto their kids before they are ready. 'Just let me know when you want the pill,' they tell their thirteen-year-old. They don't stop to think maybe the girl is not ready to hear this. It can be a lot more subtle. The mother may be fully unaware that by buying her daughter the latest seductive clothes and make-up, she is pushing her into what *she* would have liked to have done when she was young, before the sexual revolution. Once she has the girl living out her fantasy, there is also the mother's competition with the girl, *plus* her own guilt at what she has done. It may be unconscious, but it is very confusing to the daughter. Recently I was talking to a girl who is very sophisticated for her fifteen years. She laughingly said her mother always told her that if and when she needed birth control, to come to her. 'But you should have seen her face when I actually did!' she said. Most girls are not so sophisticated, and they don't laugh about it. They don't know what to do. And finally, there are many girls who really wish their mothers would say, No, *and mean it*. They can't handle all this freedom at fifteen or seventeen—their own growing up, and often their mother's as well. The girl doesn't know what the mother wants from her. The mother doesn't know herself. In the gut of the liberated Manhattan mother you very often find the same doubts and anxieties I see in women who have just arrived from Central and South America, from the heart of the macho culture. Feelings she hasn't really dealt with. So she sends out the contradictory message to her daughter: 'This is the modern age, do what you like!' But when the girl comes home at three in the morning, the mother screams at her that she is acting like a whore."

"It's very unconscious," says Dr. Robertiello, "a mother's unexpressed desire for a girl to have a sexuality she never had. Often there is a specific admonishment against it, which is like a reverse suggestion to do it. For example a girl will come in and talk about the date she's been on, and how she almost had sex. The mother will smile—giving the nonverbal message of approval—even while she gives her holy hell and tells the girl she will break her neck if she ever does it."

A double message like this undermines our reasoning powers and gives us no clear-cut line of separation. In our muddle, not knowing which way to go, we surrender our will. Either we allow ourself to be swept away by the man, or we turn back to mother. Neither is an autonomous choice. It is just a need to depend on someone. We listen to mother's contradictory commands, and in true symbiotic fashion, act out both halves of mother's conflict. One day we are "good," and say No to the boy. The next day we are "bad" and become pregnant. What more could mother want?

I ask Dr. Robertiello how a mother could possibly be sending out a message for her daughter to get pregnant. "Pregnancy and intercourse," he said, "are often confused and tied together in people's minds. Getting pregnant is proof of getting laid. If you are thirty-five and married and six months pregnant, that is not a sexual idea. But if a girl has a friend, let's say, who gets pregnant at fifteen, she can read the light in her mother's eyes: Boy, that is a sexy, bad girl."

If mother tells us that she is not certain that 2 and 2 are 4, we smile and say we have no doubts ourselves. In the area of arithmetic, at least, we are separate from her. If her words about our pregnant fifteen-year-old friend are negative, but we see that excited light in her eyes, we respond to her excitement. Despite all our own real fears and attitudes about getting pregnant, down deep we don't think it is so bad at all. We have taken in mother's unconscious wishes and act on them as if they are our own.

In a survey of girls who went to a campus contraceptive clinic versus those who did not, Ira Reiss found the clinic girls believed they were attractive to men twice as frequently as nonclinic girls. The clinic girls also more frequently felt they had as much right as men to initiate sex. "What the pill does," says Dr. Reiss, "is put choice in the hands of the female. It tells her, 'Look, if you don't want to have intercourse, that's your right, but you have to have a different reason to say No than fear of pregnancy. That can be taken care of. You are going to have to make up your mind without pretenses.' "[11]

Choosing to use the pill is evidence of a good deal of integration. The clinic girls are saying by their behavior that they are entitled to sex. By acting on what they say, and going to the clinic to be prepared for the consequences of their actions, they show their behavior, attitude and gut reactions are in line.

To my mind, their autonomy is illustrated in another area in which most women usually betray great insecurity: *they did not wait for a man to tell them they were sexually attractive.* Their actions tell me that they made their own evaluation of their looks and bodies, and, having decided they were attractive, decided to reap the reward for it by getting into sex.

I would emphasize however that it was not going to the clinic that made them more autonomous than the girls who did not. That is reverse reasoning, confusing cause with effect. They were more separate *before* they went. That is *why* they went. The pill did not make them autonomous. Their autonomy enabled them to decide to use the pill.

Psychoanalytic theory used to say that if a girl entered into premarital sex, especially if it were an unhappy experience or ended with pregnancy, it was an expression of rebellion. Sex was seen by the girl as a way of getting back at the restrictor, doing exactly the opposite of what mother wanted. That is still often the case, but nowadays psychiatrists have come to see that rebellion is one of the symptoms, not the complete statement of the overall problem—which is lack of separation.

Rebellion should not be mistaken for separation. As long as the effort to break away is seen not as a blow for ourselves but as a reaction to the parent, it is still a symbiotic proceeding. Rebellion becomes separation when the goal is self-fulfillment, not mere frustration of something the parent wants us to do. Says Dr. Robertiello, "Rebellion within the family is often a sign of how much we are still tied to the family—fighting someone from whom we should have been separated a long time ago."

The difficulty in understanding rebellion begins with the romantic glow that folklore has given the world. To researchers in human development, it has a very specific, time-related meaning. When we are two, rebellion is appropriate. This is the No-saying stage children go through. Another rebellious period comes in adolescence, but by this time, just saying No is not enough. Certain moves toward autonomy have to accompany the sixteen-year-old's rebelliousness or it is inauthentic, a sign of attachment. We may have more sex than we really want, or drink too much, but at the same time, if we are meeting our academic requirements, handling money responsibly, it can be said that the rebellious elements are in the service of separation.

But at twenty-five, thirty-five, the time for rebellion should have been long over. If we are not taking care of ourself, not paying our bills, turning up late for work, having a lot of sex without really enjoying it, then rebellion is immaturity. The rebellious person who must always put a minus sign where she is asked to put a plus is merely reacting to somebody else. She is not free to go her own way, to choose not to argue. She is ever tied, ever waiting. Give me something to say No to.

We look at the very young today and envy them their sexual ease and apparent lack of guilt. Despite all that has been written, said, experienced, and thought in the past decade, most of us have not reached the kind of free-flowing sexuality young people seem to have been born with. They seem to be so accepting of their sexuality; the word used for them is "liberated"—which is another way of saying they are separated.

It is the old philosophical problem of appearance and reality. To the outside eye, they may indeed seem free. They appear to have won the rebellion against those antisexual rules which cost us so much. In our fight for autonomy, sexuality was the one battlefield above all others. To have won any degree of freedom there, was more difficult than anywhere else.

For those of us raised before the sixties, the rules were hard and fast—especially about sex. Mother made no bones about wanting to repress and inhibit our sexuality—or our retaliatory anger. *No* was the clear message her attitude gave us. *No* was reinforced by her behavior. *No* came to us from her gut reaction. She was all of a piece: we could either conform to mother's ideas, or gather up our strength and say, "The hell with you, Mom. I'll do it my way." She gave us firm ground on which to plant our defiant feet. In the anger and quarreling, separation between mother and ourselves gains definition; we may not have attained autonomy, but at least we knew where she stood.

If we've been raised in too permissive a manner, separation can become difficult. The rules are vague and elastic. Rarely is the permissively raised child out-and-out forbidden to do this or that. We were merely presented with more attractive alternatives. In this way our own desires were manipulated and used against us. We weren't told not to play with that nasty little boy next door. Whenever he appeared on the horizon, mother took us to the drugstore for an ice cream instead. If we got kicked out of college, that was unfortunate, but a new school was found which was more tolerant of our special temperament. If we broke the parental rule about sex (if there was one), it was not the end of the world. Even if we insisted on a fight, wanting to clarify the difference (separation) between us, mom once again quickly shifted ground, to join us. "Oh, I'm so glad you feel free to express anger at me! What a healthy thing to do!" How do you separate from somebody so glued to you with admiration? Anger is not allowed to do one of its principal jobs: separate me from you. You never get a clear-cut No; no firm ground is offered from which to push yourself off.

It is difficult. We love mother, but there she is, *surrounding* us. We want to separate from her (even if we don't use the word) but we can't get a fix on the problem. If we want to run away to India, she'll pay for the ticket and remind us to phone collect when we want to come home. Never having been let go of, we can't let go ourself. Permissively reared people have had no experience of separate relationships, and so never look for them. We gravitate to what we know. Permissive girls choose permissive boys, and they glom together.

On the surface, relationships like this seem freer, easier than those between sharply defined people. If one partner wants to go to a movie and the other wants to go to a ball game, neither insists on dominance; it needs hardly any discussion to decide to compromise and go ice skating. This is not the first choice of either, but the relationship has not been roiled, even for a moment. Everything is soft, blurred, hazy, friendly. Even sex becomes nondifferentiated. (It is no coincidence that the permissive era is the Unisex era.) Young people do not regard each other today across the differences of sex as if the other were from Mars. They have been raised to relate to other people without fuss, without fighting, *without separation*. Sweetness, gentleness, amiability are all.

"Thank God," says the mother of seventeen- and eighteen-year-old daughters, "the young people I meet nowadays are not so hassled by sex as I was. They seem to have found a natural relationship with one another. My girls connect with boys in a friendly manner. Young people have much closer, deeper relationships today. This whole nightmare thing of sex doesn't seem to arise like it did in my generation. Sex doesn't play a huge part in their lives."

As far as friendliness and lack of fear goes, this is certainly an advance. But this woman says one thing that is perhaps more important than she is aware. She says sex doesn't play a huge part in her daughters' lives—a fact which relieves her anxiety. What she intuitively understands is that being closer, caring deeply about someone of the opposite sex doesn't necessarily mean you see him in a sexual light. If you are afraid of, or envy, your daughters' sexuality, you think these "friendly" developments are positive.

People who come out of a background of being coddled, who are not allowed to develop separately, indeed often do have sex—but it doesn't mean they are autonomous. It can mean the opposite: that they are using sex—which is one of nature's methods of helping us grow up—to remain childish instead, to create a nice, warm relationship with this other person which is similar to that one they once had with mother, which they never had to outgrow, and which is all they know. Proof of this is that such "sexual" relationships between young people often cease to be sexual at all; they soon become fond and fondling palships. Or maybe they were that all along: "I slept with a lot of guys before I lost my virginity," many young women tell me. "We didn't have sex. We just liked each other and were good friends." Is being "free" of sex such an unqualified good?

Says Dr. Schaefer: "The kind of symbiotic union you see today in kids who at thirteen and fourteen are already going steady delays separation . . . is a defense against separation. You see them together, day and night. They tend to have low-energy relationships. Symbiosis drains them of interest in anything outside the little womb they've built. They sit side by side in a room, silent, polite, friendly; just being together is their choice against all the variety that life can offer." It can hardly be said to be a real choice if they did not feel the freedom to explore the alternatives first.

Some sociologists have gone so far as to suggest the days of the double standard may be coming to an end. That too is a gain, but if monogamy is settled on without choice, where is freedom? "It used to be that only girls were like this," says Betty Thompson, "but today we see boys acting the same way, refusing even to look at another girl." On the surface it may look like love and fidelity. In a few years, we may see it differently. That is when symbiosis has so killed off whatever degree of sexuality there was between them that they flood the divorce courts, crying, "I need my own space!" Freedom to have sex together has been bought at the price of never giving each other air to breathe.

If people raised in nonpermissive times envy the freedom from sexual guilt of young people today, Spock-reared people seem to have lost their elders' ability to work toward well-defined goals and aims in life. "The rebellion of the permissive generation is aborted almost from the start," says Dr. Robertiello. "They often have a hard time finding what they want. They are looking for the rose garden that mother promised them." Their freedom is illusory since they reject reality to look for what does not exist.

Says Betty Thompson: "When you are indulged, when everything is done for you, you do not grow up with a recognition of the realities of life. You break your bicycle, and mother says, 'Don't worry, we'll buy you a new one.' If mother and father saw to it that you got everything you wanted, there just hasn't been any practice in being responsible for yourself. What is not available is a recognition that everything in the world cannot be bought. When a girl says, 'I don't want to carry a diaphragm when I go on dates,' it is an evasion of responsibility, it is regressive in the sense of character development. It is not romantic, it is not being separate and adult. It is babyishness." Carelessness, lack of forethought and disorder may masquerade as freedom to the outside eye. But they tie us with chains of consequence.

At seventeen our problems with autonomy arise from one direction; at thirty-seven they come at us from another. Lack of separation is where both lines meet. Autonomy is the declaration and affirmation of the self; sex is one of its expressions. "I am a woman and this is my body and my life. I will do what I want with both because that is what I want, not because I want to get back at you."

It took me twenty-one years to give up my virginity. In some similar manner I am unable to let go of this chapter. Unanswered questions run endlessly through my head like ticker tape: how does the daughter's loss of virginity affect her relationship to her mother? Shouldn't she wait until she has left home to lose her virginity so that her mother won't be involved? Doesn't the fact that a girl hasn't yet left home mean she is not yet ready to have sex?

It is August. Everyone is at the beach but me and, luckily, Richard Robertiello. Once more I trudge past the baseball players in Central Park to see him. Dr. Robertiello hears me out. "Nancy," he says, "you are asking the wrong questions. They show you are still trying to protect some false structure. You are trying to place the issue of a woman's sexuality within the framework of her relationship to her mother. Sex, more than anything else, should have nothing to do with mother. Why should losing her virginity have anything to do with what goes on between her and her mother? You talk as if the mother *knows* the girl is having sex, that she is inside the girl's head, the way she was when the girl was a baby and thought mother could read her mind. *That is symbiotic thinking.* So what if someone has sex while she is still living at home? Privacy and secrecy do in fact aid separation. Your questions, the inability to finish this chapter, are all about how to continue the tie to mother while being a sexual person. No wonder you can't answer them. There are no answers—you can't be sexual and symbiotic with mother at the same time."

That is preposterous. My sexuality has always been my badge of separation, my identity. Richard Robertiello has failed me. I storm out of his office.

In a dream last night I am back in London where I once lived. I am at the printers, watching illustrations being laid out for a book I have written on economics, a subject I know nothing about. Soon I will be exposed as a fraud! Suddenly an even more terrible anxiety hits me: I haven't telephoned my mother. There is no way in the dream I can get to a phone. I wake up in terror.

In reality, months may go by without me talking to my mother. It is no accident that wrestling with ideas of loss of virginity immediately bring me to a dream of losing my mother. This chapter has revealed a split in me. Intellectually, I think of myself as a sexual person, just as I had intellectually been able to put my ideas for this chapter down on paper. Subjectively, I don't want to face what I have written: that the declaration of full sexual independence is the declaration of separation from my mother. As long as I don't finish this chapter, as long as I don't let myself understand the implications of what I've written, I can maintain the illusion, at least, that I can be sexual and have my mother's love and approval too.

The shame of still needing, still wanting to be tied to mama even after we're grown, is universal. "I feel it myself," Dr. Robertiello once told me. "I'm always pointing to my sexuality as proof of my autonomy." Separation is a process nobody completely attains. We can only keep trying. Gone are my illusions that I am an individual person who has this terrific sexual identity. How humiliating! At least Richard Robertiello isn't separate either.

Chapter 10

THE SINGLE YEARS

Even as a child I had a great respect for money. Other little girls didn't share my passion. When I was ten I held rummage sales. My mother smiled nervously. When I was thirteen I blushed when they teased me about the glass bank on my desk, but as much as I hated being different, I wanted money more. I saved my allowance, along with coins I filched from coat pockets in the hall closet or won from my sister in Monopoly. Susie couldn't save money any more than she could win a game.

The glass bank was shaped like the world, and as I saw the lower half of Africa disappear behind my stash, I had a good feeling. But there was no one I could share it with. The only person who seemed to enjoy money as much as I was my grandfather. He had a great deal of it, and what I admired most was his ease with money. Unlike my mother, he treated money without apology. This is how you move around the world, his manner said with great logic, as he paid restaurant bills and bought himself and other people beautiful things. Handling money made my mother anxious, and she raised me never to discuss the price of anything. Her attitude baffled me since clearly you couldn't even buy groceries without money. Why was money so secret and distasteful?

I grew to associate the dirtiness of money with the vile part of me.

Except for my allowance, I never asked my mother for money; something more than cash, I realized, was being exchanged. If I wanted something badly enough, I often stole it. Meanwhile, my mother sighed at how my sister "let money slip through her fingers," her words more a girlish lament for the two of them than a criticism: this is how women are. I understood it was nicer to be like them than like me. It was a dreadful dilemma: how could I have what money gave my grandfather if I grew up like my mother, dependent on him? But if I grew up like him—unfeminine—who would want to take care of me?

As I grew into my teens, I hid my secret interest in money as I hid my growth by bending my knees when I danced. Surely someone would take care of me if I were littler and poorer. The bent knees made for painful spinal problems in my thirties. But the need to put my head on somebody's shoulder, when dance partners were running two to three inches shorter than I, outweighed everything. When it became the fad to pry the heels off our loafers, I was thrilled: another inch lost. "You are ruining your skin," my mother said as I baked in the Carolina sun. Tan was less prominent than white. "Wait until you're thirty," she warned. She might as well have told me to wait until I was dead. My only problem was getting through being fifteen.

When I was nineteen and told my mother I wanted to go to Europe, the idea was so far-fetched she agreed to match whatever money I could save, just to close the discussion. She could no more imagine me saving that kind of money than she could picture a daughter of hers so far away from home. She had never left the East Coast, and when in her early thirties she had to travel alone by train from Charleston to Buffalo, her father had given her an elaborate typed itinerary of people she should telephone at checkpoints along the way. To be fair to her, she didn't hedge when I produced my half of the money for my trip. And though I had outrageously underestimated the cost, I never cabled home for more. Nor did she offer. The bargain had been struck between us: it is one thing for a little girl to save money in a glass bank of the world, but when she breaks the bank and leaves home for a world the mother never knew, she has changed the relationship for good. In the game of who-takes-care-of-whom, the last chips had changed hands. "Not enough to live on, too much to die on," was how my husband described young women's allowances from home in one of his novels.

I was right not to ask for more; you cannot take money without strings. I couldn't afford to be angry at her stinginess then; I still needed her. I am wrong to be angry at her now, not that right and wrong have anything to do with nursery angers. There are two sides to any mother-daughter story of separation; on my side, I wanted to leave home for a bigger world. On her side, I was leaving her. What neither of us could say was that I wanted more than she had, to become more than she was.

Her abdication made it easy for me to go, but even when you want the territory, it always comes too fast; you never understand that leaving her means being by yourself. As much as I wanted independence, as hard as I tried for security in the woman I made myself into, I have always missed her, missed being tied to her. I have always been afraid that my self-confidence made me less feminine, less like her, and so less liable to find the connection with men I wanted so desperately. I was the one who had left her, but my emotions said I had been abandoned. Unfairly, I blamed her for letting me go, for making me so dependent on men for what she could never give me and for which money was never a substitute.

I never trusted my looks. In the Persian fairy tales, the genie locked in the bottle swears for the first thousand years to reward his liberator. During the second thousand, he vows to take revenge on whoever lets him out. By the time my looks came I had already wished for them too long. Raised to believe in the power of beauty—but in other people—I had long compensated with personality. I smiled even in my sleep. Who could resist me, failed at beauty though I was? Then, in the middle of my first job, I acquired the fine curve of an ass. I saw a face in the mirror people turned to look at. But it was never more than that, a reflection that might disappear. What I believed in was the old, smiling, charming but funny face I had grown up with. My too-late looks were like sudden riches that buy you entrée to a world into which everyone but you was born; you never trust them. I learned to wear my skirts tapered and ass-tight, and to cross my legs with a finesse beyond my years. I loved the compliments and worked to get them, but it was as though they were meant for someone standing behind me.

I went at my first job with a fervor. When the praise came for the amount of advertising space I sold, I winced with embarrassment. I could not take it in either. Though there was some reality here. It is disturbing to be praised for the wrong skill and I knew selling newspaper advertising space wasn't my real work. I wanted to be a writer, to say things in a way that allowed Nancy Friday to be perceived. I wanted to do something that was really my own so that I might believe in the praise I was starved for. But when writing assignments came up, I made excuses, ran in the opposite direction, doubled and tripled the hated advertising that was a cinch to sell with my new ass and my old personality. I did only the most rudimentary reporting. Why? I would ask myself. It was a terrible puzzle because I had never failed at anything, I would take any dare. What was I afraid of?

I compromised. Instead of success I could believe in, I went after success other people believed in. I got my reward from other people's opinion of me rather than my opinion of myself. It was like getting food after it had been chewed, with all the flavor and nutriment removed. Superficially it worked. Men pursued me, better jobs were offered, I had an identity in the eyes of the world. My boss fell in love with me; for a moment I thought I could take it in that he had seen me, and what he had seen was what he loved. But the excitement of conquest soon turned—as always—to the fear of loss. I knew he loved not me, but the marvelous and meretricious portrait I had projected. One unguarded moment, and he would see the jealous, insecure child beneath, who needed to hang on to him for dear life; one glimpse and he would run away. All my signals told the world I was a successful, sexual, professional woman. I knew my shabby secret: I had never tried what mattered most.

I took my men and my jobs home to mother. I think I enjoyed them most there. In her home they acquired a final polish, and gave my history with her definition it had not had before. I never understood women who took their anxieties home; I only went there in triumph. I don't know what I liked more, my mother's admiration of my single life, or my own feeling of added life when I experienced my world in her house. In my twenties it seemed I had been given the magic opportunity to rewrite our lives together. No longer was home the place I had to leave, but the place I chose to come to. No longer was I wicked for wanting to leave her; now I came home bearing gifts, stories, successes, and people I could share with her. And at last there was something she could give me.

I was proud of my mother. You could put her in a barn and by the way she placed a chair it would become hers. Once I left her I could love her. Distance gave value to all the things around her I had grown up with: the golds and greens and whites of her living room, the flowers, the silver cigarette boxes, the white wicker furniture on the lawn, all were dear to me as they had never been when it had all been mine, when it was all I had. Even her anxiety and shyness that had so upset me as a child were now lovable; they were rallying emotions for all of us. We would follow her into the big comfortable kitchen with our martinis before dinner, as though we didn't want her out of our sight, as though to protect her. She would lay elegant tables, prepare wonderful food with an effortlessness I hadn't remembered she had. I began to see talents in my mother I wanted for myself. "I don't know why we always end up in the kitchen," she would blush and smile at this new man I had brought home, and I would touch her and say, "But, Mom, this is where we want to be," loving her now that I hadn't become like her.

I warmed, I softened, I lost my nervous edge in her house. Men seemed to love me more there. I brought them to her, knowing she was on my side. One night in her pretty four-poster guest room and, as in a fairy tale, they were mine for life. What was it about her that drew them to me? I would go out of my way to give them time with her alone. After growing up feeling everyone but me had something with their mothers, now when all my friends were at odds with their families, my mother and I were in bloom. We had things to exchange: she enjoyed my life, and when my lovers saw me with her, it seemed I gained a missing dimension in their eyes: I was a single, sexual person who could take care of herself, but surely they must see that the daughter of a woman as feminine as this must also be a woman herself.

Fascinated by my life as she was, my mother didn't want the details. She never asked why I didn't marry one of the men or pursue any one of the careers instead of hopscotching around the world. And I never offered the information. Neither of us wanted her anxiety. I learned to put my arm around her, to tease her about her red hair and her naïveté with jokes. I began to call her Rusty, a childhood name no one else used. Occasionally I tried to be alone with her. But when the merriment and the men were absent, I would sense the old sadness in her—of what?—and the old guilt in me—but of what?

Very late one night after my stepfather had gone up to bed, she launched into the old refrain. "I never have to worry about Nancy," she said to the man beside me. "She could always take care of herself." So long as I was living at home, these words had aroused a kind of pride in me. Now that I was on my own, I realized how false they were. A well of anger rushed up in me so fierce I wanted to strike out at her. "Is something wrong, darling?" my mother said. "No, nothing at all," I replied. My words were like ice.

In fairness today, I can see it was almost impossible for my mother to understand my anger. What was there she could do for me? I had my apartment waiting in the city, my job in my pocket, my man beside me. I was more self-sufficient, less in need of her than ever. No matter. Without another word, I went up to bed.

By morning, the incident had been forgotten. But I knew the anger at her was there now and I grew to fear another outburst the way an epileptic fears a seizure. I didn't want to hurt her, but even more, I did not want to know there was something in me totally unaffected by grown-up success, that I could control no more than an infant can control its crying.

I tried to make up for everything with men. To get the nourishment of a lifetime from them. There was such a vast supply of energy and love, I never wanted to marry. Why stop when around each corner there was yet another man who would enlarge my life? From different men I learned about literature, theater, art, and politics. It never occurred to me that I could get from my work what men did.

My jobs were important to me and I worked hard at them but there was a built-in catch to success. If I stayed with any job long enough, my super-responsible approach to work would lead to promotions and higher salaries—jeopardizing what I needed from men. They would see the aggressive, "unfeminine" person who had always hidden inside me, showing herself to the outside world only as charming, industrious, but essentially nonambitious. I could be lovable only as long as I wasn't handed too much authority, and so turned down jobs that might lead to vice-presidencies; and worked even harder at my glamorous but short-term projects to show I was nevertheless serious. I was convinced that only men could feed me. When they didn't call I died a little; when we argued I couldn't keep my mind on my work and when I sniffed rejection in the air, total paralysis took over. But I never telephoned home with anything but good news. Even when I was down, I honestly believed only men could save me.

Ben is the one man in my life I am not proud of. I met him at a party and had he asked me to marry him right then and there, I would not have considered the proposal any less keenly than I did in the months that followed. He was a total throwback, as beautiful and dumb as the Unobtainable Prom Kings of my adolescence. He was everything my family wanted for me: he belonged to the right clubs, knew all the right people, and he smelled good. While every reasonable, valued, and intellectual instinct in me rejected him, some old forgotten me cried, "Take me, make me!"

I sat at his feet and filled his pipe while he read Edgar Guest. I lowered my hemlines and groveled to please his friends grown dull and quarrelsome on too much money and no work. As I undid myself for him, I saw the rejection coming and lay beside him, unable to sleep; for the first time in my life, unable to leave him. I told myself I wouldn't marry him, but I already knew he wouldn't ask. Ultimately I made it come true by convincing myself I couldn't live without him. "Suffocation," he said.

I called my mother. Her voice greeted me, free of the usual anxiety she felt for my sister. I did not tell her Ben and I were finished. I wanted to reverse the bargain, undo the shift in responsibility made so long ago when I had become sharer in my mother's guilts, protector of her timidities. I wanted to be her child again. "Why do you always treat me as if I could take care of myself?" I asked her. "Why don't you ever worry about me?" My mother's voice faded.

She had no way of dealing with this anger from a daughter whose jobs and men shone with power and mastery over a world she had never known. "Oh, Nancy," she said, "one day you'll settle down with someone nice, you'll be ready to build your nest." It wasn't what I wanted to hear. The desperate me that needed someone to take care of her—who needed a mother—had finally emerged and declared her fear. My mother was calmly passing the job on to a man who was running away from me. I knew in that terrible moment of regression, with all my glittering defenses down, that she had never wanted the job of being my mother in the first place. It had been a false bargain all along: I had never left her. Like Ben, she had left me. I had always said, "I quit" to avoid the humiliating knowledge that I had been fired.

She had always silently warned me that while men were alluring, the answer to all of life's problems, they were somehow dangerous too. She had turned out to be right. I could not go on alone. I wanted someone. I needed a mother. I needed to let her know she had never been a good one.

These things were unspeakable. I wanted to hurt her, to arouse her at last to worry about me, to provoke that profound anxiety in her which was the counterpart to what I was feeling myself. Hadn't she been left by my father? Reunited with her at last in a symbiosis of terror and grief over lost men, I would not be alone. All the fear I had spared her during all my life had not been spared at all. I had merely saved it up and presented it to her in one big bill. I wanted to gain my revenge because she had left me so weak. Oh, I did. I surely did.

Our single years! The first time on our own, our second chance to form ourselves. Total self-reliance, sure sense of value may never be won, but they are goals to try for. Our single years begin one of our great rites of passage. Life becomes more fluid and malleable, old forms and structures are shattered, new ones emerge. This is our chance to outgrow mother's training in passivity, her fear that without someone to lean on, we are nothing.

"I think it's important for a woman to have time on her own after high school or college, and before she marries," says an eighteen-year-old. "You can find out that you can support yourself. That you don't have to have a man to survive. So many girls get married right away. It's frightening never to find out you are able to take care of yourself. You think you must always depend on somebody else."

Imminent independence and separation give this young woman a sense of adventure and power. Life with all its options is about to unfold. At eighteen, we feel we can do anything. "I'd love to have my own apartment," she continues. "My brother left home at seventeen, but my mother doesn't think I can handle it." With every step forward we have to fight mother's legacy of fear.

Here's the other end of the spectrum:

"I love my marriage," says a thirty-two-year-old woman, "and yet it has made me more frightened than when I was single. Without my husband and children, who am I?" Neither her husband's arms around her nor her child's head on her shoulder can ease the anxiety: what would she do when/if they leave her? She has attained the goal her training promised would end all insecurity, but it hasn't. When this woman's daughter grows up, how can she be expected to encourage the girl to leave?

In poignant form, these two women recapitulate different stages of our early drama of separation from mother. At first we are hungry for a life of our own, for freedom, no strings, to go our own way. Behind our youthful vigor and eagerness to explore, a lifelong anxiety waits for us. Children and a husband are a fulfillment, but they are also hostages to fortune. We regress; we grow as dependent on them as once we were on mother. Pop radio is filled with songs about girls aching with loneliness, but statistics show that never-married young women with college educations, earning decent salaries, are the least depressed segment of population. On the other hand, TV commercials show us smiling young mothers, supposedly secure in their marriage, home and family—but the same statistics say that married women with small children in the household are among the most depressed people of all.[1]

The eighteen-year-old rushes into life. Who is to say she will not end up with the thirty-two-year-old's hopelessness?

The fear of freedom—which we dress up and call the need for security—is rooted in the unresolved half of us which is still a child, still looking for a man to replace the mother we never successfully left. So long as we have our need for symbiosis, we will not believe we can make it on our own. The child thinks that if she becomes too "strong," too independent, mother will decide she can make it on her own and neglect her. We keep ourselves little. It means we must continue to live as a child: powerless.

Love puts the child in us back to sleep. When we doubt love, lose love, or become inappropriately afraid that in a world of 4 billion people we will never find love again—we must learn to look back to that little girl. The fear is hers—which is why it baffles us so. Rather than railing at fate or the perfidy of men—which is easy but not the real issue—it would be better to re-examine the relationship of that child to her mother of long ago. "I'm sorry, I wasn't myself," we explain when our rage gets out of hand, when in the throes of lost love we've spied on him jealously, when the fury is not proportionate even to the vile hurtful thing he has done. Of course we weren't ourselves: that was the rage of the frightened child who still sees the threat of desertion as imminent death.

"The pervasive problem for many women," says sociologist Cynthia Fuchs Epstein, "is their basic low opinion of themselves." If so many of us are dependent, helpless, anxious creatures, how can we believe that men may love us? Of course they will wise up and get out sooner or later. The work of our single years is to turn this opinion around.

The first job is to prove to ourselves that we are agents in our own lives, not passive patients forever operated on by other people. Marriage may be beautiful, but all too often it is a call back into symbiosis: the desire to merge and lose our identities in someone "stronger," more valuable than ourselves. Attaching ourselves to him for life itself, without him we fear we will die. What does it matter if he says, "I love you"? Words are easy to say, compared to the importance they hold for the symbiotic child within.

"My wife is extraordinary," a man tells me with genuine pride. "She is a wonderful mother, cook, and when I look at all the trouble some of my friends are having with their wives, I get down on my knees and thank God I have such a terrific woman." This man wouldn't think of leaving his wife. But she tells me privately that she lives in the fear that he will meet another woman. "A brilliant man like him," she says. "What does he see in me?" Having no feeling of self—outside him—she does not exist in her own eyes.

Says Dr. Schaefer: "Women's desire to subordinate themselves to the man is the pattern of dependency learned from mother. To escape the feeling that she may be ornamental but nevertheless fundamentally valueless, she becomes the 'woman who is behind the successful man.' She will not try on her own. But even as she succeeds, even as she makes the man more successful, more valuable, her own feelings of self-worth diminish. The bigger he gets, the more frightened she becomes that he will leave her, a nobody."

Until our single years, we lived by other people's rules. It is salutary now to find the sky does not fall if we question them. The childhood need to be 100 percent safe 100 percent of the time is the biggest danger to life of all. If we do not have time on our own to test the ground, we will remain as afraid for ourselves as mother was. Along with the money we make goes the right to spend it as we like. If mother pays the rent, she has a voice in where we live. *New York Magazine* quoted a twenty-one-year-old girl who was asked to make a political commercial. She agreed because her family would like it. "As long as I live with them," she said, "I'm expected to be a Republican."[2]

In our single years we have our first chance to act so that the existential evidence of our lives tells us that we are new—helpless children no more. If we can successfully make the break away from home and discover we can live without the immediate emotional backup of mother and family; if we choose friends who reinforce our individuality rather than because they are "nice" or live nearby; if we meet men with whom we can explore pleasures mother never allowed; let the experiences of life happen and find in even the painful ones that there is an excitement in knowing an existence larger than we dreamed possible; and get a job which not only delivers the thrill of economic self-sufficiency but builds up our self-esteem because we do it well—we have set up a bank account in our own name on which to draw for the rest of our lives. *I enjoyed living by myself once. If I have to, I can do it again. My world does not stop if other people leave. Their going will sadden me. It will not finish me.*

Our anxieties seduce us by coming up disguised as politeness, common sense, "safety first"—even as strengths. I used to think I made myself up. I hear the same phrase so often from young women I interview today. Our lives are so different from our mothers'. And yet I know that no matter how much I accomplish in my work and marriage, a frightened part of me remains untouched by success. I wasn't born with this fear, these constant needs for reassurance of love. "I'm a very independent woman, very ambitious," a twenty-seven-year-old woman tells me. "I don't have a man in my life now because I can't find a man who treats me as an equal—but also makes me feel like a woman, taken care of." In her mind, there is no conflict between being "equal" and being "taken care of." "The reason I turned down the promotion I was offered," says another young woman, "is that I want to enjoy my freedom, the variety of life. I love my work and I work hard at it, but I don't want it to be all I care about. I don't want to be like a man."

It is a sentiment I shared when I was single. But I know now freedom was the last thing I wanted, the true freedom that comes from being my own, self-sustaining woman. The freedom I was preserving by not working "like a man" was a stance to show anyone I cared about that while I was successful, I was not too successful. I needed him. How could I take on the responsibility for a really big job when at any moment I might have to rush out to the airport to persuade my lover not to fly to Paris without me? How could any job be worth the danger that I might not be able to go with him? To the symbiotic self, separation is not freedom but mortal danger.

Leah Schaefer was recently asked to write an article for a national magazine. She tried, but couldn't, and finally resigned the assignment. "I told them I didn't have the time, but I realized it had something to do with the amount of recognition the article would bring. I can handle success on a one-to-one basis, in the privacy, almost secrecy, of a therapeutic situation. The amount of recognition I'd get in a magazine that millions of people would read froze me. I'm still working on my separation from my mother." Dr. Schaefer's mother died five years ago.

In our single years, we have a powerful ally in the fight to separate and grow up. It is our sexuality. It makes us take chances, pulls us here and there, brings us into a world larger than the family, fills our life with excitement, dangers, pleasures, and disappointments that make us grow even as we learn to handle them. That is why mother's house now seems too small for the two of us. So long as we live with her, we must do so by her rules. It is almost impossible for her to give us more space within the same rooms, under the same roof, where she protected and ordered us about for eighteen or twenty years. "I think there are some women who are comfortable in their own sexuality," says Sonya Friedman, "but I know they are not comfortable in their daughter's. The daughter at eighteen is at the peak of what the American culture calls her sexuality, while her mother is considered nearly over the hill. *Vogue* magazine may assure their forty-year-old readers that life begins at forty, but these women grew up on ludicrous songs like, 'You're Sixteen, You're Lovely, and You're Mine.'"

The moment it was born in us, mother singled out sex as her greatest enemy. More than anything else, she knew sex would separate us from her. She could not even call it by its right name. Instead she would say, "You're so irresponsible," "Don't talk back to me," "Why must you close your bedroom door, wear those tight sweaters, those high heels," etc. Now when we want to leave, to have a place of our own, we too cannot say it has anything to do with sex. We are her daughter and lust is not ladylike.

"My mother couldn't come out and say it, but I knew when I left home she was thinking, 'You want to move out so you can sleep around!' What she said was, 'Why do you want to move out? You have a nice home here.'" The speaker is a twenty-six-year-old woman who is writing her master's thesis on the difficulties women find in leaving home. "Even though I'd moved out when I got married, when I got divorced and went back to school to get my post-graduate degree, I moved back in with my parents. I lived at home for two years, until I could support myself. When I began to look for an apartment of my own it was treated like a tragedy, on the level of a virgin going out into the bad, dangerous, sexual world. The fact that I'd been married made no difference to my mother. But I knew I had to go."

When her daughter leaves, mother is often caught between what she knows and what she feels. The graduate student continues: "Of the forty women I interviewed for my thesis, every single one had trouble leaving unless it was to get married. The women's movement hasn't really reached all that many people, even in a supposedly liberal place like New York. The great majority of mothers who responded to my questionnaire equated the daughter's moving out with rejection. A typical mother said, 'I can understand a person needing to live alone.' *A person*. Not her daughter. These mothers don't want to act the way they do but they are driven to it."

This study included only forty women of various educational and economic classes, but my own research shows that even highly educated, liberal, career-oriented mothers feel anxiety about the daughter leaving. Says a forty-five-year-old woman who manages a staff of fifteen people at her office: "I raised three daughters and worked the whole time they were growing up. But when the youngest was eighteen and leaving, I went through hell. I just didn't want to let go, even though, intellectually, I knew I had to. I had a husband and a job I loved, but that didn't help. I felt rejected."

According to the U.S. Census Bureau, 40 percent of women aged twenty to twenty-four were single in 1975, almost double the number for 1960. These figures seem to suggest a revolution. In terms of real estate, they may be: an apartment of our own gives the illusion of separation. Emotionally, how independent are we? We may feel a kind of emotional blackmail from mother when we leave home, or she may help us furnish the new one-room apartment and cheerily wave bon voyage as we pull away to a new life. Either way, we pack her anxiety along with our suitcases. Says Mio Fredland: "Daughters know their mother's true feelings like they know the inside of their pockets."

With mother's fears roiling uneasily beneath our surface, it is not surprising that the revolution so far is mostly skin deep. Once she's left home, the daughter is delighted to have a job and money of her own, but when she's offered a promotion, she hesitates. She doesn't want to become so career-minded men will feel they have little to offer her. She experiments with sex, but still wants to be swept away: she is contraceptively unprepared almost a third of the time. When she is with her friends, she is the brave new person she always wanted to be. When she goes home, she reverts to the dutiful daughter she wanted to leave behind. (She even speaks differently.) When she meets new people, she tells them what she thinks they want to hear, not what she feels. At a party, she does not think, Who is there here who interests me? Instead, she wonders, What do these people think of me? The morning after a satisfying date or a good sexual experience, the pleasures of the night before have turned to anxiety: will he call again?

Do any of these describe you?

We talk a brave game of independence and make a point of lighting our own cigarettes. Underneath, we still doubt the authenticity of what we project. Mother may have talked a good game too. Underneath she is afraid her daughter cannot make it on her own. (She never was good at it herself, when she was single.) We live not with mother's official declarations of confidence but with her inarticulated fears.

"More girls may be living on their own today," says Sonya Friedman, "but the umbilical cord is still there. It is the telephone." To relieve our "guilt" we phone mother. The cure is never complete because what we feel is not guilt. After all, we have not committed some dread crime. What the symbiotically tied daughter calls *guilt* is really *fear*—fear that with every step toward independence, every step away from mother, we have lost her.

"What arouses the most guilt in you?" I ask a woman.

"My mother."

"What is the worst thing you can imagine?"

"A phone call in the night telling me she died."

I had a chance to interview this young woman's mother. From *her* side, the story runs this way: "I know my daughter feels guilty about not coming home for Christmas. I felt the same when I was her age. So this year, I went and spent Christmas with her. I love to see her, but I felt underfoot at her place. I'd really rather stay home with my friends. I love my daughter and I'd have felt guilty if I left early, so I stayed till the end of the holidays." So much *guilt,* so much *love.* The semantic confusion is only surpassed by the emotional confusion in which mother and daughter place one another.

We disguise our attachment to mother with the miles put between us, and with the evidence of our new job, a sexual life. For instance, before she returned to college to get her Ph.D., and become a therapist, Leah Schaefer pursued a successful career as a jazz singer. She moved around the country, supported herself, and had sexual relationships with men—a life that seemed as different from her mother's as possible. Who could say she was not independent?

When she was twenty-four, she decided to have plastic surgery. "I was living in Hollywood," she says. "If I hadn't been in show business, I don't think I could have had the narcissism and courage to do it. On my father's side, they have these perfect noses, like I have now. But I had a long Roman nose, like my mother. The kind with a hook in it. During the nose operation I had a local anesthetic. I was able to hear what was going on. There was this terrific crack. The doctor said, 'The hook is gone.' I had this sudden wild feeling of having lost something.

"I thought I hadn't told my mother about the operation so as not to worry her. The real reason was because I was changing a feature on my face that was like hers. In fact, when I got rid of this hook in my nose, it was a real emotional separation—*the first time I'd unhooked myself from her*. Gradually I began to believe in my attractiveness. Since adolescence I'd been crazy about boys, but this nose was the bane of my existence. When I sang in a trio, I was sure people weren't saying, 'Don't they sing great' but, 'Isn't that an ugly girl with a terrible nose?' Suddenly I had boy friends, dozens of them. I thought it was because my nose was better. Later I realized that until I'd had that operation, I'd never thought of myself as different, separate from my mother. My mother was a person who denied her sexuality, denied it was an important thing. So I had denied it too. I used to think it was the physical act of changing my appearance that separated me from my mother. My real separation was the emotional one of beginning to think of myself as sexual. It wasn't how I looked but how I felt about myself that attracted the men."

Our sexuality is running in the right direction. Before we marry, for the first time in our lives a bond is being formed which can be more powerful than the one we had with mother. It is the bond with men. "It used to be a bit of folk wisdom," says Dr. Robertiello, "that men should try out all sorts of sexual experiences before they married. The same now applies to women. Sexual experience doesn't have to be unbridled. If you are Catholic or Southern Baptist, for instance, you will have stricter limits than others. If you don't let yourself do anything else, then at least go to church where you can sit opposite or near a man. Women should try to give themselves experience *vis-à-vis* a number of men so that the male sex becomes less frightening and remote—so that the woman can learn she is able to attract and interest a man. For some people this might mean holding hands . . . for others, a series of orgies. The single years are the time to be as experimental as possible."

The single years are the time to enlarge and reinforce whatever degree of separation has been so far achieved. Otherwise, we will make our new ties with men into a form of regressive symbiosis, and sexual excitement will give way to safety. What we have with him will no longer be electric and powerful, but at best warm and friendly; at worst, merely a bargain in mutual control and dependence.

Good experiences build our desire for more autonomy. Bad ones hurt but teach us we can survive. Life is not so frightening on our own. With the beginning of self-confidence, some of the poisons of feminine life can begin to diminish. We get over the fear that if someone we love goes away we will never find another. Our need to grapple lovers with hoops of steel is eased, lessening the chances that they will cry suffocation (symbiosis) and go. We learn the ways in which we are our own enemy.

Experimenting with a number of men, different relationships, helps put the finger on what is "always" going wrong. Men hurt us. Men leave us. At least half the fault must be ours: *we chose them*. "Even if you have a psychological compulsion to make it only with bad guys who do you in," says Dr. Robertiello, "it is better to go through it ten times than not to get involved with men at all for fear of being hurt. That way, you will at least get a feeling of the location of your problem, and look around for ways to solve it." In the privacy of our single years we have time and opportunity to begin the work.

Privacy aids separation. For the first time in our lives, nobody knows what we are doing. Unless we tell them. "My husband and I always told our daughter Katie that some things are private," says Leah Schaefer. "Not hidden or denied, but private. Now she understands when we close our door. Sometimes she locks her own door and says, 'I want some privacy.'"

Without practice in privacy when we are very young, we are ever after uncomfortable with it. If our closed bedroom door was meaningless, if mother was always "straightening" our bureau drawers, asking questions about our friends and telephone calls, we grow up with the uneasy feeling that privacy is a guilty idea. We suspect no secret of ours is safe, that someone always knows what we are thinking. We feel "guilty" when we do something mother wouldn't like; we can't be sure there is no way for her to find out. As if in reaction, some women rush to tell their mothers everything. We may say that sharing our lives with mother, keeping closely in touch with her, is gratitude, paying her back for all she did when we were little. And yet, under the guise of being dutiful and loving, aren't we forestalling the fear that mother might find out? Aren't we asking her to be a collaborator and condoner of our sexuality?

"Has my mother asked if I'm still a virgin?" says a twenty-two-year-old. "I told her I was, but I lied. I'm not. When she asked if I would tell her when I did have sex, I said No, it was my own business." This young woman only lives a few blocks away from her mother; she is shy, self-effacing and has not been much involved with men. But her degree of separation, her efforts to establish it, are superior to another woman who travels constantly around the world and has sex frequently with many different men: "My mother and I are really great friends, though we're very different women. We talk constantly on the phone. I even called her from France the first time I had sex. Recently, I had bad luck and got pregnant. I called her and said I had to have an abortion. She was sweet about it, but she didn't give me the feeling of support I really wanted. It was a downer. I wanted her to call me three times a day, or even get on a plane and come take care of me."

This woman wants it both ways, to tell her mother about her sex life, to be a buddy, and to have her mother take care of her too—as her mother did when she was a child. "Sex should be something you do on your own," says Dr. Schaefer, "and for which you take responsibility. Telling your mother about your sexual life respects neither her privacy nor your own. It opens you up to her influence, one way or the other. You are giving her too much power to comment, to give or withhold approval, in an area in which she doesn't belong."

It is a difficult issue for both parents and children. Says Dr. Robertiello: "I'm not against my daughter having sex. That is her separate decision to make. But if she brings the boy home to spend the night with her, that's different. She's invading *my* privacy, bringing me into a situation I don't want to be part of. Liberal parents who don't like kids to bring their lovers home are often called hypocrites. I don't believe they are. If it bothers parents, they have the right to say, 'Don't do it in front of me. It's not my business.' Children have a right to their sexuality, but parents have a right not to be made party to it."

Some mothers want their daughters' sexual lives to be private, because it gives them a freedom too. "Sometimes my daughter tells me more than I want to hear," says the mother of a twenty-four-year-old. "All the excruciating details of her romances. When she was nineteen, she asked me to go with her to get a diaphragm. I said no. It seemed *too* intimate. She knew I didn't disapprove, but I thought some of her life as a woman has to be her life. If you aren't prepared to go without your mommy to get a diaphragm, then you're too young to be getting one."

A twenty-five-year-old woman tells me that she doesn't mind her boyfriend sleeping over at her apartment, but she is nervous if her mother calls while he is there. "I have this uncanny feeling she can see over the telephone, and knows he is naked in my bed while I'm talking to her. I don't want her to know. I guess I have a real double standard." This young woman has turned a healthy situation around and criticized herself for keeping her sexual life private from her mother. She should keep it private. And yet, if she is still so symbiotically tied that, like a child, she feels her mother can read her mind over the telephone, it is not surprising that the experience is filled with anxiety. Dr. Schaefer's comment is that she is doing the right thing. "In time, simple repetition of the experience will rid her of this anxiety."

Like everything in life, the more we do something, the more expert we become, the less inhibition is felt. You can't get there without practice. The idea is so simple, and yet, without having been given any practice in being independent, young women of eighteen and twenty are plunked down in new lives. Problems of separation, never having been worked out at the appropriate age, suddenly come at us now in a chilling manner. We are unprepared, having been rewarded all our lives for *not* being self-reliant. The first time we go to a party without a man, we do it in fear and trembling. After the fifth time, it is easier. Practice is everything. Little boys got it. We did not.

Meeting and knowing a variety of men in our single years can help us see our capacity for life was greater than we ever dared think. One man, grabbed on to too soon, can ground us in the way we've always been. The symbiotic dependency of most marriages does not allow women to grow. The divorcée or widow finds herself alone again in the world at age thirty or fifty, dealing with men as if she were a teenager. "If he leaves me, I'll die!"

Most of us will marry. No one can promise it will last. Our love may be in other people. Our security is in ourselves. If we goof our way through our single years, not paying our bills, losing our keys, writing home for the rent money, our days filled with little more than waiting for Mr. Right, basing our value not on achievement but on the men who didn't work out—we will have established an ominous memory of ourselves. Mother was right: we are too frail to survive on our own.

The irony is, our drifting, irresponsible behavior was half expected. Given our training, you might even say we have succeeded. "That's how women are," people sigh, half exasperated, half charmed—and they proceed to write a check to bail us out, offer shoulders for us to cry on when we are fired for being chronically late, when we can't recover from yet another broken heart. That is *not* how women are. It is how we become.

Things seem to be changing. The single woman looks down at us from every billboard—the symbol of our time. Pop heroines on TV, in films, and magazines make unmarried life seem so glamorous and easy. If you can't make it, baby—these successful, on-the-job creatures seem to be saying—there's something wrong with you. Everybody else is. Pseudo-role models like the *Cosmo* girl promise us the single life in all its glory, just for the price of a magazine. Reach out, and success, love, independence and freedom too—they can all be yours.

And yet there is a built-in lie to the single girl as heroine. It is the hidden agenda—habits of dependence we have been trained to think of as our central feminine core. A way of rating ourselves lives on, deep within our value system. It is based on our first role model and is backed up by the entire culture. It says the single woman is "unfinished."

When Helene Deutsch entered the university, her mother "thought it was a blemish on our whole family that I was going to study medicine. She wanted me to marry, to be like other girls. Was she proud of my success? Proud is not the word, though I supported my parents with the profession she did not want me to enter. When I eventually married, we had two witnesses. After the marriage, the first thing they did was to contact my mother. It was only then that my mother felt I had given her something solid."

Helene Deutsch is ninety-three. But when I interview a woman sixty years younger, I hear the same refrain: "My mother was pleased at my success in my job. After all, she'd wanted me to go to college. But among her friends, she is the only mother whose daughter hasn't married. Finally when I got promoted and a story about me appeared in the hometown paper, she had something to show them. I was pleased that she was proud of me, but it hurt a little too that her neighbors' opinions are so important. I know the best thing I can ever give my mother will be my marriage . . . if I ever do."

Says Dr. Deutsch: "Mothers today may want their daughters to become doctors and lawyers, but first they want them to marry. Why not? It is better for a woman to be married. Perhaps if the daughter is a big success in her career, then the mother won't be disappointed that she didn't marry. A mother would rather see her daughter married and a mother than anything else, but if she is famous enough in her work, that can satisfy the mother's narcissism, the normal narcissism."

Work rewards for young women even today come so slowly. "The only people who seem to really want them," says Jessie Bernard, "are men. It's difficult for young women to find a spot in the world equal to their talents." In most jobs you begin at the bottom. Getting married, you begin as a success. It seems such an easy solution.

Many men today have begun to say they believe women have a destiny outside the nursery and kitchen. They may even smile at their father's chauvinism in saying he prefers women who are "feminine" and "non-aggressive." *But when they become serious about a girl of their own, these are the qualities they look for.* Sociologist Mirra Komarovsky points out in her book *Dilemmas of Masculinity* that the same liberal male who says he believes in the women's movement often wants to marry a woman who will stay home and keep house for him. He can't see why she can't pursue a career and run a perfect home too. As one student in Komarovsky's study put it, it is all right if the mother of a pre-school child takes a full-time job, "provided, of course, that the home was run smoothly, the children did not suffer and the wife's job did not interfere with her husband's career."[3]

And yet I would like to add a word here in men's defense. One of the great cries of our time is that women are held back because "men won't let us." Sometimes this is true. Very often it is neither men nor society which holds us back. We do it ourselves. If the goal for women is self-reliance, we must understand why we succeed or fail in terms of ourselves—without the convenient, catchall excuse of male malevolence.

"Even though I tell you I want to be a lawyer," says a twenty-one-year-old, "there is something in me that works against my independence. It comes out in my relationships with men. My boy friend says he believes in my career, but when he tells me, 'I don't want you to do this or that,' I hear myself automatically saying, 'OK, I won't do it.' It's like being hypnotized. It's frightening to know this can happen to you." She has heard the voice of the symbiotic child within herself talking. A man did not put that child there.

Says Smith College economics professor Jeanne McFarland: "We send young women ambivalent signals. We give them this terrific education so they can compete. On the other hand, we say—what you really need is to find a husband. So go slow on competition. Men don't like women who compete. Men like their women on the pedestal—goddesses of nurturing and socialization and all the other 'good' things men don't have time to be. It's a mixed signal: compete, but don't do it too well." Can we be surprised if despite all the current talk about women making it, down deep we are afraid? We have more to lose than to gain from autonomy.

Here's a twenty-nine-year-old, highly successful woman journalist: "Last weekend, I spent the whole time in bed with my new boy friend. I hadn't taken that time out with a man in almost a year. Imagine! We just locked the doors and made love and talked and it was wonderful. All the tension went away. I forgot about my work. Monday, I went back to the office and Tuesday night I saw him again. I had these feelings of hostility even in the taxi before I met him. I was difficult with him, hostile, from the first minute. 'Shit,' I thought to myself, 'I've blown it, it's dead with him.' But in a couple of hours we'd got it back. I don't think I can keep it up with him, though, because I work so hard and my work's so important to me. It's as though I can't afford these weekends. I want them but they frighten me. It took me a day to get back into my work, and then when I did see him, I was hostile again."

Women like the journalist in the story above, to whom work is important, are often afraid of getting involved with a man for fear they will lose their juice and incentive to work. Having tasted the pleasures of autonomy, she pushes the man off because of fear she will be sucked back into a dependent relationship. The real addiction of course is her unresolved symbiotic needs. She is afraid, once the door is open to her old, denied, baby feelings, that they will come rushing back to grab her. The intensity of the desire to be dependent is vividly seen in the hostility she shows the man who inadvertently tempts her back into it.

The reverse of the coin is seen in the story of a thirty-four-year-old woman whose fears were aroused, not by the man getting too close, but because success threatened to cut her off from him. A fashion merchandiser, her work keeps her traveling from New York to California. Off and on for the past eight years, she has been living with an actor whose work keeps him traveling too. "That was fine with both of us," she tells me. "We discussed marriage but everything was going so well, we both said, Not yet. I'd miss him, but when we got together, it was very intense, wonderful. Last year I was promoted to vice-president, the first woman in my company. I'd arrived. Suddenly, I was on the telephone to him all the time, crying, 'Why aren't you here? I need you,' I'd wail. 'I want your arms around me!' I was weeping all the time, accusing him of desertion, feeling lonely when I should have been on top of the world." As a result of these new demands she began to make, the affair ended. A relationship that might not have been every woman's choice but was exactly what these two people wanted foundered in the face of the anxiety her success in work brought with it.

For most of us, the end of the single years comes none too soon. They are like a hectic trip to Paris. Exciting, but, "Gee, it's good to be home!" And home, of course, is marriage. It is the pattern we know best. Even if we had a broken or unhappy home, we still have at least the fantasy of family life. "What are your goals in life?" asks the American Council of Life Insurance in its annual national survey: "A happy family life? Making a lot of money? A fulfilling career? The chance to develop as an individual?" In 1975, a full 80 percent of the respondents, male and female, eighteen years old and over, chose a happy family life. *This does not mean they had one.*

We have an unforgettable model of how to be a wife, patterned not just on how mother was with father but, more significantly, on how we were with her. We are the couple—mother and me—that we will try to re-establish with others. The more we needed her, the more she rewarded us. When we are grown, dependency is still the norm ever held before us. It is like holding a martini in front of the alcoholic.

"What happens," says Dr. Robertiello, "is that the cultural idea of women's dependency reinforces the women's own childhood training. This is the single greatest trap held out to women. It might be called *the* feminine option."

Like many traps, it is baited with honey.

This option says that any time a woman wants, she can give up on herself and find a man to take care of her—so why struggle to establish herself in the first place? This supposed privilege is so deeply planted in our psyche that we are often not aware that we use it as our ace in the hole. "Men are so competitive. I don't see the point in working so hard." Of course society applauds the woman who feels this way, who just marks time until she takes the option. She is one less competitor to worry about, someone who will take on all the unpaid work of housekeeping, etc., that men don't like to do. Dropping out on ourselves, giving responsibility for our life to a man, is not the mark of a woman but of a child.

Nearly three out of five first brides (57.9 percent) are twenty years or under.[4] For many young women, the height of bliss is still to marry on graduation day. Only eighteen and she has achieved lifelong security! The divorce courts are filled with people who discovered too late the meretricious glamour of that promise.

Says sociologist Cynthia Fuchs Epstein: "Most women don't think they have any alternative to being a wife and mother. They just don't think success is possible for them. It's not in their spectrum of expectations. Not until they get into the marketplace and get decent jobs do they see there is some possibility for success."

Often, it takes the experience of a failed marriage for a woman to realize that the supposed lifelong security of having a husband can be a painful myth. "Women like these," continues Dr. Epstein, "often become very career-oriented. They don't necessarily stop seeing men, but their anger at a shattered illusion has opened their eyes. They learn they can't look to men to be their sole gratification."

Work-oriented women, however, face problems that men do not. Says Dr. Epstein: "There are few supports for women to say to a man, 'I can't see you tonight, I have to work late.' Women aren't used to thinking of themselves as plunging totally into work. This is not to say we couldn't. It is just not a resource we have developed yet."

Faced with pressures like these, many career-oriented women choose not to marry early. In a study done by Professor Elizabeth

Tidball on women achievers selected at random from *Who's Who of American Women,* she found that among 1,500 prominent women, only about one-half were married.[5] They had postponed marriage an average of seven years after their bachelor degrees so that they could give full attention to their careers. In Margaret Hennig's study on twenty-five high-level women executives, *all* began by feeling that marriage and career were an either/or choice.[6] When they were about twenty-five, in Dr. Hennig's words, they "stored their femininity away for future consideration." Around age thirty-five, they reassessed their lives, got in touch with their shelved femininity, and about half of them married.

We don't know how angry these women were at having to play down their sexual lives in order to get ahead. I would have been. All of us have seen the anger of women who did make this choice—women without men. Someone or something—men, society, the structures of work in our culture—has let them down. There are exceptions, women on their own, living happily and wholly without men. Part of the respect they engender is due to perception of how few women ever solve this problem: to live without men without anger.

For the vast majority who have not solved the problem, it might be said that the logical place for their anger to be directed would be at the anachronistic training which linked femininity with dependence—but that would mean turning anger back, onto mother. The anger goes forward instead, to the prince who has not presented himself, in a kind of generalized bitterness toward all men.

Says Dr. Cynthia Fuchs Epstein: "Women are very torn in work situations. They have to make a whole set of decisions based on different priority systems—including love, friendship, marriage and children—not all of which co-ordinate." If a woman becomes involved with her career, she's afraid love will suffer. If she gives too much time to her love life, she is afraid it will be at the expense of her career.

I feel these pressures myself: walking past a mirror today, I saw my mother. On my face was the expression of hers I like least: anxiety. The harder I work, the less womanly I feel.

"Nancy, I hear your questions, but you haven't taken in my answer." The speaker is a psychoanalyst. I have been asking her why women laugh off these feelings of value that come with success. Her reply runs from my mind like water. I have to phone her again in the evening to get her to repeat what she said. I plan a dinner party so that I may at least hear some praise for my feminine accomplishment at cooking, but I am working so hard at writing that I cancel it—feeling more depressed, less womanly than ever. My husband and I have a terrible row and I bury myself in the papers on my desk, depriving myself of his company. Why? The repression lifts for a moment: I am leaving him before he leaves me—a game I first played with mother when I was six.

Madness.

Do not think that because I have written this down that I can make it work for me. I have already forgotten it. Freud was disappointed at first that his patients' new self-knowledge did not immediately ameliorate their condition when he made them aware of their unconscious conflicts. It was as if he had lit a lamp in a cartoon for his patient. "I see it!" the patient would cry. And then the lamp would go out, the patient would "forget" once more, the conscious ground not won at all, dark repression closing in.

Psychoanalysts have long become accustomed to the necessity of *working through* these bits of insight, making patients aware of the repressed connections again and again before they are truly grasped—the liberating, emotional truth integrated for good. Practice, once again. We women resist knowledge of ourselves and our mothers. We prefer our fantasy relationship and so we cannot put to work what we know about the two of us:

A psychiatrist with whom I have conferred shows the chapter on competition in this book to his wife. They have a fourteen-year-old daughter. The girl's mother reads it, commenting all the while, "Yes, yes, that's interesting, but it doesn't apply to me." An hour later, she bursts into tears. "In a week or two," he tells me, "she may want to talk about it. Didn't you also deny that certain material we've discussed was relevant to your life until months, maybe a year later?"

Repression is an unconscious process. It has nothing to do with intellect or how smart we are. We may remember every fact ever learned and have an IQ of 160, and still resist "knowing" the facts of our relationship to mother—and how they are played out with different people in our lives.

The fear of losing mother doesn't even require having had an emotionally nourishing relationship with her in the first place. Some women openly dislike their mothers, others cannot recall a gesture of warmth, a moment of closeness. It is not necessary to have loved your mother, even for her to have been there for you, for the symbiotic need to exist. Sometimes, in fact, the hardest mother-daughter relationship to face is the one that is only a wish-fulfillment fantasy.

For women like this, the culturally idealized mother-daughter relationship is more important than reality. As children we miss the symbiosis we didn't have so acutely that we are perhaps even more desperate for it than women who were less deprived. It is too painful, too humiliating to admit. Casually, we say, "I simply wasn't close to my mother," or with relief, "Thank God, my mother didn't smother me the way she did my sister." Another defense is angry dismissal: "When my daughter was born, I was determined she wouldn't grow up as I did." Verbal formulas that are like cosmetics hiding our scars.

"My parents are very uptight about sex," says a twenty-nine-year-old single woman. "I don't want sex always to have to be part of some big, emotional intimacy, some ongoing relationship. I like to be able to have sex without strings. Recently I met a guy I liked a lot and went to bed with him the first night. It bothered me that he didn't call again. When I did get a note from him he didn't even refer to that night." When I suggested that it had been a humiliating experience, she protested adamantly. "No, no, it wasn't humiliation. It's just that I haven't wanted to see other guys since." At the end of the interview when I am leaving, she stops me: "Goddamnit, I did feel humiliated." The curtain of repression had lifted for a minute. Will she ever be able to integrate her attitude—wanting sex with no strings —with her gut reaction of despair when a man takes her up on it?

"When a woman goes to bed with a man and he doesn't call," says Dr. Robertiello, "she feels humiliated. It's like being used, duped, conned. It goes back to that early feeling of betrayal and loss of that first person who led you to believe that if you 'gave' to her, she would always be there for you." In her conscious mind, this woman has made a personal, rational decision about men. On the unconscious level she is still reacting to them as if they were her mother.

Men don't share our conflict. The more successful he is, the more a man feels he can get the best women, sex, and love. Where the sexes differ is that *we get involved with men symbiotically*—displacing our need for mother onto our husband or lover. No wonder we have more difficulties apportioning our time—so much for love, so much for work—than men do. In symbiotic love, the need is so great it swallows all time and nothing is left over for anything else.

"I always believed I could have love and work," says Dr. Schaefer, "and therefore I did have them. I was brought up with this belief because both of my parents loved to work. It just seemed natural to love *and* to work. Men used to say, 'If you married me, I would let you work.' I used to say, '*Let* me work?' I didn't need their permission. It is their training that makes women think they must exclude men from their lives if they want interesting work. What we believe is what we make happen."

Though the work we do and the reward we get may tell the world we are equal to the man, women live with a special day-to-day risk most men don't know. "It's so unfair," a woman tells me. "On every level I am his equal, except I know he has the ability to walk out. He won't be happy, but still he can go to a bar and drink, see his friends. He'll probably work harder and get his mind off me. I'm mesmerized until he telephones. I resent it."

It is like an intermittent disease: we are only as professional as the last assurance he still loves us. The power of the emotion we feel as the man walks out the door began with our fear, as a child, of being left. We never outgrew it. With no practice in being alone, we think we cannot survive it. Men respond to our fear. It makes them feel more powerful. This reinforces an old, sad lesson: our weakness is our strength.

In terms of work that builds independence, there is no reason to think of jobs merely in snobbish or elitist terms. The woman who can run a switchboard gets a feeling of mastery and competence. If we can do small repair jobs around the apartment—unplug a drain or fix a blown fuse—it is one more area in which we have learned to dominate the nitty-gritty details of life, without depending on a man. The woman who is proud of her position as an irreplaceable secretary gets as much feeling of value from her job as does the woman vice-president. The world may put different monetary or status value on what they do, but as far as helping to confirm feelings of autonomy, both are equally desirable.

While the value of earning a paycheck that supports you cannot be overestimated, some women find that their most emotionally nourishing work lies outside an office. They may paint or write on weekends, go into politics or put in time with the Red Cross. This doesn't say, however, that the self-esteem of the dilettante or Sunday painter is automatically reinforced. The activity must be important enough to be worth the sacrifice of extra time, labor, and social activities. Otherwise, it isn't emotionally valuable enough for us to gain feelings of autonomy. Without real commitment, it is only a game. If it doesn't matter if you lose, you gain little if you win.

Today's cry is freedom; none cry it more loudly than the single woman who demands it even while she is out finding someone to surrender it to. "Why can't I find a man to take care of me?" is a common complaint, even among Leah Schaefer's women patients who have jobs or careers. "I tell them," Dr. Schaefer says, "that the world is filled with men who feel more manly by taking care of women. But there is a payment you must make; you can't expect a man to take care of you, and also tell him what to do. The way you pay for being taken care of when you are little is to be the kind of person mother wants you to be. The same price must be paid to a man. Many women want it both ways. There is nothing wrong with wanting to be taken care of, I tell them, just as long as you know the price of what you are getting."

Women accuse men of being afraid of closeness, being unable to love, etc. It may be that the man is responding to the unspoken half of the female message of love: "Take care of me." He may indeed love her. What frightens him off is not the closeness, the intimacy, but his fear of the burden. Even if the men we meet in our single years have been trained to feel that carrying the woman is the mark of a man, they may be too young, still too far down the financial ladder to be able to do it. Perhaps they are not yet ready to give up their freedom. "The problem for the woman," says Dr. Schaefer, "is that this idea, in which love means somebody to take care of her, is so deeply rooted, she herself doesn't realize she's laying it on the man. All she thinks is that he's cold, awful, unfeeling, he's rejected her. The idea of loving her, and taking care of her too—they are so intertwined, she can't tell one from the other. Wasn't that how her mother's love was?"

Matina Horner wrote her doctoral thesis on women's "motivation to avoid success" in 1968.[7] By the early 1970s her ideas had become part of folk wisdom. What she said spoke universally and immediately to women in an area we had never been able to explain to ourselves. Never mind that other sociologists argued her findings were incomplete, that they were based on a study of only ninety women at one university. "Of course!" we exclaimed, "that explains my anxiety, my failures, my ambivalence about work. I am a woman just like any other. I have the feminine fear of success!" Our fears were not biological but socially conditioned. What was learned could be unlearned. Besides, it was all the fault of the paternalistic society anyway.

I sometimes wonder if Dr. Horner's conclusions haven't done women more harm than good. Having the zippy phrase—fear of success—in advance of trying, it becomes a self-fulfilling prophecy. We recognize failure as an old friend, the very mark of our womanliness. We make the same mistake in reading certain feminist fiction. Eager for identification with other women, we recognize ourselves in the heroines—beaten down, harassed, often humorous even if self-deprecatingly so. It is nice to know we aren't the only ones who feel uncontrollable rage when our husband comes home late, loss of identity if he doesn't come home at all. It doesn't follow, however, that identification with someone else's failures makes us better equipped to overcome our own.

Nevertheless, I feel Dr. Horner was right. We do fear success; but the phrase is useless unless we see it in context. Fear of success used to be explained with emphasis on oedipal retribution: if you beat mommy out for daddy, she will seek her revenge. I think this is true of both sexes, but women do not fear mother's rivalry and anger as much as her loss. There is a shading of emphasis here that runs along sexual lines. Our problems of separation are not parallel to men's. A man doesn't have to leave another man to gain his independence. A boy can be a rival to his father and/or use him as a model—but in either case, continue to get love and support from mother. A daughter, however, often feels she must choose a field distant from mother's in order to reinforce separation. For many women, competition with men is much easier to face than competition with another woman.

"In developing strategies for winning, women have much quicker understanding than men," says George Peabody, who is a doctor of Applied Behavioral Science. He invented The Powerplay Game, by which corporations try to teach employees on the way up methods for success in business. "But again and again, we find women hesitate—to the point of stupidity—to put what they know into play. They aren't stupid, so you have to ask why. They think their superior strategic and political planning is somehow cheating. When they enter the office, they park this kind of skill at the door. In Powerplay, they tend to want to give back all their winnings when the game is over. Many are afraid to beat out the other girls. They don't want to destroy relationships."

I know a travel agency staffed by women that has "eliminated" competition by doing away with titles. "When a senior position is open," one of the partners says proudly, "we don't make a big deal of it. Competitive feelings don't get stirred up. Someone gets the position and that's that." The story makes my heart sink.

Who is fooling whom? When there is no open power relationship, it does not mean there is no power relationship at all. Everybody knows who decides that the office will open a branch in Florida, who decides Mary Anne will get that lush assignment to Paris while Sally will type up the reports. Some people want to run organizations, some do not. Unless the rules of competition are spelled out, nobody is comfortable. The dominant personalities rule the roost by their own rules, and usually for their own comfort, while paternalistically (!) telling the subordinates they are one big happy family with the good of all as the common goal. Nor do the people at the top win totally: because their place in the hierarchy is unacknowledged and thus nonlegitimate, they suffer from anxiety too.

To deny women their right to feel competitive reinforces old stereotypes of passivity. Power is being exercised, but everyone pretends it is not. Only we are nasty enough, competitive enough to feel angry. Better shut up, pretend not to be competitive at all. To do anything else is to risk being labeled unwomanly. Even as we pass laws to force corporations to put more women into management positions, there are few women who will step up and say with self-confidence, "I am a competitive person." Back in the boardroom, it is decided not to give a female executive that big job in Chicago. "Women just aren't tough enough to hack it at the top. We'd better go with Harry."

We think we will be rewarded for being good girls, for not making waves. The other guy gets the promotion.

In *African Genesis,* Robert Ardrey says that the most neurotic, unhappy animal in the world is the American woman: she is trying to do something "nature" did not adapt her to do.[8] I totally disagree—beginning with the fact that while we are animals, we are something more too. Nature did not adapt us for playing the piano or flying airplanes. We taught ourselves. If we take this idea of *training* and substitute it for Ardrey's quasi-religious notion of *nature,* I could agree with him.

"Why has there never been a woman who has been the bridge or chess champion of the world?" asks Dr. Robertiello. "The way this question is usually put by male chauvinists is, 'Why haven't there been more great women artists, scientists,' etc.? The answer is a function of the culture in which women are brought up. After all, in comparative IQs, women come out brighter than men."

Working for yourself, getting ahead, usually means beating out another person, *breaking a bond*. Says Dr. Peabody: "Women have been trained to be somebody's 'other,' not to have an independent sense of identity. When you get to be Number One, you can't be somebody's other. If your lifelong habit is to think of your identity only in terms of being somebody's wife, somebody's secretary or assistant, it is scary not to be in that position. It means you have no identity. But as soon as you can tell women that it's not cheating, not naughty, to go after what they want, that they can do it and still be feminine—that assertiveness does not mean putting other people down—then women can give themselves permission to use their great skills and they move marvelously. It is almost a shock to them to find people don't fall apart when they say No."

We have been trained not to initiate, but to respond—not to choose but to be chosen. "My job," Dr. Peabody continues, "is to help women over the fear of clear self-definition and self-responsibility; it's the only way to move into top management. Sometimes it takes six to eight months to get even the best women through that knothole. But they can learn!"

In most women's lives, the rewards for seeing ourselves as capable and valuable on our own come late, after our deepest beliefs have been formed. It is like trying to learn to be a ballet dancer in your twenties. Our psyche has already been conditioned to respond only to certain kinds of praise; it is difficult to adjust to a whole new range of stimuli, attractive as they may be.

"You're terrific!" says the boss. "What a job you did!"

We blush. He really didn't mean it. It was a fluke; we'll never be able to pull it off again.

This is the split in which we live. We may hear praise when it is given. We just can't believe it. We see recognition of our accomplishments as a kind of flattery, mistaken or insincere. But if you cannot take in praise and recognition during the uphill battle to get a hold on who you are, how long are you going to stick with it? We have been trained to gain confidence not through efforts for ourselves but through meeting the needs of others. "Women," says Jessie Bernard, "are the ones who keep families together. All the studies show that women are the mediators in kinship relations." We are good at compromise. Men take the extreme positions that, right or wrong, define identity. They let people know "where they stand." "A lady," the old proverb used to run, "gets her name in the newspapers only twice in her life. When she marries and when she dies."

A successful woman tells me, "I work so hard. I know I do my job well, but when people praise me, I think, 'Oh, they're just being nice.' Why can't I just smile, say, 'Thanks a lot,' and maybe buy everyone a drink the way men do to nail the good feeling in? But no, I just slink away after the compliment, as if I've done something shameful." She has—she has separated herself from the other women. Not only is she slightly ashamed of the competitive glow she felt for being praised, but she is frightened too. We are overwhelmed with the fear of growing too big. We are losing our right to the feminine option: becoming so self-sufficient no man will want to take care of us.

I do not believe that "making it" is an absolute good, and that anyone who does not try is infantile. I might even say the opposite. But it is one thing to decide you don't want power, to make a conscious decision that the rat race isn't worth it, that you don't want to become unfeeling and domination-hungry "like a man." All this is reasonable, even admirable. But it is something else to pretend you aren't trying for success because you don't want to become masculinized, when the real reason is that you are surrendering to your baby fears that success and autonomy will separate you. Choice cannot be truly made unless it is conscious.

The notion of choice is beset with philosophical difficulties, but in our own lives it is usually possible to distinguish between genuinely deciding we don't want something, and merely crying "Sour grapes." A woman who has just come out of a devastating love affair says, "To hell with men, now I'm going to concentrate on my career." To the outward eye, she may then seem purposive and self-contained, but unless she finds someone to provide the closeness and intimacy we all need, she may simply be practicing denial when she says, "I can take care of myself. I don't need a man."

Another woman "chooses" not to see men because "they don't give me the support I want, either emotionally or financially." Hearing a woman speak out is still such a rarity that we often take her loud declarations as strength of character. It is important to ask, Is her choice that of an adult or the demands of a disappointed child?

Says psychoanalyst and sex therapist Helen Kaplan: "We are in a transitional period. Women want to be successful on our own, but we

still look for superdaddy, who will be more successful still. In terms
of numbers, there are more men available to the career-oriented
woman. She is more likely to be sexually active than the home-
oriented person. But the great number of work-oriented women are
thrown by the notion that most men they meet are less successful
than they are. For women like these, a man who is less powerful than
they may not be attractive."

Women marry up, men marry down. Says sociologist Cynthia
Fuchs Epstein: "For all the talk about the women's revolution, there
are no figures to indicate this is changing." And yet if women could
get over our learned need to attach ourselves to someone more powerful than we—and accept the more democratic notion of a relationship between peers—new numbers of men would become available to us. "I won't even go out to dinner with a man who makes less
money than I do," says a divorced woman who is an advertising copy
chief. She eats dinner, night after night, alone.

It is not our success but leftover, childish symbiotic needs that
push so many men out of our lives. In cool and sophisticated disguise, these needs surface in our grown-up years. Jackie Onassis went
from President Kennedy to Aristotle Onassis. How many men can
there be left for her if she continues on that trajectory? As it is, popular speculation is that she will never marry again.

Says Dr. Kaplan: "I think many men are happy to accept women
of superior accomplishment. *We* aren't able to accept ourselves yet.
We keep on thinking we have to look for men superior to us. Women
have to learn that their self-esteem cannot depend on 'superior'
males. We shouldn't need daddy."

A man who is tight with money destroys our illusion that we have
found the powerful, overabundant father who will give us everything
we feel we cannot earn for ourselves. "When a woman marries," says
Sonya Friedman, "and finds out her husband is cheap, or she buys a
dress and he has a fit, it's tremendously jarring. Stinginess is the one
thing women resent more than anything else. They can even tolerate
impotence, sadism, and infidelity. Cheapness rules him out."

Symbolically, nothing says you are big and strong as forcibly as
money. The last thing I want to do here is set up money as the kind
of value for which men have thought it worth killing themselves—but
it is vital that women understand their choices regarding money, how
often unconscious separation anxieties get played out in our attitudes
toward the dreamy stuff.

From the time we are children, we begin to learn not how to earn money but how to manipulate for it. Half the fights between mother and father are about money. We sense her feeling that if he loved her more, there would be more money available for him to give her. Money is proof he wants to take care of her. (It is a truism of psychoanalysis that when a child steals money from her mother's purse, she is stealing love.) If mother had to earn money for herself, that would mean she was not so dependent on daddy, not nearly so loved by him. What we must do is turn the whole game around. Instead of making money ourselves, which means we are separate, unloved and independent, we want to have our husband put us on an allowance, as mother did. This uses money not to threaten the symbiotic connection but to establish it more firmly.

The man thinks setting up a reward system of giving the woman something extra to buy a new dress is his idea; the woman is at least complicit in this maneuver from the start. When we are grown and have a "big daddy" of our own, we still like to get that nice little extra something for being "a good girl." In this way, money becomes involved with closeness, rather than separation. "Nevertheless," says Professor Jeanne McFarland, "while the wife is proud of how she can cajole money out of him, she knows the real money power is with him. When the man threatens to leave her, instead of quickly thinking of ways to support herself, she feels the old paralysis. By the time you're a wife, you don't really have economic options because you've bought the model that says you're dependent."

When the American Council of Life Insurance asks in its annual national sample, "What does masculinity mean to you?"—each year at least 80 percent of the population answers, "A good provider." (Sexuality is so far down the list it doesn't get a mention.) For the single working woman trying to find her elusive identity, this means one thing: in becoming too good a provider, she becomes unfeminine. She is depriving a man of his role in life, emasculating her own man—should she have one. At AT&T, women can get a college education on company pay while going up the corporate ladder. "If the gulf between what she makes and her husband's salary is not too wide," says Personnel Director Amy Hanan, "she takes advantage of the offer. But when it is too wide, the marriage is often jeopardized. It is too much of a threat."

Traditionally, when women had money of their own, a bank, a husband or father took care of it. This socially sanctioned ignorance masks an immense concern with money, along with a feeling of powerlessness. Says Jeanne McFarland: "Women profess a stupidity about money, they are willing to take on this foolish caricature in order to buy the socially accepted role of womanhood. I don't know any woman, however, who actually lives out this stereotype."

Women, who made up 33 percent of the national labor force in 1960, now account for 40.7 percent, a proportion that was not expected to be reached until 1985.[9] Economist Eli Ginzburg calls the flood of women into the work force "the single most outstanding phenomenon of our century."[10] And yet most women like to give the impression that "the man of the house" runs the money, while they not only contribute to it but make most of the consumer decisions.

All of which leads to dreadful arguments because of the double message women send out: Little me, I know nothing about money, take care of me. At the same time we broadcast: Money is very important, I can't make it, so you've got to make enough for both of us, and if I do make it, then goddamn it, I'm going to make a lot of the big decisions about it. (To say nothing of the third message: Despite all I've just said, I want to feel you're making the decisions anyway.)

"The issue of what money does for a woman and what it doesn't is a puzzle," says Emily Jane Goodman, lawyer and co-author of *Money, Women and Power*. "If she doesn't have a man to turn it over to, she is in a dilemma. A shorthand way of saying it is, What woman goes out and buys herself a Porsche? It boils down to a sexual thing. For men, financial success is a very sexual experience. For women, it is not. If we make money, we don't really know how to enjoy it in the same way as a man. We do not accumulate men, we do not accumulate wealth. We don't see them as interchangeable. Men are not sexually attracted to us by our wealth and power. If money is indeed an aphrodisiac when obtained by men, it is a turn-off when obtained by women."

Even if we can come to terms with the role reversal inherent in the idea of earning more than our husband, we have to live with the disapproval in other people's voices: "I don't like the way people looked askance that I made more money than Jack," says a divorced woman executive. "I tried not to let it bother me. In the end, it got to him. I know money, my money, was the reason we split."

One way to solve our childish need to have a man more powerful than we is to "choose" to make less money ourselves. Very rarely have I heard a woman say she wanted to make a million. I can't count the number who've told me, "I want to marry a millionaire." By deliberately deciding to leave the issue of making money to someone else, by marrying *up* so we feel we have someone powerful to lean on, we have not strengthened the grown woman within, but reinforced the baby.

As undeniably and simply as rain makes you wet, a paycheck is proof we can make it on our own. Once we have succeeded in a job, once we have the feel of money, it loses much of its awe. We know how much it costs to earn; how to spend it, save it, what it can do for us. It no longer is some mystery that only men can understand. Money in your pocket gives you firm ground on which to stand. Until we have an economic alternative to marriage, we have no alternative at all. We will try to make it perform a function it is not meant to do. Love does not easily survive a power relationship in which one partner can economically blackmail the other.

When we were little, if mother had a job or career, we may have resented her for not being there when we got home from school. In the same way, if she did not subvert her sexuality in the service of motherhood, we resented that she wasn't comfy, and homey, like all the other moms. When we are grown, we may realize she gave us something better: the image of sexuality, of independence, of a woman earning money, spending it, enjoying the freedom from anxiety that comes with knowing you can support yourself if anything happens. "The girls who are being best taught that autonomy presupposes economic independence," says Jeanne McFarland, "are those who have career mothers."

Sometimes, even as we pursue career and sexuality, we continue to be angry she wasn't the way we, as children, would have liked. Anger is a way of maintaining some form of tie. As long as we remain fixed on resentment of what she didn't do, we don't have to think of what we must do for ourselves. "Children," says Jessie Bernard, "have always had the option to call on mother for help and support until they were fifty. Mother must have the right to say, 'OK, I've done my share. I'm finished.'"

"The money I would ordinarily have given my daughter, I spent on a trip to Paris," a woman tells me. "The day I got on the plane, I said to myself, 'This is my declaration of independence!'"

Chapter 11

MARRIAGE: THE RETURN TO SYMBIOSIS

Bill and I decided to get married our first hour alone together. He had never touched me. I had known him two years and during that time I had not expected he should. I had always been with another man, he had been with someone too. One morning I phoned and said, "It's my birthday." "I'll get my shoes shined and take you to lunch," he said as casually as if we had been meeting for years. We went to the Drake and sat in the darkness at the far end of the bar. "When you and I begin," he said with our first martinis, "it's not going to be like all the other times."

Nothing in me argued. "You get out of your thing with Tom," he said, "and I'll get out of mine. I'll be waiting." We never had lunch. When we left the bar, we paused on the corner of Fifth Avenue and 55th Street and looked at one another. We had decided to spend the rest of our lives together and we had never kissed.

My call to him had said I was a very separate person. It was what drew him from the very start. "I love it that I'm not your life," he said. The only advice my mother ever gave me about men was "Marry a man who loves you more than you love him." She didn't hand it to me like a bulletin. I can't even remember the context in which it was said. I thought I'd dismissed it as yet one more of my mother's well-intentioned, but mostly irrelevant, bits of advice. The eerie way that sentence has remained isolated in my mind says how profound an effect it had on me. I wasn't ready to marry; my life as a single woman was at its zenith. But I never doubted this was the man for me.

Because he loved me more than I loved him? Other men had loved me for different reasons. When they asked me to marry, when they spoke of their love, I did not respond—I could not match the emotions they were talking about. Bill saw the part of me I wanted to become.

Bill wasn't ready to get married either. He had written several books on the pleasures of bachelorhood. I loved what he saw in me that had made him change his mind; as I grew to love him more, I became more the person he admired. And yet I have always felt I defrauded him. He had seen me on a good day. The woman who called him, the woman who left men easily and flew around the world on her own, was only independent until she was in love. I was only secure as long as he loved me more than I loved him. The way he loves me binds me to him. "Don't ever leave me," I whisper to him at night. It puzzles him. He thinks of me as the woman self-determined enough to write books like this. I am, but I am that frightened person too.

I have always liked it that my mother is so attracted to Bill. She responds to him physically. When she's on the dance floor with him she never wants the night to end. She never criticizes him as she does my sister's husband. The first time I took Bill home, my mother gave a cocktail party. A local banker offered Bill a job. "We're sailing to Europe," Bill announced. Mother looked from him to me. "On the same ship?" she asked, and then quickly rose above that first clutch of anxiety. "How romantic!" she said. Because I was with a man she respected, she acted like a woman instead of a mother.

Before we sailed, she and my stepfather came to New York. Bill was taking part in a literary symposium. Very quickly it changed from polite conversation to a heated argument about "What has happened to fucking in literature?" During the intermission, Bill looked uneasily at my mother. "Shall we leave?" My mother was crushed. "Oh, no!" she said, "let's stay." Afterward we went to a bar in the Village. "Once," my mother said, "when I was twenty-eight, I met a man in a railroad station. He was an army captain. There was a line in front of the telephone booth, and he gave me his place. That night he took me to dinner. When I got to daddy's the next day there were roses from the captain. He wanted to see me again, but I couldn't. . . ." Her voice trailed off. She was smiling, flushed. My stepfather had gotten up from the table and was sitting a few feet away at the bar, staring at my mother. He had never heard this story. "Why didn't you see him?" I asked, fascinated by something I had never seen in her before. "Because," she said, "daddy wouldn't let me." "I'll tell you what, Jane," Bill said to my mother. "We'll make up for the adventure you missed. There's a taxi outside. Let's the four of us get in and go to Kennedy and take the first plane to Puerto Rico. We'll buy the toothbrushes there." When we dropped mother and Scotty off at their hotel that night, she was still pleading, "Oh, Scotty, forget your business appointments tomorrow. *Let's go!*"

Seeing me with Bill changed our relationship. It opened up something in her she hadn't dared expose before. Had I become the mother, giving her permission to give in for once to the antic side of her nature? Was it competition? Had she just slipped into my skin? Probably a bit of all these reasons, but mostly I think it was exhilaration that I had gotten past a barrier and in so doing had made the way safe for her. I felt comfortable with Bill and me in the lead because I believed more in us than in them. "Marry a man your mother is half in love with," is the advice I give my single women friends.

Four months later when we cabled her from Rome that we were getting married, she swallowed her fear of flying and came to Europe for the first time. We had planned a beautiful wedding at Michelangelo's Campidoglio—Rome's city hall. Afterward, there was a wedding lunch at the Casina Valadier—it had been Napoleon's son's villa, overlooking the fountains of the Piazza di Popolo. As I planned the details of the menu, the flowers, the ceremony, and the parties surrounding those days, I think I had her pleasure in mind as much as Bill's and my own. It was our wedding, taking place on ground we had chosen, but for the first time in my life when a judgment of taste had to be made, I did it her way. The night before the wedding, I asked Bill to move out, not just to another room but to a different hotel. While my mother was speeding forward to meet her adventurous daughter, I was retreating back to her.

I argued with Bill all the way to the altar. Terrible fights up until the moment I swore to the man in the red, white, and green sash of Italian civil law that I would live in Bill's "stanza" (room) forever. Much as I wanted to be married to Bill, I didn't want everything to stop—the men, the travel, the possibilities for change. Did half of me hope Bill would call it all off? I'll never know. The moment I married, I was triple married. Overnight I became a wife. I wrote home to mother for recipes. I bought a series of prim little double-seamed dresses. I banished even the remotest thoughts of infidelity by never looking at another man. I gave all the money to Bill; no, I didn't even want my name on the checks. I would just ask him for cash when I needed it.

I loved the picture of my mother with her man and me with mine, as two jolly couples. When they came to New York we would take them dancing. When they came to Italy, we would abandon our work and drive them to Florence or Positano. I was meticulous about the arrangements and would call ahead to be sure they got the best room, the one with the cantilevered bathroom so my mother could lie in her tub surrounded by the Mediterranean. "Nancy, you're planning too many things," Bill would say as I scheduled activities to please them from dawn to midnight. "No, no," I would say, and call the restaurant to be sure the fiddler remembered my mother's favorite tune was "Fascination." Now that I was married, I wanted to be a good daughter; now that I was married, I was able.

When men approached me I felt the old excitement, but it frightened me. One night at a bar, a man said, "You are too much together, you and your husband." Five minutes earlier, when I had rejected him, I had felt a twinge of regret. Now I took his criticism as a compliment.

When we moved to London we found a beautiful house for sale. Being writers, we had no credit rating. "I'll write mother," I said. "Don't," Bill said. "Don't ask your mother for money." "It's not asking for money," I pointed out. "We're just asking her to countersign a loan." I reminded him of how often my mother helped out my sister and brother-in-law. I had never asked her for anything, not in my whole life. How could she possibly say no? I smiled at Bill's resistance. He didn't have a close family like mine. "One for all and all for one!" was my grandfather's toast at family dinners. I smiled now when I said it, but had grown up believing in those words. I wrote mother. I remember the day her letter arrived, a fat envelope on the hall table containing five pages explaining why she couldn't countersign the loan. Bill put his arms around me. He didn't say a word.

I didn't answer my mother's letter. My silence was nothing as simple as a desire to get back at her. I needed desperately to understand. When I can't sleep, Bill's joke is that "Even in her dreams, Nancy is always asking 'What does it all mean?'" The pain I felt questioned my whole relationship with my mother, a lifetime was balanced in the air. If family was so important, if being a good daughter was superior to being good at anything else—then why was this refusal my reward?

My mother's letters over the subsequent months never mentioned the issue of the loan. "I'm sorry you're so busy, darling," she would write. "I wish you'd find time to send just a note." When I did write at last, I did not mention the house, but the subject roiled in me like a storm.

Six months later we found another, less expensive house which we bought on our own. It is the only place I have ever lived that I felt was *my* home, Bill's and mine. Was it because we bought it without assistance? Only partially. Unlike other places we had lived, I had no hesitation decorating that house. I knew exactly what I wanted. One sunny afternoon as I was lying on an antique British officer's campaign bed in a sitting room that fit me like a second skin, I picked up a book on women's sexuality. The author's theory was that the basis for a woman's orgasmic potential lay primarily in her trust of men, first developed in her relationship to her father. "But what about mother?" was my immediate response. The idea for this book was born in that house.

Eventually my mother and stepfather came to visit us. Content in my new home, past angers forgotten, I went into my old good-daughter gear and staged a lavish cocktail party so they could meet our English friends.

Bill and I took time off from work and flew to France to show them the Paris we loved. Late one night, when I was seated beside my mother in a restaurant, she edged toward me on the banquette, almost cuddling up to me. I wanted to shove her away. Instead, I leaned far away from her toward Bill—half furious, half repentant and guilty that I could not give her the affection she wanted from me. Sometimes the anger would rise in the middle of a tour of Notre Dame, or a walk through a department store. Once I got up and left her sitting alone in the Café de Paris. We never talked about these scenes, she never ceased to show me a smile the next time we met. My anger seemed to belong to another person, another time. It did.

Oh, perhaps she should have countersigned that loan. Perhaps it was wrong of me to ask. These are questions that have no answer. Who was right, who was wrong can never be fixed. The anger that came out of the collision between my expectations of my mother and her own estimate of what she could or could not do for me—that was real. It was the beginning of my responsibility to be me.

So sweet is the first feel of marriage that we give up everything. We abandon our names, say good-bye to old lovers and friends, and close our savings and checking accounts, putting everything in our (his) name. We are losing our credit rating for life—should this man ever die or leave us—but we don't want to hear those arguments. We have come full cycle. We are home. Nothing has ever felt so right as putting ourselves in his hands.

The uncertain rewards of autonomy now seem like so much rebellion, merely a childish phase we had to go through to get here. "When I was single," a divorced woman of thirty-two says, "I had this crazy life. A terrific apartment, work that sent me all over the world, lovers. . . . Oh, the men I used to fall in love with! Then I got married. I stopped seeing my single friends. Even though I had argued with my mother for years about how provincial she had become by living in the suburbs, my husband and I moved out of the city ourselves. Mother and I became great friends. When I married, I started re-enacting my mother's life, like a sleepwalker. I used to refer to my single years as 'my rebellion.' Now I refer to my marriage as 'my regression.'"

When we marry, we don't know how to be. We intend to "make up" our marriage with this man we love, just as we planned to make ourselves up when we were single. We will incorporate only those warm and loving aspects of mother's marriage, and throw out the rest. One day our husband says angrily, "You are just like your mother." Nothing cuts so deep.

Everything reminds us of her. When we decorate our house, when we stand at our kitchen stove, or buy clothes to fit our new married persona, who comes to mind? When he pays the bills, when he tells us how to cope with the world and holds us in his arms, promising love forever, what we feel is what we once had with her. Or grieve that we did not. In our union with him we are reunited with her.

"What makes symbiosis hard to break through," says Dr. Robertiello, "is that it is so endorsed by society. This sticky, gooey closeness between mother and daughter is seen as some idyllic, wonderful thing. In fact past age one and one half or two, it's an absolutely terrible thing. When you have this symbiotic dependency between a mother and daughter who is eight or eighteen, it's nothing to cheer about. If the woman is twenty-five and married and still telephoning mommy every day, it means there's something wrong. Society always prefers to endorse people's insecurities rather than their health, independence and tradition-breaking possibilities." An almost superhuman conscious effort is demanded if we are to maintain our individuality in marriage.

"Lean on me," our husband says. Little does he realize the profundity of the invitation. "How was I to know," says a divorced man, "what she meant by asking me to take care of her? Of course I said yes. It made me feel proud of myself, and competent."

"I need a lot of sleep," his wife would say.

"Fine," was his reply. "Just tell me when you're tired, and we'll leave the party."

"No, you don't understand. You must tell me when to go to bed. If you leave it to me, I'll stay up all night and be wretched tomorrow."

"I was too dumb to recognize what a dirty bargain was being struck," the man says. "From then on, she could be as irresponsible as she liked and if anything went wrong, it was because I hadn't taken care of her. Who was I supposed to be? Her mother?"

Not for independence, not for an apartment of our own, not for experimenting with jobs, careers, work, sex, men, but for this—*this* is what mother raised us to be good at: to live for, through, and protected by, others. It makes us feel more at peace than anything we ever did for and by ourselves.

When we were single our independence may have reminded us how much like our father we were—he too had a life away from home and mother. Many married women still say father was the determining person in their character, the one who shaped their attitudes. It is understandable. Mother stands for worry, anxiety, fear. She is connected with the baby embarrassments of dependency, feeding tantrums, etc. All that is long behind us. We are like father now—women of the world. But who was our sexual model? The act of marriage makes us feel more womanly. Is that identification with father? We have taken mother's model into ourselves; an added strength runs through our veins. With the circle of gold on our finger, we wake like sleeping giants. Lying on his breast, we feel omnipotent, as once we must have done lying on hers.

Our marriage puts mother's heart at rest too. It is proof that she has been a good mother. Accomplishments prior to marriage may have made her proud, but they also put distance between us. Marriage builds a bridge back. She helps us decorate the house, sends us *The Joy of Cooking,* lends us money. *She is available.* We think the change is in her. It is we who have changed, taking a step back in time to meet her again. So complete is the reunion it doesn't matter if our husband is richer or more powerful than her own: she lives in our triumph as if it were hers. Marriage is the great equalizer.

"All my life I wanted my mother's approval," a woman says. "For her to say, 'Well done!' Nothing I accomplished in my single years did it for me like finding a husband. Now she wants my approval." We think our reunion with mother is self-chosen, that it is a step forward in our relationship, growth toward maturity. Because she treats us as an equal now, phones for advice, and even depends on us in a way she never did before, the assumption is we are bigger people. The truth is that in marriage we become the little girl who once took down the cookie sheet and imitated mommy. We also become mommy.

Very often the new mother-daughter friendship comes at the expense of what should be our prime union—with our husband. We do not mean to ally with her, but whose standards are we living up to when we give up our identity? Did he ask it of us? When a husband is unfaithful but the wife does not take the same freedom for herself, to whom is she remaining true? If sex once divided mother and daughter, The Rules in marriage make us friends again. Monogamy is the vow made for our husband but even more to placate the introjected mother within. The Rules make a prison, but they give us rest; they inhibit each woman equally.

"After we'd been married six months," a thirty-year-old woman recalls, "my husband said he didn't want me to talk to my mother on the phone so much. 'I don't want you to see her,' he said, 'until you understand a new habit you've gotten into. If I want to put a chair here, the table there, the two of you get together and decide they would look better in a third place. She's done it for years to your father. I won't have you lining up against me with your mother. You and I will decide and then we'll tell her how we want things done, if we tell her at all.' He was right. I wasn't even aware of slipping into this thing with mother—which, in a way, was against him."

Hence, the terrible mother-in-law jokes that men tell.

For some people, the blissful "in love" stage of the honeymoon may go on for years. We idealize the other person—and through him, ourselves. "It is a very heightened symbiosis," says Dr. Robertiello, "a merger with the fantasized ideal. The other person is seen not as he is, but as the glorious person we want him to be." The unspoken self-flattery here is that we must be pretty special too, to have been chosen by this incredible being. For others, reality presents its harsh face when the two weeks in Bermuda end and he calmly goes back to his job or golf foursomes. He walks out the door alone, and doesn't think of it as betrayal at all. When he leaves home for work in the morning, his feeling of doing the right thing is unmistakable. Much as we love our new house, our new name, they have not brought us what we expected of marriage. The rational self knows the mortgage must be paid, but somewhere within we feel his 9 to 5 life—*anything separate from us*—is a rival. We want love, more love, love without end. Doesn't he want it too?

We are told we are womanly to need love so badly but the issue is not love. It is the longing to be merged. If we take a job for a salary our new family needs just as much as it does his, why don't we feel as wholeheartedly right about working as he does? "Everything is OK," he says reassuringly. We don't believe him. The independence of a job, life in the office with other people, do not seem to complement what we have at home, but carry jeopardy. New friends and adventures when we were little, sex itself, were all the more exciting because they were *away* from mother, but that was why they were tinged with anxiety too. We didn't tell her about these experiences because we believed they would frighten her; the truth is we were frightened that if she knew, she would get angry. Our tie to her would be weakened. This way of thinking was confirmed when we found out later that more men, more success and accomplishment often lost us the love of other girls. They experienced our gains as somehow leaving less of the pie for them. How can our husband be any different? How can he not fear the added life we get from work as a betrayal too? Won't he love us less, even leave us?

A successful career woman tells me she feels no conflict at all between marriage and career. "It was my husband who encouraged me to continue my job," she tells me proudly. But when we part, she calls me back: "I've been thinking," she says. "Sometimes I do feel guilty that I'm not there with a hot meal when Jim comes home from work. It's irrational, but there it is. There's this niggling fear that maybe I'm disenfranchising myself from my femininity. He's never said anything, but I feel it."

The anxiety here is not between husband and wife but within the woman herself. On TV, she sees commercials of families moving ever together in tight, compact groups. She has her own history of closeness within her childhood family. She and her husband may have worked out more economic divisions of time; she may be getting rewards more real and appropriate from her marriage—but it is not what she was raised to look for. The majority of American divorces—higher than ever last year—come in the second year of marriage. The third year is almost as bad. More women than ever are working outside the home, but our culture has taught us so successfully that a woman's place is tied to a man as securely as once we were tied to mother that we are guilty about our efforts to be free. Men too have been raised to think of women in this way. Though they may give our work separate from them verbal encouragement, the other half of the unspoken double message is often there too: why aren't you the way my mother was with my father?

It is important to emphasize that wanting to be taken care of is not always negative. Men and women are drawn together because we all need a close, intimate relationship. In a good one we can satisfy each other's needs with pleasure, or at least at low psychic cost. To be held in someone's arms, to be able to say, "I'm scared, lonely, tell me everything will be all right. Comfort me and I'll do the same for you when you feel this way"—that is not asking to be guaranteed against all the vicissitudes of life. The woman who says this is merely asking for a resting place, a fueling station in which to gather her strength to go on again. It is not quitting the job of adulthood, nor submitting to a superior-inferior relationship. It is the pause that refreshes.

When "take care of me" means asking someone to permanently interpose himself between us and reality, the wish is destructive to the self, and therefore to the marriage. In the 1936 movie *Dodsworth* there is a scene I once would have dismissed as cute movie dialog. Walter Huston's wife has a shipboard flirtation with suave David Niven and quickly finds herself beyond her depth. Humiliated, she says to her husband, "Sam, you've got to take care of me. I frighten myself. And if I'm bad, promise you'll beat me." Walter Huston dismisses this as foolish woman talk, but the need to be nurtured, disciplined, and protected by a man as if he were our mother speaks of unformed identity: take care of me, tell me how to be, who to be, let me be your child.

This behavior is often found in women whose total orientation toward life is a kind of reliving out of the dissatisfactions they experienced from a cold, nongiving mother. Even in sex, such a woman expects to be passively gratified at all times, with little concern for the man's needs or satisfactions. If her primary aim is to be nurtured, to be petted, soothed, *suckled* (in any of its unconscious disguises including the sexual), it is not orgasmic satisfaction she is looking for; I've heard men say sex with women like these makes them feel, not refreshed, renewed and satisfied, but exhausted.

A psychiatrist describes a sexual problem she often sees in women: "She won't do anything during sex because that means giving. All she wants is to receive. She speaks of sex as 'letting him make love to me.' The idea that she might make love to him is inconceivable. She just wants to lie there. The typical mother of a woman like this simply hadn't been there, emotionally or physically, when the woman was little. Therefore, the daughter's orientation toward life was that she had to be constantly reassured, told how good she was, to be nurtured and done for. She can't give, partly because she was afraid she would be smacked down if she did, but mostly because she has very little to give." You can't learn to give without having been initially given to.

I don't think most women question the rightness of expecting a man to take care of them. We have been raised to think that handing men our will is as precious a gift as our virginity. A friend of my husband's speaks about a woman he met after fifteen years of marriage. "I didn't realize it was an affair, at first," he said. "I had always thought of women—especially a wife—as some kind of burden, some heavy weight you had a duty to carry around on your back. This new woman is such fun, she pulls her own weight at all times. So I didn't realize I was entering something serious with her. Now that I realize it is serious, I don't want the feeling of lightness I get from her to stop."

No wonder so many couples who have lived together worry that marriage may ruin what they have. "We're as much as married now," one of them may say, "what would be different if we went through a legal ceremony?" But marriage does change us; it brings a formal element into our lives, the rigidity of the model of our parents. The friend of my husband's mentioned above, who began an affair after fifteen years of marriage, had been as symbiosed as his wife. It wasn't just his wife who fell into old patterns, he did too.

Women too can find breaking symbiosis exhilarating. A woman

who had been faithfully married to an increasingly indifferent husband for the past ten years tells me about her affair: "I began to think there must be something wrong with me because I never wanted to confess to my husband. I just frankly enjoyed the relationship very much. It's hard to explain, but it had been a very close friendship for many years, before it turned into an affair. We had worked together for six years. My job has been responsible for a lot of growth on my part."

Without putting any value judgment on adultery, let's try to understand what this woman is saying about symbiosis and freedom of choice. What surprised her is how little guilt she felt—as opposed to how much she had always assumed she would. Once she'd experienced the security and self-esteem that came from having a job and life apart from her husband, she could reassess her marriage, decide it was not fulfilling her needs—and do something about the decision. Symbiotic dependence upon her husband had been broken—as evidenced by the fact that she feels no need to "guiltily" inform him. What she is doing is separate from him, her own affair. No wonder she enjoys it so much.

Having a life of our own outside marriage does not necessarily mean we will go in for adultery. Instead, when he goes off for a business trip, we don't simply wait for him to return but take an art class. If he wants to go to a Chinese restaurant but we want to go to a movie, we meet again after each has done his/her thing and it doesn't feel like an unhappy, lonely compromise. The evening leaves us feeling refreshed, each pleased for a little time on her/his own, glad to see each other again. Symbiotic union puts a premium not on doing what the individual wants but on finding something with a low enough common denominator so both can do it together. It is a low-intensity relationship.

It isn't even safe—you never know when, without even looking for it, one partner is suddenly going to be swept off his/her feet by some new person who comes along as a reminder of all the electricity life once offered.

"Before I was married, I functioned very independently," says psychologist Liz Hauser. "I had a job that took me all over the country. I was months on the road, on and off an airplane almost every day. But when I married at twenty-seven, I went directly back into a symbiotic thing. It's really where I'd been all along. When I was growing up my mother used to say, 'Now when you get married, you won't move away. You'll have a little house nearby.' I would not say a word but I had my plans. I wanted out of all that smothering and overprotecting. But if someone hung on to you too long when you were little, or you didn't get enough mothering, you tend to go through life not knowing how to relate except symbiotically. When I got married it was simple transference. There is tremendous regression in symbiosis with the mate, if you haven't settled it earlier. It's important to stress this because women may be able to recognize their regressive behavior in their marriage easier than they can with their child. Marriage is less sacred than motherhood. Our child is where we want to face separation last.

"I was self-supporting before marriage, but after—I began waiting for him to come home and bring me news of the outside world. I was upset that he wasn't there all the time. I began to think of myself only as his wife—no other identity. And so I only felt really alive when he was around the house, when we were together. When he was home, I wanted him to talk to *me*, to be with *me*. I didn't want to travel anywhere without him.

"The moment wasn't real, time wasn't whole when he was absent. *That* is the symbiotic bind. After about six months, he said to me, 'For God's sake, get yourself something to do and go do it.' I knew he was right. I was whining and whimpering like a baby because he was busy with his work, not with me. So I went back to work, thank God."

Symbiosis is not a dirty word. When we are grown, fleeting, temporary symbiosis and merging can play as lovely a role as it did in infancy. There are times when we don't want to be separate, when it is indeed exhilarating within a loving relationship to feel merged—a satisfying sense of closeness, almost a transcendent oneness with the other person. For instance, if we would let ourselves feel this kind of depth of union with our husband or lover tonight, it would be a marvelous experience. During sex, when we suspend our adult lives and get back into those almost primitive feelings of symbiosis that we once had as trusting infants, the joining with the other person is going to give the sexual experience all kinds of different dimensions than it would have had we stayed on an adult level.

The feeling of life that comes from symbiosis isn't exclusive to sex; you can feel it in other moments of deep intimacy with a person. Creative people experience it when they suspend their day-by-day adult consciousnesses and dip back into buried emotions, their earliest, unconscious experiences, to dredge up raw, powerful feelings and ideas to be sublimated into art. *What distinguishes bad symbiosis from good is the loss of choice.*

When the need for symbiosis is so desperate that you cannot turn it on or off at will, you lose your sense of self. The other person, the outside world, loses its urgency and excitement, sex becomes tame, autonomy is gone. Pleasurable, positive symbiosis is entered into at will, enhancing moments of union with the other so that both feel a larger identity than ever before; and yet it is easily broken or interrupted when it is time to separate, to be people with your own ego, autonomy and jobs to do in the world. The conventional name for the feeling is "being in love." In destructive symbiosis the two people meet, feel the initial enlargement of the self due to merging of identities—but can't seem to part. They stay glued to one another. Absence from the partner is tinged with anxiety, peace comes only when they are together. But with so little stimulation and energy coming into the situation, they use each other up. They go stale, but still can't let go.

Women have an important confusion about being taken care of emotionally, and being taken care of financially. It compounds the problem of symbiosis, and so will be discussed here at some length. The difficulty begins with the fact that men and women see money's role in their lives in different ways. This causes almost hopeless frictions compounded by the fact that all of us have been trained to think there is something intrinsically not nice in talking about money at all.

Psychoanalysts speak of stubborn aspects of behavior in the same way they speak of misers or stingy people: they say these are "anal retentive" character formations. It surprises no one to learn that stingy people are often constipated. Whether you believe in psychoanalysis or not, ideas like these resonate on a deep, intuitive level of everyday wisdom; they help explain a great deal about people's furtiveness about money. Most of us have noted how someone would rather tell you his most intimate bedroom secrets than reveal his yearly income. Therefore, it is easy to see that money discussions between husbands and wives begin with a great handicap. Money is symbolic of too many aspects of emotional life to be dealt with on a simple, factual level; too many angry repressions—equations of money, filthy lucre and shit, for instance—are boiling just beneath the surface.

By the time a man is old enough to think of marriage, he is usually on his way to having solved the material side of living. Socialized masculinity tells him that as long as he is a good provider, women will tend to his emotions for him. "Take care of me," he says when he comes home from the office. He means he is exhausted by the battles of the day, and wants his wife to help him feel better. He is asking for emotional support.

The wife too is exhausted by battling it out with the carpool, the repairman, the PTA, and her loneliness. "Take care of me," she says. Her emotional request is as legitimate as his, but she wants more from him. You might say there is a hidden clause in her request. In defense of women, it must be added that this usually operates outside our conscious knowledge: mixed in with any request to be emotionally taken care of is the expectation that this includes being taken care of financially as well—an assumption men do not fully understand. From here, it is easy to fuse and confuse emotional and material needs: we expect that meeting one need implies the man is ready, willing, and able to meet the other too. That is what love "means." If he buys us expensive gifts, a house on the lake, or takes us for a trip to Paris, the economic half of the gift becomes suffused with a romantic, emotional glow: he has "proved" he loves us.

"I will marry for love," a woman says, but the unspoken half of her definition is that love will make her feel free of material anxieties. It is only after marriage that many women become aware that what they love is not just the man but the material security he is supposed to bring. Married couples fight over money more than any other single cause.

On the other hand, a marriage in which all bills are paid promptly is not necessarily a happy one. It is only a negative event, an anxiety subtracted. The cliché is old and tired, but that is because it is so often true: a man often works so hard and long to make the money for the marriage that he has little time or energy left for emotions. After the house in the suburbs, two pretty children and charge accounts at five expensive stores, a wife in a marriage like this may realize she is emotionally starving to death, right in the midst of material plenty. "Why did she leave good old reliable Charley, with his solid job as vice-president at the bank, to run off with a guitar player?" people ask. "She must be crazy." She is hungry. Her confusion and merging of two different needs—financial and emotional—into one, led her to a dead end.

Not every wife in this situation runs off, of course. She may look for the emotional support she needs elsewhere. Charity work, children, adultery, women's consciousness-raising groups, alcohol, divorce itself. Some of these options may work, some may not; questions of value are not the point here. I want only to show that while a woman may turn to various outlets in her search, perhaps a wiser start would be to look at her assumptions. Mother's love and milk gave her both emotional and material well-being; in fact, they were indistinguishable one from the other. When she met a man who could materially take care of her, did she assume—as it had been with mother—she would automatically feel emotionally taken care of too?

Money is the rub, and when marriage fails, often enough it is money which women use to "get back at him." How much of the unrealistic amounts asked for in divorce settlements are meant for support, how much for revenge? When they were in love, she told him money didn't matter, love was all. Now that the unrealistic promise of symbiotic love has failed, money matters very much. But, says lawyer Emily Jane Goodman: "When I tell women that if they do not own and control their own money, they do not control their lives, I always meet resistance. 'Oh, no,' they say. 'I'm the one who keeps the checkbook, pays the telephone bills on time, we have a joint account,' etc. They never want to face that when he stops putting money into the joint account, everything stops."

A cliché says that women control the wealth of the United States. It supports women's refusal to understand our powerlessness over money. If women own the major share of stocks on the New York Stock Exchange, it somehow is supposed to mean we don't have to get angry about impotence over money in our individual lives. "If you are convinced you are part of the ruling class that controls the nation's wealth," says Emily Jane Goodman, "it's hard to get angry over the fact that in your family, you have no say about the money at all."

The day all this changes is when the wife goes to an attorney to seek a divorce. Up to now, she's "chosen" not to know her husband's income, she doesn't know whose name the house is in, what are their total assets in stocks, bonds or whatever. "Who, me? My husband handles all that." When her lawyer asks for figures, income tax statements, bank balances, etc., in order to make a case for alimony and/or child support, the soon-to-be-ex-wife can only weep.

"Women come into my office in divorce cases," says Ms. Goodman. "They've been beaten by their husbands. 'Do you know what assets your husband has?' I say. Their reply is, 'No, but all I have to do is ask him. I know he'll never try to trick me.' It is almost impossible to make her see that this is the man who broke her nose. Why does she think he's going to be level with her about money? Her attitude is, 'If I don't trust him, everything has been in vain.'" If a child cannot trust her mother, what is the purpose of living?

I have heard many an otherwise articulate single woman stammer in her efforts to express her confusion when, the morning after the night of love at his place, there is the matter of the long, expensive taxi ride back to her apartment. Should she pay it herself when he makes four times her salary—merely because she is sufficiently liberated to see herself home? She wants to be equal, but she is broke. Isn't there an easy way for him to slip her $10? Even if he does it gracefully, why does she still feel angry, humiliated, like a greedy child who has just wheedled an extra $10 allowance? No one wants to talk about money, she doesn't know how, but it is her reality.

A common defense wives adopt against economic powerlessness is to live by a kind of unspoken formula. "Your money is our money, but my money is mine." When the husband wants to know how she can justify not pooling all her money, she cannot tell him. Feeling sneaky and sly, she squirrels away part of the housekeeping money in a cookie jar or secret account. She has some unconscious feeling that money—keeping money, hiding money, *her* money—is not nice. On a more conscious level, she has been trained never to mention it. Saddest of all, the amount being withheld is not going to give her autonomy anyway.

My own feeling is that far from behaving childishly, women who defend the unspoken formula "Yours is ours and mine is mine" may be showing a certain amount of common sense. Says psychologist Sonya Friedman: "I don't think it's unrealistic for a woman with no income to put money away as a margin of safety. In marriage counseling, I often see men who are getting ready to leave their wives. He sells the home, then puts her in a new $80,000 house with a $70,000 mortgage and departs, keeping most of the cash realized on the sale of the old house for himself. A woman must always ask herself, 'Am I being financially wise to depend on him totally?'"

Millions of women do contribute to the family income. More than 30 million women work outside the home today—over one-third the labor force.[1] When children must be fed or clothed, there is no question of whose money is whose. A recent University of Michigan survey shows that a third of working women are the sole wage earners of the family.[2] Some women have been raised by their mothers to think of themselves as providers and take pride in it. Other women find feelings of deeply satisfied symbiosis with the husband and children when they hand over their paycheck for the good of the family. "It is when the money in the family rises above the baseline of survival," says Dr. Friedman, "that the trouble starts. It's up to him, the wife thinks, always to provide the economic baseline on which they live. If she earns anything, it is on top. He is not supposed to count on it. She thinks she is entitled to do whatever she wants with her money." She has been raised to think she needn't earn any money at all, so if she does, it is extra, hers alone. And if a money need should arise that she considers to lie within his province of day-to-day family expenses—like a repair bill for the car—and he asks her to help pay for it, she may stubbornly resist.

She usually gives in to him on everything else. Why does she balk here?

Ever since we can remember, mother has held out marriage as the grand payoff for all our sacrifices and restraints. It is put as a kind of reality principle: deferring satisfaction today will lead to a greater reward tomorrow. If we curb our temper, deny ourselves sex, give up assertiveness—all will bring a better man, a safer marriage, one in which it is the man's job to support us. For the wife to contribute money to her own support is to break the symbiotic illusion that the husband will always take care of her.

Money is power, the woman without money is a victim. Most wives realize this means they are living on the edge of a financial precipice. But to say it might make it come true. "When my wife told me she was putting her salary into a savings account in her name," a highly successful surgeon tells me, "I was mildly surprised. But I didn't mind. She makes only a fraction of what I do. She has a good reason to want a nest egg of her own. I've been married four times. I hope this is the last, but if it isn't, her standard of living could go from upper class to welfare overnight." Seen this way, the wife who insists on keeping whatever little money she can earn in her own name is trying to right an unequal power balance—a balance that our society still rigs in favor of men and their greater earning ability. She is also responding to fear: if he breaks the symbiotic promise to take care of her by asking her to pool her money, how can she know he will not break the rest of it and leave her?

It is difficult to tell a husband: "I'm not getting enough emotion from you." It sounds neurotic and childish. It is easier to say, "Why don't you ask for a raise? Why can't we take a trip to South America? The people next door have a new car. Can't we?" Asking for pleasures that money can buy when what we really feel is emotionally poor makes money arguments family-killers. Trapped in role-playing postures, talking about one thing when they mean another, and unable to understand the difference between emotional and material "taking care of," both husband and wife are doomed to endless Rashomon arguments. Each is defending unnamed positions the other doesn't suspect.

"Ask a housewife if she's happy," says Jessie Bernard, "and she'll say, 'Oh, yes, I'm just as happy as can be.' And yet she's taking all these tranquilizers. . . ." In northwest Washington, D.C., Dr. Bernard goes on to report, "The suicide rate among women is higher than almost anywhere else—even though it is a very prosperous area." In fact, since 1950, the number of female suicides in this country has practically doubled.[3]

A woman may resist the new tide of feminism and reject all its tenets, but she cannot forget she has alternatives her mother did not. Grandmother may have gotten enough narcissistic gratification through identification with her husband, his achievements and her status as his wife. Today, television makes it impossible not to know many women out there are getting a lot more out of life. This is not to say being a housewife and mother is not enough for millions of women. It obviously is. But if you are the sort of person who wants more than being *Mrs.* Harry Brown, living through him may not be enough. He is not taking in enough air, life, success and/or achievement for two.

"But the insufficiency," says Dr. Schaefer, "is not seen by the woman as her problem. She thinks it is his. She may feel like a nobody, but the way she puts it is: 'Oh, I'm very happy, but I wish George were better organized so he could get a better job.' Her implication is, If I were George, I could do it better. Another wife will say to her husband, 'If you just tried harder, with all your brilliance you could be making a lot more money.' To the superficial observer, this sounds like the wife has unbounded confidence in her husband. *He* knows this is criticism."

Dr. Schaefer continues: "A woman like this is afraid to take the risks her husband does. She would like a more interesting, stimulating life, but she sees it as something only he can get for her. It never occurs to her the problem is hers. She is so meshed, so dependent on him, she can't see where he begins and she leaves off. She fears that separating out a problem as her own will divide them—that it will force her to act on her own. 'Why not get a job?' I suggest to a woman like this. 'You're terrific with clothes, you could sell dresses in a boutique.' But she is terrified. 'Oh, no, I could never fill out one of those sales slips!' she says. She clings to him and complains instead."

To people like this, the contemporary message that women have a responsibility for their own gratification in life seems like so much theoretical hooey. A woman who is as talented as her husband will put him through law or medical school because she has been trained to feel the life she will get from his success far surpasses what she could get on her own.

In those marriages where roles are shared—where women help carry the financial load and men help in the housework and raising the children, studies show, says sociologist Jessie Bernard, "that women end up working at least 25 percent more than the men."

"Wives have too much at stake to admit unhappiness," says sociologist Cynthia Fuchs Epstein. "You really can't interview people about how happy they are. I did a survey on women lawyers married to male lawyers, and in practice with them. Though these women told me they were living in husband-and-wife partnerships of utter equality, when I observed the actual behavior of a good proportion of them, I found the women were doing the 'housekeeping' of the law firm—the hiring, firing and administration—while the husbands went out, met the clients and did the interesting cases in court. By outside standards, these were very assertive, commanding women. By their own standards, they were 'happy,' but when they said theirs was an equal partnership with their husbands, they were deluding themselves. When you were around them for a while you saw how the women deferred to their husbands. They made the meals, they asked, 'More coffee, dear?' They took the back seat."

There has been a recent backlash among certain male writers who warn that unless women return to traditional roles and get out of the male marketplace, a whole new generation of frustrated and angry males will be unleashed upon the world.

I would like to talk about the rage of women.

We bear a burden of anger all our lives. Just like men, some of us are more angry than others. Although some authorities would like to convince us that men's greater potential for anger is sex-linked (hormones, testosterones, etc.), I remain unconvinced. The difference between the angers of the sexes is that women's are the more repressed.

If I choose to discuss anger within the context of marriage, it is not because I believe there are no happy marriages. I know many. And yet any institution sold to women as a reward for lifelong inhibition must cause anger and disappointment. But how many women can name marriage itself as a source of our turbulence? More often than not, we were the one who most wanted to get married. Besides, if not marriage, what *do* we want? Divorce? That is too fearsome. "The more I talk to a woman," says Sonya Friedman, "the more anger I uncover. All the depression, the going to sleep early, not having energy, the fact that it's three in the afternoon and she is still sitting around in her housecoat—all these are various forms of anger. 'I'm bored,' she says, 'I went through all this schooling, I used to have dreams but now I know they aren't going to be met. I'm even afraid to go back to school, to get out there and compete.' Most of the anger has to do with the way she was raised. Marriage, she was told, would be the answer to all problems. The typical American housewife has no identity apart from her husband, so can't let the anger out. Her only way to deal with it is to turn it upon herself. That is why so many women are depressed."

I was very moved by the following interview. The woman is thirty-five years old. At first I thought her gentleness of speech was part of her early, learned passivity. What she said made me realize it is the calm that comes after the battle of facing one's own raging emotions.

"My mother died five years ago, of emphysema. She was submissive and my father was very dominant. All my life, I watched her swallow her anger. Mother was such a gentle, loving person. She wouldn't want me to bottle up the turbulent emotions I've been going through but she never showed me how to get them out. I thought my parents had a perfect marriage because I never heard them fight. It was a difficult experience for me, working out my anger toward mother after she died. But it was a freeing experience too, to be able to admit the anger, the hate, as well as the love. Part of my anger is having held back getting my postgraduate degree until my husband had his. From my mother, I got the feeling that, as a woman, I had to let him go first. I had learned that kind of deference to men from her, and I was angry at her for teaching me this. I married someone totally different from my father and have had trouble accepting his regard for me. I have only recently stopped thinking of him as weak for what is in essence his high opinion and tender feelings for me. I couldn't appreciate this because I was looking for what mother had settled on. I have deep respect for my mother and for my father. I am not angry at my father. I am angry at her because I am like her, because she taught me to be like her. Because she loved me, she taught me to swallow my anger."

Speech is the least harmful outlet for anger. The easiest way to dissipate it or to change the environment in a beneficial way is with words. But one of the first things girls are deprived of is the direct translation of thought into speech. While we are little, the clever, articulate child is mother's darling. It is the commonplace experience of pediatricians that little girls learn to speak earlier and more fluently than boys. As we become young women, this changes. The subtle training in silence begins.

We learn that spontaneity in speech can lose you people. We learn to edit our thoughts, to reduce strong emotions to bland euphemisms. "When I go places with my husband," says a thirty-year-old woman, "I'd like to participate more in the discussions. But by the time I've formed a sentence in my head, the talk has already gone on to a new subject."

We are not practiced in spontaneity. What fluency in speech this woman picked up in college has been lost in the ten years she has spent at home raising children. She does not regret the choice of motherhood; she just can't understand her uneasiness about joining in dinner-party conversation. "Many men aren't necessarily bright, but that doesn't stop them from going nonstop. Why can't I let myself get in a word?"

Like any other facility, the conduit between brain and tongue requires use if it is not to go rusty. Without practice, the prospect of humiliation, fear of saying the wrong thing and finding ourselves stranded midsentence, keeps us silent.

We also have the social disadvantage of a woman's voice. I've often sat in my own living room and heard my opinion ignored as if I were invisible; the same idea spoken five minutes later in a sonorous male voice is applauded. These experiences do not equip us to handle differences of opinion about a movie or even teasing about a tennis game. How can they equip us for the sudden and violent emotions of anger?

How many women have you ever heard express hostility intelligently? Our voices become charged, not with anger's force and determination, but with an anxious quality that makes listeners turn away. They are afraid we will lose control; they are "bored" by our over-emotional delivery. "That's how women are. They can't argue logically." What drives us to fury is not the illogic of our argument, but inexperience in speaking aggressively. We ourselves fear hysteria. I have watched socially organized groups of intelligent women disintegrate into anxious little knots of dismay when faced with someone's inability to speak her anger at another woman who is present. It is easier to show anger to a man: it was a woman who taught us to suppress our rage. Tears and weeping are the only sound of anger we are allowed.

Without female models able to show us how to vent anger in socially acceptable ways, we fear the emotion, deny it. "When I was in college," a woman tells me, "I took fencing lessons. Part of the rules are that you are required to stomp aggressively on the floor to start a match. You don't have to say a thing, just *stomp!* That was the part I loved best."

In her book on rape, *Against Our Will,* Susan Brownmiller describes a self-defense karate class in which the male instructor ordered the women students to hit him as hard as they could. He assured them they could not hurt his professionally hardened muscles and gave them permission to be as aggressive as they liked. Ms. Brownmiller reports that at first not a single woman could allow herself to hit the instructor with all her force, and many could not strike a blow at all.[4] Learning how to protect ourselves begins as an emotional problem.

Because society would rather we always wore a pretty face, women have been trained to cut off anger, much as surgeons in the nineteenth century, for similar reasons of keeping "the sex" tame, popularized the clitorectomy. "Help me," we cry, running to psychiatrists, surgeons, doctors, priests, or even back to mother. We say we are "nervous" and take tranquilizers, aspirin, gin and courses in Total Womanhood. We say we are "happy" but find ourselves unaccountably suffering from headaches, ulcers, or chronic fatigue. We say we are bored and gamble, take lovers or spend too much money in the department store. We say we are not in the mood and deny our husband sex. We say we are menopausal and live in states of chronic physical and/or mental anguish for a decade. There is a respectable body of medical opinion which believes that our buried, long-smoldering anger can even lead to the silent explosion of the body against itself: cancer. Our anger against the false idealization of marriage is so unacceptable that we have turned it against ourselves in the profoundest sense of the word.

A forty-five-year-old woman speaks: "I was married at high noon at St. Patrick's Cathedral. You can't do better than that. I did so many things right. I suppose I was acting out my mother's desires. When she was growing up, she didn't have the opportunities so she made them for me. She was a career woman, worked all her life, and she expected me to be an achiever too. She got a lot of vicarious pleasure out of whatever my sister and I did, but she never gave us praise directly. We'd hear it from her friends. So there was this ambivalence we got from her: 'You should do better than I did . . .' but a feeling of jealousy too.

"Along with making my mark in the world, I was brought up to marry and raise a family. My mother used to pray for me to St. Anne . . . you know, 'St. Anne, get my daughter a man.' When I was twenty-eight and still not married, she switched to St. Jude, the patron saint of hopeless cases. This set up a kind of split in me. Especially on the job. It is hard to work alongside a man, and even compete with him for the same promotion—but nevertheless need his approval as a woman at the same time.

"Marriage made it easier for me to be nice to my mother. When I married, I stopped working. I was going to be the typical Irish Catholic East Side New York young matron. But my husband died and I had to go back to work. That was fifteen years ago, and I've made a professional success of my life. But I am left with this anger. If I had been raised to be even normally aggressive, I would not have had to always assume the soft position in career situations; I always needed male approval of me as a woman before I could think about getting it as a professional and a peer. All those years of smiling at men who were less capable than I. . . .

"Nowadays, my mother depends on me. I am not angry at her any more for withholding her approval when I was a kid. That's how she was. She called me at the office today and asked if she should wear a pants suit on an airplane. A few years ago, I would have been angry at her for bothering me with such a stupid question at work. Today, I have my anger under control. Perhaps I have mellowed. I made time for her call, even though it meant I had to delay a meeting. At this point, I guess I view her very much as I do my children. It's a responsibility, part of my dues-paying. It leaves me with a good feeling. The latent hostilities, the things that bugged me when I was younger, are still there, but I avoid them."

The woman in this interview died of cancer a year after I spoke to her. Her two daughters are being raised by her sister, who asked if she could read the interview. "It made me sad to see how emphatically my sister denied being angry about certain things," she wrote me. "She said that because she understood, she didn't have to get mad. . . . How I wish she had been angry at some things, some people. She wasn't even angry about life's final assault on her."

Says Dr. Schaefer: "I see so many women whose lives are dominated by the idea, 'He won't let me.' The whole women's movement is based on personal responsibility, but many people think as soon as they've liberated themselves, all the goodies will drop in their lap. They think, Now that I've dumped the old man who was holding me back, now the boss will give me, the world is going to give me, the sisterhood is going to give me. Because women were never raised to be autonomous, they don't understand the personal responsibility needed to make the liberation slogans mean something." We want to be "free" but taken care of anyway.

The bottled-up fury resulting from overidealizing marriage as the solution to all our problems makes for a kind of agoraphobia. "You might even call it 'housewife phobia,'" says Sonya Friedman. "It is not uncommon, and describes the great number of women who don't like, or are afraid, to leave the house alone. It has to do with the fear that once she gets out there in the wide-open spaces, she'll get this irresistible urge to run away."

A private detective who works for a large agency in New York gives me a description of the average runaway housewife. It reads like someone in a TV soap opera: she got married at nineteen, had children shortly thereafter, and has had little or no work experience. She's thirty-four when she differs from her more conventional sisters and disappears to find a new life.

In a symbiotic marriage, you feel protected, close—in fact, so close that no separation can be tolerated. Any emphasis put on individual choice, any anger expressed, is betrayal. I've heard this kind of marriage called "the long quiet walk, hand in hand, to the grave." A psychiatrist I know calls it the "tit-lined coffin." Men have long run away from it. Women are beginning to.

"I was a lot more passionately in love with other men than the man I married," a woman tells her marriage counselor. "There was an actor I was crazy about. He was extremely emotional, and it gave our affair that extra zing. But the idea of marrying him? It frightened me. So I married someone I thought was stable as a rock, like my father. By the time I saw that behind Larry's surface calm he was selfish and unreliable, it was too late. I was already emotionally dependent on him. He would stay out late. He wouldn't telephone. I blamed myself. I was going slowly, desperately mad. But the next morning, I wouldn't want to muddy the waters. There were so many things to do that I would forget my desperation. I made breakfast, got the children off to school and always tried to put a good face on things."

Our culture rewards women for swallowing their anger and/or directing it away from its source. The compulsive housekeeper, the lioness of the Anti-Porn Society, the nonstop charity-worker, the overprotective and critical mother who does it all for someone else's good—who can fault these people out loud? We don't know where they get their energy, we don't know what they get out of it. We may avoid them and their company; but we can't call them bad women/wives/mothers.

Very often, these women are obsessive/compulsives—suffering from forms of behavior that seem to have nothing to do with anger. Unlike depressed people who turn their anger within, against themselves, the obsessive/compulsives express theirs outwardly—but in such an indirect way they never need face their furies at all.

While usually discussed together, compulsions and obsessions differ slightly. Compulsions are repeated acts of behavior, like constantly emptying ashtrays while the smoker is using them, or fluffing up the sofa pillows the minute somebody gets up. If you've ever been around compulsive people and seen how they fray the nerves of anyone they come into contact with, you will recognize that a great deal of hostility is being loosed nonspecifically into the environment. On the other hand, obsessions are not actions, but thoughts. Obsessional people have their minds constantly flooded with repetitive ideas—like the woman who is ever worried that something terrible has happened to the children, that her husband will leave. Once again, anger has taken on a disguise, a constant conjuring-up of pain, loss and death. Nobody has happy obsessive thoughts. Both obsessions and compulsions are repetitive because underground anger must be defended against, over and over.

"What I remember most about my mother," says a twenty-eight-year-old wife, "is the incredible amount of anger she brought to little things, like tracking dirt across the kitchen floor. She would get as hot about a button missing as she would at a sin like lying. I've decided her anger was because she was afraid. Each thing I did wrong was a clue that I was so careless I would do something far worse. I see her anger in myself nowadays toward my little girl, and it frightens me."

Says Sonya Friedman: "Women have problems with anger because they don't have a sense of security within. Women go from being an extension of their families to being an extension of their husbands. Most marry before they complete growing. The man usually has more power, so whatever sense of identity she has can easily be snuffed out. Men don't *do* this *to* women, they do it *with* women's compliance. Women have been so conditioned for marriage that they buy the contract, the trade-off of autonomy for dependence. Later they cry: 'What can I do to save my marriage?' You have to tell these women there are no ready-made answers. Maybe in time they get in touch with their anger, but that means going back to the beginning to when they first learned the double-edged reward they got from mother was paid for by playing down their self-confidence and independence.

Dr. Friedman continues: "Anger is positive. When a woman is unhappy about her marriage, but apathetic, I know it's going to be a tough job to help her. If she's angry, I know I've got a good shot. If I can get a woman to see that she's bought a shoddy bill of goods, she doesn't go into anger. She goes into rage."

Says Dr. Sidney Q. Cohlan: "Just as no child ever meets the mother's fantasy, so does no mother ever live up to the daughter's fantasy of what a mother should be." To continue the fiction that we have some ideal relationship with mother behind the superficial, day-by-day frictions, we often invent a pat phrase to sum up what we have with her. Like sentences in code, they disguise the real situation. "Mother and I get along fine these days, as long as we don't live too near one another." Or, "I don't blame my mother for the way she raised me, she did the best she could." Indeed, unless mother was one of the rare malevolents, she *did* do the best she could. Nevertheless, what she did or did not do, hurt us. The child within is furious still. If you will go back and reread those two sentences quoted just above, you will see there is anger in each one.

"The job of the grown-up part of you is not to deny that angry child within," says Dr. Robertiello. "If you do, that child is going to get out and displace the anger onto other people, like your husband, or take it out in psychosomatics, depression or compulsions."

Here is an example of how a twenty-five-year-old woman both knows and doesn't know that she is angry at her mother: "My mother had this idea that if you didn't talk about sex it wouldn't happen. Even when my sister became pregnant and had to have an abortion, the matter was never discussed. I went into marriage a virgin because I believed what my mother said. That if you were a good girl everything would turn out all right. But all my life I've wondered how important that was. I know it wasn't my mother's fault, but I feel cheated that I was never able to talk about feelings, emotions when I was growing up. I have this anger toward men, and I don't want my daughter to see it. But she can't help but see my resentment toward my husband. He's a good man. I married him because I loved him and because he was accepted by my family. I wanted my mother to approve of my marriage."

This woman is angry at her husband because he didn't make the dream come true. She says she doesn't blame her mother; that is supposed to mean that she's not angry with her—which is not the case at all. Side by side with the love she has for her mother is another emotion: fury. We have trouble understanding that we can be angry and forgiving at the same time. The two are not mutually exclusive. We think if we hate someone we hate them all the way through. This is to misunderstand the split between the conscious and the unconscious, between the adult self and the child.

The solution is not to call up mother and give her hell for what happened twenty years ago. *It is not today's mother we are in a rage with.* She probably wouldn't understand what we are talking about. Or mother may be dead—which does not mean we are not still angry at her. "It is only when you understand the source of your anger," says Dr. Robertiello, "that you may be able to stop displacing it onto your husband or yourself."

There is a big difference between being angry at someone and "blaming" them. If a psychotic comes up and socks you in the nose because he thinks you are his boss's wife, you may be angry, but you don't blame him. You can understand that he is not a responsible person. You might even be sympathetic. But still you got the slap in the face, it hurt, and you're angry. In a similar manner, perhaps what mother did or didn't do came from the best intentions. That doesn't lessen the sting. You were hurt. You were angry. "So it behooves you," says Dr. Robertiello, "to acknowledge your anger and not hide from it by saying, 'Poor mom, she did the best she could.' Just knowing that your anger is inappropriate to the present situation, that it is childish, helps put things in perspective. It frees you from having to relive the past situation in the present."

Part of the problem is that even when we are grown, the little girl within is still fixed, *vis-à-vis* mother, at some period of life so primitive, so imbued with leftover ideas of infantile omnipotence, that there is no distinction between anger and annihilation. Our unconscious won't allow us to feel, let alone express, our rage at mother. To do so brings with it the guilt and fear of killing her. "Thoughts of rage against our mothers are just not acceptable," says psychiatrist, Dr. Lilly Engler. "The only thing more difficult to face is a mother's rage against the child. That is almost impossible. There's too much guilt."

Besides headaches, depression, ulcers and other illnesses, repressed anger can also take the form of sexual masochism—an abhorrent idea which is often gratuitously applied to all women. Freud found it in so many of his female patients he thought it was biological, that it came with our genes. He was wrong, of course. It is cultural and can be changed.

As an example of the roots of a particular kind of psychosexual masochism, take the mother who says to her child: "You've been naughty. Wait till your father gets home." Says a young mother: "In our house, discipline was always handled by my father. I'd be sent to my room to wait until he got home, and I'd sit there quivering. I was terrified of my father, and I would say that my fear of rejection from men stems from him. But even more than I feared him, I needed my mother's approval. It seemed she was the only bulwark I had against him. She dominated the household, including him. And so having established him as the fake authority figure, the bad guy, she would then use him. We would conspire together. If I were going out she'd say, 'Be in by twelve, but if you're really having a good time, call me and I'll tell him it's not as late as he thinks.' "

In time, this woman came to regard her mother as a victim of this terrifying male creature who had to be cajoled, lied to, and above all, controlled—or his savage temper would be loosed. She goes on:

"It was only when I got far enough away from home in distance and time that I began to see what a raw deal my father had. I used to think he was such an ogre, but my mother *ran him*. There is a parallel in my own marriage, in that I accepted the face-value aspect of my parents' marriage. When my husband would storm and rage at me— for ten years he told me I was frigid, castrating and sexually nothing at all!—I accepted it. That's how men were supposed to be—perpetually storming and angry. I never could get mad back at him because my mother had shown me that a *real woman* handles a man with the soft answer and the cunning trick. If I stormed back at him, it would be acting like a man!"

When mother sets up the father as the daughter's disciplinarian, the unspoken message is: "I'm mad at you, but I'm not going to express it because women don't. The bad guys, the sadists of the world, are men. That's what daddy is—he's going to hurt you." Later, when the daughter is married, she does what she has been taught is woman's role: she looks to the man to put her down, to hurt her psychologically or even physically. She may hate it, but it feels right to her. It's what she's been taught to expect. She's a woman, isn't she?

Most important of all, and with dire consequences for women's sexuality, when she does feel angry she maneuvers the man to express it for her, as mother did. She projects her anger onto him. She tricks, goads or taunts him into expressing his rage—for instance, by letting him somehow find out that the $20 dress really cost $75. Then she has the melancholy satisfaction of having made herself the victim of the man's anger. He is vile, but male. She is submissive, but female. The psychosexual pattern, established as a child, is lived out by the woman.

On the other hand, if our needs are to be as symbiotic and unseparate from our husband as possible, we will not do anything that might arouse his anger. Instead of using him to express our anger, we turn it inward. We feel we are failures, become insomniacs, compulsive housekeepers, victims of obsessive ideas of aging, death. One very frequent face this inner fear and anger wears is that of the controlling woman. The nagging, critical, hen-pecking little woman.

Says Dr. Friedman: "We think the controlling wife is so sure of herself. The opposite is true. Very often there is such a terror of *being* controlled or abandoned that she assumes control. A woman who had a very controlling mother often becomes inflexible herself because she has this fear of becoming the helpless child again, on the bottom. She controls the man before he can control her or leave her. But the more she nags and controls him, the more she fears his retaliation—the more she becomes terrified he is going to get fed up and leave her. Any spontaneous impulse on his part must be checked because the next one might be the impulse to leave her."

In human relations, fear is almost always counterproductive. The more a wife fears the husband will leave her, the more she nags, the more she will try to run him like a child. He gets fed up with all the tears, the going through his pockets for evidence, the anxiety. He goes.

As the girl watches her mother play martyr rather than express her anger directly, she learns techniques of masochistic manipulation. "Oh, that's all right," mother tells father, "don't worry about me if you have to work tonight. I'll just have dinner alone." This kind of nonexpressive, nonassertive behavior once again tells the girl she must bow to men's evil ways. The message is: "Any resentment or anger that women might show is nothing compared to men with their tempers, ruthless business ethics, their delight in wars and the may-hem of Sunday pro-football games." Techniques of passive-aggres-sion are being taught—a method of letting the man know you are angry at him, all the while denying you are, giving him no handhold with which to grasp the problem. Passive-aggressive actions may be very subtle, not conscious or even verbal: withholding an appropriate response, for example. A classic case is the man who becomes aware that he has said or done "something." "What's wrong?" he says to his wife, who has gone dead and silent 'on him. "Oh, nothing," she replies. She says it without feeling although everything about her—her face, body, her attitude and posture—is screaming that everything is wrong.

These methods of avoiding expression of anger create an alliance between the women in the family; often it is a method of avoiding sexual competition. Setting daddy up as the bogey man warns the daughter off from wanting to be close to such a stormy, hurtful crea-ture. Only mother is unfailingly kind and nice. It is a way for mother to win the almost universal competition between the parents as to whom the child loves most.

After marriage, in any quarrel, the man is set up as the aggressor, we are the victim. We knew it would come to this. Men only bring pain. Men can't love. A basic insecurity is being expressed: it all depends on this other. His anger, loss, disappearance, or death wipe us out. We would be unnatural if we did not at times resent needing someone so much. But our very dependency forces us to smother any hostility. If the marriage breaks up, we have more to lose than he. Says Dr. Sonya Friedman: "Mothers tell their daughters, 'It's up to you to make the marriage work. It takes 80 percent from you, only 20 percent from him.' No wonder all the studies show that women tend to blame themselves for whatever goes wrong in a relationship."

Except for sex. That is the man's job, 100 percent. If this is so, how is the wife to cope when sex doesn't run smooth? "Sam couldn't keep his hands off me before we were married," a young wife sadly says. "Now he couldn't be less interested." The only advice she gets from popular wisdom is to experiment on the safe margins: try a new perfume, go off for "a second honeymoon" to Hawaii. Says Dr. Schaefer: "The wife is not conditioned to realize that she's just as responsible for their sexuality as he is. She can't imagine initiating sex in totally different ways, to vary the usual active/passive roles." "You're cold and frigid!" cries the man, his anger at peak because he knows he is at least half at fault. But he is the sexual expert. If he labels us a sexual dud, we believe him. It is *all* our fault.

It is only in some buried, central core of being that we know better. It is here where the residual anger lives.

There is little we can do about it. The power relation has been set since adolescence: we are the malleable clay, he is the master sculptor. Do with me as you will. The tyranny of the orgasm begins: true sex, real sex, orgasmically fulfilled sex with your husband will make a different woman of you, a real woman, a prettier woman, one more relaxed, more energetic, happy to be alive. In our secular society, a kind of sexual mysticism is one of our last faiths, and the "right" orgasm comes to be its tangible sign.

It is a medical fact that many women report having wonderful feelings about sex without orgasm, just as it is true that many women have orgasms without sexual pleasure, or happiness. Freud's heavy legacy is the notion that "vaginal orgasm" is in some mysterious manner the measure of womanliness or psychic health. "A very dependent and neurotic woman can be very orgasmic," says Dr. Robertiello. "In my clinical experience I have found women in the back wards of psychiatric hospitals who are multiorgasmic. There are other women who are well-functioning, who enjoy sex, but who have never had an orgasm in their lives. When we say there is a diminution of sexuality with the loss of the self in symbiosis, we must not confuse sex with orgasm. We don't know what makes some people have orgasms and others not. There are no exact correlations between sexual pleasure and orgasm."

"The reason a woman chooses sex to demonstrate her rage," says Sonya Friedman, "is that it is the only weapon she has. On the surface her tendency is to accept the blame, but underneath, because she can't be assertive in any other way, she withholds sex. In almost every marital problem I see, there is sexual incompatibility. Men don't understand that sex doesn't begin in the bedroom. He thinks he can criticize her, yell that she's a lousy mother or housekeeper, and then take her into the bedroom where she'll receive him gladly. He has been able to separate love and sex, but most women cannot. For him, marriage is not the central core of his life. For the full-time wife and mother, *it is*."

A significant number of women do not hold out on their husbands totally but use sex as a form of barter—candy for getting something she wants from him, when she feels guilty or afraid he might leave her. The penalty of turning sex into a commodity in this manner is that it—and she—are reduced to a cheap bribe, and the man who takes that foolish bribe is a chump. Respect is gone from the marriage. So is romance and genuine excitement.

Withholding sex is not always a coldly conscious maneuver. The wife may get sudden headaches; she is tired, fatigued, she says the children may hear them, etc. It doesn't matter that by denying the man she is denying herself. She is gaining something preferable to sex in her state of dependency: the poisoned joys of control.

Says Dr. Friedman: "When a woman turns her anger upon herself and becomes nonsexual or nonorgasmic, she is doing several things. On an unconscious level, she refuses to give him the deepest part of herself, perhaps the only area in which she feels full control. Many women simply don't want to share sex with the man they are married to. I see a lot of women who are selectively orgasmic—just as some men are selectively impotent. It has nothing to do with technique. She is angry, bitter. She doesn't want to give this pleasure to him, to let him see her abandon herself. She doesn't want him to see he has this kind of power over her. She doesn't want to enhance his pleasure. If a woman goes into marriage thinking he must take care of her, which includes making her sexual, fully orgasmic and fulfilled, she's too frightened to tell him what she wants."

Dr. Friedman continues: "To change this way of thinking in which the man is responsible not only for her sex but also for her orgasm is simply not possible for many women. Making herself understand that sex is for her own pleasure, something she actively does for herself, demands rethinking her entire sexual training." We would rather be silent, angry, and asexual.

It is a common enough idea that orgasm correlates very strongly with the trust a woman feels for her sexual partner. "If you are angry, wary or suspicious," says Dr. Engler, "then you feel you must control yourself. You have to control him too. If you are constantly trying to control, you can't let go and be spontaneous in sex or anything else."

Some men are trustworthy and good as gold—and still their wives are unable to let their suspicions go. I do not think that ease in sex is merely a matter of faith in the man, or his knowledge of erotic tricks. Along with Erik Erikson, I believe "basic trust" is first learned in the relationship to mother. Father is immensely important, of course, but unless he genuinely shared in our early mothering, it is years before he enters our life with any degree of significance. One of the fundamentals of our attitude toward our body is the attitude toward it of the person who held, bathed, and toilet-trained us. Was that father? Trust is the issue in sex. It may be altered, affected, augmented, or diminished by what goes on with men. It begins with mother.

Leah Schaefer once told me that when her mother refused to lend her the money that would help finance her training to become a therapist, the resulting anger gave her courage enough to write her book *Women and Sex.* "But from the time I began my research," says Dr. Schaefer, "my relationship with my mother improved. It may have taken anger to get there, but increased anger was not the result of facing it. The opposite was true. My relationship to my mother improved to the day she died because I was released from my old rages against her."

The child is afraid to sexually defy mother. The woman carries her inhibitions with her into experiences with men, but now he is the one at fault: he did not "give" her an orgasm. And yet, simple logic tells us that either partner can only be 50 percent responsible. It is easier to blame our husband than to rearouse our buried furies at mother.

Nevertheless, if the rages of childhood are faced and expressed—if only to ourselves—they do not kill any real love between mother and daughter. I am beginning to see that there is nothing I can ever do that will destroy my mother. I can be as sexual, as free, as different from her in my work and life as I choose, but can have a relationship with her too. It will be far more real than the mythic All-Loving Mommy I had been unconsciously holding out for.

I had always resented feeling that to keep my mother's love and approval I had to be perfect. I had to show her what she wanted to see, and not the me who had grown up in the years away from her. What I know now is that this pact I had set up killed any chance of being myself whether I was with her or not. And wasn't I doing the same to her?

We make our own ghosts.

Chapter 12

A MOTHER DIES.
A DAUGHTER IS BORN.
THE CYCLE REPEATS

During our honeymoon I began to menstruate two weeks early. It had never happened before. I took it as a sign: the mystery of marriage was full upon me. Ten months later, I had a pregnancy scare.

The words are apt because I was as terrified as a sixteen-year-old. Marriage had once loomed like The End of adventure. Now pregnancy threatened like the finish of life itself. With the fervor of a nun, I prayed I was mistaken.

I went to a young American doctor on one of those pretty, shady streets just off the Via Veneto, who confounded me still more with his disdain for a married woman who did not want to be a mother. Afterward I met Bill at the Café de Paris. We sat at one of the cramped tables indoors instead of our usual place on the sidewalk with a view of the afternoon *passagiata*. Bill ordered me a brandy. I was shaking. What was so terrible? Why were we acting like two conspirators hiding from the consequences of a dubious act? We thought it had to do with not being able to afford a family yet. We wanted more time for ourselves. Or so we said. The idea that we simply did not want to be parents was something neither could voice.

I don't think I was really married until two or three years after we'd gone through the ceremony. "Playing at marriage" was how I'd describe that first year in our pretty apartment in Rome. Play-acting in a foreign country. How can the mere signing of a document change a life? Young girls imagine being married so long; when reality comes, it seems a dream. It took me time to become a wife, to give up my fantasies of what marriage would be. I did not love Bill that first year or two, not as I would grow to. I was right to be worried that day. Children, Bill and I had decided, would come later. We were both still absorbed in our marriage. Bill was beginning a new career, as a writer. We were young. We never doubted that one day we would be parents. Not now.   •

Several years later my mother and I were going through a revolving door in Bergdorf Goodman's when I caught the tail end of a sentence: ". . . and the magazine said that birth defects are more frequent among couples who do not have sex frequently . . ." *What?*

Had my mother said that? By the time I caught up to her, she was deep into discussions about the palest shade of lipstick with the saleswoman at the Estée Lauder counter. My mother's medicine cabinet is filled with barely used tubes and vials of cosmetics. They are the softest colors available but she still can't bear to use them. I wasn't sure whether I wanted to pick up on her comment. She settled the issue by buying us each a lipstick brush and heading for the shoe department. She had always avoided any discussion of sex.

"Can't you two write about anything else?" she would ask. "Don't you know there are other things in life?" It was never really criticism —these half-embarrassed, half-titillated remarks over martinis. She was playing her part. We had ours: to be "different," not like her neighbors' children, not like my sister, who'd had three children in the first four years of marriage.

I have always wondered if I blew it that day at Bergdorf's. Was it a mother-daughter talk on babies she was after? I think not. She had all the grandmother role she could handle: my sister spoke to her daily about the children, relied on her for advice and financial support, and suffered her constant criticism; which my mother took as her right. My sister might be a mother herself, but in my mother's eyes she is still thirteen, wears too much make-up, talks too fast, overdresses, and shouldn't smoke.

No, to this day I do not think my mother was urging me to get on with beginning a family. Out of her own dark history of being left with two babies to raise on her own when she was twenty, I feel she was obscurely trying to warn me that there are unpredictable hazards in marriage, that all the lovely fantasies of motherhood do not automatically come true at the end of nine months, and that there is sometimes a stiff price to pay. More than being put off by Bill's and my "preoccupation" with sex, she was warming her hands at our fire, trying to tell me that if I became a mother, this quality in us that she enjoys might be lost. To this day, I don't think she regrets that Bill and I decided not to have children.

Four years ago I went off the pill. We were living in England and a close friend was having a baby. My London doctor—like gynecologists in every country we'd lived—kept pointing at the clock and making doomsday noises: I was not getting younger. What is frightening is that I don't remember Bill and me sitting down to have a discussion about parenthood. We seemed to have come to this crossroad of our lives by an almost negative route: since we had always assumed one day we would have children, when the time struck me as right—a friend of my own age having her first baby—he just went along with it.

"We drifted into that decision-without-making-a-decision," Bill recently said. "Neither one of us was expressing his own wishes. We had not gone along with conventional ideas about jobs, career, money, where and how to live, or what we wanted out of marriage. But this one was too big, too deeply implanted in us. In our own defense, we have to remember this was before the whole nonparenthood movement came to consciousness. Still, backing into that decision to have a child meant we'd lost confidence in ourselves. We were surrendering to unconscious assumptions about what the world seemed to be asking of us. *They were right.* Never to have a child was too large a decision to question by our own values. As for me, I was undercut in my reluctance by feeling I must be strange, inhuman, not to want to be a father. Alienation from my true feelings made me indecisive and passive. I didn't feel I had the right to make you live by my strangeness."

The whole exercise wasn't an idea I entered into passionately either, merely one I assented to, and with less weighing of the pro and con than the decision to move to another country. Nevertheless, since my friend had had trouble conceiving, I too began taking my temperature every morning and keeping charts. I even went into the hospital for a day to have everything checked, to be sure I was in tip-top shape for the trip. (In the back of my mind were ten years of gynecologists' queries: "What, never been pregnant, never had an abortion?" they would say, giving no points at all for carefulness.) I was going to be as responsible about having a baby as I'd been about not having one. Once pronounced in perfect running order, I set about getting pregnant.

The dispassionate nonquestioning of the decision still puzzles me. Like Bill, perhaps I too thought I didn't have the right to keep fatherhood from him. It is frightening to think that we, who always discussed every aspect of our lives together, were so passive and silent about this. Being married, living together, moving around the world as we willed—*that* was natural for us. To have a child—*that* was the really radical thing for us to do, not our style, not born of our own imagination. And yet we accepted it, even though we knew that if I did conceive, our lives would be totally and dramatically changed. With no guarantee at all that the change would be for the better.

I was passionate about one aspect of motherhood: it must be a boy. The idea of a little Bill with dark hair and big brown eyes was a wonderful fantasy. Growing up without a father, I told myself that I'd had enough of living with women. Nothing but a boy would do, I said to Bill, as we were driving to Mexico on a shaky assignment that might enable us to live there a year. Infrequent as our talks were about children, joke as I might about my insistence on a boy, I was deadly serious about not wanting a daughter. Something in me knew I would never, for instance, let her take journeys like this into the unknown. I would be a mother more afraid for her daughter than for herself.

Two months after I went off the pill I was back on it. Once again it was not really a conscious decision about motherhood. Work demanded we return to New York; starting a family was being postponed as haphazardly as it had been entertained. A year later I switched from the pill to a diaphragm, and about two years ago Bill and I decided not to have children. No, to put it correctly, the decision went like this: One day he said, "Isn't it a good thing that we didn't have children?"

Today I look over my history of contraceptions, pregnancy scares, temperature charts, and I wonder what the hell two intelligent people were doing, never consciously making a decision about one of the most important steps in their lives. I said that I wasn't really married until the second or third year; today, the way I am married makes the first six years look like an acquaintance. I sometimes tell Bill I don't even mind growing old so long as we're together. The life we have made, the kind of marriage we have applied talent and imagination to create, would change if there were a child. No matter how much we loved that child, no matter how good parents we were, Bill and I would be different. I do not know that it would be better. I know the kind of wife I am, and I have an idea of the kind of mother I would have been.

Those things I like best in myself are never far from the things I like least: anxiety, which I hope brings a creative tension to my work, fear that makes me want to be close to someone. To the degree that on any given day that I can believe in what my husband feels for me, and in my work, that is the degree to which I have surmounted that day's residual anxiety of being my mother's daughter. I can handle the anonymous telephone call in the night, my fears of failure and success, the neighbors' opinions. They no longer run me because I acknowledge the space between the me I am today and the me I used to be. I can pull it off for myself. But if I had a daughter, I could never trust that she could be as lucky. That space between autonomy and fear would narrow and I would make her anxious with my own anxiety. To protect her I would limit her world, and thereby my own. It would put what I have with Bill and my work into question. I would be my mother's daughter all over again.

When I was interviewing Helene Deutsch for this book, she spoke of the maternal instinct. "Are you telling me, Dr. Deutsch," I asked with some incredulity, "that one day I'm going to wish I'd been a mother?" "Yes," she said without hesitation, "you will always regret never having had a child." Even now words like this fill me with anxiety. They seem to speak the wisdom of the ages. A moment later I have my certainty back. Today, should a person talk about these regrets, my reply would be that I will never try sky diving, or be the President of the United States. These must be very fulfilling too. I have learned to live without them.

I don't expect my story is exactly like any other woman's but I suspect most of us have had ideas like these. I will always have a fantasy of a son. I imagine Bill talking to him about the books he read when he was a boy, Norse mythology, and *The Water Babies*. Because I have decided not to have a child doesn't mean I never dream of what might have been.

Let's begin with a story of classical mother-daughter role-modeling:

Peggy is cooking her first big meal for her parents since her marriage—a glorious Virginia ham. Standing up to carve, her new husband asks Peggy why she sliced off three or four inches from the shank end before baking. Peggy looks surprised. "Mother always does it that way."

Everyone at the table looks at Peggy's mother. "That's how my mother did it too," she says, a bit puzzled. "Doesn't everyone?"

Peggy phones her grandmother the next day, and asks why, in their family, has the shank end always been cut off before baking. "I've always done it that way," grandmother says, "because that is how my mother did it."

It happens that four generations of women are still alive in this family. A call is put in to great-grandmother, and the mystery is solved. Once when her daughter—Peggy's grandmother—was a little girl and learning to cook, they were baking a large ham. The family roasting pan was small, and so the shank end had been cut off to make it fit.

Four generations of women, each one ignoring present reality, each one conforming, unquestioningly, to a circumstance that was no longer relevant; each one certain in her mind "that's how you do it" because she had seen her mother do it that way. An amusing story, an illustration of how we incorporate those parts of mother we choose to imitate—like her skill in cooking—but right along with them we also take in less rational and unexamined aspects all unaware.

It is here that one of the great feminine mysteries begins. Everyone else can see we've taken in many of mother's most negative character traits; we cannot. We deny it, treat the imputation as an accusation, get angry and deny it again. And yet one day we realize that we are acting to our daughter exactly in the same repressive way mother once acted to us. How did it happen? We swore it never would. We would show our child only the wonderful warmth and love we got from mother. As for the rest—mother's nagging, anxiety, sexual timidity and general lack of adventurousness—why, we would just leave them out. And yet, generation after generation of daughters become women still carrying the inheritance of mother's sad luggage, passing it on to daughters of their own.

Why does the cycle repeat?

Says Dr. Schaefer: "There are times when I catch a glimpse of my-self in the mirror, and I hate the way I look. It is when I most look like my mother. It's a kind of driven expression she used to have when she was busy with one of her projects. When I was a child, I was very close to my mother. I adored her, but when I saw that pur-poseful, nothing-will-get-in-my-way look on her face, I hated it. Lately, I've realized it wasn't the driven trait I hated in my mother. It was how she *behaved toward me* when she was this way. It meant she was so busy with her charity work that she would ignore me.

"I couldn't admit to myself that I hated her. I had to think it was the driven *quality* that I disliked. In other words, I was saying that this characteristic was not my mother. My real mother—she was this other good, kind person who always had time for me. This driven, purposeful side of her was a foreign aspect, someone else. *I had split the good mother off from the bad one.* I refused to recognize the bad side. Then, when I had a daughter of my own, I came to realize that Katie hated me for having this same quality. When I was finishing my thesis I was locked away in my office for weeks. One night Katie said to me, 'I hate you, I don't like you anymore. Stay in your office for-ever.' I felt awful. I had ignored her in the same way my mother had me. I had repeated exactly what I hated most about my mother."

The pathos of the parental double bind is in this story. Mother didn't nag or restrict us because she was cruel. Dr. Schaefer didn't lock herself away from her daughter because she was selfish. There was a lot of reality in Leah Schaefer's need to write her thesis, get her degree, complete her training; she had to support herself and her daughter. Remembering her own unhappiness as a child when her mother was unavailable to her, one might think she would have *made* more time for her daughter. That is not how the unconscious works. Since she was acting as her mother had, *it felt right.* To maintain her tie to her own mother, to avoid anger at that mother of childhood, Leah Schaefer *became* her mother.

Why do daughters repeat in their lives many aspects of mother, in-cluding those they hated? Says Dr. Robertiello: "Two mechanisms are at work. *Role-modeling* is largely conscious, and has a lot to do with those parts of the 'good' mother we liked. For this reason, it is usually the work of a moment's introspection to see that mother's ease with strangers, and our skill at entertaining, are connected. At some point, role-modeling shades into *introjection*. This process is harder to understand because it is mostly unconscious, and is marked by a lot of repressed anger directed against the 'bad' mother. We take in her negative aspects in order not to see them in her. If they are in us, we don't have to hate her—and run the risk of her retaliatory anger. We are the bad ones. The evil, split half of mother has been introjected."

Even a child who has been deserted or sent away cannot think, "Mother doesn't want me." She has to rationalize. "Mother loves me, but is punishing me because I've done this or that bad thing. The fault is not in mother. She is trying to correct me. She is sending me away out of love, so I'll learn to be better. She is good. The badness is in me."

A more everyday example might be when mother refuses to let us go to the movies with friends. We hate her, splitting her off from the good mother who bought us a pretty dress yesterday. However, should one of our friends say, "That's mean, your mother is too strict," we rush to mom's defense. "Oh, no, I probably deserve it," we say. "I've been a real pain around the house lately." We don't like to hear our parents, especially mother, criticized by others. It externalizes the bad mother, threatening release of our pent-up rage, which would destroy the relationship. It is easier, safer to feel we are bad, not she.

This process is automatic, unthinking, unconscious and inevitable. The child cannot take the fearful loneliness that hating mother brings. Introjection is an almost mindless union in the depths of being, a merger at the level of the baby who could not bear—and indeed could not survive—being separated from mother.

In ideal developmental circumstances, by the end of the first year the child will have fused the image of the good and bad mother into one person—she will have come to the realistic conclusion that mother is a mixture of both. This is a highly sophisticated idea, a judgment of such difficult and mature perception that even adults have difficulty with it. We get stuck with a kind of dichotomous view of the people with whom we are intimately involved, repeating with them the split we never resolved with mother. If we get mad at our husband, he becomes the biggest bastard in the world, and our entire marriage to date has been a mistake; the next day, when he brings us flowers, we realize that he's really the sweetest guy of all time. It is a child's way of seeing the world—the way we liked to see movies when we were little. The white hats were all good. The black hats were all bad. Any effort on the screenwriter's part to show us that there were shades of gray in the good guys, some redeeming features in the bad, ended by confusing us. It is only when we are able to achieve a higher level of psychic integration that we can accept others as a mix of good and bad and not swing to extremes when they disappoint or hurt us.

In his book *The Uses of Enchantment,* Dr. Bruno Bettelheim examines why so many fairy tales of witches and deadly dragons survive—even though they were passed down through the centuries unwritten—while most published contemporary and supposedly "creatively healthy" children's stories are soon forgotten. As each generation verbally passes on the version of what it heard from the generation before, all unnecessary, contingent, or purely personal elements are dropped. The dross is burned away. Only those elements with golden meaning for every succeeding age survive. In the end, says Dr. Bettelheim, fairy tales become universal stories, "communicating in a manner which reaches the uneducated mind of the child . . . [they speak to the child's] budding ego and encourage its development, while at the same time relieving preconscious and unconscious pressures."[1]

One of the elements that gives the old fairy tales their power is the frequency with which they deal in images of the mother, split into good and bad. Cinderella is treated miserably by the cruel stepmother, but the kind fairy godmother makes her into a princess. In story after story, there is this opposition between a wicked stepmother, or evil old fairy, and a protective, magical figure who is on the child's side. In writing about how Little Red Riding Hood's grandmother suddenly turns into a wolf wearing the benevolent old lady's clothes, Dr. Bettelheim says, "How silly a transformation when viewed objectively, and how frightening. . . . But when viewed in terms of a child's ways of experiencing, is it really any more scary than the sudden transformation of his own kindly grandma into a figure who threatens his very sense of self when she humiliates him for a pants-wetting accident? To the child, grandma is no longer the same person she was just a moment before; she has become an ogre."[2]

As we grow up, we repress the attachment the needy child within still has to the powerful mother of infancy, and come to the seemingly mature conclusion, "Oh, well, there are some parts of mother I don't like, but I understand why she was that way. They are not important." The "bad" parent is being ignored. We both know and don't know there are parts of mother we dislike.

While we are young enough to live at home, there is even a degree of tolerance for those aspects of mother that irritate. We can afford to see them because separation anxiety is not too great: we are both living under the same roof. We may hate or rage at mother, but there she is, waiting. An hour later, a kiss and a few tears, and symbiosis is back, strong as ever. Even if we are not affectionate, she is physically near, available.

As we get older and the tie to mother is weakened by physical or psychological separation, introjection gathers momentum. When we move into an apartment of our own, when we find a job, take a lover, get married and have a child of our own—in all these important rites of passage away from her, as we take one step forward, we take another one back, and find ourselves doing things her way. *Becoming like her overcomes our separation anxieties.*

It is a kind of symbolic rapprochement. Just as the infant who crawls away from mama into the next room gets frightened and rushes back for confirmation that she is still there, so, emotionally, as we edge away from mother in our adult lives, do we incorporate parts of her. Having her with us—*in* us—makes the journey less fearsome.

We are offered a promotion at the office. It is deserved, we can do the work. But mother's entire life warned us, a long time ago, that people don't like aggressive women. We decide to stay with the job we've been doing. "I'm not all that competitive," we say, "not career mad." We have lovers but are never free of mother's anxiety that men will trick and desert us. It is unsettling. We can almost see ourselves, split into a double image: the woman who goes to bed with men and enjoys sex, the woman who wakes up the next morning already wondering, Will he telephone tonight? These are mother's fears. Which woman are we? We are both.

The process of introjection continues even if we never see mother any more, even if she is dead or living in Paris. It is not the present mother who is being introjected, but that bad one of long ago, whom we could not afford to "know" was making us so unhappy we hated her. When we have an outburst of fury at someone, how often is it because what that person is doing makes us aware of something we dislike in ourselves?

When we were little and saw mama running her house, we admired how firm she was with the repairman who did a bad job, the department store that sent the wrong bill. She spoke her mind, got the job done. We're as good at these things as she. But we also remember her panic when father was driving and took a wrong turn, how angry she got over spilled milk, her fear of noises in the house when alone. Above all, we have introjected her anxiety about sex.

Marriage is our chance at last to become as sexually daring as we would like. Instead, we are preoccupied with furniture, neatness, entertaining. The clothes we wore when we were single had plunging necklines. Now we run to suburban styles that don't raise an eyebrow. The reason sex was easier when we were single was that we had never seen mother unmarried and without a child. This was a role we could create on our own. She was far away—emotionally, at least—and we felt the zip of at least temporary separation. Marriage reunites us with her. To openly declare our sexuality now would make us too different from the picture of how she was as a wife. We would have to face our anger at last at that frustrating mother who hated the sexual pleasure we wanted from the time we were infants, who made us renounce it to keep her love.

When we become mothers ourselves, introjection speeds up even more. When we hold our little girl in our arms, we are reminded of mother, feel at one with her, as never before. Since sex was always a powerful force toward individuation, it is hardly surprising that sex is one of the first things to go.

To please mother, we gave up the right to our bodies and erotic gratification when we were little. Now when baby touches her genitals, we don't just frown. As mother did to us, we take her hand away. We become child-centered caretakers, madonnas, "not always thinking about sex." Mother used to be the enemy of sex. We are tired of the war. For our daughter's sake, and our own, we join her. Continuity is preserved.

When we were single, the joys of sexuality were their own reward and reinforcement. Allowing the same autonomy to our daughter is too risky. We have no models of a mother who encourages her daughter's sexuality. To ensure our little girl does not get any funny ideas, we present her with the right one: a nonsexual image of ourselves. Nothing must excite forbidden thoughts in our daughter. Soon, nothing excites them in us either.

Most women I interview are aware they became less sexual after motherhood, but cannot say why. They were too tired, they had to listen for the baby's cries, etc. Good reasons, but not convincing. If you want something badly enough, you establish priorities so you get it. Child psychologist Helen Prentiss looks at the issue subjectively and objectively:

"Before my daughter was born, I had been very proud of my sexual union with my husband. More than anything, I felt this distinguished me from the kind of woman my mother was. But when I became pregnant, I began to lose this contact with him, with the feeling I'd always had opposite him. I knew Jack loved my body, but that was my old slim body. How could he be turned on by this fat lady? He would put his arms around me, start kissing me, but I would make excuses. It felt wrong, sex, and me almost a mother. I was into this whole other picture of myself—one of those warm, clean, dedicated mothers you see in women's magazines. Those pretty women don't have sex! They're good mothers, and I was going to be one too.

"My own mother being around a great deal speeded this idea. She was always dropping by with clothes for the baby, helping me fix the nursery. It was very reassuring to have her around because I was a little scared. Even though I was teaching courses in child psychology, being responsible for a baby loomed up as a frightening responsibility. Just as my mother had always steered away from 'knowing' about the strong sexuality Jack and I had between us, so did she steer right into knowing all about my pregnancy. Suddenly she seemed to have all the answers, just as she hadn't had any before I was pregnant. She told me about her pregnancies. She even admitted having doubts about being a good mother!

"As she and I became closer, my physical thing with Jack diminished. It was as though I couldn't have both—my closeness with her and with Jack. Sex became something silly or frivolous, perhaps a bit shameful, that you did before you became a mother. Now that I was pregnant, well, this was serious business, and those long hours in bed, those nights and mornings Jack and I used to spend exploring one another, closed away from the world—they seemed like selfish devilishness, kid stuff. So, you see, because I entered into motherhood without any clear assessment of myself, of my priorities in my own life and with my husband, I just automatically slipped into this picture of my own mother. Unwittingly and without any hesitation in the world, I gave up one of the most important things in my life and with my husband—our sexual tie.

"It was as though I'd been programed from birth like some female

Manchurian Candidate. I just allied with my mother in this feminine mystery she and I shared, and Jack was left out—some Dagwood Bumstead who perhaps had been necessary to get the whole thing started, but now it was time for him to get out and let us women handle the realities of life. It was almost as though what I was setting up with my mother was against him!"

Dr. Prentiss went on to say that while she knew—theoretically, intellectually, from everything she had read and lectured on herself—that it is necessary for a mother to be as symbiotic as possible with her baby during the first months of life, this union should not be allowed to interfere with what goes on between husband and wife. "There's a six-week prohibition against sex after the baby is born. Well, in my case six grew into ten, and what with me listening for the baby every time Jack touched me and feeling like this Super Mother, I would say, '*Jack, please!*' in this tone of indignation, as though he'd touched the Holy Grail.

"In my mind, I knew that without a connection to your adult identity, you stay symbiotically tied to your baby long beyond the period when you should let your child start to separate. Sex is the call of the adult world, reminding you of who you are. Reminding you that you may be a mother, but you are a woman too, a wife. But deeply as this knowledge was planted in me, something deeper, more unconscious, was working too. Sex had always been one of the strongest forces working on me to get out in the world, to leave home and become my own person. I loved my mom but I wanted a bigger life, and when I met Jack, sex with him became the final definition that divided me, in my mind's eye, from the picture of my mom. I was a different kind of woman, or so I thought. Holding this baby in my arms changed all that. It never occurred to me that Jack might like to be included in taking care of Sally during those first months. And since I seemed to have no confidence in him, he lost whatever confidence he might have had in himself. He stopped volunteering. So there I was—a case out of one of my own textbooks. Symbiotically tied to my baby, reunited with my mother, and excluding my husband from 'our' (me, my baby and my mother's) life!

"I got an enormous amount of emotion from this thing with my baby. And my libido, if you want to use those kinds of terms, was very much directed toward the baby. All my libidinal energy went there. My body was still not the beautiful body it used to be, my

narcissistic view of myself was diminished. I just didn't feel like a
sexual woman. I can see now that all my old notions—all my mother's
old notions—had come back: that sex was dirty, or selfish. *It was un-
motherly.*

"If you don't think about sex during those first months when you
are so meshed with your baby, you wake up six years later not a
woman, but a mom. Being sexual and being a person with a strong
sense of who she is are ideas that are very tied together. Women cannot focus on this enough. It is hard enough to be sexual people before we become mothers. The outside world may see us as sexual
women, but inside we are not at home with that idea ourselves. It's so
easy—and dangerous—to lapse back into being a 'nice lady,' a mother.
Giving yourself to union with your child at the beginning of your
baby's life is healthy and necessary. After that, it is resignation from
the problems, joys, and pleasures of an adult life of your own."

Resignation or not, it is what most women do. "Not in front of the
children," sounds like a musical-comedy joke, but it is a fact of marital life. We gladly make the sacrifice because it is "for our child's
good." The idea is debatable. Frustration and anger lie just behind
the curtain we have pulled down between ourselves and our sexuality.

If we have to sacrifice so much for her good, well—she'd better be
damned good. We are determined not to be as inhibiting as our own
mother, but much stricter codes of conduct are enforced on our
daughter than our son. After the latest outburst at the girl, we sit
down and get hold of ourselves. Never again! How frightening it used
to be when we were little to have mother furious. And so we start out
once more with the best intentions: to be calm, cool, kind, to let her
do things her way. But even as we act out this part, an inner anger
comes up to sabotage all good intentions. It is not possible to be this
"perfect" mother without comparing the ideal way we are trying to
act, with the restrictive way mother used to be. To see this comparison too clearly would be to become furious at the old "bad" mother
hidden in the unconscious. This rage would separate us from her.
That is intolerable. The anger gets diverted, back onto ourselves,
onto our husband, the unfairness of the world in general. Part of it inevitably spills out onto the daughter.

Why should she get this perfect treatment when we had such a
hard time? One part of our anger becomes subverted, and is experienced as a kind of forgiveness. "When women have children of their
own," says Dr. Mio Fredland, "they begin to feel much more em-

pathetic with their mothers. They make up old quarrels. They realize what their mother's life was like. They forgive whatever obscure angers have plagued them in the past, and they become loving and close. Especially if they have a daughter. There's a strange kind of direct line between mother, daughter, and granddaughter. My own mother told me that while she loves my brother's children, she doesn't have this same feeling about them as she does about my little girl. They didn't come out of the uterus of the child she carried in her own uterus. My mother looks ahead to the child my daughter will bear in time, and sees her own immortality. She is transformed by the idea, rejuvenated."

"A major reason," says Dr. Sirgay Sanger, "why women's anger at the mother often diminishes when they have a child is that the good mother image can now be acted out in real life. The negative, internalized image can be repressed, and there is the existence now of a new capacity—to love the new baby with a pure, unfettered giving of one's self. This is the mother one wished to have and to be. There often exists a euphoria after birth that women radiate. It casts a glow of warmth over her family, her husband and friends. It is also biologically necessary for the early growth and development of the infant. Post-partum depression in some ways is not a depression of the usual variety. It is a limiting of the euphoria. The woman's feeling that here is her chance to heal and solidify her sense of being a worthwhile and productive person has been punctured. The desire—'I want to be the good mother to my infant'—explains why some women who never asserted themselves before can say no now in the name of that infant. The wish for a perfect mother has been transformed into becoming that perfection."

You hear it again and again: "When I became a mother, I began to understand what my mother went through. I'm not so mad at her any more." Fine—unless this forgiveness goes beyond healthy recognition of the real problems of motherhood and becomes the strengthening of the original symbiosis. Does this "understanding" mean identification with everything in mother we once hated? Does rapprochement give us permission to act as she did, to overprotect our daughter and so limit her separation? Is the green light on once again for bringing all mother's old anxiety, nagging, sexual repression and inhibition to bear upon another generation?

When we have a child, we think we will be able to give up the old symbiotic need of mother (call it by what name you will), and find new security with our baby. Instead of needing someone to take care of us, we will be happily fulfilled by taking care of someone else. This is a kind of distorted notion of separation: because I will be most tied to my infant daughter, I will be less dependent on my mother for union and strength.

To nobody's surprise, the new mother finds the need for her own mother increasing. By this I don't mean the need for physical help and practical advice so much as the longing for an emotional reconciliation, a bonding with her. Now, more than any other time in our lives, when we hold our helpless baby in our arms, we cannot afford the old angers at mother. Ironically, mom herself is mellowing, becoming more like the mother we always hoped she would be. But not to us—to our little girl.

Says psychologist Liz Hauser: "My mother was loving and patient with my daughter Liza and would play cards with her for hours. When I was little, I got the idea that you should always be doing something productive. So I don't have the patience for cards. She didn't smother Liza as she did me because there was enough separation. That's why it is so much easier to be a grandmother. The sticky symbiosis never began, so you don't bring all that anxiety and fear to the relationship, the need to hold on. As for me—no sooner do I get through listening to a patient tell me how much she hated it when her mother nagged her, than I'll go home and begin on Liza. 'Look at your room!' It's so hard to remember to do things differently with your daughter than your mother did with you."

Before motherhood, we tried to find with men and other women what we missed with mother. Our husband may have failed us in that search for a perfect, blissful union. (How could he not?) Becoming a mother ends the search. We will never be alone again. We will find in the bond with our baby's need for us an identity we can recognize, all the emotion we want.

Says the poet Anne Sexton in "The Double Image":

> I, who was never quite sure
> about being a girl, needed another
> life, another image to remind me.
> And this was my worst guilt; you
>   could not cure
> nor soothe it. I made you to find me.[3]

"As a new mother," says Liz Hauser, "part of what you're looking for in this heavenly blurring of dependency and closeness between you and your child is the desire to be taken care of yourself. If you didn't get enough mothering when you were a baby, this is your chance to do the mothering. It is as if you can make up to the baby for what you didn't get yourself. So in your befuddled, symbiotic way, you get the feeling of tight attachment and unending love. *But you are not the one being taken care of.* The child is getting it all. There is an immense satisfaction in being a mother but not the kind of satisfaction you wanted. You are not the child in this relationship. You are the mother. This is the problem of symbiosis: undefined boundaries. You don't know where you leave off and the child begins. Eventually you become angry because your child is not satisfying your needs."

Dr. Hauser may be speaking in terms of psychological theory, but she is speaking from the inside too. She is a mother with a daughter of her own. All the women quoted in this chapter are both mothers and professionals trained to handle symbiotic problems. And yet they could not avoid nonseparation themselves when they had children. The almost hypnotic way symbiosis took them over is a warning of how delusory may be the boast, "I'm raising my daughter in a totally different way than my mother raised me."

Dr. Hauser continues: "To think your daughter is somehow going to make up for what you missed yourself as a baby is like hanging around a bakery when you're hungry and just smelling the brownies. It isn't satisfying, but it's irresistible: at least you are *around* mothering. Eventually, of course, out of this unsatisfied hunger are born the terrible angers that mothers feel. Their children are 'selfish' and 'ungrateful'—angers that are all the worse because they are so defended against and unadmitted. But if you stop to think about it, you can see that the mother who is raging against her child because the child isn't giving her enough, isn't grateful enough—she has turned the tables around. It is as if the mother is the baby, screaming at *her* mother for love. She's twenty, thirty, forty years old, and she's still raging for that tight, all-encompassing love infants need.

"One of the first things I heard when I was studying psychology," she continues, "was the remark, 'Of course she's hostile. She's dependent, and dependent people have to be hostile.' That idea stuck with me. It's simple, but it is the whole dynamic. If you're utterly dependent, then you're always waiting for someone to give you a handout—even if it is a small baby. You expect that baby to *give* to you, and in that sense you are dependent on your child.

"I've made these mistakes, felt these angers myself. I love Liza and I get a tremendous feeling when I make her happy. But sometimes it's like there's an endless request going on. This is natural to a child, but to the mother, it can seem like the little girl is a bottomless pit. You can't satisfy her. You want her to stop and be happy at what she's got. Your anger boils up. I can remember so vividly being on the other end and hearing the words I say to Liza from my own mother: 'Now, you've already had this, we've done that together, you should be grateful you have so much and not keep asking for more and more. . . .' This is why women should be aware of separation before they decide to become mothers. They should run checks on themselves after the baby is born. For instance, when you get terribly angry at a child that's been crying and won't stop, ask yourself if the intensity of your anger at that moment isn't derived from your own frustrations that the baby is making you miserable when you want *her* to make *you* happy. All those feelings of closeness and security and mother love you've been dreaming about—where's your payoff?"

There is a story ascribed to Freud about an eagle who had to bring her three children to safety when a flood covered the earth and they were too young to fly the great distance. She picked up the first child in her talons and began to fly. "I will always be grateful to you, Mother," said the baby eagle. "Liar," said the mother, and dropped him into the flood. The same thing happened with the second child. When the mother picked up the third little eagle and began flying him to safety, this eaglet said, "I hope I will be as good a parent to my children as you are to me." The mother saved that child.

The debt of gratitude we owe our mother and father goes forward, not backward. What we owe our parents is the bill presented to us by our children. Having a daughter is one of life's fulfillments, but to expect her to reward us in a time, place, or manner of our choosing is to distort the nature of the parent-child relationship.

Over vast periods of time, the process of evolution weeds out any trait that is not fundamental to the survival of the race. Conversely, anything on which the race depends cannot be left to whim, fashion, or accident: it must be carried forward in the gene. I believe the rewards of motherhood are biologically imbued, but the degree of satisfaction can vary with circumstances. The new mother who feels her baby nursing at her breast does not have to be told she is happy. A slum mother with nine children who finds she is again pregnant may feel differently. Biology and anatomy go on whether we like it or not. The unmarried mother may decide she will have her baby put out for adoption. When the baby is born she is suddenly caught up in a rush of emotion. She wants to keep the baby. She is certain her decision is right. Is she? There is no "correct" answer. What I wish to discuss here is individual choice. Motherhood furnishes great feelings of worth and value, function and pleasure. The question some women are beginning to ask is, Is there something else I would rather do with my life that would be more satisfying still? In a recent public-opinion poll, three out of four people—men and women alike—thought it OK for women not to have children.[4] My own feeling is that this reflects our changing attitudes—not necessarily our deepest feelings: *it's OK for other people, not me.* But if most women don't think of marriage without children as a permissible option, can it be said that they *chose* to be mothers?

Says Dr. Prentiss: "My own story sounds like I made a conscious decision about motherhood, but it was only an illusion. As a child I always felt I was getting only my mother's 'official' emotions—what she thought would be good for me. Not her real emotions. And so I learned to show her only what she wanted to see, the daughter in me —not the full person. The result was that while we were loving, it was not very honest. This is what I wanted to make up for in children of my own. Especially a little girl, because I could understand a girl's feeling. But don't let me mislead you. It sounds like I was deciding to have a baby for this reason or that. The fact is that I never decided at all that I would or would not have a baby. I never consciously felt I had a choice. I always assumed I would get married and have a child. It was part of the sequence that was already set up for me. I just knew I would be a mother. Every woman was. This kind of automatic falling into a role has caused me and my daughter a lot of trouble."

Having a child is still so expected of us, so programed into our development, that we drift into what is perhaps the most important act of our lives. Our reasons for becoming mothers—difficult as they may be to get at—are the first clue as to whether we will maintain our own identity, and let our child grow into a person—individual and separate from us.

The manner in which a woman relates to her child is one of the marks of her development—or arrested development. If she related symbiotically to her mother, and does the same with her husband, it cannot be said she has grown. Only the cast of characters has changed. In time, the wife may become a bit more independent of her husband, but when their daughter is born, the symbiotic switch is made to the girl. "It goes from mother to husband to daughter," says Dr. Robertiello, "but the woman's emotional age, her stage of development, remains fixed. She has not grown up one single day. The husband has just been a kind of intermediate stage between the old symbiosis with mother and the new one with the daughter. The woman, as an independent individual in her own right, never fully emerged."

Everyone—man or woman—has a stake in preserving the idea of unique identity. *"I'm me!"* Few things threaten this notion of autonomy so much as being told we are like our mother.

Last night at dinner I was asked what I was working on. "A book about the mother-daughter relationship." Instantly, the four women present turned to listen, ignoring the men. "What aspect are you writing about now?" one asked. "How we become like our mothers," I said. The light faded from four pairs of mascaraed eyes. "Oh, no, I'm not at all like my mother. It was my father—my grandmother—who influenced me most."

Denial. Flat denial that the woman with whom we once lived so intimately—who taught us how to speak, to eat, to walk, to dress ourselves, and on whose smile we lived—had any determining influence. Two of the four said they loved their mothers, but still repeated that their greatest influences were other people. I felt as though I had just heard it denied that two and two are four.

Of course other people—father, Aunt Sal, or an older sister—may be crucially important, but why deny so vehemently that mother was too? Why hold our attachment to these other figures as evidence of our uniqueness? Says Dr. Robertiello: "It sounds much more adult and self-affirming to say you are like your aunt or grandmother, with whom you don't have that sticky closeness and half-remembered dependencies. To say you are like your father is best of all. It implies decision. After all, he is a man. It says you are sexual, while to be like mom is practically to label yourself nonsexual. To declare you are like dad brings in choice. Being like mother sounds automatic and passive. Being like father shows a certain strength of character. You've crossed the sexual line, you're big enough to move easily in a man's world. You are one hell of a woman and you did it all yourself!"

Cutting the symbiotic tie between mother and daughter can be aided by identification with father or an aunt, but it is best begun through an effort of absolute honesty, introspection, and memory. We have to see who mother was, and who we are. What was mother really like when we were little? Was she withholding, not quite attentive enough? Or did she overprotect, intrude, and make us fearful of life without her? Have we been able to face both the good mother and the bad, to know what we love and what we hate, and begun to fuse them all at last without sentimental gloss?

If the reason for having a child is to give yourself an identity, to replay childhood over again the way it should have been, to preserve the marriage, to have someone to live through, or a half dozen other crippling reasons, separation will be very difficult. The daughter cannot be let go because *she is doing something for you.* If she leaves and becomes her own person, you lose your identity, function, the chance to live life all over again.

Making a conscious decision about motherhood is one of the most liberating things that can be done both for ourselves and the unconceived child. Even if we want to become a mother for unrealistic reasons, *just knowing it,* says we are more separate than someone who doesn't make a decision at all, who passively slides from growing up into getting married and then automatically has a child. That kind of sequential thinking—or nonthinking—says we have no real feeling of self. The woman who says, "I want a child because I want to hang on to my husband," has been proved again and again to be acting for wrong and self-defeating reasons, but even she is ahead of the wife who gives birth because that's what you do if you're a woman. Right or wrong, the first woman has decided, she has been active, and taken the responsibility for becoming pregnant.

Deciding that we want a child, knowing why, helps us escape the feeling "they" made us do it. If motherhood is disappointing, if the work of having a baby is more than we reckoned, remembering it was our own idea helps put a damper on making the child feel responsible for being alive.

If the inexorable pattern of repetition between mother and daughter is to be changed, all the denied aspects of our mothers and ourselves must be faced. We have the right to acknowledge at last the fury felt when we were five and she neglected us. But she has the right, now that we are twenty-five, to be allowed to be less than perfect. Seeing mother plain, seeing her whole, a mixture of good and bad, is in itself an enormous step toward separation. Even better, it helps us from cutting ourselves off from her so totally that we throw away all our good inheritance from her, as well as the parts we don't like.

There are two times in women's lives when the unconscious drive to become the mother we dislike speeds up. The first is when we become mothers ourselves. The second is when our mother dies.

Even beyond the grave, mother continues to be split. The person who died was good. The bad person lives on in us, vile daughters who did not appreciate mother enough while she was still alive. It is a complex business, this eerie monument we make to our mothers within ourselves.

"My mother died six years ago," says Leah Schaefer, "and I'd had problems of separation from her all my life. I think I took my biggest step toward autonomy when my daughter Katie was born. In my years of psychoanalytic study and practice, I'd come to an intellectual grasp on the symbiotic problem between my mother and me, but I'd never been able to resolve it. When Katie was born, I was forty-two. Only then was I ready to take this giant step in separation from my mother. If I say I did it for the sake of my daughter, I know now it was I who benefited from it most. I had always thought it was my mother who insisted on keeping this symbiotic hold on me. Typical wishful thinking, the sheerest projection. I learned I was the major contributor to keeping alive this suffocating attachment between my mother and me.

"All my life I had never denied my mother anything. If I wanted to do something she might not like, I did it secretly. I always believed something terrible would happen if she knew of this other me, my secret self. She would die or reject me if I defeated or denied her. When Katie was born, she wanted to come live with us. I realized that if she did, it would be the end of me. If I gave in to her, as I always had in the past, she would just take over my life and my child. I understood the symbiosis between my mother and me, I could handle that. But now I was a mother and I wanted to raise my daughter to be the individual I was still trying to become. Telling my mother No, that she could not move in with us, was one of the major turning points in my life—a lifelong dependency on her broken.

"It didn't kill her, she didn't reject me. In fact, it was the best thing I ever did for both of us. We think we cannot be straight with our mothers, that they can't take the honesty of who we really are. But it is we who are the cowards, the babies; we are afraid that if we stand up to them, they will abandon us.

"It was a terrible confrontation when I told my mother No. We both cried. I felt miserable, as though I'd put a knife in her heart. Then several days later, she announced she was returning home to California. 'I think married people need to live alone,' she said to me, as though she had come to this decision herself. She was perfectly content with the explanation. She was basically a very independent person, but she had this terrific tie to me, her only daughter. When we said good-bye she was as light-hearted as I'd ever seen her. I felt miserable. You know what my biggest emotion was after she'd left? One word kept running through my mind: *rooked!*

"All my life had been one big compromise because I'd believed that if I ever denied my mother anything, it would mean a withdrawal of her love. I'd had my secret life where I did those things she wouldn't approve of anyway, but it had been paid for by all this guilt. The revelation that I could be myself in front of my mother, tell her No, and that she didn't die and I didn't die, that nothing terrible happened—was incredible. I was married and the mother of a daughter of my own, but emotionally I was still acting like a child who had to have her mother's approval. It was the purest symbiosis. All those years I had spent being less of the person I wanted to be because I also felt I had to be her kind of person. Now, here she was tolerating my separation from her very happily."

Dr. Schaefer continues:

"Before my mother died, I was with her in the hospital. She was confused, her loss of memory troubled her. My mother had never been able to accept my profession, she believed in *physical* medicine, not mental therapy. But now I was able to give her back some of the rewards of the work I'd been able to pursue because of the habits of professionalism she taught me. For the first time in my life, I could help her, talk to her about her past, about her husband and our family, remind her who she was. I was able to give her what she wanted most in those last weeks: her sense of self. When I said good-bye to her that last time, she turned away and began to talk to my brother. She never could stand separation.

"The break with my mother that began when my daughter was

born allowed me to begin to see in myself, before she died, the good things I had inherited from her. My mother's dedication to her work made her effective and admirable. I had hated it as a kid because it left me out. Now that I had gained some distance from her, I could see this wasn't 'compulsive' but rather, it was professionalism. Without this dedication to my work, I would not have been able to support myself, to make her last days in the hospital easier, or to pay her final bills. Unless I had separated from my mother, I would never have allowed myself to see the value of how I am like her in the best ways."

The idea of *melancholia*—in connection with the death of someone toward whom we have ambivalent feelings of love and hate—was developed by Freud and one of his disciples, Dr. Karl Abraham.[5] It is very different from genuine mourning. To mourn a mother who has died is a healthy process, the acceptance of loss, a gradual letting go. It is a sign she was "a good enough" mother, and that our feelings about her were relatively unambivalent—much more love than anger or hate. "Even if she was not a good enough mother," says Dr. Robertiello, "if you have come to terms with that idea before she dies, you may be able to avoid melancholia. If you can recognize her for what she was, that is a mature evaluation. You have at least begun separation."

In the melancholic, grief is not wholehearted because the ambivalent rage at the bad mother of infancy has not been resolved. Sorrow cannot be fully expressed and so gotten out. Old feelings of infantile omnipotence come to plague the daughter: her unconscious conscience accuses her of murder.

It is too terrible an idea. We must deny our hatred for the bad mother more strongly than ever. This repression seems to solve the problem. We begin to walk like mother, talk like her; *we become her.* We take in all those parts that once we hated. In this way, we can answer the self-accusation that we are glad she is dead: we are keeping her alive!

By turning our aggression inward, hating those aspects of her we have introjected, we do not have to see it is really directed at her. We hate ourselves instead. The result is a sadness and self-hate that goes on and on, feelings of futility and bewilderment, flashes of seemingly pointless rage amid a general air of depression. Melancholia. The introjection of the bad mother after she dies is a mystery. It has been too universally remarked to doubt.

Dr. Robertiello: "My father had his first heart attack six months ago. It gave me time to face what was coming. I never got on well with my father. All my life I had denied I was like him at all. And yet, during these last six months, I became aware that I was taking in the aspects of my father I'd always hated: his imperious nature, his hypochondria, and all the rest. This was introjection and I realized that if I didn't face my father squarely, the kind of man he was—good and bad—the guilt when he died would be too great. The melancholia would have gone on for years. I knew only a more complete separation could stop the process. Otherwise, I would have continued to hate my father totally. I would never have seen the many good things I took over from him. As it was, I felt: The king is dead. Long live the king!"

Four years ago I told my mother's sister that I was going to write a book on the mother-daughter relationship. She said, "Nancy, some day your mother is going to die. How can you do this to her?" I was startled, guilty, hurt that my aunt would think that I was setting out to injure my mother. Why did she automatically assume any unblinking examination of the mother-daughter relationship must be hurtful? Simple projection, forbidden images of the repressed "bad mother" surround notions like these. If we daughters feel enormous guilt at the thought of our mother's mortality, mothers too mirror our anxiety about taking a hard look at the relationship with eyes rendered unsentimental by the importance of death. Why is honesty so fearful? What can there be between us that is so bad that two lives must be spent, each showing the other only what they feel the other can tolerate—while simultaneously seeing in the other only what we want to see?

Says Dr. Robertiello: "If people say it is cold and calculating to analyze who you are, and who your mother is—to acknowledge what you hate and love in her—they are still trying to hold on to her as children. They are afraid to think these things because at some deep level they still fear she can be hurt by their thoughts. They are also demanding that she be immortal, postponing their separation."

"If only I had been able to tell my mother how much I loved her while she was still alive!" a woman tells me. "She had her faults but they were just reflexes. She couldn't help nagging and criticizing any more than you can help sneezing when your nose itches. It was just something built into her nervous system. Now, I'll never be able to tell her what I really felt for her. It's too late."

It is a conversation I find chilling, sad, and bewildering. If anything, this woman is even more nagging and critical than her mother. It has led to her divorce from her husband and alienated her daughter. Even when we have a destructive relationship with our mothers, why do we turn it all around when she dies, and only talk about our love for her?

When I began this book, I too would have told you that I loved my mother and all my angers at her were unimportant. "She didn't mean to hurt me. That's just the way she was, a bad habit." In the service of maintaining a fantasy that beneath her "bad habits" was all-encompassing love, I'd refused to recognize the "bad mother" of childhood. I once would have said that ignoring my petty angers was my adult way of keeping the relationship to my mother affectionate and easy. I know now this "forgetting" only ensures the angers beneath are kept alive and boiling.

The usual way to avoid the fear of seeing there are parts of mother we hate is to sentimentalize her. Literature tells us very little about what really goes on between children and their mothers. The saccharine sweetness of Mother's Day poetry protests too much.

Says Dr. Robertiello: "These forms of sentimentality are a defense against anger. Rather than feel like a murderer, we doubly repress our hostility with a smile. Whatever it is we didn't like—her nagging, the controls she tried to put on us, her sexual repressiveness—we say they weren't important. We 'understand' them. Which means we forgive them, and try to focus instead on the 'loving' parts of her, and how much we loved her. To talk like this is not proof that you loved your mother, but that you are sentimentalizing. The word 'love' is used to cover so many destructive emotions, like possessiveness, anxiety, et cetera. You tell yourself soft remorseful lies that protect her—which means you are blurring your own perception that you are repeating her. You are stuck with your rage, and the only way you can keep that alive is by incorporating into yourself the parts of her that you hated. It's all in the service of continuing the symbiosis, even though mother may be far away or dead." In the unconscious where the first connection was forged, the mother of our infancy never dies.

When we are not sentimentalizing her, we go to the other extreme. If the telephone call home didn't go well, if she said the wrong thing during our visit, all the old angers rise up again. We were right to decide to be as different from her as possible. She becomes the measure of everything we dislike—which means we will denigrate or hate every echo of her we find in ourselves. Everything in the "bad mother" is bad, and so if we have her straightforwardness and honesty, we will say it is unkindness and hostility. Leah Schaefer took in her mother's professionalism and called it being a compulsive worker. If we have mother's powers of organization, we will dislike ourselves for being bossy and controlling.

No matter if the world or our husband loves us for these qualities. That only means we are temporarily fooling them. If they don't find us out, they are dumb. If they do, they will leave us. Our choice is to be loved by a fool or not to be loved at all.

"It was denial of what really went on between my mother and me," says Helen Prentiss, "that made me hide out and symbiose with my daughter. To deny your sexuality is a way of avoiding competition with your daughter. I hope to break the chain women pass on from one generation to another—that paralyzing nonaggression, noncompetitive pact. I know you can be a good mother and sexual too—even if it took me a long time to find it out. It's so simple. I can explain it to my six-year-old but I could never get it through to my mother."

At this stage in our lives, mother probably needs us more than the other way around—but we are still afraid to ask her those difficult but clarifying questions about childhood. Her involvement in our introspective process of separation can help, but is not necessary. The question is, If our questions should lead her into a rage so violent that she throws us out of the house—to name the worst fantasy—what has been lost? Only the illusion of symbiotic love.

Most of us need to get over the fear that separation is going to kill her. Being a good mother to a thirty-five-year-old (dependent) daughter is just as confining and anachronistic as playing the good daughter when we are grown with a daughter of our own. Mother is stronger than we wish to give her credit for. Part of this fear of hurting her is puffing up our own importance. Another part is just wishful thinking, maintaining the symbiosis. Both ideas may be summed up by the thought, "She cannot live without me." Another part is, "My anger is so terrible, that if I show it to her, it'll kill her."

The Greeks had a word for all this: *hubris*. It meant a kind of overweening self-importance, pride, and arrogance. It always led to destruction. Now that we are grown, to decide that mother must be protected as if she were the child—isn't that hubris too?

Guilt is the name we give anxiety at the fear of losing symbiosis with mother. Guilt is what we feel when we leave her ourselves. All our lives, whenever we say good-bye, there is this feeling we have not been able to give her something she wanted. What does she want from us that we can't seem to provide? Next time we meet, we promise ourselves, we will try harder, we will be "a good daughter," we will give her this magic something that will make her happy. But the next time we fail again, and after she dies we know we have failed forever.

I have heard ideas like these from many women, and in a recent talk with Dr. Robertiello mentioned how often I'd felt them myself. We'd been talking about introjection, and about his father's death; it had occurred while I was writing this chapter. I went on to say that I hoped what I'd learned from my research would "help me avoid all that old sadness and guilt the next time I go home and it comes time to say good-bye." Richard shook his head in mock despair. "Ah, Nancy, Nancy," he said. "You still haven't integrated what you know intellectually with what you feel down deep. It is not guilt you feel, that you cannot make your mother happy. You feel *anxious* that you do not say the right thing, open the magic door, through which all the love you once wanted from her would come flooding through. You still cannot let go of your infantile need of that magic mother of long ago. Your mother is still vigorous and alive, but if you don't come to understand what you are doing, you will continue to blame yourself after she dies. The forsaken feeling will not be that you didn't make her happy, but that you did not do or say the magic thing that would force her—in the sense of infantile omnipotence—to love you as you have waited for all your life."

How many times have I said in this book that my mother and I are totally different women? Oh, I have acknowledged certain minor virtues I got from her—housekeeping, an easy hostess, etc. But compared to those qualities of hers I have always disliked but taken over anyway—her anxiety and the fear which lies beneath my surface independence—how paltry appeared my "good" inheritance. I have always thought I had to leave home to reinforce the qualities in myself I wanted because I felt by nature my mother is a very timid person.

For every step I have taken away from her—my sexuality, my work, the whole dramatic design of my life which overshadows her conservative one—I have been aware of her tugging at my heels, pulling me back. Maybe I "made myself up," but there is not a daring thing I have ever done that has not been accompanied by anxiety. At the beginning of this chapter I had said that one of my strongest reasons for not becoming a mother was I did not want to turn into the kind of nervous, frightened mother she had been to me. Alone, I can control the helpless mother who lives inside me. A mother myself, I would become just like her.

Helpless? Why do I automatically associate that word with her? A woman who raised two daughters on her own, who ran her house smoothly, paid her bills on time, and never set a table or planned a trip where anything was left out? Is she indeed so timid and afraid, so unlike me—the adventurous daughter? To turn that around: am I so unlike her?

I have mentioned the silver cups she won in cross-country steeple-chasing. She demeans this courage as if it were girlish stupidity, and stored the cups in the basement until I retrieved them. They are now in my home, polished—a tribute to something I too am reluctant to acknowledge. Whenever Bill tells people how responsible and well organized I am, it rankles me. Why have I always seen these qualities in myself as something I must hide, not to be proud of? So long as I could not recognize and appreciate them in my mother, and was determined to see her "helplessness" as the mark of being a woman, being capable and organized made me sound masculine.

It has taken me the entire writing of this book to acknowledge in my heart that the qualities I am proudest of in myself I learned from her. It is unbelievable to me now to think I did not know them last week. "Why, you look just like your mother!" a woman said to me recently. I thought she meant I was wearing my mother's tight, anxious look. But she was thinking of something else. "The last time I saw her," this woman went on, "your mother bid a grand slam. It was four o'clock in the morning, and she made it!"

Stories of my mother's courage have always excited me. The photos of her I love so much hang over my desk—jumping a horse over a high brick wall, wearing a daring two-piece bathing suit twenty-five years ago when she was my age. Why have I refused to credit her for the abilities and emotions I have tried to incorporate in myself?

At one time I would have told you that more than anything else, my sexuality differentiated me from my mother. But she likes men tremendously, and they her. When we are together, I am usually the one who calls the evening to an end; she'd prefer to dance all night.

More important, why have I always discounted that when my mother was seventeen she ran away with the handsomest man in Pittsburgh, and married him against her father's wishes? I used to make her elopement sound like some out-of-character phenomenon, as if the idea had been totally my father's and she had only passively gone along. The fact is, my "asexual" and "timid" mother was into sex *four years younger than I, who didn't give up her virginity until twenty-one!*

In my absolutism about having made myself up out of no cloth taken from her, I have disinherited myself from my grandmother too. Didn't she leave her dominating husband and their oldest children when she could no longer stand the tyranny—and that in the 1920s, long before liberation, long before the time when a decision like this could be thought anything but mad and irredeemably unfeminine?

There is a strong current in the women in my family that I am bound and determined not to recognize. I come from three generations of sexual, adventurous, self-sufficient women. Is this not more exciting, more profound, than the shallow notion of making myself up? Aren't these the qualities I want most to reinforce in myself? In the service of maintaining a childish tie to a mother who never existed, I have turned my back on the best of my inheritance.

I am suddenly afraid that the mother I have depicted throughout this book is false.

Does this mean that everything I have written so far is false?

"No!" says Dr. Robertiello. "Like everyone else you keep changing your idea of your mother. One day she's good, kind, and loving. The next day, she's frightened, timid, and asexual. One day all you can see is your anger. Right now you want to go into a period of seeing her as all good. Either way, it means you are still avoiding the job of seeing her realistically. You are determined to invest your mother with magic importance—to see her, not as a human being, but in some childlike, monolithic, total way. *That is the way the baby sees her mother.* You are still lost in that first attachment to her, as you were when she was the Giantess of the Nursery."

Seeing mother divested of the symbiotic glamour she once held for us means she becomes another person, someone else, outside of us. Which means we have separated at last. As long as we remained symbiotically linked, there was always hope that it was not too late to get from her the perfect love we always wanted. Now we are grown, and know we never will. We must give up the fantasy and look elsewhere.

The idea is sobering. It is maturing too. Most important of all, it is the truth.

I can see now that while 'I liked my sexuality and wanted to give my mother no credit for it at all, that part of me rested on an uneasy base: if my mother, my image of femininity, was "asexual," then my own sexuality must be "masculine." I was proud of it, but didn't trust it. In this way, until we learn to fuse our mother into one person, we will be at war with ourselves. The cries and slogans of liberation from outside can serve at best to cheer us on. There is no changed history for women until each faces her own.

I said in the first chapter of this book that I'd often wished my mother had had my life. Hubris again, snidely competitive, and damned impertinent too. I don't think she'd want it. The more I grow away from her and define myself, the more I see in her this other person she was before she became Nancy Friday's mother. That is the magic: not that we can ever re-create that nirvana of love that may or may not have existed between us as mother-and-child, but that once we have separated we can give each other life, extra life, each out of the abundance of her own.

Recognizing the woman who can bid a grand slam at four in the morning when the rest of the world is asleep, I sleep better myself. Now that I have granted her the right to have run off with my father at seventeen because she was a sexual adventuress at heart—and not because it was some atypical bit of foolishness which had nothing to do with her true character at all—I can be proud of that part of myself that is a sexual woman too.

NOTES

CHAPTER ONE

1. Will McBride and Helga Fleischauer-Hardt, *Show Me* (New York: St. Martin's Press, 1975).
2. See D. W. Winnicott, *Playing and Reality,* pp. 47–52.
3. Adrienne Rich, *Of Woman Born,* p. 259.
4. Edward Shorter, *The Making of the Modern Family,* pp. 168–169.
5. Helene Deutsch, *The Psychology of Women,* vol. I, *Girlhood,* p. 151.

CHAPTER TWO

1. D. W. Winnicott, *The Maturational Processes and the Facilitating Environment.*
2. Erik H. Erikson. The theory of basic trust runs throughout Erikson's work. See *Childhood and Society,* 1950. Also *Psychological Issues* (1959), pp. 55–56: "For the first component of a healthy personality, I nominate a sense of basic trust."
3. Margaret Mahler is a pioneer in ego psychology and child development. Her theory of the nature of the child's attachment to the mother (symbiosis) and the gradual breaking of this attachment (separation-individuation) has been one of the major contributions to psychoanalytic theory in recent decades. This theory was set forth in *On Human Symbiosis and the Vicissitudes of Individuation,* vol. I, *Infantile Psychosis,* 1968. She has recently written *The Psychological*

Development of the Human Infant, 1976, which is a continuation and elaboration of her theories.

4. Erik H. Erikson, *Childhood and Society,* p. 247.

5. *Ibid.*

6. Heinz Kohut, M.D., a practicing psychoanalyst in Chicago, is one of the most important psychoanalytic theorists on the subject of narcissism. His book *The Analysis of the Self* affirms the development of narcissism as a healthy drive that is necessary for the formation of a positive self-image.

CHAPTER THREE

1. Leah Schaefer's doctoral study was completed in 1964, at Teachers College, Columbia University. It is titled "Sexual Experiences and Reactions of a Group of 30 Women as Told to a Female Psychotherapist." This study grew into her book *Women and Sex,* published by Pantheon in 1973.

2. John Bowlby is an English psychoanalyst whose books on attachment and separation are considered classics in the field. His work has focused on the effects of the child's separation from its parents, his argument being that an early closeness to mother is the bedrock of later emotional stability and that anxiety is caused by fear of loss of this attachment. See *Attachment and Loss,* vol. I, *Attachment;* and *Attachment and Loss,* vol. II, *Separation.*

3. Margaret Mahler, *On Human Symbiosis and the Vicissitudes of Individuation,* vol. I.

4. Quote from the poem "Effort at Speech Between Two People," from the book *Waterlily Fire, Poems 1935–1962* by Muriel Rukeyser, p. 3.

5. See Seymour Fisher, *The Female Orgasm.*

CHAPTER FOUR

1. Germaine Greer, *The Female Eunuch,* p. 142.

2. Clara Thompson, "Penis Envy in Women." *Psychiatry,* vol. VI, 1943, pp. 123–125.

3. Quoted from a review by Anatole Broyard of *The Curse: A Cultural History of Menstruation,* by Janice Delaney, Mary Jane Lupton, and Emily Toth. Review appeared in *The New York Times,* September 21, 1976.

4. Karen Page's studies were conducted in 1971 and 1973. Her findings appeared in an article, "Women Learn to Sing the Menstrual Blues."

Psychology Today, September 1973, pp. 41–46. Karen Page is a psychologist at the University of California at Davis, where she continues to do work on this subject.

CHAPTER FIVE

1. *American College Dictionary.* New York: Harper, 1950, p. 246.
2. See Reuben Fine, *The Psychology of the Chess Player.*
3. Jessie Bernard tells me she has seen informal studies in recent years that show girls are beginning to remain on the honor roll right through high school. In the *Journal of Counseling Psychology* (January 1975, pp. 35–38), Rosalind C. Barnett statistically demonstrates in a study of 988 females and 1,531 males from ages 9 to 17 that boys tend to prefer high-prestige occupations, the more they enter adolescence. The article is titled "Sex Differences and Age Trends in Occupational Preferences and Occupational Prestige." "What do these differing studies say to us?" asks Jessie Bernard. "That we're still very much betwixt and between."
4. Aurelia Schober Plath, *Letters Home by Sylvia Plath,* p. 38.

CHAPTER SIX

1. "The age of the menarche [onset of menstruation]," says Seymour Reichlin, M.D., chief of the endocrine division at the New England Medical Center Hospital in Boston, "has changed from 17.5 years in about 1860 to 11.7 years in 1976. We are talking about Western societies. The relevant factor is size; a girl can't conceive and bear a live child until her body has the fat content to carry her through a pregnancy. A certain height and weight is necessary for the onset of puberty. And with the better nutrition and freedom from infections today, young girls are reaching this height and weight earlier."
2. Lillian Hellman, *Pentimento: A Book of Portraits,* p. 119.

CHAPTER EIGHT

1. Sigmund Freud, "A Case of Paranoia Running Counter to the Psycho-Analytic Theory of the Disease," *Standard Edition of Complete Psychological Works of Sigmund Freud,* p. 261.
2. Quote appeared in an interview with Elizabeth Ashley by Ila Stanger.

The article was titled "Extraordinary Women Talk About the Single Life," *Harper's Bazaar,* March 1975.

3. This study was titled "The Effects of Mass Media on the Sexual Behavior of Adolescent Females" and was distributed by The American Association of Sex Counselors and Therapists, of which Dr. Schiller is executive director.

4. Margaret Hennig's doctoral dissertation was done in 1970 for the Graduate School of Business Administration at Harvard University. It is titled "Career Development for Women Executives." Her work was further developed in the book written with Anne Jardim, *The Managerial Woman.*

CHAPTER NINE

1. A. C. Kinsey et al., *Sexual Behavior in the Human Female,* p. 170.

2. Leah Schaefer, *Women and Sex,* pp. 88–106.

3. Robert Sorenson, *Adolescent Sexuality in Contemporary America,* pp. 129–145.

4. This study was done on 300 undergraduates at the University of Iowa in 1963. The study is contained in a book by Ira Reiss, *The Social Context of Premarital Sexual Permissiveness,* pp. 105–125.

5. This is an ongoing study being conducted by Ira Reiss.

6. These findings were in the same study quoted above, Note 4.

7. Mirra Komarovsky, *Dilemmas of Masculinity: A Study of College Youth,* pp. 78–81.

8. SIECUS Study Guide No. 5, "Premarital Sexual Standards," p. 14.

9. Zelnik and Kantner's figures were published in 1972 by the U.S. Commission on Population Growth and The American Future. This study was only on 15- to 19-year-olds. "But recent national samples," says Ira Reiss, "conducted by the U.S. Department of Health, Education and Welfare, back up both Kinsey and Zelnik and Kantner."

10. I heard of this study from Ira Reiss. The study was done by Robert Walsh and was his Ph.D. dissertation, 1970, titled "Survey of Parents and Their Own Children's Sexual Attitudes." The study began in 1967 and is ongoing. Walsh did his research at Illinois State University, got his degree at the University of Iowa. He is teaching now at Illinois State University.

11. This survey was conducted on 500 coeds at the University of Minnesota between the years 1970 and 1972. It was titled "Premarital Contraceptive Usage: A Study and Some Theoretical Explorations," and was published in the *Journal of Marriage and Family,* August 1975, pp. 619–630.

CHAPTER TEN

1. See Jessie Bernard's paper "Homosociality and Female Depression," *Journal of Social Issues,* to be published in 1977. In this paper, Dr. Bernard states that "never married women fared better in terms of mental health than never married men." She cites the studies done by psychologist Lenore Radloff which show that "The never married [women who were] heads of households in which the household income was $16,000 and over—presumably successful career women—fared spectacularly well [in terms of mental health]. As well, in fact, as married men, usually the best off in all studies. It is interesting that the category of never-married was the only one in which women showed up better than men."

2. Quote from an article, "I Weep for the Party of Lincoln and My Father," by Richard Reeves, *New York Magazine,* August 30, 1976, p. 8.

3. Komarovsky, p. 31.

4. Figures are for 1975, from the U.S. Department of Commerce, Bureau of the Census.

5. M. Elizabeth Tidball is a professor of physiology at George Washington Medical Center in Washington, D.C. An account of her study on achieving women appeared in *The Executive Woman,* vol. 2, no. 6, February 1975, pp. 1–2.

6. Margaret Hennig's doctoral dissertation was done in 1970, at the Graduate School of Business Administration at Harvard University. It is titled "Career Development for Women Executives."

7. Psychologist Matina Horner was a doctoral student at the University of Michigan. Her dissertation is titled "Sex Differences in Achievement Motivation and Performance in Competitive and Non-Competitive Situations."

8. Robert Ardrey, *African Genesis,* p. 165.

9. Figures quoted from the U.S. Labor Department, as they appeared in the article "Women Entering Job Market at An 'Extraordinary Pace,'" by Robert Lindsey, *New York Times,* September 12, 1976.

10. Eli Ginzburg is a Columbia University economist and chairman of the National Commission for Manpower Policy. This quote appeared in the *New York Times* article cited above.

CHAPTER ELEVEN

1. Figures from the U.S. Labor Department. Almost 48 percent of American women over 16 years of age now work or want a job. Some economists think that within two or three years it is possible that half of American women over 16 will be in the work force.
2. Dr. Joyce Brothers, "How to Be Unafraid of Success," *Harper's Bazaar*, January 1976, p. 96.
3. In 1950, 3,848 women committed suicide. In 1974, 7,088 women committed suicide. These figures were obtained from U.S. Department of Commerce, Bureau of the Census, Statistical Abstract of the U.S. 1976.
4. Susan Brownmiller, *Against Our Will*, p. 403.

CHAPTER TWELVE

1. Bruno Bettelheim, *The Uses of Enchantment*, pp. 5–6.
2. *Ibid.*, p. 66.
3. Anne Sexton, "The Double Image," *To Bedlam and Part Way Back*, p. 61.
4. In a national sample, the American Council of Life Insurance asks: "It is perfectly all right to be married and to choose not to have children." In 1973 and 1974, three out of four adults, age 18 and over, agreed with that statement. In 1976, it went up to 83 percent in agreement, which is four out of five people.
5. Sigmund Freud, "Mourning and Melancholia," written in 1917. *Standard Edition*, vol. XIV., pp. 243–258. See also Karl Abraham, "The Process of Introjection in Melancholia," *Selected Papers*, pp. 442–453.

BIBLIOGRAPHY

Abraham, Karl. *Selected Papers.* London: Hogarth Press, 1927.
Ardrey, Robert. *African Genesis.* New York: Atheneum, 1961.

Bardwick, Judith. "The Dynamics of Successful People." *New Research on Women.* Ann Arbor: University of Michigan.
Barker-Benfield, G. J. *The Horrors of the Half-Known Life: Male Attitudes Toward Women and Sexuality in Nineteenth Century America.* New York: Harper & Row, 1976.
Barnett, Rosalind C. "Sex Differences and Age Trends in Occupational Preference and Occupational Prestige." *Journal of Counseling Psychology.* Jan. 1975, Vol. 22 (1), pp. 35–38.
Bernard, Jessie. *The Future of Marriage.* New York: World, 1972.
——. *The Future of Motherhood.* New York: Dial Press, 1975.
——. *Women, Wives, Mothers: Values and Options.* Chicago: Aldine Press, 1975.
Bettelheim, Bruno. *The Uses of Enchantment.* New York: Knopf, 1976.
Blos, Peter. *On Adolescence: A Psychoanalytic Interpretation.* New York: The Free Press, 1962.
Bowlby, John. *Attachment and Loss.* Vol. I, *Attachment.* New York: Basic Books, 1969.
——. *Attachment and Loss.* Vol. II, *Separation—Anxiety and Anger.* New York: Basic Books, 1973.
Brothers, Joyce. "How to Be Unafraid of Success." *Harper's Bazaar,* Jan. 1976, p. 96.

Brownmiller, Susan. *Against Our Will: Men, Women and Rape.* New York: Simon and Schuster, 1975.

Delaney, Janice and Mary Jane Lupton. *The Curse: A Cultural History of Menstruation.* New York: Dutton, 1976.

Deutsch, Helene. *The Psychology of Women.* Vol. 1, *Girlhood.* New York: Bantam Edition, 1973.

———. *The Psychology of Women,* Vol. 2, *Motherhood.* New York: Bantam Edition, 1973.

Erikson, Erik H. *Childhood and Society.* New York: Norton, 1950.

———. *Identity, Youth and Crisis.* New York: Norton, 1968.

Fine, Reuben. *The Psychology of the Chess Player.* New York: Dover Publications, 1967.

Fisher, Seymour. *The Female Orgasm.* New York: Basic Books, 1973.

Freud, Sigmund. *Standard Edition of Complete Psychological Works of Sigmund Freud.* London: Hogarth Press, 1957–1964.

Friday, Nancy. *My Secret Garden.* New York: Trident, 1973.

Goodman, Emily Jane and Phyllis Chesler. *Women, Money and Power.* New York: Morrow, 1976.

Greer, Germaine. *The Female Eunuch.* London: MacGibbon and Kee, 1970.

Haskell, Molly. *From Reverence to Rape: The Treatment of Women in the Movies.* New York: Holt, Rinehart and Winston, 1974.

Hellman, Lillian. *Pentimento: A Book of Portraits.* Boston: Little, Brown, 1973.

Hennig, Margaret. "Career Development for Women Executives." Doctoral dissertation for the Graduate School of Business Administration at Harvard University, 1970. Developed into a book, *The Managerial Woman,* co-authored with Anne Jardim. New York: Doubleday, 1977.

Horner, Matina. "Sex Differences in Achievement Motivation and Performance in Competitive and Non-Competitive Situations." Unpublished doctoral dissertation for the University of Minnesota. 1968.

Hunt, Morton. *Sexual Behavior in the 1970's.* Chicago: Playboy Press, 1974.

Janeway, Elizabeth. *Man's World, Woman's Place.* New York: Delta, 1971.

Kaplan, Helen. *The New Sex Therapy.* New York: Brunner/Mazel, 1974.

Kinsey, A. C., et al. *Sexual Behavior in the Human Female*. Philadelphia: W. B. Saunders, 1953.

Kohut, H. *The Analysis of the Self*. New York: International University Press, 1971.

Komarovsky, Mirra. *Dilemmas of Masculinity: A Study of College Youth*. New York: Norton, 1976.

Maddux, Hilary C. *Menstruation*. New Canaan: Tobey Publishing, 1975.

Mahler, M. S. *On Human Symbiosis and the Vicissitudes of Individuation*. Vol. I, *Infantile Psychosis*. New York: International University Press, 1968.

——. *The Psychological Development of the Human Infant*. New York: Basic Books, 1976.

Masters, William H. and Virginia E. Johnson. *Human Sexual Response*. Boston: Little, Brown, 1969.

Mitchell, Juliet. *Psychoanalysis and Feminism*. New York: Vintage, 1974.

Money, John. *Sexual Signatures*. Boston: Little, Brown, 1975.

Page, Karen. "Women Learn to Sing the Menstrual Blues." *Psychology Today*. September 1973.

Plath, Aurelia Schober. *Letters Home by Sylvia Plath*. New York: Harper & Row, 1975.

Pomeroy, Wardell B. *Girls and Sex*. New York: Delacorte Press, 1969.

Reiss, Ira L. *The Social Context of Premarital Sexual Permissiveness*. New York: Holt, Rinehart and Winston, 1967.

——. "Premarital Contraceptive Usage: A Study and Some Theoretical Explorations." *Journal of Marriage and Family*. August 1975.

Rich, Adrienne. *Of Woman Born: Motherhood as Experience and Institution*. New York: Norton, 1976.

Robertiello, Richard C. *Hold Them Very Close, Then Let Them Go*. New York: Dial, 1975.

——, and Grace Elish Kirsten. *Big You, Little You*. New York: Dial, 1977.

——, and Rena M. Shadmi. "Dynamics in Female Sexual Problems." *Journal of Contemporary Psychotherapy*. Vol. 1, No. 1. Fall 1968.

——. "Masochism and the Female Sexual Role." *Journal of Sex Research*. Vol. 6, No. 1. Feb. 1970, pp. 56–58.

——. "Penis Envy." *Psychotherapy: Theory, Research and Practice*. Vol. 7, No. 4. Winter 1970.

Rukeyser, Muriel. *Waterlily Fire, Poems 1935–1962*. New York: Macmillan, 1962.

Schaefer, Leah Cahan. *Women and Sex*. New York: Pantheon, 1973.

——. "Female Adolescent Sexuality." An unpublished paper given at International Forum on Adolescence, Jerusalem, Israel. July 1976.

Schiller, Patricia. "The Effects of Mass Media on the Sexual Behavior of Adolescent Females." Study distributed by the American Association of Sex Educators and Counselors.

Sheehy, Gail. *Passages: Predictable Crises of Adult Life*. New York: Dutton, 1976.

Sex Information and Education Council of the U.S. *SIECUS Study Guide* No. 5 (revised edition), "Premarital Sexual Standards." New York: SIECUS, 1967.

Sexton, Anne. *To Bedlam and Part Way Back*. Boston: Houghton Mifflin, 1960.

Shorter, Edward. *The Making of the Modern Family*. New York: Basic Books, 1975.

Sorenson, Robert. *Adolescent Sexuality in Contemporary America*. New York: World Publishing, 1972.

Stanger, Ila. "Extraordinary Women Talk About the Single Life." Harper's Bazaar, March 1975.

Sullivan, H. S. *The Interpersonal Theory of Psychiatry*. New York: Norton, 1953.

Thompson, Clara. "Penis Envy in Women." *Psychiatry*. Vol. VI, 1943.

Tiger, Lionel, and Robin Fox. *The Imperial Animal*. New York: Holt, Rinehart and Winston, 1971.

Weideger, Paula. *Menstruation and Menopause*. New York: Knopf, 1976.

Winnicott, D. W. *The Maturational Processes and the Facilitating Environment*. New York: International University Press, 1965.

——. *Playing and Reality*. New York: Basic Books, 1971.

Zelnik, Melvin, and John Kantner. "Sexuality, Contraception and Pregnancy Among Young Unwed Females in the United States." In U.S. Commission on Population Growth and the American Future. *Demographic and Social Aspects of Population Growth,* Vol. 1 of Commission Research Reports. Government Printing Office, 1972.

Preface to the Second Edition

KAISER: When Bob Boynton retired in 1991, he followed through on a plan that he had told me (and others) about two years earlier. He cleaned out his office, closed his lab, gave away all of his technical books and reprints, and announced that he planned to give up vision research. From this it was abundantly clear that he had no intention of revising *Human Color Vision*, which he published in 1979.

There have been tremendous advances in our knowledge of human color vision since then. Consequently, by the early 1990s a revision of this book, which was previously well received, seemed appropriate. When I told Bob that I would like to take on the task, he gave his approval and immediately had the copyright transferred to me. He also made it clear that he did not want to be much involved with the revision.

BOYNTON: Quite correct. Although I had very much enjoyed my academic and research career, I had, indeed, decided to change fields in whatever was left of my lifetime after retirement at age 67. I had every confidence in Pete Kaiser's ability to handle the revision, and wished him luck with the project.

Shortly thereafter, and quite independently of Pete's proposal to prepare a second edition, the Book Publishing Committee of the Optical Society of America (OSA) came up with the idea of a limited reprint edition of *Human Color Vision*, and upon discovering that Pete held the copyright, approached him for permission.

KAISER: I told OSA that they should contact Bob, and that if he agreed to the reprint edition, it would be all right with me.

BOYNTON: I was flattered that OSA would want to reprint the original edition. And so we agreed, provided that I be allowed to prepare pages of errata to identify the errors that had come to my attention. Somehow, by the time I completed that task I began to realize how difficult it would be to have no role in revising the book I had written so many years ago. Consequently, I volunteered to read and comment on each revised chapter, but only for a quick once-over just before submission to the publisher.

KAISER: This was good news from my viewpoint. Then Bob kept getting more involved, and I did nothing to discourage him. Later he volunteered to take "a first crack" at revising Chapter 8. Toward the end, he volunteered to write the initial draft of a new chapter on naming, ordering, and recognition of surface colors, which is Chapter 11.

KAISER & BOYNTON: This is how the second edition of *Human Color Vision* turned out to be a collaborative effort, one which, in all likelihood, will be the last of the research-based interactions that we have enjoyed as long-standing scientific and personal friends for nearly thirty years.

Steadfastly, we have retained the pedagogical and scientific philosophy of the first edition as described in the original preface. This is first and foremost a textbook, not a reference work that attempts to represent a complete compendium of color science and color vision research. We use this text as a vehicle to introduce the reader to many of the important and relevant roles that physics, psychophysics, photochemistry, anatomy, and physiology play in color vision. Much of the content necessarily relates to vision in general, and not only to its chromatic aspects. We have attempted to acquaint the reader with the various research methods used to enhance our understanding of human color vision. As in the first edition we introduce some demonstrations that can be done at home, and which, if taken seriously, will enhance understanding of the concepts under discussion.

We are grateful to the following scholars who reviewed one or more chapters: Geoffrey Boynton, David Brainard, Richard Brown, Gershon Buchsbaum, Hoover Chan, Mike D'Zmura, Rhea Eskew, Don Hood, Ken Knoblauch, John Krauskopf, Barry Lee, Gene Martinez–Uriegas, John Mollon, Kathy Mullen, Alan Nagy, Jay Neitz, Maureen Neitz, Ralph Nicholls, Joel Pokorny, Martin Regan, Alan Robertson, Julie Schnapf, Steve Shevell, Vivianne Smith, Andrew Stockman, Roger Tootell, Jimmy Troost, Matt Valeton.

KAISER: I am especially indebted to Yasuhiro Nakano for supplying the tutorial on color vision mathematics and to David Brainard for supplying the tutorial on cone contrast and opponent modulation color spaces. Both of these tutorials appear in the Appendix. I thank Matt Valeton for the calculations required for Table 6.1 and for the assistance with the text associated with Table 6.1.

KAISER & BOYNTON: Although we received considerable help from all of the scientists mentioned above, we obviously assume complete responsibility for errors that may appear in this book. Our reviewers and contributors submitted their best judgments to us. The decision to accept their contributions and the manner in which they were implemented rests with the authors. Nevertheless, there can be no doubt that this second edition of *Human Color Vision* was immeasurably improved by the interaction we had with our generous scientific colleagues.

We are pleased that the Book Publishing Committee of the Optical Society of America agreed to publish this second edition. At the Society Office, we have enjoyed the pleasant and fruitful interactions with Alan Tourtlotte, Kelly Cohen Furr, Aaron Taylor and Maggie Deegan whose efforts in coordinating the production of this book are most appreciated.

KAISER: In the first edition Bob acknowledged those who had significant influences on his professional development. At this point I would like to acknowledge the early support of James P. Thomas who introduced me to vision research. I would like to also thank Bob for introducing me to the mysteries and enjoyment of color vision research and for being a continuing collaborator and source of inspiration.

BOYNTON: And I would like to thank Jim Thomas for suggesting Pete to me as a possible post-doc at an Optical Society meeting that Jim and I attended back in the 1960s. Pete came to Rochester, and we had great fun together, in the course of which — while trying without success to develop a method for measuring large color differences — we developed the minimally distinct border method of heterochromatic photometry. Years later, Pete spent a year at UCSD, where we worked together once again, this time examining the role of the S-cones in wavelength discrimination.

KAISER & BOYNTON: We both owe more than can be expressed to our wives, Linda Kaiser and Allie Boynton, who, in sum, have put up with us for more than eighty years. It is with love that we dedicate this second edition to them.

Boynton was supported for more than 38 years by the National Eye Institute (NEI) as well as the institutes from which NEI eventually evolved. Kaiser has been supported since 1968 by the Natural

Sciences and Engineering Research Council (NSERC) of Canada. We both very much appreciate the support we received from these agencies.

P.K.K., Toronto, Canada
R.M.B., Del Mar California
May 1995

Preface to the First Edition

Through the application of scientific method for about four hundred years, substantial progress has been made toward an understanding of how human beings are able to appreciate and gauge the colors of things. Before that, such an understanding had been wholly lacking. The principle aim of this book is to put forth some of our current concepts about the nature of such color perception.

With the general reader as well as the formal student in mind, I have tried to build each chapter from fundamentals without assuming any special background beyond that furnished by some lower-division study of general science and mathematics. My approach is scientific and rather theoretical. Nevertheless it is hoped that those who are concerned with color aesthetics and color technology will find my treatment of human chromatic mechanisms to be of some value. (Such a group would include artists, textile and ceramics workers, graphic arts designers, and color TV and photographic engineers.)

Despite our inability to solve the mind-body problem, it is scientifically productive to suppose that a definite anatomical and physiological substrate underlies all that we see, colors included. Similarly, it is important to be convinced that a physical world exists, one which would persist without the need for humans or other creatures to populate and perceive it. To be consistent with these essential assumptions, my approach necessarily utilizes concepts drawn freely, and in roughly equal proportions, from physical, biological, and behavioral science.

I propose no radically new theory. Instead, because I am convinced that we have by now achieved a substantial number of solid concepts about color, these are the ones that are developed and stressed. Although these ideas will undoubtedly require substantial modification and elaboration in the future, they seem unlikely to be completely overthrown by some paradigmatic revolution. Still, at the frontiers of research, theoretical ideas vary considerably and these must be held tentatively. For pedagogical purposes I have not hesitated to use models that I prefer, and to which I have occasionally contributed, without confusing the issues by discussing all possible elaborations or an excessive number of alternatives. Despite such simplification, fact and fancy should be discriminable. Moreover, enough references are given, many of them quite recent, to enable the interested reader to pursue various theoretical issues in the light of the conceptual framework provided here, and to learn more about the experimental evidence upon which these ideas rest.

Experimental data are presented mainly to illuminate theoretical ideas that are distributed throughout the book. In an effort to illustrate the nature of modern empirical visual science, a few experiments are described in considerable detail. In the early chapters, readers are invited to try a simple experiments of their own; these appear in boxes. And by means of historical examples, it is clear that theory not based upon experiment is vacuous.

There are many people to thank. An initial draft was read by my colleague, Donald MacLeod, to whom I am especially indebted for his penetrating and scholarly suggestions. After revision, each chapter was reviewed by at least one expert of my choosing. This permitted the correction of many errors and led to some substantial rewriting. While he was on leave at UCSD from Santa Barbara, Jack Loomis volunteered to read these penultimate revisions and made many helpful suggestions, as did an anonymous reviewer selected by the publisher.

The following are the scholars who reviewed one or more chapters: Howard Baker, John Boles, Frank Clarke, Julian Hochberg, Carl Ingling, Naotake Kambe, Lloyd Kaufman, Donald Kelly, Yves LeGrand, John Mollon, Walter Makous, Dirk van Norren, Thomas Piantanida, Joel Pokorny, and Vivianne Smith. They gave freely and generously of their time and expertise, and I thank them all. Please do not blame any of them for deficiencies that remain. I am also indebted to W. David Wright, one of the founding fathers of modern colorimetry, for his help in producing an abridged version of some delightful reminiscences about his role in that development, to be found in the Appendix.

At Holt, Rinehart, and Winston, I wish to acknowledge the support and assistance of Joan Green, psychology editor, as well as that of four patient predecessors with whom I interacted over nearly a decade: Tom Davies, Deborah Doty, Terry O'Reilly, and Roger Williams. For improving my efforts in many ways, and for coordinating the production of this book, a very special vote of thanks is due to Brian Heald.

Thirty years ago, Lorrin A. Riggs introduced me to visual science, and I owe much to him. On a pair of sabbatical leaves I learned a great deal from W. S. Stiles, F. J. J. Clarke, K. T. Brown, and D. N. Whitten. On the home front, two major sources of inspiration and tolerance have been my wife Allie, and my father Merrill H. Boynton.

For more than twenty years, my research has been supported by the National Eye Institute (NEI) or by one of the institutes of the U.S. Department of Health, Education, and Welfare form which NEI eventually evolved. I very much appreciate this support. Because doing research provides insights and perspectives attainable in no other way, my own work is cited disproportionately in this book. NEI has also supported many graduate students and postdoctoral fellows who worked in my laboratories at the University of Rochester and the University of California, San Diego. From them, I have learned more than I could teach. I hope that they will enjoy this book, because every one of them contributed to it.

La Jolla, California
R.M.B.

Contents

Chapter 1   Science of Color Vision: A Brief History

Chapter 2   Subjective Color Phenomena

Chapter 3   The Visual Stimulus

Chapter 4   The Eye: Anatomy Underlying the Perception of Form and Color

Chapter 5   Visual Pigments, Spectral Sensitivity, and Color Matching

Chapter 6   Sensitivity Regulation

Chapter 7   The Encoding of Color

Chapter 11   Naming, Ordering, and Recognizing Surface Colors

Appendix

References

Index of Names

Index of Subjects

Chapter 1

Science of Color Vision: A Brief History

INTRODUCTION

It has been said of science that ". . . a full scientific story, especially one that has been unfolding over historic times, can be a lovely thing, like a classical symphony or a gothic cathedral" (Botstein, 1986). By saying "If I have seen further, it is by standing on ye sholders of Giants" Newton was perhaps the most famous person, if not the first, to have expressed this sentiment (Merton, 1965). Paying attention, if even only briefly, to the history of color vision, is to gain an appreciation of the unfolding of a lovely thing and to learn about the early giants on whose shoulders some of us attempt to stand.

Those with normal color vision usually take it for granted and do not think much about it. Today, color is all around us. However, it was not so many decades ago that the norm in still photography, motion pictures, and TV was black and white images. These black and white images make it patently clear that hue is usually not required to recognize objects. Nevertheless, colors are important for esthetic reasons, for identification, and, most importantly, for safety reasons (for example traffic signals). As it turns out, we almost always associate color with specific objects. If one attempts to separate color and form unusual things happen. For example, if one looks at a mackintosh apple through a small peephole in an opaque screen its redness will have a different appearance than when the whole apple is viewed. Even more dramatic is the case when all structure is removed. If one places half a ping pong ball over each eye and then looks at a colored light, the color will fade rather quickly. Consequently, in order to understand color perception it is necessary to understand how we perceive objects in the first place. For this reason we are concerned with spatial as well as with chromatic vision. Color perception or color vision, as it is frequently called, is currently the subject of intense empirical study. It has, however, been the subject of interest for thousands of years.

EARLY GREEK CONCEPTS

How are we able, through the sense of vision, to discern the nature and color of objects far removed from our bodies — objects with which we are obviously not in physical contact? The ancient Greek philosophers correctly reasoned that something must pass between our eyes and the objects that are visually perceived. The basic elements of nature at that time were conceived to be earth, air, fire, and water. Empedocles, who suggested in the fifth century B.C. that the "eye is like a lantern," may have been referring to the fact that, under certain circumstances, the eyes of animals appear to be self-luminous. (This observation will be explained in Chapter 5.) Another observation that undoubtedly influenced the early Greeks is the phenomenon of visual phosphenes. In the dark when eyes are rapidly moved or if one applies pressure against the eye visual sensations may result. These sensations are called phosphenes, which the early Greeks attributed the sensation to fire within the eye. It was possibly on the basis of these phosphenes that Plato developed an emanation theory of vision, according to which an inner fire gave rise to visual rays shooting outward from the eye in the direction of a perceived object.[1]

It was not considered necessary to do experiments in those days, but even so it was obvious that, for man at least, no vision occurred in the total absence of light. So Plato was forced also to propose the existence of outer rays of light that were supposed to interact somehow with the visual rays. In the absence of experimentation, especially as we know it today, the Greek philosophers depended on observation. They primarily paid attention to the physical attributes of their environment. For example, light seemed to emanate best from very smooth and therefore shiny surfaces. An example of such a surface is water. As a consequence, in addition to assuming a fire within the eye the Greeks also attached great importance to the "water" in the eye.

Epicurus later rejected the emanation theory, preferring instead some rather wild ideas about what was transmitted from external objects to our eyes. He specifically considered and rejected the notion that rays of any kind were involved. Instead he thought that tiny husks (replicas) "maintain the similarity of the objects in colour and form, enter into our sight and into our thought according to the proportion of their size and with very rapid motion."[2] Not a very useful proposal, surely.

Among the ideas about which most of these early philosophers agreed, were the notions that black and white should be regarded as basic opposites, and that other hues are derivable from a limited number of more fundamental ones. Plato, as reported by Stratton (1964), believed that color is a "flame from bodies, a flame whose parts correspond to the organ of vision" (p. 145). Theophrastus, referred to by Stratton as one of the early physiological psychologists, did not agree with Plato. Theophrastus is reported as believing that color is responsible for our seeing color. By that one would assume that Theophrastus would accept the idea that "the rays are colored," an idea specifically rejected by Newton in the seventeenth century A.D.

There was no agreement about the nature of the limited fundamental hues from which others were derived. Although the notion of color mixture was prevalent, there was little understanding or agreement concerning just what was being mixed, or where, or why.

Plato recognized that one could not know another's perceptual experience.

> . . . neither that which impinges upon, nor that which is impinged upon, but something which *passes* — some relation — between them, and is peculiar to each percipient. For the several colors can scarcely appear to a dog or to any animal as they appear to a human being; nor, indeed do they appear to one man as they do to another; or even to the same man at one time as they do at another (Beare, 1906, p. 55).

This statement contains a remarkable series of early insights about species and individual differences in color perception (Chapter 10), with an added hint of awareness of the process of chromatic adaptation (Chapter 6).

That the physical nature of surfaces had something to do with their perceived color was also widely appreciated: Democritus thought that hard surfaces appeared white and rough ones black, while Plato wrote of the "surface limit of the diaphanous in a determinately bounded body" (Beare, 1906, p. 60) as being important. He also correctly thought that the degree to which light penetrates a surface was significant for the purpose of color rendering. Aristotle was especially specific in believing that reflection was an important process for the production of color.

But despite such occasional flashes of insight, wrong ideas abounded, and no effort was made to settle disputes by experiment. The following quotation is offered as a horrible example of some of Plato's ideas that were very wide of the mark:

> That which dilates the visual current is *white*, the opposite is *black*. When a more rapid motion [than that of white], belonging to a different kind of fire, impinging on and dilating the visual current right up to the eyes, forcibly distends and dissolves the very pores of the eyes, causing a combined mass of fire and water — that which we call a tear to flow from them, and being itself fire meeting the other fire right opposite: then, while the one fire leaps forth as from a lightening-flash, and the other enters in and becomes extinguished in the moisture, colours of all varieties are generated in the encounter between them, and we feel what we call a *dazzling* sensation, to the external stimulus of which we apply the terms *bright* and *glittering* (Beare, 1906, p. 51).

Another Platonic idea which we know today to be wide of the mark concerns the efficacy of experimenting with color mixing. On the subject of mixing colors, Stratton (1964, p. 145) quotes Theophrastus on Plato as:

> But as for the precise proportions, he says that one ought not to state them, even if one knew, since we have neither a necessary nor a probable account to give of them; or should one, upon experiment, find the event far otherwise, there need be no surprise; for God alone can bring such things to pass.

The importance of the brain in perception was appreciated very early, for example by Plato, although some (like Aristotle) preferred the heart as a sentient center. Dissection was practiced by the Greeks and the gross anatomy of the eye had been explored. The more obvious internal ocular components, including lens, vitreous, and various layers of the eye (with the retina) were known,[3] and the optic nerve was recognized as the connection between eye and brain. But the idea of probing a system to test its response was one whose time had not yet come.

Much of Greek anatomy and physiology was incorporated into the teachings of Galen. Judged by the length of time his views were accepted — about 1,500 years — he was the most influential physiologist ever known. Galen was a strong proponent of a specific form of emanation theory. He stated that the brain was "an organ where all sensations arrive, and where all mental images and all intelligent ideas arise." He believed that rays were discharged in the direction of an object: these emerged through the pupil, interacted with the object, and then returned to the eye. He taught that the brain was in communication with the eye by means of a visual spirit flowing back and forth through a hollow optic nerve. The visual rays, entering the eye following their return from the perceived object, interacted with the visual spirit in the lens of the eye. The latter, having come from the brain, was now flushed back into it, carrying with it the replicas of objects seen.

Even if true, the foregoing would explain little unless one understands what happens in the brain. What would permit the replicas of the outer objects, carried into the brain by the visual spirit, to be interpreted there? Although Galen was not specific on this point, there emerged over the years the concept of the "sensorium," still popular with some sensory physiologists as late as the twentieth century A.D.

The sensorium is a hypothetical place in the brain where input from the sense organs is presumed to be delivered in order to give rise to our sensations and perceptions. Sensorium is a concept that makes little sense unless it is tacitly assumed, not very usefully, that some little creature exists there who can look at, and thus interpret the meaning of, the incoming replicas. Even today it is exceedingly difficult to think clearly about what is involved here. Our knowledge about the final, interpretive stages of the visual process is rudimentary. Concepts such as "association cortex" and "integrative centers" represent no real advance and the discovery that vision is represented in more than twenty areas of the brain only compounds the mystery. The final stages are so bound up in the seemingly insoluble "mind–body" problem that they may forever resist experimental analysis. To the historians of the future, it is likely that the early Greek ideas about these matters will look no worse than some of our current concepts.

THE MIDDLE AGES

Following the decline of ancient Greek civilization, records of what had been learned were to some degree retained and utilized by the Arab culture. During the middle ages, when little scientific interest was apparent elsewhere, there lived among the Arabs a remarkable natural philosopher named Abu Ali Mohammed Ibn Al Hazen, mercifully known also as Alhazen (965–1039 A.D.), who rejected the emanation theory of vision. In agreement with the first Arab philosopher-scientist, Alkendi, Alhazen became convinced that an optical image of the sort produced by a pinhole camera (with which he experimented) was produced in the eye. Upon viewing the image formed by a pinhole camera obscura, one can see that it contains much important information about the external world.* Although the image is two-dimensional, very dim, and usually lacking in fine detail, objects nevertheless can be perceived in their proper geometrical relation to other objects and their surrounds. Moreover, the colors of objects appear to be retained in such a reproduction.

It is easy to build a pinhole camera, and for those not familiar with this device (widely heralded as the proper way to view a solar eclipse), the following description may be helpful. Take a shoe box and cut two holes in one end, each of about a quarter inch (6.25 mm) in diameter. One of these holes should be near the edge, the other about in the center. Take a piece of aluminum foil and punch a small hole in it with the tip of an ice pick, or one end of an unbent paper clip. Tape this over the center hole, so that the hole in the foil is within the hole in the box. Take the box out of doors on a sunny day; stand with the sun at your back, so that its light shines on the pinhole. Use the second hole to look into the box. An image of the sun will be seen on the opposite wall of the box. If the hole is not too small, images of artificial lights can also be seen, and it will be noticed that they are inverted.

In Alhazen's time, it was by no means clear that the pinhole camera had anything in common with the eye. It was correctly believed that light entered the eye through the pupil, but the diameter of the eye's pupil (at least 2 mm) is much too large for it to act as a pinhole. Because dissection was prohibited in the Arab culture, Alhazen was forced to depend heavily upon recorded Greek anatomy. Alhazen suspected that an image was present somewhere in the eye and he presumed, following the teachings of Galen, that it would be located in the crystalline lens in the middle of the eye. Although mistaken about this, Alhazen had the important insight that there must be points in the eye corresponding to points on perceived objects. He was also correct in supposing that light from an object was reflected to the eye following illumination by a source of light, and that the apparent color of an object depended to some extent upon the color of the light, as well as upon some property of the object (see Fig. 1.1).

Much later, during the Italian Renaissance, the great painter-scientist Leonardo da Vinci (1452–1519) turned his brilliant mind toward some of the problems of vision. He was a leader in the development of perspective drawing, which had been completely unknown to the Greeks. He also realized that a pinhole, located in an otherwise opaque screen, is capable of producing behind it an image of objects out in front. Assuming that light travels in straight lines, he reasoned that there must also be a plane in front of the screen that corresponds to the one behind, excepting that geometrical relations in the forward plane will be normal, whereas the image to the rear is inverted. Leonardo found that, by placing a plane of glass before the eye and tracing carefully an outline of perceived boundaries in the

---

*Asterisks draw attention to simple experiments (see boxed text) that can be conducted with common equipment. These experiments illustrate and amplify points raised in the text. Numbered superscripts refer to endnotes.

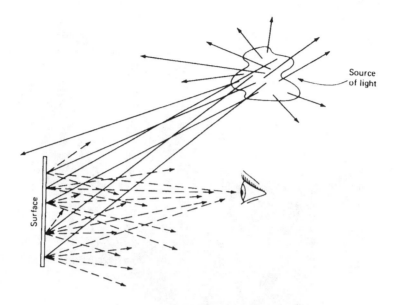

Figure 1.1   Alhazen apparently knew that the color of a surface depends in some way on the color of the light incident upon it, as well as on some property of the surface, which scatters the light incident on it in various directions, including toward the eye. This differs importantly from Galen's idea, which was believed for 1,500 years, that something is discharged from the eye toward the surface.

visual field, the eye itself somehow assumed the role of the pinhole: a replica so derived appeared to the eye as being in proper perspective (see Fig. 1.2). Leonardo also became convinced that there was some kind of image inside the eye, and he made drawings in which he unsuccessfully attempted to sketch just how the image-forming rays might behave.

But his efforts proved fruitless because nothing was yet known about the laws of light refraction (Chapter 3), and for all his genius, Leonardo was not destined to discover them. He was also seriously hampered in his efforts by a curious and irrelevant preoccupation, one that Alhazen had also suffered from: Leonardo thought that the image in the eye must be right side up. This fact should give us pause. He was assuming that, in order for the world to appear right side up, the ocular image must be oriented in the same way. Many philosophers have been troubled by this problem. But this assumption is necessary only if one holds to an old view of perception, which Boring (1942, p. 224) describes as follows:

Figure 1.2 Principles of perspective, according to which the three-dimensional object is rendered in proper perspective with points on the object located in the window as if taut strings were drawn toward the eye and allowed to intersect the plane of the window. Illustration is from Pirenne (1970), who attributes it to Brook Taylor (1811), in *New Principles of Linear Perspective*.

> The older theory of perception regarded the mind (the soul, the sensorium) as a personal entity within the head, shut off from the external world but seeking information about it and perceiving the representatives (images, copies) of objects that the nerves bring to it. This was the common-sense theory: a cranial homunculus able to perceive directly anything that comes within range of its apprehension. The mind, according to such a view, would see the image on the retina and would see it inverted because it is inverted. Thus, since the mind does not see objects without inversion, there was a problem [to account for the perceived right-side-up world, despite the upside-down retinal image].

Today the view is widely accepted among behaviorally oriented experimental psychologists that this concept of mind is not particularly useful. Furthermore, one perceives objects, not images. The term "image" is a very slippery one, whose referent is somewhat obscure even in optics. As applied to brain processes or conscious events, it becomes a hopelessly vague notion. The idea of a sensorium, with a little creature inside to view what is coming in, seems related to a kind of naive faith that the end product of vision, as it appears in the brain, must somehow represent — in some more or less obvious way — the geometry of visual space. It was common to find, in introductory treatments of vision, statements implying that although the retinal image is upside down, we are spared the perception of an inverted world thanks to the heroic effort of the brain, which turns it right side up again (e.g., Rainwater, 1962; Lawson *et al.*, 1975)[4]. The error contained in this kind of thinking is at least as serious as the earlier error of the emanation theory of vision. For surely the brain does nothing at all to the retinal image, if that image is regarded, as it must be, as a purely optical phenomenon. As Johannes Müller pointed out in the nineteenth century, the brain receives nerve signals, not light. Müller formally generalized this concept to all sensory processes and called it the "doctrine of specific nerve energies."[5] With regard to vision, the doctrine of specific nerve energies implies that regardless of how the visual system is stimulated it produces a visual response. These messages normally have their origin in the patterning of light received at the retina, but neither the amount nor the quality of information contained in the retinal image is in any sense altered by transformations of that image such as inversion or left-right reversal.

KEPLER AND THE RETINAL IMAGE

The seventeenth century marks the start of the modern era for the study of light and vision. Gradually, though with much difficulty, the habits of speculation and of appeal to ancient authority began to be replaced by more astute natural observation, experimentation, and a willingness to challenge established views. There was surely much to learn about color, a subject about which total confusion still prevailed in the 1600s.

Descartes (1596–1650) would soon promote an influential and scientifically useful philosophy that treated humans partly as machines, drawing a clear distinction between objective and subjective domains. The subjective/objective dichotomy can be traced to Aristotle and Democritus. Aristotle thought color was dependent on the eye as well as the object. Democritus, on the other hand, considered color as something purely subjective (Stratton, 1964). In the sixteenth century, without microscopes, microelectrodes, or radiometers, investigators lacked the means by which to understand or measure either the physical light stimulus or the response of the eye. It was still not clear whether color was embodied in light, object, eye, or soul. Despite a knowledge of ocular gross anatomy and a growing suspicion that rays of some kind caused an image to be formed some-where in the eye, spatial vision was not yet correctly understood any more than it had been by the Greeks or Arabs.

Lenses were described by a Franciscan friar, Roger Bacon in 1267 (van Helden, 1989). In his *Opus Maius* he wrote about thick pieces of glass spheres placed over one's reading material to make reading easier; a solution particularly useful for the aged. van Helden further reports that "before the end of the thirteenth century craftsmen in Italy had begun making thin biconvex glasses and putting them into frames so that they could be worn in front of the eyes" (p. 2). Positive lenses had been used to improve the performance of the pinhole camera by G. B. Della Porta in 1589. But the study of lenses had a curious history: they were considered not to be scientifically respectable. Bacon, for example, was considered a magician, especially as a result of some extravagant claims with regard to what could be achieved with the glasses. To use lenses, it was thought, would lead to distortions of per-ception that must be carefully avoided by the objective investigator. Even Galileo encountered difficulties. Because his spyglass (as he called his telescope) revealed phenomena that were not visible to the naked eye, he had to counter the argument that the spyglass deceived him. For a very long time the manufacture and use of lenses was left to artisans and practitioners, who used them without understanding how they worked. van Helden (1989) tells us that toward the end of 1609 Galileo had made significant progress in developing a 20 power "spy glass." Galileo's discoveries became quickly known and van Helden adds that by 1610 "Galileo's name was on the lips of learned men all over Europe" (p. 87). From Ronchi (1970) we learn that Galileo was ". . .a man who strongly influenced any scientific subject to which he turned his attention . . ."(p. 95). Ronchi further notes that when Galileo published his findings in his *Sidereus Nuncius*, The whole aca-demic world, with an impressive unanimity, ranged itself against Galileo" (p. 97). He was accused of allowing the telescope to deceive him and make him the observer of not real things but illusions.

Johannes Kepler, a contemporary of Galileo, was a noted astrono-mer who believed in the heliocentric theory of Copernicus. In the field of optics, he was the first to understand how positive lenses work, and why their use permits enlargement of the aperture of a pinhole camera, leading to the double benefits of increased brightness and improved image quality. There had been substantial resistance to Kepler's early observations with his telescope, related to the fact that his crude lenses had produced severe chromatic aberration, giving rise to the perception of colors where none were otherwise evident. (Chromatic aberration is discussed in Chapter 3, p. 87). At the beginning of the seventeenth century opticians, mathematicians and philosophers summarized the value of this new device as follows: "the telescope shows images larger than the real objects or nearer; it shows them colored and distorted therefore it misleads us and cannot be used as an instrument of observation" (Ronchi, 1970, p. 95).

In addition to being forced to live with this kind of "scientific" negativism, Kepler was also concerned with the ever present danger of persecution by religious zealots. The accomplishments of early scientists such as Kepler cannot be fully appreciated without taking into account the inhibiting effects of this kind of epistemological and social climate. Today the science of physics provides a way of describing the world that is grossly at odds with biblical descriptions, as well as with the way we perceive it. Now we take for granted that science advances with the development of instruments that extend human senses, permitting the measurement of that which otherwise is too small to be seen, or of radiation or matter to which human end organs are wholly insensitive.

Proceeding from his understanding of optical relationships, Kepler reasoned that the crystalline lens within the eye was required to form an image in the eye, and so the image could not be in the lens itself. He inferred instead that the receptive layer for image reception was at the back of the eye, in the retina. He seemed keenly aware, more than most of his predecessors had been, that this is the end of the trail so far as light is concerned in the visual process. Some other substance or process must intervene at this stage; one that is somehow capable of appreciating the light. But Kepler's speculations about how this might work were woefully wide of the mark, being clearly influenced by a religious and mystical turn of mind that was still natural even for men like Kepler, who were beginning to stake out the territory of modern empirical science.

Kepler was also mistaken about a basic fact of purely optical importance, believing incorrectly that no light refraction takes place at the cornea of the eye, which is in fact the principal refractive interface. Despite this error, Kepler was correct in believing that the retinal image was small, inverted, and systematically related to points in space. Moreover, it was colored: "Green is depicted green, and in general things are depicted by whatever colour they have."

In 1595, according to Polyak (1957), an Italian named Aranzi actually had cut a hole in the back of an animal eye, and by placing a translucent screen there, he had directly observed the colored image that Kepler was later to imagine. Kepler was apparently unaware of Aranzi's work, which was too far ahead of its time to create much attention. In 1625, long after Kepler had drawn his conclusions, Christoph Scheiner repeated Aranzi's experiment in Germany. Its significance was immediately recognized, and Scheiner is usually cited today as the one who first accomplished the demonstration. Descartes, in his *Dioptrique* (published in 1637), also reports having done this experiment.

The formation of retinal images may seem to have relatively little to do with color vision. Therefore it is worth stating again that a proper explanation of color vision is not possible without a general understanding of the visual process, in particular the physics and physiology underlying its spatial aspects. After all, if Democritus had been correct that color is something inherent in tiny replicas entering the eye, then the task of color vision today would be to capture and dissect these replicas, and to perturb them in order to discover which of their features contains information that is specific to color. Instead, the problem becomes one of analyzing the distribution of light on the retina, and of understanding what aspect of this light is capable of giving rise to sensations of color.

NEWTON'S BREAKTHROUGH

Throughout the period of history so far described, nothing was known about the physical nature of light, although the science known as *geometrical optics* was gradually being developed. This is a branch of optics that treats light as being comprised of rays that move in straight lines and suffer refraction when passing from one optical medium to another (see Chapter 3). These concepts are mainly useful for predicting the location of images, which is done these days by computer. But geometrical optics fails to describe many important features of physical reality and is unable to deal with most of the physical aspects of color. To do this requires an understanding of the physical nature of light (physical optics) and this work did not advance rapidly until the nineteenth century.

Almost everyone knows about Isaac Newton's famous experiment in which he broke white light into its spectral components by passing a beam through a prism. Newton understood geometrical optics very well, as a perusal of his *Opticks* (1730) will show, and his experiments with prisms were probably the most important in the history of color science. What is often overlooked is that Francesco Maria Grimaldi (1608–1663), who died at the age of 45 when Newton was 23 years old, had considered the "undulatory theory" of light. Moreover, Grimaldi defined three "simple" colors as red, yellow, and blue. Ronchi (1970) attributes the birth of trichromatic theory to him.

Although Grimaldi anticipated Newton, clearly the precision and detail Newton exercised in his research and interpretation causes historians to place the origins of modern color science with the work Newton published in his *Opticks*.

Newton's biographers are fond of pointing out that he purchased his prisms at the Stourbridge fair, almost as if to imply that he was on a lark and might accidentally have discovered spectral dispersion while looking through one of them on his way home. So far as the source of supply is concerned, he was not, after all, able to order them from Edmund Scientific or Bausch and Lomb. And Newton was by no means the first to disperse white light with a prism, or to note that colors resulted.[6] But when he got his prisms back to his rooms at Trinity College he set up his experimental conditions with care and precision, and was masterful in interpreting the observations that followed.

If a thick beam of white light is dispersed by a prism, a continuum of overlapping spectra is produced and these mainly recombine to produce white: only at the edges are residual fringes seen. Newton reduced the size of his incident light beam to dimensions small enough to minimize the overlapping spectra, but he kept the beam large enough to allow sufficient light for clear visual observation of the spectrum that was formed. Newton's light source, the sun, was of course the most intense available; his aperture — used to limit beam size — was a small circular opening in an otherwise opaque shutter. The prism that he used, a regular triangular one, was set at the precise angle of minimum dispersion. According to already established principles of geometrical optics, this condition should have produced a perfectly circular spot of light on his receiving screen. What Newton observed instead was a shape of the sort that would be traced out by a continuous succession of overlapping circles, consisting overall of a splotch of light with straight sides and rounded ends, longer than its width by a ratio of about five to one, and changing gradually in color from violet at one end to red at the other.

Newton extended his experiment in important ways. A narrow colored band was selected from the spectrum and was passed through a second prism (today we refer to such an arrangement as a double monochromator), as shown in Figure 1.3. Newton reported that there was no further dispersion or change of color. In another experiment, he recombined the dispersed rays of the initial spectrum and found that white light was thereby restored. From these and other observations, he concluded that white light was in fact a mixture of colored lights, and that the rays corresponding to each color took different paths through the prism.

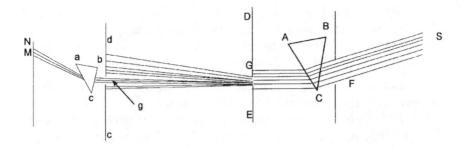

Figure 1.3   Newton's diagram of one of the experiments described in the text. Light from the sun, coming in at the right, is dispersed by prism, ABC, and a small part of the beam is selected by aperture, G, in screen, DE. The dispersed spectrum is seen along de. Another small aperture, g, picks off a narrow part of the spectrum and delivers it to a second prism, abc. If g is sufficiently small, no further dispersion is seen. (Adapted from Newton, 1730/1952)

Newton appreciated the continuous nature of the spectrum. In his *Opticks*, he wrote:

> The Spectrum did appear tinged with this Series of colors, violet, indigo, blue, green, yellow, orange, red together with all their intermediate Degrees in a continual Succession perpetually varying. So that there appeared as many Degrees of Colors, as there were sorts of Rays differing in Refrangibility (p. 122).

Here, although Newton identified certain regions of the spectrum in terms of "ROY G. BIV" (the acronym that many of us learned in school), his perception of graded colors in the spectrum led him to conclude that the hypothetical rays of spectral light were also graded continuously — an idea that turns out to be correct (see Chapter 3). Newton also was careful to point out that the light rays themselves are not colored, but should be regarded instead as providing only a disposition for eliciting one or another color sensation if delivered to the eye (Newton, 1730/1952, p. 124).

> And if at any time I speak of Light and Rays as coloured and endued with Colours, I would be understood to speak not philosophically and properly, but grossly, and according to such Conceptions as vulgar People in seeing all these Experiments would be apt to frame. For the Rays to speak properly are not coloured. In them there is nothing else than a certain Power and Disposition to stir up a Sensation of this or that Colour.

Yet when Newton said that white light was a mixture of colored lights, it was not clear whether he meant that the mixture was to be regarded as being a physical affair or if it depended also upon the eye for its occurrence. Lacking any definitive evidence about where color mixture occurs, Newton characteristically chose not to take a firm stand on this important matter.

What is most impressive about this work is that it removed color from the perceived object, where it had been relegated since the ancient Greeks. Instead Newton placed the stimulus for color perception in the rays reflected from the object. And he went a step further, showing experimentally that the color of an object was related to its ability to reflect the colored rays of the spectrum selectively, also making the critical observation that monochromatic light, approximated by isolating just one part of the spectrum, is only more or less reflected by a surface, but is not otherwise changed in character.

The idea that white light is comprised of a mixture of colored lights was so contrary to common sense that, although it was widely adopted by post-Newtonian physicists, it absolutely outraged the famous German poet-scientist Johann Wolfgang von Goethe,[7] who had observed that colors appear only at the edges of white objects when they are viewed directly through prisms. He repeated some of Newton's experiments and did many of his own, concluding that Newton's conclusions were mistaken and could only have been reached under the bizarre and contrived circumstances of Newton's experiments. This kind of dispute has been common in the history of science. It arises between those who favor difficult and controlled experiments and those who, like Goethe in his time and the Gestalt psychologists of a later era, tend to favor a more naturalistic form of observation. While the latter claim that the whole of a complex process can never be understood by taking it apart (a concept we saw earlier attributed to Plato on p.3), their opponents find it difficult to imagine how progress can occur by any other route.

Some of Goethe's objections were not without foundation. Because Newton had claimed that there was no further dispersion when a small part of the spectrum was passed through a second prism, there could be no further appearance of color fringes. In repeating the experiment, Goethe noted that faint color fringes did in fact appear. Today we know that this happens because a narrow spectral band is not the same as pure monochromatic light. Newton had either failed to observe this variation in color, or he may have decided to ignore it as a second-order effect. Given that he had just invented the calculus, we must assume that he understood the nature of limiting conditions. If so, he reached the correct conclusion by ignoring effects that, though inevitable in real experiments with finite wavebands of light, would not occur at the theoretical limit.

There is an important history lesson here. The foregoing illustrates a style of research that can sometimes lead quickly to strong and important inferences. Yet when deviations from an expected result occur, one ignores them at great peril. In another instance, Newton himself was not so fortunate. By using crossed spectra he had attempted to determine whether white light could be produced in the overlapping square by the mixture of only two colors. He failed to find this, observing instead a slight residual color.[8] From this he concluded that it would not be possible to get white from a mixture of only two pure spectral colors. This time he had no theoretical basis for what to expect in the limiting case, and he guessed wrong. Nevertheless, there was nothing otherwise incorrect about what he reported, and in this case, where he did not understand so well what to expect, he was careful to report exactly what he observed.

Newton had also asserted that chromatic aberration in telescopes could never be corrected. This would follow if, as Newton had thought, all kinds of glass had the same characteristics of chromatic dispersion. But they do not (see Chapter 3, p. 87), and multiple-element color-corrected lenses were in fact developed during Newton's lifetime. Goethe, who was born twenty-two years after Newton's death, took this as evidence that Newton had been wrong not just about optical glass, but about almost everything. Although Goethe's diatribe against Newton was of unusual intensity, such scientific conflict is not itself unusual. Helmholtz and Hering (see pp. 23–25) were to be at odds later, and there are plenty of unmentionable examples that could be cited from the present era of color science.

TOWARD EXPLAINING THE APPEARANCE OF THE SPECTRUM

For much of his life, Newton favored a corpuscular theory of light. It sometimes happens with the greatest of scientists that they eventually carry out themselves, sometimes perhaps without intending to do so, the very experiments that prove most damaging to their cherished beliefs. Working with juxtaposed plates of glass, one flat and the other just slightly curved, he produced and carefully studied what are now called "Newton's rings." Although Robert Hooke had previously conducted this experiment, once again it was Newton who performed the quantitative analysis, through which it proved possible to more fully understand the implications of these rings.

Vasco Ronchi, in his fascinating book on the history of light and vision (1970, p. 176), writes:

Newton's measurements and calculations established that the dark rings were always formed where the thickness of the film [of air between the two glass layers] was a multiple of a given value, namely 1/89,000 part of an inch (0.285 micron) for light of a bright yellow and that the bright rings occurred where the thickness had a value which was between those of the dark colour... [and] that the ratio of the thickness required to produce red and violet rings was 14 to 9.

Here Newton had almost in his grasp the relation between wavelength and hue, but it eluded him. His results are easy to understand by wave theory. The rings are caused by interference, which in turn depends upon the wave nature of light and the occurrence of constructive and destructive interference (Chapter 3). Destructive interference would create dark rings in the condition where the transmitted and reflected waves are 180° out of phase, or shifted by half a wavelength. This occurs at a separation of 0.285 nm in yellow light. The full wave would then be 570 nm, and this turns out be an accurate estimate of the wavelength of yellow light.[9] The ratio of 14 to 9 corresponds to that between 650 to 417 nm; wavelengths that appear red and violet respectively. Thus, Newton was the first to develop a method for measuring the wavelength of light, although he failed to recognize it as such.

Earlier Newton had undertaken the first experiment that related the wavelength of light to the appearance of hue. His procedure was to mark the places in the spectrum that corresponded to the midpoints of his seven zones of hues, and then to ask others to do the same. He concluded from this that there was reasonable agreement among observers.

Sherman (1981) describes an interesting controversy that took place in the early 1800s among some of the leading scientists of the day, including, among others, Wollaston, Brewster, Heschel, and Airy. The controversy concerned the appearance of the spectrum. What is interesting in Sherman's account is that it underscores the importance of experimental replication. The controversy was finally solved and laid to rest by Helmholtz because he bothered to replicate as precisely as possible earlier experiments. He was able to duplicate previous observations and determine their causes and artifacts. Then he preceded to do the experiment properly and solved the puzzle. Helmholtz showed that internal reflections in the optics of the equipment used to generate the spectra and intra-ocular scatter were responsible for the observations reported by Brewster.

There are perhaps three reasons why the correlation between the degree of refraction and hue was not measured until recently. (1) *It is controversial whether sensations can be measured.* For example, neither Hering nor Helmholtz would attempt such measurement in the nineteenth century, although both were keen introspectionists who understood the physical nature of light. Hering described the appearance of colors and how they should be arranged in a proper color diagram. Helmholtz went to great lengths to select color terms that satisfied him as being proper descriptors of the points of the spectrum marked by Fraunhofer's solar lines, but his description was qualitative only. (2) *The appearance of the spectrum depends upon its intensity.* This is known as the Bezold–Brücke hue shift, about which Helmholtz had earlier commented, especially with respect to the loss of reddishness when violet lights are raised to high brightnesses. (3) *The appearance of any color depends, to a surprising extent, upon its surroundings.* The appearance of one part of a spectrum is influenced by the rest of it. To judge spectral colors properly, it is necessary for a narrow spectral band to fill a visual field of the desired size with light of uniform quality. The effects of context and surround on color perception are exceedingly important (see Chapters 2 and 11 as well as the concluding section of this chapter).

TRICHROMACY

The basic idea behind trichromacy is that it is possible to match all spectral wavelengths by use of only three primary colors. In addition, it was hypothesized over 200 years ago that there must be three kinds of physiological entities in the eye responsible for processing the light from these three primary colors. For many years sole credit for these ideas were given to Thomas Young and Hermann von Helmholtz. In fact Young's contribution lay dormant for some years until Helmholtz revived it and thus gave birth to the Young–Helmholtz trichromatic theory of color vision.

In a succession of papers starting with Gordon Walls (1956), we have now learned that the eighteenth century was a fertile time for the field of color and the concept of trichromacy in particular. Jakob C. Le Blon, an artist-printer, published a book in c.1723, which describes a process of printing reproductions of paintings with a three color process and which describes the process of color mixing (Sherman, 1981; Mollon, 1982). In 1956, Walls published a fascinating paper which shows that George Palmer proposed a physiologically based trichromacy more than twenty years before Young's now famous pronouncement quoted below. Palmer, however, did not appreciate, as did Young, that the physical variable underlying hue was continuous (Mollon, 1987). In 1957, Robert Weale published a paper entitled *Trichromatic Ideas in the Seventeenth and Eighteenth Centuries*. Weale states that in 1757, twenty years before Palmer's paper, Michael Lomonosov reported on a theory of light and colors, which contained the fundamental ideas of three primary colors. Weale tells us that Lomonosov named red, yellow, and blue as the three primary colors and proposed that all other colors are formed from the mixtures of these. Weale also quotes Lomonosov as stating: "Gyration will freely act in the retina of the eye so that all colours will affect vision" (p. 650). The reader then learns that Lomonosov was influenced by Mariotte, who predates him by about a century, and that Mariotte "derived his three primaries from an examination of the spectrum" (p. 650). According to Weale, Young "never claimed priority in matters relating to colour vision" (p. 650). Where trichromatic theory is concerned Helmholtz is primarily responsible for bringing Thomas Young to modern fame. Weale's historical treatment concludes that the acceptance of trichromatic theory was speeded up by the authority of Young's ideas as revitalized by Helmholtz.[10]

According to Helmholtz (1924, v. 2, p. 162), "Pliny tells us that the ancient Greek painters knew how to prepare all colors with four pigments . . . and even in the celebrated fresco, The Marriage of the Aldobrandini, dating from Roman times, the profusion of pigments is very small, as Davy's chemical investigations showed." In addition to mixing lights, Newton had also mixed pigments, but he attached little significance to the critical difference between these two operations. It is interesting that Newton, for all his genius, did not make the correct observations with respect to mixing blue and yellow light. He said one obtains green (Newton, 1730/1952).[11] Helmholtz (1962) cited Le Blon, DuFay, Tobias, Mayer, and J.H. Lambert as physicists who subscribed to a notion of three fundamental colors.[12] We have to interpret Helmholtz's designation of physicist in the very broadest terms. According to Mollon (1979), Le Blon was a printer, and according to Lee (1991), Mayer was a professor of Economy with interests in physics, mathematics, astronomy, and geography. Judging from Walls' story about tracking down the origins of George Palmer, we know that the accuracy of Helmholtz's referencing could have been improved. Nevertheless, the important point is that the eighteenth century was important for trichromacy. With trichromatic color mixing being well established and these ideas integrated into visual function by Lomonosov and Palmer it set a perfect stage for Thomas Young to correctly hypothesize the relationship between physiological trichromacy and the continuous nature of the spectrum.

Let us now take a closer look at Young's famous 1802 statement of trichromacy articulated, for the first time, in physiological and correct physical terms.

As it is almost impossible to conceive each sensitive point of the retina to contain an infinite number of particles, each capable of vibrating in perfect unison with every possible undulation, it becomes necessary to suppose the number limited; for instance to the three principal colours, red, yellow, and blue, and that each of the particles is capable of being put in motion more or less forcibly by undulations differing less or more from perfect unison. Each sensitive filament of the nerve may consist of three portions, one for each principal colour.[13]

This statement embodies most of the important ideas of modern trichromatic theory, for which there is now overwhelming experimental support, as will be seen in Chapter 5. Although the statement does not go so far as to recognize that defective color vision was related to the existence of the "sensitive filaments," Young did, in fact, attribute Dalton's color defective vision to his lacking a fiber which is responsible for seeing red (Hunt, Dulai, Bowmaker & Mollon, 1975). Because Palmer's statement predates Young's it would appear that he was the first to recognize that color defective vision is the result of problems in one or more of the visual receptors. Young's famous statement of trichromacy contains the implication that the wavelength of light (which, as we will see in Chapter 3, is reciprocally related to its frequency of vibration) varies continuously across the spectrum, consistent with what Newton had supposed. Young explains that the relation between wavelength and hue depends essentially upon the ratios of activation among three processes: this is the basic idea of trichromacy. The alternative hypothesis that each receptor (or "sensitive point of the retina") could respond in some differential way to each wavelength is rejected, with the substitution of the idea (now known as the principle of univariance — see Chapter 5) that a receptor can respond only more or less vigorously, depending upon how well it resonates with the frequency of the incoming light. Because light comes in a continuous series of frequencies, it is not possible to conceive of an infinite number of receptors, each sharply tuned to only one frequency. Three types of receptors might do, if these were to have overlapping spectral sensitivities such that each wavelength produces a different ratio of responses among them. It should be recognized that these prophetic ideas were developed before anything at all was known about the physiology of the retina: the argument was largely a logical one, being no more than a plausible hypothesis based upon known physical facts.

As noted above, Palmer was the first to attribute defective color vision to a problem with retinal receptors (Weale, 1957; MacAdam, 1970). MacAdam quotes Palmer as follows (p.48):

It is quite evident that the retina must be composed of three kinds of fibers, or membranes, each analogous to one of the three primary rays and susceptible of being stimulated only by it. Equal sensibility of these three classes of fibers constitutes true vision; any deficiency of sensibility as well as excessive sensibility of any class constitutes false vision.

If by false vision[14] Palmer was referring to color defective vision, then clearly (as MacAdam points out) "Palmer was being as modern as possible" (p. 49). We know today, at least for congenital defective color vision, that color deficiency is a problem rooted in an abnormality of one or more of the cone receptors.

The development of color vision theory has often profited from the part-time efforts of some very great physical scientists. Bertrand Russell states without qualification that, in his opinion, Newton was the greatest scientific genius of all time. If so, Thomas Young could surely qualify as a very close second. His work on vision had begun early. For his study of visual accommodation (or the focus of the lens in the eye) he was elected to fellowship in the Royal Society in 1793 at the age of twenty-one (nine years younger than Newton). Young worked in an astounding variety of scientific fields, and color vision was for him only a minor interest. For this reason he did not choose to spend much time promoting trichromatic theory. Perhaps he was not convinced that it was correct: the number three was, after all, offered very tentatively; no proof that this was the correct number of particles was given, and none was sought. More important than the number of postulated color receptors was the idea that no one class of them could, by itself, carry a message from which hue could be deduced. But Young had no proof of this concept either.

Unlike the specialized scientific interests we see today, in the eighteenth and nineteenth centuries most scientists who made significant advances in the field of color had rather diverse interests. Le Blon, we already noted, was a printer. Lomonosov, as described by Weale (1957), was working in geography, electricity, oratory, and grammar. In addition, he owned a factory that made stained glass.[15] Walls (1956) guessed that George Palmer was a chemist, but Mollon (1985) deduced that he was a merchant specializing in colored glass. Newton, in addition to his color work, made numerous other significant advances, perhaps the most notable of which are related to the law of gravity and the invention of calculus. Thomas Young is described by Sherman (1981) as ". . . one of the acutest men who ever lived" (p. 3). He made significant contributions in medicine, philology, physics, actuarial calculations, mathematics, and Egyptology.

In any event, for many years Young's ideas on color were not very widely accepted; this fact is illustrated by noting that David Brewster, a very respectable optical physicist, seriously proposed as late as 1855 that there were but three fundamental kinds of light, called red, yellow, and blue, and that all physically realizable lights, including spectral ones, contained mixtures of these three.

Hermann von Helmholtz initially rejected Young's trichromatic statements. However, in the second book of his monumental three-volume *Handbook of Physiological Optics,* which remains the greatest work in the history of visual science, Helmholtz revived Young's trichromatic statement and brought it to the prominence we know today.

Helmholtz almost defies classification.[16] He studied medicine at the Friedrich-Wilhelm Institute in Berlin, where he came under the influence of the world's first professor of physiology, Johannes Müller. While a very young man, Helmholtz was the first to measure the velocity of nerve conduction. He authored the principle of conservation of energy, invented the ophthalmoscope, did almost as much work in audition as in vision, and was an absolutely first-rate physicist, mathematician, psychologist, and physiologist. He eventually became professor of physics at the University of Berlin.

The *Handbook* was first published from 1856 to 1866, when Helmholtz was between 35 and 45 years of age; a second edition appeared 30 years later, during the last decade of his life. A third German edition was posthumously published from 1909 to 1911, with editorial additions by A. Gullstrand, J. von Kries, and W. Nagel. The work was considered so important that it was translated into English by J. P. C. Southall and others in 1924, and was published by the Optical Society of America, with additional appendices and editorial comments. In his second volume, Helmholtz wrote:

> Young's theory of the colour sensations, like so much else that this marvelous investigator achieved in advance of his time, remained unnoticed, until the author himself [Helmholtz] and Maxwell again directed attention to it. It is sufficient to assume that the optic nerve is capable of sensations of different kinds, without trying to find out why the system of these visual sensations is just what it is. (p. 163)

Helmholtz refers here to James Clerk Maxwell, another nineteenth century scientific genius, who is probably best known for his vector equations describing electromagnetic fields.

Helmholtz's first sketches of overlapping spectral sensitivity curves are shown in Figure 1.4. It is probably unfortunate that he talked about fundamental sensations, rather than receptor processes, because curves of this kind (although they explain color matches) do not explain color sensations; a point that will be elaborated shortly. Maxwell, after doing some ingeniously simple experiments using reflecting surfaces on a spinning top (the ancestor of the modern color

1. The eye is provided with three distinct sets of nervous fibres. Stimulation of the first excites the sensation of red, stimulation of the second the sensation of green, and stimulation of the third the sensation of violet.

2. Objective homogeneous light excites these three kinds of fibres in various degrees, depending on its wave-length. The red-sensitive fibres are stimulated most by light of longest wave-length, and the violet-sensitive fibres by light of shortest wave-length. But this does not mean that each colour of the spectrum does not stimulate all three kinds of fibres, some feebly and others strongly; on the contrary, in order to explain a series of phenomena, it is necessary to assume that that is exactly what does happen. Suppose that the colours of the spectrum are plotted horizontally in Fig. 21 in their natural sequence, from red to violet, the three curves may be taken to indicate something like the degree of excitation of the three kinds of fibres, No. 1 for the red-sensitive fibres, No. 2 for the green-sensitive fibres, and No. 3 for the violet-sensitive fibres.

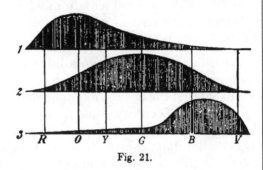

Fig. 21.

Figure 1.4   Helmholtz's three overlapping spectral sensitivity curves, and the text that goes with them, from Helmholtz (1924). This is a basically qualitative account, as indicated, for example, by the use of color names to identify the spectrum. Curves like these, representing the results of actual measurements, will be found in Chapter 5. Note that Helmholtz has plotted the spectral colors in an order that is reversed relative to the modern convention.

wheel), conducted the first color-mixture experiments that made use of spectral light. He was, thus, the first to provide quantitative data that we relate today to the absorption spectra of the three kinds of cone photopigments in the retina (Chapter 5).

OPPONENT-COLOR THEORY

In the late nineteenth century, a German physiologist named Ewald Hering[17] developed a viewpoint about color vision that was largely based upon the subjective appearance of colors, rather than upon physical experiments like those of Maxwell that involved only color matching. The trichromatic theory, as put forth by Helmholtz, is inadequate to account for the way colors appear. It cannot reasonably explain, for example, why red and green lights mix to produce yellow (a color qualitatively different from each of the components in the mixture), or why this yellow, if mixed with blue, can produce a perfect white. Helmholtz did not consider it worthwhile "to find out why the system of these visual sensations is just what it is." Ever since, most trichromatic theorists have been physicists, for whom the appearance of colors often is regarded as being of little scientific interest.

But the appearance of colors did concern Hering, who also wanted to show why one never sees reddish greens or yellowish blues. Hering speculated that the answer might lie in an "opponent-color" process. More than a half century would pass before there was a shred of direct physiological evidence to support this idea, but abundant evidence has been developed since 1950 (see Chapters 4 and 7). Hering suggested that the visual system might be capable of generating signals of two opposite kinds, depending upon wavelength. This is an idea that was not favorably received by either the physicists or physiologists of that era, being squarely at odds with both the Young–Helmholtz theory of color and Müller's doctrine of specific nerve energies.

Opponent-color and trichromatic theory competed for a long time. What is interesting is that there should have been a competition at all. In his *Outlines of a Theory of the Light Sense* (translated by Hurvich & Jameson, 1964) Hering, in a footnote (p. 48), agreed with Aubert that these two theories co-exist. The relevant part of the footnote (quotation from Aubert) is as follows:

> . . . the opponent-colors theory and the Young–Helmholtz three color theory "could, with some modifications very well exist side by side if one strictly distinguished between the *process of excitation and the process of sensation*," and used the three-color theory for the former and my theory for the latter.

This brief passage would seem to indicate that Hering acknowledged the peripheral trichromatic processing of visual activity resulting from the retina being excited and that this peripheral information is transmitted along the visual pathway and becomes involved with the process of sensation where opponent processing takes place.

Because of some very ingenious psychophysics as well as more direct physiological and optical techniques, we know, today, that the processing of chromatic information starts in the receptors according to the trichromatic theory and this information is transformed in the retina to a level of processing that is consistent with the opponent processing theory. This two stage model, as it is called, has its origins in the 1920s and is presaged in 1905 by von Kries. The psychologist G. E. Müller and the physicist Erwin Schrödinger worked out plausible zone theories to handle the problem. Judd (1951) provides an excellent summary of this early zone approach to color vision. According to such models, of which there have been many since, the initial trichromatic color separation, of the sort that Young had proposed, leads next to an opponent-color stage. The direct evidence for this will be considered in Chapter 7.

THE RECENT PAST

The past sixty-five years have seen a rapid development in visual science generally, and color science in particular. The work is too technical to permit a simple summary. Nevertheless this chapter will be concluded with a very brief overview of a few modern developments.

The CIE System

Until 1931, the concept of color had no precise scientific basis and colors could be specified only by appeal to physical samples. In that year, the International Commission on Illumination (CIE)[18] adopted a system of color specification which has lasted to the present time. The basic data with which the founding fathers of colorimetry worked were color-mixture functions of the sort that Maxwell had originally obtained. A standard set of color-mixture values based mainly upon extensive experimental investigations in England by W. D. Wright and by J. Guild, was adopted. The idea was to reduce any spectral radiance distribution (Chapter 3) to only three variables, and to state that, for color vision, any two stimuli describable by the same values of each of these variables, no matter how physically different, would be defined as colorimetrically identical. Because the color of a surface does not change very much when intensity is changed without change in spectral distribution, it proved possible to reduce the identification of color to only two variables that could be represented on a two-dimensional chart known as a chromaticity diagram. The properties of such a diagram will be explained in Chapter 5. The particular one adopted by the CIE, which will be minimally utilized in this book, is discussed in Appendix Parts I, II, and III.

Although very useful, there are many limitations to this system. For one thing, the color matches that it predicts apply only to a hypothetical standard observer, and not exactly to any particular human being. For another, it is valid only for restricted conditions of viewing with small fields that are neither too bright nor too dim.

And, finally, the chromaticity diagram does not represent color appearance very well, and although there is really no reason why it should (see Chapter 8), it has often been used for this purpose.

Anatomy and Physiology

The improvement in the nineteenth century of the light microscope and histological procedures permitted the discovery of rods and cones as the photoreceptors in the eye, and provided the basis for the duplicity theory that will be described in Chapter 4, according to which cones are the receptors for color vision. Yet it has been difficult to show clear anatomical differences among the three cone types that are believed to exist in primates, or to extract their photopigments, which were thought to be responsible for absorption of light. A class of cones outside of the fovea has been observed, which appear a little larger and more circular than others. In a review article, Boynton (1988) suggested that these may be the short wavelength sensitive cones. Fortunately, it has proved possible to examine cone pigments by less direct techniques (Chapter 5).

Biological tissue is electrically active, and the recording of such activity (electrophysiology) began in the nineteenth century and has advanced to a fine art. Direct physiological evidence to support the notion of three classes of cones and of opponent-color responses at subsequent neural stages, now exists (Chapters 4 and 7). Many workers today are recording from the more central parts of the visual brain, presumably a step closer than the retina to visual consciousness.

Until recently, inferences about mechanisms of color perception could be made only indirectly on the basis of psychophysical evidence (for example, experiments on color matching using human subjects and behavioral measures). A wide spectrum of research techniques now exist that should, in the years ahead, move us closer to a complete description of how the human color-vision system actually works. Much of this book is devoted to an examination of the state of such evidence today, considered in terms of what it implies about how we see color. As this subject advances, psychophysical experiments will continue to add to our knowledge of color vision, and these will be stressed. Many of these experiments could have been done many years earlier, although some depend heavily on technical advances in the area of stimulus presentation. But even where they were technically possible at an earlier time, the state of anatomy, neurophysiology, and photochemistry would not have suggested the usefulness of some of the experiments of today, which test implications of theories rooted in the more direct techniques, but not fully testable by them. Conversely, the data of the psychophysicist, together with theories developed from such data, provide a framework within which the electrophysiologist conducts his research.

Chromatic Context

In the spring of 1958, a student in Boynton's physiological optics class at the University of Rochester showed him a clipping from the *New York Times* describing a demonstration by Edwin Land, president of the Polaroid Corporation, that had been done the previous day at a meeting of the National Academy of Sciences. According to the newspaper account, Land had photographed a scene with two cameras, one of which had a red filter in front of its lens, the other, a green one. Positive black-and-white slides were prepared from the resulting negatives and placed in two slide projectors. One of these delivered its light to the screen through a red filter, whereas the other was used without any filter at all. With the images in perfect registration, a full gamut of color was seen in the resulting reproduction. The student wanted to know what Boynton thought about this report.

His reply was that there was probably a mistake in the *New York Times* account. He was wrong: the description of what Land had done was entirely accurate, and it was also true that Land had claimed that a "full gamut" of color experience had resulted. As a conclusion to this chapter, we wish to expand upon this incident for a variety of interrelated reasons.

• In his report of this work, Land (1959a) begins by stating (p. 115): "We have come to the conclusion that the classical laws of color mixing conceal great basic laws of color vision. There is a discrepancy between the conclusions that one would reach on the basis of the standard theory of color mixing and the results we obtain in studying total images." Boynton's orientation toward color had indeed been in the classical tradition. Given Boynton's reaction to the *Times* account, he concluded that there was truth in what Land said.

• Nevertheless, there is no logical reason why one would consider that the classical laws of color mixing (see Chapter 5) should conceal anything about the laws of color vision. If they do it is because one has inappropriately extended the interpretation of color mixing data. Helmholtz was guilty of this and the modern tradition of associating particular regions of chromaticity space with particular hues perpetuates the error. For example, Helmholtz (1924) wrote:

> When we speak of reducing the colours to three fundamental colours, this must be understood in a subjective sense and as being an attempt

> to trace the color sensations to three fundamental sensations. This was
> the way Young regarded the problem; in fact, his theory affords an
> exceedingly simple and clear explanation of all the phenomena of the
> physiological color theory. (v. 2, p. 143)

When using three primary colors to match another color the major
thing that has been learned is that a match has been made. When
such data are used, for example, to locate a color in the CIE chromaticity diagram, all one knows is that the test color and the mixture
plot on the same coordinates and that they would appear identical
to the CIE standard observer. Or, to be more precise, CIE colorimetry specifies ". . . a colour in terms of a trichromatic colour-matching equation" (Wright, 1991). But these data do not tell how the colors appeared to the standard observer, or to any other observer.

• Despite a great deal of work from his and other laboratories,
the "great basic laws of color vision" to which Land alludes are very
far from being fully formulated. When Land and McCann later stated
(1971) that "there is no predictable relationship between flux at various wavelengths and the color sensation associated with objects"
(p. 1), they could have meant: (1) that to predict the appearance of
a color, one must in principle know about the colors in the surround;
(2) the "great basic laws" are not yet known (so that even if the surround colors are specified the prediction cannot be made); or (3) if
the surround colors are known, the prediction of color appearance
can be made.

• We agree with (1) and (2) above, but reject (3). Land and his
associates have formulated some of the necessary principles and are
able to make some reasonable predictions. Many such predictions
are not very accurate, even in a completely abstract situation, and
they ignore the effects of memory color and psychological context
that must eventually be taken into account (see Chapter 11). Much
of what Land did was not as new as he thought, nor were his predictions of color appearance superior to some earlier ones (see Judd,
1960, and Walls, 1960, for reviews).

• Nothing like "a full gamut" of color is possible in the Land
demonstration. McCamy (1960) demonstrated this beautifully by
putting Land and Kodachrome images side by side. In the same talk,
using the Land images, he induced members of the audience to shout
out the color names of various objects as an assistant gradually and
surreptitiously dimmed one of the projectors: the names kept coming even after the light had been turned off entirely.

So far as Land's work is concerned, the reader is referred to two
Scientific American articles (Land, 1959c, 1977); to the pioneering work

of Helson (1938, 1963); of Helson and Michels (1948) and Judd (1940); to Land's two original papers (1959a, b); and to McCann, McKee, and Taylor (1976). For more recent analyses and commentary of the retinex theory we suggest that the reader see the papers written by Brainard and Wandell (1986) and by Sharpe (1987).

SUMMARY

The question of how, through the sense of vision, we are able to discern the nature and color of remote objects, has been raised repeatedly throughout recorded history. Speculations of the Greek philosophers, who did not indulge in experimentation, were clever but mostly wrong. For example, it was widely believed that rays were discharged from the eyes (emanation theory) and that tiny replicas of perceived objects could be released by such rays, to be delivered through the pupil of the eye and from there flushed through the hollow optic nerve to the sensorium in the brain.

In the middle ages Alhazen rejected emanation theory. Instead, he argued that an image of some kind, perhaps similar to that formed in a pinhole camera, was passively formed within the eye. Later, Leonardo da Vinci came close to a full understanding of visual optics but he failed because of his conviction that the retinal image could not be inverted. The German astronomer Johannes Kepler was the first to understand the basis of image formation by positive lenses and was, thereby, able to conclude that there must be an inverted retinal image.

Visual science has profited greatly from the part-time efforts of some great physical scientists. For example, although not the first to disperse the spectrum, Isaac Newton fully understood the implications of this experiment (when properly executed) for color vision. He demonstrated that the colors of objects relate to their spectral reflectances. He also stated correctly that the rays of light are not themselves colored; rather they contain a disposition to elicit color percepts in an observer.

By studying the rings formed by juxtaposition of plates of plane and slightly curved glass, Newton also demonstrated the wave properties of light and pointed the way toward the measurement of wavelength. Johann Wolfgang von Goethe rejected Newton's analytical approach and objected to most of his conclusions. Such conflict between analytic and holistic approaches is still present today.

Lomonosov (1757), Palmer (1977), and Young (1802) laid down the basic principles of trichromatic vision, although they had remarkably little to go on.[19] Hermann von Helmholtz made the first sketches of three overlapping curves of spectral sensitivity conceived to provide the initial physiological basis for color perception. Although his curves were only qualitative, they were, conceptually, a remarkable prediction of the cone spectral sensitivities as we know them today.

Opponent-color theory, which dealt with color appearance rather than color matching, had its origins with Ewald Hering. Opponent-color and trichromatic theories competed for a long time. Coalescence of these theories started in the 1920s and has continued to the present time.

A set of standard color matching curves was adopted in 1931 by the CIE, along with a chromaticity diagram upon which to represent colors. Anatomical and physiological work had its beginnings in the nineteenth century and has advanced over the years as new techniques have been developed.

The chapter concludes with mention of the fact that the appearance of a color depends importantly upon its surroundings.

NOTES

[1] To obtain information concerning the early Greek concepts about color, we have relied mainly upon the following sources: Beare (1906), Boring (1942), Helmholtz (1924), Polyak (1957), Stratton (1964), Ronchi (1970), and Sherman (1981). The Greek philosophers and writers whose ideas are summarized here lived at approximately the following times: Democritus, 460–370 B.C.; Plato, 427–347 B.C.; Aristotle, 384–322 B.C.; Epicurus, 342–270 B.C.; Galen, 130–200 A.D.

[2] This is part of a longer passage described by Ronchi (1970, p. 27) as "controversial." Another translation is given by Hernnstein and Boring (1965, p. 90) as follows: ". . . models, similar in colour and shape, leave the objects and enter according to their respective size either into our sight or into our mind; moving along swiftly, and so by this means reproducing the image of a single continuous thing and preserving the corresponding sequence of qualities and movements from the original object as the result of their uniform contact with us, kept up by the vibration of the atoms deep in the interior surface of the concrete body." The need to rely on translation, wherever it occurs, inevitably raises added ambiguities in attempting to understand the original author's intent.

[3] See Chapter 4, especially Fig. 4.1 on page 93, where current conceptions of these and other structures are considered.

[4] In the slim and generally rather neat *Golden Library of Knowledge* book on Vision, Rainwater (1962) puts it this way: "The image formed on the retina is upside down and is reversed from right to left. We are not aware of this inversion and reversal, as our brains are able to decode the information from the retina and keep our world from seeming topsy-turvy" (p. 10). Somewhat better (but not much), Lawson *et al.* (1975), in one of the standard introductory psychology texts, wrote: ". . . the lens of the human eye . . . produces an inverted retinal

image so that if we were looking at a person he would be imaged on our retina with his head down and his feet up. . . . Inasmuch as we never see directly our retinal image and because the entire image is inverted, we see the world upright by ignoring the inversion information in the retinal image produced by the human lens" (p. 147). The point that is missed by Lawson *et al.* is simply that there is no "inversion information" to be ignored: this would be available to us only if we did "see directly" our retinal image. As they correctly state, we do not.

[5] Today we know that all nerve fibers are fundamentally alike. It is not "nerve energies" that are specific: rather, it is something very special, about which we still know very little, about the specific regions of the brain to which specific nerve fibers project and the type of chemical released at the termination of each fiber.

[6] In a letter to Boynton, Dr. J. D. Mollon of the University of Cambridge has passed along the following information: "Prisms (long thin ones, with knobs on, such as Newton used) were probably sold widely at fairs, being intended to be hung up at windows or on chandeliers, to produce colors. I recall a letter from Newton to Oldenburg published in the Philosophical Transactions of the Royal Society for 1671 in which he speaks of buying a prism 'to try therewith the celebrated Phaenomena of Colours.'"

[7] A very nice review of the scientific side of Goethe's work is given by Magnus (1949).

[8] Very narrow spectral bands are needed to get white from two components; with bands as wide as Newton used, some inhomogeneity would be expected.

[9] A dark spot is always observed at the point of contact between a glass plate and the slightly curved surface of the glass that contacts it. This is evidence of phase reversal because if such reversal did not occur in the wave reflected at the point of contact, the center spot would be light, not dark. In order to achieve the first dark ring concentric with the central dark spot, the separation must be increased so that the full distance traversed by a wave, in the space between the curved and flat surface, is exactly one wavelength. Because this space is traversed twice, the physical distance must be exactly half a wavelength. For more detail about Newton's rings, see Strong, 1958, p. 222.

[10] If the reader is intrigued by this abbreviated account of Helmholtz's role in the early part of modern color vision we strongly recommend Sherman's *Colour Vision in the 19th Century*. It is fascinating reading.

[11] Under PROP. IV Theor. III Newton wrote: "For the yellow and blue on either hand, if they are equal in quantity they draw the intermediate green equally towards themselves in Composition, and so keep it as it were in Æquilibrion, that it verge not more to the yellow on the one hand, and to the blue on the other, but by their mix'd Actions remain still a middle Colour (p. 133)." One might think that perhaps Newton was discussing the mixing of pigments, but it seems quite clear he was discussing the mixing of light.

[12] Helmholtz cited LeBlon, 1735. In a personal communication John Mollon reported that there is no known publication by Le Blon with this date. The other citations by Helmholtz are DuFay, 1737; Mayer, 1758; and Lambert, 1772.

[13] Quotation originally from Young (1802) as given by MacAdam (1970), p. 51. In 1777, George Palmer had published a book on *Theory of Colors and Vision* (London: Leacroft, 1777) in which his first "principle of vision," as given by MacAdam on page 41 of his book, is: "The surface of the retina is compounded of particles of three different kinds, analogous to the three rays of light; and each of these particles is moved by his own ray." Trichromatic theory in this form apparently

accepts the doctrine that light rays exist in discrete classes, and misses the point so clearly elucidated by Young (and which had also been understood by Newton), according to which light exists in a continuum of frequencies and is responded to by sensitive elements having broad and overlapping tuning curves.

[14] A better translation than "false vision" [*les vues fousses*] is probably "impaired vision", which in this context would mean color defective vision.

[15] Mollon (personal communication) reports that Lomonosov was primarily a chemist.

[16] Crombie (1958) has published a very readable short biography of Helmholtz.

[17] In 1964, M. Hurvich and D. Jameson performed a noble service for visual science by translating Hering's, *Outlines of a Theory of the Light Sense* originally published in 1905, 1907, and 1911. This is also a good source of biographical material about Hering.

[18] The letters "CIE" stand for "Commission Internationale de l'Éclairage", which is the French version of "International Commission on Illumination."

[19] For the Lomonosov reference see Weale (1957); for the Palmer reference see Walls (1956), Weale (1957), and Mollon (1985).

Chapter 2

Subjective Color Phenomena

INTRODUCTION

When Newton correctly stated that "the rays are not colored," he implied that color, rather than being a physical phenomenon, does not exist until the eye of an observer receives the physical input. In this sense, all color perception is subjective. Why then have a special chapter on "subjective color phenomena"? We argue that a useful distinction can be drawn between subjective and objective colors, and most of this book is concerned with the latter.

By *objective colors,* we generally mean the perception of color consistent with what is normally expected in response to a particular spectral distribution of energy, whether or not that distribution is known. In contrast, Shute (1981) defines *subjective colors as ".* . . produced within the visual system without being related directly to specific wavelengths of light impinging on the eye" (p. 141). For example, all normal observers presented with a flashing light of 570 nm will call that light yellow, which makes it possible to use such a light as a traffic signal. The objective perception of red and green traffic signals represents the difference between life and death. Consider, however, a rapidly spinning disk inscribed with a black and white pattern (see Fig. 2.1). One would not, *a priori,* expect to see hues on the disk, but almost everyone does perceive faint colors. Even though there is some consensus about the hues of these colors,

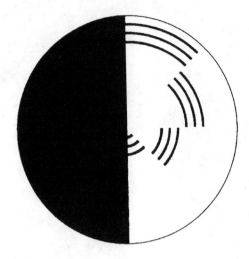

Figure 2.1 This circular disc is called Benham's top. When it is spun about its center subjective hues will appear in the position of the arcs even though there is no hint of hue when the disc is static.

they are considered subjective because, if the disk is viewed when stationary, only black and white are seen. Subjective colors are also experienced when one looks at a black and white TV when there is no signal and the screen is filled with signal noise (sometimes called "snow"). If inspected closely (provided one can pay attention to what is actually seen, rather than what is known to be objectively present) colored specks will definitely be observed. Steady fixation of a finely ruled black and white grating (Fig. 2.2) can also result in the perception of subjective colors.

Other examples abound. After steadily fixating an objective patch of red light for several seconds, an adjacent area, objectively homogeneously white, will appear to contain a greenish patch approximately the same size and shape as the red one. This phenomenon is called a *complementary (negative) after image*. Observers can prove to themselves that this perception is indeed a subjective phenomenon and not part of the white area on which they are attending. The greenish afterimage will move with one's gaze proving that the greenish perception is not physically part of the white area at which one is looking. So-called *simultaneous color contrast* occurs when, for example, one views an objectively gray patch embedded in an objectively red surround, a condition that causes the objectively gray patch to appear greenish.

Figure 2.2   If the reader fixates near the center of this lined pattern faint subjective hues will be observed.

A particularly unusual subjective color phenomenon is called the *McCollough* (1965) *effect* after its discoverer. Following exposure for several minutes to alternating patterns of vertical black-green gratings and horizontal black-green ones, objectively black and white gratings will appear to be colored: vertical gratings appear reddish, horizontal ones greenish. (It has been claimed that some observers, after viewing the McCollough gratings, have seen colors when looking at zebras!) Clearly the McCollough colors are subjective. They are not ordinary afterimages, because steady fixation of the colored fields is not required (or even desirable) to induce the effect; also because the after-effect can last for weeks rather than seconds.

Subjective colors are studied not only because they are interesting in their own right, but also with the hope that they can help us to understand objective color vision and the physiological processes underlying it. Shute (1981) contends that objective colors are initiated by the differential activation of the three kinds of cone photoreceptors. He believes that subjective colors are seen when this initial receptor stage of vision is bypassed. To the extent that this is true, subjective colors afford a means for studying the post-receptoral processing of color vision. In Chapter 7 we will see how Ewald Hering used his observations of subjective colors to begin the formulation of the important opponent process theory of color vision.

THE COLORS OF OBJECTS

The properties with which objects are endowed include such things as shape, weight, and color. The shape and weight of an object clearly can be specified physically with rulers and scales; such specifications correlate with our judgements about the size of objects (whether visually or tactually obtained) and with their felt heaviness when the objects are lifted.

The perceived color of an object differs from its perceived size, because vision is the only sense through which color can be judged.[1] Whereas it is possible to judge the shapes of objects by our visual impressions of them, and to compare these with tactual experiences involving the same objects,[2] such associations in the case of color are manifestly impossible. There is no way that a person who has been blind from birth can have any appreciation of what is meant by the color of an object.

Is there, for color as for length, a physically measurable property of an object that is related to its perceived color? The answer is yes: this property is called the *spectral reflectance* of the object's surface. As Newton correctly observed, a spectral light can only be more or less reflected from a surface; otherwise it remains qualitatively unchanged. Thus, when white light[3] shines upon a surface, the wavelengths of which the light is comprised will be reflected more or less equally. Such reflection, if it is approximately equal as a function of wavelength will produce a surface appearance that is neutral, i.e., black, gray, or white, depending upon the percentage of light that is nonselectively reflected. Differential reflection of wavelength, when it occurs, is usually correlated with the perception of hue. For example, if long wavelengths are reflected more than short ones, the surface will appear yellow, red, orange, or brown. These relationships will be discussed in much more detail in the following chapter. For now, it is helpful to know at least this much about the physical basis for the perception of an object's color.

We tend to take for granted that color is a property of the surface of an object. When we change the color of a surface by painting it, it is difficult to avoid the impression that the color which was originally in the paint has now simply been applied to the surface. Moreover, we recognize that, should we scrape the surface of an object, its color may change, as when we scrape the yellow paint from a pencil, and see the more neutrally colored wood beneath. On the other hand, similar scraping of a red crayon will reveal that its color resides not only on its surface, but also within it. Thus we note that the inside of an object may have a color also, but one which is perceived only by exposing it to light and to our vision. The color that we see depends upon some property of the object's surface when it is exposed to light and this light is reflected into our eyes.

If color is somehow on the object and an inherent property of its surface, one would not expect it to change according to the conditions under which the object is viewed. To a first approximation, including many of the important conditions of ordinary viewing, this appears to be the case. For example, look at a yellow banana under artificial light, and then take it outside in the bright sunlight.[4] Its color does not seem to change very much under these two drastically different viewing conditions. When the perceived color of an object does not change, despite such changes in lighting or viewing conditions, the phenomenon is called *color constancy* (see Chapter 11). It is related to the more general fact that many different physical stimuli can give rise to the same or similar sensory impressions.

From the standpoint of evolution and survival, color constancy is obviously a very good thing. Only to the extent that color is in fact a stable property of the surface of an object may we discern the important properties of the object. We can, for example, tell whether a banana is ripe or not, and do so whether we are indoors or outside. The physician may judge the pallor of a patient's skin. The secretary knows that the yellow copy is to be filed. The cartologist can designate whether areas of his maps are to be regarded as land or water. Color constancy does not always hold, however. It is a common experience, for example, to find deviations in constancy when attempting to buy additional material to match the color of something that was previously purchased. Suppose one goes to the store with a sample of the material of which more is needed. This material could be wool, cloth, vinyl, wallpaper, almost anything. Upon reaching the store the clerk is shown the material and asked for an additional quantity. "You are in luck" the clerk says "here is an exact match." After careful scrutiny the material is accepted as a match. At home, however, great disappointment is experienced when it is discovered the match no longer is acceptable. How could that be? Actually the answer is probably quite simple. At the store the material undoubtedly was viewed under fluorescent lighting. At home it was probably viewed under ordinary incandescent lighting. This experience illustrates the problem of *metamerism* which will be discussed more fully in Chapter 5 where the reason why the precise colors one sees is a joint function of the pigments in the material and the spectral distribution of the illuminant is explained.

In the context provided by these examples color is an important property of objects. This commonsense view is hard to deny. But there are serious problems with this view. If color is a property of a surface, how can we explain the following facts?

• Almost all colors disappear under low illumination (for example, under the light of the quarter moon).*

> Take a magazine outside on a moonlit night; try to tell which of its illustrations are reproduced in color and which in black and white.

• For some observers, the so-called "color-defectives" discussed in Chapter 10, objects that appear very different in color for the normal observer, may appear unambiguously alike.

• Objects that are seen as highly colored, and easily discriminable in daylight, lose their color when viewed under low pressure sodium vapor light, frequently used for street lighting.

We will explain these facts later. For now, let us note that color is a latent property of a surface which may or may not become manifest. Suppose that you see a red book on your bookshelf. You cannot reasonably doubt that if you leave the room the book will still be there, as red as ever. If you turn the lighting down to a very low level, its redness will disappear, though you still see the book. The typical observer under this condition will probably maintain that a red book is still there, in the same sense that the observer would also argue that the fine print on its cover, no longer visible in the dim light, is still present, continuing to form words and sentences as before. In referring to the latent content of what is on the book's surface, the observer will say that not only is the book itself still there, but that there is yet fine print on the cover, and moreover that the book is red. To test this hypothesis the observer need only to turn up the lights.

We must be sympathetic with the commonsense viewpoint just described. Indeed, it is pointless to suppose that a book disappears when the room is made totally dark, or when an observer leaves the room: the book is presumed to have a physical existence that transcends the view of any particular observer. Similarly, it does somehow seem useful to suppose that, as the light level is lowered, the book is still red and the fine print is still on its cover, even though it is no longer visible. What is needed, where color is concerned, is a physical description of those qualities of the surface of the book that are responsible for the appearance that it has for a normal observer under appropriate viewing conditions. These qualities could be supposed to survive even under conditions that abolish the sensation of color. The key to this, as previously noted, is reflectance. The way that reflectance supplies the physical basis for color vision will be discussed in the next chapter.

DIMENSIONS OF CHROMATIC EXPERIENCE

The nature of color experience depends to a significant degree upon the mode of perception. Evans (1964), who has written extensively on this subject, distinguishes between what he calls a "light mode" and a "surface mode" of perception. This distinction corresponds closely to one that has long been in the literature, between the perception of "aperture color" and of "surface color" (sometimes also called unrelated colors and related colors). Surface color is the normal mode of color perception, where colors apparently belong to the surfaces of objects. Aperture color results whenever the color is presented in such a way as to make its localization impossible with respect to an object. One way to do this is with a "reduction screen,"[5] which permits a view of only a small element of a surface, eliminating all cues that could relate it to some portion of a real object.

As an example of the profound difference between what is seen in these two modes of perception, imagine a scene in which a chocolate bar is brightly lit by an obvious and visible spotlight, and there is a ripe orange in another part of the scene that is seen under more general and dimmer illumination. There is no doubt that the colors of the chocolate and the orange are very different when they are seen as object colors, in the context of the overall scene. Now suppose that a reduction screen is placed between the observer and the scene. This reduction screen contains two small holes in it, so that by moving one's eye the observer can first see (as an aperture color) only the chocolate, and then (also in aperture mode) the surface of the more dimly lit orange. It is quite possible for these two aperture colors to appear identical. A more exact test could be made by using a telescope having a very narrow field of view, and by arranging for it to pick up a semicircle of light from one or the other of the objects, depending upon how it is aimed. By adding an adjacent and variable comparison field (to form a full circle) it would be possible to match the color of the chocolate, and then to verify that the match held also with respect to the orange.

The use of a reduction screen or a telescope provides a percept that is highly correlated with the actual spectral light distribution coming from the object being sampled. When a full scene is viewed, the context effects that arise are of two sorts. One sort, which is very

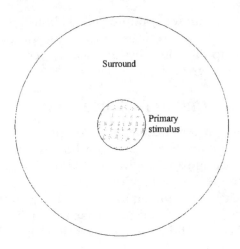

Figure 2.3   General appearance of the simplest stimulus configuration possible that permits the assessment of a surround field upon the appearance of an aperture color, called here the "primary stimulus." The appearance of the primary stimulus varies enormously, depending on the color and intensity of the surround.

complicated, results from the fact that real objects are seen, together with the various sources of illumination that are present. The other sort, somewhat simpler, has to do with the action of colors in the surrounding field; these effects can occur also in a completely abstract setting.

The aperture mode of perception is by far the simpler to deal with, and for this reason, the focus of this book will be upon it. Using current jargon of computer science and cognitive psychology, we prefer the "bottom up" approach. After all, if we are not able to understand the relation between stimulus and response for this relatively simple situation how would it be possible to understand more complex perceptions of which this simple one is only one component?

The concept of the aperture mode of viewing can be enlarged, after Evans, to include not only a central circular spot — the primary stimulus — but also a uniform concentric surround (Fig. 2.3). As noted, the appearance of such a central spot will depend not only upon the physical characteristics of the light contained within it, but also to a surprising extent upon the characteristics of the light in the surrounding region. (The nature of the surround's influence is discussed in Chapter 7.) To allow good experimental control of such fields, they are produced with projectors or special optics; nevertheless, it is legitimate to consider them as aperture colors, devoid of reference to any particular object, because this is how they are seen.

To begin with the simplest of all possible cases, let us consider first the aperture mode of perception, in the special case of zero surround. What should be visualized here is a single, circular spot of light, having a rather ethereal appearance, imprecisely localized in depth, seen in an otherwise completely dark environment. Although it requires a carefully contrived laboratory situation to produce a stimulus having such an appearance, a distant signal light, seen at night, is a common example that comes fairly close. Such a stimulus is perceived as self-luminous, probably because our experience teaches us that this is most probably the physical case. It should be noted, however, that a white piece of cardboard, carefully illuminated with a spotlight, can also produce the same appearance — provided that the light source is shielded from view, the light scattered from the illuminating beam is too weak to be directly visible, and any light escaping around the edges of the cardboard is absorbed in a suitably contrived light trap.[6]

A related experiment is to turn off all light in your room and project a small spot of light (using a slide projector) onto a dark screen, such as a piece of black cardboard hung from a thread in a doorway leading into another dark room. In this way, if done carefully, you should be able to illuminate only the black cardboard. Try varying the intensity of the spot by filtering out some of the light by putting your fingers in front of the projector (very close to it). The spot can easily be seen as if it were a piece of white paper attached to the black cardboard, provided that it is not too bright; at brightness higher than an actual piece of white paper could reflect, it will appear self-luminous. To change the appearance immediately back to black, introduce a small piece of white paper in front of the black card.

> This works especially well if the projector can be kept out of sight, and if observed by someone who has no idea of how the demonstration was set up. But even when you know what is happening, the sensory effects are quite compelling. This demonstration has been attributed to Gelb and often is referred to as the Gelb effect (Graham, *et al.*, 1965).

Hue, Brightness, and Saturation

It is generally agreed that such a disembodied stimulus has a color that can be described as varying along three psychological dimen-

Figure 2.4   This illustration depicts the arrangement of saturated colors around a closed circle, where the psychologically unique hues are represented at the cardinal points as shown. (N.B. because of printing difficulties these colors may not reproduce accurately). Other colors, not shown, would be located inside the circle, showing progressively greater desaturation of each until white is reached at the center.

sions: hue, brightness, and saturation. The dimension of brightness is easiest to understand. At one extreme, the stimulus is just barely visible; at the other extreme it is dazzlingly bright and painful to regard. Further increases in physical intensity will not necessarily make it appear brighter and it may be dangerous to look at, as would be the case if the central portion of the sun were viewed through a reduction screen. There are many discriminable steps of brightness along the continuum between these two extremes; it is a continuum that correlates most highly with the physical intensity of the light.

Although hue is generally considered to be a single dimension of color experience, it is actually more complicated than that. For the aperture color with dark surround, combinations of four color names plus white are sufficient to describe the chromatic content of what is seen: the color names are red, yellow, green, and blue (Boynton, Shafer & Neun, 1964). All combinations are possible excepting those including red and green, or yellow and blue. For example, blue-greens are common experiences, and a given blend of blue-green can vary from a very pastel, or pale, hue (almost white) to one that is much more richly chromatic. But reddish greens and yellowish blues are almost never seen.[7]

Because whiteness can coexist with any of the hues, and because white somehow does not seem to be a color in the same sense as are the other four, it is conventional to denote as hue the experiences of red, green, yellow, blue, and the permissible blends of pairs of these, and to introduce the term saturation to signify the relative white content of a stimulus perceived as having a particular hue. The dimensions of hue and saturation can be conveniently represented in a two-dimensional color diagram as shown in Figure 2.4. The circle represents each hue at high saturation.

Hue varies continuously around the circle, for example starting at 9 o'clock, from pure red clockwise, through yellowish reds (oranges) to pure yellow; then through a gradation of yellowish greens until pure green is reached at 3 o'clock; next through a succession of progressively more bluish greens culminating in pure blue at 6 o'clock; and finally back to red through a range of reddish blues (purples). For any particular hue — for example pure blue — the white content can vary gradually from the very high saturation shown on the outer circle, to zero at the center. Hues of equal saturation, but less than that represented on the outer circle, would be represented upon concentric circles having smaller radii. The reader should be aware that it is difficult to produce "pure hues" with printing inks. It is even more difficult to maintain sufficient printing ink quality control to insure that all reproductions are identical. Because the human eye is extraordinarily sensitive to hue differences, it may be that none of the chips in Figure 2.4 will perfectly represent a unique hue as just described. Unique red is a special case when it comes to producing it with lights. Unique green, yellow, and blue can all be produced with the aid of a monochromator. Monochromators produce lights called spectral lights. It is not possible to produce a unique red with a monochromator because all spectral reds will contain at least a small amount of yellow in them (Hurvich, 1981). Thus, to produce unique red a little blue light must be added to spectral red. The blue light will cancel the small amount of yellow thus producing unique red.[8]

The diagram in Figure 2.4 has no necessary referent whatever to the domain of physics. A color circle of this sort could be put together by giving observers a sample of colored papers, including those

Table 2.1   Rules for Pure Hues

Name of hue	Cannot coexist with	Also is devoid of hues shown, with which it can potentially coexist
red	green	yellow or blue
yellow	blue	green or red
green	red	blue or yellow
blue	yellow	red or green

shown in Figure 2.4 and some intermediate steps, whose physical properties could be completely unknown. The instructions to the subjects might be merely: "Arrange these chips of colored paper in some reasonable and ordered way." Given enough time and patience, most people would order them according to the kind of diagram set forth in Figure 2.4, although the orientation is arbitrary.

Some additional remarks should be made about psychologically unique hues. The explanation of unique hues requires an appeal to subjective experience. Most people agree, for example, that there is a "pure" yellow which has the following properties: (1) Unique yellow is neither reddish nor greenish. Most yellows are tinged with one or the other of these, though never both at the same time. (2) Unique yellow cannot coexist with blue. Similar arguments can be made for three other pure hues, and can be summarized as shown in Table 2.1.

In terms of the color diagram of Figure 2.4, unique hues can have a geometrical representation. The hues that potentially can be present with any particular unique hue on the circle are those that are adjacent to it; those which cannot coexist are opposite to each other. Color space, so represented, divides itself into four quadrants as shown in Figure 2.4. The first quadrant (upper right) consists of yellow-green mixtures of various saturations, containing a quarter of the total possible color experience. Within this quadrant color changes are continuous, and qualitatively alike in that all colors are greenish, yellowish, and whitish, to varying degrees. At the border defined by unique yellow, which separates the upper right quadrant from the upper left, there is a qualitative change. In the upper left there are yellow red mixtures of various saturations. The upper quadrants are vertically separated by a narrow band of unique yellow.*

Look carefully at the other quadrants of Figure 2.4, and work out analogous statements to describe the color sensations that are represented there. There are also four "balanced hues," one of which is orange (located midway between unique red and unique yellow). By balanced hues is meant a color with equally perceived amounts of unique hues. What color names can be used to describe the other three balanced hues?

A purely subjective, or psychological, diagram of this sort is not a satisfactory point at which to leave the description of color experience, but it is the best that we can hope to do without recourse to physical measurements. Such a representation does, nevertheless, seem to give an ordered account of color experience, and it is one that has proved useful to interior decorators and artists, as well as to color scientists.

Effects of Surrounds

Using our bottom-up approach, let us now consider what happens when a surround color is introduced, as in Figure 2.3. If we confine our attention strictly to the central spot, we will find that three surprises are introduced by the addition of a surround, and that each of these surprises corresponds to a new dimension of subjective experience. Consider first the case of a white spot with a white surround. This condition produces simultaneous contrast. If the white surround is made brighter than the central test spot, the spot will appear darker. If the surround is made bright enough, the central spot will appear black. If the surround is then suddenly removed, it will once again be evident that there is light physically present in the central spot, and it appears white, not black. Without the surround, the central spot never appears black, even when reduced in intensity until it is nearly invisible. This trick of providing a bright surround to produce dark colors is well known to artists.

As the central spot is progressively reduced in intensity, for a given intensity of the surround, a point will be reached where the spot appears as black as it can possibly appear, so that further reductions in the intensity of the spot will not make it appear any blacker. This is called the point of subjective black, and it depends upon the ratio of intensities of central spot and annular surround, as well as upon other factors, including the size of the spot. Subjective blackness has been studied intensively (Werner *et al.* 1984; Cicerone *et al.*, 1986; Volbrecht *et al.*, 1989).

For an intermediate level of the ratio of surround to spot intensity, the spot will be darkened, but not made black. Evans (1974) wrote of this as the introduction of a "gray content." This terminology seems satisfactory, so long as we recognize that the gray content may become so strong as to yield black. The appearance of the central spot is so critically dependent upon the surround that it is sometimes difficult in the laboratory to tell whether the surround intensity has been increased or the spot intensity decreased, since either will result in a darker spot and — to a lesser extent — a brighter-appearing surround. But by looking at only the central spot or annular surround with the aid of a reduction screen, the two possibilities can easily be distinguished.

Let us consider next the case where the surround is white, and the center spot is highly chromatic. Evans described the appearance of such a chromatic field, as its intensity is increased relative to a fixed surround, as follows:

> At some low value of luminance, relative to the surround, of the order of 1% or less, the color is seen as black. . . . For all colors, as this ratio is increased the appearance of the color passes through a predictable series. At first the blackness decreases, the hue appears at low saturation mixed with black or dark gray. As the ratio continues to increase, gray decreases and saturation increases, until a point is reached at which the gray has disappeared. This point is usually considerably below and in some cases very much below a luminance match with the surround. As luminance is still further raised, the color becomes fluorent[9] and saturation continues to increase. The saturation and this fluorence continue to increase up to and slightly beyond a luminance match with the surround. Above this, brightness continues to increase but the fluorence disappears and saturation decreases. The color takes on the appearance of a light source (Evans & Swenholt, 1967, p. 1319).

A further complication in the case of dark colors is the introduction of at least one completely new experience of hue, namely brown, which is produced by surrounding a yellow or orange with a brighter annulus of white light. This helps us to understand how the chocolate bar and the orange, viewed through a reduction screen as previously described, could look alike. Brown, like black, is a sensation that seldom appears without a surround field.[10] The reader may wish to read an interesting article by Bartleson (1976), entitled "Brown." Although brown shares some of the properties of unique hues, current research does not permit the definite labeling of brown as a unique hue (Bartleson, 1976; Fuld, Werner & Wooten, 1983).

Other dark colors, such as maroon, olive green, and navy blue, appear to be qualitatively more similar to their brighter counterparts than brown is to yellow and orange. The existence of the dark colors adds a great deal to the entire range of possible chromatic experiences, and greatly complicates their description.

Even more impressive and more complicated effects can occur when chromatic fields are used both in the test spot and the surround, or in more complicated ways in the visual array. One of the more complex arrays that has found its way into color science is the so called Mondrian pattern used initially by Land in the experiments to referred to in Chapter 1. These patterns have a marked similarity to the paintings of the Dutch painter Piet Mondriaan. The relatively complex Mondrian patterns have been systematically studied psychophysically by McCann and colleagues and by Arends and colleagues (e.g., McCann, McKee & Taylor, 1976; Arend & Reeves, 1986) and physiologically by Zeki (1980; 1990). We will return to this subject in Chapter 11.

MISCELLANEOUS COLOR PHENOMENA

In this section, a variety of interesting phenomena having to do with color perception will be described. Some will be illustrated with color plates, but many will not; some are demonstrations that can be set up easily in the laboratory, or even at home; others require special materials or techniques that would make this difficult. All are chosen because they make some contribution to our appreciation of human color perception, but not all of the points that they make can be made clear in this chapter, since only after an exposure to some of the physical and physiological principles of color is this possible.

Effects of Lighting

Figure 2.5 (from Evans, 1948, p. 55) shows a collection of marbles illuminated under two extremely different conditions. Looking at the top set, the experienced observer will recognize immediately that (1) the marbles are shiny, and (2) they are illuminated by a concentrated source of light — perhaps the sun or a flashbulb. Looking at the bottom set, the reader can not be so sure of what is seen. Although both pictures may seem to depict the same kind of marbles, the possibility exists that the balls in the bottom set are diffuse — possibly made of cloth, painted with a very flat paint, or cut from styrofoam. These possibilities would appear more likely if all of the balls were uniform in color, for example like the blue one at the far right which indeed appears as if it could be made from something other than glass, for example, cardboard. The variegation of color on most of the other marbles, and some of the highlights that remain (despite the attempt at diffuse illumination) provide clues that the objects almost certainly are marbles seen under diffuse illumination, and not discs or balls of yarn. The latter illusion could be greatly

Figure 2.5   The marbles at the top were illuminated by a concentrated light source; those at the bottom, by diffuse and uniform lighting. (After Evans, 1948.)

enhanced by blackening in the shadow areas, making them look more like the ones in the top picture. There is much less ambiguity about what is seen in the top picture. In the real-world situation it is of course most unlikely that such a collection of objects would have painted upon them white specks located in just the positions where they would have to be, were they actually highlights. Of course, this is exactly the trick artists use to create the illusion of highlights.

For most observers, the colors of the marbles in the top picture will appear somewhat more saturated than those in the bottom one. It would be very surprising to reach out to touch one of the marbles at the top, and not find it smooth and hard to the touch. One may not be quite so sure about the balls at the bottom, especially the blue one at the right. It could be soft and squashy, or at least quite roughly textured.

The highlights seen in the collection of marbles at the top are, of course, images of the source of illumination, seen by reflection from the convex surface of the marbles. In one case, the bluish-gray marble at the far left, a very poor image of the source is also formed underneath and behind the marble, providing information that this object is at least partially transparent. The hard surface of a marble, as we shall see in Chapter 3, reveals its hardness by means of the mirror-like (specular) reflection from its surface, and its color by diffuse reflection of light from the layers just underneath. The specular reflection does not alter the distribution of wavelengths in the reflected light, relative to those that are incident. Thus one can actually gauge the color of the source from these highlights; therefore it is by no means necessary to look directly at the source of illumination in a scene to know what its color is. This is undoubtedly an aid to color constancy, and one which would be lost under diffuse illumination, or if all surfaces reflected only in a diffuse manner. Most illumination is a mixture of concentrated and diffuse: this is what we get on a sunny day, from the combination of direct sunlight and skylight. This is also what the professional photographer often chooses to use for best form and color rendition. Most surfaces reveal a mixture of specular and diffuse reflectance.

The marbles of Figure 2.5 may also be used to illustrate again some of the effects of using a reduction screen, associated with the differences between aperture and object color. A reduction screen that permitted the viewing of only the highlight from one of the marbles at the top would, of course, obscure all information about the color of the marble.

Physical Analysis of Complex Scenes

Color Television

Starting with Chapter 3, we will be concerned with the physical specification of the stimulus for color perception. A major purpose of this book will be to explain our perceptions of colored objects as these relate to an objective description of these objects, one that can be given through the use of physical measuring instruments. Because they are simpler, laboratory situations involving stimuli such as discs, annuli, and split fields will be greatly stressed. But the real world is much more complicated, as, for example, in the case of the marbles just discussed.

Is there any hope of achieving a purely physical description of such a complex scene? The answer is yes, and the trick is to break up the scene into a large number of elements, each of which is homogeneous and therefore amenable to a simple physical description. This is exactly what lies behind the illusions created by color television. A color TV screen consists of about a million phosphor dots which glow red, green or blue when irradiated by an electron beam. There are no white glowing phosphors or any other phosphors than the red, green, and blue. All the colors seen on the TV screen result from the eye mixing the light of the red, green, and blue phosphors. For example, if the three primary phosphors, which occupy contiguous elements on the TV screen are excited, and the viewer is unable to resolve the spatial location of these three phosphors, that small spot on the screen will appear white. In a physical sense, the color TV image is nothing more (or less) than this collection of glowing dots, each of which can vary in brightness, but not in hue.*

> With the aid of a magnifying glass, carefully examine these elements. Note the spatial arrangement of the three phosphor types, and the absence of any white or yellow dots.

In a static scene, the illusion of color TV depends upon the limited ability of the visual system to resolve spatial detail. The impression of continuous temporal flow in a changing scene depends upon the limited ability of the visual system to keep track of time. (These matters will be dealt with systematically in Chapter 9.) Where color vision is concerned, special interest attaches to the fact that these elements need be of only three different colors, rather than continuously variable as in the actual scene. A larger point to be gleaned in the present discussion is this: to the extent that color TV can simulate impressions that would be received by looking directly at the scene the camera sees, then to this extent one can legitimately consider the visual scene to be comprised of a very large number of homogeneous elements, known as *pixels*.

Each of us who has seen TV can judge this for ourselves. A major concern of artists is to understand the extent to which such simulation works, and to learn the tricks that are needed to compensate for the fact that viewing a painting or a motion picture or a TV tube cannot exactly simulate the experience of viewing the scene being reproduced. But even if we had never seen television, we could conclude a great deal from watching the behavior of others. That people will sit transfixed for hours, watching a million dots of three colors whose individual intensities are changing, reveals at once that something much more interesting than a mere collection of dots is represented there.

The principle behind generating a colored scene with only three colors is not unique to color television. As we saw in Chapter 1, it is also used in printing colors. Newspapers sometimes use a principle similar to that of the TV to generate colors. Many tiny dots, which are not resolvable at normal reading distances, are combined to make colors in a manner similar to the combining of glowing TV phosphors. This technique was also used by artists who painted using the pointillist technique (Jameson, 1989; Ratliff, 1992).

Successive Contrast and Afterimages

In his Ives Medal address to the Optical Society of America in 1958, Deane B. Judd demonstrated that the color one sees may depend upon colors no longer in the scene, to which the eye has previously been exposed. A section of the written summary of his talk is reproduced below. (In this quotation, the phrase "orchid plaque" is used to describe a patch of light on the screen, probably circular in shape, having an "orchid" [light purple] hue.)

> . . . a slide was projected that consisted of red, yellow, green, and blue quadrants. The members of the audience were requested to fixate the center of the slide for about 15 sec, then the slide was removed, and after a second or two there appeared (apparently to each member of the audience) the after-image complimentary of the four hues: that is, by means of the retinal areas previously exposed to the red quadrant, the white screen appeared blue-green similarly, or other segments of white screen appeared purplish blue, red-purple, and orange. This is the classic demonstration of successive contrast, or the projection of a negative after-image onto a white surface. This after-image requires fixation for several seconds for its appearance. It moves with the eye, and has no object character.
>
> To show that there is an instantaneous type of adjustment in chromatic sensitivity of the visual mechanism, an orchid plaque was shown against a gray background under which conditions the color perception was that of a light purplish red of moderate saturation. Then it was presented against a brilliant magenta background. The color perception was then reported by many in the audience as gray. It was noted that the transition from orchid to gray took place without perceptible time delay, and that the color was stable. Furthermore, the color was perceived as belonging to the plaque in the same sense that the light purplish red color of moderate saturation was perceived to belong to it when viewed against a gray background (Judd, 1959, p. 326).

Simultaneous Color Contrast

The orchid plaque demonstration Judd showed his audience is synthesized here by showing the reader Evans' four urns in Figure 2.6 (Evans, 1948, facing p. 178), which are all printed with exactly the same ink. Note the changes in both lightness and hue are caused by

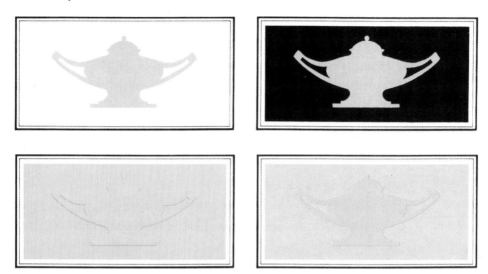

Figure 2.6   The four urns are all printed with ink exactly of the same color, and will yield the same sensation if a reduction screen is used. The striking differences in color among the four urns are due entirely to the surrounds against which they are depicted. (After Evans, 1948.)

the simultaneous presence of differing backgrounds. And finally, in Figure 2.7 (Evans, 1948, facing p. 192) is an excellent illustration of the von Bezold "spreading effect." The effect, which is also called the "assimilation phenomenon" (Hurvich, 1981, p. 175), works as if it is combining adjacent colors rather than accentuating the differences between adjacent colors as contrast does. Color contrast is usually achieved by placing rather simple fields next to each other. The von Bezold "spreading effect" works best when repeated stimulus patterns of appropriate dimensions make up the display as seen in Figure 2.7. Hurvich shows a pattern somewhat simpler than that shown in Figure 2.7 and it also demonstrates the effect and points out that the effect is not due to an optical mixture of colors within the visual system. He contends that ". . . the physiological basis of this effect is the spatial nonuniformity of the retina and its cellular organization. . ." (p. 176).

One of the first to systematically study simultaneous contrast was M. E. Chevreul who, upon taking a position as Director of Dyes for the Royal Manufacturers at the Gobelins in 1824, reported that "I saw that the want of vigour complained of in the blacks was owing to the colour next to them, and was due to the phenomena of contrast of colours" (p. 48). Chevreul, up to this time, was a noted and ac-

Figure 2.7   Evans caption reads: "As there is no overlapping of inked areas in these designs, they consist only of three colors in addition to the white of the paper: a red, a blue, and black. The visual appearance of any area of red or blue, however, depends in part on the colors of the adjacent areas. The blues surrounded by black appear darker and more saturated than those surrounded by white, and different in hue from those surrounded by red. The shifts in brightness are opposite to those that would be predicted on the basis of contrast effects. This phenomenon is call the 'spreading effect,'" (The opposite to contrast is also known as "assimilation.") (After Evans, 1948.)

complished chemist who took on the additional task of studying these contrast phenomena, and herein lies the beginnings rather intense investigations of simultaneous contrast. The interested reader is encouraged to seek out Chevreul's book *The Principles of Harmony and*

Figure 2.8   Each sector of this step-tablet is of uniform lightness, as can be confirmed by masking the adjacent sectors. The nonuniformity of brightness is related to the influence of adjacent areas that are either lighter or darker than the one being examined. Lateral inhibitory mechanisms in the retina and brain are believed to be responsible.

Contrast Colors and Their Application to the Arts. The translated version of this book was revised and reissued in 1987 by Faber Birren.

Perceived Nonuniformity from Surrounds

Figure 2.8 shows a series of steps from black on the left to light gray on the right, each of which, incredibly, is physically uniform within the boundaries that delimit it. To prove this, cover all but one of these areas with opaque pieces of paper or cardboard. As soon as the paper is removed, allowing more than one step to be seen, the scalloped effect appears. The more steps that are seen at once, the more compelling is the effect. In this example it is the lightness of each patch that varies from one side to the other; each appears lighter at the left, contrasting with the darker panel to the left, and darker at the right, contrasting with the lighter panel to the right.

Effect of Intensity

The perception of the color of objects depends importantly upon the amount of light that is available to illuminate them. The exercise below is designed to illustrate some of the perceived changes in color that occur as a function of intensity.*

Here is a demonstration that can easily be done at home. A variable intensity of light source, using a dimmer, is helpful, but it can also be done by turning the lights off and on, and shielding them in various ways. The demonstration will be described as if done with tungsten light, varied in intensity by means of an inexpensive dimmer. Use it to operate a 15W bulb, and place it, exposed, somewhere in the corner of an ordinary room filled with ordinary objects. The entire room should be without windows, or have heavy enough drapes to exclude the evening light. A bookcase filled with books is particularly suitable. Have available some magazine illustrations, some printed in color, some in black and white, and spread them around on the floor — or better, have some-one else do this for you. Set the dimmer at a very low setting so that the lamp itself can barely be seen, and enter the room, having first exposed yourself to a high level of interior illumination in an adjoining room.

At first, nothing will be seen. Then, gradually, the outlines of the contours that ·are longest and of highest contrast — such as the edge between a white doorframe and an adjoining dark wall — will be seen. Gradually, smaller objects will become visible, including the books in the bookcase. However, if the conditions are set properly, none of the books on the shelf will have any color, although they will vary in lightness, which will permit them to be discriminated. Introspection will reveal that visual sensations under this condition are totally achromatic — black, white, and gray — possibly tinged with a bit of bluishness. It is impossible to tell which of the illustrations spread on the floor are printed in color. Now, as the intensity of the light source is slowly increased, all objects in the room will be seen more clearly. The first hue to be perceived will be red — not very strong or distinct, but definitely present. Red areas of the colored illustrations on the floor will appear dull-reddish, and a basis for discrimination between the two types of reproduction will be evident.

As the intensity of the lamp is increased further, more and more hues will be seen. The distinction between the illustrations on the floor will become obvious and, at the highest level, chromatic perception will become more or less normal. But a single 15W bulb in the corner of a room is not really sufficient to mediate good color perception, which can be easily demonstrated by switching on all the regular lights in the room.

One of the important phenomena to be observed as the level of illumination is increased is the reversal of brightness relations that takes place between some adjoining objects. Specifically, if a red and a blue book are located side by side on the shelf, the blue one will look much lighter than the red one (which will probably appear black) at the lowest level of illumination, although neither will have any hue. So long as hue is not present, this relation will remain. When the level of illumination is reached that first permits the perception of red to be associated with the red book, its lightness will begin to increase relative to the blue one. At some higher level, they will appear equally light and of different color, and at the highest levels there will be no doubt, if the books are properly chosen, that the red book now appears brighter than the blue one. Why are brightness relations affected in this way by changing the light level? And why does color vision fail totally at very low levels of illumination? It turns out that both of these phenomena have their origin in major classes of receptors (the rods and the cones) in our retinas. We will consider these receptors and their functions in Chapter 5.

The observation that red and blue books in close proximity to each other can show changes in relative brightnesses as light is increased from exceedingly dim to bright was first described in detail by Purkinje. Helmholtz (1924) had an interesting way of describing the *Purkinje Phenomenon.* "In dim twilight the cap of a German infantryman, which is blue with a red band, does not look different from that of a sanitary officer with its dark blue band" (p. 357). Helmholtz (1924) quotes Purkinje while observing colors in the morning twilight as follows: "Blue is what I saw first. The shades of red that are usually brightest in daylight, namely carmine, vermilion, and orange, are for a long time the darkest, and not to be compared to their ordinary brightness" (p. 358). The Purkinje Phenomenon is attributed to the change where the amount of light is just at or below threshold for cone vision but above threshold for rod vision. The cones are specialized receptors for daylight and color vision where as the rods are specialized for night vision and are color blind.

SUMMARY

A variety of subjective color phenomena has been described, and some simple experiments have been discussed that are easily done without specialized equipment and can be used to illustrate some of these phenomena. Such observations should provide convincing evidence that color vision is a very complex phenomenon, and that the color of an object depends not only on the nature of the paint on its surface, but also on the color of the light used to illuminate it, the intensity of that light, and the chromatic characteristics of other surfaces located nearby. There are many more demonstrations that could be provided, but the ones recommended in this chapter should be sufficient to illustrate the complexity of color perception and to develop an increased awareness of one's sensations, where color is concerned. But an eternity of such demonstrations would not suffice to explain the mechanisms within the eye and brain that are responsible for what is perceived. For this, it is necessary to study the physics and physiology of the subject. This study will begin in Chapter 3.

NOTES

[1] We will return to this point again in the next chapter. See especially endnote 2 on page 90 of Chapter 3.

[2] The seemingly reasonable idea that visual perception depends for its development upon tactual experience seems, by and large, to be a false one. When the two senses are put into conflict vision nearly always predominates. As Gregory and Wallace (1963) have pointed out, one cannot draw any safe conclusions about normal visual development based upon the kinds of difficulties that are

experienced when pattern vision, lacking from birth because of defects in the optical system of the eye, is, through surgery, rendered possible for the first time in adulthood. In a textbook, Rock (1975) summarizes a great deal of evidence to show the primacy of visual over tactual perception.

[3] As Newton first noted, the light itself is not colored. The use of color names to describe light is therefore technically incorrect. Such usage will nevertheless be permitted in this book, but Newton's caveat, "the rays are not coloured," should be kept in mind.

[4] Artificial light, for example, tungsten incandescent, and daylight are physically quite different. As a result, the light reaching the eye, after being reflected from the banana, contains a very different physical mixture of wavelengths, depending upon whether it is viewed under daylight or artificial incandescent illumination.

[5] The use of the term "reduction screen" is attributed to Katz (1935), who spoke of "surface color" and "film color."

[6] Great care is needed to achieve the illusion of a self-luminous color when a surface color is actually presented. See Uchikawa, Uchikawa and Boynton (1989) for details of such a set-up.

[7] *Science* published a paper with the provoking title "On Seeing Reddish Green and Yellowish Blue." The authors [Crane and Piantanida (1983)] presented observers with a display that caused the main part of a red/green or blue/yellow bipartite field to be presented so that there was no relative motion of the stimulus on the retina. In other words the retinal image was stabilized. This is an unusual laboratory condition and certainly not something that one would normally experience. Nevertheless Crane and Piantanida report that under these conditions observers report that the ". . . entire region can be perceived simultaneously as both red and green (or yellow and blue.)"

[8] In an early use of color naming to gauge the appearance of spectral lights, Boynton and Gordon (1965) found unique red did appear in pure form for long wavelength stimuli, provided they were presented at a relatively low luminance.

[9] Evans uses the term "fluorent" to describe an appearance similar or identical to that experienced when viewing fluorescent (Chapter 3, endnote 11) surfaces. The color appears to glow and has an exceptionally vivid appearance. Along with the gray content induced by bright surround fields, the appearance of "fluorence" adds a second new dimension to the test spot when it is seen within a surround.

[10] Hochberg (personal communication) has called attention to the fact that sensations of brown can sometimes arise by successive as well as by simultaneous contrast.

Chapter 3

The Visual Stimulus

NEED FOR A PHYSICAL DEFINITION OF THE STIMULUS

Samuel Johnson is reported to have said, "We all know what light is; but it is not easy to tell what it is" (Falk, Brill & Stork, 1986). Because light is the stimulus to which the eyes respond, it is incumbent on us to make an attempt to tell what it is.

We use our various senses to infer that there is a world outside our own bodies; one that is filled with objects that seem to have a physical reality. Most of us see desks, tables, people, animals, automobiles, and so forth — objects seemingly arranged in meaningful ways in an external world. Physical scientists, in addition, pay attention to molecules, photons, subatomic particles, magnetic flux, and so forth. Most of these physical entities are difficult or impossible to visualize and can be "seen" only in the same cognitive sense that a blind person might say "Yes, I see what you mean." Such physical concepts are sometimes made easier to understand when an attempt to visualize the concept is made. These concepts are also used to build models whose behavior matches our observations. We learn to diagram an atom as having a spherical nucleus surrounded by little whirling balls, although we are cautioned (if we are well taught) that this is only a representation, nothing more than a metaphorical visual crutch, crudely representative of mathematical relations that provide a more accurate description.

In casual, everyday activities we have come to rely on our observations by direct perception. These abilities probably evolved as a result of our adaptation to, and survival in, our external environment. If, say, magnetic fields carried significant information for us, we probably would have evolved with magneto-receptors. That we have not may be taken as evidence that there are other forms of physical disturbances available in the sea of energy within which we live that are more significant for our survival. We have developed specialized receptive equipment that is specifically tuned to what is most important.[1] Although our perceptions work well for us much of the time, we should be prepared to understand that they are limited. In our understanding of color vision we must force ourselves to realize that, although our observations are of a special kind, they are limited and it is frequently necessary to use special devices to make indirect observations of our visual environment.

Survival on earth is not dependent on an accurate perception of the universe or, until very recently, even on what is happening on the other side of the mountain. We usually survive without being able to see microorganisms, although occasionally they are lethal. It must be emphasized that the perceptual powers that we do possess, utilizing our unaided perceptual capacities, are impressive indeed. We may suppose that, if we could see the microscopic world or react directly to static magnetic fields (as some birds apparently do), the capacity to do so would only have evolved at the expense of the significant and presumably more important perceptual powers that we possess instead.

Although we cannot directly perceive the world in a way that accords with its description in physical terms, there is no reason to deny the physical existence of ordinary objects, such as a blue book on the desk. You can, after all, confirm its existence in many ways: by feeling it, by lifting it to discern its heaviness, by blowing on its surface in order to sense the reflected wind, or by slapping it hard so as to hear the sound that this makes and to feel a sting in your fingers. You can hold the book to the light and note that it is impossible to see through it. You can try to bend it in order to gain an impression of its physical resistance. All of these events interact to confirm your perception, initially based on the remarkable act of vision at a distance, that there is indeed a book lying on your desk. Yet of all the properties that the book seems to possess, its color is something special because you are unable to confirm it by any of these other operations; only your eyes can tell you that the book appears blue.[2]

As was pointed out in Chapter 1, it is obvious that we are not in direct contact with such remote objects whose forms we can recognize and whose colors we can identify. We seek in this book to deal with current conceptions of how such visual perception is possible. We have seen that prescientific efforts to gain such understanding led to concepts that were necessarily speculative, and usually untrue. It is evident that we are not in mechanical contact with the visual object that is perceived. Rather, light reflected from the object enters our eyes, stimulates our retinas (strictly speaking, the retina is an extension of the brain), and indirectly activates our brains. Somehow, from this activity, we gain an appreciation of the presence of the object and of its color.

It is tempting to fall into a trap, as the Greek philosophers and, more recently, the Gestalt psychologists did, of defining the perceived object as constituting a "stimulus for vision." To say that one perceives a pen lying on the desk because the "pen" stimulates the eyes is not to solve the problem of perception, but merely to state that perception occurs. What we require instead is a sufficiently detailed description of the object that is independent of the object's subjective appearance. Anything less inevitably begs the question.

Ideally, physical descriptions should be free of the raw power of people's sensory processes. This power is so important in everyday life and is so vital to certain fields of endeavor, such as art and literature, that it may be difficult to accept the view that, for the clear understanding of this power itself, a different (and more difficult) description of the stimulus is required. The physical environment so conceived has a nature and presence that does not depend on whether anyone is around to perceive it. The tree falling in the forest produces a physical sound whether or not anyone is there to hear it. A description of the pen on a desk should be possible using concepts that do not presume that the pen necessarily will be perceived by anyone, but which does assume that it has a physical existence that can be given an independent description.

PRIMARY STIMULUS FOR VISION

If one receives a blow to the head, it is not uncommon to have a visual sensation. We frequently say that we "see stars." It is also possible to have a visual experience by pressing firmly on the eye through closed eyelids. It has been demonstrated that a visual experience can be achieved by passing a mild electric current across the eye. (While the reader may wish to press on the eye, he or she is definitely cautioned not to pass an electric current across the eye.) While the eye will respond to such mechanical or electrical stimulation, the visual receptors clearly have not been designed for these purposes. The receptors are designed to receive and process electromagnetic energy from a very narrow part of the electromagnetic spectrum that encompasses wavelengths between about 380 and 750 nm. This part of the spectrum is called light, and light is the primary stimulus for vision.

LIGHT

In the 1792 edition of the *Encyclopedia Britannica* it is stated[3] that: "It is obvious . . . that whatever side we take concerning the nature of light, many, indeed almost all the circumstances concerning it, are incomprehensible and beyond the reach of human understanding."

One hundred seventy-six years later, in the September 1968 special edition of *Scientific American* on "Light," Gerald Feinberg wrote[4]:

> At present the photon theory gives us an accurate description of all we know about light. The notion that light is fundamentally just another kind of matter is likely to persist in any future theory. That idea is the distinctive contribution of 20th-century physicists to the understanding of light, and it is one of which we can well be proud.

Photons

The quotations above provide us with a starting point for our discussion of light, which is the primary stimulus for color vision. We see from these quotes that the early view that light could never be understood has given way to a modern conceptualization that light consists of particles, called *photons*.

A photon is an indivisible unit of radiant energy. The amount of energy associated with a photon of wavelength λ is

$$E = \frac{hc}{\lambda} \tag{3.1}$$

where E = energy (erg), $h = 6.626 \times 10^{-34}$ J $\cdot$ s (Planck's Constant), $c = 2.997 \times 10^{8}$ m $\cdot$ s^{-1} (velocity of light), and λ = wavelength. Put another way, a photon is the smallest amount of energy associated with λ; thus, short wavelength photons "pack more punch" than long wavelength ones because short wavelength photons are of a higher frequency than long wavelength ones.

The brighter a light is, the more photons are contained in it. Because photons are discrete packets of energy it is not possible to absorb a fraction of a photon. When a photon is emitted from a source it immediately moves at the speed of light. It is a mistake to assume that a photon can occupy a specific position. Light has a zero rest mass: despite this, photons are never at rest, and in their actual state of motion they possess energy and momentum. It is thus to be expected that a beam of light should be capable of exerting pressure on a physical object, and it is reassuring to find that this actually happens.[5] But the momentum possessed by each photon is exceedingly small, despite its velocity (which in a vacuum is the highest attainable in nature). For most purposes, including vision, the pressure that light exerts is negligible and has nothing to do with the extent of its stimulating capacity.

During the life of a photon, the energy it possesses is maintained at an exact value, and to a first approximation it moves in a straight line. In a vacuum, it would continue to do so forever. As discussed below, other fates are possible for photons that move within environments containing other particles of matter with which photons may interact. Photons that emerged from distant stars, hundreds or even millions of years ago, reach our eyes unchanged. It is conceptually important, and awe inspiring, to realize that these particles of light are in no sense "tired" and they do not lose the capacity to stimulate the eye during their long journey to earth. On the other hand, when we look at a mountain that is 50 miles away, light reflected from that source takes 0.00027 s to reach our eyes. We will see in Chapter 9 that the physiological latencies involved in visual information processing are orders of magnitude greater than this, meaning that even if light did travel with infinite velocity — as the ancients believed — there would be very few situations where one could tell the difference.

Because light within a homogeneous medium moves in straight lines, inferences can be made about the location of its origin. We will see below something of how the eye does this, by mapping all light that originates from a given point in space upon a restricted region of the retina. The path of light corresponds to what is called, in geometric optics, a ray.

A typical environment containing a source of illumination is packed solid with such light rays because such an environment will also contain numerous reflecting surfaces. (If one were in an environment where all surfaces were perfectly absorbing and there were no visible particles in the air, then one would see the light source and nothing else.) Given a reasonable sampling time, an arbitrary point in a normal environment would have rays passing through it in all possible directions. If the amounts of light per unit time defining these rays were all equal, there would obviously be no basis for pattern vision: such a situation exists in a perfect *Ganzfeld* and is approximated in an Arctic whiteout, being inundated by a superdense fog, or in the center of an integrating sphere.[6] In the real world sources of light are nonuniformly distributed; their output varies with direction and surfaces vary in their reflectivity. Consequently, if one were able to sample a given point in the environment one would find that the rate of photon flow in certain directions would exceed that in others. At each location in the environment where an eye might be, the proximal basis for visual perception lies in the distribution and directionality of light that enters the pupil of an eye located there.[7] The color of an object is related to the distribution of wavelengths of this light.

Photons or Waves

The idea that a wavelength of light can be associated with the behavior of an individual photon has it origins in the early 1900s with the work of Max Planck. Jenkins and White (1957) noted that

> . . . visible light of ordinary intensities contains so many photons that their average behavior is accurately given by the wave theory provided that the interactions with individual atoms of matter do not involve quantized energy states of the latter (p. 623).

Light consists of small packets of highly localized energy. This packet, which we have been properly calling a photon, is able to ". . . communicate all of its energy to a single atom or molecule" (Jenkins and White, 1957, p. 611). When discussing the optics associated with light we will make reference to the wave theory, and when we discuss the absorption of light by the receptor photopigments we will make reference to the particle theory of light. In anticipation of using both theories, we introduce them briefly in this chapter.

If a photon moves with frequency v and in a plane perpendicular to its direction of travel at the speed of light c, then some distance will be traversed during the time required for the particle to move through one cycle. This distance is called *wavelength* and it is inversely proportional to the frequency: $\lambda = c/v$ (Fig. 3.1). When considering light moving as a sinusoidal wave it is necessary to define the concept of a *wavefront*. A wavefront is "an imaginary surface representing the locus of points in wave motion for which, at a given instant, the phase is the same" (Cline, Hofstetter, and Griffin, 1980).

An experiment demonstrating the wavelength nature of light goes as follows. Imagine a beam of light passing through a pinhole aperture (a_0) and that this light then is incident upon a pair of very narrow slits, a_1 and a_2 (Fig. 3.2). The distribution of light that results was first shown by Thomas Young (1807) and is represented as an *interference pattern* represented on the far right of Figure 3.2. This interference pattern can be understood by recognizing that the light, after

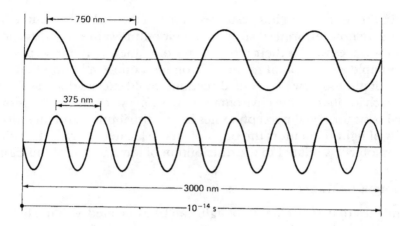

Figure 3.1   Relations between wavelength and frequency of vibration. In 10^{-14} s, light will travel about 3000 nm. Extreme violet light (375 nm) vibrates through 8 cycles during this time, so the distance λ that it travels during one cycle is 3000/8 = 375 nm. Extreme red light vibrates more slowly, covering 4 cycles during this time; the distance that it travels is 3000/4 = 750 nm. The distance that light travels during one cycle of vibration defines its wavelength.

traversing slits a_1 and a_2, forms wavefronts. These wavefronts produce *constructive* and *destructive* interference patterns in the plane labeled *C*. In those places where the two wavefronts are in phase, constructive interference occurs and the light will be bright. Where the two wavefronts are out-of-phase, destructive interference occurs and the light will be dim. This experiment does a good job of demonstrating the wave nature of light. However, the full story is not so simple.

Feinberg (1968) reported that G. I. Taylor conducted a version of the Thomas Young experiment at the University of Cambridge in the early 1900s using extremely low exposures of several months duration, and found an interference pattern on the photographic plate used to collect the light. In 1967, Pfleegor and Mandel, at the University of Rochester, reported doing this same kind of experiment under conditions where the rate of light arrival at the receiving plane was so slow that light interaction was not possible. Very sensitive detectors were used to register where each photon arrived at the plane behind the slits. Over a very long period of time, the distribution of photon incidence that built up was the same as that obtained under the more usual high-intensity conditions where interactions between photons seemed possible. The implication, as Dirac (1958)

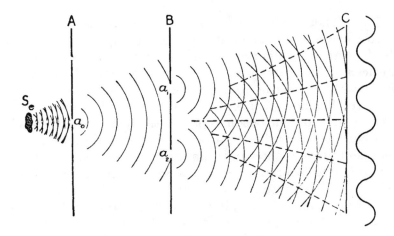

Figure 3.2 Interference produced by coherent light passing through a pair of slits. Where light is vibrating in phase, amplitude is doubled (dashed lines); amplitude is less everywhere else and is zero in the center of regions flanked by dashed lines. A receiving screen at C results in an amplitude distribution as shown at the far right. (After Ditchburn, 1976 p. 105.)

had earlier expressed it,[8] is clear: "Each photon then interferes only with itself." Dirac went on to say that "interference between two different photons never occurs." Although Pfleegor and Mandel's experiment fails to prove the second statement, their result is consistent with it. Feynman (1965) gave a different and more intuitively palatable explanation. He contends that what builds up on the receiving plane is a distribution of the *probability* of photons hitting various points along the receiving plane. The brighter areas represent areas of high-probability hits and the darker parts areas of lower-probability hits. For the condition where there are very few photons over a period of time being emitted, he contends that they arrive like discrete particles, but the probability of their arrival is determined as the intensity of waves would be. Consequently, photons sometimes behave like particles and sometimes like waves. They ". . . behave in two different ways at the same time" (Feynman, 1965, p. 138).

Wavelength and Hue

The wavelengths of photons to which the eye is sensitive are in the range of about 380 to 750 nm. Although the perception of hue cannot be reliably mediated by a single photon, the use of large enough numbers of them (high intensities) under otherwise appropriate conditions leads to a reliable correspondence between wavelength and hue. The shortest perceptible wavelengths appear violet, or reddish blue. As wavelength is increased, the reddish component diminishes and disappears at about 470 nm, at a point called *psychologically unique* blue. (Recall, from Chapter 2, that this is a blue that is neither reddish nor greenish.) As wavelength is further increased, the appearance of blue becomes progressively more greenish; a balanced blue-green is achieved around 490 nm and then the green component predominates and unique green is reached in the range of about 500 to 515 nm. The longest wavelengths of the spectrum appear to be nearly (but not quite) a pure red (Hurvich, 1981; Abramov, Gordon, and Chan, 1991). Shortening the wavelength from 700 nm introduces a greater yellowish component; a balanced red-yellow (orange) is seen at about 600 nm. Further shortening of wavelength causes the red component to diminish until psychologically unique yellow is reached at about 575 nm. The range between about 515 and 575 nm appears as yellow-green blends and a balanced yellow-green occurs at about 550 nm.* The reader may wonder why we cannot be more precise about the wavelengths that produce these hues. In point of fact, it is possible to precisely determine the hues that individual observers will report at specific wavelengths (Boynton and Gordon, 1965). However, inter-observer variability requires the less precise statements we make above when referring to human observers in general.

> Refer to the color diagram of Figure 2.4 and indicate around the color circle the wavelengths that correspond to the psychologically unique hues and the balanced blends. Note that there is no wavelength corresponding to the balanced sensation of reddish blue and there is no wavelength which corresponds to unique red — e.g., a red with no red or yellow component.

SOURCES OF LIGHT

Natural Illumination

No creature — not even a cat — can see in the dark. All visual perception demands that a source of illumination be present to irradiate the objects that are seen. Sunlight, which has presumably always been available to guide the evolution of eyes, is still very important. The solar radiant energy begins as gamma radiation comprised of wavelengths at least a million times too short to see. This radiation is spread out into longer wavelengths "by absorption and re-emission processes throughout the sun's bulk" (Henderson, 1977, p. 15). The distribution of wavelengths in sunlight is further altered following

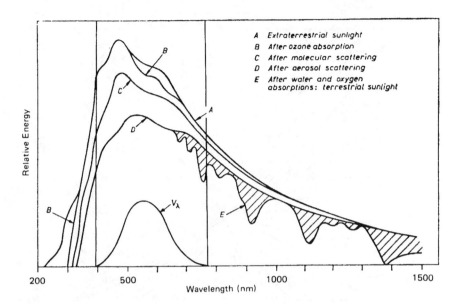

A   Extraterrestrial sunlight
B   After ozone absorption
C   After molecular scattering
D   After aerosol scattering
E   After water and oxygen
     absorptions: terrestrial sunlight

Figure 3.3   The topmost curve (A) shows the spectral distribution of sunlight as it enters the earth's atmosphere. The other curves show how the amount of light is reduced, and its spectral distribution altered, by additional factors as shown. The relative spectral sensitivity of the eye, under conditions where color vision prevails, is given as V_λ at the bottom. This shows that the eye is sensitive to a region of the spectrum where the radiation reaching the earth from the sun is most plentiful. (After Henderson, 1977, Fig. 1, p. 48.)

interaction with the earth's atmosphere. Figure 3.3 shows how extraterrestrial sunlight has its spectrum altered by absorption and *scattering*. By the time sunlight reaches the earth, all wavelengths are still richly represented throughout the visible spectrum.

Artificial Illumination

The production of artificial light originally required that something be burned in open air. The flame of a candle is an example of such a source. Its spectral output in the shorter wavelengths of the visible spectrum is deficient, relative to that of daylight. In general, the same is true for *incandescent lamps* (ordinary light bulbs) in which a filament is heated until it glows. The gas-filled enclosure is designed to preserve the life of the filament. When operated at very low current, no visible radiation is produced by such a lamp. As the applied voltage is increased, causing an increase in current flow through the filament, its tempera-

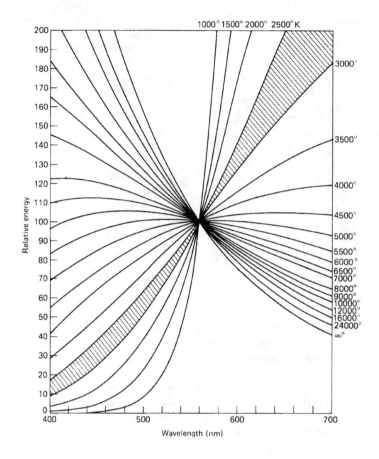

Figure 3.4   Spectral distribution of light emitted from a "complete radiator" (which tungsten closely approximates) as a function of temperature. These curves are normalized at 560 nm and, therefore, do not show that the absolute amount of energy emitted grows, at all wavelengths, as temperature is increased. Ordinary tungsten lamps operate in the range (shaded) from 2500° to 3000°. Over this small range, the efficiency of such lamps increases from about 8 to 22 lumens per watt. (From *The Science of Color,* 1953, p. 261.)

ture is raised and the spectral distribution of the emitted light changes so that the level of short wavelength energy relative to long wavelength energy increases, as depicted in Figure 3.4. Associated with increased voltage is a change in the color of the filament, or of a white object illuminated by it, that varies from appearing dull to bright red, then through orange to yellowish white, and, finally, to a definitely bluish white. The deficiency in the shorter wavelengths is eliminated at the highest temperatures, but at the cost of a drastic shortening of the life of ordinary light bulbs. The quartz-iodide lamp, now used in many slide projectors, automobile head lights, ordinary household lighting, and laboratories, solves this problem by causing much of the tungsten that leaves the filament to redeposit itself back upon the filament, rather than upon the inside wall of the lamp enclosure.

Good *color rendering* depends on a continuous spectrum like that provided by sunlight or incandescent lamps. Color rendering refers to the effect a light source has on object color appearance. Incandescent lamps generate large amounts of infrared radiation, resulting in more heat than light. This limits the efficiency that can be provided by this kind of artificial light, as measured in *lumens per watt.* The lumen is a measure of the amount of visually effective light. The watt, a unit of physical power, refers in this case to the energy supplied as input to the lamp, which is, of course, what the consumer pays for. It is not surprising that when *fluorescent* lights, which are much more efficient, were developed in the 1930s, they almost immediately started to become popular for commercial lighting and are now widely used for this purpose as well as home lighting.

A fluorescent lamp contains a mercury vapor which, when energized electrically, emits ultraviolet radiation that itself is invisible. The manner in which this radiation is converted into visible light is explained by LeGrand as follows:

> . . . the inside of the envelope, or tube, [is coated] with a fluorescent layer, which absorbs the 253.7 nm radiation and emits, as a result, a continuous spectrum of longer wavelengths. . . . [T]he spectral emittance of the fluorescent light is a maximum at about 440 nm for a coating of calcium tungstate, 480 for magnesium tungstate, 525 for zinc silicate, 595 for cadmium silicate, 615 for cadmium borate and 665 nm for magnesium germinate. Usually about 16% of the energy consumed by the lamp reappears as fluorescent light (1968, p. 25).

Fluorescent lamps produce about 60 lumens per watt. (See Figure 3.4 for data on tungsten incandescent sources.) The spectral lines of a fluorescent tube, which may contain a mixture of these substances, are merged so that there is a continuity of radiation throughout the spectrum. Especially for the most efficient lamps, which are deficient in long-wave radiation, fluorescent lamps are poor for color rendering. The subtle colors of human complexions are not improved by such fluorescent lamps. Incandescent sources, which are rich in long wavelengths, are often used to spotlight roast beef in areas otherwise lit by fluorescent light. Otherwise an expensive red roast looks like a cheap overcooked cut, and even the completely uncooked meats in the supermarket can look grayish and unappetizing.

There are many other light sources in common use these days. A full treatment of these is not necessary here, and can be found, for example, in the *Illuminating Engineering Society Handbook*[9]. These other sources include arc lamps, like the xenon source used for commercial motion picture projection (and in many vision labs), and the sodium vapor lamp, sometimes used for highway illumination because of its exceptional efficiency. The spectral lines of the xenon arc are greatly smeared under pressure, resulting in an excellent spectral distribution for color rendering. The low-pressure sodium vapor lamp, on the other hand, emits mostly yellow light from a narrow band of the spectrum and only very weakly elsewhere; nearly total color blindness occurs when objects are seen illuminated by its rays. High-pressure sodium, which is often used for street lighting, has better spectral properties because of the pressure broadening in vapor of the spectral lines.

WHAT HAPPENS TO LIGHT WHEN IT ENCOUNTERS VARIOUS MEDIA?

When light travels and encounters a medium other than that through which it has been traveling several things can happen. It can be *transmitted*, meaning it passes through the medium relatively unimpeded. Light can be *reflected*, which is what we commonly experience when looking into a mirror. If the substance is appropriate, the light will become completely *absorbed*. It can be *refracted*, which gives a rod its bent appearance when partially submerged in water. When light encounters substances that are not completely transparent it can be *scattered*. These effects on light are represented in Figure 3.5. One other action of light will be discussed and that occurs when light passes quite close to an opaque edge. When this happens a process of *diffraction* occurs. Each of these optical effects will be discussed in more detail in the following.

Transmission

When light moves from one location to another it moves through some medium. That medium might be glass, air, the various components of the eye, or even a vacuum. When this occurs we speak of light being transmitted or the transmission of light (Fig. 3.5). So far nothing has been discussed about the effect of the medium through which light travels. Except for a vacuum, there is no such thing as a perfectly transparent medium. The fact that light requires no medium for its transport is a fact only grudgingly conceded by physicists in this century: the idea of an "ether" that supposedly existed for this

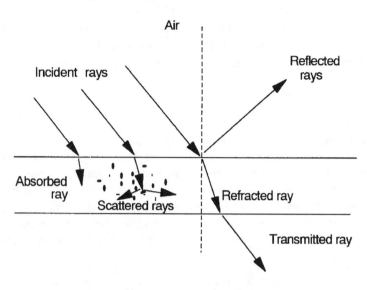

Figure 3.5 The various ways in which light rays interact when encountering a transparent medium like, for example, glass.

purpose, even in a vacuum, had long been in vogue. Experimental evidence capable of testing, yet failing to support, the ether concept finally led to its demise (the famous Michelson–Morley experiment).[10]

Transparent media have an effect on light because they contain atoms that interact with photons. Some of the atoms absorb photons (we will deal with absorption below). Others change the flight path of a photon, and this is called scatter (see below). The flight paths of photons that once having entered a medium are able to pass within it without change of direction define the *image-forming rays*, and these are almost always the ones that are important for vision. Image-forming rays that pass through the atmosphere are little altered by it; it is also the case that photons traveling along these paths do so with negligible reduction of speed compared to that in a vacuum. Apparently these photons get through the widely spaced molecules of the atmosphere without interacting with them.

Transparent media other than the atmosphere, such as glass, have a much higher molecular density and it is not possible for photons to pass through (even though very few of them may be absorbed) without interacting with the atoms of the glass. But these interactions produce, in addition, a very important result, namely a reduction in the velocity of the photon compared to what it would be in air. This is not a small effect: ordinary glass or water will reduce the speed of light by about a third. The speed of light in a vacuum divided by the speed of light in a medium defines the *index of refraction* of that medium (1.33 for water).

Reflection

Most of the time we see objects only because they reflect light to a greater or lesser degree than their backgrounds. Offhand it might seem that reflection should be a rather simple matter. From the subjective view of Chapter 2, glossy surfaces reflect light at the same angle of incidence and without any change of color. Whereas glossy surfaces are very smooth, matte surfaces have tiny surface imperfections that cause light to scatter and somehow have the ability to change color.

Most writers who deal with the topic of reflection, even at the highly technical level that is necessary to understand the principles of color printing or photography, assume that the reflected light from a surface is some portion of that which was incident. Light is incident upon the color print: some of it passes through the outer glossy surface and through the layers of selectively absorbing dyes. The spectral distribution of the light (numbers of photons as a function of wavelength) is altered by the double transfer through the dyes, both before and after reflection from the white paper beneath. There may be internal reflections, which is a problem of *scatter* (see below), and there are many other technical problems to deal with, but surely the light that is reflected from the print is the same light that illuminated it.

On the contrary, the physicist Victor Weisskopf writes:

> The overwhelming majority of things we see when we look around our environment do not emit light of their own. They are visible only because they reemit part of the light that falls on them from some primary source, such as the sun or an electric lamp. What is the nature of the light that reaches our eyes from objects that are inherently non-luminous?

> In everyday language we say that such light is reflected or, in some cases, transmitted. As we shall see, however, the terms reflection and transmission give little hint of the subtle atomic and molecular mechanisms that come into play when materials are irradiated by a light source. (Weisskopf, 1968, p. 60.)

Reemission implies that the photons reflected from an object are not the same ones that are incident upon it. Nevertheless, with the relatively rare exception of fluorescent materials[11] such physical theory states that the wavelength of the emerging photon is exactly the same as that of the incident one. The numbers of emerging photons never exceed the numbers of incident ones. The time delay involved in the substitution of one photon for another is too short to measure. Therefore, so far as the potential visual effects of emerging photons are concerned, they might as well be some of the same ones that were incident upon a surface. No conceivable detector, whether eye or otherwise, could tell the difference. Therefore, we shall assume that any emerging reflected photon is the same as one of those that was incident, meaning that individual photons reflect without losing their identity. Making this assumption allows us to trace the fate of a hypothetical individual photon as it interacts with matter, both outside and inside the eye.

Recall from Chapter 2 that the most important property of a surface for perceiving its color is diffuse spectral reflectance. This is a statement about how the probability of a photon being reflected from a surface, in an unpredictable direction, varies depending on the wavelength of the incident photon. Although much remains to be learned about how surfaces in nature manage to do this, the fact that they do is crucial for color perception.

Absorption

When a beam of light enters some medium, for example a dark glass, not all of it will emerge out of the other side (Fig. 3.5). Some of this light will become scattered and emerge from the glass in unpredictable places (see discussion on scatter below). Some of the light is absorbed by the atoms contained in the medium and is converted to heat: that which is converted to heat is said to be absorbed. The more transparent the medium is, the less absorption will take place. The extent to which absorption takes place is wavelength dependent. For example, if you take a monochromatic light of say 470 nm (unique blue for many people) and shine it on a filter whose maximum spectral transmittance is at 470 nm, this light will pass through with little absorption. If, on the other hand, the 470 nm light is shone on a filter that has a maximum transmittance at 650 nm (a red filter), then a great deal of this short wavelength light will be absorbed.

Refraction

Refraction refers to a change in the direction of light as it passes from one medium to another. Consider, as in Figure 3.6, a wavefront obliquely approaching a block of glass, coming from air. A part of the wavefront gets into the glass first and must slow down; the part still

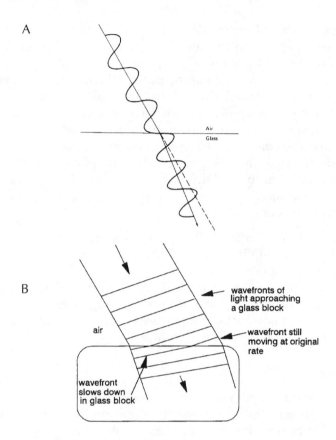

Figure 3.6   A. Refraction of light at an air-glass interface. The change in direction of a photon is associated with a reduction of velocity and a decrease in wavelength. B. The reason light bends when entering a more dense medium like glass, at an angle, is that those photons that enter the glass first slow down while those that have not yet entered continue at their original speed.

outside continues at its original rate. The only way that a wavefront can enter the glass and maintain its integrity is to change its direction. An analogy may help here: imagine two wheels mounted on roller bearings on opposite ends of an axle, entering sand from a concrete roadway. If the direction of entry is perpendicular to the edge of the roadway, both wheels will leave the roadway at the same time and will be slowed in the sand by the same amount, so that the unit as a whole, defined by a line perpendicular to the axle, will continue to move in its original direction. But if the entrance is oblique, the sand will slow the rotation of the inner wheel before the outer one is affected. In order to

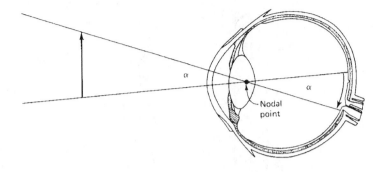

Figure 3.7   Nodal point system for determining the location of a retinal image.

preserve its integrity, the unit must change direction as it enters the sand. The more formal treatment of refraction invokes Huygen's theory of secondary wavelets and the interested reader is referred to a text-book on optics (e.g., Jenkins and White, 1957; Falk *et al.*, 1986).

Refraction is what allows images to be formed in eyes and cameras. As Kepler first understood, positive lenses can be used to cause bundles of diverging light, incident upon one surface of a lens, to converge again on the other side to form an image, which must be upside down, as shown in Figure 3.7. (Refraction will be dealt with again at the end of this chapter.)*

> The inversion of the image in the eye can be directly appreciated by pressing gently, though the eyelid, on the lateral surface of the eye, with the eye turned inward and the pressure applied as close as possible to the lower orbital ridge. The pressure phosphene that results will be perceived in space up and opposite, localized in that part of space where a light source must be located in order to form an image on the retina at the region where the external pressure is applied.

Scatter

Scatter (Fig. 3.5) occurs whenever the reradiation of photons by the molecules of a transmitting medium is other than in the forward direction. Such photons become useless for, and often degrade, spatial vision. The light that we see when a beam pierces a smoky room is visible only because of scatter. In a perfectly transmitting medium, beams of enormous intensity could pass just before our eyes and we would not see them. There is appreciable light scatter over long distances even in clear atmosphere, and a great deal of it occurs under other conditions, especially in fog. There is a surprisingly large

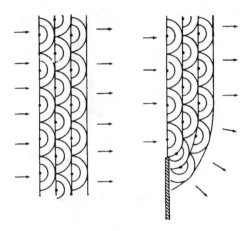

Figure 3.8   When wavefronts encounter an edge the will not be cut off sharply at the edge but bend around it as shown. This effect is called diffraction.

amount of scattered light in the eye itself, which has significant effects for vision. An extreme example of ocular light scatter occurs when the lens of the eye becomes cloudy, which is called a cataract. This condition is common in the elderly but can occur at any age.

When scattering particles are large, as they are in the eye, scatter is largely independent of wavelength and is concentrated in a forward direction. When the particles are small, as in the atmosphere on a clear day, shortwave photons are much more likely to be scattered than long-wave ones; this is the physical basis for the blue of the sky.

Diffraction

If a light encounters an opaque (nontransparent) object, it will be either absorbed or reflected. If it passes the edge of such an object at a considerable distance, the presence of the remote object will have no ability to influence the light path and it will go by just as it would if the object were completely removed from the scene. But if a light passes very near the edge of a surface, it will appear to bend around the edge. This is called *diffraction*. Huygens, in the 17th century explained this phenomenon as follows. Invoking the wave theory of light, one can consider light as a series of wavefronts moving along the path taken by the light. Each point on a wavefront acts like a new spherical wave source. As can be seen in Figure 3.8, when the wavefront encounters an edge, the curved part of the front will contain a new source that sends light off on an angle away from the original direction of light propagation. Some of this light is sent behind the opaque surface edge, giving the appearance of the light "bending" around the edge.

Diffraction sets an upper limit on the ability of any optical system, including the eye, to image each point as a point. In the pinhole camera, diffraction is very great and the image quality is poor. As the pupil of the eye becomes larger, the image blur due to diffraction becomes less. This relates to the fact that opening the pupil allows a smaller proportion of the incoming light being processed by the eye to interact with the edge of the pupil.

THE FATE OF A SOLAR PHOTON

Consider a photon, on its way toward the earth from the sun, which ultimately might enter an observer's eye, thus contributing to vision. Unless the photon is traveling through outer space in the direction of the earth, the initial probability that it will enter into an earthling's vision is nearly zero. To a first approximation outer space is a perfect vacuum; therefore, the path of a photon will be in a straight line (neglecting weak magnetic field effects) and it will miss the earth. Photons that miss the earth in this manner are most unlikely to have a second chance, with the exception (which we shall ignore) of some of those that travel in the direction of the moon or other objects in the solar system (see path a in Fig. 3.9) from which they may reflect.

Next consider photon b, which is headed for the earth at a grazing angle. The greatest probability by far is that it will pass unmolested through the atmosphere. If so, it will emerge from the other side of the atmosphere and cannot possibly contribute to visual stimulation. Such photons must have their direction of travel altered to be potential contributors to vision. This happens fairly frequently. If a photon interacts with an atmospheric molecule two possibilities exist. It may be absorbed by the molecule, increasing the latter's agitation and thereby adding its tiny share to atmospheric temperature. Such a photon will travel no farther and no longer is in contention as a visual stimulus. A second possibility is scatter, which can occur in any direction within the full 4π steradians of solid angle surrounding the molecule, including straight ahead (in which case the scatter would be undetectable and might as well never have occurred), and straight back along the path of incidence. Where scatter is concerned, the probabilities involved are very complex and depend on the wavelength of the photon as this relates to the properties of the molecule with which it collides. For a photon incident upon the earth's atmosphere at a grazing angle, the result is that the photon, which would

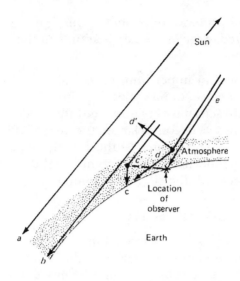

Figure 3.9   Various ways in which a photon coming from the sun might, or might not, reach the eye of the observer.

almost certainly have missed striking a planet free of atmosphere, instead has a finite probability of being scattered toward the surface of the earth (c', c in Fig. 3.9)

Consider next photon d headed directly toward the surface of the earth. It may also be absorbed or scattered before reaching the earth. If scattered, it may be directed into space (d') or toward a different terrestrial point than that toward which it started (d). On a clear day, the greatest chance is that the photon will escape collision with atmospheric molecules and continue on its trip to earth.

From the standpoint of an observer on earth, a group of photons that originate from the same place may reach the eye in more than one way. We do not, and should not, look directly at the sun (although its rays very often enter the eye in peripheral vision while we are trying to look somewhere else). Imagine that the eye is pointed straight toward the sun (e). Given the origin of a photon at a particular point on the sun, there is a certain probability that, having traveled through space and having avoided collision with atmospheric molecules, it will continue directly to the eye. More important is the fact that sunlight illuminates everything around us, and some of this light is reflected toward our eyes. Few objects are self-luminous; most are seen as a result of reflection. So this is another path that an individual photon might take: from sun to object to eye. Yet another photon may start out in a direction deviant from that which would stimulate the eye directly. Instead, it is scattered in the atmosphere and, therefore, appears to be coming from some place other than its original source. Scattered light is what makes the sky light up. Almost everyone has seen, on television or in photographs, the effect of an absence of such light scatter on the moon, where the sky is jet-black even at midday because the moon lacks atmosphere. A final possibility is a scattered photon that strikes an object and is then reflected or scattered into the eye. Most objects that are seen in the shade on a sunny day owe their visibility to this effect: on the moon, they generally would not be visible. On a cloudy day, all objects owe their visibility to illumination provided by scattered light.

THE IMPORTANCE OF DIRECTION

A prerequisite to gauging the color of an object is to discern that the object exists in the first place. To gain the recognition at a distance that is characteristic of such object vision, it is necessary somehow to extract salient information from the dense pattern of rays that are found in any complex real-world environment. To do this requires spatial vision, which may be defined as an ability to detect the discontinuities in such patterns of rays caused by the presence of the object.

Imagine yourself in a classroom illuminated by a combination of light from the window and overhead fluorescent fixtures. Consider that you are sitting somewhere in the middle of this room, and that a white piece of cardboard is attached to the wall at the front of the room. At the location of the pupil of, say, your right eye, there will exist a complex array of photon flight paths, or rays — some coming directly from the sources of radiation, others reflecting from the various surfaces in the room, including the cardboard. Suppose now that an arrow, about 1 m long, base down and tip up, is drawn on the cardboard with a green felt pen. If anyone were to ask "what has just been drawn on the cardboard?" all will agree that it is a green arrow.

The usual textbook explanation of how this image inversion happens is shown by the ray diagram in Figure 3.7. The arrow is shown at the left with just two rays emerging from it — one from the base and one from the tip. These rays cross in the eye and produce an image, which is upside down, upon the retina. The image is green, and the arrow is seen. This explanation is inadequate in the extreme. In the first place, the green arrow, which is not self-luminous, does not have the capacity to reflect photons only in the direction of the eye. Second, the light reflecting from it comes from all along the length of

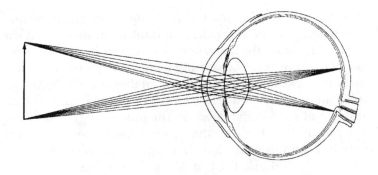

Figure 3.10 Actual path of rays through the eye.

the arrow, not just from the ends. Third, the retinal image must be processed; its existence does not "explain" vision.

Pretending for the moment that the arrow is self-luminous, let us concentrate on the light coming from its tip. A critical point is that photons emerge from this point in space in all possible directions within the half-sphere in front of the cardboard. There is not just one ray headed magically toward the middle of the eye as shown in Figure 3.7. (If this were so, moving the head slightly would cause the arrow to disappear; actually, of course, one can move freely around the room and see the arrow from just about any vantage point.) A truer situation is diagrammed in Figure 3.10. With the eye in any particular location, the rays of interest are the diverging ones that strike the cornea of the eye over a range of locations such that the rays passing through the cornea also pass through the pupil of the eye. We ignore, for purposes of analysis, all other rays.

We have known, since Kepler, that the optics of the eye brings this bundle of rays to a focus on the retina where the so-called retinal image of the arrow tip will be formed. Because of the diffraction limitation and other factors, it is both theoretically and practically impossible for an optical system to image a point exactly as a point. Instead, the point will be imaged on the retina as a more-or-less Gaussian (bell-shaped) spread function. Nevertheless, it will be convenient to imagine that there is a point image on the retina, keeping in mind that this represents a serious oversimplification.

What then is the meaning, if any, of the diagram in Figure 3.7? The explanation has to do with the concept of the *nodal point* in optics. The behavior of any coaxial optical system, however complex, can be predicted by a model of the type shown in Figure 3.11. Given the object

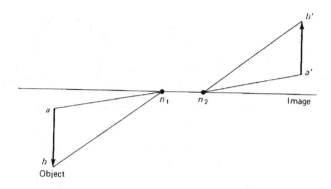

Figure 3.11 Use of the nodal points of an optical system to determine image location in a known place.

point, two nodal points, and a known location of the image plane, the approximate location of the image can be calculated by drawing a line from the object to the first nodal point, and another line from the second nodal point, parallel to the first line, until it intersects the image plane. The eye is an unusual optical system, because the rays entering it from air proceed to a denser medium from which they do not again emerge. Partly for this reason, the two nodal points of the eye are very close together, and, although their locations vary slightly depending on the state of accommodation of the eye, they may be considered for many practical purposes as being coincident, located about 7 mm behind the vertex of the cornea of the eye. Assuming a single nodal point means that the location of an image on the retina of the eye can be easily determined to a first approximation. Simply draw a line from the object, through the nodal point, and determine where it strikes the back of the eye. But no photon actually follows such a path, unless it passes along the optical axis of the eye. The actual path is usually much more complicated because refraction takes place at the corneal surface and at a number of other places within the eye where there is a sudden change in the index of refraction. To represent the formation of an image in the eye as if actual light rays cross at the nodal point is a useful concept for an approximate calculation of retinal image location and for defining the *visual angle* subtended by an object. If taken with respect to the nodal point, visual angle is the same outside as inside the eye. Figure 3.12 shows that, because of similar triangles, the angle subtended by the image on the retina is the same angle as that subtended by the object at which the observer is looking. Using simple trigonometry allows one to determine this angle by knowing the size of the object and its distance from the eye.

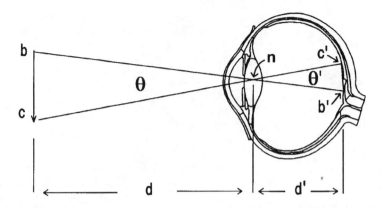

Figure 3.12   The visual angle of an image on the retina can be calculated by measuring the angle subtended by the object outside of the eye. $\theta = \theta'$ because nbc and nb'c' are similar triangles. Therefore, for a given θ, the subtense of the retinal image depends on the ratio of d' to d.

The fact that the arrow on the cardboard is not self-luminous complicates the matter considerably. Imagine a nondirectionally sensitive photocell[12] at the location of the eye, and suppose that a reading of its output is taken before the arrow is drawn on the cardboard. After the arrow is drawn, the number of photons per unit time received at the photocell is decreased, but by how much? It is worth taking time out to do the calculation — at least approximately.

To simplify the problem, we will imagine a black object on a white background, the latter consisting of the half-sphere of Figure 3.13 with a nondirectional photocell located 10 meters from the back of the half-sphere. Assume that the surface of the sphere is uniformly illuminated and, for the moment, that the green arrow is replaced by a nonreflecting black line, 0.002 m wide and 0.3 m in length. All areas of the sphere will affect the photocell equally, except the area that is black. The area of the black region is 0.0006 m², whereas that of the hemisphere is $2\pi r^2$, which is slightly more than 600 m². The result is that the decrease in the rate of photon incidence upon the photocell, caused by the black line on the sphere, is less than 1 part in a million.

But the eye can do better than this. The line so far described subtends a visual angle of about 0.35 minute of arc. A black line of this width can be discriminated very easily. Hecht, Ross, and Mueller (1947) reported that under ideal conditions they could see a wire 1/16 inch

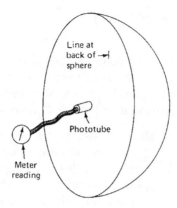

Figure 3.13   Adding the line at the back of the sphere, though it is clearly visible, would not cause a significant change in the output of the nondirectional phototube.

in diameter at a distance of 1 mile. This works out to about 0.5 second of visual angle. Thus, for an easily visible line, a reduction in the amount of light received at the photocell could be less than 1 part in 10 million. No nondirectional device could possibly discriminate such a small difference; the ability of the eye itself to discriminate variations in the intensity of a uniform field is more like one part in a hundred (see Chapter 6). The remarkable fact that the observer easily sees such a line must therefore be critically dependent on the ability of the eye to sort out photons according to their direction of incidence and to disregard most of these as irrelevant to the task at hand. In essence, this is what the formation of a retinal image accomplishes by translating differences in angle of incidence of photons upon the eye into spatial location upon the retina.

There is, of course, much more that could be said on the matter of spatial vision. For example, how do we localize an object in depth? How do we judge the size of an object? How does the visual system deal with the inevitable blur of the retinal image caused by the fact that points are not exactly imaged as points? In this book on color, we will not deal much further with these interesting issues. It is hoped, however, that the following point has by now been well established: Without pattern vision there could be no vision of real objects, and because color is usually a perceptual property of real objects there can be no study of the color of real objects without becoming involved to some extent with the problems of pattern vision.

WAVELENGTH, PHOTON ENERGY, AND RETINAL IRRADIATION

One of the triumphs of twentieth-century physics has been the clarification of the relation between the wavelength and the energy of the photons that make up light at that wavelength. (The reader is reminded that each photon also has wave properties.)

The quantitative relations between the wavelength of a photon and its frequency of vibration have already been mentioned. Given that all photons travel at the same velocity in a given medium, whatever their frequency, it is perhaps intuitively clear that those photons of higher frequency are more energetic than the ones of lower frequency; it turns out that the two quantities are directly proportional to each other. This, then, is the picture to bear in mind: longwave photons are of lower frequency and are less energetic than shortwave photons.

Probably the most basic property of a photon is its frequency. This does not change as a photon enters a medium of higher index of refraction. Because the photon now moves more slowly, its wavelength must shorten. No energy is lost. Therefore a photon of red light at 650 nm will have its wavelength shortened to 487 nm inside a medium, such as the eye, with an index of refraction of about 4/3. Frequency, which is $4.6 \times 10^{14} s^{-1}$ outside the eye, is the same inside. Despite the fact that frequency is a better metric for measuring the spectral aspect of light than is wavelength, the use of wavelength in visual science is so well established that we will also follow this convention.

In describing various experiments to be reported in chapters to follow, it is necessary to decide in what units of intensity to report the visual stimuli that have been employed. A bewildering variety of units has been used for this purpose. The subject of *photometry* deals with the definition of such units, and this is required because the eye has a sensitivity that differs depending on wavelength of the photons that are absorbed in the retina. To specify the visual stimulus strictly in terms of the numbers of photons incident upon the retina would be meaningless, unless the wavelength distribution of these photons were known so that their visual effectiveness can be evaluated.

There exists a unit of *retinal illuminance*, which is the density of light incident upon the retina, called the *troland* (td). The usual definition of the troland requires first that the entire system of photometry be developed. One of the better photometric tutorials is found in LeGrand (1968). Chapter 4 of Wyszecki and Stiles (1982), provides another excellent treatment of photometry.

We shall avoid such photometric details here simply by noting that, at a wavelength of 555 nm, photons have a frequency of 5.4×10^{14} Hz and an energy of 3.58×10^{12} erg. This energy results in approximately one million photons per second per square degree of visual angle,[13] incident upon the retina, to produce a retinal illuminance of 1 td. A general equation relating the number of trolands (N_t) to the number of photons (N_p) per sec per deg is:

$$N_t = 8 \times 10^{-7} N_p Q(\lambda) \tag{3.2}$$

where $Q(\lambda)$ is a measure of the relative spectral sensitivity of the eye on a quantal basis (see "Energy- vs. Photon-Based Sensitivity" in Chapter 5, p. 128). This in turn relates to $V(\lambda)$, the photopic luminosity function (see Note 3, Chapter 8, p. 354 and Appendix, Part I), by

$$Q(\lambda) = V(\lambda) \cdot \frac{555}{\lambda} \tag{3.3}$$

where λ is in nanometers. $Q(\lambda)$ has a value of 1.0 at a wavelength of 555 nm. Because this is the wavelength of highest sensitivity for the light-adapted eye, $V(\lambda)$ has a value of less than 1 at all other wavelengths. The total variation of wavelengths of visible photons is less than two to one. Late in the nineteenth century it was established that the visible spectrum is but a narrow band in a total spectrum of electromagnetic radiation that covers some 22 logarithmic units (decades), as shown in Figure 3.14. To deal with very long wavelengths in a manner analogous to the way it handles visible ones, an eye would have to be scaled upward proportionally in size. To deal with very short wavelengths an eye would have to be microscopically small. Moreover, it is not likely that x-rays, which pass easily through most objects that are significant to us, would be effective messengers about the outside world. Visible light apparently has just the right wavelengths to reflect from objects in useful ways and to permit the evolution of a compact and efficient pickup device, the eye.

DISPERSION AND CHROMATIC ABERRATION

Although Kepler was the first to understand in a general way how lenses work (as we saw in Chapter 1), the principles of light refraction that underlie their function were not quantitatively understood until late in his lifetime. In notes that were not discovered until their author's death, Willebrord Snell wrote in 1621 that "the place of the

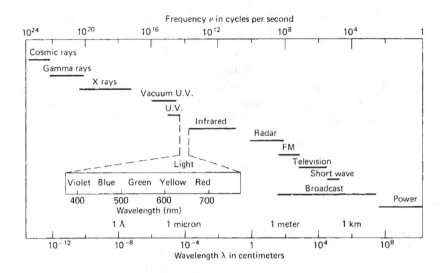

Figure 3.14   The visible spectrum is a relatively narrow band in the total spectrum of electromagnetic energy, as shown here (from Riggs, 1965).

image follows in each case a well-defined perpendicular in such a way that always the incident ray observes to the place of the image from the point of incidence its own perpetual proportion" (Sabra, 1967, p. 99). What this means[14] is illustrated in Figure 3.15a. Ray *AB*, incident upon interface *MN* (for example, that between air at the top and glass at the bottom), is refracted as shown. If a perpendicular to the interface is erected anywhere to the right of *B*, the ratio *BD/BE* is constant, no matter what the angle of incidence of *AB* with respect to the interface *MN*. In 1637, Descartes published the law of sines, usually referred to as *Snell's law*, in the form that we now know it.[15] For this purpose, the simpler construction shown in Figure 3.15b was used; the relations that Snell discovered can be expressed instead as:

$$n_1 \sin\theta_1 = n_2 \sin\theta_2 \qquad (3.4)$$

where n_1 and n_2 are designated as, and in fact define, the relative refractive index of each medium.

Snell's law permits an extremely accurate calculation of the direction of the refracted ray, provided that the indices of refraction of the media are known. Conversely, measurements of the deviations of

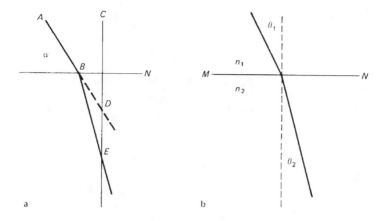

Figure 3.15   a. Snell's law in the form that he discovered it: BD/BE is constant, no matter what the angle of incidence, α. b. Snell's law in the form given it by Descartes: $n_1 \sin\theta_1 = n_2 \sin\theta_2$.

such rays provide an easy and practical way to measure the relative indices of refraction of any two optical media. It will be recalled that these relations can, in principle, also be determined by measuring the relative speed of light in the two media. But this is not easy to do, and nothing was known anyway about the speed of light at the time Snell made his discovery.[16]

Newton's dispersion of white light into its spectral components shows that refraction varies with wavelength. When light slows down, for example when entering glass from air, the photons that comprise that light slow to different degrees, depending on their wavelengths. The photons with the highest frequency (and which, therefore, have the shortest wavelengths) slow down the most and show a larger change in direction than those with lower frequency. Therefore, the *index of refraction* of an optical medium is not a single value but a continuous series of values that vary as a function of the wavelength of the light.

But the full story is yet more complicated. The rate at which the refractive index varies with wavelength differs from one optical medium to another. The higher the rate, the greater the dispersive power of the medium. Because refraction varies with wavelength, whatever the dispersive power, a simple lens always refracts short-wave light more than long-wave light, causing *chromatic aberration* to occur. It is common to correct for this in manmade optical systems by judiciously selecting optical glasses of particular refractive and dispersive powers which can be used together in multielement lenses.[17]

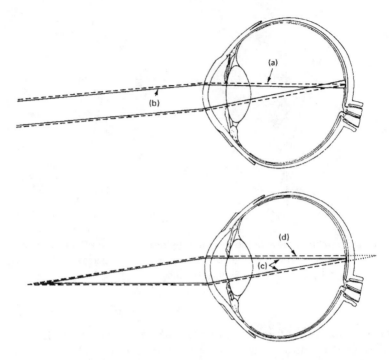

Figure 3.16 Chromatic aberration in the eye. Distant targets can never be in focus for violet light (b). Near targets can be (c), but not simultaneously for red light (a), (d).

Perhaps because eyes are not made of glass, no such correction for chromatic aberration has evolved. If the eye is accommodated (focused) on a distant red target of wavelength 700 nm, a distant violet one of 400 nm will be seriously blurred (Fig. 3.16). If focus is held on the distant red target, the violet one must be brought to within about 0.5 m of the eye before good focus is achieved. This means that normal eyes are seriously *myopic*—in the vernacular, "near-sighted" — for distant blue targets, and, therefore, there is no possibility that the mixed rays from a white target can all be optimally focused upon the retina. Because there is no way to accommodate for distant blue targets, it is not surprising that the eye tends to accommodate instead for longer wavelengths than this, allowing the short-wave components of the retinal image to be seriously blurred.

Yet we do not ordinarily perceive the expected effects of such chromatic aberration, which would be a visual world whose edges are tinged with chromatic fringes. Why not? This is an important problem for color vision, and we shall return to it in subsequent chapters. Leaving the details for later, the following factors seem to be involved in the attempt to understand this interesting problem.

- Selective absorption occurs in the eye media, reducing the effectiveness of blue light and thereby effectively shortening the visible spectrum (Chapter 5).

- The short-wavelength-sensitive cones enter importantly into the perception of hue but very little into the perception of contour. Because these cones absorb mostly short-wave light this is in effect another spectrum-shortening device, but one that is selective for contour (Chapters 5, 8, and 9).

- The *Stiles–Crawford effect*, attributable to the directional sensitivity of the cone photoreceptors, reduces the effectiveness of rays entering the margins of the pupil (Stiles and Crawford, 1933a); these marginal rays produce the greatest amount of chromatic aberration (Fig. 3.16).

- When prisms are mounted before the eyes, the chromatic fringes that they produce upon the retina are at first very evident in sensation. But if the prisms are worn for a long time the fringes become very much less evident and may even disappear. This indicates that neural machinery exists, which is capable of compensating for consistent relations between fringes and contours, somehow expelling the part of the message that carries no real information about the outside world (Kohler, 1962).

SUMMARY

The use of physical concepts to help understand human color vision is important, because it avoids a tautology that is inevitable if, as is often done, the stimulus for vision is described according to how things look.

Of the various ways to regard light, its conception as a collection of swiftly moving photons is especially useful for vision. The frequency of each photon is inversely related to its wavelength; this frequency carries the initial chromatic message. Among the properties of light that are important for vision is its tendency to move in straight lines except when scattered, diffracted, refracted, or reflected. The optical system of the eye causes diverging light from points in visual space to converge and form an image at the retina. Spatial vision, thus mediated, is essential to color vision because the latter normally relates to, and is affected by, specific regions of space.

Reflection is important because the visual properties of object surfaces, including their colors, depend upon it. Diffraction limits the optimal quality of any image, including the one in the eye. Scatter is helpful because the diffuse light that it provides from the sky helps to fill dark shadows. Refraction is essential for image formation in eyes and cameras.

The direction of photon travel is critically important for vision. As an example it is shown that unless the directions of incident photons can be sorted out, the percentage of change in the total number of photons reaching the eye, from an easily visible target, is orders of magnitude too small to register.

The relation between the wavelength and energy of photons is easily and clearly understood within the framework of modern physics. The energy of a photon does not change as it moves from one medium to another, nor does its frequency of vibration. In passing from air to glass, for example, a photon slows down and its wavelength decreases.

The standard unit of light intensity to be used in this book is the troland, which is proportional to the number of photons per second per square degree incident upon the retina, weighted according to the photopic spectral sensitivity of the visual system.

The eye is subject to a serious amount of chromatic aberration, which nevertheless seems to have no seriously deleterious effect upon spatial vision.

NOTES

[1] There is no way to be certain that magnetic fields could not tell us a great deal about what we require to know about the physical world. However this may be, we certainly know that vision provides much of our information about the outside world, though perhaps not quite the 90% once claimed by the American Optometric Association. Because vision is so important it is reasonable to expect that light interacts with objects in especially useful ways, and that we have been able to evolve sensory devices that are able to extract whatever is most important from the radiation patterns in which we find ourselves imbedded.

[2] From time to time, one sees reports that colors can be discriminated by some people through the tactile sense. A blindfolded person surely could tell the difference, say, between a white cat and a black cat in the sunlight because the black cat would feel warmer than the white one. The discrimination would then be based on a correlation: cats that absorb the most infrared radiation (heat) are also those that tend to absorb the most visible radiation, so hot cats also tend to be black. If the light reflected from objects is restricted to the visible spectrum, there is no scientifically acceptable evidence that colors are discriminable by touch (see Makous, 1966; Kaiser, 1983).

[3] According to Henderson (1970, p. 1.)

[4] An article by Feinberg (1968) is the lead article in the September 1968 issue of *Scientific American*, devoted exclusively to light. The 11 articles in the issue have

been republished, along with a number of additional articles from other issues of *Scientific American*, in *Lasers and Light*, with introductions by Arthur L. Schawlow (San Francisco: Freeman, 1969).

[5] See, for example, the textbook by Strong (1958, p. 58). We will not give references for all of the physical concepts introduced in this chapter, all of which are treated in detail in standard texts. We have tried to eliminate most of the mathematics and to encourage visualization of optical concepts. As a result, our treatment is not entirely rigorous.

[6] An integrating sphere is used in photometry to measure all of the light in a beam (for example, that passing through a filter that scatters light) or to mix two beams. If the inside of a sphere is painted white, light admitted through a small hole will be diffusely reflected many times and will appear to "light up" the sphere uniformly.

[7] See Boynton (1974) for an elaboration of these ideas.

[8] Dirac (1958, p. 9); also quoted in Scully and Sargent (1972).

[9] Kaufman, J. E. (ed.), *IES Lighting Handbook*, New York: Illuminating Engineering Society, 1993.

[10] See for example, Ditchburn (1976, p. 404) or almost any other optics textbook.

[11] Here and in the discussion to follow, fluorescence is ignored. Surfaces that exhibit this phenomenon are widely used these days in advertising displays, producing very vivid colors that seem to glow almost as if they are self-luminous and in detergents as whitening agents. Fluorescence occurs when light is absorbed by the surface and is then reradiated at a longer wavelength. If this is to be regarded as reflected light, then clearly it is not inevitable that the wavelength of incident photons is preserved in reflection. Fluorescence usually plays a very minor role in object perception.

[12] A nondirectional photocell is one that will react in the same way to any photon incident upon its receiving surface, whatever the angle at which it strikes that surface. Most detectors are directionally sensitive: photons incident perpendicular to the surface are more likely to register than those striking at a grazing angle. This is true of the cone photoreceptors of the human eye (the so-called *Stiles–Crawford effect*).

[13] A square degree of visual angle would result, for example, from the viewing of a square that subtends one linear degree of visual angle on each side. It could also be produced by a circular spot having a diameter of $(2/\sqrt{\pi}) = 1.128°$. One square degree is also equivalent to 3.046×10^{-4} steradian.

[14] According to Kingslake (1974, p. 799), Snell's use of the word "image" to describe the intersection of ray paths and construction lines is not at all in accord with modern usage.

[15] Descartes gave Snell no credit and was later accused of plagiarism. It is however, entirely possible that Descartes arrived at "Snell's law" independently.

[16] The prevailing view held that the speed of light was infinite. Newton thought it finite but predicted incorrectly from his corpuscular theory that light should travel faster in glass than in air.

[17] Typically, only three wavelengths in the visible spectrum are corrected and some deviation of the others is allowed.

Chapter 4

The Eye: Anatomy Underlying the Perception of Form and Color

INTRODUCTION

Thomas Young (1807) introduced his lecture On Vision as follows

> The medium of communication, by which we become acquainted with all the objects that we have been lately considering, is the eye; an organ that exhibits, to an attentive observer, an arrangement of various substances, so correctly and delicately adapted to the purposes of the sense of vision, that we cannot help admiring, at every step, the wisdom by which each part is adjusted to the rest, and made to conspire in effects, so remote from what the mere external appearance promises, that we have only been able to understand, by means of a laborious investigation, the nature and operations of this wonderful structure, while its whole mechanism still remains far beyond all rivalship of human art (p. 447).

Although we have learned a lot about the visual process in the last 200 years, Young's eloquent statement is as apt today as when he wrote it. We cannot do justice in one short chapter to the topic of retinal anatomy. There are three excellent references to which the reader is directed for a more complete story: *The Vertebrate Visual System* by Polyak (1957), *The Vertebrate Retina* by Rodieck (1973), and *The Retina* by Dowling (1987). For a very recent review of the mammalian retinal

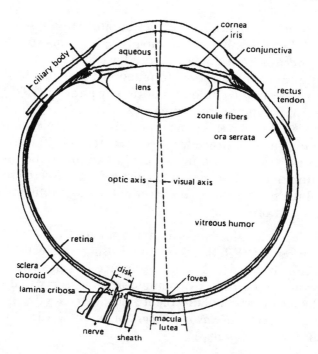

Figure 4.1   This cross section of the eye was originally prepared by Salzmann (1912) and with modifications, has been widely reproduced. This figure is reproduced from Rodieck (1973), p. 3. Not all of the features that are labeled here are discussed in this chapter.

functional architecture, the reader is referred to Wässle and Boycott (1991). In this chapter we will consider the eye's anatomy primarily as it contributes to our understanding of human color vision.

Since the time that Kepler first understood the optics of the eye, it has been realized that the retina, and not the lens, constitutes its photoreceptive component (Fig. 4.1). The basic structure of the retina has been known since the 1870s, when staining techniques were developed that rendered some of the critical retinal structures visible under the light microscope.[1] Polyak (1941, 1957) summarized a wealth of detail about the structure of the retina at the level of magnification that light microscopy permits. However, because the light microscope left many details unclear — in particular the connections (synapses) between nerve cells — correlation between structure and function was not easy. Rodieck's and Dowling's books describe many of the technological advances that have occurred since Polyak wrote *The Vertebrate Visual System*. The scanning electron microscope provides pictures of the vertebrate retina not available to Polyak and the visual anatomists who preceded him. Advances made in the recordings from single neurons have also permitted a wealth of understanding about retinal function not available in the 1950s. One very interesting technique reported by Kaneko (1970) involves the electrophysiological recording of single retinal cells with a micropipette, after which this same pipette is used to inject a yellow dye into the neuron. This procedure confirms the specific neuron from which the electrical recording was taken and shows the investigator the structure of the intact neuron. The reader is directed to Dowling (1987), which shows some of these retinal photographs and provides references to more recent work.

For vision, electrical records first appeared in 1860, when the electroretinogram (ERG) was obtained using an electrode applied to the cornea of a frog.[2] The next advance to which we already alluded involves recording from single units in the visual system of animals by the insertion of tiny recording electrodes that nestle close to active cells (*extracellular recordings*) or in some cases impale the cells (*intracellular recordings*).[3]

In this chapter we shall consider some of the basic findings about the nature of the eye, especially those that have been revealed by optical and anatomical methods. This will provide the background necessary to consider concepts about sensitivity regulation (Chapter 6) and neural mechanisms of color vision, including those in the brain, in Chapter 7. The photochemistry of vision will be considered separately in Chapter 5.

THE MOBILE EYE

The retina cannot effectively function independently of the eye that contains it, or of the other structures in and around the eyeball that allow an image to be formed, permit the eye to move, and thereby enable it to sample the visual environment. The human eye, one of the most complex structures in the body, is just a little less than an inch in diameter. It deviates from a sphere in that its posterior part is somewhat flattened, and there is also a pronounced bulge in front caused by the transparent *cornea*, which for optical reasons, in an eye of this size, must have a radius of curvature less than that approximated by the eye as a whole.*

> The corneal bulge can easily be verified by closing the eyelids and lightly touching the outer surface of the eyelid with a fingertip while rotating the eye slowly from side to side.

Each eye[4] is located in the eyesocket, or *bony orbit*, a cone-shaped cavity that points slightly outward relative to the midline of the head. The eye, thus recessed, is also cushioned by surrounding fatty tissue. The functional significance of such an arrangement may be three-fold: (1) Being located high in the body, the eyes have a good vantage point from which to survey the environment. (2) The eyes are located very close to the brain, which permits the transmission pathways from eye to brain to be both short and well protected. (3) The recession of the eyeballs into the bony orbit, together with the surrounding fat and the covering lid, minimize to an important degree the probability of serious injury to this vital organ.

Movement of each eye is controlled by three pairs of *extraocular* (outside-the-eye) muscles that determine the position of the eyeball within the socket. Each time we change our point of fixation, an exquisitely coordinated relaxation and contraction of these muscles causes a change in eye position. When the position of the head is fixed and there is no predictable motion of objects in the visual world, only *saccadic* eye movements can be made.[5] These so-called "*saccades*," of which we are typically unaware, are ballistic and largely preprogrammed, meaning that once such an eye movement is under way, little modification of it is possible. If the head is turned from side to side while an object is fixated, the eyes roll smoothly in the opposite direction, tending thereby to remain fixed in space. With the head fixed, smooth, *pursuit* eye movements can occur that permit the tracking of external objects, provided that these are moving in predictable ways over distances that are not too large. An act such as following the flight path of a tennis ball also requires head movements, controlled by muscles in the neck, upon which tracking movements of the eyes are superimposed. Small errors of this tracking system are compensated by saccadic eye movements that are superimposed upon the smooth ones.

The literature on eye movements is enormous.[6] A great deal is known about their neurophysiological underpinnings. For most of the basic experiments on human color vision the head is not free to move, and the subject is instructed to fixate upon a black dot, a point of light, or on the center of a more complex target. However, the ability to fixate is limited by small eye movements, called *physiological nystagmus*, that occur even during the most intense effort to fixate. These small movements have been found to be necessary to maintain vision; the entire visual world appears to fade away if eye movements are artificially eliminated.[7]

The Act of Fixation

Whenever we wish to pay visual attention to an object we fixate it, with little awareness of what we are doing, by moving our eyes so that the image of that object will fall on a specialized region of the retina, the *fovea centralis*. This is a depression in the retina represented near the bottom of Figure 4.1. Though it comprises a small percentage of the total retinal area, the fovea is critically important for the perception of visual detail* and also for color vision. The signals leaving the fovea activate a disproportionately large part of the visual brain. The act of fixation is important not only in everyday life but also in the vision laboratory, where, by assuming that a subject can follow the instruction to look at a fixation target, the experimenter can know to which part of the retina a stimulus is directed.

> While looking squarely at one of the words near the center of this page, attempt to read some of the others without moving fixation from the original word. Although many words are visible, only those quite near the fixated word will be recognized. It is an interesting fact of perception that we are normally unaware of the impreciseness of our peripheral vision. (See also p. 115.) Most people with substantial blind areas in the peripheral retina, such as can be caused, for example, by glaucoma, fail to notice them, whereas blind spots in the central retina, which can be caused by looking at the sun, are immediately obvious. Each of us has a blind spot of which we are unaware unless special efforts are taken to notice it. See the simple experiment described on page 105.

OPTICAL ELEMENTS OF THE EYE

Cornea

The cornea, through which light enters the eye, is transparent despite a complex lamellar structure. At the outer corner of the eye is the *lacrimal gland*, which secretes tear and mucus solutions. Tears are necessary to help maintain the normal exchange of oxygen and to control the water balance within the cornea, which otherwise will become cloudy, scattering so much of the incoming light as to seriously degrade the retinal image. Blinking of the eyelids helps to maintain the distribution of tears across the cornea, filling in its microstructure and thereby improving its quality as an optical interface. The cornea is also richly endowed with pain receptors, which function, along with the eyelids, to help protect the eye. Probably everyone is familiar with the intense discomfort caused by even a tiny piece of grit caught under the eyelid.

The cornea is the primary refractive element of the eye because its index of refraction is substantially greater than that of air; the refractive indices of other structures in the eye are more similar to that of the cornea than to air. Thus, the smoothness of the corneal surface, and its index of refraction, are very important. Recall from Chapter 3 that, by *Snell's law*, the greater the difference in refractive index between two optical media, the greater is the amount of refraction that will occur. The indices of refraction of the ocular media relative to air are approximately as follows:[8]

cornea	1.37
aqueous	1.33
lens (cortex)	1.38
lens (core)	1.40
vitreous	1.33

Vision is unclear under water because water (1.33) and the cornea have nearly the same refractive index. The optical power of the cornea is nearly lost and severe "farsightedness" (*hyperopia*) results. The use of watertight goggles permits air to intervene and restore normal corneal function. When corneal contact lenses are worn to correct refractive errors in air, the anterior surface of the contact lens, which together with the intervening fluid has about the same refractive index as the cornea, simply replaces that of the cornea.

Unlike man-made optical surfaces, which for ease of manufacture are usually sections of spheres, the radius of curvature of the cornea is less at the margin than at the center. This is a type of aspherical curve that a lens designer can use to help eliminate spherical aberration, which otherwise results because spherical surfaces refract the marginal rays too much relative to those passing near the center of the lens.

Iris and Pupil

The *iris* controls the entry of light into the eye. The variable opening within it, the *pupil*, determines the amount of light that can pass through to the retina, doing so without altering the field of view. In other words, light can reach any region of the retina having passed through any region of the pupil. The annular iris, which determines the "color of the eye" when viewed from the front, varies in width to alter the size of the pupil as a function of the level of illumination of the retina. However, its size depends also upon a host of other factors, including the size and region of the retina stimulated, spectral and temporal characteristics of the light, and emotional reactions having nothing necessarily to do with vision. The constriction of the pupil that occurs with increasing external illumination is not nearly sufficient to keep the illumination of the retina constant (see Chapter 6).

The quality of the retinal image depends upon the size of the pupil. When the pupil is very small, the image is degraded by diffraction; when it is very large, the effects of spherical and chromatic aberration are most serious. The neural organization of the retina changes as a function of retinal illuminance, to provide one of the mechanisms of light adaptation to be discussed in Chapter 6. The pupil appears set for a slightly clearer image than the neural processing machinery can use (Campbell & Gregory, 1960). For example, at very low levels of external luminance, very little detail is perceptible because the low rate of photon incidence upon the retina is sufficient only to excite a few rod receptors. The rods are organized into very large receptive fields, meaning that photons falling as far as a degree apart (0.3 mm) on the retina have effects that summate spatially. Visual resolution in dim light is therefore limited by the receptive field spacing and cannot be modified by changes in pupil size. At high levels of external luminance, optical aberrations are perceived if pupil size is artificially enlarged, as will be recognized by anyone who has had an ophthalmological examination during which a drug was used to enlarge the pupil. The spatial resolution of the neural processing machinery is finely tuned for high illumination, so optical aberrations introduced by an inappropriately enlarged pupil are resolvable.

The response of the iris muscle depends upon the action of light upon the same photoreceptors that mediate vision. Some of the signals derived therefrom are sent to the midbrain for processing and lead to signals that are directed back to the iris musculature. The pupils of both eyes change size together in what is known as the *consensual* pupillary response; this means that both pupils grow smaller when light is delivered to only one of the eyes.

Much of the experimental evidence to be discussed in this book has been derived from studies in which the subject's head is fixed by biting on a dental impression; subjects are instructed to regard a fixation point and light is beamed through the pupil of the eye in what is known as the *Maxwellian view* (Boynton, 1966; LeGrand, 1968; Westheimer, 1966). For such research, the pupillary response is an unwanted nuisance because it causes the amount of light entering the eye to vary no matter how exactly the external stimulus may be controlled. The effects of pupillary fluctuations are eliminated in the Maxwellian view by making the light beam, as it passes through the pupil, smaller than the smallest pupil (about 2 mm in diameter). If the Maxwellian view is not used, a small *artificial pupil* (a hole in a thin metal plate) can be positioned immediately in front of the eye. In addition to negating the effects of the natural pupil, the artificial pupil cuts off a part of the peripheral visual field. This is not a problem in vision research when the central visual field is being studied.

An important advantage of a small pupil over a large one relates to the *depth of focus*. In the middle panel of Figure 4.2, the eye is accommodated for distance, resulting in a *blur circle* on the retina, as explained in the figure legend. If the pupil were made smaller, the entire bundle of rays that are shown converging toward a point behind the retina would be made smaller; in the limit there could be a very narrow pencil of rays constrained nearly to the visual axis. Reducing the size of the pupil therefore decreases the size of blur circles on the retina, whether these are caused by inappropriate accommodation or by aberrations, thereby increasing the range within which objects will be in reasonable focus for a particular state of accommodation. This improvement in depth of field will be familiar to camera buffs because the same principle applies to photography. One pays a price for it, however, in loss of retinal illumination and increased blur due to diffraction. For the eye, a 3-mm pupil usually produces optimal image quality. The reader is cautioned not to take the photographic analogy too far. The photographer can manipulate the amount of light reaching the film by controlling the *f* stop and exposure duration. Under normal viewing conditions such controls are not readily available to the visual system. As already noted, the pupillary response is insufficient to control the whole range of illumination to which human observers respond.

Lens

The lens of the eye is a complex multi-layered structure whose shape changes during the act of *accommodation*. This process allows objects at various distances from the eye to be clearly imaged, though not all at the same time. If extracted from the eye the human lens bulges and appears yellow because it selectively absorbs short-wavelength light. This selective absorption occurs more so for older eyes than younger ones. This selectivity of transmission influences the color vision of an observer in ways that will be discussed in the next chapter. Such extraction is common in surgery for removal of a *cataract*, which is a clouding of the lens, common in old age.

The greatest change in lens shape during accommodation, takes place at the front surface of the lens. When the eye is focused for a

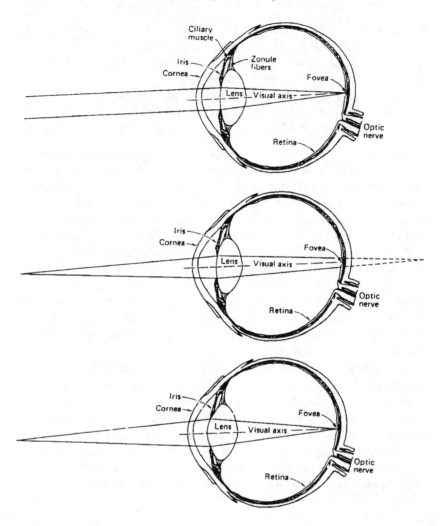

Figure 4.2   Top: The lens of the eye, which will bulge if removed, is held in a flattened position by the action of the zonule fibers that support it. Light from a distant source provides parallel rays, seen entering from the left. The cornea provides most of the refraction needed to bring the rays to a sharp focus at the fovea. Middle: The fixated object has been brought close to the eye. The shape of the lens has not changed and the refraction at the cornea is no longer sufficient to form a point image on the retina, because the rays striking it are now divergent. Instead, a circle of light intersects the retina and the image is blurred. If a hole were cut in the back of the eye an image would be formed behind it, as shown by the dotted lines. Bottom: Contraction of the ciliary muscle releases some of the tension of the zonule fibers. This is the act of accommodation. The lens changes shape, especially at its anterior surface. This added refractive power is now sufficient to re-store a sharp image on the fovea.

distant object, the *zonule fibers*, which hold the lens taut, exert their maximum pull. As an object is brought nearer, the retinal image will blur unless an adjustment is made (Fig. 4.2). Contraction of the ciliary muscle, which rings the eye, is able to release some of the tension that otherwise is exerted by the zonule fibers, allowing the front surface of the lens to bulge. This action adds optical power to the total system, restoring the focus of the image. Maximum accommodation occurs when the ciliary muscle is sufficiently contracted to reduce the tension exerted by the zonule fibers, allowing the lens to assume its maximum bulge. When humans age a condition known as *presbyopia* gradually sets in; although the ciliary muscle remains active, the lens looses its capacity to bulge. By age 60 or so, it usually becomes "stuck" in the flattened shape, making near vision of fine detail impossible without correcting spectacles or contact lenses.

Sclera

The white *sclera* which constitutes the tough outer tunic of the eye is contiguous with the transparent cornea. Unlike the cornea, which is exquisitely sensitive to pain and has no blood supply at all, the sclera is heavily vascularized, has few pain receptors, and is somewhat more difficult to penetrate. The sclera is contiguous at the back of the eye with the sheath of the optic nerve.

Vitreous and Aqueous

A photographic camera has rigid walls, but the eye would collapse were it not filled completely at an intraocular pressure greater than that of the surrounding atmosphere. About two-thirds of the eyeball is filled with the *vitreous*, which is partially a gel and partially liquid interlaced with peculiar membranes. The *anterior chamber* of the eye, between cornea and lens, is filled with an exceptionally clear fluid called the *aqueous humor*. The aqueous is continuously generated and absorbed. It controls the intraocular pressure, which must be high enough to maintain the integrity of the eye, but not too high, or the cells of the retina will be destroyed. When the intraocular pressure is too high the condition known as *glaucoma* exits.

THE RETINA

The vascular supply of the retina is the only component of the central nervous system that is directly visible, this being possible with the aid of an *ophthalmoscope*, which the examiner uses to look into the eye through the pupil. The sensory structure of the retina cannot be visualized this way because the retina is largely transparent and its critical features are of microscopic dimensions. What is seen is called the *fundus*; it has an orange-red hue that is characteristic of the retina's vascular supply. Upon this background, the vessels that supply the circulation of blood to the retina are easily visible. To learn anything about the microstructure of the retina, it must be removed from an eye, subjected to histological procedures (slicing, fixing, staining and so forth), and viewed with a microscope.

The human retina is less than half a millimeter thick over most of its extent. It contains a total area of about 1100 mm², about that of a silver dollar (Taylor and Jennings, 1971), and has a volume of about .25 cm³. Within this small volume are found something like 200 million nerve cells that are directly involved with the processing of visual information, distributed across the retina in a very highly organized fashion.

Most of the volume of the retina is contained within the inner and outer limiting membranes (Figs. 4.3, 4.4). The *inner limiting membrane* separates the retina from the vitreous humor, which is shown at the bottom of Figure 4.3.[9] The *outer limiting membrane* is located about four-fifths of the way toward the top of this figure and, in turn, is separated from the outside surface of the eye by about 500 μm of tissue that includes the *receptors, pigment epithelium, choroid, and sclera*. The choroid is a pigmented layer lying just inside the sclera, whose function it is to absorb much of the light that passes through the sclera, which otherwise would reach the retina from the wrong side.*

> By pulling the lids wide apart with the fingers on a sunny day, the effects of stray light entering the eye through the sclera can be directly appreciated. The effects are most easily seen if sunlight directly strikes the eye while the observer is looking at objects seen in the shade. The resulting stray light casts an apparent veil over everything and reduces contrast. Other important sources of stray light in the eye include scatter from the cornea and lens, but these are harder to demonstrate.

The retina also contains radially oriented cells, called *Müller cells*, that are not shown in Figures 4.3 and 4.4. These serve a structural function because, in addition to extending all the way from the inner to the outer limiting membrane, they also exhibit lateral processes that fill up much, if not all, of the space within the inner retina not occupied by nerve cells or blood vessels. Little is known about the functions of Müller (glial) cells. Dowling (1987, p. 237) reports that ". . . most of the ERG recorded from the intact eye comes from these cells." Rodieck (1988) tells us that the Müller cells are active in various metabolic and ionic functions.

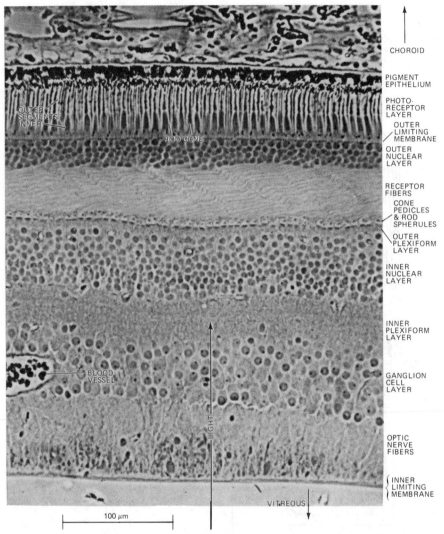

FIGURE 4.3 Cross section of the human retina about 4° from the fovea. (From Boycott and Dowling, 1969.)

The sensory part of the retina begins with the outer segments of the photoreceptors which lie outside of the *outer limiting membrane* (Figs. 4.3, 4.4). In the outer plexiform layer, near the *cone pedicles* and *rod spherules*, are the dendrites of the *bipolar* and *horizontal cells*. The cell bodies of the bipolar and horizontal cells lie in a thick region of the retina known as the inner nuclear layer, which also contains the cell bodies of the *amacrine cells*. These, unlike the horizontal and bi-

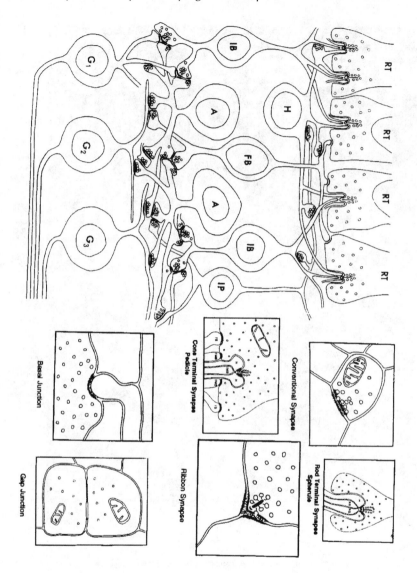

Figure 4.4   A schematic diagram of the retina. The purpose of this diagram is to illustrate the kinds of synapses that occur. It is useful to use this figure in conjunction with Figure 4.3, which shows a light micrograph of the retina. The leftmost figure shows an overall schematic. The schematics in the boxes show the synapses in greater detail. All of these schematics were drawn from electron micrographs. Symbols: RT – receptor terminals, H – horizontal cell, FB – flat bipolar cell, IB – invaginating bipolar cell, IP – interplexiform cell, A – amacrine cell, G – ganglion cell, IMB – invaginating midget bipolar, FMB – flat midget bipolar, RB – ribbon bipolar. (Modified from Dowling, 1987, and with permission of the Royal Society of London.)

polar cells, make no direct contact with the photoreceptors. Although there are some exceptions, the horizontal cell bodies tend to be located outermost, the amacrine cell bodies innermost, and the bipolar cell bodies intermediate in the *inner nuclear layer.*

The direct centripetal pathway for carrying visual information is from receptor to bipolar to ganglion cell. The nuclei of the latter form the ganglion cell layer. The region between the ganglion cell and the inner nuclear layers, containing the various connections among bipolar, amacrine, and ganglion cells, is known as the *inner plexiform layer.*

The ganglion cell axons that emerge from the inner end of the ganglion cell bodies are the optic nerve fibers that connect the retina to the *lateral geniculate nucleus* (LGN). In order to exit from the eyeball, all of these fibers course laterally in the eye as far as may be necessary to reach the optic disc. The full collection of *optic nerve* fibers, about a million of them, leaves the eye at the *optic disc;* they are contained outside the eye within the sheath of the optic nerve.*

> The blind spot is the sensory counterpart of the receptor-free optic disc, and is one of the easiest so-called entoptic phenomena to demonstrate. On a piece of white paper, draw a horizontal line about 15 cm long and then draw a 2 cm 'x' at the right end of it. With the left eye covered, look squarely at the line, using the right eye at a viewing distance of about 30 cm. Look first at the 'x', and then shift fixation along the line to the left. A point will be reached where the 'x' disappears. For this condition, the image of the 'x' will be upon the nasal retina, about 16–18 degrees from the fovea, corresponding to the location of the optic disc. Continued movement of fixation leftward along the line will cause the 'x' to reappear as its image comes out of the blind spot on the other side. If the 'x' is removed and the experiment repeated, the blind spot is not perceived. Nor is it seen in everyday life.

Retinal Neurons and Connections: A Closer Look

We will now take a closer look at the various components of the retina. Because this book is primarily concerned with color vision we focus primarily on the cones and their connections. When turned, the left side of Figure 4.4 is a summary diagram representing that which is found in the vertebrate retina (Dowling, 1987). It represents primarily the cone retinal pathways. On the right side of Figure 4.4, again taken from Dowling (1987), are shown examples of various interneural connections found in the retina. These are shown here to help the reader who attempts to delve into the primary literature and encounters discussions of these connections. The details concerning them are beyond the scope of this book; however, the reader is encouraged to look at Dowling (1987) for an eminently readable description of the retinal structures.

Figure 4.4 was made possible by a series of investigations by Dowling and his colleagues (see Dowling, 1987 for appropriate references). These investigators systematically developed a number of indicators that made it possible to identify important features in electron micrographs of retinal tissue. Often, using these indicators, one can tell which region of the picture belongs to what type of cell and discern where synaptic connections exist. It is evident by comparing the light microscopic representation of the retina in Figure 4.3 with the drawing derived from electron micrographs in Figure 4.4 that the sizes of various structures, and the thicknesses of the retinal layers, are considerably distorted in the latter figure. The reader should remember that Figure 4.4 is a diagram of connections and not of literal neuroanatomy.

Whereas a global overview of a portion of the retina is best accomplished by light microscope (Fig. 4.3), it is due to the electron microscope that details represented in Figure 4.4 are known. Ultimately, what one would like to know is exactly what each part of the retina looks like and what its function is. One might expect that because details as represented in Figure 4.4 are technologically possible the development of exact information about the retina is just a matter of time. However, as Boynton (1979) noted in the first edition of this book, we can expect that as the anatomists' ability to visually enlarge the retina improves, we will surely increase manyfold our awareness of what we do not know. Furthermore, Dowling (1987) points out that if we use an electron microscope to examine just one cubic millimeter of the retina enlarged 10^4 times one would need about 10^8 micrographs. The task ahead for visual scientists is impressive indeed. Fortunately, anatomical procedures are not the only ones that help us to understand how the visual system functions. In a subsequent chapter we will take a closer look at how recording the electrical signals of single neurons helps us to understand what the anatomy does.

Some of the retinal layers are named for the cells contained in them. Two other classes of layers are called the plexiform (inner and outer) and the nuclear (inner and outer). The *plexiform layers* generally contain the synapses of neurons whose nuclei are elsewhere. The outer *nuclear layer* contains the nuclei of the receptors. The inner nuclear layer contains the nuclei of the horizontal cells, the bipolar cells, and most of the amacrine cells. A close look at Figures 4.3 and 4.4 will help the reader identify these retinal layers and the various components discussed below.

Photoreceptors

There are two classes of photoreceptors: *rods* and *cones*. The rods are used primarily for vision under the very low light levels (*scotopic*) and the cones are used for high or daylight levels (*photopic*), for color vision, and for seeing fine details. Figure 4.5 shows sketches of a human rod, foveal cone, and extra-foveal cone (Dowling, 1987, p. 22). The reader will note the apparent morphological similarity between human foveal cones and rods. The similarity results from so many cones being packed into such a small space; the fovea. Functionally and photochemically there are distinct differences between cones and rods as noted below. Although color vision (with the exception of some rod-cone interactions) is dependent on cone receptors, it is instructive to look as some attributes of rods. Because of the greater amount of rod photopigment and the ease with which it could be extracted, much early photopigment research was done on the rods. It is only in recent years that advancing technology has permitted a closer look at what the cones are doing. One of the more exciting technological advances is the ability to suck individual rods and cones into a micropipette so they can be individually stimulated (Baylor, Nunn & Schnapf, 1987).

The outermost parts of each photoreceptor extend beyond the outer limiting membrane as if punched through it; the membrane helps to hold the receptors in position. Rods differ from cones, both morphologically (Fig. 4.5) and functionally. Rod outer segments consist of a large number of laminations, usually referred to as *discs*. Each disc contains an estimated 10,000 molecules of *rhodopsin* and each molecule is capable of absorbing a photon of light. Rhodopsin molecules do not move from one disc to another, or between receptors. There are about 1000 discs in each rod and about 10^8 rods in the eye, so the total number of rhodopsin molecules in the eye is on the order of $10^{15.}$

The structure of the outer segment has been known since the work of Sjöstrand in 1953; the estimates of the numbers of molecules per disc are indirect (see Wald, Brown & Gibbons, 1963). It has also been established that the discs of rod outer segments are continuously replenishing themselves. New discs are formed at the base of the outer segment, near a constricted region (*cilium*) that connects the outer and inner segments. The discs move upward (toward the outer surface of the eye) at a rate of about 10 μm per day, eventually reaching the end of the outer segment, where they are sloughed off and are "eaten" by the pigment epithelium, into which the outer tips of the photoreceptors project (Young, 1971).

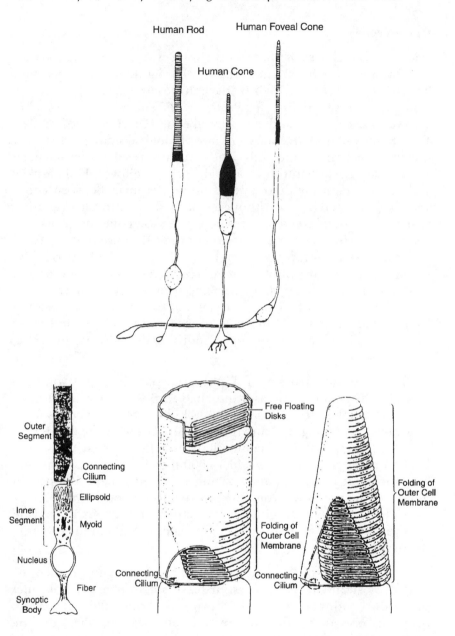

Figure 4.5 Top: This diagram illustrates that the human foveal cone looks very rod-like. It is not until one looks at extra-foveal cones (middle receptor) that they take on a cone-like appearance. (from Dowling, 1987) Bottom: At the left is a generalized conception of the important structural feature of a vertebrate photoreceptor cell. At the right are shown the differences between the structure rod (left) and cone (right) outer segments. (From Young, 1970, 1971.)

Rhodopsin is easily extracted from rod outer segments (see p. 131). Although the extraction of human cone photopigments has never been accomplished, their characteristics have been examined by physical techniques to be described in the next chapter, and they are of the expected three different kinds. Cone outer segments also have discs, but upon close examination it is found that, rather than being self-contained as in rods, they are formed by an infolding of the cone membrane as shown in Figure 4.5. Evidence that cone discs are also replaced has been reported (Young, 1978); this occurs at different times for rods and cones during the diurnal cycle.

Another difference between rods and most cones is the shape of their outer segments, as seen in Figure 4.5. Except for the ciliary region, the overall shape of rods is cylindrical; they were appropriately named on the basis of their shape by early anatomical workers. The inner segments of most cones, by contrast, are much fatter and taper near the outer segment to give them their conical form. However, as noted above, the cones in the central fovea are rod-like (Fig. 4.5) in shape and actual dimensions, suggesting that shape is probably not the most critically distinguishing feature by which to classify rods and cones.

The remainder of each photoreceptor lies inside the outer limiting membrane. Rods have a connecting cilium separating their outer segments from the cell nucleus, from which another fiber leads to the termination of the rod, called the *spherule*. Cones, again, are different: the nucleus is more immediately juxtaposed with the inner segment; from it runs a long fiber connecting the nucleus to the foot of the cone, known as the cone *pedicle*. Cone pedicles differ from rod spherules in a number of respects. The pedicles are small foot-like in appearance (Fig. 4.4). The rod terminals look like little spheres, hence the name spherules. They have multiple indentations called *invaginations* at their base, which are seen in the right half of Figure 4.4. Three processes enter each invagination. The central one of these leads to a bipolar cell, always of the same type, originally called a *midget bipolar* by Polyak (1957). (An exception to this has been reported by Stell, Lightfoot, Wheeler, and Leeper [1975] in the goldfish retina, where the central process sometimes is from a *horizontal cell* — *see* Fig. 7.9.) Compared to rod spherules, the cone pedicles lie somewhat deeper in the retina, they are much larger, and they are considerably more complex.

Horizontal Cells

The photoreceptors synapse onto two major classes of neurons: the horizontal cells and the bipolar cells (Fig. 4.4). The somata of horizontal cells lie near the outer margin of the inner nuclear layer and their dendrites and axons are located in the outer plexiform layer (Wässle and Boycott, 1991) Two types of horizontal cells (H1 and H2) have been identified (Boycott *et al.*, 1987). H2 horizontal cells have dendrites and axons that only contact cones. H1 dendrites contact cones but have an axon that contacts only rods.

Horizontal cells that contact both rods and cones do so in a peculiar way. The primary contact is with cones in the neighborhood of the horizontal cell body. The contact with rods is quite distant, mediated by a very long axon (*telodendron*) whose terminal arborization makes contact with rods (Kolb, 1970). Horizontal cells are estimated to cover as much as 1000 µm laterally in the retina. A typical cell has seven groupings of dendritic terminals, believed to represent connections with seven cones. It also seems likely that any given cone is in contact with from two to four horizontal cells.

It is speculated that horizontal cells receive information from cones and pass it back again to cones. Their synaptic relations with the cones — the way that their processes flank the centripetal contact that cones make with the bipolar cells — suggest that they exert some sort of modulating influence upon the signals being passed from cones to bipolars. Another possibility is that, by feeding back upon the receptors, they actually influence the potentials generated by the receptors themselves. In any case, horizontal cells appear to tie groups of receptors together.

Early work with horizontal cells in fish and turtles showed that they were chromatically selective, in the sense of generating responses of opposite polarity depending upon stimulus wavelength. It is now realized that mammalian horizontal cells, unlike those for fish and turtle, are not chromatically selective. Wässle and Boycott (1991) are unequivocal on this point, stating that "No such chromatic responses have been found from mammalian horizontal cells" (p. 452).

Bipolar Cells

A great deal of work has been done on *bipolar cells,* sufficiently so that Boycott and Wässle (1991) devoted an entire paper to the *Morphological Classification of Bipolar Cells of the Primate Retina.* Here we can only highlight some of the more salient points as they relate to human color vision.

Six major classes of bipolar cells have been identified.

1. Blue cone

2. Diffuse flat cone

3. Diffuse invaginating cone

4. Midget flat cone

5. Midget invaginating cone

6. Rod

Cell classes 1 through 5 involve cone-specific synapses. Bipolars in class 6 synapse with rod receptors. The blue cone bipolar synapses specifically with short wavelength sensitive receptors. Several functional attributes have been determined. The diffuse bipolars are not chromatically selective and appear to serve a luminance type function, whereas the midget bipolars are chromatically selective. Both the rod and cone bipolars have dendritic trees in the outer plexiform layer where they synapse with the receptors (Fig. 4.4). Their axons are in the inner plexiform layer where they synapse with amacrine and ganglion cells.

The flat and invaginating bipolars can be seen in Figure 4.4. They are respectively labeled as FB and IB for flat and invaginating in the main part of the figure. In the diagram showing cone terminal synapses the neuron labeled IMB represents an invaginating midget bipolar. Those labeled FB and FMB are respectively flat bipolars and flat midget bipolars. The invaginating bipolars are so called because the are located within the pedicle area called the *triad*. The flat bipolars synapse with the base of the cone pedicles.

Magnocellular and *parvocellular* pathways contain neurons whose signals go to or come from the magnocellular and parvocellular layers of the lateral geniculate nucleus.[10] A great deal of research on these pathways has been conducted in the last 15 or 20 years and we will deal with it further in subsequent chapters.

Boycott and Wässle (1991) report that flat bipolar cells contact neurons assumed to be OFF ganglion cells and invaginating bipolars "meet" ON ganglion cells. Diffuse bipolars terminate in the same strata of the inner plexiform layer as parasol ganglion cells causing Boycott and Wässle to observe that the midget/diffuse bipolar dichotomy could be the basis of the parvocellular and magnocellular pathways. They note that if all of these assumed connections are verified then the visual signals which are segregated into the putative magno and parvo pathways have their origins at the cone pedicle synapses.

Amacrine Cells

Amacrine cells are axonless neurons that synapse in the inner plexiform layer with bipolar cells and the dendrites of ganglions cells. Their somata lie near the inner border of the inner nuclear layer, within the inner plexiform layer or, more rarely, within the ganglion cell layer. Like the horizontal cells, amacrine cells tend to send their dendrites laterally across the retina. Rodieck (1988) reports that Cajal coined the name a-nacrine, which from its Greek roots, means ". . . a cell lacking a long process (axon)."

Interplexiform Cells

Whereas all of the neurons noted so far were known to Cajal in the nineteenth century, the *interplexiform cells* were first reliably reported in 1969 (Dowling and Ehinger, 1975). These neurons have been seen in both old and new world monkeys. While the cell nucleus is located among the amacrine nuclei their processes extend from the inner to the outer plexiform layers; hence their name. Not very much seems to be known yet about these neurons with respect to their influence on the vision but it is believed that their function is to send signals from the inner to the outer plexiform layers. Because the interplexiform cells seem to send signals toward the receptors, it is possible that they participate in some sort of 'feedback' system.

Ganglion Cells

The third nuclear layer is comprised of ganglion cells of which there are two major types. Some of these neurons have diffuse dendritic structures that are located throughout the inner plexiform layer and others have stratified dendritic structures that spread to one or more of the levels of the inner plexiform layer. Whereas the dendrites of the ganglion cells occupy the outer plexiform layer, their axons make up the optic nerve which leaves the retina at the optic disc and travels to the lateral geniculate nucleus. Morphologically there are two major varieties of ganglion cells: midget and parasol. These names refer to the general shapes of the neural structures of these cells.

The details of the connections among the six sensory cell types just described are of vital importance for understanding, or even speculating about, spatial and chromatic information processing in the retina.

The Fovea Centralis

The anatomy of the fovea centralis differs in several important respects from the rest of the retina. It is a curious feature of the vertebrate retina, implicit in what has already been discussed, that light must pass through so many retinal layers before finally reaching the photoreceptors. (Note the arrow labeled "light" in Fig. 4.3) Moreover, there is an extensive vascular system in the retina that invades the inner nuclear, inner plexiform, and ganglion cell layers. (Part of one blood vessel is visible at the bottom left in Fig. 4.3.) With the exception of the blood vessels, the other retinal structures are relatively transparent to light, so that to be clearly visible by light microscopy they must first be stained. A variety of staining techniques is available, some of which selectively invade neural tissue.

The blood vessels are not transparent; therefore they cast shadows on the receptor layer of the retina. These shadows normally are not seen, for two reasons. First, there are no blood vessels in the central fovea, where we see most critically. Second, the vessels occupy a fixed position, buried within the retina, so that their shadows upon the photoreceptors are stationary under normal conditions of seeing. This constitutes a natural form of stabilized retinal "image" which prevents the retinal vasculature from being seen except under unusual circumstances.*

> Using a flashlight (a penlight will work best), shine the light obliquely upon the sclera in an otherwise dark room. Wiggling the light slightly is helpful. What should be seen is a map of the retinal vasculature, like that of Figure 4.6, seen as if projected outward in space. It should be possible to discern, with practice, that there are no vessels at the point of fixation (corresponding to the fovea). This subjective vascular map will, of course, move with the eye.

Figure 4.7 illustrates the curious specialization that exists only in the fovea. First, the retina is less than half as thick in the fovea as in the remainder of the eye. The change in thickness creates the depression, or pit, from which the term fovea derives. Despite the thinness of the foveal retina, the outer segments of the photoreceptors are actually longer than anywhere else. They are also thinner and therefore more closely packed. All other neural tissues in the fovea, including the cell bodies of the foveal cones, are laterally displaced (Fig. 4.7).

If one were somehow to insert an electrode radially into the retina at the location shown by the arrow in Figure 4.7 in order to stimulate the ganglion cell body located there, the apparent location of the light that would be seen would differ from that caused by photic

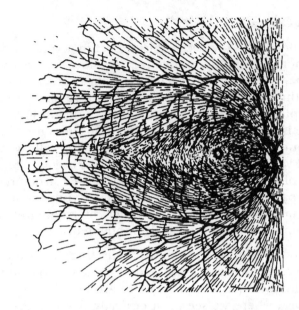

Figure 4.6   The thin lines show the pathways of the optic nerve fibers. The heavy lines are the blood vessels of the retina (see box describing how reader can see their own retinal blood vessels). The optic disc. is at the far right; the fovea centralis appears as the encircled region to the left of the disc. This drawing is based on the anatomy of the rhesus macaque monkey, but is very similar to that of the human retina (from Brown, 1965 and Polyak, 1941).

excitation of the receptor at the point along the retina toward which the arrow points. The result of such electrical stimulation would appear as if nearer to the point of fixation, because the electrically excited ganglion cell is one that normally would be excited by photons striking near the center of the foveal pit.

The anatomy of the foveal pit has important implications for the resolution of fine visual detail. In order to resolve a highly detailed optical image, it is necessary to have a high density of photoreceptors. Although retinas vary, foveal cone densities as high has 281,000 per square mm have been reported in human eyes (Curcio, Sloan, Packer, Hendrickson & Kalina, 1987). The cone density is unequivocally higher in the fovea than other retinal areas. To have a retinal image of excellent optical quality formed upon the photoreceptors, it is necessary to reduce the scattered light within the retina as much as possible; this is neatly accomplished with the foveal depression. The improved spatial resolution that results is not accomplished at the expense of sensitivity to light. On the contrary, the fovea of the light-adapted retina is its region of highest sensitivity.*

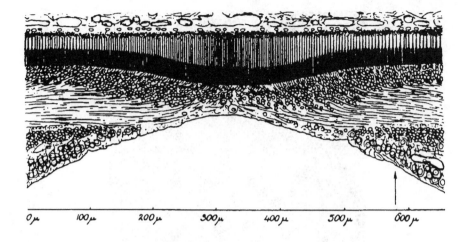

0μ   100μ   200μ   300μ   400μ   500μ   600μ

Figure 4.7   Central fovea of the human retina. (From Polyak, 1957.)

> Using a hard pencil, make a very light gray dot in the center of a sheet of blank white paper. Under strong illumination, move the point of fixation away from the dot and notice that it disappears. This is not a general result, however. The dimmest perceptible spots of light that can be seen in the dark, when the eye is well dark adapted (see Chapter 6), are seen by rods alone and disappear when directly fixated. To see them, one must shift the point of regard slightly to one side. This is quite easy to demonstrate on a starry night.

Figure 4.8 permits a visualization of how human cones are arranged in the central fovea. This "central bouquet" of cones is the region of visual fixation. As one moves from the center the diameters of the cone inner segments increase and have at least doubled at only 0.05 mm from the center, corresponding to less than 10 minutes of visual angle. There are no rods whatever in the central fovea. Farther out, the cones become fatter and rods to begin to appear. At the margin of the foveal pit there are many more rods than cones per unit area, although the fat cones still occupy more space than do the slender rods. Another interesting feature noticed in the central fovea seen in Figure 4.8 is the non-random organization of the receptors.

A quantitative estimate of the distribution of cones in the human retina is given in Figure 4.9. We show two sets of data. Figure 4.9A shows the rod and cone distributions from Østerberg (1935) and Figure 4.9B shows more recent estimates of cone density from Curcio *et al.* (1987). The data of Curcio *et al.* are similar to that of Østerberg published 52 years earlier. They are based on four retinas and pre-

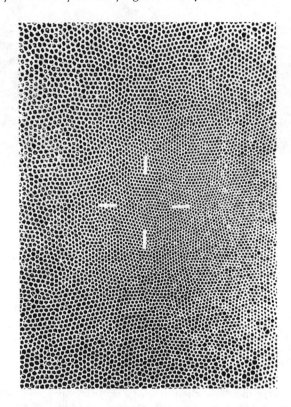

Figure 4.8   A light micrograph of the human foveola (within the pointers). This is a tangential section through the inner segments of the receptors. Note that this mosaic appears to be subdivided into polygonal subunits. This is a ×900 magnification. (From Ahnelt, Kolb & Pflug, 1987.)

sented on a log–log plot (Fig. 4.9B). Ahnelt *et al.* (1987) reported central fovea cone densities for two retinas of 238,000 and 178,000 cones/mm² respectively and Curcio *et al.* reported densities ranging from 96,900 to 281,000 cones/mm². The weighted mean peak density from the six retinae in these two recent papers is 177,266 cones/mm². This weighted mean density is still higher than the 147,000 cones/mm² reported by Østerberg. Curcio *et al.* found, as did Østerberg, that there is a slight temporal-nasal asymmetry in cone density.

The emphasis upon the importance of the foveal region of the retina should not be permitted to obscure the importance of cones in the peripheral retina.* Only about four percent of the cones are in the fovea. When considering the relative densities of rods and cones in the peripheral retina, account must be taken of the much larger cross section of the peripheral cones relative to the rods. In attempt-

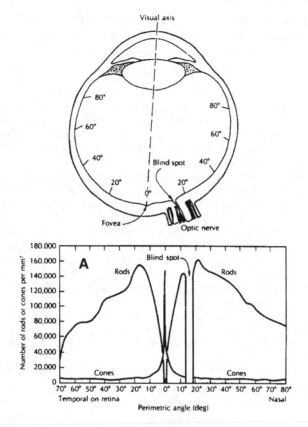

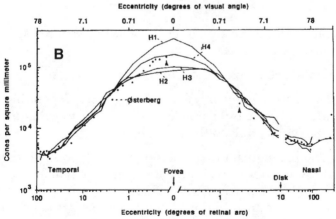

Figure 4.9 A. Rod and cone density as a function of retinal location (from Cornsweet, 1970) B. Cone density as a function of retinal location (from Curcio, et al., 1987). These data are from four retinas (H1, H2, H3 & H4), and are plotted on a log–log plot, which accounts for the difference in curve shape when compared with the cone data in A. The solid circles are a replot of Østerberg's classic data.

ing to estimate the relative probabilities that a photon will be absorbed in a rod or cone, the density values of the cone curve of Figure 4.9 would need to be multiplied by something like a factor of ten.

> The following demonstration illustrates the importance of peripheral vision. Take a long mailing tube, and while covering the left eye, try to move about in a room while looking monocularly through the tube. It would be easy enough to read the "20/20" line on an acuity chart this way, and by that criterion be judged to have normal vision. But the actual visual loss is almost catastrophic: as the head moves, the world appears to sweep by the end of the tube in the opposite direction; orientation is difficult and walking very dangerous. Even in a very familiar room, it is hard to direct the line of sight toward a known object designated as the target; with the full visual field this occurs rapidly and easily, and clearly depends upon peripheral vision. This demonstration would give the reader some idea of the tunnel vision experienced by people with advanced *retinitis pigmentosa*. (This ailment is congenital and starts in the periphery and does not affect central vision until its final stages. Unlike the case for glaucoma, for which there is treatment, currently there is no cure.) Remove the tube (or open the other eye) and note that the perception of color in the peripheral visual field, corresponding to the peripheral retina, is very evident.

We were not overly concerned with rods here because rods cannot, by themselves, mediate color discrimination (Chapter 5). However, to the extent that rods are functional in the same eye that contains cones, they potentially complicate color vision. Therefore it is interesting to note the following:

• In some cases there are direct contacts between rod spherules and cone pedicles.

• Horizontal cells connect to both rods and cones.

• Bipolar cells connect only to rods or to cones, depending upon type, but whereas cone bipolar cells connect only to ganglion cells, rod bipolars connect only to the amacrines.

It seems apparent that the retina is replete with possibilities for interactions between rods and cones. At the light levels required for good color vision, rods do not contribute to vision to a significant extent, at least in the central retina. In the central fovea this is true because no rods are stimulated there by a small light source; elsewhere the rods saturate (Aguilar & Stiles, 1954) at luminances corresponding roughly with those provided by high levels of indoor illumination, whereas the cones of course continue to react discriminatively. The structures that seem to be concerned exclusively with rod vision include the rods themselves, and the rod bipolars, which connect only to rods.

SUMMARY

The major focus of this chapter is upon the retina, where receptors (rods and cones) absorb photons and produce the first signals of vision. But the retina comprises only a tiny part of the mobile eye, which normally samples the visual environment in a complicated series of saccadic and smooth movements. The eye is always in motion, even during the act of fixation. Nevertheless, a cooperative observer can fixate well enough to localize, within reasonable limits of accuracy, the region of the retina being experimentally stimulated.

The optical elements of the eye, which allow the formation of the retinal image, are described. Most light refraction occurs at the optical interface between air and cornea. The iris controls the entry of light into the eye, helping to maintain an image quality that the retinal nervous system can fully utilize, while serving also as one mechanism of light adaptation. The act of accommodation allows the lens of the eye to change its shape so as to modulate the optical power of the eye, keeping objects at various distances from the eye in good focus.

The various layers of the retina, as revealed by light and electron microscopy, are described. The outer segments of the rods and cones contain the essential photosensitive pigments that react to the absorption of light. The fovea centralis is an important and highly specialized retinal region lacking in blood vessels, where the other structures of the kind that cover most of the retina are laterally displaced so that a high quality image can be formed there. This is also the retinal region of highest spatial acuity, greatest light-adapted sensitivity, and optimal attention value. The central part of the fovea is devoid of rods, and the density of the long and slender cones is at a maximum there. The remainder of the cones in the eye are literally cone shaped, have a much larger cross section, and are found in the peripheral retina.

Electron microscopy has begun to reveal in detail some of the elaborate connections among the nerve cells of the retina. Of particular interest are the horizontal cells that interconnect the cones. However, because the horizontal cells to not each synapse with just one type of cone there is no evidence in primates that they mediate chromatic vision.

Evidence suggests that the parvo and magnocellular pathway distinction has it origin at the cone pedicle. The midget bipolar cells convey chromatic signals do midget ganglion cells and diffuse bipolar cells convey achromatic signals to parasol ganglion cells. The latter project to the magnocellular layers of the LGN and the former to the parvocellular layers.

NOTES

[1] The Golgi stain proved to be especially valuable. It has the curious property of selectively staining only a small proportion of neurons. The use of the new staining techniques was taken up most vigorously by the famed anatomist S. R. Cajal, whose work on the vertebrate retina has been translated into English by R. W. Rodieck (1973) as an appendix to his comprehensive and highly recommended textbook, *The Vertebrate Retina*. Cajal was the first to show that all vertebrate retinas contain the same basic elements in about the same configuration.

[2] We shall return to the electroretinogram, though only briefly, in Chapter 7. A comprehensive summary of this subject, including its early history, has been provided by Armington (1974).

[3] A summary of bioelectric recording techniques is available in a three-volume set edited by R. F. Thompson and M. M. Patterson (1973, 1974).

[4] Although it is important that there are two eyes rather than only one, monocular color vision differs little from the binocular variety. Most of the time, in this book, we will pretend that vision occurs through only one eye.

[5] Saccadic movements of the eyes are very rapid (up to $800°s^{-1}$), therefore the accelerative forces that they produce cannot be negligible. Richards (1968) has suggested that a decrease in visual sensitivity occurs during a saccadic eye movement, due to shearing forces acting upon the receptors. The neural machinery of the eye must be able to withstand such forces. Because the tissues of the eye are not rigid there can be no empty space in the eye. Most people have a perceptible amount of debris in the vitreous, which is free to move to some degree within the vitreal jelly; these are called muscae volitantes. They appear subjectively as "floaters" in visual space, whose motion can be induced by making eye movements. Donders reported floaters that remained in the visual field for 17 years (Zoethout, 1947, p. 105).

[6] For a brief and readable summary of the eye movement control system, see Robinson (1968). For more recent surveys of the subject, see Monty and Senders (1976) and Carpenter (1988).

[7] An encyclopedic coverage of research on the fading of vision with stabilized retinal images has been published by Ditchburn (1973).

[8] These values are from Zoethout (1947, p. 55). They refer to a schematic eye developed by Gullstrand.

[9] Figure 4.3 displays the retinal cross section in the conventional way, with the outside of the eye at the top, and the inside at the bottom. In this representation, light is incident upon the retina from the bottom of the diagram and travels toward the top. The top of the retina, as shown here, is also called distal or scleral; the bottom, proximal or vitreal. Near the fovea, a line drawn from the center of the eye would pass vertically through Figure 4.2; for that reason such a direction is called radial.

[10] The magnocellular and parvocellular pathways, or the cells contained in them are frequently referred to as the parvo or P, and the magno or M pathways or cells. So retinal ganglion cells whose axons synapse with parvocellular neurons of the LGN are sometimes referred to as *P cells* and those that synapse with magnocellular neurons of the LGN are sometimes referred to as *M cells*. Ganglion cells are sometimes referred to by their initials which relate to morphology, e.g., M for midget and P for parasol. Unfortunately, the midget ganglion cells project to the parvo LGN layers and the parasol ganglion cells project to the magno LGN layers. Another confusion in the literature of which the reader should be aware is that M cells not only can refer to magno and midget, but also to middle wavelength sensitive receptors. Lee (personal communication) attempts to circumvent this confusion by referring to **PC** (parvocellular pathway) and to **MC** (magnocellular pathway) cells.

Chapter 5

Visual Pigments, Spectral Sensitivity, and Color Matching

INTRODUCTION

To attain an understanding of color vision we must consider complex events at different levels. In searching for an explanation, a natural place to start is with the physical events leading to the stimulation of the photoreceptors, because it is here that the process of color vision begins. Yet a consideration of the physics of color (Chapter 3), far from accounting for what we see, confronts us with a strangely complicated situation that does not seem to correspond in any simple or direct way with our visual experience. Newton's experiments with prisms (Chapter 1) illustrate this: a surface that appears white may be sending to the eye a stimulus compounded of photons of every possible wavelength, and yet the resulting sensation of a simple uniform white does not reveal this complexity. To understand this complexity requires more than an eye: it also requires physical instrumentation. In this sense, our sensations fail to do justice to the physical reality of the observed events. Certainly they do not represent these events in all their aspects.

Color vision would be impossible if there were not some relation between the physical stimulus and what is subjectively experienced. The complexity of the physical stimulus warns us, however, that the relationship cannot be a simple one. To understand color vision, we must understand this relationship, and the key to such understanding lies in the processes that intervene between reception of the physical stimulus on the one hand, and visual experience on the other. These processes occur in the intricate machinery of the visual pathways whose description began in Chapter 4. A considerable portion of the remainder of this book will be devoted to tracing the visual signals as they are transmitted through the visual pathway, and to examining what is known or hypothesized concerning the nature of these signals and their transformations in retina and brain.

The guiding assumption behind any attempt to understand vision in terms of its physiological underpinnings is that visual experience depends at any particular time upon the specific events that are taking place in the visual pathway. Suppose, for example, that the eye were removed and a pattern of action potentials could somehow be sent down to each of the million fibers of the optic nerve (in the direction of the brain), which is exactly the same as that produced by viewing a natural scene with eye and nerve intact. What will be experienced as a result of the artificial stimulation of the optic nerve should, according to our guiding assumption, be indistinguishable from the natural scene as perceived with the visual system intact.

Suppose that we knew in minute detail the exact state of someone's visual pathway at a particular instant: would we then be able to characterize the nature of his visual experience? The answer is "no," unless we would also have available a catalog of all possible states of the visual pathway and their corresponding percepts. But we do not possess such a catalog, and we never shall, because the number of possible states of the visual pathway is inconceivably large; as is the variety of possible visual experiences.

That the catalog required to document the relationship between pathway states and perception would be impossibly cumbersome is illustrated by a simple calculation based on the analog of color television. The red, green, and blue phosphor dots that make up the color TV picture (recall the exercise on page 50) number altogether about a million. Thirty separate pictures are delivered each second in order to provide a convincing illusion of motion and seemingly continuous visual input. Although brightness varies continuously in natural scenes, a reasonable depiction of brightness in a scene can be had with as few as eight discrete levels (Graham, 1958). Therefore, to specify the character of a color TV picture for only one second would require a table of $1,000,000 \times 30 \times 8$ or 240 million values. The situation in the visual pathway where the optic nerve leaves the eye is roughly the same: about 30 specifications per second of one of eight quantized levels of spike frequency in each of about one million optic nerve fibers would be needed to characterize the visual message.

In fact, our only knowledge of physiological events is based upon general principles. We have no means of determining in any detail what is actually happening in a particular person's visual pathway at any particular time. Response indicators such as the electroretinogram or the evoked cortical potential, which will be described in Chapter 7, are orders of magnitude too crude to qualify. The electroretinogram and evoked cortical potentials provide response indications of large cell populations and can be effectively used to provide useful information. But progress in understanding vision must be based on the discovery of general principles in the subjective realm that can be related to what we know, or can hope to learn, about the operation of the visual pathway.

Because they are directed toward the discovery of simple general principles, basic experiments in visual science often make use of stimulus displays that may at first seem to be ridiculously simple. Yet, it has been repeatedly shown that simple general principles will best reveal themselves in such perceptually impoverished situations and that the principles discovered there are also applicable to vision in more complex everyday environments. To readers who are trained in physical science this will be recognized as a normal way to proceed.

The general class of investigation that has proved most useful for building a bridge between physiology and perception is the psychophysical experiment. In this type of study, the physical stimulus is kept simple, as just discussed, and so is the response: the observers (often called subjects) are not free to describe what they see in just any way that they choose. As we shall see in numerous examples to follow, an observer's behavior is very much constrained. Simplification of procedure on the response end of the experiment carries with it the same kinds of advantages that accrue from simplifying the stimulus.

In attempting to build a bridge between physiology and perception, it helps very much to have the stimulus specified in purely physical terms. The paradigm below illustrates this:

Psychophysics: Physical stimulus → Behavioral response

Physiology: Physical stimulus → Physiological response

This procedure allows a correlation to be made between the behavioral and physiological responses, especially when exactly the same physical stimuli have been used in both cases.

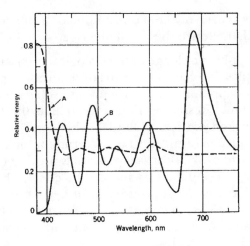

Figure 5.1   Curves A and B are the relative spectral power distributions of two colors that appear identical. Two colors that look the same but have different energies as a function of wavelength are called metamers. (From Judd & Wyszecki, 1975.)

THE MATCHING OPERATION

One of the simplest and most fundamental experiments in color vision proceeds as follows. The subject is asked to fixate the center of a small disc, divided into two halves that can be separately illuminated. When the two halves of the disc are illuminated with light of the same spectral composition (so as to produce, for example, a white appearance in each half), the subject then sees the two halves merge so that the disc appears as uniformly filled. This is not surprising, for the disc is now actually physically uniform. Suppose now that the spectral composition of the light illuminating the left hemi-field is altered, without any change being made on the right. It is not surprising that the two hemi-fields will now appear different in color. Sometimes spectral differences between two fields will go undetected by a subject, who continues to see a uniform white circle. Failing to perceive the physical difference between the two halves is not due to inattention but rather to inherent limitations of normal color vision.

To illustrate the fact that normal subjects may be regularly fooled, the two lights A and B, whose spectral distributions are shown in Figure 5.1, are matches for normal observers under conditions where normal cone vision is operative. Two such stimuli, which are physically different but visually indistinguishable, are called *metamers*. Stimuli that physically match, and for that reason also look identical, are called *isomers*. For stimuli that are physically different within the visible spectrum, metamerism is the exception rather than the rule; exact or even near metameric matches seldom occur outside the laboratory. This is fortunate, and it suggests that the amount of color discrimination that we possess is sufficient for all practical purposes.[1]

Two physically different lights will constitute an exact color match only under certain mathematically specifiable conditions. These constraints governing color matching are the most precisely established of the general principles relating to vision, and they have proved to be of cardinal importance for understanding the nature of the physiological processes involved in color vision.

METAMERIC MATCHING AND
THE SPECTRAL SENSITIVITY OF ROD VISION

In Chapter 2 the point was made that color vision fails totally under dim illumination. As a preliminary to the analysis of true color vision it is instructive to consider first the characteristics of colorless night vision (*scotopic vision*). Scotopic vision, as it turns out, is mediated by rods whereas daylight vision, including color vision, depends upon the activity of cones (*photopic vision*). Because these two varieties of photoreceptors share certain basic characteristics, rod vision can be considered as a prototype for cone vision, one that is simpler and easier to analyze.

The failure of color vision at low light levels is not directly due to any impoverishment of the physical stimulus. Objects retain their characteristic spectral reflectance whatever the illumination level, and moonlight differs little from sunlight in terms of its relative spectral distribution. Our inability to discriminate among different colors when using only rod vision is a consequence of a fundamental limitation in the rods themselves. They fail to distinguish between physically different radiations for reasons that will shortly be explained.

Although in rod vision we are totally color-blind, we still manage to distinguish between some differently colored objects. This is possible because objects may still vary in their relative lightness.[2] Otherwise night vision would be impossible and we would be totally blind, rather than merely color-blind. But the brightness difference between two objects can be eliminated for rod vision merely by reducing the amount of light reaching the eye from the lighter object without any change in relative spectral distribution.

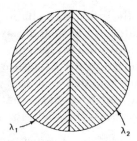

Figure 5.2   The appearance of a bipartite, or split, field as seen by an observer. The two halves of the field radiate monochromatic lights of different wavelengths. If the fields are dim (i.e., below cone threshold) it is always possible to adjust the intensity of one half of the field so that the two halves match exactly: the border disappears (if the hemi-fields are perfectly juxtaposed) and the field is visually homogeneous.

A Matching Experiment

We can bring this problem into the laboratory and examine it, for example, by using the bipartite field of Figure 5.2. Suppose that each half of the field is illuminated by monochromatic light, with different wavelengths in the two halves: λ_1 for the left side, and λ_2 for the right. Suppose further that the intensities of the fields are set at such low levels that only the rods can detect them. What appearance will the bipartite field now present to the subject? Because the difference in color between the two halves of the field is not detected by the rods, the field might appear as a uniform disk. In fact, this happens only under rather special circumstances, namely when the relative intensities of the two hemi-fields are such as to exactly eliminate any difference in brightness between the two. Normally the two hemi-fields will differ in brightness; therefore, in order to investigate the color-matching properties of rod vision, the experimenter must make arrangements to eliminate that brightness difference. This is most conveniently done by giving the subject a means to control the light intensity[3] in one of the hemi-fields. If subjects are instructed to adjust the intensity so as to abolish any difference in brightness between the hemi-fields they find that, once the brightnesses are equated, the two halves merge to form a uniform disk. This is what it means to be totally color-blind. There are some abnormal subjects (see Chapter 10) who would be able to produce a uniform disk for lights of any two wavelengths even at high intensities. Whereas these subjects are totally color-blind all of the time, all of us are totally color-blind under conditions where rods alone are functional.

Precisely what relative intensities are required to eliminate brightness differences and produce these matches for rod vision? This can be determined experimentally by placing a light detector in place of the subject's eye. By occluding first the left and then the right hemifield, the number[4] of photons impinging on the eye from each hemifield can be measured separately. It turns out that two lights of equal brightness for rods are by no means equal in any physical sense. For instance, when one hemi-field is illuminated with light from the longwave end of the spectrum (that would appear red at high intensities) and the other is illuminated by a light that appears blue or green, the long wavelength hemi-field must provide more than 10,000 times as many photons to the eye in order to match the other light. Rod vision, then, is not equally sensitive to photons of all wavelengths.

Terminology

To reduce confusion as much as possible, spectrally related terminology should be used unambiguously. Such unambiguity has not been readily available in the color vision literature. We will use the following conventions in the remainder of this book.

Hue names (red, green, blue, etc.) will refer to percepts. See Chapter 11 for a discussion on color names.

Stimuli will be referred to in one of three ways. (1) Wavelength specification. (e.g., 650 nm). (2) I_L, I_M, and I_S are generic representations of wavelength for unspecified stimuli. They respectively refer to long wavelength, middle wavelength, and short wavelength lights. (3) When the wavelength is specified we note it by I_λ (e.g., I_{650} for a 650 nm light).

When referring to the spectral sensitivity of cone receptors (often called cone fundamentals) we use the letters **L**, **M**, and **S**. These letters respectively refer to the long wavelength, middle wavelength, and short wavelength sensitive cones.

Spectral Sensitivity

The matching experiment may be used to define the relative sensitivity of rod vision to various wavelengths of monochromatic light. This is done by having the subject make matches between a fixed standard light in, say, the right hemi-field and each of various test wavelengths delivered in turn to the left hemi-field. Each time that a new wavelength is introduced on the left, the subject adjusts its intensity to make it match the standard, and then a physical light detector is used to measure the number of photons provided at the matching intensity. The results of these measurements specify the numbers of photons required at each of the wavelengths tested in order to produce a constant effect for rod vision.

The *relative sensitivity of rod vision* for the various wavelengths can now be defined as follows. At each wavelength of the test (left) field, take the reciprocal of the number of photons required to match the standard; the resulting number defines the relative spectral sensitivity of rod vision for that wavelength. Relative sensitivity is highest for wavelengths near 500 nm, because it turns out that in this spectral region the number of photons required for a match with the standard is least. Relative rod spectral sensitivity values are usually standardized by expressing each sensitivity value as a fraction of 1, with the unit value being assigned to the wavelength of greatest sensitivity. Lights of all other wavelengths, therefore, have a relative sensitivity of less than 1. Sensitivity measured in this way is sometimes called quantized spectral sensitivity to distinguish it from energy-based spectral sensitivity. The latter depends upon measures of energy, rather than of photons.

Energy- vs. Photon-Based Sensitivity

We have just seen that quantized sensitivity depends upon measuring the numbers of photons required for a constant effect. More often energy-based sensitivity is measured instead, and because the energy of a photon varies with wavelength, as we saw in Chapter 3, these measurements are not equivalent. For instance, when an I_L light includes 10,000 times as many photons as an I_S one, the energy supplied by the I_L light is less than 10,000 times that supplied by the I_S (recall that the longwave photons are vibrating more slowly). Because the energy of individual photons is inversely proportional to wavelength, I_{660} light supplying 10,000 times as many photons would supply only about 7,000 times the energy of a I_{460} light. Because *sensitivity* is reciprocally related to the amount of stimulation required for a certain visual effect, energy-based sensitivity (the reciprocal of energy required) is relatively greater in the long wavelengths than is photon-based sensitivity. The ratio of energy-based to photon-based sensitivity is proportional to wavelength. In this book we will describe the eye's spectral sensitivity both ways, with emphasis on the photon-based measure. Because the visible spectrum covers less than an octave of variation in wavelength, the two measures of sensitivity do not differ very much.

Need for a Logarithmic Ordinate

Spectral sensitivity for rod vision is shown two ways in Figure 5.3. At the top are shown the reciprocals of the energies required for a match,

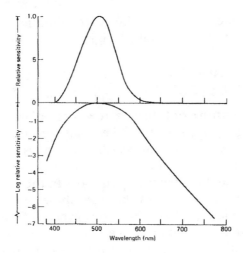

Figure 5.3   Top: Relative spectral sensitivity for rod vision, measured as described in the text, using a field like that of Figure 5.2. Bottom: The same curve, except that the ordinate values are scaled logarithmically. Note the way in which this brings out the details in the tails of the curve, which are lost in the top curve. The ordinate values are plotted as sensitivity. Sensitivity is the reciprocal of energy required for the criterion response. The abscissa plots wavelength on a linear scale.

normalized to 1.0 at the peak. This is exactly as described earlier in this chapter. At the bottom, the logarithm of sensitivity is plotted instead. Because the logarithm of 1 is zero, the curve assumes this value at its peak, and all other values, because they represent fractions, are negative. At wavelengths where the tails of the curves at the top appear to have run into the baseline, and whose ordinate values therefore could be mistaken for zero, a finite sensitivity actually remains, which is much more accurately represented on the logarithmic curve at the bottom. We will see later in this chapter that the tails of cone spectral sensitivity curves are critically important for understanding color vision; in order to achieve an accurate graphical impression, the logarithmic ordinate is essential.

It is only in a loose sense that we can refer to the "ends" of the visible spectrum. If radiation in the near infrared or ultraviolet is intense enough, it can be seen. Nevertheless, the notion that the visible spectrum has limits is valid because of the very rapid descent of spectral sensitivity at extreme wavelengths. Outside the range from 385 to 645 nm, more than 10,000 times as many photons would be required to stimulate rods, compared to the wavelength of maximum sensitivity. Outside these limits, therefore, photons are so unlikely to be effective that they can usually be ignored.

ON THE NARROWNESS
OF THE VISIBLE SPECTRUM

Why is the eye sensitive only to a narrow range of wavelengths within the electromagnetic spectrum? Like many questions about vision, this one can be interpreted in two different ways. First, it could be taken as a purely physical question: why are infrared and ultraviolet lights so unlikely to be effective upon rods? In the case of ultraviolet light, the answer is simple; it is because these photons are heavily absorbed by the lens and are thereby prevented from reaching the retina. In young people the lens is almost transparent to long wavelength light, with absorption increasing progressively toward the shorter visible wavelengths. During life, the lens grows thicker and less transparent, especially at the shorter wavelengths.[5]

Since infrared radiation does reach the retina, why are we so insensitive to it? It has been shown that the decline in spectral sensitivity near the long wavelength end of the spectrum can be attributed to the lower energy values that are associated with the more slowly vibrating photons at longer wavelengths. (This will be elaborated upon shortly.)

A second way to answer the question about why the visible spectrum is so narrow is to consider the consequences for vision if the range of detected wavelengths could somehow be enlarged. This seems to pose a query about the purpose of the system, an approach to understanding that would be branded as "teleological" by some, and dismissed out of hand. This approach to biological questions, though admittedly risky, often produces interesting insights. It is not necessary to decide, or even to ask about, whether the "design" of the system has been provided by trial and error through evolution, or is due to the efforts of some Great Designer. However it may have come about, the design of the visual system is so clever and exquisite that one cannot examine it without concluding that, at the very least, Nature is no fool.

From the design standpoint, then, we note that the yellowness of the lens, which is associated with its selective absorption of I_s light, is not preordained. For example, when compared with humans, cats and the African primate Galago (bush baby) have much more transparent lenses than humans, that transmit most of the incident light even at 400 nm.[6] The longwave limit is not absolutely fixed either because a variety of cold-blooded animals have higher sensitivity than we to the near infrared. Why then have these enlarged visual capacities been denied to humans?

Consider the benefits and disadvantages of ultraviolet vision. The benefits are limited because ultraviolet radiation in the usable range of wavelengths is sparsely represented in the natural environment, so that sensitivity to these very short wavelengths would increase the effective intensity of the retinal image by only a small amount. Probably more important is the harm that the added shortwave light would do because of the eye's marked and uncorrected chromatic aberration (p. 88).

What about the infrared limitation? Pirenne has suggested (1948, pp. 53–54) that very high sensitivity to infrared would be undesirable because the human body continuously radiates a quantity of infrared radiation commensurate with body temperature. This body heat is present inside the eyeball, so if we were sensitive to infrared light we would probably see it as a luminous fog that would tend to obscure the visibility of external objects. Thus, we may have evolved a low infrared sensitivity in order to avoid this fog, along with a lens that screens out ultraviolet light that would otherwise obliterate details because of chromatic aberration.

MONOCHROMACY AND THE MOLECULAR BASIS OF VISION

Rhodopsin: The Rod Photopigment

To generate a visual sensation light must be absorbed within the retina, and the retina must somehow register that absorption by itself undergoing a change that will initiate the process leading to sensation. With this in mind, many investigators have looked for signs that light can affect the state of the retina. The first successful experiments were reported by Franz Boll in 1876 (see also Hubbard, 1977). He found that if he removed an eye from an animal and aimed it at a brightly lit window, subsequent examination of the retina under dim light showed an image of the window still present on the retina as a kind of photographic record which Boll called an *"optogram."* Where it had not been exposed to light, the retina appeared purplish pink, but the part where the image of the window had fallen had become almost transparent. From this demonstration Boll concluded that the retina contained some kind of pinkish substance that became transparent when exposed to light.

Not long after Boll's first observations, this substance was isolated by chemists from retinal extracts and was given the name *rhodopsin* from the Greek words rhodos, meaning red, and ops, the eye. The fact that this substance was present in the retina at a considerable concentration, and underwent a change (becoming relatively transparent when light fell upon it), at once suggested that rhodopsin might play a critical role in the process of vision. Subsequent experiments have confirmed this, and have established a link between the pinkish color of rhodopsin and the spectral sensitivity of night vision.

The pinkish color is characteristic of rhodopsin from the eyes of many animals, including humans. The color is determined by rhodopsin's absorption spectrum, based on the variation with wavelength of the probability that a photon will be absorbed in rhodopsin. Photons that are not absorbed are mostly reflected, and the purplish-pink color is seen because rhodopsin reflects more of the spectral extremes than of the middle portion of the spectrum.

Because only absorbed light can cause a change in rhodopsin, visual sensitivity is greatest for the wavelengths that are most absorbed by it. The correlation between the perceptions of night vision and the absorption spectrum of rhodopsin is so close as to make it virtually certain that the effects of light upon rhodopsin, rather than upon other substances, are responsible. In terms of the paradigm mentioned earlier:

Psychophysics:	Relative numbers of photons of various wavelengths	$\Rightarrow$ Constant behavioral response
Physiology:	Relative numbers of photons of various wavelengths	$\Rightarrow$ Constant photochemical reaction

It should be emphasized that these relations do not absolutely prove that a photochemical reaction is the basis for the constant behavioral response. But the highly quantitative nature of the agreement strongly supports the hypothesis of a causal link.

Rhodopsin is not, as we shall soon see, the only visual pigment, and it is not involved at all in normal color vision at high light levels.

Nevertheless, because the principles of its reactions are probably the same as for cone photopigments, and it has proved much easier to examine, some further examination of the photochemistry of rhodopsin is worthwhile. What is the nature of the change that rhodopsin undergoes when it is exposed to strong light? Thanks principally to the investigations of George Wald, for which he was awarded a Nobel prize,[7] we know that rhodopsin passes through a long sequence of separately identifiable states before reaching the colorless condition in which Boll first observed it.

Mechanisms of Absorption in Rhodopsin

When a rhodopsin molecule absorbs a photon, it will be effective for vision only if it can raise the internal energy of the system of electrons in the rhodopsin molecule so that it exceeds a critical level. The gap between the baseline energy level and the critical energy level is usually too large to be bridged by a very long wavelength photon. If the baseline energy level were constant, we might expect the visible spectrum to terminate abruptly at some long wavelength beyond which photons are suddenly too feeble to be effective. But the random variation of the baseline, which is caused by thermal fluctuations of electron energy, allows any long wavelength photon some chance of producing a molecular effect, even if this chance is very small. For this reason, lights of long wavelengths can be seen if they are strong enough to provide enough photons to counteract the high odds against success for any one of them.

Infrared vision has been demonstrated at least to one micron of wavelength (1000 nm) (Griffin, Hubbard & Wald, 1947). For wavelengths in the range from about 660 nm and beyond, it has been observed that sensitivity varies with wavelength according to a simple function compatible with the physical explanation just provided:

$$\log S_\lambda = k + (a/\lambda) \tag{5.1}$$

where S is the sensitivity at wavelength λ, k is a constant independent of wavelength, and a is another constant having a value of about 14,600 if wavelength is in nm. This equation means that sensitivity in the far long wavelength part of the spectrum (700 nm) changes by a factor of about 7 percent per nm. This value varies slightly with wavelength. But if we rewrite Equation (5.1) in terms of frequency of vibration, v, instead of wavelength, we get

$$\log S_\lambda = k + a'v \tag{5.2}$$

which means that, as the frequency of vibration of a photon increases (which shortens the wavelength), log sensitivity rises linearly. Equation (5.2) holds good for both cone and rod vision. Physical considerations suggest that the value of the constant a' should depend upon the individual's temperature. Brindley and Lewis (cited in Brindley, 1960), following a lead from the Dutch scientist Hessel DeVries, heated and cooled subjects over a small but sufficient range to produce corresponding changes in spectral sensitivity.[8]

Rhodopsin and Human Spectral Sensitivity

The identification of rhodopsin as the visual pigment for human night vision was first firmly established by Helmholtz's most illustrious student, Arthur König, in 1894. For his experiments, König constructed a sophisticated *spectrophotometer*, a device that could direct a beam of spectral light of any chosen wavelength into a solution, in order to measure the quantity of light passing through it. König had planned to begin his experiments using animals, but chance presented him with a pair of fresh human retinas just after he had gotten his apparatus ready. Being very careful not to bleach any, he extracted the rhodopsin from the retinas and put the pinkish solution in his spectrophotometer. He then passed light of several wavelengths through the solution, doing this in turn as he spanned the visible spectrum and recorded how much light of each wavelength was transmitted.

Next, König bleached the rhodopsin and made a similar set of measurements on the bleached solution. In this second set of measurements, rhodopsin — having been fully bleached — was not absorbing any light. The difference between the measurements before and after bleaching therefore represented light lost by absorption in the rhodopsin before bleaching. It was then possible to estimate the absorption spectrum of rhodopsin in the following way: Denote the tested wavelength by λ and the intensities of the light passing through the rhodopsin solution, before and after bleaching, by $I_1(\lambda)$ and $I_2(\lambda)$ respectively. The amount of light absorbed by rhodopsin at each wavelength is $I_2(\lambda) - I_1(\lambda)$.

Expressed as a fraction of $I_{2\lambda}$, the absorbed amount is

$$\frac{I_{2\lambda} - I_{1\lambda}}{I_{2\lambda}} \, .$$

The variation of this fraction across the spectrum traces out the absorption spectrum. If what matters for vision is the amount of light absorbed by rhodopsin, the absorption spectrum of rhodopsin must determine the spectral sensitivity of rod vision. König found this to be true within experimental error: absorption was maximal at about 500 nm, and fell off progressively on either side of that wavelength.

König put the comparison between the absorption spectrum of rhodopsin and human spectral sensitivity on a quantitative basis. Consider again the spectral sensitivity of Figure 5.3, which was obtained by asking an observer to choose the intensities that made each wavelength, taken in turn, look the same as a fixed standard stimulus. If it is true that the observer detects these lights according to the effects that they have on rhodopsin, a prediction can be made about the absorption spectrum, based upon the visual matches. At any given wavelength, the amount of light absorbed by rhodopsin is proportional to the intensity of the incident light, with a constant of proportionality given by the absorption spectrum of rhodopsin. This proportionality depends upon the probability that any individual photon will be absorbed, multiplied by the numbers of such photons that are available. The amount of light absorbed by rhodopsin from stimuli of different wavelengths can be made equal by setting the intensities to be inversely proportional to the values of the absorption spectrum at the wavelengths in question. For example, if a change in wavelength reduces the probability of photon absorption to a tenth of what it had been before the change, the initial absorption can be regained by pouring in ten times as many photons. Because spectral sensitivity as measured psychophysically is by definition the reciprocal of the amount of light required for a match to the standard, the prediction is simply that the spectral sensitivity of night vision and the absorption spectrum of rhodopsin should be proportional.

A complication, recognized by König, is that a significant amount of shortwave light is lost in vision by being absorbed, mainly by the lens, before it can reach the visual pigment. When this is taken into account, König found the proportionality principle to hold within experimental error: visual spectral sensitivity was found to be proportional to the absorption spectrum of rhodopsin multiplied by the spectral transmittance of the eye media.

König's groundbreaking research set the stage for Crescitelli and Dartnall (1953), who extracted rhodopsin from a human retina, measured its spectral absorption, and then compared it to the average scotopic spectral sensitivity from 50 observers. In order to make the comparison, Crescitelli and Dartnall had to compensate for light loss due to reflection at the cornea and loss by pre-retinal media. The comparison between the psychophysical function and the rhodopsin absorption function (which they called visual pigment 497) was sufficiently good to permit the authors to conclude:

> Apart from the violet region of the spectrum where variations in individual observers make the allowance for pre-retinal absorption uncertain, the sensitivity data are in excellent agreement with the constructed curve for visual pigment 497 . . . This strongly suggests that visual pigment 497 is the scotopic pigment of human vision. . . . (p. 196)

It should be mentioned that Crescitelli and Dartnall were conservatively cautious in describing their preparation by acknowledging that it was a crude preparation containing impurities. Nevertheless, it would appear their conclusion is valid when one considers later research.

The Principle of Univariance

König's observation, that similar sensations result when rhodopsin absorbs equal amounts of light at different wavelengths, would not be logically inevitable even if rhodopsin were the only operative visual pigment. We need one further assumption to make it so, which the visual physiologist William Rushton called *the principle of univariance* (Estévez & Spekreijse, 1982). According to this principle, *the effect of absorbed photons upon the visual pigment is independent of their wavelengths.* The biochemical evidence supports this assumption by showing that the initial action of light upon rhodopsin is to cause a conformational change in the rhodopsin molecule of the sort depicted in Figure 5.4, known as *photoisomerization.* If visual perceptions are generated as a result of such actions, equal numbers of molecules isomerized must lead to indistinguishable perceptions. The photopigment molecule does not know anything about the wavelength of the photon that isomerized it: only the fact that the event has taken place is signaled. Because of this, lights of any two wavelengths can cause equal amounts of isomerization, provided that their intensities are adjusted to take into account the relative probabilities that photons of these two wavelengths will cause isomerization to occur. Without the limitation imposed by the principle of univariance, we might be able to distinguish colors by using only one visual pigment; because of univariance, we fail.

Additional Complications

The problem of prereceptoral absorption has been considered as one factor that would be expected to cause a difference between

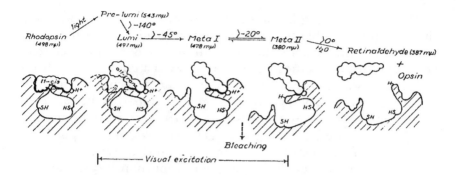

Figure 5.4   *Isomerization* refers to a change in the configuration of a molecule, with other changes of its constituent atoms or linkages. In this depiction from Wald (1968), the absorption of a photon is shown to cause a change in the configuration of the chromophore of rhodopsin, which initially is in the 11-cis form and is locked onto the protein base of the molecule as shown at the far left. As it straightens to the all-trans form, as a result of absorbing light, and is dissociated from the protein base, the chromophore has participated in the process of bleaching.

spectral sensitivity as found psychophysically and that obtained in the chemistry lab. There are other complications that must also be taken into account.

• It is important to be precise about the units in which the amounts of light at various wavelengths are measured. Because the number of molecules isomerized depends upon the number of photons absorbed, and not upon the energy of each absorbed photon, the light must be measured in numbers of photons (rather than in energy units).

• Spectrophotometry on whole retinas suggests that the absorption spectrum of the rhodopsin retina exhibits a *"long wavelength shift"* when compared to the absorption spectrum in solution, with the wavelength of peak sensitivity moving slightly toward the longer wavelengths.

• In extracting visual pigments solvents must be used and these selectively absorb some light as a function of wavelength: this places a selective "filter" in the test-tube that must be taken into account in the chemistry lab, just as the preretinal absorption must be dealt with in the psychophysical experiment.

• The products of bleaching also absorb light, and although their concentration depends upon the amount of bleaching that has occurred, the light which these photoproducts absorb does not contribute to vision.

The long wavelength shift of whole retinas is not yet understood, although it is possible that the fraction of incident light that is retained within the receptor may vary with wavelength. More can definitely be stated about the matter of units. Even a photon of relatively high energy will isomerize only the particular molecule that absorbs it. This has been established by experiments comparing the *absorption spectrum* of a rhodopsin solution with its *action spectrum*[9]. If the amount of light is measured in photons, the action spectrum is proportional to the absorption spectrum. But if the amount is measured in energy units, the two functions differ by a factor proportional to wavelength. The visual matching experiment is, in effect, a determination of the action spectrum, and exact agreement with the absorption spectrum can be expected only if the light is measured in photons.

Matches of Monochromatic Lights

The principle that when lights of different wavelengths isomerize equal quantities of rhodopsin, the resulting perceptions are indistinguishable, leads to a concise mathematical statement of the conditions for a visual match between two spectrally dissimilar lights in night vision. The sensitivity of rhodopsin in the eye (including the effects of preretinal absorption) may be defined by the average number of molecules isomerized per photon of wavelength λ incident upon the eye. This quantity will of course be less than 1.0 (often much less); denote it by S_λ. Similarly, let S_μ stand for the sensitivity at wavelength μ. Suppose now that in a split field like the one in Figure 5.2, one half of the field is illuminated with wavelength λ and the other with wavelength μ. The intensities of these two fields may be represented by the numbers of photons incident upon the eye (per unit time) from each field, and these quantities may be labeled I_λ and I_μ respectively. The number of photopigment molecules isomerized per unit time will then be $I_\lambda S_\lambda$ on the side of the field illuminated with wavelength λ, and $I_\mu S_\mu$ on the other side. The two halves will be visually indistinguishable if these products are equal; that is, if the following equation is true:

$$I_\lambda S_\lambda = I_\mu S_\mu. \tag{5.3}$$

Matches with Complex Spectral Distributions

Equation (5.3) makes a statement only about the condition for a match between two monochromatic lights. Most objects stimulate the eye with a continuous spectral distribution, where light of all wavelengths is represented. Can the principal that "equal isomerization means equal sensation" be generalized to predict the conditions for a match between spectrally complex stimuli? The answer is "yes." Recall from Chapter 3 that photons act independently of each other. This is also true for the act of absorption: individual absorptions occur between individual, noninteracting molecules of rhodopsin. This means that the total number of isomerizations may be obtained simply by adding together the contribution from each wavelength in the stimulus. This additivity in the action of photons upon pigment has important consequences for visual matching that can be tested experimentally and found to hold. If stimulus A is indistinguishable from B, and C is indistinguishable from D, then A + C = B + D. In fact, all of the rules of algebra work: as another example, if A = B + C, then 2A = 2 (B + C). This rule is especially important because it states that a match made at one intensity level will hold at another intensity level, and it turns out that color matches for cone vision also follow these rules within rather wide limits (Wyszecki & Stiles, 1980).

The principle of univariance makes it possible to treat spectrally complex stimuli in the same way as monochromatic stimuli. In each case the visual effect of a stimulus can be represented by a single number, which stands for the number of molecules of photopigment that are isomerized by the stimulus.

To determine the effect of a spectrally complex stimulus, the spectrum must first be divided into narrow bands, and the effect of photons within each such band must be found separately by multiplying the intensity provided by the stimulus within each band by the sensitivity of the photopigment to that band of wavelengths, just as was done for monochromatic lights in deriving Equation (5.3).

The total effect is then found by adding together the effects of each spectral band. Stimuli of different spectral composition will match if their total effects on the pigment are the same. In the limit, where the spectral bands are extremely narrow, this process may be summarized for matching fields for spectral distributions λ and μ by writing

$$^{\lambda}\!\int I_{\lambda} S_{\lambda} d\lambda = {}^{\mu}\!\int I_{\mu} S_{\mu} d\mu, \tag{5.4}$$

where the limits of the definite integrals cover the visible spectrum, usually taken to be from 380 nm to 750 nm.

TRICHROMATIC COLOR VISION AND ITS BASIS

The Shift from Rod to Cone Vision

Having completed a long digression into the realm of rod vision, where we are all color-blind, we are ready now to tackle the more complex problems of trichromatic cone vision. Superficially, the phenomena of color vision at high light levels, where the cones are active, seem to be very different from those of scotopic vision. For example, the transition from color-blind night vision to colored cone vision involves a dramatic breakdown in the additivity of visual matching that has just been described for rod vision. A long wavelength and short wavelength light that look the same at a low scotopic light levels will not continue to match, but might appear red and blue respectively, and at different brightnesses, if the intensities of each are increased by the same factor into the photopic range. The brightness difference occurs because of a dramatic change in the spectral sensitivity of the eye that is associated with the advent of color vision: whereas in scotopic rod vision sensitivity is greatest near 505 nm, in cone vision it is greatest near 555 nm. If long wavelength and short wavelength lights match for night vision and both are increased proportionally in intensity so as to stimulate cones, the short wavelength light will appear exceedingly dim relative to the long wavelength light. An additional increase of its intensity of the short wavelength light, by as much as a hundredfold, may be necessary to restore a brightness match, after which the two fields will continue to differ in hue.

One way to measure the difference in spectral sensitivity between photopic and scotopic vision is to determine thresholds under conditions designed to favor the exclusive stimulation of cones in the one case, rods in the other. (The concept of threshold and a discussion of psychophysical methods useful for measuring thresholds, will be found in Chapter 6, starting on page 206.) Cones can be uniquely stimulated by confining the stimulus to the rod-free foveal region of the retina. Rods can be preferentially stimulated by imaging the stimulus on a peripheral part of the retina, where rods predominate. Wald published the results of such an experiment in 1945; these data are shown in Figure 5.5. The rod curve has the expected shape and a straightforward interpretation along the lines just discussed. The interpretation of the cone curve, because three different kinds of cones are involved, is more complicated (see Chapters 6 and 9). The curve for cones 8° from the fovea is based upon the initial perception of hue.

The ordinate values in Figure 5.5 are the reciprocals of the radiometric amounts of lights (energies) required for threshold visibility.

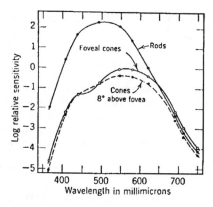

Figure 5.5   The curve labeled "Foveal cones" was obtained by determining the intensity required for threshold visibility of a 1° foveal test flash (on an energy basis) and plotting the log reciprocal of that value (sensitivity), normalized to 0 at the peak. The curve labeled "Rods" was obtained using a stimulus of the same size, positioned 8° in the periphery, with the sensitivity units on the same scale as those for the cone curve. As the energy of the peripheral stimulus is increased (downward on the graph), the peripheral stimulus eventually appears colored; the threshold for the perception of hue is shown by the dashed curve. The distance from the solid curve at the top to the dashed curve is called the photochromatic interval, which is highly dependent on wavelength. (From Judd, 1951, originally from Wald, 1945.)

For example, at 500 nm, the rod curve has a sensitivity value of about 2.4 log units, corresponding to a threshold energy value of –2.4 log units. As energy is increased at that wavelength, the stimulus appears progressively brighter, but no color is seen in the periphery. Finally, when an energy level of about 0.7 log units is reached, which is about 1000 times higher than the threshold for rods, only then does the blue-green hue of the 500 nm stimulus finally become apparent. Shifting its retinal location to the fovea again reduces the stimulus to threshold. The range between the absolute threshold for rod vision and the first appearance of hue is known as the *photochromatic interval.* This interval, expressed as a ratio, is about 1000:1 (3 log units) at 500 nm; it is virtually nonexistent at long wavelengths.

This change in the relative brightness of blue and red objects was first described in 1823 by Purkinje, a Czech physiologist and follower of Goethe, who made many subtle observations that have helped in the understanding of the visual process. The shifting of the eye's spectral sensitivity toward longer wavelengths as the light level is increased, or toward short wavelengths when it is decreased, has been termed the *Purkinje shift.* *

> Take two pieces of colored paper, one blue and one yellow, each about two or three inches square. Select the colored papers so that the yellow member of the pair is definitely lighter than the blue one when viewed under daylight. Then, after the eyes have become dark-adapted under conditions of very low illumination (moonlight would be excellent), note that the blue member of the pair appears much lighter than the yellow. Both will now appear colorless.

The failure of additivity in the transition from colorless night vision to colored day vision, and the change of spectral sensitivity associated with it, are not due to violations of the principles of either univariance or of additivity at the pigment level. Rather, they are signs that visual pigments other than rhodopsin and their host receptors are responding. Cone color vision, as it turns out, has the same relation to the properties of the cone photopigments that colorless rod vision bears to the properties of rhodopsin.

In night vision spectrally dissimilar lights can be matched to one another simply by varying the intensity of one of them. What it means to have color vision is that no such complete identity match generally can be made at photopic levels with fields of different colors. If a bipartite field has a standard white-appearing light on the left-hand side and a monochromatic red-appearing light on the right, the two halves cannot be made to match by adjusting the intensity of the red. The light level must be high enough to ensure cone vision and yet not so bright that discomfort, glare, strong and persistent afterimages, and marked bleaching of the cone pigments occur. Cone color vision has limitations, less drastic than those of rod vision, but similar in principle. Even the cones can be fooled into allowing a metameric match between spectrally dissimilar lights.

Complementary Colors

A special case of metamerism occurs when *complementary monochromatic lights* are mixed to match a white-appearing light. For example, this can be done with a long wavelength light that is mixed with just the right amount of monochromatic light of a suitable wavelength from the short to middle wavelength range of the spectrum. Despite their visual similarity, the white that is created from monochromatic complementaries is physically very different from the matching white that may include significant amounts of light from every region of the spectrum. The possibility of making white by mixing comple-

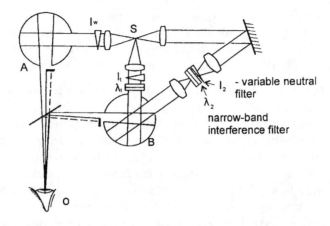

Figure 5.6   An apparatus that could be used to make color matches of spectral complementaries vs. white. Light from source S enters integrating sphere A; a half circle defined by the second opening in the sphere is seen by the observer O. Source S also directs light of wavelength I_1 through one opening of integrating sphere B, and that of wavelength I_2 through a second opening of the same sphere. Lights completely mix inside the sphere. Observer O sees the back side of sphere B through a third opening in that sphere, as a half circle juxtaposed with the one in A.

mentaries illustrates a limitation of human color vision. But it is a limitation that reveals itself only under such precise circumstances that Newton, as we recall, thought it impossible. For the match to occur, the following three conditions must be met exactly:

- For a fixed wavelength of I_L light, the I_M light must be of the appropriate wavelength.

- The amount of I_M light relative to the amount of I_L must be correct, so that the mixture appears neither blue-green nor red.

- The intensity of the resulting mixture must be such that it does not look brighter or dimmer than the standard.

With an apparatus like that of Figure 5.6, capable of creating uniformly colored fields of nearly monochromatic light and mixtures of colored lights with precise intensity control, a good white can be obtained without any difficulty. A complementary wavelength can be found, not only for I_L, but also for most spectral lights. However, I_M spectral lights (495 to 570 nm) have no exact spectral complementary: they yield yellowish tints when mixed with long wavelengths and bluish tints when mixed with short ones. They do have complementaries, but these are not in the spectrum; it turns out that purple appearing light (mixtures of long and short wavelengths) are required to produce them. The explanation for this is related to the spectral sensitivities of the cone photopigments, and will be explained shortly.

If there is too much of one complementary in the mixture, the result will be a color resembling more or less the hue of whichever component is present in excess. When this happens the match can be restored by adding, to the near white, a suitable amount of the spectral complementary of the hue that dominates the mixture of spectral colors. This has led to a way of specifying colors where each color is described by (1) the wavelength of the spectral light that must be mixed with white in order to produce that color, and (2) the proportion of the spectral light that must be introduced in order to produce it. These quantities are respectively called the *dominant wavelength* and the *purity* of the colors specified. It should be noted that conditions (1) and (2) must both be met. If (1) is met but (2) is not, the perceived hue will be more or less correct, but the saturation will be wrong. If (2) is met but not (1), the saturation will be more or less correct, but the hue will be wrong. For purples, no dominant wavelength can be specified. Instead, the complementary wavelength is given.

For nonspectral colors (colors which do not plot on the spectrum locus of a chromaticity diagram, where purity is less than 1 (see Appendix, Part I) the units in which the white and spectral lights are measured must be specified. The units that seem to be the most natural ones — numbers of photons, or energy, or trolands — have not proved convenient in practice, and other units have been developed. (The particular units adopted by the CIE are explained in the Appendix, Part I.) A second important ambiguity in the specification of colors by dominant wavelength and purity is that the choice of white is somewhat arbitrary. Several physical definitions of white have been proposed. One is to define it as a light that provides the same energy in each band of wavelength across the spectrum. Another is to define it as a spectrum that provides the same number of photons in each band of vibration frequency. It turns out that neither of these lights is truly white because when presented in a dark surround they appear bluish to most observers. The less bluish is the equal-energy white, and in color specification it has been most often used as the reference for specifying dominant wavelength and purity. In any event, it is not correct to refer to dominant wavelength, purity, or complementary colors unless the context makes clear the nature of the reference white.

Physiological Basis for Metameric Whites

Why must three conditions be met in order to match an equal-energy white with a mixture of complementary colors? We have already seen the answer in the prophetic statement of Thomas Young on page 20: a white matches a mixture of spectral complementaries providing that both stimuli have identical effects on the three different cone photopigments. When this happens, each pigment in turn behaves in accordance with the principle of univariance, and none of them can tell that there is any difference between the two stimuli. When all three pigments cannot tell, then any possible basis for distinguishing two colors as being different is lost. If the spectral sensitivities of the three classes of pigments is known, then it is possible to calculate, from any known physical intensity distribution, the relative rates of photon absorptions in each of the three classes of pigment. From this it is possible to specify any physical stimulus in terms of three values that are proportional to the absorption rates in the three kinds of pigments.

All of this has been appreciated in a general way since the time of Maxwell and Helmholtz, but the absorption spectra of the three classes of cone pigments were not known to them, nor did they know that pigments were specifically involved. It is surprising to learn that the extraction of human cone pigments has so far proved virtually impossible[10] whereas we recall that Boll first did it for rhodopsin more than a hundred years ago. One consequence of the lack of direct evidence about cone pigments was the emergence of quite a few "doubting Thomases" who have proposed various schemes to explain color perception that either ignore the principle of univariance, or flatly deny it. Common to most of these theories has been the claim that all cones are alike, and that any individual cone can sort out wavelength from intensity.[11] We now have excellent evidence about the cone pigments which is discussed next.

THE SEARCH FOR CONE SPECTRAL SENSITIVITY CURVES

The attempt to determine the spectral sensitivity of cone receptors has been a protracted endeavor in the history of color science. We shall see below that the early attempts that used psychophysical methods gave results that are remarkably similar to those obtained using the more direct methods of retinal densitometry, microspectrophotometry, and suction electrophysiology. These latter techniques are more direct than the psychophysical approach because they attempt to measure the actual spectral absorbance or sensitivity of individual cones. On the other hand, the psychophysical results are necessarily dependent on various procedures that assume single classes of cones are being stimulated. Although these assumptions are quite reasonable, inferences must nevertheless be made about the spectral sensitivity of individual cone receptors. The power of psychophysics has been sufficient to provide results that were confirmed by the direct methods. Moreover, psychophysical methods can sometimes yield data that are more accurate than those obtained using direct approaches.

Knowledge of the cone absorption spectra is an important component of color theory. Because this information is so important, the search for it has been an intense one. In Chapter 7 we will see that it is possible to impale single cones in fish and turtles. In these species it has been shown by this very direct means that the expected three classes of cone receptors do exist. We will also show that by sucking individual human cones up into a micropipette it is possible to stimulate and record the electrical activity of single cones. Results from experiments such as these are important, and obviously provide direct support for the idea of trichromacy. Another direct physical technique is called microspectrophotometry, which is basically the method that König pioneered, but refined to the point where the absorption of light in the outer segment of a single cone can be measured. This has been done by building spectrophotometers with beams so small, and sensitivities so great, that the tiny amounts of absorption that are involved can be detected. During the early exploitation of this technique in the 1960s, a handful of primate cones (including a few human ones) were examined. So far as they went, these results were consistent with the trichromatic view. Most of those who worked originally with the method soon gave up. Paul Liebman (1972), who stayed with it longer, offered no evidence on human cones, and has had discouraging things to say about the accuracy of the method. Bowmaker and his colleagues, whose early work started in the 1970s, have continued investigating receptors of many species including humans. We will take a closer look at some of their results below. Before taking a closer look at these direct attacks on cone spectral sensitivity, it is interesting to note that very recent psychophysical and genetic evidence suggests that human color vision is not necessarily trichromatic, but may be dependent on as many as five photopigments (Neitz, Neitz & Jacobs, 1992) by one report. Smith & Pokorny (1995) report that there is the possibility of 17 L-pigment opsins and 11 M-pigment opsins, which can affect the spectral peak absorbances of these pigments.

RETINAL DENSITOMETRY

Most people will have had the experience of being examined by an eye-care practitioner who used an ophthalmoscope to visualize the fundus. This instrument works because some of the light that is delivered into the eye is reflected out through the pupil, which enables the examiner to visualize the fundus. That which is not reflected is absorbed in various places within the eye and especially in and near the retinal tissues. As we noted above, various psychophysical experiments have led color scientists to believe that there are photopigments in the outer segments of the receptors. We have already seen that this certainly is the case for the rods. To be effective the photopigments must absorb light. If they do absorb light then that light will not be reflected out. Retinal densitometry is a direct measurement that is based on this principle. When a beam of light is delivered to the eye some of this light will be absorbed in the visual pigments of the retina, and some will pass through unabsorbed, to be reflected from the back of the eyeball. If this light escapes absorption again during its outward passage through the retina some of it will emerge through the pupil of the eye, where it can be measured with a photometer.

The intensity of the emerging beam serves as an index of visual pigment concentration in the retina, for the following reason. Suppose, for instance, that the retina contains enough visual pigment to absorb half the light at each passage through the retina. In that case the reflected beam apparently will emerge at only one quarter of the intensity that it would have had in an eye with no visual pigment present. If the retina is now flooded with a very strong light, one strong enough to bleach nearly all of the visual pigment, the intensity of the reflected beam will increase by a factor of four, and the fact of this increase can be used to gauge the amount of bleaching that has taken place. Having said all this, the reader is now cautioned not to take the foregoing quantitative example literally, because the actual situation is far more complicated.

Because little of the incident light reemerges from the pupil, it is not surprising that the pupil of the eye typically appears intensely black, except for the specular reflections that produce highlights at the cornea and lens. Some animals have a retroreflector, called the tapetum, behind the retina that allows the receptors a second chance to catch the light that is not absorbed on the initial passage; by directing it back toward the pupil the added absorptions occur in the appropriate receptors to help form a reasonably good image. (Examples of retroreflectors are the surfaces used on license plates in some states, labels on the sides of boxcars, and road signs.) Retroreflection causes the eyes of cats to appear to glow under conditions where those of humans do not, and it is also why the light in the cat's eye can be seen only from a vantage point close to the source that illuminates the eye.*

> In a dim room, and with the subject looking straight at the camera, take a flash photograph. If the flash bulb or lamp is located near the camera lens, the pupil of the eye of the subject will appear a brilliant red in the resulting photograph. Moving the flash away from the optical axis of the camera will eliminate this. Doing this in an initially dim room ensures that the pupil will be large, permitting more light to be reflected from the fundus than would be true for a smaller pupil. To see the fundus of another eye under continuous illumination requires a high-intensity source of light and some means to put the observer's eye on the optical axis of the eye being scrutinized. Helmholtz (1924, pp. 249 ff.), invented the ophthalmoscope, which is commonly used by eye-care practitioners for this purpose. Cornsweet (1970, p. 447) tells how to build an ophthalmoscope with inexpensive components.

Retinal Densitometry On Cones

Weale, Rushton, and their collaborators obtained the first early results in humans, which provided direct evidence that these purported photopigments actually exist[12]. They found evidence for the long wavelength and middle wavelength sensitive photopigments. Retinal densitometry is not a very sensitive technique and because there are far fewer short wavelength receptors than long and middle wavelength receptors, it is not surprising that this method did not yield evidence of short wavelength sensitive photopigments. Further, the insensitivity of retinal densitometry only permitted plotting the topmost portions of the cone spectral absorption functions. Psychophysics, as it turns out, yielded virtually the same results in those portions of the sensitivity function where the two methods are applicable. Psychophysics, however, was able to measure more than a log unit further down the function and, therefore, gauge a broader range of sensitivity.

Retinal densitometry provided the first objective evidence for the existence of the long and middle wavelength human photopigments. Even though subsequent methods, namely microspectrophotometry and the suction electrophysiology, have given us far better data, it is of historical interest to review the densitometric data and how they were analyzed. The interested reader might wish to read about the caveats pertaining to retinal densitometry that were thoroughly discussed in Boynton (1979).

An interesting difficulty was encountered with the long and middle wavelength sensitive cones because their spectral sensitivities overlap considerably. Consequently, it is impossible to uniquely stimulate only the L- or only the M-cone with the rather strong bleaches that are required. A clever solution to this problem was found by Mitchell and Rushton (1971a). They used dichromats as subjects. If a protanope is missing the long wavelength photopigment, which Rushton called *erythrolabe,* and if the technique is insensitive to the short wavelength photopigment, which he called *cyanolabe,* then the only pigment left to measure is the middle wavelength *chlorolabe.* In this text we refer to these as L-, S-, and M-photopigments, respectively. By analogous logic, L-photopigment was measured using deuteranopic observers who were ostensibly missing M-photopigment. Their results are shown in Figure 5.7. Three sets of curves are shown. The one labeled A is a test to determine whether, indeed, only one photopigment was being measured when a protanope was the subject.[13] The small circles plot the changes in double density when the dark adapted fovea was bleached by red (Ilford 205 gelatin filter) light. The small squares are from a similar experiment but the bleaching light was a blue-green (Ilford 623) light. The large circles are data for a bright white bleach after the red bleach and the large squares are a bright white bleach after the blue-green bleach. Rushton (1963) reasoned that if more than one pigment were being measured in this protanopic subject, then the bleaching results with the two chromatic colors would yield different spectra as would the bright white bleaches which were conducted after the chromatic bleach. Because of the close correspondence between the circles and squares, Rushton concluded that only one pigment was bleached. In Figure 5.7B retinal densitometric results (vertical lines) are compared with the spectral sensitivity of the protanope determined by color matching (triangles). The continuous curve is a replot of Pitt's (1935) data from six protanopes. Figure 5.7C shows analogous data for a deuteranope. The vertical rectangles are the retinal densitometry data, the triangles are psychophysical data, and the continuous curve a replot of Pitt's (1935) six deuteranopes. The correspondence between psychophysics and retinal densitometry permits the conclusion that Rushton has measured M-photopigment and L-photopigment.

MICROSPECTROPHOTOMETRY (MSP)

Retinal densitometry measures the cone spectral absorption *in situ.* In the 1960s, a new technique was developed that measured the cone sensitivity *in vitro.* Although the basic idea behind microspectrophotometry is quite simple, its implementation is very detailed and diffi-

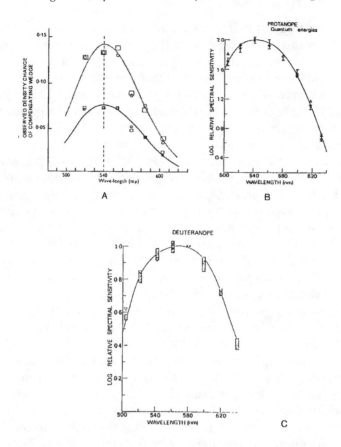

Figure 5.7   In A, Rushton's 1963 measurements show changes in the amount of
light reflected from the eye of the protanope for two very different
colors of the bleaching light. In B and C, data of Mitchell and Rushton
(1971) show the action spectra of the protanope's and deuteranope's
remaining pigment. The triangles in each case plot spectral sensitivity
values measured psychophysically, and the solid curves are for
protanopes and deuteranopes investigated by Pitt (1935).

cult. Basically, a piece of retina is placed on a microscope slide, at
first with no light reaching it. Then two microscopically narrow pencils of light are passed through the tissue. One pencil goes through
the specimen to penetrate an outer segment of the receptor with its
constituent photopigments. The other pencil goes through a portion of the specimen not containing an outer segment and its
photopigments. The container holding the tissue, the solutions in
which the tissue is placed, and the tissue itself all have spectral absorbances and these have to be factored out in order to measure the

spectral absorption of just the photopigment. That is why these two beams of light are used. Early MSP data on human cones were made *axially*, meaning that the investigators attempted to pass the light into the receptor lengthwise (Marks *et al.*, 1964; Brown and Wald, 1964). Bowmaker & Dartnall (1980) reported that measurements made this way caused an ". . . uncertainty whether the measuring beam had passed through the chosen outer segment without invading other cells." (p. 502). *Transverse* observations are free from this uncertainty and have been used with rather great success since the early 1970s. However, because the natural flow of light is axial, it is necessary to make corrections in the data obtained the transverse method.

Human retinas are almost always obtained under less than desirable conditions. Such conditions include less than healthy eyes, enucleation under less than optimal experimental conditions, and the use of an eye that may be received by the investigator many hours after death. We relate these problems not to denigrate the human MSP research but to give the reader an idea of why so little human work has been done. Furthermore, the reader can now understand why finding that certain species of monkey make excellent physiological models for studying human color vision has been most welcome (De Valois and Jacobs, 1968; DeValois *et al.*, 1974; Schnapf *et al.*, 1987; Kraft *et al.*, 1990).

To obtain really good tissue from humans requires the co-operation of the donor and the ophthalmic surgeon. Bowmaker and Dartnall (1980) received such cooperation and obtained a fresh dark-adapted human retina in sufficient time to make 48 transverse MSP measures from the fovea and parafovea. The cooperation among the patient, surgeon, and scientists made it possible to apply a light-tight bandage over the eye to be enucleated on the evening before the surgery. The surgery, which was performed because of a malignant melanoma of the choroid, was conducted under deep red light in an otherwise darkened operating theater. The enucleated eye was immediately placed in a light-tight Dewar flask containing ice, delivered promptly to the research laboratory, and the first measurements were made 170 minutes after the eye was removed from the patient.

In Figure 5.8 the equipment and data collection are arranged so that the experimenter knows precisely how much chromatic light is being delivered into the retina by each of the microscopically small pencils of light rays. The piece of retina is placed between the condenser and objective lens of an inverted microscope. Figure 5.8 is a schematic diagram of the microspectrophotometer designed by Liebman and Entine (1964). With some improvements this is the instrument used in Bowmaker's lab.

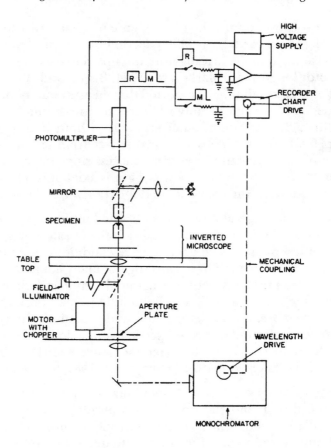

Figure 5.8   A schematic diagram of a microspectrophotometer used to measure the spectral absorbance of retinal receptor photopigments (from Liebman & Entine, 1964). Light from the monochromator is directed up through the table top and through the specimen and is finally collected by the photomultiplier which sends the information to the recorder chart drive yielding curves as seen in Figure 5.9. See text for addition explanation.

In order to obtain baseline instrumental readings two pencils of light (only one of which is shown in Fig. 5.8) are projected through a portion of the specimen not containing an outer segment. The spectral absorbance of the photopigment is obtained by passing one beam transversely through an outer segment and the other through a part of the tissue not containing an outer segment. The difference between the amount of light that passes through the outer segment and that which does not, provides a measure of the spectral absorbance of the photopigment. Sometimes, for example when measuring shortwave cones, an additional step is taken. After the photopigments have been assayed, the retina is bleached with a strong white light and the spectral absorption of the photopigment is measured again (Bowmaker *et al.*, 1991).

The first microspectrophotometric (MSP) data were collected from vertebrates but not from primates because the latter have much smaller cones. The first primate MSP data were collected by Marks, Dobelle, and MacNichol (1964). They cite several of the vertebrate studies, the earliest of which was reported in 1957. Although the early studies (including the groundbreaking primate study that included human cones) were frought with difficulties they did mark an important beginning. Marks *et al.* (1964) reported spectral sensitivity for L-, M-, and S-cones obtained from both monkey and human retina. These data support and extend psychophysical cone sensitivities, and those obtained by retinal densitometry, by showing that there are at least three classes of cone photopigment. They extend earlier work by directly measuring the S-photopigment. (Recall that retinal densitometry was too insensitive to measure these receptors.) After reviewing the retinal densitometry and psychophysical data, Marks *et al.* reported that:

> From none of these [psychophysical] experiments could it be determined whether the pigments are segregated in individual cones or whether two or more of them are present in each receptor. Our experiments indicate that the former is basically true (p. 1181).

Thus the second extension was to show that each cone had its own single pigment. Figure 5.9 shows typical records obtained from a human retina (Bowmaker & Dartnall, 1980). The lower curve in each record is the instrumental baseline and the spectral absorbance of the photopigment is derived by taking the difference between the two functions in each record. The resultant spectral absorbance functions for each photopigment are shown in Figure 5.10. These functions were obtained from three S-cones, 11 M-sensitive cones, and 19 L-cones. The curve labeled 498 represents the average spectral absorbance from 11 rods.

The reader will recall that in Rushton's retinal densitometry research he compared his absorbance data with spectral sensitivity functions determined psychophysically. Bowmaker and Dartnall (1980) made a similar comparison with their MSP data. In Figure 5.11 they compared the rod MSP results with the CIE scotopic luminous efficiency function. The longwave MSP data were compared to Stiles's π_5, the middlewave MSP data were compared to π_4, and the shortwave to π_3 (see Chapter 6).[14] The open symbols represent Stiles's data and the closed circles the CIE scotopic luminous efficiency function. The continuous curves are

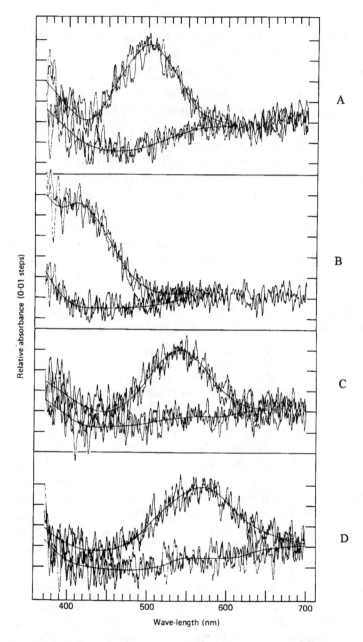

Figure 5.9   Microspectrophotometric recordings from human receptors. Records for rhodopsin, the photopigment found in the outer segment of rod receptors are shown in A. Panels B, C & D, respectively, show the records from S-, M-, and L-photopigments found in the outer segments of cone receptors. The solid line was drawn through the middle of the noise. The difference between each pair of curves gives the spectral absorbance of the photopigments. (From Bowmaker & Dartnall, 1980.)

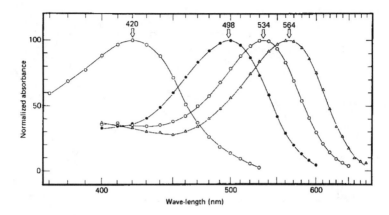

Figure 5.10   The mean spectral absorbances of receptor photopigments in the outer segments of human receptors. Closed symbols are for rhodopsin, the photopigment found in rods. The open symbols are from S- (420), M- (534), and L-photopigments (564). These curves are derived from data as shown in Figure 5.9. (From Bowmaker & Dartnall, 1980.)

the sensitivity function derived from the MSP data. To accomplish this comparison, Bowmaker and Dartnall had to factor in the preretinal absorptions of the lens for all four pigments and the macular pigmentation for the L- and M-cones. The macular pigment was not factored in for the rods because the data for these were collected 5° from the fovea. One other correction was needed to make the MSP comparable to psychophysics. Because MSP was performed by projecting the light stimuli transversely through the receptors, optical density corrections had to be made because psychophysically light travels axially. As the reader can see, the agreement for the long and middle wave functions is quite good. The shortwave agreement is less good, but Bowmaker and Dartnall caution that the MSP is only the average of three records. With regard to the rods, the investigators wrote:

> The discrepancy between the CIE, scotopic sensitivity function and our derived sensitivity for rods is thus difficult to account for, especially so in view of the clear correlation of our derived psychophysical sensitivities of the three classes of cones with the mechanisms of W. S. Stiles. There seems little doubt of the discrepancy, however, and an explanation is needed for it (p. 510).

The Stability of Relative Spectral Absorption Curves

The percentage of light absorbed in a solution of pigment molecules depends upon three factors: (1) the probability that a pigment mol-

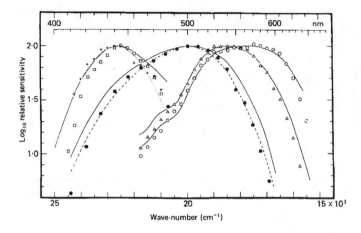

Figure 5.11   A comparison of sensitivity functions determined psychophysically with the spectral absorbance of receptor photopigments determined microspectrophotometrically. The solid curves were calculated from the data in Figure 5.10. The psychophysical comparisons are with the Stiles π-mechanisms: open circles – π_5 triangles – π_4 crosses – π_3 squares – $\pi 1$, (the latter measured 8° eccentrically), filled circles – CIE scotopic spectral sensitivity. To make these comparisons allowances had to be made because the psychophysical data reflect not only the spectral absorbance of the photopigment but also of the pigments in the lens and the macular lutea. The dotted curve was obtained from the Dartnall nomogram assuming a λ_{max} of 420 nm. The dashed curve was calculated from rod data after correcting for lens absorption and assuming an axial absorbance of zero for rhodopsin. (From Bowmaker & Dartnall, 1980.)

ecule, if it encounters a photon, will absorb it; (2) the concentration of the solution, which depends upon the density of pigment molecules (which is a function of the concentration of the solution); and (3) the path length through which the measuring beam is allowed to pass. For the discussion that follows, assume a fixed path length and assume that the concentration may be varied. If the concentration is low, the probability that a pigment molecule near the end of the path will absorb a photon is little different than for one near the beginning. The absorption spectrum depends only upon the characteristics of the constituent molecules. So long as this is true, increases and decreases in concentration will not alter the relative absorption spectrum. If the pigment concentration is high, the probability that a photon will reach molecules near the end of the path will be selectively changed as a function of wavelength, depending upon how much absorption has already taken place in the molecules nearer the front of the path. This has been called "self-screening" (see Dartnall, 1962, p. 339, for an excellent treatment of the details of this argument).

Over a considerable range, color matches are independent of the intensity of the light (Burns & Elsner, 1985). On the basis of the considerations just outlined, it is to be expected that these matches should fail if the concentration of cone pigments is high and can be varied due to bleaching. This is because these matches depend upon relative spectral sensitivity curves whose shapes would change. Retinal densitometry tells us that little bleaching occurs over the normal levels of photopic vision where most of our color vision occurs, and where most color matching experiments have been done. Because of this, the intensity of the light within this range is not an important variable: it is the relative degree of stimulation of the three kinds of cone photopigment that matters. On the subjective side, the apparent hue and saturation of lights does not change very much over the intensity range under discussion here (although the changes that do occur are of considerable theoretical interest).

Various estimates of the densities of cone photopigments suggest that they are high enough to cause a significant change in spectral sensitivity curves with strong bleaches,[15] and it is found that metameric color matches do begin to fail at bleaching intensities (Wyszecki and Stiles, 1980). But we will not deal further with these interesting issues here. Rather we will assume that the relative spectral sensitivity curves of cone pigments are, for practical purposes, invariant.

SUCTION ELECTROPHYSIOLOGY

The most recent method for evaluating the spectral properties of the photoreceptors involves drawing the outer segment of a receptor into a fire-polished, salinized glass micropipette (Fig. 5.12), which is connected to a current-to-voltage converter, then measuring its electrophysiological response when stimulated with light (Baylor *et al.*, 1979; Nunn and Baylor, 1983; Baylor, 1987; Baylor *et al.*, 1987; Schnapf *et al.*, 1987; Kraft *et al.*, 1990; Schnapf *et al.*, 1990).

Baylor (1987) reported that, "A single photoreceptor's electrical activity can be measured non-invasively by recording its membrane current." (p. 36) (We assume he uses the term non-invasive because the receptor is not impaled by an electrode.) Baylor *et al.* (1987) noted that, whereas microspectrophotometry is limited to spectral regions

Figure 5.12   Suction electrophysiology. A micropipette draws up a single receptor into its tube. Light passes through the end of the micropipette and the outer segment receptor within it. At the other end of the micropipette an electrical contact receives the electrophysiological signal via the electrolyte in the tube. (From Baylor, 1987.)

of strong absorption, the suction electrode method permits recording of photocurrents over a wider range of wavelengths. Bowmaker and colleagues have been successful in making MSP measurements from human L-, M-, and S-cones. The suction method has been used on human L- and M-cones but S-cone measurements have been obtained only from monkey retina. The technique is sufficiently sensitive to measure single photon events from toad rods (Baylor, 1987).

Spectral sensitivities of individual receptors were measured from toad, monkey, and human retinas. As with other techniques, and for the same reasons mentioned above, the first measurements were made in each of these species on rod receptors. The spectral sensitivity of single rods was as expected from human psychophysics. Because here we are primarily concerned with human color vision, we will focus our attention on suction electrophysiology conducted on human retinas.

DeValois and Jacobs (1968) and DeValois *et al.* (1974) demonstrated the commonality between macaque physiology and psychophysics, and the commonality between macaque psychophysics and human psychophysics. They inferred that human and old world

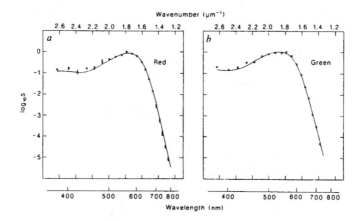

Figure 5.13   The data points are the spectral sensitivity of human L- and M-cones measured by suction electrophysiology. The solid lines are the average spectra of L- and M- cones of monkey Macaca fascicularis. (From Schnapf, Kraft & Baylor, 1987.)

macaques have virtually the same color vision system. The suction electrode method leads to this same conclusion by showing that the L- and M- human and monkey cones have virtually the same spectral sensitivities (Schnapf *et al.*, 1987; Kraft *et al.*, 1990).

For our purposes, Figures 5.13–5.15 present some rather informative results. Figure 5.13 presents the spectral sensitivity of human L- and M-cones. The long wavelength data are the average of five cones and the middle wavelength data are from one M- cone. The smooth curves are the average spectra of L- and M-cones of Macaca fasicularis (Schnapf *et al.*, 1987). These data represent the relative reciprocal number of photons required to attain a criterion electrophysiological response. Figure 5.14A shows monkey cone data for all three classes of receptors (Baylor, 1987), which have been used to compute the relative intensities of each photopigment required to match the wavelengths represented on the abscissa (Fig. 5.14B). The smooth curves are the human color matching data of Stiles and Burch (1959), which will be discussed in detail in the next section. For the time being, it suffices to point out that the fit of the monkey data to the human is acceptable. Finally, Figure 5.15 (Schnapf *et al.*, 1987) added the sensitivity of the L- and M-cones by weighting the L-cones 1.69 times more than the M. This calculation was then compared to CIE $V_M(\lambda)$, which is the photopic luminosity function frequently used by vision researchers (smooth curve in Fig. 5.15)[16]. The reader can

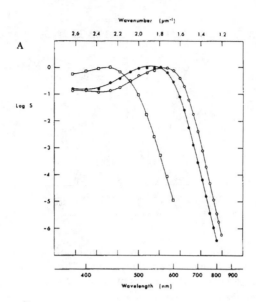

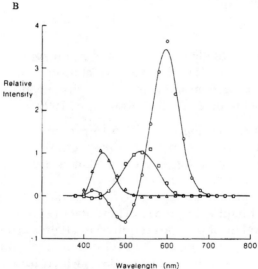

Figure 5.14   A. Spectral sensitivity of macaque S-, M-, and L-cones measured by suction electrophysiology. The upper scale is the wavenumber and the lower
scale the corresponding wavelength. Note that these are very similar to
the data in Figure 5.13 except that in humans it was not possible to
record from S-cones. B. Prediction of human color-matching functions.
Data points were calculated from the suction electrode derived spectral
sensitivity functions from macaque receptors. The continuous curves are
the 10° Stiles & Burch color-matching functions. The suction electrophysiological data were modified to take lens and macular absorption
plus self screening of cone pigments into account. (From Baylor, 1987.)

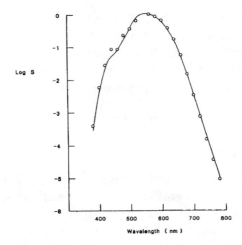

Figure 5.15   The sensitivities of the L- and M-cones were added together by weighting the L-cones 1.69 times more than the M-cones (open circles). These sensitivities were taken from Figure 5.13. The continuous curve is the CIE $V_M(\lambda)$ photopic luminosity function. (From Schnapf, Kraft, & Baylor, 1987.)

see that the fit between the suction electrode generated data and the $V_M(\lambda)$ is quite good. These suction electrode data clearly support DeValois' finding that old world monkeys and humans have very nearly the same color vision system. This is important because as will be seen in subsequent chapters we can learn a lot from monkey experiments of an invasive kind that could never be carried out with humans. We are fortunate to have such an excellent animal model.

Suction electrophysiology yields data over a range of about five log units from the peak of the sensitivity curve, compared to only a bit more than two log units for MSP. Moreover, the data obtained using the suction electrode technique are considerably more similar to those obtained by psychophysics, and less variable than the results obtained by MSP or reflection densitometry. However, we should not count out MSP yet because Bowmaker's group, at this writing, is still actively exploiting this technique which is the only objective technique so far that has been able to assess human S-cones. Further, because these investigators are able to examine 40–50 receptors from a single retina, information about cone receptor distribution probably will be forthcoming.

The methods of MSP and psychophysics have produced data showing variability of spectral sensitivity within cone types suggesting that there may be subclasses of them. Very recent psychophysical and genetic research has also provided evidence for these subclasses (Neitz, Neitz & Jacobs, 1991). Baylor *et al.* (1987) found very small variability measures of their spectra positions leading them to conclude that they did not find subpopulations of pigments within each major class. We need to remember, however, that this applies to monkey cones and caution needs to be exercised when extending this conclusion to humans.

COLOR MATCHING

In subsequent chapters, we will see that very precise specifications of the shapes of the cone pigment curves are required in order to understand chromatic discrimination (Chapter 8) and color deficiencies (Chapter 10). Accurate data for these curves are now available. The detailed evidence has been achieved by MSP, suction electrophysiology, and psychophysical methods. It might seem incredible that the use of procedures that involve the intact human subject could reveal such curves more accurately than the direct methods, but it is true. The most important psychophysical experiments have been those on color matching, which, as we saw in Chapter 1, began with Maxwell more than 100 years ago. Although color-matching data from normal trichromats do not yield a unique set of cone spectral sensitivities, an accurate set of these sensitivities should predict the color-matching function. The remainder of this chapter will largely be concerned with this evidence, and with showing how it relates to the action spectra of the three types of cone photopigments.

Hypothetical Curves

To introduce this topic we deal first with sets of hypothetical spectral sensitivity curves. For convenience it will be assumed that the three classes of photopigments are uniquely contained in long, middle, and short wavelength cones, and that phenomena such as the "long wavelength shift" of rhodopsin (p. 137) can be ignored, so that the spectral curves of the pigments and those of the receptors are proportional. The curves to be sketched in this section are wrong, but they prove useful for pedagogic purposes. We will work our way through a few sets of them that will gradually take us fairly close to the real ones. This will help to introduce various principles that are difficult to make clear when starting with the real curves.

Curves That Fail to Overlap

The most obvious respect in which the curves of Figure 5.16 differ from the real cone absorption curves is that they fail to overlap. Curves

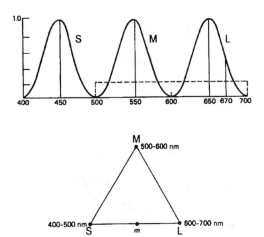

Figure 5.16 An initial set of hypothetical sensitivity curves that do not overlap. In the color triangle at the bottom, spectral colors plot only at the corners.

of this sort imply that a photon of any particular wavelength can be absorbed in only one of the three types of cones. This arrangement would be disastrous for good discrimination of spectral colors: the principle of univariance applies separately within each of the spectral bands covered by the three pigments, so within each of these ranges there could be no discrimination at all of stimuli whose wavelengths are restricted to this band. From the standpoint of efficient photon collection (especially near 500 nm and 600 nm where the tails of the curves descend to zero) this is also a very poor arrangement.

A major purpose of a color mixture experiment is to specify any arbitrary stimulus, called the test, in terms of a mixture of three components (often called *primaries*). As previously noted, two such stimuli will match whenever the photons delivered to the eye from the mixture field are absorbed in all three classes of cones in the same way as those delivered by the test stimulus. From the curves of Figure 5.16, it should be intuitively clear that the choice of usable matching wavelengths is at once both arbitrary and constrained. Each must fall somewhere within a spectral band defined by the sensitivity curve of one of the cone types: although these locations are not critical, it is necessary that no two of them fall within a single such band. (A fourth stimulus would of necessity fall in the same band as one of the original three; within that band an infinite number of combinations of relative intensities of those two stimuli could cause the same absorptions to occur, and thus the color match would not be a unique one.) By adjust-

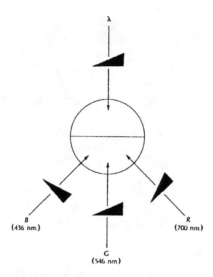

Figure 5.17   Schematic arrangement of stimuli for a color-mixing experiment. A test
stimulus is delivered to the top of the split field, while a mixture of three
primaries is delivered to the bottom. All are adjustable in intensity by
means of neutral density wedges. An arrangement must also be provided so that any one of the primaries can, in turn, be added to the test
stimulus in the top field. (From Boynton, 1971.)

ing the intensities of the three components in turn, it should not be a
problem to produce in this way an equivalent stimulation of all three
types of cones, thereby achieving a match with any test stimulus.

The Mixture Experiment from the Subject's Perspective

Such an experiment requires an apparatus capable of delivering the
test stimulus to one half of a bipartite field, and the components of
the mixture field to the other. Recall that photons do not physically
mix, so what is actually needed is a means for causing the entire mixture field to radiate its photons, for all three component wavelengths,
uniformly toward the eye. There are a variety of ways to accomplish
this, one of which has already been considered in Figure 5.6 in connection with the special case of mixtures of complementary colors.
Figure 5.17 is intended to represent all possible methods schematically. If it helps to have something definite in mind, recall and extend the use of the integrating spheres of Figure 5.6, or imagine that
the mixture field is built up from the superimposed images of half
fields delivered from three slide projectors. With the latter arrange-

ment, narrow-band interference filters could be placed in front of each projector to select the matching wavelengths, and the intensity of each component could be continuously varied by means of variable transformers supplying the lamps of each projector. A fourth projector, with its semicircular image reversed, could be used to provide the adjacent test stimulus.[17]

Consider 450, 550, and 650 nm as the wavelengths of the three matching components (primaries). As an example to show how the experiment goes, attempt to specify a test stimulus of 670 nm by a mixture of these three mixture components. The subject's task is to manipulate the three intensities of the mixture field in order to produce an exact match with the 670-nm test. A bit of trial and error would establish that the appropriate amounts of the 450 nm and 550 nm primaries must be zero because no match can be made if any finite amounts are tried. This is true because the 670 test stimulus fails to stimulate either the S- or M-cones, so it is necessary in making a match that the mixture field should also fail to do so. Once this is discovered, then the task that remains is easy to understand, being identical in principle to the single-pigment matches of rod vision (p. 125). After the match is made, physical measurement would reveal only half as many photons in the matching field as in the test. This difference compensates for the greater sensitivity of the L- cones at 650 as compared to 670 nm; the argument is the same as that for rod vision discussed earlier.

The test stimulus need not be monochromatic in order to be matched. Suppose that it consisted instead of a continuous range of photons covering the range from 500 nm to 700 nm, as shown by the dotted lines in Figure 5.16. It can be seen at a glance that such a stimulus causes equal excitation of both the L- and M-cones. In attempting to match it, the subject would discover once again that the I_{450} primary is useless; but both of the remaining two would be needed. The match would now require equal numbers of photons to be absorbed from each component of the mixture, in order to cause equal stimulation of the L- and M-cones, just as for the test. If the test stimulus were further extended at the same photon level to include the remaining spectral region from 400 nm to 500 nm, then the subject would also require the I_{450} mixture component to make the match.

The primaries used in the matching experiment need not be monochromatic either. For the curves of Figure 5.16, one of them could, for example, be of any spectral distribution confined to the range of wavelengths from 600 to 700 nm (I_L). No matter what this distribution might be, such a stimulus could only serve to activate the L-cones.

Suppose that it overlapped a bit into the adjoining spectral region: could a match then still be made? If the test stimulus were monochromatic the answer would be "no" because such a test stimulus would activate only one kind of cone, whereas the assumed primary would activate two of them. This is similar, as we shall see, to what happens with spectral primaries when the sensitivity curves overlap.

A final comment about these nonoverlapping curves is that they would permit a fair discrimination of colors that depend upon continuous curves of reflectance covering the entire spectrum, which, as we will see in Chapter 11, is a reasonable description of most reflecting surfaces.

Necessary Relations between Stimuli and Perceptions

An important psychophysical assumption that underlies the matching operation now needs to be made explicit. The relationship between physics and perception must permit the subject to converge upon a solution when making a color match. It surely would not do, for example, for low levels of excitation of L-cones to yield perceptions of red that suddenly changed to green at higher levels. Further, it seems necessary for the correlation between physical intensity and brightness, as delivered via one type of cone, to be monotonic over the range being examined; otherwise there would be at least two physical intensities that could cause the same perception and unique matches could not be made. Although the psychophysical relationships may be complex, the perceptions that are generated as a consequence of photon absorptions in the three cone types must relate in some sensible and continuous way to the amounts of these absorptions.[18]

THE TRILINEAR TRIANGULAR
COLOR DIAGRAM INTRODUCED

Newton first suggested that colors could be represented on a two-dimensional diagram. Maxwell (1855) later made this idea more explicit by introducing the use of *trilinear coordinates* to describe the results of his early color experiments, carried out with a spinning top upon which sectors of colored papers were attached. Although (as Maxwell fully realized) such coordinates are ideal for the representation of color mixtures, trilinear coordinates have seldom actually been used for that purpose. For example, the CIE has officially adopted the use of *Cartesian coordinates* for its chromaticity diagram (see Appendix, Part I). Yet, the use of a triangular chart instantly clarifies relationships that are otherwise obscure, and for that reason the color triangle will be introduced here.

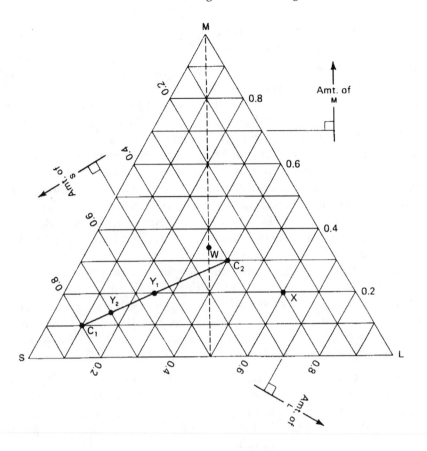

Figure 5.18   Color diagram in trilinear coordinates (color triangle). The features illustrated by this diagram are explained in the text.

Consider the equilateral triangle of Figure 5.18. The colors represented by the unique excitation of each of the three kinds of cones are plotted at the corners of the diagram. Side SL is positioned horizontally and, therefore, has an appearance similar to the x-axis of the more familiar Cartesian coordinate system. The proportion of M-cone activity required in a color match is represented as the perpendicular distance above the SL axis, in the same way that an ordinate value is represented in Cartesian coordinates. The proportions contributed by the other two types of cones are represented in the same way (to appreciate this it might help to rotate the diagram so that the primary under consideration is in each case at the top). Thus, there are three coordinates obliquely related to each other; the proportion of total excitation represented by a particular kind of cone is represented as the distance along a perpendicular erected from the side of the triangle opposite the labeled apex.

This triangular diagram has a special property that makes it ideal for representing color matches. Given any point within it, such as X in Figure 5.18, the sum of the distances from that point to the three sides is always the same.[19] For the point X shown, L = 0.6, M = 0.2, and S = 0.2. A limiting case occurs when X is located at one of the corners. For example, if it is at M, this implies that the color match requires only M-cone response. If one of the components of the mixture field were able to stimulate only M-cones, then the other two components of the mixture would have to be extinguished in order to make the match. This level of M, whatever its actual response (which would depend upon that of the test field being matched) is specified as 1.0 because this is a diagram to represent proportions of the three cone responses, not their absolute responses. The dotted line from SL to M, therefore, has a unit length and divides SL into two equal parts. The locus of all cone responses that represent equal amounts of S and L in the match is given by this line; at M, these amounts are zero, whereas at the other end of the line — at a point midway between S and L on the line SL — they are 0.5.

A point W at the very center of the diagram is equally far from each side, the distances therefore being 0.333 in each case. These examples help to demonstrate that the position of any color in this diagram shows very nicely the relative excitations of the three kinds of cones caused by any stimulus.

Such a triangular diagram is shown in Figure 5.16, under the nonoverlapping spectral curves. All spectral cone responses between 600 and 700 nm are represented at L. Those between 500 and 600 nm are all at M, and the remainder are plotted at S. Although for monochromatic stimuli no cone response can plot anywhere except at the corners, complex stimuli that activate both L- and M-cones (but not S) can be represented along the side LM of the triangle according to a *"center of gravity"* principle. According to this principle, combined cone responses lie along the side of the triangle at a location that depends upon the relative amounts of each component required to make the match. For example, a color at m (Fig. 5.16) would be one that requires equal amounts of S- and L-cone response to match it. A color that requires four times as much L as S will be located four-fifths of the distance from L toward S on the line LS. All possible combinations of L and S plot somewhere along this line.

The proof of the center of gravity principle is fundamental and requires that color equations be written. Such equations summarize the information contained in the triangular color diagram, and apply similarly to diagrams in Cartesian coordinates that express the same information.

Color Equations

It was mentioned on page 139 that the operations of color matching obey the rules of ordinary algebra. In this relation, the "=" sign of algebra translates to "matches with" in the laboratory, and the "+" sign implies the superposition of lights by one or another of the methods already described. Negative quantities of light cannot be produced in a colorimeter, but the algebraic equivalent is to add that amount to the other side of the equation. Later in this chapter we will see how this is done in the laboratory to permit matches that otherwise would not be possible.

A few examples may help. Suppose that a match is made between a spectral light I_{570}, that appears yellow, and a mixture of I_{650} and I_{515} primaries. We may write

$$y(I_{570}) = r(I_{650}) + g(I_{515}) \qquad (5.5)$$

where (I_{570}), (I_{650}), and (I_{515}) stand for the stimuli being used, whose amounts are y, r, and g. Read this equation: "y units of (I_{570}) are matched by a mixture of r units of (I_{650}) and g units of (I_{515})." (For now, we will not worry about the units.) Suppose now that we add some other color, say b units of (I_{470}), to both sides of the colorimetric field. Algebraically:

$$y(I_{570}) + b(I_{470}) = r(I_{650}) + g(I_{515}) + b(I_{470}) \qquad (5.6)$$

and the two sides of the equation, having been equal before, remain equal because the same quantity has been added to each side. This could be tested experimentally by adding a veil of short wavelength light to the previous match, for example by reflecting it to the eye from a piece of glass so that it covers the entire field. Experimentally, as well as algebraically, the match will hold.

Suppose that the intensity of both halves of the field were increased by the same factor, say 2. The equation will now read

$$2y(I_{570}) = 2r(I_{650}) + 2g\ (I_{515}) \qquad\qquad (5.7)$$

and the equation remains valid. Experimentally, what is required is to double the numbers of photons reaching the eye from both halves of the field, without altering their relative spectral distributions. This is most easily done by making the match initially with a neutral filter in front of the eye, one which absorbs exactly 50 percent of the photons incident upon it without regard to wavelength. After the match is made, the filter is removed, and although both halves brighten, the match holds.

These properties of color matches are what should be expected by the trichromatic theory introduced earlier in this chapter. The original match exists, by this view, because photons are absorbed at the same rates by all three classes of photopigments despite the physical differences represented by the two sides of the equation. In the first example, the addition of short wavelength light of the same amount to both halves of the field would be expected to cause additional photons to be absorbed by the three photopigments in the same way for both halves of the field, and there is no reason why this should destroy the match. In the second example, provided that the action spectra of the three cone types are not altered by the added light, the doubling of the numbers of photons will not alter the physiological identity[20] originally implied by the two sides of the color equation.

As a final example of a property of color matches that makes their mathematical expression useful, consider their stability under conditions of chromatic adaptation, a subject to be discussed more fully in the next chapter. Suppose that, following the match $r(I_{650}) + g(I_{515}) = y(I_{570})$, the eye is strongly adapted to a long wavelength light, after which the original fields are viewed. The I_{570} half of the field, which previously appeared yellow, will now appear decidedly green. But the $I_{650} + I_{515}$ side of the field, which also previously looked yellow, also now appears green. The fields in fact will continue to match, although their appearance is grossly changed. This example illustrates that, although color equations express the conditions for a color match, they do not tell us anything directly about what the matching colors look like.

Center of Gravity Principle

Now we can examine the center of gravity principle using an intuitive approach with the aid of Figure 5.18. (A more analytic approach is found in Appendix, Part III). Recall that the triangular diagram in Figure 5.18 is supposed to represent the excitation of the long (L), middle (M), and short (S) wavelength sensitive cones.

Note in Figure 5.18 that there are two colors depicted in the diagram: C_1 and C_2. These represent the relative excitations that these two colors cause in the L-, M-, and S-cones and can be defined in *unit amounts* as follows:

$$C_1 = l_1(L) + m_1(M) + s_1(S). \tag{5.8}$$

Because Equation 5.5 is in unit amounts, it follows that $l_1 + m_1 + s_1 = 1.0$. By the same logic we define Equation 5.9.

$$C_2 = l_2(L) + m_2(M) + s_2(S) \tag{5.9}$$

Again, it follows that $l_2 + m_2 + s_2 = 1.0$

Now if we mix C_1 and C_2 where in the triangular diagram would the resultant mixture plot? The reader surely must ask, does it not depend on how much of each component one uses? Indeed that is the case. Consequently, by writing the equation in *unit amounts,* we can express the mixture as follows:

$$C_3 = c_1(C_1) + c_2(C_2). \tag{5.10}$$

And, as with the previous equations representing unit amounts, we note that

$$l_3 + m_3 + s_3 = c_1 + c_2 = 1.0$$

Now suppose $c_1 = c_2 = 0.5$. Intuitively we would expect that equal mixtures of C_1 and C_2 would plot halfway between C_1 and C_2 in the triangular diagram. We can examine our intuition quantitatively. Recall that when a stimulus plots at a particular apex it is assumed to uniquely stimulate the cone represented there. If, for example, a stimulus plots at L it is assumed that stimulus uniquely stimulates the long wavelength sensitive cone and does not stimulate the middle or short wavelength sensitive cones.

Recall that to determine the coefficient for a stimulus one rotates the page so that the relevant cone faces up and then one counts the number of units from the base to the location of the stimulus. The base has a value of zero and the apex representing the unique excitation of a cone has a value of 1.0.

$$C_1 \text{ plots at } 0.1L, 0.1M, 0.8S$$

$$C_2 \text{ plots at } 0.4L, 0.3M, 0.3S$$

Above we asked where would C_3 plot if it was an equal mixture of C_1 + C_2? Let us divide the coefficients in half and then add C_1 and C_2.

$$C_1 : 0.05L, 0.05M, 0.40S$$

$$C_2 : 0.20L, 0.15M, 0.15S$$

Now adding C_1 + C_2 we obtain:

$$C_3 : 0.25L, 0.20M, 0.55S.$$

The reader will note that C_3 plots at the point Y_1 in Figure 5.18. We leave it as an exercise for the reader to prove to that point Y_2 is the result of mixing 4 units of C_1 with 1 unit of C_2.

Trichromatic Units

We have been treating the color triangle in Figure 5.18 as representing the relative cone excitation caused by stimuli of varying chromaticities. It is also possible to use the triangle as a stimulus color mixture diagram. In such a case the apexes would represent the primaries used to perform the color matches and would respectively be labeled I_L, I_M, and I_S for long wavelength, middle wavelength, and short wavelength primaries.

By definition, if equal "amounts" of I_L, I_M, and I_S stimuli are mixed, the mixture falls at the center of the color triangle. These amounts could be expressed in terms of photons, ergs, or trolands, but none of these turn out to be convenient. Another possibility is to let the position of a point in the color diagram represent the relative probabilities of photon absorption in the three kinds of cone photopigment. But this could be done only if these relative probabilities were known. Although, as we shall see, the shapes of the relative spectral sensitivity curves are now quite well established, such a specification is not possible because their relative heights are not known.

It is important to understand that color matches do not depend upon these relative heights. Suppose, for example, that a color match were made and that the numbers of molecules of L-photopigment in the retina were suddenly halved. A given stimulus, say one at about 580 nm that appeared yellow before, would now activate the L-cones relatively less than before and the appearance of the color presumably would change toward green, in much the same manner as in the case of adaptation to I_L light mentioned earlier. But, again, both sides of the field should change in the same way, providing no basis for upsetting the color match. Indeed, all of the L-photopigment could be removed and without upsetting the match, as in the case of the protanope (Chapter 10), who will accept the match of a normal observer.

If two fields match exactly, then each will in turn match the same additive mixture of I_L, I_M, and I_S components of a mixture stimulus. If the units of measurement for the I_L component of two identical stimuli are the same, equal numerical values imply equal amounts of that component. The same is, of course, true for the I_M and I_S components. But the units in which the I_L component is measured need not be the same as those for the I_M or I_S. It would be bizarre to do it, but it would be permissible to measure I_L in ergs/sec, I_M in photons/sec, and I_S in trolands.

One scheme that is used in practice is to abandon all of the familiar units and introduce new ones, known as trichromatic, or T-units. One could decide that the center of the color triangle should represent a white-appearing light that matches an equal-energy spectrum. If so, the decision implies that equal "amounts" of the I_L, I_M, and I_S mixture components produce this white. The T-units are specified by an auxiliary experiment in which the subject is asked to match an equal–energy stimulus using a mixture of the three mixture components. The amounts of each of the components of that mixture are then defined as equal under the matching condition, no matter how different they might be in radiometric or photometric units. A consistent result of this type of match is that the number of trolands of short wavelength light is quite small relative to the numbers of

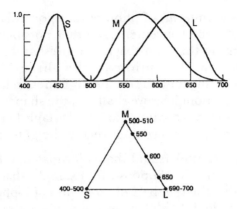

Figure 5.19 A second set of hypothetical spectral sensitivity curves. These differ from the first set (Fig. 5.16) in that the L- and M-curves now overlap. The result is that the spectral stimuli from 500 to 600 nm are now represented continuously along the LM side of the color triangle.

trolands of the long wavelength and middle wavelength primaries. This correlates with the fact that an amount of I_S that adds very little to the brightness of a pre-existing I_L, I_M mixture has the capacity to greatly alter the hue of the field.

L- and M-Curves that Overlap

We can move a step closer to reality by broadening the absorption curves of the assumed L- and M-pigments so that they partially overlap, as shown in Figure 5.19. If these curves implied the same probabilities of photon absorption at their peaks, then the crossing of the L- and M-curves at 600 nm would imply that a photon of that wavelength would stand an equal chance of being absorbed by either pigment. The curves have been drawn so that there is a range from 500 nm to 510 nm where the probability of absorption by the L-cones (and the S cones as well) is zero, and another range from 690 to 700 nm, where only the L-cones can absorb photons. Test stimuli falling within either of these ranges can therefore be matched by using only a single primary, provided that it is chosen to fall also within the same band of wavelengths as the test stimulus to be matched.

Suppose instead that the primaries are chosen to be 550 and 650 nm as before. In this case there will be some test wavelengths that can still be matched by a mixture of the two primaries, namely those that fall in the range from 550 to 650 nm. A test stimulus at 600 nm, which stimulates these two types of cones equally, can be matched by equal amounts of the two components, assuming that the L- and M-absorption curves are symmetrical as shown. Note that each component of the mixture is absorbed to some degree by the "wrong" type of cone, which did not happen in the initial example of Figure 5.16, where the L- and M-curves were not permitted to overlap. With the new curves, test stimuli in the range from 650 to 700 nm, and from 500 to 550 nm, cannot be matched by a mixture of 550- and 650-nm primaries because these test stimuli produce a greater imbalance in the relative stimulation of the two types of cone than do either of the components of the mixture. For example, a test stimulus at 695 nm uniquely activates L-cones, whereas the I_{650} mixture component does not. To make a color match in this case, the I_{550} primary must be placed on the "wrong" side of the field to be added to the 695-nm test.

Letting I_L stand for the long wavelength primary, I_M for the middle wavelength one, and T for the test, we can state the conditions for the match as

$$T + g\ (I_M) = r(I_L). \tag{5.11}$$

What is the amount g of the I_M primary that must be added to the test? It must be an amount that, when mixed with the test, will reduce the ratio of L- to M-cone excitation to 4, because this is the ratio of L- to M-cone excitation produced by the 650-nm component acting alone on the other side of the field. The reader can prove this by drawing horizontal lines from the intersection of the vertical line with the two curves at 650 to the left hand ordinate. The lower line will intersect at 20, the upper at 80; hence a 1:4 ratio. To find this value, first express the test stimulus and the two primaries by their relative absorptions by the L- and M-cones:

$$I_L = 0.8(L) + 0.2\ (M)$$
$$I_M = 0.8(M) + 0.2\ (L) \tag{5.12}$$
$$T = 1.0(L).$$

If we translate the requirement for a match of Equation (5.11) into these terms:

$$1.0(L)+ 0.8g(M)+ 0.2g(L)= 0.8r(L)+ 0.2r(M), \qquad (5.13)$$

the value g must be such that the two coefficients for (L) sum to four times that for (M) on the left-hand side of Equation (5.10). This condition is achieved when

$$\frac{1+0.2g}{0.8g} = 4 \qquad (5.14)$$

The value of g that satisfies Equation (5.14) is 0.333. Therefore the relative amount of I_M that must be mixed with the test in order to allow a match with the I_L primary is 0.333.

If we assume that the corners of the color triangle represent unique cone excitations then we can replot the spectral colors as required by the new curves. The point L still represents the location of a stimulus that would activate L-cones exclusively, which now covers the range from 690 to 700 nm. Because the I_{650} primary now stimulates the L-cones 4 times as much as the M-, it therefore plots four-fifths of the way from M toward L. Similarly, the I_{550} primary plots four-fifths of the way from L toward M. A stimulus of 600 nm, which stimulates L- and M-cones equally, plots midway between. By measuring ordinate values everywhere between 500 and 700 nm, the L/M ratios for all other spectral colors in this range can be determined and plotted in Figure 5.19 according to the center of gravity principle.

Broadening the S-Curve

The foregoing curves are still very fanciful because of the failure of the S-cone sensitivity curve to overlap with the others. To remedy this, the S-cone curve has been broadened in Figure 5.20. Over the range from 400 to 500 nm, all spectral stimuli continue to plot at the S- corner of the diagram because it is still true that S cones are exclusively activated by stimuli in this range. But the range from 510 to 590 nm reveals something new and interesting because for the first time in this series of examples, all three types of cones are assumed to be activated by spectral lights within this band of wavelengths. As an example of what this implies for the color triangle consider where a stimulus at 550 nm will plot. This wavelength is assumed to be absorbed equally by L- and S-cones, but by M-cones 5 times as much as for either of the others. If a photon is absorbed, the probability that it will happen in the M-cones is then 5/7. For the L- and S-cones, this probability is 1/7. This point plots as shown in Figure 5.20.

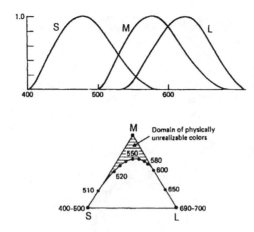

Figure 5.20   In this third set of hypothetical spectral sensitivity curves, the S-curve has been broadened to overlap the other two in the spectral region from 500 to 600 nm. These wavelengths are represented along the curved locus shown crossing the color triangle.

The locations of a number of other spectral stimuli have also been shown in Figure 5.20. Stimuli from the longwave end of the spectrum to 600 nm, which activate only L- and M-cones, fall along a straight line connecting L and 600 nm. In the region from 600 to 510 nm, the spectral locus is curved and this turns out to be characteristic of any part of the spectrum where three kinds of cones are stimulated. Below 500 nm all stimuli again plot at the S corner. Because mixtures of any two stimuli fall along a straight line that connects them, we can see at a glance that in the region of the spectrum where all three curves overlap to generate a curved spectral locus, no monochromatic light can be matched by a mixture of any two lights of other wavelengths. Note also that the M-cones can no longer be uniquely stimulated by any real light.

A Final Set of Curves

One more set of curves (Fig. 5.21) will take us fairly close to reality. We now extend the L-and M-curves farther into the short wavelengths. (If there is to be wavelength discrimination in the short wavelengths, then at least one of these curves must extend to 400 nm.) In Figure 5.21 the tails of the L- and M-curves have been extended so that they overlap throughout most of the visible spectrum, and the S curve has been given a breadth intermediate between the shapes that were assumed in the previous examples.

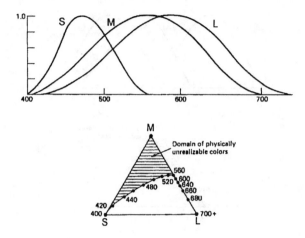

Figure 5.21 A fourth and final set of hypothetical spectral sensitivity curves. These approach those of real human cones in their qualitative aspects.

These curves are qualitatively similar to the real ones to the extent that the L- and M-curves are similar in shape and lie relatively close together, whereas the S-curve is different in shape and is also rather well separated from the other two, falling to zero at the longest wavelengths. The consequences of assuming these revised curves may be seen in the color triangle of Figure 5.21.

Physical Mixture Components at the Corners of the Diagram

Maxwell, who first used the triangular color diagram, had no information about cone pigments; therefore he plotted the physical components of his matching field at the corners of the triangle. This differs from what has been done in the foregoing examples, where each of the corners has represented the unique excitation of one type of cone. The spectral sensitivities of the cones overlap. Therefore, the colors represented at the corners of our diagram cannot match real lights that always activate more than just one type of cone. For this reason, the colors represented at the M-corner of Figure 5.21 (and for that matter all colors in the shaded region) can be called "imaginary."

If physical mixture stimuli (I_L, I_M, I_S) are specified instead at the corners of the diagram, a stimulus that would uniquely activate M-cones would be represented along an extension of the line L_M, beyond M to the upper left in Figure 5.21. This would imply that some I_L must be added to I_M in order to allow a real stimulus to match it.

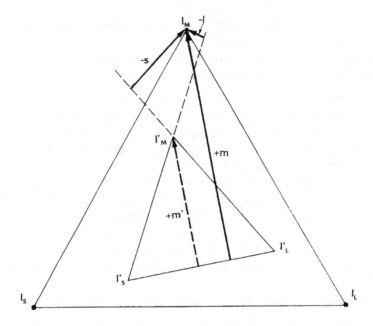

Figure 5.22 I_S, I_M, and I_L are imaginary primaries, lying outside the domain of real colors and those that can be matched by an additive mixture of real primaries I'_S, I'_M, and I_L. This construction show how imaginary primary I_M can be represented in terms of real primaries.

We can provide a further physical interpretation of the meaning of imaginary matching stimuli with the help of Figure 5.22. This time we will suppose that none of the three types of cones is capable of being uniquely stimulated by a real light. Let the triangle $I'_L I'_S I'_M$ enclose the domain of real colors that can be generated by mixtures of three physical lights. The larger triangle $I_L I_M I_S$ represents the enlarged domain of colors encompassed by a set of imaginary primaries, perhaps, but not necessarily, those corresponding to the spectral sensitivities of the three types of cones. Consider, as an example, the representation of the imaginary component I_M in terms of the real stimuli. The line labeled "+m" is drawn as a perpendicular from $I'_S I'_L$ to I_M. The length of this line specifies the proportion of I'_M that is needed. It implies that the proportion of I'_M is much greater than the unit amount (+m′) that can be physically achieved.

To determine the proportion of I'_L needed in a match for I_M first extend the line $I'_S I'_M$. The short perpendicular from this line to I_M is in a negative direction, because I_M falls above and to the left of the extension of $I'_S I'_M$. A similar construction reveals a need for an even

larger negative proportion of the I'_S component. These three proportions are now represented as distances labeled +m, –l, and –s.
These show the proportions of the three primaries needed to make
the match with I_M. As before, the sum of the three values is unity.

Place a mixture of the negative components I'_S and I'_L in one part
of a bipartite field, say on the left, where they will be seen as a purple.
Place the I'_M component on the right side of the field. Now the meaning of the imaginary primary I_M is this: if a unit amount of the imaginary primary I_M could somehow be added to the purple mixture in
the left side of the field the result (with suitable intensity adjustment)
would permit a match with I'_M on the right side of the field. In other
words, the purple mixture specifies a physical light that would be
required in order to desaturate the imaginary primary I_M until it
matches the real I'_M. Because light cannot be physically subtracted,
I_M is physically unrealizable, and it is in this sense that it is imaginary.

Transformations from One Set of Primaries to Another

Given a set of color-mixture curves that are based upon one set of
primaries, it is possible to calculate the color matches that these curves
imply for any other set of primaries. The primaries, or mixture components of the two sets, are assumed to differ in their spectral distributions; these may or may not be monochromatic. Such a transfer
from one set of primaries to another is possible because, as previously indicated, the laws of color mixture follow the laws of ordinary
algebra. The problem is best handled in the context of matrix algebra, where the solutions of the simultaneous equations required for
the transfer are routine. The reader will find a tutorial on such transformation in Appendix, Part III.

DATA FROM ACTUAL COLOR-MIXTURE EXPERIMENTS

Accurate sets of color-mixture functions were obtained long ago by J.
Guild (1925–1926) and W. D. Wright (1928–1929) in England.
Wright's curves indicated the amounts of the three spectral primaries that were required to match other spectral colors throughout
the visible spectrum. In 1931, the CIE settled upon a standardized
set of functions, derived by change of the assumed wavelengths of
the primaries into a new system said to represent the color matches
of a "standard observer" (Judd, 1933). When it became evident that
there was a problem with the CIE values in the short wavelength end
of the spectrum, Judd (1951a) published a correction that raised the
values of all three functions somewhat at wavelengths shorter than
about 450 nm. In 1959, Stiles and Burch reported the results of a

very careful investigation, carried out under CIE sponsorship at the National Physical Laboratory, the basic standards laboratory of Great Britain. The work yielded results that fell midway between the CIE values and Judd's corrected curves in most cases. Stiles and Burch reported only the average data of their 10 observers. In 1987, Trezona found and published the individual data for these 10 observers.

Stiles's Mixture Curves

The results of Stiles's determinations are shown as the solid curves of Figure 5.23. These are drawn through 49 data points, which fall so accurately upon the smooth functions that in most cases they cannot be seen. Also shown for comparison are the original CIE values and Judd's corrections of these. Stiles's curves show the amounts of the three spectral primaries at 644, 526, and 444 nm, required to match 46 other wavelengths in the spectrum. For convenience we will refer to these as the red, green, and blue primaries. The functions are presented in separate panels, one for each component of the mixture field. These show the relative energies that are required to match the test wavelength indicated on the x-axis. The relative energy values are scaled independently for each light so that the amount of a primary used, when it matches its own wavelength, is taken as 1.0 no matter what the actual energy. Most of the determinations were made at 500 td, although somewhat less light than this was available at the spectral extremes. It should be recalled that, within limits, color matches do not depend upon the absolute intensity level that is used; Stiles's intensities mostly fall within these limits.

Each function is plotted on a logarithmic ordinate. Although this is unconventional for representing color-matching data, it is necessary to show accurately values that are small relative to the peaks of the curves (recall the discussion of log scales on page 128). The fact that the low values can be accurately measured by the psychophysical method of color matching means that very small amounts of light absorption have very important effects upon color matching, as well as on the perception of color upon which such matching depends.

The direct method of reflection densitometry, it will be recalled, was able to only skim the top of the cone sensitivity function. MSP was somewhat more sensitive. The recently developed technique of suction electrophysiology measures cone spectral sensitivities with about the same sensitivity as psychophysics.

In Figure 5.23, each panel shows function that are interrupted at three places by vertical lines. These represent the wavelengths of the

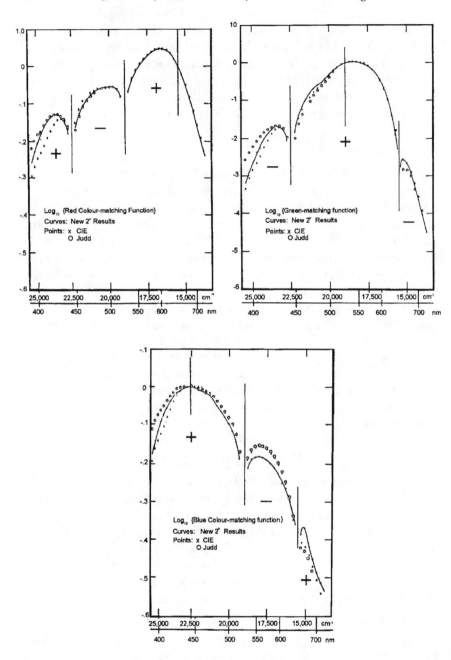

Figure 5.23   Color-mixture curves for 2° fields as determined by Stiles (1955). Each panel represents the amounts of one of the three primaries used in mixtures matching the spectral wavelengths shown.

primaries for which the amounts of the other two primaries, being zero, cannot be represented on the logarithmic ordinate. Where the test stimulus is of the same wavelength as one of the primaries, the ordinate value is, by definition, zero (the logarithm of 1). Within each panel, the spectrum is therefore divided into four regions. In four of the resulting twelve regions, negative proportions of a primary are represented; because negative numbers do not have logarithms, Stiles chose to indicate the logarithm of absolute values, together with the sign of the original values whose logarithms are plotted within each section of the curve.

From the shortest wavelengths tested to the wavelength of the blue primary, positive amounts of blue and red stimuli are required for a match, while small amounts of the green primary must be added to the test wavelength. In the next region of the spectrum (between the wavelengths of the blue and green primary components of the mixture field) positive amounts of the blue and green are required, while small amounts of red must be added to the test field. In a third region between the wavelengths of the green and red primaries, positive amounts of red and green are needed in the mixture field with small amounts of blue added to the other side. Beyond the wavelength of the red primary at the right, the red stimulus accounts for most of the mixture, together with a small negative amount of green and a tiny positive component of the blue.

Unit Coordinate System of Plotting

A way of plotting color mixture data that has proved very useful is shown in Figure 5.24. In this plot, the amounts of the three primary stimuli required to match each spectral wavelength are adjusted so that the ordinate values always sum to unity. The proportions of the red, green, and blue components are thereby directly given, and these can be used to represent colors in a color triangle or a chromaticity diagram. They are known as *chromaticity coefficients*. The details of the procedure used to obtain these particular curves are clever and worth understanding.

Earlier in this chapter (p. 173) it was noted that the units in which the primaries of a color match are specified are not ordinary ones. The system used in Figure 5.24 was developed many years ago by W. D. Wright (1928–1929). It makes use of two reference wavelengths that are located about midway between pairs of primaries (in this case 488 and 580 nm). We will call these the blue-green and yellow

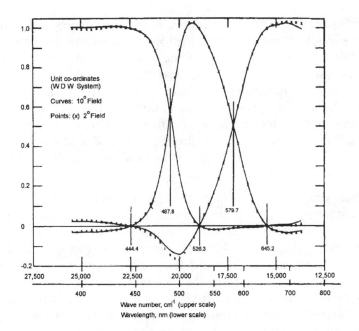

Figure 5.24   This way of plotting Stiles's color mixing data was developed by W. D. Wright. The amounts of the three primaries required to match each spectral wavelength (represented on the abscissa) are adjusted so that the ordinate values always sum to 1.0. See text for procedures used to obtain these particular curves.

reference wavelengths respectively. A color match is made, independently of the spectral determinations, in which the yellow reference is matched with a mixture of the red (645 nm) and green (526 nm) primaries. By convention, the amounts of the red and green are stated to be equal for this condition. A similar but separate operation is carried out for the blue (444 nm) and green lights, which are adjusted to match the blue-green reference; this defines equal amounts of these two stimuli. The fact that the green stimulus is used twice permits it to serve as a bridge between the units of red and blue. Here is a step-by-step example to illustrate how this works.

• Select some amount of the red primary, say 100 td. The subject is given control of the intensity of the green stimulus and of the yellow (580 nm) reference.

• The subject adjusts the amount of green in the mixture with the red in order to produce a yellow that matches the yellow reference. To make the match exact for brightness as well as hue, the observer simultaneously adjusts the amount of yellow reference. Suppose that it turns out that 200 td of the green primary stimulus is needed for the match. (A very small amount of the blue stimulus may be required, added to the reference, in order to make the match exact.)

- The 200-td green primary is mixed with the blue. The blue-green reference is the main component of the other half of the field, but a modest amount of the red stimulus will be needed to desaturate it. The subject therefore adjusts three stimuli (all except the green) to make a match. Suppose that 5 td of the blue component is required in the match.

- The troland amounts of the red, green, and blue mixture components in the two matches are in the ratio of 100 : 200 : 5. To specify the amount of a mixture component in any subsequent color match, in *trichromatic units,* the troland values are reciprocally adjusted: the red troland values are multiplied by 2, the green by 1, and the blue by 40.

The clever part of this scheme is that it eliminates from the color equation the effects of prereceptoral absorption, which vary considerably from one subject to another. The method works because the quality of a monochromatic light cannot be changed by the action of an absorbing medium; as Newton demonstrated, only the amount is altered. For an observer with a very yellow (short wavelength-absorbing) lens, for example, the energy required to achieve a unit trichromatic amount of the blue component will be higher than for an observer with a clear lens. Yet for both subjects, a unit trichromatic amount of each of these lights implies the same stimulating power at the retina.

When this procedure is followed, the agreement between observers is very good. A set of curves for 10 observers tested by Wright (1946) is shown in Figure 5.25.[21] Although the wavelengths of the primaries used by Wright are slightly different than those that yielded Stiles's curves of Figure 5.24, the general features are the same.

SPECTRAL ABSORPTION
CURVES OF HUMAN CONE PIGMENTS

We have seen that color mixture curves have shapes that depend upon the choice of wavelengths of the primaries used to determine them, but that all such sets of curves represent the same color-matching behavior. "Imaginary" components of a mixture field cannot be physically realized because they imply a degree of selectivity of absorption in cone photopigments that cannot be achieved by real lights because of the overlapping nature of the spectral absorption curves of real

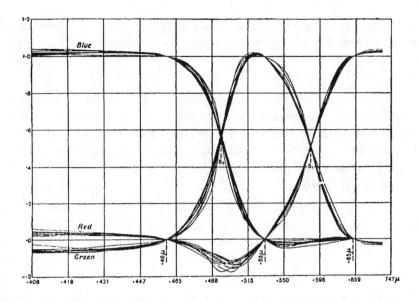

Figure 5.25 Color matching data of W. D. Wright, for several subjects plotted in the unit coordinate system. (From Wright, 1946.)

cones. There are many triads of imaginary primaries that yield color-mixture curves whose values are all positive; if the domain of real colors plots entirely inside a color triangle whose corners define the components of the mixture field, an all-positive set of curves is indicated.

The actual absorption curves of human cone pigments must be related to the data of color-mixing experiments because a color match implies equal absorptions for each member of the metameric pair within the three kinds of cone pigment. The absorption curves of the actual pigments must also be all-positive because negative absorption has no physical meaning. Therefore, of all the possible sets of imaginary mixture stimuli enclosing the domain of real colors in the color diagram, there is one (and only one) such set that specifies the relative absorption spectra of the actual pigments contained in the outer segments of L-, M-, and S-cones of the human eye.

Importance of Data from Color Variant Observers

The search for these curves, which has been a long one, has nearly ended. The key that has unlocked their hiding place has been found within the eyes of certain color variant observers (see Chapter 10). It depends upon the finding that the color vision they exhibit is not different in principle from that of normal subjects, but is impoverished specifically because they lack one or another of the normal cone photopigments. Not all color-variant observers meet this requirement; those who do are called *dichromats*.

Left with but two types of cones, the dichromat needs only two primary components in order to make a color match. If given three knobs to adjust, each controlling the amount of one of the components of the mixture, his matches are neither unique nor reproducible, and it is only by chance if the resulting match is also acceptable to a normal observer. There will be much more to be said about abnormal color vision in Chapter 10, but the facts mentioned here should be sufficient to make it clear why the dichromat is so important for the understanding of normal cone pigments.

Dartnall's Standard Shape

In 1953, H. J. A. Dartnall demonstrated that a wide variety of photopigments that had been extracted from many different species had absorption spectra having the same shape,[22] if plotted on the basis of wavenumber (proportional to frequency of vibration). Although many different wavelengths of peak sensitivity could be found, a template based on the curve shape for any one of them could be used to represent any of the others, simply by shifting it laterally along the wavenumber axis.

The shape of the standard curve is shown in Figure 5.26, where it will be seen to have a smooth principal peak. If extended to shorter wavelengths, the curve would continue its rise, producing a secondary maximum called a *cis-peak*. For a pigment like human rhodopsin, the cis-peak is in the ultraviolet and can play no role in vision.

Dartnall's standard curve is an empirical generalization. There exists no adequate chemical theory to show exactly why it should be true that discrete shifts of curves having the same shape, if plotted in this particular way, should occur. We will not deal here with any theoretical ideas that have been advanced, except to say that the explanation for the shape of the linear longwave slope, which was dealt with on page 133, is consistent with Dartnall's template. The important point is that it works, and if the concept could be extended to the treatment of the pigments of human cone vision, then their exact shapes would be known if the wavelengths of peak sensitivity could be established with sufficiently high accuracy.

This hope has been frustrated. In the first place, there is a bad fit between the Dartnall template and the spectral sensitivity curves of

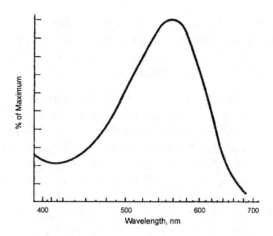

Figure 5.26   Dartnall's (1953) standard curve for a pigment with a peak sensitivity at 560 nm.

protanopes and deuteranopes. The most careful analysis of this discrepancy is due to Smith and Pokorny (1972) and Stiles and Wyszecki (1974). The latter authors posed the question: Is it possible to find a set of Dartnall pigments such that, with preretinal absorption taken into account, they are adequate transformations of color mixture data? The answer is "no." Most of the difficulty seems related to the shape of the longwave pigment (L-photopigment). Smith and Pokorny approached the problem by taking a careful look at protanopic and deuteranopic spectral sensitivity data available in the psychophysical literature (all of it consistent with the physical evidence of retinal densitometry). Figure 5.27 illustrates what they found. When the data are plotted on a wavenumber scale, the data for protanopes and deuteranopes coincide. The dashed curve in this plot represents the Dartnall template. The discrepancy is mainly at the long wavelengths, and although it is not large, it is highly significant for color vision. Again, the tails of the curve prove to be important. When Smith and Pokorny had a retrospective look at the pigment absorption data in the literature, they found many other instances where their curve shape fitted the experimental data somewhat better than did that of Dartnall.

S-photopigment, on the other hand, seems definitely to be a pigment of the original type. It is a curious fact that, despite the elusive nature of this "short wavelength-catching" pigment from the standpoint of physical measurement, its characteristics have been the easi-

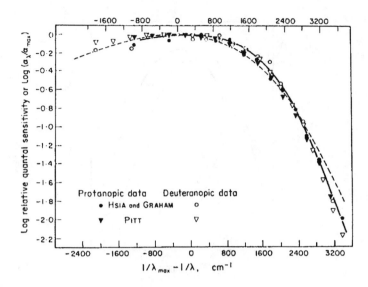

Figure 5.27 Log relative quantal sensitivity as a function of wavenumber for protanopes and deuteranopes. All curves have been scaled to unity at their maxima and they have been shifted laterally for best fit. The dashed line is Dartnall's standard shape; the solid line is from Vos and Walraven (1971). (From Smith & Pokorny, 1972.)

est of all to reveal by psychophysical methods. Some of these methods will be discussed in the next chapter; the most obvious data once again have come from a class of color-variant observer, the *S-cone mono-chromat*.[23] These subjects apparently have only S-cones and rods (see Chapter 10), so it is easy at high intensities to measure the spectral sensitivity of their S-cones psychophysically. The resulting curve is excellently fitted by Dartnall's original curve shape.

Smith and Pokorny's finding strongly suggests, though it does not prove, that deuteranopia is caused by a loss of M-photopigment and not by fusion: it seems unlikely that a single template could be used to fit the sensitivity curves of protanopes, from whom it is virtually certain that L-photopigment is missing, and deuteranopes as well, if in fact the deuteranopes possessed both kinds of pigment. Rushton's view (p. 149), based on retinal densitometry, is therefore supported.

The smooth curve drawn through the data in Figure 5.27 is due to an earlier analysis by Vos and Walraven (1971). The set of cone sensitivity curves derived by these authors is very similar to a set proposed by Smith and Pokorny. Both are probably very close to the

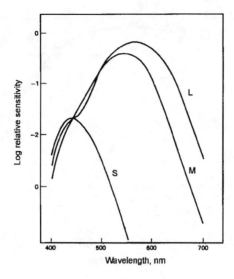

Figure 5.28   The spectral curves of Smith and Pokorny. These come very close to representing the relative spectral sensitivities of L-, M-, and S-photopigments of the human retina. The relative heights of the curves are discusses in the text. The values of these curves are given in the Appendix.

actual curves. This section will be concluded with a brief description of considerations leading to the curves that are shown in Figure 5.28 (also given in tabular form on page 558). Before itemizing the facts that these curves attempt to predict, one additional concept needs to be elaborated.

Spectral Sensitivity Functions for Photopic Vision

Spectral sensitivity for rod vision can be unambiguously obtained, as we saw on page 134, because a metameric match is achieved and both halves of the field therefore appear identical. The measurement of analogous functions for photopic vision is a more difficult problem, one that will be discussed more fully in Chapter 9. These functions, which are also called spectral luminous efficiency functions, or *"luminosity functions"* for short, are ambiguous for cone vision because, as noted earlier, two wavelengths of equal luminosity for cones are perceived as being qualitatively different. Luminosity functions have nevertheless been obtained for normal subjects at photopic levels of intensity, and these have been compared with the less ambiguous curves that come from dichromats. Vos and Walraven

(1971) used luminosity data of normal subjects not only to help specify the relative spectral sensitivity curves for the three types of cones, but also to suggest where these curves should be displayed vertically, relative to one another, in a sensitivity vs wavelength plot. Otherwise, their analysis also depends heavily upon a consideration of the characteristics of dichromats.

The curves of Figure 5.28 have the following properties:

• They account for color mixture curves of normal subjects.

• If the L- and M-curves are added together, they predict the luminosity function of the normal observer.

• If either the L- or M-curve is eliminated, the remaining curve accounts for the luminosity curves of protanopes and deuteranopes respectively (S-cones are assumed not to contribute to luminance).

• If it is assumed that the heights of these curves are proportional to the relative numbers of cone receptors of the three types in the retina, then a reasonable estimate of the relative numbers of L-, M-, and S-cones in the foveal region is about 32 : 16 : 1 respectively (Walraven, 1974). The S-cone curve is reasonably consistent with other estimates of its shape, as for example that derived from the data of S-cone monochromats (see p. 457).

SUMMARY

Human vision begins with the absorption of photons by the photopigments that reside in the outer segments of the photoreceptors. One of these, rhodopsin, is found in the outer segments of rods. When a photon is absorbed, it isomerizes the rhodopsin molecule and initiates the sequence of events leading to vision. The probability of photon absorption varies with wavelength, but once a photon is absorbed, all information about its wavelength is lost. Any two arbitrary spectral distributions may therefore be matched for their effects upon rhodopsin simply by varying the intensity of one of them. Because rods contain only rhodopsin and operate over a low range of intensities below the cone threshold, rod vision is color-blind. Color vision depends upon the absorption of photons in the three kinds of cones, which contain different pigments. Unlike rhodopsin, these have resisted direct chemical analysis.

It appears likely that a given type of cone contains only one kind of pigment. Stimuli that differ in their spectral distribution may also appear identical in cone vision; these metameric matches are much more restricted than for rods and most spectral distributions that differ physically cannot be made to match at any adjustment of relative intensity. Metameric matches occur in the special cases where the same rates of photon capture occur in each of the three types of cones, by being absorbed at the same rate by L-photopigment (the L-cone pigment), M-photopigment (M-cones), and S-photopigment (S-cones). As for rods, once a photon is absorbed by a cone pigment molecule, the visual system has no information about its wavelength. The initial basis for color perception therefore lies, as Thomas Young suspected long ago, in the relative rates of light absorption by the three types of photopigments.

The exact shapes of the pigment absorption curves are critically important for understanding color vision. The method of microspectrophotometry permits direct measures of the transmittances of cone photopigments, but primate data are scarce and noisy, serving only to confirm the trichromatic view in a general way. Retinal densitometry, which can be practiced on living human subjects, measures the change in light reflected from the back of the eye as this varies with the bleaching of the photopigments. Although more extensively used than microspectrophotometry, it has suffered from two limitations: (1) S-photopigment, though certainly present, cannot be observed by this technique; (2) the method "fails in the tails" for L-photopigment and M-photopigment because the important lower limbs of their absorption spectra cannot be assessed accurately. Suction electrophysiology does better.

Nevertheless, the shapes of the absorption curves of human cone photopigments are known with reasonable accuracy from inferences drawn from human psychophysical experiments. Color-mixture experiments with normal and dichromatic subjects have been especially helpful in this regard. In principle, any light can be represented by a point in a color triangle, as Maxwell first showed, where distances from the three sides specify the proportions of the three components of the mixture. If the corners of the diagram represent the physiological primaries, then a given location in the triangle can specify, at least in principle, the relative probabilities that a photon will be absorbed by each of the three types of pigment. These probabilities are the same for all metamers that are represented by that point.

The power of color-mixture data for revealing physiological facts lies first of all in the discovery that the numerical data and operations of color matching are isomorphic with the numbers and operations of ordinary algebra. This permits the writing of color equations to express the results of color-mixture experiments. Depending upon the choice of primaries that are used in such calculations, the colors of the spectrum can be specified by an infinite number of sets of three curves. Only one of these can represent the set of three physiological primaries whose values are proportional, if preretinal absorption is taken into account, to the action spectra of the three types of cone photopigments. This choice has been made mainly on the basis of the data from dichromats who lack one or another of the normal cone pigments.

NOTES

[1] If humans did not experience metamerism then many of the manufactured items, for example in an automobile, would not appear to be the same color. It is necessary sometimes to use different pigments to color plastic, vinyl, and the cloth from which upholstery is made. Metameric surface color matches usually break down a little when viewed under some of the variety of common illuminants (daylight, incandescent lamps, fluorescent tubes, and various other types of discharge lamps).

[2] The word *lightness* is used to refer to the perceived correlate of the reflectance of a surface, as opposed to the brightness of a disembodied aperture color. It will be recalled from Chapter 2 that there is a profound difference between these two modes of viewing. Most of the basic color science under discussion in this book is based on experiments where aperture colors have been viewed, as these are simpler to interpret. Surface color is considered in Chapter 11.

[3] Whereas the word "intensity" is used here (and elsewhere in the book) in its generic sense, it will always stand for a physical measure. Strictly speaking, what is under discussion in this section is radiometric intensity per unit (projected) area of the field, known as *radiance.*

[4] If the fields are continuously exposed, the significant measure is not the number of photons in the exposure, but their rate. It will be seen in Chapter 9 that the number of photons is the physical correlate, which determines the threshold visibility and suprathreshold brightness of very brief flashes. The word "number," as used here, could stand either for the number of photons per unit time (rate) in an extended stimulus presentation, or the total number presented during a very brief flash.

[5] Weale (1963). For a review, see Ruddock (1972).

[6] Cooper and Robson (1969).

[7] Wald's Nobel lecture, delivered in Stockholm on December 12, 1967, has been published in *Science* (Wald, 1968). This provides a good review of his work, including that concerned with human color vision and color blindness.

[8] Brindley's discussion of this subject is on pages 251 and 252 of the first edition of his book, published in 1960. The topic has been dropped in the second edition (Brindley, 1970).

[9] An action spectrum is the relative energy needed to produce a constant visual effect.

[10] Wald (1937) extracted a cone pigment called iodopsin from the chicken, and Bridges (1962) reported extracting two cone pigments from the pigeon. No primate pigments have ever been extracted.

[11] Some comments of Rushton (1966), triggered by his reaction to such theories, make choice reading. For example (p. 1130):

"Vision is a subject infected by a type of speculator from which most subjects are immune — the speculator who delights in suggesting what is fantastically improbable, and then challenging the world to prove his particular fantasy impossible. Speculators are concerned to conceal the cracks in their structure. Scientists study the relevant observations at first hand. . . . Speculators rely on popular sources, review articles, student textbooks, etc. . . . Most important of all, the scientist's theory leads to predictions that can be tested experimentally, and which he generally is employed in testing: by means of this his theory may be improved. The speculator is not concerned with experiments or indeed in meeting the reality behind his speculation at all. His speculations seldom lead to new and testable predictions and consequently remain a patch of sterility in the fertile forest of experimentation."

[12] Although Brindley and Willmer (1952) had described a retinal densitometer, they did not successfully measure the effects of bleaching, and the first full papers from the Cambridge laboratory were those of Campbell and Rushton (1955), and Rushton, Campbell, Hagins, and Brindley (1955). In 1953, Weale described an application of the method to the observation of "Photochemical reactions in the living cat's retina" in the *Journal of Physiology*. He first described the procedure in the *Annual Report of the Institute Ophthalmology* 1950–51 (p. 18).

[13] In retinal densitometry, complications due to stray light can sometimes lead to double-peaked curves even though a single pigment with a single peak sensitivity is present (Rushton, 1965b, p. 34).

[14] The π mechanisms are defined and discussed in Chapter 6. Suffice it to say that current evidence indicates that π_1, π_4, and π_5 have spectral sensitivities similar to, but not identical with, the S-, M-, and L-cone fundamentals.

[15] Working the other way round, Miller (1972) estimated the density of L-photopigment and M-photopigment by measuring the effects of bleaching on the spectral sensitivity of protanopes and deuteranopes. His density values fall in the range from 0.4 to 0.6.

[16] $V_M(\lambda)$ is the CIE photopic luminous efficiency function (CIE, 1990) as modified first (1951) by Judd (1951) and then by Vos (1978).

[17] Colors may also be "mixed" by means of half-silvered mirrors, by repeating them in rapid succession (Chapter 9) or by presenting them as large numbers of interlaced tiny dots, each too small to be resolved by the eye. The latter is the principle used in "pointillist" painting and color television.

[18] Grassman anticipated this in part long ago when he wrote (Helmholtz, 1924, p. 133 v. 2): "When one of two kinds of light that are to be mixed together changes continuously, the appearance of the mixture changes continuously also" (Grassman's second law). It may be helpful for some readers to appreciate that color matching is akin to solving three simultaneous equations by iteration. To be successful at this, it is necessary to know whether a change from what has gone before in one of the coefficients has allowed one to move closer to, or farther from, a solution. Similarly, when the subject changes the amount of one of the primaries in the mixture, he must be able to tell whether that change has caused the fields to appear more or less similar than before.

[19] We are indebted to A. Eisner for the following proof, which requires that it be shown that the sum of the lengths of the perpendiculars erected from the three sides of an equilateral triangle to any point inside the triangle is a constant equal

to the altitude of the triangle. If a is the length of an altitude and s is the length of a side, the area of the equilateral triangle is $A = \frac{1}{2}as$ because all three sides are equal. Now divide the full triangle into six right triangles by means of the dotted lines from the internal point to the three corners. The area of the full triangle must be equal to the sum of the areas of these six triangles. Therefore:

$$A = \tfrac{1}{2}gz_1 + \tfrac{1}{2}gz_2 + \tfrac{1}{2}by_1 + \tfrac{1}{2}by_2 + \tfrac{1}{2}rx_1 + \tfrac{1}{2}r\,x_2$$

$$= \tfrac{1}{2}g(z_1 + z_2) + \tfrac{1}{2}b(y_1 + y_2) + \tfrac{1}{2}r(x_1 + x_2)$$

$$= \tfrac{1}{2}gs + \tfrac{1}{2}rs + \tfrac{1}{2}bs$$

$$= \tfrac{1}{2}(g + r + b)s$$

Therefore

$$\tfrac{1}{2}as = \tfrac{1}{2}(g + r + b)s$$

$$a = g + r + b.$$

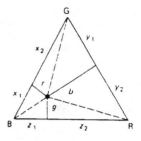

[20] The expression "physiological identity" was coined by F. J. J. Clarke (1960), p. 376.

[21] Starting on page 126 of his book *Researches on Normal and Defective Colour Vision,* Wright (1946) explains the special system he developed for specifying the trichromatic coefficients as described here.

[22] Two such curves are in fact required, depending upon animal species. It was not revealed earlier in this chapter that the photochemical process in the eye depends upon a store of vitamin A from which one of the important components needed for regeneration is derived. Humans possess one type of vitamin A called vitamin A_1, some other animals (for example, fish) possess vitamin A_2.

[23] In the literature, this type of observer is frequently referred to as "blue-cone monochromats." We avoid this terminology in favor of restricting hue names for chromatic percepts.

Chapter 6

Sensitivity Regulation

INTRODUCTION

People with normal vision are capable of making chromatic and achromatic visual discriminations over an enormous range of light intensities. Although it is not pleasant to do so, one can, for example, read in midday under direct summer sunlight, and yet see well enough on a hazy night to avoid large objects while walking around under feeble, haze-filtered starlight. For these daily visual extremes, the ratio of intensities is about 10^{10}, or ten thousand million, to 1. On a logarithmic scale, this enormous range is about equally divided between scotopic (rod) and photopic (cone) vision. When rods alone are stimulated there is no color vision, for reasons given in the previous chapter. Accordingly, this chapter will mainly deal with visual discriminations that occur within the photopic range. Nevertheless, it will again prove instructive to consider the simpler rod system as a prototype.

Before beginning a discussion of the technical aspects of visual sensitivity control, a pair of illustrations from everyday life will help set the stage. Consider that none of the stars visible on a clear night sky are seen during the day. Yet the increment of light added to the retinal image, by the image of a star, is unchanged when the sun rises. The difference must therefore have something to do with the nature of the visual system, and the way it responds to such increments with and without background illumination. Scattered light from the sun, which illuminates the sky, will add to the light from a star. The increment of retinal illumination provided by the star, by itself sufficient to render that star easily visible against the night sky, becomes insufficient to allow the perception of the same star against the bright daytime sky. The effect is not absolute, for brighter objects can still be seen. The moon, for example, has an intensity at night that is roughly equal to that of the sky by day. In the daytime, the luminance of the moon adds to that of the sky. The ratio of intensities of moon-plus-sky to sky alone is approximately two to one– easily sufficient to allow the moon to be seen. In fact, an object the size of the moon could still be detected (though just barely) even if its intensity were only about one percent that of the sky.

Although the increment provided by a star in the daytime is the same as it is at night, the percentage of light that it adds decidedly is not. The invisibility of stars in the daytime could easily be understood if the sensitivity of the eye were found to depend upon ratios, rather than increments. The idea that sensory systems react in such a way is captured in *Weber's law,* which states that "$\Delta I/I$ = constant." This is perhaps the oldest law in visual psychophysics. More than one hundred years ago Fechner wrote in his *Elements of Psychophysics* that "The law as applied to vision had, in the past, been stated by Bouguer, Arago, Masson, and Steinheil in connection with other investigations, and later by myself and Volkmann, without, however, anyone's paying much attention to it."[1] It turns out that for vision Weber's law applies only at high intensities and even then not always perfectly. Nevertheless, there is more truth to it (except at extremely low levels of illumination) than to a law stating that the sensitivity to increments is what remains constant.

A further example from everyday life serves to illustrate another crucial point about sensitivity regulation, namely that changes in visual sensitivity take time. Because of this delay, entering a dimly lit enclosure, such as a theater on a bright day, can be a most difficult experience. At first the aisle is not visible unless illuminated, and it is quite impossible to tell whether a seat is occupied, or for that matter even whether there are seats. In the dark theater visibility gradually improves; gross outlines become discriminable, for example the boundary of an aisle. Later it is possible to tell whether a seat is occupied, and eventually a familiar face can be recognized. Vision in the dimly lit enclosure will gradually improve and eventually (in about 30 minutes) reach a state that is optimal for that amount of illumination. (Recall the exercise on page 55.) This process is called *dark adaptation.* The reverse process, which occurs upon leaving the dimly lit enclosure, is called *light adaptation* and is completed in about five minutes.

CHROMATIC ADAPTATION: A TRIPLE PROBLEM

The basic information about color received by the brain derives initially from the relative degree of activity among three classes of cones. If we lived in a world where photopic illumination never varied, we could forget about the problem of adaptation. But instead there is at least a million-to-one range of luminances with which the cones must contend. The cones and their associated pathways deal with this range by adapting automatically in order to keep themselves within a sensitive range. We will see that there are many mechanisms needed to accomplish this, and that doubtless there are others yet to be discovered. All these somehow manage to work in concert and with such incredible precision that the colored appearance of things changes relatively little over most of the range of stimulus intensities. This resistance to changes of color appearance is one aspect of an important field of study called color constancy, which will be dealt with in some detail in Chapter 11. Where color vision is concerned it is not just the sensitivity of a unitary photopic system that is under continuous adjustment, but rather that of a system with three inputs.[2]

The mechanisms of adaptation are nevertheless easily capable of changing perceived hue. This change is an aspect of what is called *chromatic adaptation.* Try the exercise described below,* and the subjective effects of chromatic adaptation will become evident.

> Normally we see colors about the same way with each of our eyes. Test this by covering one eye at a time, switching your view of various colored surfaces seen in the environment. (For a few readers there may be slight differences, which probably will not have been noticed before.) Now, while covering the left eye, stare for 15 to 30 seconds at a bright light, such as an incandescent lamp or the sky. Upon repeating the original experiment, definite differences will be seen depending upon which eye does the looking; these will fade over time as the exposed eye recovers its original state of sensitivity. During the period when the two eyes differ, looking with both eyes will result in an intermediate sensation. This demonstration shows that a major part of the chromatic balance is independently determined by independent mechanisms within each eye. The fact that the two eyes normally mediate the same sensations results from the fact that they are normally in the same state of adaptation (for example, both eyes are exposed to a bright source); it also shows the almost incredible precision of identical control by the separate eyes.

Underlying this demonstration are parallel mechanisms, existing independently within each eye, that orchestrate a process of sensitivity adjustment that normally keeps all systems precisely tuned, preserving the delicate balance required for stable chromatic perception. Most of these mechanisms work independently within each eye. This is true of the photopigments that absorb the light, of the cones that contain them, and of all the retinal machinery that was discussed in Chapter 4. The demonstration shows that the colored appearance of things can easily be upset by adapting the eye to unusual conditions. But if the two eyes receive almost the same input, as they normally do, the adaptive machinery is so precise that there is normally no difference at all in the perceived color of objects as they are viewed alternately with the two eyes.

NUMBERS OF PHOTONS INVOLVED

It is helpful to develop some conception of the numbers of photons that impinge on the retina for the range of conditions in which color vision occurs. The least amount of light entering the central part of the pupil[3] required for foveal vision corresponds to about 0.1 td. By Equation (3.2) (p. 85) this corresponds at 555 nm to 125,000 photons per square degree on the retina during each second. In order to see such a threshold light, an exposure of only 100 ms is as effective as one that lasts an entire second (1,000 ms). Therefore, 12,500 photons in the briefer exposure are sufficient to arouse a visual sensation.

Because there are about 10,000 cones in one square degree of fovea, the numbers of photons arriving in 100 ms at threshold are on the same order of magnitude as the number of cones. Because not all arriving photons are absorbed, there are evidently fewer photons absorbed than there are cones.

Suppose that a white page reflects 80% of the incident light, and the black print 5%. A few calculations will show what this implies at three levels: (a) threshold, (b) a good level of illumination for reading, and (c) outdoor sunlight.

	Trolands (completely reflecting surface)	Photons per 100 ms per sq. deg. of retina (page)	Photons per 100 ms per sq. deg. of retina (print)	Page–print difference	Print to page ratio
Threshold	0.1 td	10^5	6.25×10^3	9.375×10^4	0.0625
Reading light	1,000 td	10^9	6.25×10^7	9.375×10^8	0.0625
Sunlight	100,000 td	10^{11}	6.25×10^9	9.375×10^{10}	0.0625

The percentages of light reflected from a white page and black print do not depend upon illumination level because the percentages relate directly to the probability that each incident photon will be reflected, and this probability, although it differs for print and page, is not affected by light level. Thus the ratio of print to page luminance is 0.0625, whether the values that enter into the calculation of this ratio (itself dimensionless) are expressed in trolands, numbers of photons, or whatever units. From the table one can see how, as illumination level is raised, the print-page *difference* in photon density at the retina increases from 9.375×10^4 to 9.375×10^{10} photons per square degree of retinal area during each 100 ms. A difference of 937.5 million photons, provided by reading light, would under sunlight result only if the print to page ratio were increased to .990625. This could be done by using a very light gray ink, but such letters would be very difficult to see, being at less than 1% contrast, under any light. [Contrast is defined in this case as the difference between the print and page values divided by the page value. Although there are other definitions of contrast, this is a good one to use when the critical (test) area to be discriminated–in this case letters–is small relative to the background, because positive contrasts (test area brighter than the background) produce nearly equivalent visual effects (Blackwell, 1946)].

Sensitivity to contrast generally improves as illumination is increased, in violation of Weber's law, and our ability to see objects against their backgrounds in fact improves–as we all know from everyday experience–as the level of illumination is raised. But our ability to see an object of fixed intensity, such as a star or traffic signal, decreases.

THE USE OF BACKGROUND AND TEST FIELDS

In Chapter 5, we saw that a simple bipartite field, used for color matching, has unexpected power for generating data useful for understanding the spectral sensitivities of the cones. For studying adaptation, a different stimulus configuration has often been used, one that is equally simple. *Background fields* are used to control the state of adaptation of the eye. The size of these fields does not matter very much, so long as it subtends about six degrees or more of visual angle. In many experiments the background is presented continuously to maintain the desired state of adaptation. Then, while the subject is still looking at the field, a *test flash* is superimposed upon the adapting field. If a small flash appears at the point of fixation it can easily be confined to the rod-free area of the fovea. Threshold foveal flashes are frequently measured and are defined as that intensity of the flash required for it to be just barely visible. The test flash is too brief and feeble to affect the state of adaptation being probed. With this technique many things can be varied, especially the intensity and spectral composition of the background field.

Background fields, if presented steadily, can raise the threshold of perception for superimposed test flashes (recall the stars). But backgrounds near threshold intensities have no such effect: only when their intensities are about 30 times greater than threshold do they begin to elevate the threshold of the added flash. Such a background would, in a 100-ms period, deliver nearly 300,000 photons to the flash area, corresponding to about 30 photons per cone. At 100,000 td, the 10 billion photons involved would provide about 1 million photons per receptor. These threshold statistics show that an individual cone is able to register, at least some of the time, the arrival of a single photon. Yet that same receptor must also be able to withstand the assault of more than a million photons in a 1000-ms exposure. The ability of the eye to adjust its sensitivity so that it can respond effectively over such very wide ranges of light intensity is called *visual adaptation*. Subsumed within it are the specialized problems of light, dark, and chromatic adaptation.

PHOTOGRAPHY AS AN ANALOG

To make good photographs the film exposure must be appropriate to the amount of light falling on the external scene, which in turn is proportional to that imaged by the optics of the camera at the film plane. As many would-be photographers have learned to their sorrow, seriously underexposed film leads to photographic prints that are black all over, whereas severe overexposure leads to photographic whiteout.

The potential amount of information in a photograph is related to the number of discriminable spatial elements that comprise it, multiplied by the number of discriminable steps of brightness that can be provided by each element. Extremely inappropriate exposure, whether too great or too small, causes the loss of all information that the photograph otherwise might have conveyed.

Because cameras and eyes look at the same scenes, both are faced with the same problem of attempting to respond appropriately to the amount of incoming light. Because of the incredibly sophisticated design of the eye, inappropriate exposure happens relatively seldom, and then usually only to a modest degree. Because cameras are simpler than eyes, and most readers will have had some experience with photography, the principles of proper photographic exposure will be described in order to provide background for what follows on the sensitivity regulation of the eye. Despite the usefulness of the eye–camera analogy, the reader is warned that eyes and cameras do not usually solve their problems in the same way. It is the problems, not their solutions, that are common in the two cases.

It is necessary to pause for a moment to introduce another photometric concept, in relation to the troland unit introduced in Chapter 3. *Luminance* is a technical term that refers to the intensity per unit area of light coming from a surface toward the eye. In referring to quantitative measures of luminance in this and chapters to follow, the unit of *candela per square meter* (cd/m^2) will be used exclusively. For the purposes of this book all we need to know about this unit is its relation to the unit of retinal illuminance, the troland (introduced on page 84). By definition, a surface external to the eye having a luminance of 1 cd/m^2 produces a retinal illuminance of 1 td if the pupil area of the eye is 1 mm^2. For an external surface of fixed luminance, the retinal illuminance produced by it increases in proportion to the area of the pupil. Neither the area of the surface nor its distance from the eye affects either luminance or retinal illumination.[4]

In order to produce a photograph that depicts objects, the luminances of various areas in the scene must differ. Objects stand out because they are either brighter or darker than the backgrounds against which they are seen. (For the moment, we neglect the role of color differences.) Because many scenes do not depict actual sources of light, we consider here only those that depend upon reflected light for their rendition. We shall ignore also certain important problems in connection with the highlights caused by specular surfaces. Assuming uniform illumination and a flat scene (recall the marbles at the bottom of Fig. 2.5), the total range of luminances depends entirely upon the range of reflectances of the objects that are there. Some objects reflect more than 90 percent of the light incident upon them. No matter what the illumination, those that reflect about 70 percent or more appear white, whether directly viewed or seen in a good photographic reproduction. At the other extreme, objects that reflect less than 4 or 5 percent of the incident light appear black. Therefore the range of intensities that a photographic print must provide, which corresponds exactly to the range of reflectances that it can produce, need not be greater than about 20:1 in order for the lightnesses of the original scene to be reasonably well depicted.

If the illumination falling upon all scenes were constant, the design of cameras and eyes would be greatly simplified. Because constant illumination yields a fixed range of object and background luminances, a camera could be designed with a fixed lens opening and shutter speed, allowing the film always to be exposed within its most

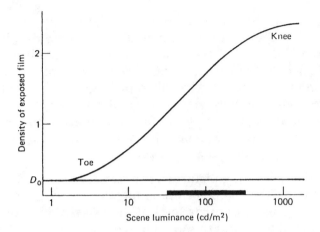

Figure. 6.1   This curve shows how the density of a photographic negative increases as a function of the scene luminance. Plotted on the abscissa is the luminance of the external scene, assuming a fixed diaphram at the camera lens. The black rectangle on the abscissa corresponds to a 20:1 range of luminances; the density of the exposed film increases rapidly and nearly linearly through this range.

sensitive range. But as already noted, the actual range of illuminations under which cameras and eyes function is enormous. A highly reflecting surface in the sunshine has a luminance of about 20,000 cd/m^2 whereas the same surface by moonlight would register at about 0.02 cd/m^2. This implies a ratio of incident illuminations of about 1,000,000 to 1.

A typical curve for photographic film is shown in Figure 6.1. The ordinate shows the density[5] of the exposed and processed negative. The abscissa represents, at the plane of the film, the luminance of an external scene. This film, like all such materials, is most sensitive to illuminance variations in a mid-range. Here the slope of the curve is highest, being less so at the extremes labeled 'toe' and 'knee'. Any luminance less than about 2 cd/m^2 fails to increase the density of this film above its unexposed value; a photographic negative thus exposed will be virtually transparent, and if printed in the usual way, the picture will be black. Any exposure greater than about 2,000 cd/m^2 will expose the film to its maximum processed density of about 2.4; this corresponds to an almost opaque negative that transmits less than 0.5 percent of the light incident upon it. When processed in the ordinary way, the print will reflect more than 90 percent of the incident light, and it will appear white.

This range of 1000:1 is broader than the 20:1 required to depict a flat scene. But the most useful range is far less than this, because both the toe and knee of the characteristic curve yield only small density changes relative to the middle portion; this implies a loss of information in these regions. Excellent photographic reproduction results only from exposures constrained to the middle portion of the curve, corresponding roughly to the 20:1 variations of discriminable luminances in the original scene. This range is shown in Figure 6.1 as a black rectangle along the abscissa.

In order to take good pictures it is necessary to keep the illuminance level at the film plane, corresponding to the mid-range of scene luminances, at the appropriate level. If the external level of illumination is too low to permit this, then longer exposures can be used. But once the longest practical exposure is reached, no solutions are possible other than to seek a more sensitive film or a larger lens opening. On the other hand, as the level of external illumination is raised, it is easily possible to keep the film exposure constant by progressively reducing the lens opening, decreasing the exposure time, or both. Whether done automatically, as in many modern cameras, or manually, these adjustments have been used by millions of photographers. Let us now return to vision.

LIGHT AND DARK ADAPTATION

The term *adaptation* has the general meaning of adjusting to, or getting used to, some kind of situation. The expression is used in diverse scientific contexts ranging from the evolution of species characteristics to the tendency of neurons to fire at a constant rate following an initial transient discharge. Even within the much more restricted domain of visual science, the term unfortunately has more than one technical meaning.[6] In contexts outside our concern, the word may refer to adjustments that one makes following prolonged observations of slant, tilt, prismatic distortion, or gratings.

Perhaps the most common theme running through all these examples is the notion that adaptation is not immediate; instead, the process takes time. The change in sensitivity that the eye undergoes in response to changes in luminance level, as we have seen, is no exception. Dark adaptation can be extremely slow (about 30 minutes), whereas the reverse process of light adaptation, although faster, is by no means instantaneous. These facts permit the following generalization: although a high level of visual information transfer is possible over an enormous range of intensities, the range at any particular time is much more restricted.

Measurement of Sensitivity

Sensitivity is defined as the reciprocal of the stimulus energy required to elicit a fixed response (often called a *criterion response*) from an observer. The strength of the visual percept, *brightness*, ranges from just barely visible to the brightest light that one can imagine. Its investigation is rendered difficult by the inaccessibility of subjective response magnitude. Brightness is not directly measurable in the same sense that physical quantities are, because a perception is a private, unshared experience. Although numerical estimates of brightness have been attempted with surprising success in many scaling experiments,[7] these methods have not often proved useful for those whose interests include the underlying mechanisms of perception. For example, it would be possible to do an experiment where brightness ratings were recorded as a function of wavelength for a series of equal-photon stimuli. At photopic energy levels, the peak of the resulting curve could be identified without much ambiguity. But the meaning of all other points on the curve would be obscure, and impossible to relate, say, to the action spectra of cone photopigments. The methods of classical psychophysics yield data that plot entirely along physical scales, which makes them much easier to relate to underlying mechanisms (as in the example in Chapter 5 of scotopic spectral sensitivity and its relation to the very similar action spectrum of rhodopsin).

Consider an average human being with an average, normal visual system. Assume that we have no information about the linearity of the visual system or the linearity of the observer's responses. Let us also assume when we shine light into an observer's eye the observer can tell if the light is brighter or dimmer than a previously observed light. We can assume that a monotonic relation exists between the intensity of the light delivered to the visual system and an observer's verbal response representing the brightness of the light. As the light's intensity increases the observer will say the light is getting brighter. Eventually the amount of light will be so great that it no longer appears to increase in brightness.

Suppose the task is to find the spectral sensitivity of the visual system. We could start by stimulating the visual system with equal numbers of photons at various wavelengths. If the observer's task is to tell us about the brightness of the light we can determine which of the wavelengths that we present appear the brightest. That is to say we could determine the wavelength of peak response. Unfortunately, all other responses would be ambiguous, due to a lack of observer's response scale and due to a possible nonlinearity of the observer's visual system.

We can get around this problem in several ways. One way would be to change the experiment by determining the minimum number of photons as a function of wavelength required to elicit the response, "Yes I see the light." Because of observer and stimulus variability it would be necessary to repeat the measure at each wavelength multiple numbers of times to obtain a reliable measure. This approach produces an *action spectrum*. It is a particular action spectrum, namely a measure of the minimum number of photons required to produce a *threshold* visual response.

Thresholds

Threshold responses can be implemented in a variety of ways. In addition to determining the minimum number of photons required to elicit a psychophysical response of "Yes I see the flash of light," physiologically one might determine the minimum number of photons required to elicit a criterion number of spikes per second, or required to elicit a criterion voltage change when dealing with graded potentials.

There is a general problem in science that the act of measuring a state or process often interferes with the state or process being examined. Measuring thresholds that make use of the weakest possible stimulus does not eliminate this concern but does help to minimize it. However, anyone who has ever observed dim light flashes will realize that judging whether a flash is seen or not involves a nontrivial decision process. Observers must adopt a criterion according to which they will say "yes" or "no" in response to a given sensation. Different observers adopt different criteria and a given observer's criterion can vary from one time to another. This change in criterion has been demonstrated in experiments where some of the flashes are randomly presented as blanks; that is no light is delivered to the eye, though care is taken to produce all the preparatory signals and usual shutter noises. Some observers report as many as 30 or 40% *false positives* under these conditions, other observers report virtually none. These methods allow the experimenter to record whether a response is correct or incorrect rather than merely to note whether the observer reports "yes" or "no." Many variations on these methods have been developed and are discussed in standard texts.[8]

Mechanisms of Light Adaptation

When visual messages reach the retinal ganglion cells, they become encoded, for the first time, in terms of nerve impulse frequency (see Chapter 7). The useful range of frequencies within each cell is not great, ranging from zero to about 100 spikes per second. Such a range of frequencies seems about right for encoding the range of luminances present in a scene, provided that the illumination level does not change. But it is obviously all wrong for encoding a million-to-one variation in light input. Because the photopic visual system nevertheless handles such a range, some form of gain control is necessary to keep the frequency of optic nerve discharge within the useful range.

Suppose that adaptation were fully compensatory and took place entirely at the level of the individual photoreceptor. If the process worked with perfect spatial and temporal precision, this would mean that the output from each receptor would always be adjusted so that, no matter what the input, the output would be the same. But vision begins with a spatio-temporal pattern of retinal illuminance. Just as in the photographic analog, this pattern contains all the information that is available to be detected and transmitted. A perfectly precise adaptive mechanism, because it would render the output of all photoreceptors constant, no matter what the input, would thereby eliminate all transfer of information. The foregoing tells us what not to look for. We might expect instead to find regions of the retina that are interconnected for purposes of adaptation, and we can anticipate also that adaptation should be a process that has sluggish temporal characteristics.

Could the adaptive machinery operate to attenuate the light input in the manner of an automatic exposure control on a camera? If it could, this would serve to keep average retinal illuminance constant over the whole scene despite changes in external scene luminance, without wiping out the information contained in the point-to-point illuminance variations. It might seem that the pupil of the eye could serve this function because it does admit light and therefore affects retinal illumination in proportion to its area, just as the iris diaphragm of a camera similarly affects the exposure of the film. Moreover, the pupil automatically becomes smaller as the amount of light incident upon the eye is increased.

In a camera the only mechanism of adaptation for a fixed duration of exposure is the size of the camera's aperture, which controls the amount of light reaching the film plane. This control is designed to be completely compensatory and to keep the illumination at the film plane constant no matter what the external scene. But in the eye the maximum change in pupil area resulting from the over millionfold range of photopic luminances is about 16 fold, which reduces the effective retinal illumination by this same factor. Therefore, as external luminance increases, so does retinal illumination, though not quite in proportion.

BLEACHING AND REGENERATION KINETICS

In addition to the adaptive mechanisms noted above, the photographer has one additional mechanism to cope with the amount of available light. The film placed in the camera can be very fast (meaning very light sensitive) or slow (not so sensitive). Obviously it is not possible to change the retinal receptors as a function of the available light. However, the photopigments in the outer segments of the receptors bleach when exposed to light. In the bleached state they do not contribute to the process of generating a signal to be passed along the visual pathways. In the absence of light the photopigments regenerate. Actually this statement is an oversimplification because a certain amount of regeneration occurs in the presence of light. For complete regeneration to take place no light can enter the eye. Thus, it can be appreciated that bleaching and regeneration of photopigments are important factors in adaptation. Retinal densitometry contributed critically to the study of the rates of bleaching and regeneration of visual photopigments. As we saw in Chapter 5, the bleaching of photopigments increases the amount of light in the test beam reflected from the fundus. When the bleaching light is extinguished, the test light (itself too weak to bleach significantly) is exposed to monitor the amount of unbleached rhodopsin in the retina. The test-beam intensity declines as expected toward the unbleached level, indicating that the retina's supply of unbleached rhodopsin is being replenished.

Bleaching

Rushton (1972) investigated the time course of bleaching during exposure to light. Quite high light levels were required to bleach a large fraction of rhodopsin, a fact which at first seems hard to reconcile with the high sensitivity of rod vision. Indeed, only in bright daylight would as much as 50 percent of rhodopsin be bleached. The quantitative study of bleaching is made easier by the slowness of rhodopsin regeneration, for if the bleaching light does not last longer than a few seconds, only a very small and insignificant fraction of the rhodopsin will regenerate during the exposure. It is, therefore, relatively easy to measure the amount of rhodopsin bleached after various intensities of exposure to light, provided that the fraction of rhodopsin bleached is directly proportional to the number of photons in the bleaching exposure, a result in agreement with the expectation that each absorbed photon bleaches only one pigment molecule—the molecule that absorbs it.

This proportionality between the number of incident photons and the number of bleached molecules of rhodopsin cannot continue indefinitely because there are only a finite number of rhodopsin molecules present in the retina (though it is a very large number, as we saw on p. 107). Thus the situation is formally similar to the regeneration process. For example, if at a particular moment the bleaching photons have converted half the rhodopsin into the bleached state, there are then only half as many molecules as before ready to absorb subsequent photons; at this point in time bleaching should therefore proceed at only half its initial rate. The corresponding differential equation is

$$\frac{dp}{dt} = \frac{-Ip}{N},$$ (6.1)

where I is the intensity of the bleaching light and N is a scaling factor that has a value depending, among other things, upon the units in which the light intensity I is measured, p is the amount of unbleached pigment, and t is duration. Because the rate of bleaching decreases with the fraction of pigment remaining to be bleached, Equation (6.1) implies that the amount of unbleached pigment will also decline exponentially as

$$p = e^{(-It/N)}.$$ (6.2)

Notice that in this case, where the duration of exposure is short enough to make regeneration negligible, bleaching depends only on the intensity-time product It. This represents the total amount of light delivered during the bleaching exposure, without regard to its distribution in time. This *intensity-time trade-off* is characteristic of many visual functions (Hood & Finkelstein, 1986). For most of these, however, the limits within which this trade-off holds true are much shorter than for bleaching.

Regeneration

Since the discovery of retinal photopigments, visual scientists suspected that there was a relationship between recovery from bleaching and rod dark adaptation. Some of the earliest work using retinal densitometry was concerned with just this relationship. As already noted in Chapter 5, there was not a one-to-one correspondence in this relationship; there being less bleaching than expected. The replacement of rhodopsin, it was found, is a relatively slow process, but not as slow as the recovery of sensitivity in dark adaptation as measured psychophysically: most of the rhodopsin returned in about 5 minutes, whereas dark adaptation takes at least 30 minutes. The precise time course of rhodopsin recovery offers some insight into the process involved. Initially, 0.25 percent of the rhodopsin returns with every second spent in the dark after the bleaching exposure. If recovery were maintained at this rate, one might think that all of the rhodopsin would return in 400 seconds. But this is not how recovery works: the rate of recovery is not constant, but rather it is proportional to the deficit that remains to be made up. Instead of 0.25 percent of the total rhodopsin supply returning every second, it is 0.25 percent of the amount remaining to be replenished that appears each second. For example, if 50 percent of the rhodopsin has already regenerated at some particular time in the dark, only 0.125 percent of the total will be added during the following second.

Mathematically this behavior may be described by a simple differential equation

$$\frac{dp}{dt} = \frac{1-p}{400},\tag{6.3}$$

where p is the amount of unbleached rhodopsin (assigned a maximum value of 1) and the left-hand side of the equation stands for the rate at which p changes with time t measured in seconds. To satisfy this differential equation, p must vary in time in accordance with an exponential function:

$$p = 1 - e^{(-t/400)},\tag{6.4}$$

which is what Rushton observed (Fig. 6.2). When only a part of the rhodopsin was initially bleached, the same differential equation is found to hold, with the same time constant of 400 seconds, and the pigment returns along the same time course shown in Figure 6.2, except that it starts at some larger value of p, appropriate to the lesser amount of unbleached pigment immediately after the bleaching exposure.

This behavior of rhodopsin during recovery from bleaching exposure strongly suggests that the bleached rhodopsin itself is the source for replenishing the store of unbleached rhodopsin. The rate of recovery would then be expected to slow down as recovery approaches completion, as implied by Equation (6.2), because the store of bleached rhodopsin is now much less abundant than it was soon after bleaching. For this reason the restoration of rhodopsin to its unbleached form is termed the regeneration of rhodopsin, on the assumption that it is produced in the retina by a reisomerization and recombination of the products of bleaching. This implies that the retina has a fixed total pool of ingredients for manufacturing rhodopsin.

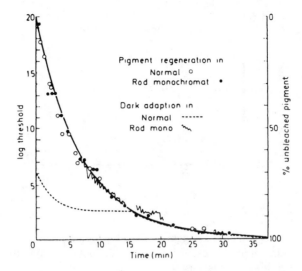

Figure 6.2   The points represent retinal densitometric measurements of the fraction of unbleached pigment (right-hand ordinate) as a function of time in the dark following an exposure that bleaches almost all of the rhodopsin in the eye. These data were obtained from an observer who had only rod receptors. The smooth curve drawn through these points is similar to Equation (6.4). The uneven line represents psychophysical threshold settings, obtained by the method of adjustment; these should be referred to as the left-hand ordinate. Most of the psychophysical curve cannot be seen in a normal subject, whose sensitivity during the early phase of dark adaptation is controlled by cones as suggested by the dotted line. (Adapted from Rushton, 1972, p. 377.)

Bleaching and Regeneration Kinetics Combined

With light exposure longer than a few seconds, the regeneration that occurs during the light exposure can no longer be ignored. In the general case, the behavior of the pigment can be described by adding together the changes that are produced, moment by moment, by both bleaching and regeneration:

$$\frac{dp}{dt} = \frac{1-p}{400} - \frac{Ip}{400I_0} \tag{6.5}$$

This equation is achieved by adding together the right hand sides of Equations (6.3) and (6.1). The scaling factor N has been replaced in the bleaching term by $400\,I_0$: the value I_0 is the intensity that bleaches 1/400th of the pigment per second, and that would bleach all of it in

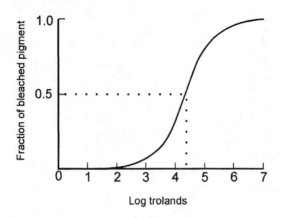

Figure 6.3   Proportion of photopigment bleached as a function of log trolands of retinal illuminance. This is a plot of Equation (6.6) in the text, with a half-bleach constant $I_0 = 4.3$ log td.

400 seconds if the initial rate of bleaching could be maintained. In fact, however, regeneration always acts to prevent bleaching of all of the pigment, and it can easily be shown that if the eye is exposed indefinitely to light of constant intensity, p will adjust itself toward some steady value. The resulting value of p can be found by setting the left-hand side of Equation (6.5) to zero, which is equivalent to saying that the net rate of bleaching, dp/dt, is zero. This yields

$$1 - p = \frac{I}{I + I_0} \tag{6.6}$$

which shows that the percentage of bleached pigment is not substantially increased until the intensity I approaches the value of I_0, the intensity for which the fractions of unbleached and bleached rhodopsin are 0.5, known as the halfbleach constant. This very important equation is shown graphically in Figure 6.3. Among other things, it states that

• At low intensities, where I is small relative to I_0, there is a very nearly linear relationship between I and the fraction of unbleached (and bleached) pigment.

• At high intensities, where I is very large relative to I_0, the rate of photon absorption Ip becomes nearly independent of I and is equal to the maximum rate of regeneration that is reached when nearly all the pigment has been bleached.

• The range over which p goes from about 90% to 10% is restricted to about a hundred-fold (2 log unit) range of intensities, centered upon I_0.

Cone Photopigment Kinetics

Similar experiments carried out with foveal measurements, using normal subjects as well as protanopes and deuteranopes, have established that the same principles apply as have been outlined for rhodopsin. The following are the main points to be noted:

• The information on bleaching and regeneration of cone photopigments was obtained using the method of retinal densitometry. This technique was not sufficiently sensitive to measure the S-photopigment. However, a more recent method of microspectrophotometry has confirmed the existence of S-photopigment in humans and the suction electrode method has confirmed these photopigments in monkey cone receptors.

• The bleaching and regeneration kinetics of the L- and M-photopigments appear to be identical.

◦ The following equation applies:

$$\frac{dp}{dt} = \frac{1-p}{120} - \frac{Ip}{120 I_0} \tag{6.7}$$

The meaning of Equation (6.7) is that cone bleaching and regeneration proceeds more rapidly than that of rods. The value of I_0 is around 20,000 td and is not very different from that for rods. Equation (6.6) also describes the steady-state bleaching for cones.

The primary and direct effect of bleaching upon the sensitivity of the eye is easy to understand. If, for example, 90 percent of the initial supply of pigment is bleached away, leaving only 10 percent of the photopigment molecules available to absorb photons, then ten times as many photons would be required in a test flash to achieve the same visual effect as in the dark-adapted state. In other words, sensitivity is proportional to *p*, the fraction of unbleached pigment. Such loss of sensitivity because of the direct effects of bleaching will hereafter be called the *depletion effect of bleaching*.

An important fact about the depletion effects, true both for rods and for cones, is that the rise in threshold associated with bleaching is enormously greater than depletion alone could cause. This is most evident in rods. The output of the rod system appears to saturate at about 1000 td, implying that the rods and/or the pathways to which they connect are responding with a maximum signal (Aguilar & Stiles, 1954). All discrimination based on rods is lost. Yet the amount of rhodopsin bleached at saturation is only about two percent, which would by itself raise the rod threshold by such a small amount that it would be very difficult even to measure by psychophysical methods. Fortunately, cone vision normally takes over completely by the time 1000 td is reached. But what about the upper levels of cone vision: do cones also saturate and thereby produce a total loss of visual information? The answer is that they do not for steady state stimuli: they are protected from saturating by the depletion effects of bleaching.

RECEPTOR ADAPTATION

There are logical grounds for believing that a significant amount of adaptation must take place in the cone photoreceptors. As will be shown in Chapter 7, the cones are *analog* devices, in the sense that they generate signals of graded amplitude, quite unlike the *digital* spikes that are recorded from ganglion cells. We will shortly see that, after bleaching and pupil size are accounted for, the cones still must handle light inputs covering about a 3,000-fold range. To suppose that the cones do so without adapting is to imply that their responses should be linearly related to the rate at which they absorb photons. If so, equal increments of stimulation would yield equal increments of response, regardless of the existing level of stimulation to which the increment is added. We have already seen that the overall system does not work this way (remember the stars in the daytime). Moreover, if the cone responses were linear and nonadapting, the problem of interpreting their signals by horizontal and bipolar cells would be very much like trying to make accurate voltage measurements from 1 to 3,000 volts by using an analog voltmeter without change of range. Although at one time it was not very popular to suppose that very much of the *gain control* took place in the receptors, it seems impossible to understand how a receptor could transmit a useful analog signal over such a range, without losing information in the toe and knee of its characteristic curve.

Receptor Linearity

Research on primate receptor adaptation received a major impetus with Boynton and Whitten (1970). These investigators, as well as Valeton and van Norren (1983), studying macaque monkeys (whose vision is similar to that of humans), observed by electrophysiological experiment that there is a nonlinear relation between light input and receptor output, even at very low light levels, of a type shown in

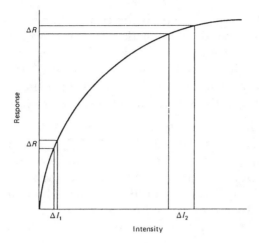

Figure 6.4   If the criterion response for perception is ΔR, and the relationship between response and stimulus intensity is nonlinear as shown, then the
threshold intensity needed to arouse that criterion response increases
from ΔI₁ to ΔI₂ for the two examples shown. Sensitivity is inversely
related to the slope of the function.

Figure 6.4. When brief flashes were used, this nonlinearity was ac-
centuated at high light levels by the impending saturation of the cones
— a phenomenon analogous to reaching the maximum density of a
photographic negative. Depletion prevents such saturation from oc-
curring in the steady state.

It is not uncommon to find apparently inconsistent results among
laboratories. One obvious factor to explore while attempting to understand the different results is the research methodology used to
collect the data. On the question of linearity versus non-linearity to
dim stimuli, it seems natural to consider the following.

Schnapf, Nunn, Meister & Baylor (1990) recording from Macaca
fascicularis monkeys, with suction electrodes, found that receptor
responses were strictly linear to dim stimuli. This method records
receptors *in vitro* whereas the late receptor potential (LRP) recorded
by Boynton and his colleagues and the fractional local electroretinogram (Fr-LERG) used by Valeton and van Norren, studied receptors
in vivo.[9] There are at least two differences that result from the *in vitro*
vs. *in vivo* approach. Schnapf *et al.* found that after bleaching their
preparations did not regenerate. The electrophysiological response
between these two techniques is also somewhat different. The suction electrode method yields strongly diphasic flash responses from

cones. This diphasic response is the result of brief flash (as short as 10.7 ms). The second phase of this response occurs many tens of milliseconds after the stimulus. The local electroretinogram (LERG) method, when the vitreous is perfused with sodium aspartate, also yields a diphasic response. But the first response is an on-response to stimulus onset and the second an off-response to stimulus offset.

Another difference is that suction electrodes record from isolated single receptors. The LERG, Fr-LERG, and ERG record from multiple receptors. This fact by itself can not account for a linear vs. nonlinear response. Valeton and van Norren analyzed this possibility and concluded that a very unlikely range of half-saturation values for individual receptors would be required to cause a conglomerate of them to yield a nonlinear response.

One might naturally ask what does psychophysics have to say about the linearity question. Unfortunately, the results here are conflicting. Geisler (1981) reports nonlinearity whereas Hood, Ilves, Maurer, Wandell and Buckingham (1978) observed linearity. It would appear that in the time since Valeton and van Norren (1983) the linearity question has not been resolved.

RANGE OF VISUAL RESPONSES AS A FUNCTION OF LUMINANCE RANGE

Four Factors

Consider the luminance range that cones must handle. Toward the upper end of that range, constant contrast thresholds ($\Delta I/I$) against backgrounds of approximately 10^5 cd/m^2 are not different from those obtained for much weaker adapting fields (Weber's law applies).

According to Stiles (1959), background fields do not begin to affect increment thresholds below about 0.3 cd/m^2 (6 td for a 5-mm pupil). This fact indicates that steady stimuli weaker than this, although visible if presented as flashes, exert a negligible adaptive effect upon the cone system. Moreover, they fade from view very readily and probably can be presumed to produce very small receptor responses in the steady state. For the purposes of the calculations to be done in this section, a value of 0.28 cd/m^2 is taken as the value near cone threshold and the response produced at this level, for a linear nonadapting receptor and fixed pupil, is defined as a unit response.

The computational example shown below is based on the monkey eye because that is a subject on which we have all the requisite information. Fortunately, it has been previously demonstrated, and

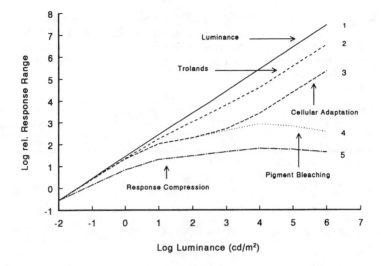

Figure 6.5   How four factors are taken into account to shrink the range of cone response. Curve 1 is for a linear, nonadapting receptor with a fixed pupil. Curve 2 results from the reduction of pupil area as luminance level is increased. Curve 3 results when the effect of cellular adaptation is combined with pupil response. When the effect of photopigment bleaching is added Curve 4 results. Receptor response compression brings Curve 4 down to Curve 5.

frequently assumed, that monkey and humans share many common physiological and psychophysical attributes. The results of the calculations are shown on the log scales in Figure 6.5, where the ordinate represents relative cone response amplitude. The abscissa shows the external luminance required to produce these responses. These responses vary from curve to curve, depending upon assumptions that will be made clear below.

These assumptions include: pupil responses, cone photopigment bleaching, cone response nonlinearity,[10] and cellular adaptation [Cellular adaptation is defined by Equation (6.10).] Cellular adaptation will be one of two mechanisms assumed to cause a shift of the cone response curve along the stimulus intensity axis, the other mechanism being pigment bleaching. Curve 1 shows what happens if none of these are considered: this is the hypothetical response of cones that (a) do not bleach, (b) respond linearly, and (c) are stimulated through a fixed, maximally dilated pupil and exhibit no adaptation. Because the real pupil constricts as luminance is increased we obtain curve 2. The reduction of receptor response caused by cellular adaptation in addition

Table 6.1   Calculated log relative response amplitude values for some of the values of log luminance plotted on the abscissa of Figure 6.5. Symbols are defined in the test equations. (We thank M. Valeton for considerable assistance in producing this table especially for including cellular adaptation.)

L_v	R_1	A	R_2		R_3		R_4	R_5
log luminance (cd/m²)	luminance with fixed pupil*	pupil area (mm²)	retinal illuminance (trolands)	Cellular Adapt. Factor	R_c/CAF	p % unbleached pigment**	pR_3	response compression
−2.00	0.28	28.04	0.28	1.00	0.28	1	0.28	0.28
−1.00	2.80	25.59	2.56	1.00	2.56	1	2.56	1.44
0.00	28.04	23.03	23.03	1.05	21.93	0.9998	21.92	6.85
1.00	280.40	18.18	181.80	1.66	109.52	0.9976	109.26	20.68
2.00	2,804.00	10.85	1,085.00	5.31	204.33	0.9781	199.86	30.19
3.00	28,040.00	6.56	6,560.00	12.40	529.03	0.8221	434.92	47.17
4.00	280,400.00	3.07	39,700.00	14.90	2,664.43	0.3235	861.94	66.17
5.00	2,804,000.00	3.83	383,000.00	15.26	25,098.30	0.0268	672.63	58.88
6.00	28,040,000.00	3.51	3,510,000.00	15.26	230,013.11	0.0017	391.02	44.28

* pupil fixed 28.04 mm²   ** calculated from Padmos data

to the pupil response is shown by curve 3. When the reduction of response amplitude that is attributable to the loss of bleachable pigment molecules is also taken into account, curve 4 results. (Photopigment bleaching does not have a significant effect until about 4.0 log cd/m².) Taking the first two factors into account reduces the response range from 8 to about 6 log units over the original luminance range of from −2 to 6 log cd/m². We assume non-linear cone response because of inherent nonlinearities in the lower part of its response range, and saturation that occurs at high intensities. Taking this non-linearity into account in addition to all four factors produces curve 5. The original response range has now been reduced from 8 to about 2 log units.

Let us now discuss the calculations that lead to the curves in Figure 6.5. In Table 6.1 the columns labeled R_1 through R_5 show the data in linear units that are plotted on log coordinates in Figure 6.5 (which shows the predicted range of receptor response under varying assumptions which are made explicit as we go along).

In Figure 6.5, curve 1 (labeled *Luminance*) represents the predicted receptor response assuming that the receptor responds linearly as a function of the luminance. We assume a fixed pupil area of 28.04 mm² at a luminance of 0.01 cd/m².

$$R_1 = 28.04 \cdot L_v \qquad (6.8)$$

where R_1 is plotted as curve 1 in Figure 6.5 and L_v is the luminance of the stimulus in cd/m².

Curve 2 (labeled *Trolands*) represents the retinal illuminance and assumes that the receptor responds linearly and only as a function of the retinal illuminance. In other words, this curve shows what happens when one takes into account the reduction of pupil size as luminance is increased (Wyszecki & Stiles, 1982 p.105).

$$R_2 = A \cdot L_v \qquad (6.9)$$

where R_2 is retinal illuminance in trolands, A is pupil area in mm², and L_v is luminance in cd/m².

Before proceeding to the next step we need to consider some preliminary concepts. Boynton & Whitten (1970) showed that the receptor responses (R) can be calculated, assuming a fixed pupil and no photopigment bleaching, by Equation (6.10)

$$R = \frac{L_v^n}{L_v^n + \sigma^n} R_{max} \qquad (6.10)$$

where L_v is the luminance of the stimulus, and σ^n is the half saturation constant. Another way of expressing this concept is by saying that σ^n is the stimulus intensity when $R/R_{max} = 0.5$, where R_{max} is the maximum receptor response. The value of n used by Boynton and Whitten was 0.7. The general form of Equation (6.10), without the exponent, was originally used by Michaelis and Menten (1913) to account for enzyme kinetics.

Initially when a receptor is stimulated its response increases. However, at some point the increase in response increments start getting smaller as the stimulus light stimulus continues to increase. Eventually a point is reached when the receptor response reaches a plateau indicating a saturation level. σ is the stimulus intensity that takes one 50% of the way towards response saturation.

Valeton & van Norren (1983) identified two half saturation constants, one when the eye is in a light adapted state (σ_L) and another when in a dark adapted state (σ_D). The cellular adaptation factor (CAF) was also derived by Valeton & van Norren, based on their experiments. These data are shown in Table 6.1 in the fifth column from the left. The following description will help the reader to understand how CAF was determined, although for a thorough understanding of these calculations one should see the original paper. Their basic equation is:

$$CAF = \frac{\sigma_L}{\sigma_D \sigma_\beta} \qquad (6.11)$$

Where σ_L is the light adapted half saturation constant and, thus, the position of the response curve relative to the luminance axis; σ_D is the half saturation constant in the dark (1,585 td); and σ_b is the reciprocal percentage of unbleached photopigment. Monkey cone pigment bleaching was obtained from Padmos' retinal densitometry data provided in the Appendix of the Valeton & van Norren paper. σ_L was determined by taking the antilog of the value calculated using the following equation:

$$Log \, \sigma_L = \log L_{vB} + \frac{1}{n}\log\left(\frac{V_{im}}{|V_{dm}|}\right) (\text{for } L_{vB} > 0 \qquad (6.12)$$

Where L_{vB} is the background luminance, $n = 0.74$, V_{im} and V_{dm} are the maximum incremental and decremental Fr-LERG cone responses, respectively, obtained from Figure 4 in Valeton and van Norren (1983).

Curve 3 in Figure 6.5 labeled *cellular adaptation* represents the response of the receptor taking into account pupil fluctuation and cellular adaptation:

$$R_3 = R_2 / CAF. \qquad (6.13)$$

R_3 represents the combined effect of retinal illuminance and cellular adaptation. CAF = cellular adaptation factor, R_2 and is calculated in Equation (6.9).

Curve 4 (labeled *Pigment Bleaching*) represents the further decrease in receptor response range due to reduction of available photopigment as a function of luminance. The pigment values (p) are the percentage of unbleached pigment. These data are found in column 7 of Table 6.1.

$$R_4 = pR_3 \tag{6.14}$$

R_4 represents the cumulative effects of the pupil fluctuation, cellular adaptation, and pigment bleaching.

Curve 5 (labeled response compression) is calculated by Equation (6.15). It includes the nonlinear receptor response taking into account luminance, pupil area, cellular adaptation, pigment bleaching, and response compression.

We calculated response compression based on R_4 as input, thus taking into account the cumulative effects of the pupil, cellular adaptation, pigment bleaching, and response compression upon the linear (luminance) response with which we started.

$$R_5 = K \frac{(R_4)^n}{(R_4)^n + (s_L)^n} \tag{6.15}$$

Where K is a scaling constant set to 170.0 so that $R_4 = R_5$ at –2.00 log cd/m², n = 0.74 and s_L is the light adapted half saturation constant (Valeton & van Norren, 1983).

A Different Approach

The foregoing approach to understanding how the visual system regulates its sensitivity is an extension of that described in the first edition of this text, with necessary revisions based on the important work of Valeton and van Norren. It is not uncommon in science that alternative models are able to account for the same phenomena, and that is the situation now as we begin an alternative analysis proposed by Graham and Hood in 1992. By focusing on incremental receptor responses to stimulus increments they show how sensitivity is maintained as adaptation level increases. Graham and Hood did not present a new model, rather they summarize and amalgamate previous adaptation models (e.g., Boynton & Whitten, 1970; Geisler, 1978, 1979; Hood & Finkelstein, 1981; Valeton & van Norren, 1983; Walraven & Valeton, 1984; Hayhoe *et al.*, 1987). The following is a qualitative description of this approach.

The overall design is schematized in the top of Figure 6.6. A_1 represents a zero luminance background, i.e., the visual system is dark adapted and the increment stimulus occurs at the same time as the background stimulus. A_2 assumes a light adapted visual system and that the background has been on for a long time relative to the

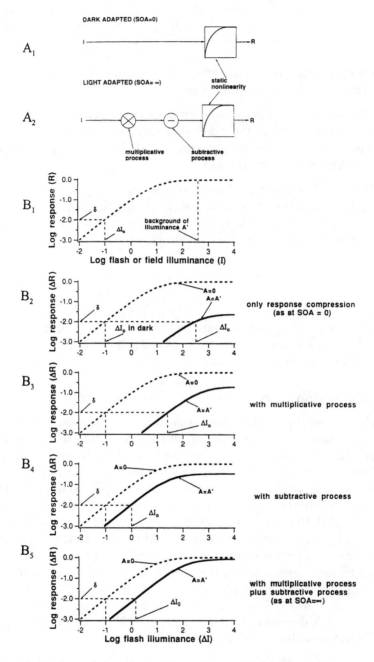

Figure 6.6 These curves show the effects of static nonlinearity, multiplicative processes, and subtractive processes in static models of adaptation. A_1 and A_2 respectively schematically represent the dark adapted and light adapted models of adaptation. In B_1 Log R is plotted as a function of Log I. In B_2 – B_5 log ΔR is plotted as a function of log ΔI. (Adapted from Graham and Hood, 1992.)

onset of the incremental stimulus. Both conditions share a static nonlinearity, which causes the response to saturate at high luminance levels, i.e., response compression. In the light adapted condition the schematic in A_2 assumes two additional processes: 1. a multiplicative, and 2. a subtractive process. These two processes are assumed to be sufficiently slow so that they have no effect when a light increment and background onset occur at the same time (SOA = 0).

Figures 6.6 B_1–B_5 show the theoretical visual responses as a function of illuminance. B_1 represents the response of the dark adapted visual system governed only by the static non-linearity (response compression), e.g., the Michaelis–Menten function of Equation (6.10). In B_2 through B_5 the dashed curves also represent response compression with no background illuminance. The ordinates in B_2 through B_5 are now the incremental response ΔR to the light increment as a function of the illuminance increment. The reduction of the incremental response, represented by the solid curve, relative to the dashed curve, in B_2 is the reduced sensitivity of the visual system due to the presence of a background illuminance. The visual system's response to the background is shown by the vertical dashed line on the right side of B_1. The assumption is made in B_2 that the background and test light increment occur at the same time. Because the multiplicative and subtractive processes are slow they are not a factor when the SOA = 0.

The result of response compression, background illuminance, and the multiplicative process is represented in B_3 by the solid curve. By multiplicative process Graham and Hood include processes analogous to receptor (von Kries) adaptation, cellular adaptation, automatic gain control, pigment bleaching, and the "dark glasses" effect. The *dark glasses effect* refers to the visual system's change in sensitivity as if a pair of sunglasses were placed before the eyes, thus decreasing the effectiveness of all lights by a constant factor (Graham & Hood, 1992). The reader can see that this multiplicative process has the effect of increasing the response by preventing some reduction in sensitivity otherwise caused by response compression.

The subtractive process (B_4) involves decreasing the effectiveness of prolonged lights (e.g., the background in the SOA = ∞ condition) by removing some of the visual signal. The subtractive process has been called "discounting the background" by Walraven (1976) and "high-pass temporal filtering" by others (Graham & Hood, 1992). The solid curve in B_4 shows that subtractive adaptation has an even greater sensitivity enhancing effect than the multiplicative process. When all of these factors are taken into account, the visual system's response to increments is nearly as great at the higher luminances as in the dark adapted state, as shown by the convergence of the solid and dashed lines in B_5. Figure B_5 assumes that the background has been on for a long time (SOA = ∞) and these combined results are represented by the solid curve.

However, Graham and Hood caution the reader that this description of adaptation is not necessarily the only formulation that might work, nor is it necessarily one that will have a bearing on psychophysical results other than those from which they have considered. Nevertheless, this summary from various laboratories is a useful approach by which to consider the problem of visual adaptation. Work in this area is in progress and significant strides have been made, but we still have a way to go before it will be quantitatively possible to understand all of the components involved with the dynamics of light adaptation.

OTHER CONSIDERATIONS
CONCERNING RECEPTOR ADAPTATION

During the past ten years important advances have been made in understanding the biochemical activity of the receptor (Pugh & Cobbs, 1986; Lamb & Pugh, 1992). Mention of this biochemistry is made only to make the reader aware of the extent to which receptor processes are being studied. Clearly this biochemistry is beyond the scope of this book. We do, however, find that the electrophysiological research has a rather direct bearing on psychophysics. We would like to recall, and thereby bring to the reader's attention, the following four electrophysiological investigations of primate receptors:

- Boynton & Whitten (1970) did the pioneering work in monkeys employing the late receptor potential (LRP).

- Valeton and van Norren (1983) used a bipolar microelectrode and performed fractional recording across the outer segment layer of the fovea rhesus monkey to obtain local ERGs (Fr-LERG). Both of these monkey investigations were extra cellular and recorded from multiple receptors.

- Schnapf *et al.* (1990) used the suction electrodes to record electrophysiological responses from single, isolated, monkey cone outer segments.

- Hood & Birch (1993) studied human cone receptor responses by using the early part of the a-wave obtained by electroretinographic (ERG) recordings. These ERGs are obtained from humans by placing an electrode on the surface of the eye. Hood and Birch used a contact lens electrode.

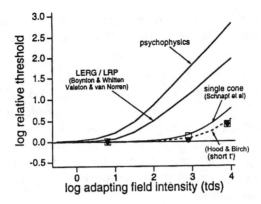

Figure 6.7   Log relative incremental threshold as a function of log adapting field intensity estimated from Boynton & Whitten (1970), Valeton & van Norren (1983), Schnapf et al. (1990), Hood & Birch, (1993) compared with a function obtained psychophysically. (See text for details.)

Hood and Birch (1993) reviewed the data from these various research methods and concluded, in agreement with other investigators, that response compression has only a small effect upon the response range to incremental lights, and that pigment bleaching is not an important factor below 4 log trolands.

Comparison with Psychophysics

Let us now look at human visual sensitivity from a slightly different perspective. If visual sensitivity were constant, the size of a just noticeable light increment would be independent of adaptation level. We would see stars during the day just as easily as we do at night. A classical psychophysical experiment for investigating visual sensitivity is to determine the intensity required to see a just noticeable light increment as a function of the background intensity. This is called the threshold vs. intensity (*tvi*) experiment (or *tvr* when light is measured in radiance units).

Let us once again see to what extent it is possible to attribute adaptation to the cones. In Figure 6.7 we have reproduced Hood and Birch's (1993) Figure 10, which compares the log relative threshold as a function of log adapting field intensity (tds) for psychophysically determined tvi functions, and for LRP and Fr-LERG determined functions, (these, respectively are the sensitivity functions determined from single cones by the suction electrophysiology and the early part of the cone ERG a-wave). An important factor to keep in mind when comparing this figure with others cited in the figure legend is that the adapting field intensity is limited to 4 log trolands so that pigment bleaching is not a significant factor.

If sensitivity were completely controlled in the receptor, one would expect to find that sensitivity functions determined by the LRP, Fr-LERG, suction electrodes, and the early a-wave would yield the same curve as that obtained psychophysically. As seen in Figure 6.7, the electrophysiologically determined functions are markedly different than the psychophysically measured tvi curve. One is led to the conclusion, therefore, that a significant amount of adaptation must take place after the receptors.

Another question that arises is why there should be different functions for the various classes of electrophysiological investigations. It is important to remember that, in vision research, the obtained results depend not only on how the visual system works, but also on how experiments are conducted, and there are differences in the way these retinal potentials have been harvested. We do not yet understand how the different techniques contribute differentially to the results, but it is an interesting exercise to speculate on the answer to this question. Although their electrophysiological techniques were not identical, both LRP and Fr-LERG studies [Boynton & Whitten (1970); Valeton & van Norren (1983)] made extracellular recordings from conglomerates of cone outer segments in monkey. So it is not surprising that they yield similar results. Schnapf *et al.* (1990), using suction electrodes, recorded from single isolated receptors, also in monkey. Hood & Birch (1993) using corneal electrodes measured the early (~ first 10 msec) part of the human ERG a-wave. The difference among the LRP, Fr-LERG, and the suction electrode studies may result from LRP and Fr-LERG studies recording from multiple receptors intact with the pigment epithelium,[11] whereas the suction electrode method dissected the outer segment from the pigment epithelium, recorded from single receptors. Perhaps there was some interference in the suction method with the Calcium transfer due to the receptor being encased in the micropipette.

If it is assumed that the suction electrode method yields the true isolated receptor response, then one wonders about the discrepancy between that method and the other methods. Two factors can be noted concerning the discrepancy. First, the a-wave is recorded from multiple cones, rather than isolated cones. Second, it is possible that the suction electrode reveals the entire diphasic response whereas the a-wave reveals only that for the first 10 msecs. Support for such an explanation would carry weight if one assumes that the LRP, Fr-

LERG, and ERG studies are not isolated receptor responses. Hood and Birch provide evidence that only the first 11 msecs of the a-wave are uninfluenced by non-receptor potentials whereas the latter part is so influenced. Accordingly, they advance the possibility that the LRP and Fr-LERG studies may also have been so influenced. There are two possibilities: 1. The retinal blood vessel clamping does not completely shut off retinal activity and, 2. there are intercone feedback loops. The fractional recording technique of Valeton and van Norren claims to have isolated cone responses. Even if we assume that to be the case, it is still theoretically possible that intercone feedback occurred. The bottom line is that one needs to be cautious when interpreting results from experiments using various methods. It is only when one obtains the same results with different methods that one can begin to gain confidence in the concordant results.

MECHANISMS OF ADAPTATION BEYOND RECEPTORS

We move now to even less certain ground and consider possible mechanisms of adaptation beyond receptors. There are at least two experimental facts that demonstrate such mechanisms must exist. We have just seen that one cannot fully account for a psychophysically obtained tvi function by looking at just the receptor response. Walraven and Valeton (1984) report that a Rushton type gain control helps to describe these changes. Psychophysical responses depend on information being processed by and/or relayed through various visual pathways before finally reaching the visual cortex. If the tvi function had a form and amplitude consistent with receptor function, then one could conclude that the limiting step is in the receptor and the resulting signal was relayed intact to the visual cortex. When psychophysically based responses are not predicted by receptor data, one must conclude that sensitivity regulating steps occur after the signal leaves the receptor. A second observation is that the ratio of threshold change that takes place when increments are flashed against steady backgrounds of increasing luminance, depends upon the area of the test stimulus.[12] Of special significance is the fact that changes in area have much larger effects upon thresholds in the dark-adapted eye than they do when the stimulus light is flashed against a bright background. This result suggests that the retinal area over which light can be integrated to produce a threshold response becomes smaller as the eye becomes more light adapted. This implies a functional reorganization of the retina, which could result either from larger pools of neural summation, or a change in surrounding areas in the center-surround organization (to be discussed in Chapter 7) such that surround-inhibition drops out at low light levels. In either case, the retina would require some kind of information related to the actual level of retinal illumination in order for it to control its own organization as a function of that variable.

Early studies of retinal sensitivity beyond the receptors were reported by F. Werblin and coworkers (Normann & Werblin, 1974; Werblin, 1974; Werblin & Copenhagen, 1974). Because the experiments were carried out on the mudpuppy, the degree to which the results and conclusions can be generalized to humans is uncertain. These studies show clearly that adaptation does occur in both the inner and outer plexiform layers. Sperling & Mills (1991) provide interesting evidence about processing that occurs in these layers from their research in monkey eye. A prime accomplishment of the additional stages of processing seems to be to keep the system functioning within the most sensitive part of its response range. By the time the ganglion cell level is reached, much of the information about absolute levels of input to cones seems to have been lost. To a degree, the same is true of human vision, but this is not completely so. With practice, one can make judgments about absolute levels that correlate fairly well with the actual level of illumination, even if the sources are shielded and there is no change in the geometry of the situation. This ability tends to be lost with large diffuse fields (although not completely so even then) and at luminance levels where the depletion effects of bleaching have taken over as the principal mechanism of adaptation. Interestingly, more recent research on goldfish, cats, and monkeys suggests that there are more cross species similarities than one might expect. Nevertheless, the information about post receptoral sensitivity control is very much like a jigsaw puzzle with many interesting pieces — but how they fit together is still to be worked out.

CHROMATIC ADAPTATION

Color Constancy

We have seen that various mechanisms serve to keep the visual system functioning over an extended stimulus range. To the extent that these mechanisms are selective within receptors and their associated pathways, color constancy will be enhanced (see Chapter 11). Suppose, for example, that one is looking at objects illuminated by a reddish appearing light. Under such illumination, in comparison with white light, the L-cones adapt more than the M-cones. Objects reflect more of the long wavelengths under this reddish illumination than they would under white light. The light reflected from these objects would, if the eye were neutrally adapted, make them appear more yellowish or reddish than normal. But the eyes are not neutrally adapted, the selective chromatic adaptation of the L-cones, relative to the M-cones, tends to restore the appearance of these surfaces toward the same hue that they would have had under white light and neutral adaptation. Under red light surfaces that normally look white tend to retain that appearance. This concept was originally proposed by von Kries (1905) and is often used in one form or another in computational discussions of color constancy. In 1986, the *Journal of the Optical Society of America, A* featured a series of papers on computational vision, most of which dealt with color constancy, a subject that will be discussed more fully in Chapter 11.

Selective Chromatic Adaptation and Cone Isolation

In the laboratory, chromatic conditions can be contrived that seldom, if ever, occur in everyday life, and with them the phenomenon of chromatic adaptation can be studied. The remainder of this chapter emphasizes these studies of selective chromatic adaptation, particularly those that have been used to estimate the spectral sensitivities of the cones.

If a test tube of rhodopsin in solution is irradiated with light, some of the molecules bleach. This bleaching causes rhodopsin to lose its purplish color, becoming transparent, and the transmittance of the solution is increased. If the solution is pure, the bleaching can be done with light of any wavelength because precisely the same effect can be produced by adjusting the various wavelengths to take account of the action spectrum of rhodopsin. If the solution is dilute enough to preclude a significant amount of self-screening (see Chapter 5), the normalized spectral absorption curves for all solutions, whatever their concentrations, will be identical. A convenient way to plot such data is on an ordinate of log absorption, in which case the curves will all have the same shape prior to normalization and if shifted vertically they will superimpose. Chemists sometimes take such unchanging curve shapes as evidence that they are working with a pure solution, one that contains only one kind of labile pigment.

Suppose it were possible to extract L-, M-, and S-cone pigments, mix them, and then subject them to the same kind of test. The curve shapes would change depending upon the wavelength and intensity of the adapting lights. A longwave light, for example, would begin to bleach the L-photopigment before the S- and M-photopigments were significantly affected; the spectral sensitivity curve would therefore narrow as a result of being selectively reduced in the longwave spectral range.

Because it has not been possible to extract human photopigments from the cone outer segments and measure their transmittance in solution, similar experiments have been done *in situ* by means of retinal densitometry and *in vitro* by microspectrophotometry (see Chapter 5), with similar results for the two methods. Here we consider the consequences of obtaining analogous measures using psychophysical techniques and intact human subjects. The purpose of such psychophysical experiments has been, in the view of some workers, to isolate and measure the properties (particularly the spectral sensitivities) of the L-, M-, and S-cone photopigments. Other investigators, led by W. S. Stiles, have taken a more conservative view reasoning that to the extent such procedures are successful, they merely measure the characteristics of unspecified cone 'mechanisms' whose exact nature cannot be deduced from psychophysics alone.[13] According to this more conservative view, mechanisms are first operationally defined through the use of certain psychophysical procedures. Their characteristics may then be compared with those of cone photopigments, cone action spectra, electrophysiological data, or whatever.

The common feature of all such psychophysical procedures is that test lights are small, weak, brief, and centrally fixated. These test lights stimulate only cones in the rod-free foveal area of the retina without materially affecting the state of the system being assessed. The task of the subject is to detect the presence (or signal the absence) of each test light, so that threshold radiances can be obtained as a function of wavelength. The reciprocals of these radiances are plotted as a function of wavelength (or wave number) and these constitute cone-mediated spectral sensitivity curves. We will see that the absolute height of such functions (on a logarithmic ordinate) is easily manipulated by varying the intensity of an adapting field upon which the test light is superimposed. More importantly (and quite unlike the case for rods) the shape of the curve is also easy to alter, which is not surprising considering that (1) at least three different photopigments must be involved, and (2) like our hypothetical pigments in the test-tube, they probably can be selectively 'adapted' by bleaching.

Unlike the case of the test-tube pigments, as we have already noted, bleaching is only one of many adaptive effects that may occur in the eye. The problem is further complicated by mechanisms of interaction, whose properties cannot be assumed but must instead be uncovered by experiment. For example, suppose that an intense long wavelength adapting light is used. Some of this light will be absorbed in M-cones as well as in L-cones, and the relative amounts may or may not be known. For purposes of exposition, assume that all of the light is absorbed in L-cones. Now we may ask: is the desen-sitization of the eye, as revealed by lowered sensitivity and altered curve shape, necessarily a consequence only of direct adaptation of the L-cones, or even of an L-cone system? Not necessarily, because there are many mechanisms of adaptation and many lateral connec-tions are known to exist among cones and cone pathways.[14] It is there-fore perfectly possible that the absorption of light in L-cones might also alter the sensitivities of M- and S-cones, even if these other two types do not absorb a single photon. Even if it can be shown that the M- and S-cones themselves are not so affected, the channels into which they feed might be.

Similar interactions may occur also with respect to the test light. Suppose it to be of short wavelength, and suppose also that it is ab-sorbed only by S-cones. Would it then be safe to assume that only the S-cones are affected by the test probe? Because the test probe (being at threshold) is weak and brief, the assumption may seem safer than the analogous assumption with respect to an adapting field. Never-theless, the assumption must be tested because the responses of indi-vidual cones are now certainly known to be affected by what their neighbors are doing.

Most of the time a psychophysical test light can be expected to stimulate cones of at least two different kinds. In the two-cone case, does the threshold simply depend upon the total amount of light absorbed, regardless of how it is distributed between the two cone types? Or does it depend only upon the responses of the type of cones that are most strongly simulated? Or are the responses of the two cone types treated as if they came from totally independent mecha-nisms? Unfortunately for those who like things simple, all of these things (and more) frequently occur, depending upon circumstances; some of the evidence will be reviewed later. Fortunately, a psychophysical procedure has been recently devised called the back-ground exchange method that has shown to be successful in isolat-ing the M- and L-cone responses.

Selective Chromatic Adaptation and Spectral Sensitivity

In 1933, Stiles and Crawford measured foveal spectral sensitivity curves, some of which are shown in Figure 6.8. Their adapting fields were of moderate intensity and surrounded the area of the test light without including it. Such surround fields were found to have a pro-found effect upon the spectral sensitivity of the eye, based on the reciprocal of threshold energies of test flashes of various wavelengths delivered to the central area. The curves seemed to have three humps,

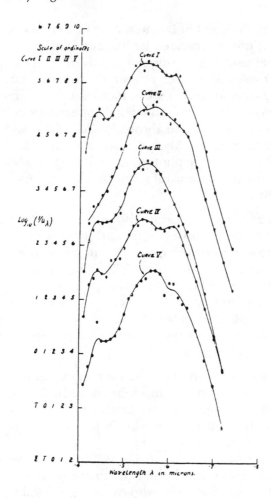

Figure 6.8   Results from Stiles and Crawford (1933b). The ordinate shows log relative threshold sensitivity of a central test flash as affected by an annular adapting field. Intensities vary between about 2500 and 4400 td, and the curves (arbitrarily displaced vertically) are for filtered lights whose appearance from top to bottom was white, blue, red, yellow, and blue-green.

and the possible connection of these with three types of cones immediately suggested itself. This study launched a 25-year series of investigations, mostly undertaken by Stiles alone, leading to the isolation of what he originally called "R, G, and B mechanisms", later to be named "π-mechanisms."

In Stiles' subsequent work, the adapting fields typically subtended about 10° and always included the test area. The test lights subtended

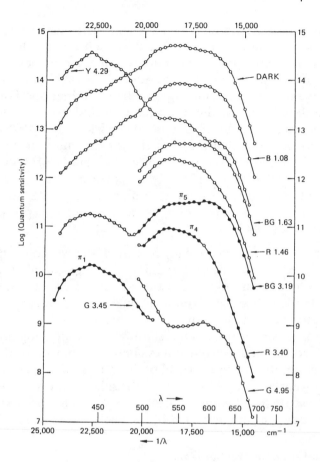

Figure 6.9   Test sensitivity curves of Stiles (1964) for a wide variety of conditions of adaptation. Chromatic appearance of the adapting fields was yellow, blue, blue-green, or red. The numerical values following the chromatic symbols specify the retinal illuminance (in log trolands) of the adapting fields . Vertical displacement of the curves is arbitrary. These curves are for quantum sensitivity, plotted on a scale which is linear with frequency, but reversed so that wavelength increases from left to right. (See text for explanation of π_1, π_4, and π_5.)

$1°$ and were usually flashed for about 100–200 ms every 3 s. Stiles measured many spectral sensitivity curves where curve shape was altered by selective adaptation to various wavelengths. A set of such functions, obtained under many different adapting conditions, is shown in Figure 6.9. These curves, which Stiles called *test sensitivities*, represent the outcome of many hundreds of hours of experimental work are based on the mean data of four subjects, obtained in a British standards laboratory under unusually well controlled experimental conditions. Thresholds were obtained in each case by determining frequency of seeing curves and interpolating the 50-percent point (method of constant stimuli). Each subject's threshold was estimated from the mean of from four to eight such determinations. For a more complete description of the π-mechanisms and how they were obtained and analyzed, the reader is referred to Stiles (1978). Stiles' papers, though logically precise, make for difficult reading. Enoch (1972) and Mollon (1982) provide useful accounts. Mollon does an especially nice job of putting Stiles' π-mechanisms in perspective with the relevant psychophysics and electrophysiology. A detailed in-depth historical review and analysis of Stiles' π-mechanisms is presented by Pugh and Kirk (1986).

The most obvious and striking feature of the two-color threshold curves (Fig. 6.9) is that their shapes have been grossly altered by the use of chromatic adapting fields. Compare, for example, Curve Y 4.29 (obtained with 4.29 log td of yellow adaptation) with the curve for the dark-adapted eye. Adapting the eye to 4.29 log td of yellow appearing light causes sensitivity to be reduced only by about 0.5 log unit at the shortwave end of the spectrum, but by about 2 log units at the longwave end (note that the relative vertical positioning of the separate curves in the figure is arbitrary). Therefore the adaptation has been selective, in the sense that 30 times more sensitivity loss has occurred in the region of the spectrum occupied by the background stimulus.

Interpretation of π-Mechanisms

The shapes of the curves of Figure 6.9 suggest that they might be understood by assuming that the overall (measured) spectral sensitivity curve, as determined under each condition of adaptation, results from the activity of three underlying processes, each of which has a different spectral sensitivity. Three such functions are defined in Figure 6.9 as portions of three experimental functions where the symbols have been filled. For example, the curve labeled π_1 was obtained by adaptation to a 548-nm field of 3.45 log td. This has brought out a spectral sensitivity that peaks in the shortwave end of the spectrum, one that could be due to the activity of S-cones, or at least of a system or mechanism fed mainly by such cones. Inspection of the figure will reveal the conditions of chromatic adaptation necessary to reveal the curve shapes of π_4 and π_5, which are the other two underlying functions shown. It should be noted that the levels of adaptation used to bring out these underlying functions are modest, the strongest being sufficient to bleach only about 12 percent of the L- and M-cone photopigments.

A problem with the test sensitivity method is that only a portion of a sensitivity curve relates to the mechanism under test, namely that for which the mechanism is much more sensitive than any other. For example, in Figure 6.9 it is virtually certain that the short wavelength portion of the function that yields π_5 for long wavelengths (curve BG3.19, open circles) is attributable to a mechanism having its peak sensitivity in the short wavelengths.

In an attempt to circumvent this problem, Stiles developed what he called the *field-sensitivity* method. For example, to isolate π_5 (the long wavelength mechanism) he selected a test stimulus of 667 nm and used that wavelength throughout the experiment. The procedure was to evaluate spectral sensitivity according to the intensities of *adapting stimuli* required to produce a criterion effect upon the test stimulus. Specifically, in the example cited, Stiles measured the dark-adapted sensitivity to a 667 nm test stimulus, and then determined, for each of a large number of wavelengths, the field energy required to elevate the threshold of the test flash by a factor of 10. The resulting curve agrees in its shape with that of the curve in Figure 6.9 at long wavelengths (filled symbols). The short wavelength portion of such a field sensitivity curve does not display the secondary hump shown by the unfilled symbols, suggesting that the effectiveness of the adapting field in raising test threshold might have been entirely mediated via π_1.

A further check on this involved the test of *displacement rules*. These rules are discussed by Enoch (1972), as well as by Pugh and Kirk (1986). Briefly, if a single mechanism is involved, any segment of a function relating log test threshold to log adapting field intensity, when their wavelengths differ, should retain its shape and merely shift vertically or horizontally with changes in test or adapting intensity. Although this is a necessary requirement for identifying a single mechanism, the displacement tests are not conclusive and it appears likely that the sensitivity of π_5, for example, does not depend only upon photons absorbed by that mechanism, but is significantly affected indirectly by other mechanisms that are more heavily stimulated than π_5 by short wavelengths.

From these data alone there is really no objective way to know whether the three π-functions are sufficiently well isolated to represent completely different mechanisms. It is possible that π_1, π_4, and π_5 have spectral sensitivities equivalent to those of the S-, M-, and L-cones respectively. If so, the color-mixture behavior of normal observers must be correctly predicted by the π-functions. Estévez & Cavonius (1977) and Pugh & Sigel (1978) provided support for π_4

and π_5 as describing the spectral sensitivity of the M- and L-cones by showing that color matching functions could be derived from the π-mechanisms. However, as Mollon (1982) has pointed out, such agreement does not prove the point. For example if more than one cone type were to contribute linearly to the spectral sensitivities of the π-mechanisms these functions would correctly predict color matches.

There are two difficulties when it comes to interpreting the π-mechanisms as cone fundamentals. First, there are five π-mechanisms (or even seven, if special high-intensity versions of π_4 and π_5, not discussed here, are admitted). Our current understanding is that there are at most five cone photopigments (Neitz, Neitz & Jacobs, 1992). Only two of the longer wavelength photopigments have been shown to have a close correspondence with π_4 and π_5 (Estévez & Cavonius, 1977; Pugh & Sigel, 1978). The S-cone photopigment corresponds to either π_1 or π_3 (Estévez & Cavonius, 1977). The second difficulty concerns the data of color variant observers, upon which derived cone sensitivity curves are largely based. Protanopes (see Chapter 10) lack the long wavelength sensitive pigment. When tested under conditions that discourage a significant contribution from rods or S-cones, the resulting sensitivity curve is narrower than π_4. A similar problem exists for the relation between π_5 and the sensitivity of deuteranopes. Bowmaker, Dartnall, Lythgoe, and Mollon (1978) believe that the results of their retinal densitometry indicate that π_5 and L-cone absorption spectra are the same. However, quite a few assumptions were made in the calculations to justify their conclusion, which seems difficult to reconcile with the narrower L-function of Figure 5.21, based mainly on data from dichromats.

Pugh (1976) has shown that π_1 consists of two components, only one of which (the shortwave part) appears to reflect the spectral sensitivity of S-cones. Using additivity experiments, involving mixtures of long- and shortwave adapting fields, he has clearly shown that the low-sensitivity, longwave hump in the π_1 sensitivity curve comes from some other source, and that, overall, π_1 is not univariant. The same is very probably true of π_2, which shows a notch at 580 nm, has a very strange shape, and cannot even be examined over much of the spectrum. The high-intensity variants on π_4 and π_5 could be explained away as artifacts caused, in one way or another, by driving the system beyond its physiological levels. The evidence for more than only three pigments (Neitz, Neitz & Jacobs, 1992) and the color matching functions predicted from the π-mechanisms make it difficult to reject the idea that π_1 or π_3 plus π_4 and π_5 are the spectral sensitivities of the cone photopigments. Still, before this correspondence can be un-equivocally accepted the problems discussed above need to be re-

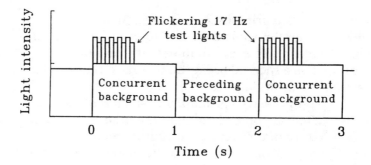

Figure 6.10 Stimulating conditions used in the background exchange method. Adapted from Stockman, MacLeod & Vivien (1993).

solved. Understanding the π-mechanisms is an interesting problem in its own right. Once accomplished it may or may not bring us closer to an understanding of the cone spectral sensitivities.

The Background Exchange Method

A new psychophysical approach for determining the spectral sensitivities of the L- and M-cones has been proposed by Stockman, MacLeod & Vivien (1993) and Stockman, MacLeod & Johnson (1993), which they call the *background exchange method*. The technique is similar to Stiles' two color threshold method except that transient adaptation is used. The reason it is difficult to obtain the isolated spectral sensitivities of the M- and L-cones is because their spectral sensitivities overlap throughout the spectrum. Because the peak sensitivity of the S-cones is well separated from that of the M- and L-cones (Figure 5.10) it is easier to measure their isolated spectral sensitivity. Stockman *et al.*, like others before them, accomplished this by using a long-wavelength (617 nm) background adapting field. The S-cones are very insensitive to this wavelength whereas the M- and L-cones are very sensitive to it. However, special effort is required to measure the M- and L- cones; Stockman *et al.* accomplished the task using their background exchange method.

Figure 6.10 illustrates the temporal sequence of the stimuli presented to subjects with one version of this method. Stockman, MacLeod & Vivien (1993) report that

"... temporally modulating the adapting field in both color and intensity suppresses the unwanted cone type(s) by a factor greater than that predicted by Weber's Law, so that the responses of a single cone class can be isolated throughout the visible spectrum" (p. 3).

Test stimuli were superimposed on a spectral background just as in the Stiles two-color threshold method. However, Stockman *et al.* made two modifications. 1. The test stimulus that is presented for 500 msec superimposed on a spectral background is flickered at 17 Hz and the observer's task was to detect the flicker. 2. Whereas in a given trial Stiles utilized only one background, Stockman *et al.* used two, one of which they called the preceding[15] and the other concurrent. These backgrounds were of different wavelengths and alternated with one another. The *concurrent background* is the field on which the flickering test field is presented and it is alternated with the *preceding background*. Both backgrounds are presented for 1,000 msec and the test stimulus is presented in the first 500 msec of the concurrent background.

The wavelengths of these backgrounds were chosen to isolate the respective cone receptors. To isolate M-cones the preceding background was 485 nm and the concurrent background was produced with a Wratten filter that was metameric with 678 nm. To isolate the L-cones the wavelengths of the preceding and concurrent backgrounds were reversed. The 485 nm preceding background had the effect of reducing the sensitivity of the M-cones significantly more than it did the L-cones and 678 nm had the effect of reducing the sensitivity of the L-cones significantly more than the M-cones to isolate the M-cones. In some experiments it was necessary to provide additional desensitization of the S-cones and this was accomplished with an auxiliary 418 nm adapting field.

One might ask: why not just use a steady strong adapting field to suppress unwanted cone activity and thereby isolate selective cones? In a study given wide publicity because of its inclusion in his Nobel address, Wald (1968) claimed to have isolated the spectral sensitivities of the L-, M-, and S-cones by the use of very high intensities of steady chromatic adaptation. But this seems highly unlikely because once high bleaching adapting levels are reached the constituent mechanisms all achieve a constant and limiting Weber fraction and selective chromatic adaptation with further increases in retinal illuminance should be severely restricted. However, when the stimuli are temporally modulated as in flicker photometry, selective suppression of cone inputs by chromatic backgrounds may exceed Weber's law. Eisner and MacLeod (1981) tested Rushton's skepticism that strong colored backgrounds could isolate cone responses and found that L- and M-cones could be depressed relative to each other by more than a log unit over that predicted by Weber's law. As we noted above, when the background exchange method is used even better cone isolation can be achieved.

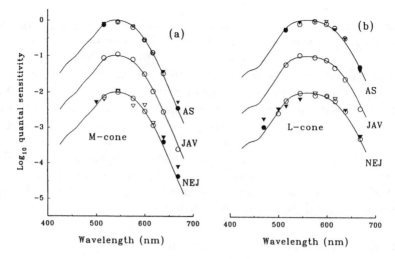

Figure 6.11   Spectral sensitivities of the M and L cones measured by bipartite color matching either following an exchange of background (from 678 to 485 nm) or on a steady (678 nm) field. Open symbols are for perfect color matches, non-perfect color matches represented with closed symbols. The background exchange condition represented by circles and the steady field by inverted triangles. The continuous lines are the Smith–Pokorny cone sensitivities. (From Stockman, MacLeod, and Vivien, 1993.)

To determine whether the suppression caused by the background exchange method is a general phenomenon, Stockman *et al.* performed bipartite color matching in the same background exchange experiment. The standard hemi-field (561 nm) was just above increment threshold with respect to the concurrent background. The subject then adjusted the test hemi-field in an attempt to match the standard and informed the experimenter if there was a residual color difference between the standard and test that could not be eliminated. If there was a color difference the subject was told to make a brightness match. The color matching experiment was also run using steady background adaptation. No attempt was made to desensitize the S-cones; therefore the matches broke down at short wavelengths due to S-cone intrusion.

The standard against which Stockman *et al.* compared their data is the set of Smith & Pokorny fundamentals, which were derived from protanopic and deuteranopic spectral sensitivity functions. Because protanopes and deuteranopes have only one longwave photopigment the usual isolation problem is obviated. Figure 6.11 shows the spectral sensitivity functions derived while performing a color-matching exercise on either a steady background (inverted triangles) or following background exchange (circles). The open symbols show the data obtained when there was no color difference between the test and reference fields when the best match was made. The closed symbols represent spectral sensitivities when there was a residual color difference when the best match was made. In each panel, the continuous line represents the appropriate Smith–Pokorny fundamental. It can be seen that the deviations from Smith–Pokorny, albeit small, are greater for the steady adaptation background than for the background exchange method. These data show that better isolation of cone spectral sensitivities is accomplished with the exchange method than with the steady background.

Sensitivity Peaks Attributable to Interactions

When we look at the spectral sensitivities curves of the cones we expect to see peaks near 570 nm, 540 nm, and 440 nm, which is near the peaks of the cone photopigment spectral absorbances. However, with some experimental procedures a peak sensitivity near 610 nm is observed. Clear evidence for this is shown in Figure 6.12, from the work of Sperling and Harwerth (1971). The result is interesting because we know that there is no photopigment in the human eye peaking at so long a wavelength (Chapter 5). The curves of Figure 6.12 were obtained by assuming that sensitivity is determined by a signal derived from the difference between inputs from the L and M cones as shown by the following equations:

$$\frac{1}{Q_L} = k_1 L_\lambda - k_2 M_\lambda \tag{6.17}$$

$$\frac{1}{Q_M} = k_3 M_\lambda - k_4 L_\lambda \tag{6.18}$$

In these equations, Q_L and Q_M represent the quantal requirements for threshold perception as mediated by L- or M-cones. The threshold is assumed to be determined exclusively by the more sensitive of these cones. The quantities L_λ and M_λ represent the action spectra of the L- and M-cones, assumed to be Dartnall template pigments peaking at 575 and 535 nm respectively. Although we saw in Chapter 5 (p. 156) that Dartnall pigments do not exactly describe human L- and M-cones, the changes in this model that would be required by the selection of slightly different cone–pigment curves would not seriously alter the fit of theory to data.

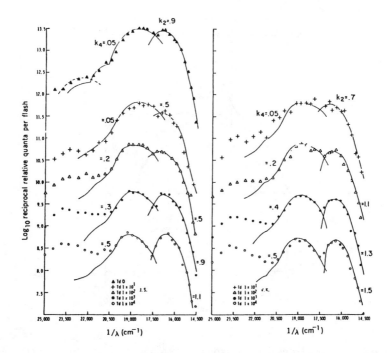

Figure 6.12 The effect on spectral sensitivity of white adapting fields of varying intensity. The curves are fitted by assuming an inhibitory interaction between L and M cones (Sperling and Harwerth, 1971).

In Figure 6.12, the constants k_1 and k_3 were set to 1.0, and the values of k_2 and k_4 were set so the model fit the data. k_2 and k_4 systematically increase with adaptation level and, therefore, are assumed to be associated with adaptation. (The model does not explain why or how adaptation level should cause the values of these 'constants' to change.)

The experimental conditions that produced these functions included the use of 45-min foveally fixated test fields, viewed either in the dark (topmost curve) or against white adapting fields at four intensities, ranging from 10 to 10,000 td.

The sensitivity of a mechanism, in the long wavelength portion of the spectrum, is assumed to be reduced by an inhibitory signal caused by activity of the second and less sensitive member of a L- and M-cone pair. This inhibitory effect would be maximum where the L- and M-cone sensitivities are equal, producing a deep notch in the function at about 580 nm. It also accounts for the peak at about 610 nm.

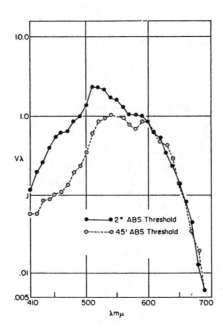

Figure 6.13 Spectral sensitivity is markedly altered by changing the size of the test stimulus. Stimuli were concentric with the point of fixation and there was no adapting field. Changes in the short wavelengths are probably due to rods, but the "notch" around 580 nm, which shows clearly only for the small test flash, is probably due to inhibitory interactions between the L and M cones. (From Sperling & Lewis, 1959.)

There is only a hint of such a notch in Stiles's data of Figure 6.8, and we may ask why this phenomenon shows so much more clearly in the data of Sperling and Harwerth. The answer probably is to be found in differences among experimental conditions. In addition to using higher adaptation levels, Sperling and Harwerth used small, brief flashes, whereas Stiles used larger, longer ones. Ikeda and Boynton (1962) showed that exposure duration affects the shape of spectral sensitivity curves but not in a manner that would necessarily bring out the notch. Sperling and Lewis (1959) compared 2' and 45' test areas with the results shown in Figure 6.13. Here the notch is clearly evident with the 45' test, much less so with the larger one.

It is also unlikely that the interactions found by Sperling and Harwerth somehow disappear at very high intensities. This is best understood by looking back at Figure 6.5; in the steady state, all lights brighter than the half-bleach intensity are very nearly equal in their visual effects. High bleaches therefore do not guarantee psychophysi-

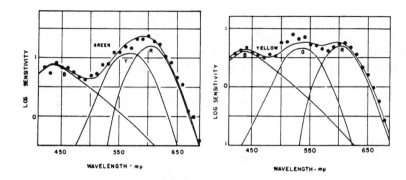

Figure 6.14   Transient adapting flashes, whose onsets occurred just before the test stimuli were delivered, produce marked alterations in spectral sensitivity. The peak near 610 nm cannot be due to a cone pigment; a notch near 580 nm, like those seen in Figures 6.12 and 6.13 is evident under a condition of yellow adaptation (right). (From Boynton, 1965.)

cal isolation of cone photopigments. Wald's curves, which do not agree very well with other estimates of cone sensitivity functions, remain unexplained.

In 1956, Boynton showed that large changes in spectral sensitivity could be produced by the use of very weak (about 2.3 log td) adapting fields, provided that the background field was presented as a flash of light presented to the dark-adapted eye. The background flash, lasting for 0.56 seconds, and the test flash, of 40 ms duration, appeared each time 50 ms after the onset of the background flash. The results for yellow and green appearing adaptation are summarized in Figure 6.14. The Sperling–Harwerth type of notch (also referred to as Sloan's notch) at about 580 nm is more evident than in Stiles's steady-state data. We can conclude that foveal threshold spectral sensitivity, determined in the presence of various chromatic adapting stimuli, brings out some evidence of the three underlying cone mechanisms. However, the rules of combination of the underlying activities appear to be complex, depending upon (1) the level of the adaptation, (2) which mechanism is most active, and (3) temporal and spatial parameters.

SOME EVIDENCE FOR POSTRECEPTORAL CHROMATIC ADAPTATION

This chapter will be concluded with a brief discussion of an interesting kind of experiment that has been attempted several times in an effort to isolate the spectral sensitivities of the three types of cones by a psychophysical technique. The method assumes, first, that adaptation takes place independently in the two eyes. This makes possible a comparison of the appearance of fields that are delivered separately to the two eyes (dichoptic viewing) but which appear to lie side by side in space. As mentioned in Chapter 2 (see also the exercise on p. 198), two such fields, if physically identical, will appear different if the two eyes are differently adapted.

With such asymmetric adaptation of the two eyes, the subject is given control of the chromaticity of one of the fields–for example, by manipulation of the amounts of three spectral primaries in an additive mixture. The task is to produce a dichoptic color match. Assume now that there are only three mechanisms in the eye, each with a different spectral sensitivity, each obeying the principle of univariance. It is further assumed that, if the two test fields can be made to match when viewed by the asymmetrically adapted eyes, the outputs of corresponding mechanisms will be the same for the two eyes. (Unless the eyes are symmetrically adapted, the physical input required to get these outputs differs.)

If this experiment is done for many different adapting and test fields, it should be possible to describe all of the results in terms of the behavior of a unique set of three spectral functions, each representing the action spectrum of one of the three types of mechanisms that were adapted (the full argument is not presented here). This experiment does not succeed. If one grants all of the assumptions, it is necessary to conclude from the results of these studies that the spectral sensitivity of at least one of the three mechanisms varies considerably from one condition to another. Thus no unique set can be derived. We can conclude from this that some or all of the initial assumptions are incorrect.

If the mechanisms with invariant action spectra are types of cones, it is nevertheless likely, as already noted, that there are mechanisms downstream from these cones which also adapt. If so, there is no reason to suppose that test lights that produce the same outputs from the cones of the two eyes will yield the same sensations after being passed through pathways that are differentially adapted in the two cases.

It is quite probable that some of the adaptation that does occur downstream involves sensitivity changes of opponent-color mechanisms.[16] If so, this would be expected to lead to extremely complicated predictions about the effects of chromatic adaptation on color appearance. Moreover, color appearance depends not only on the conditions of stimulation of a test area, and the adaptation that occurs there, but also upon the nature of surrounding fields (Walraven, 1981; Shevell *et al.*, 1988; Shevell *et al.*, 1989). There are empirical equations that are fairly useful for predicting such effects, some of which are essentially without any theoretical basis. Others, e.g., Walraven & Werner (1982) invoke the properties of discounting of a steady background and cone specific gain control utilizing π-mechanism spectral sensitivities to account for chromatic adaptation.

SUMMARY

Because the eye must operate over an enormous range of external light levels, mechanisms exist that automatically adjust its sensitivity to permit good vision at all levels. Color constancy is preserved,[17] to the extent that it is, despite the existence, in each eye, of three parallel mechanisms that must remain precisely balanced during sensitivity adjustments that occur independently within each mechanism.

Because adaptation is such a complicated process, the problems that physiological mechanisms of adaptation are designed to solve are introduced in this chapter with a photographic analog, with the admonition that camera and eye solve their common problems in very different ways. Light and dark adaptation are discussed in relation to the bleaching and regeneration kinetics of rod and cone photopigments because these changes correlate with, and may cause some of these changes in, visual sensitivity. The extent to which steady state photopic adaptation can be understood in terms of four factors (pupillary constriction, photopigment bleaching, cellular adaptation, and receptor response compression) is considered, and although these factors go some distance toward an explanation, other mechanisms of adaptation are also known to exist, and some of these are discussed.

In the laboratory, the phenomena of adaptation can be deliberately used to help understand some of the characteristics of color vision under extreme conditions of selective chromatic adaptation where color constancy breaks down very badly. As a prime example of this, the two-color threshold technique of Stiles is discussed, which leads to "mechanisms" that can be isolated and studied by psychophysical methods. It seems unlikely that these mechanisms describe the action spectra of the L-, M-, and S-cones. Newer psychophysical methods are described that appear to do so.

NOTES

[1] This statement is on page 117 of Adler's translation (1966) of Fechner's *Elements of Psychophysics*, Vol. 1.

[2] Recent research suggests that there are as many as five photopigments in the normal human retina (Neitz, Neitz & Jacobs, 1992). However, these five can be

grouped into three classes, short wavelength, middle wavelength and, long wavelength, within which variations are very slight.

[3] The central part of the pupil is important because as Stiles and Crawford (1933a) demonstrated, receptor sensitivity varies as a function of the angle with which light impinges on the receptors. For a given retinal location this angle varies as a function of pupillary area, being greater for rays passing through the margins of the pupil than for those in the center. This is called the Stiles–Crawford effect. See also page 89 in Chapter 3.

[4] The equation for this relationship is $E = L_v A_p$ where E is retinal illuminance in trolands. L_v is the luminance of the viewed surface in cd/m^2 and A_p is the area of the pupil in mm^2. Discussions of photometric concepts are available in many places. Walsh (1958) tells more about the subject than most readers will want to know. Shorter treatments are available in Boynton (1966), LeGrand (1968), Wyszecki and Stiles (1967) and Kaiser (1984).

[5] Density (D) is related to transmittance (t) as follows: $D = -\log t$, or $D = \log (1/t)$. Transmittance refers to the fraction of incident light that passes through a filter, or photographic film; this can vary from zero (in which case D approaches infinity) to 1.0 (100 percent), in which case $D = 0$. The following table of examples may help:

t	D
1.00	0
.50	0.3
.25	0.6
.10	1.0
.05	1.3
.025	1.6
.001	3.0
.0001	4.0

The placement of a curve like that of Figure 6.1 will depend upon the exposure duration, the numerical aperture (reciprocal f number) of the lens, and the type of film used.

[6] See the more restricted definition of adaptation applied to receptors on pg. 214.

[7] For many years, the chief proponent of the utility of subjective scaling was S. S. Stevens of Harvard University. Interested readers are referred to a collection of papers planned as a Festschrift in his honor (Moskowitz, Scharf, & Stevens, 1974).

[8] In the old days, "blank" trials were used in an effort to keep the subject honest and alert, and the attitude in the laboratory was that "false alarm" responses, as these are now called ("yes" responses to "blank" stimuli), were undesirable, if not downright sinful. A more modern view, embedded in signal detection theory, holds that if false alarm data are properly dealt with, it should be possible to derive an estimate of sensitivity (called d') that will remain invariant for a particular stimulus intensity despite changes in a subject's criterion. This estimate works, to the extent that it does, because a subject who uses a low criterion for "yes" responses will also generate large numbers of false alarms, whereas a high-criterion subject will produce relatively few. In practice, the criterion problem turns out not to be very serious for the class of visual psychophysics treated in this book, and large bodies of data (such as those of Stiles, discussed in the

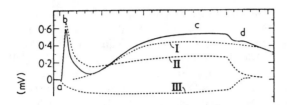

Figure 6.15   Illustrations of the a, b, c, and d waves of the ERG together with the PI, II and III components. (Adapted from Granit, 1947.)

second part of this chapter) based on simple "yes" and "no" judgments, without adjustment for criterion changes, have proved to be extremely useful. For a treatment of signal detection theory and related data analysis, see Egan (1975).

[9] ERGs are gross retinal recordings obtained with electrodes placed on the cornea. Late receptor potentials (LRPs) are recorded with monopolar microelectrodes placed near the receptors and the retinal blood supply, which services much of the retina but not the receptors, is clamped by pressure on the optic disc, thus inactivating retinal neurons but not the receptors, which rely on the pigment epithelium for their nutrients. The evidence is good, but not conclusive, that the retinal blood supply clamping eliminates all retinal electrophysiological activity except cone responses. The LRP is a negative potential, which Granit originally called PIII. The a-wave is the beginning of the LRP. These relationships can be seen in Figure 6.15. Fr-LERGs are retinal recordings obtained with bipolar microelectrodes placed across the receptors' outer segment layer. When these bipolar microelectrodes were used they referred to "fractional recording." Therefore, at Valeton's suggestion (personal communication), we refer to fractional LERGs (or Fr-LERG, not to be confused with FERG, which stands for focal ERG). These electrodes recorded from an area of 1.2° as opposed to 4° obtained from monopolar electrodes. Moreover, fractional recording with bipolar electrodes did not require chemical (aspartate) or mechanical (blood vessel clamping procedures) to isolate receptor responses. Thus, a more natural retinal preparation was used. This method does not record from isolated single receptors.

[10] The nonlinear relationship between the amount of light entering the cone and its resultant electrophysiological response is referred to as cone response nonlinearity. Although Schnapf *et al.* found clear evidence for linearity in isolated cone responses, we will use the nonlinearity exhibited by multiple cone response as found by Whitten & Boynton (1970) and by Valeton & van Norren (1983). We do this in a belief that aggregate cone responses bring us a little closer to understanding human perceptual responses.

[11] Valeton & van Norren (1983) report that the single vs. multiple receptor recordings do not provide a reasonable dichotomy to explain the differences between the suction electrode and other electrophysiological methods. Valeton pointed out that if we assume each receptor has its own half-saturation light intensity and one then adds up the responses from a large number of these receptors, one would obtain a shallower response function from the conglomerate than is

obtained from any single cone. Valeton simulated this concept and determined that to obtain a 30% shallower slope (and exponent of 0.7) from individual cones that each have a slope of 1.0 would require a standard deviation of half saturation constants that is much larger than one can realistically expect.

[12] This observation proves the point only if receptors behave independently. Although Baylor, Fuortes, and O'Bryan (1971) showed, in the turtle, that they do not, the degree of summation of cone signals is far too small to account for the psychophysical result.

[13] See Stiles (1978), for the most recent summary. The work is reported in detail in Stiles (1939), Stiles (1949), and Stiles (1953). Summaries of his approach written by others are available by Brindley (1970), Enoch (1972), and Mariott (1962).

[14] There is a rather extensive literature documenting rod–cone interactions (e.g., Arden and Frumkes, 1986) so it is not so surprising that there should be cone–cone interactions.

[15] The preceding background might be better called the "interpolated" background because it follows, as well as precedes, the concurrent one.

[16] See, for example, a study by Scheibner (1966). Also, the theory of Jameson and Hurvich specifically assumes that adaptation occurs partly at the opponent-color stage. This theory has had some success in accounting for color shifts caused by chromatic adaptation. For a summary and entry to earlier references, see Jameson and Hurvich (1972).

[17] We do not want to perpetuate the fiction that color constancy is perfect (see Chapter 11).

Chapter 7

The Encoding of Color

INTRODUCTION

What are the various roles played by cells in the visual pathway that determine color appearance? Abramov and Gordon (1994) proposed a psychophysiological linking hypothesis as follows: ". . . for any unique category of sensation (e.g., R or Y) there is a neural mechanism with response properties that match those of related psychophysical functions. Only when that mechanism responds do we experience that sensation" (pp. 456–457). In this chapter we discuss a simple color vision model, consider some psychophysical and electrophysiological approaches for studying color coding, and examine various neural structures and pathways responsible for color coding.

From the perspective provided by Chapter 5, it would be hard to doubt that the L-, M-, and S-cones are truly at the first stage of chromatic vision. Yet the achromatic attributes of pattern vision we experience when looking at black-and-white photographs must, because there are no other cones, be served by the same receptors. Those who probe the monkey cortex with microelectrodes often find cells that appear to carry a chromatic code; yet at the same time many of these same units also respond selectively to nonspectral characteristics of the stimulus. For example, a cell may respond only to the longwave end of the spectrum we call "red", but its willingness to do so may also require that the light be presented as a slit, that the slit be oriented in a certain direction, and that it move in a direction perpendicular to its axis. We therefore appear to be dealing with an interlocking system of neural elements whose collective concern is to process information about intensity, space, time, motion, and wavelength; more often than not, any single unit may be involved in two or more of these functions at the same time (Martinez–Uriegas, 1994).

We know a good deal about the first stage of chromatic processing, somewhat less about the second stage, and are still rather uncertain about the third stage. Obvious as it may be, we emphasize that visual perception does not take place in the eye: an intact optic nerve is required to send the message from the eye to the brain. Direct electrical or mechanical stimulation of the eye can lead to visual sensations only if the optic nerve is available to carry these retinal signals to the higher brain centers, in the same way that it carries light-generated signals. But direct electrical stimulation of the visual brain can also lead to visual sensations, whether or not there is an optic nerve, or even an eye. The visual sensations produced by these electrical stimulations are spatially diffuse and localized in space according to which region of the visual brain is stimulated. However, these so-called *phosphenes* lack specificity and do not much resemble ordinary visual perceptions. The pattern of brain activity induced by normal input from the light-stimulated eye is evidently exceedingly subtle and precise, and is not likely to be duplicated by direct electrical stimulation of the eye or brain.[1]

OPPONENT-COLOR THEORY

In Chapter 1 we saw that Hering first proposed the idea of a neural opponent color code in the nineteenth century. By the middle of the present century, a variety of theories had been suggested to incorporate trichromacy at the initial stage of vision with second-stage recoding into (1) red-green and yellow-blue opponent signals, and (2) a nonspectral opponent signal to transmit luminance or brightness information. In Stevens' *Handbook of Experimental Psychology*, Judd (1951b) provided the first quantitative review of such two-stage models, which tie together trichromatic and opponent coding of color signals.

Psychophysical and electrophysiological evidence supporting the opponent-color idea started to appear in the 1950s. This chapter will stress the physiological and anatomical evidence; nevertheless it will be worthwhile first to review some of the modern psychophysical work, which shows that opponent color signals exist somewhere in the visual system. Many models of color vision have been published that attempt to organize the physiology, anatomy, and psychophysics of color vision (e.g., Boynton, 1979; Hurvich, 1981; Ingling *et al.*, 1977;

Guth *et al.*, 1980; D'Zmura & Lennie, 1986; Lennie & D'Zmura, 1988; Guth, 1991; Hunt, 1991; De Valois & De Valois, 1993). We begin here with a simple version of what is frequently called multi-stage or standard model of color vision. The purpose of this simple model is not to fully explain color vision but to provide a framework within which we can discuss some aspects of the subject. With respect to this model, Boynton (1986) wrote:

> I wish to make clear that it is by no means intended to account for everything about color perception. In the first place, it is a gross oversimplification even of the domain it intends to cover. There are many important facts of color vision with which the model does not attempt to deal (p. 245).

This simple model combines what is known about some aspects of color vision physiology and color vision psychophysics. The first stage consists of the L-, M-, and S-cones (Fig. 7.1A) The second stage is an opponent processing stage resulting from subtractive processes: L – M and S – (L + M). S-, M-, and L-, it will be recalled, are the short, middle, and long wavelength cone receptors. They are represented twice in Figure 7.1A just for convenience. The r-g chromatic channel is the result of M- 0.5L with a proposed input from the S-cones, which will be discussed in a moment. The y-b chromatic channel is fed by the S-cones and the sum of the L- and M-cones. The luminance channel is fed by the sum of the L-cones and M-cones (L+M). The psychophysically based spectral sensitivities of the L-, M-, and S-cones are the Smith–Pokorny functions (see Appendix Part III). Choosing the Smith–Pokorny fundamentals is an arbitrary decision. These cone sensitivities are not far off the mark and agree reasonably well with those proposed by other investigators (e.g., Vos, Estévez & Walraven, 1990 or Stockman *et al.*, 1993). Nor are they very different from those derived by microspectrophotometry or by electrophysiology. The Smith–Pokorny functions are shown in Figure 7.1B as the S-, M-, and L- functions. The sum of L+M very nearly describes Judd's modification of V(λ). However, the S-, M-, and L-sensitivities do not correlate very well with our chromatic perceptions. For example, the L-curve is considerably higher than the M-curve near 575 nm. As a result, assuming that chromatic perception is dependent on an opponent L-M signal, one would expect from these spectral sensitivities that this wavelength would appear decidedly reddish orange. However, 575 nm is very close to unique yellow for most observers. One can also see in Figure 7.1B that between 420 and 500 nm the M-spectral sensitivity is either equal to or only slightly greater than the L. This would suggest that little green should be seen at these wavelengths. In fact, near 510 nm many people observe unique green. One way around this dilemma is to reduce the sensitivity of the L- cones by 50% as represented by the dashed "L/2" curve in Figure 7.1B.

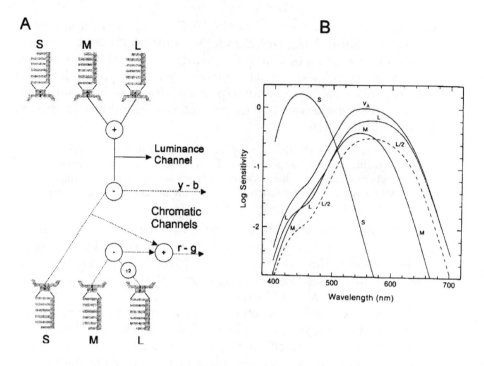

Figure 7.1   A. Simple opponent-color model of human color vision. The S, M-, and L-cones at the top are intended to represent the same three cones that are also shown at the bottom. The achromatic (broadband, spectrally nonopponent) pathway is activated by the summated output of the L- and M-cones. The r-g spectrally opponent pathway is activated by the difference in output by these same cones. The y-b spectrally opponent pathway receives a signal that is the difference between the output of the S-cones and that of the luminance channel. The signal from the S-cones added to the difference signal from the M- and L-cones helps to account for the redness seen as short wavelengths (see text), B. Spectral sensitivity of the L-, M-, and S-cones based on the Smith–Pokorny fundamentals (see Appendix Part III). L/2 (dashed curve) is the spectral sensitivity of the L-cones reduced by 0.3 log units, a factor of two; V_λ is Judd's modification of C.I.E. $V(\lambda)$; the sum of L and M very nearly describes V_λ.

The S-cones are connected to the r-g chromatic channel to help account for the perception of violet at the shortest wavelengths. Lennie & D'Zmura (1988) suggest that signals from the S-cones feed into the r-g channel with the same sign as do the L-cones.

Our understanding of stage three is still very uncertain and there are some rather major disagreements in the literature about various aspects of this stage. One of the interesting attributes of stage three is a proposed multiplexing of chromatic and achromatic signals (Lennie & D'Zmura, 1988; De Valois & De Valois, 1993). This multiplexing idea, which was originally proposed theoretically by Ingling and Martinez–Uriegas (1983), assumes that the parvocellular pathway is able to carry both chromatic and achromatic information. Which of these two is transmitted depends in part on the temporal and spatial characteristics of the stimulus. The original physiological evidence for the idea comes from Gouras & Zrenner (1979). These investigators made retinal recordings from macaque L–M ganglion cells and obtained typical spectrally opponent action spectra when the stimuli were steady state or modulated slowly. However, when the stimuli were flickered at 33 Hz a unimodal action spectrum was obtained.

There are two schools of thought concerning how the parvocellular pathway might handle achromatic information in addition to chromatic.

• The achromatic signal is a luminance signal. There is no strong physiological or conclusive psychophysical support for this position.

• The parvo achromatic signal yields brightness information, not luminance information. This suggestion was first put forward by Valberg *et al.* (1986).

The physiological evidence so far suggests that the physiological basis for luminance resides, at least in part, in the magnocellular pathway (see p. 286) (Lee *et al.*, 1988; Lee, 1993). In an attempt to see if the parvo pathway can handle luminance, Lee has tried combining the activity of various parvocellular neurons to model a luminance signal. Because he was unable to do so he arrived at the conclusion that the magnocellular pathway provides the sole underlying physiological basis for luminance. Perhaps there is no real contradiction between Lee and other investigators. Lee's physiological recordings were obtained using macaque retinal ganglion cells. This stage of the anatomy would seem to be part of the second stage of color vision. The third stage occurs in the cortex so perhaps the multiplexing of chromatic and achromatic information is strictly a cortical, stage three process.

Let us now look at two of the psychophysical methods that point to a spectral opponent processing of color vision signals.

Color Naming

A type of experiment that permits a relatively direct gauging of the appearance of spectral colors utilizes direct color scaling, or color naming (Boynton, Shafer & Neun, 1964; Abramov, Gordon & Chan,

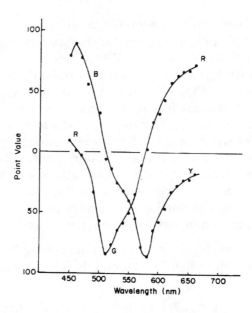

Figure 7.2   Results of a color–naming experiment by Boynton and Gordon (1965), as replotted by Boynton (1975), for the average of three subjects at 1000 td of retinal illuminance. This figure helps to illustrate the opponent nature of color vision processing.

1992; also see Chapter 11). Figure 7.2 shows Boynton's (1975) re-plotting of the Boynton and Gordon (1965) color naming data. Briefly, subjects were presented monochromatic lights at each of the wavelengths shown in the figure. They were required to judge the appearance of each stimulus by using only the color names red, green, yellow, and blue. Either one or two names could be used on each trial. For example, if the subject saw a unique yellow, only the color yellow was reported. If the color was yellowish red (i.e., more yellow than red) then yellow-red, in that order, was reported. An important outcome of the experiment was that, (excepting in a few instances involving an 8-year-old subject) responses of red-green, green-red, yellow-blue, and blue-yellow were not given, although there was no proscription against using them.

Chromatic Cancellation

Jameson and Hurvich (1955) reasoned that it should be possible to cancel the hue components of spectral stimuli by superimposing lights having dominant hues opposite to those being canceled. For example, light at 600 nm, which appears orange,[2] seems to contain both red and yellow hue components. If an observer is given a variable green-appearing stimulus, superimposed on the orange field, it is possible to adjust the amount of green light until the reddishness of the orange is completely canceled, leaving a field that appears only yellow with no apparent reddishness or greeness. This is the essence of the hue cancellation technique.

The amount of green-appearing light is used as a measure of the strength of the red component that is present in the original orange light. By using a blue cancellation light, it is possible to cancel the yellow component of the original orange, leaving a unique red. Such hue cancellation was carried out using lights of the three psychologically unique hues plus a long wavelength red,[3] two at a time in each of four regions of the spectrum (separated by the wavelengths corresponding to the unique hues of the spectrum).

Some additional observations were needed to specify the units of the cancellation stimuli. Opponent pairs of cancellation stimuli were superimposed and the relative energy values required to produce their mutual cancellation were taken as equal intensities of these two stimuli. The intensities of red and yellow appearing lights were taken to be visually equal when presented in amounts that produced the perception of a balanced orange mixture.

The results of this hue cancellation experiment, for one observer, are shown in Figure 7.3A. Log *chromatic valence,* on the ordinate, refers to the amount of the cancellation component, expressed in relative energy units, required to cancel the opponent hue of test stimuli presented at equal energy at various wavelengths. By converting the chromatic valence from log units to arithmetic units, and arbitrarily designating red and yellow as positive and green and blue as negative, the opponent characteristics are more easily visualized (Fig. 7.3B). The resulting functions provide a remarkably good description of the appearance of spectral colors. Figure 7.3B shows that the longest wavelengths are slightly yellowish red, corresponding to a large amount of green light that was required to cancel the red component and a much smaller amount of blue light to cancel the residual yellow. A balanced orange occurs at 600 nm. Unique yellow (a yellow with no hint of green or red) is represented at about 575 nm, where the red-green function crosses the zero baseline. At this wavelength neither red nor green is seen and neither cancellation component is needed; only blue light is used to cancel the perception of yellow and thereby produce an apparent white.

In the midspectral region, yellow-greens are flanked by unique yellow (a yellow with no perceptible red or green content) to the

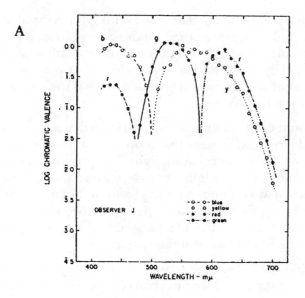

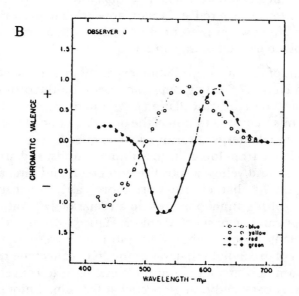

Figure 7.3   A. Results of a hue cancellation experiment by Hurvich and Jameson (1955a) in which the perceived amounts of red, green, yellow, and blue hues in spectral colors were assessed in terms of complementary colors required to cancel each hue component. B. The same data replotted by using an linear ordinate and arbitrarily making red and yellow positive and blue and green negative to more graphically illustrate opponent processing.

right, and unique green at about 500 nm to the left. As wavelength is further shortened, a small blue-green region appears that terminates at unique blue near 475 nm. Although the shortest wavelengths are seen as predominantly blue, red reappears in this part of the spectrum, and it is canceled, just as for the long wavelengths, by adding green light.

Hurvich and Jameson (1955) went on to show that functions like those of Figure 7.3 can be derived from linear transformations of color-mixture data. In their theory (and others similar to it) the outputs of L- and M-cones are assumed to subtract from each other to produce the red-minus-green opponent-color function. Similarly, L+M cone signals are assumed to subtract from those of S-cones (yellow-blue cancellation). Larimer, Krantz, and Cicerone (1974, 1975) reexamined chromatic cancellation and replicated the main features of the Jameson–Hurvich experiment. In addition they demonstrated that, although the red-green cancellation process is linear with intensity, yellow-blue cancellation is not. Therefore the hue should vary somewhat with intensity at most wavelengths, as indeed it does (the Bezold–Brücke hue shift; see, for example, Nagy and Zacks (1977) for work on this topic.

In summary, two procedures were described by which it is possible to scale the appearance of the spectrum psychophysically. When direct color naming is used, opponent hues are virtually never seen together, and the appearance of the spectrum as derived from this procedure agrees in important respects with that obtained by the cancellation method. Colors that appear red cancel colors that appear green and green cancels red; similarly, yellow and blue cancel each other and the amount of the cancellation stimulus can be used to gauge the components of spectral colors.

Evidence For Chromatic Differencing Signals

Hue cancellation implies a subtractive process, and there is convincing evidence that such a process takes place between receptors, although the exact nature of this subtraction is still controversial. The belief in chromatic difference signals at stage 2 rests upon direct evidence. But, beginning with Hering, there were those who believed in them because such difference signals seemed necessary to explain the appearance of colors, especially the dimensions of color experience described here and in Chapter 2. For example, this differencing concept is consistent with our inability to see red and green in the same place at the same time, presumably because messages meaning "red" and "green" must be transmitted through the same pathways.

Implicit in this arrangement is the requirement that the signals of the L-M pathways must exist in two qualitative states; otherwise a brain receiving such a message could not use it to distinguish one sensation from the other.

Until direct evidence began to accumulate in the 1950s, few physicists or neurophysiologists wanted to believe this. The physicists' intransigence was related to the focus of their training and concern, which was mainly with color matching related to the behavior of the cones, the class of experiment stressed in Chapter 5. Neurophysiologists, in their turn, had long been conditioned by the so-called *law of specific nerve energies,* according to which a single nerve fiber was not allowed to carry messages having more than one kind of qualitative significance.

It is interesting to speculate about the possible advantages of computing a L–M difference signal, as compared to the trichromatic alternative that Helmholtz and many other theorists had favored. In linking receptors directly to sensations, Helmholtz implied that signals from L- and M-cones are kept separate from receptors to brain. A problem with this scheme stems from the large overlap between L- and M-cone sensitivity curves, especially in the region where these curves cross. Wavelength discrimination data require that relatively small differences between signals of nearly equal strength must be reliably discriminated.

Many years ago, Hecht (1932) proposed a theory of color vision in which color-mixture data were transformed so that his resulting triad of curves seemed nearly to lie upon one another. Yet they differed sufficiently that, in a mathematical sense, they made the correct predictions about metameric color matches. Although the overlap between modern L- and M-cone sensitivity curves is much less, some remarks made by Guild (1932) about Hecht's theory nevertheless apply:

> . . . . It is perfectly easy to start with the known properties of ordinary colour vision . . . and then work out a system, such as [in Hecht's paper], which will be in exact agreement with these properties: it is only necessary to carry the arithmetic to a sufficient number of significant figures in order to do so.

> Nature, however, begins at the other end. She first constructs the visual mechanism, not on a calculating machine, but from flesh and blood and protoplasm, and the visual properties which any individual possesses are determined by the particular example of this mechanism with which he is provided.

> On any system of the type suggested [by Hecht], all the qualitative properties of vision, as exemplified in the colour-match relations, depend upon small differences in large and nearly equal quantities . . .

> The slightest deviations from a standard pattern in the various parts of
> the visual apparatus would alter the colour vision to an enormous ex-
> tent . . . (p. 157)

Thus there is no problem about small differences between large
signals, provided that one has a digital computer and can carry the
computations to a sufficient number of decimal places. But the initial cone signals of vision exist in analog form and, moreover, depend upon the statistical properties of light. The farther such signals
are carried through the visual system before being compared, the
less reliable they become. Therefore, to keep the signal-to-noise ratio as high as possible it is better to compare the signals early. A
differencing process taking place near the receptors constitutes such
a comparison (Buchsbaum & Gottshhalk, 1983).

A related issue concerns the dynamic range of subsequent neural elements, especially the bipolar cells that receive signals from cones
and pass their outputs along to ganglion cells. The factors examined
in Chapter 6 proved capable of shrinking the responses of cones to
about 150 to 1 over a millionfold range of stimulus intensities. But
150:1 is still a large ratio of activity to be carried reliably by the analog responses of bipolar cells, or for that matter in the subsequent
impulse-frequency code of ganglion cells. But the ratio of L- to M-
cone activation varies only from about 1:4 at 465 nm to perhaps 8:1
at the longest wavelengths. Ratios of this order can be reliably encoded, at a given luminance level, without exceeding the dynamic
range of bipolar cells.

The Perception of Red Re-emerges at Short Wavelengths

Most opponent models attempted to account for various aspects of
color vision by subtracting the cone outputs from each other. Clearly
a simple subtraction of M- from L-cone outputs cannot account for
the redness seen at short wavelengths. Ingling (1977) has argued
that there is an inhibitory interaction of the S-cones acting on the M-
cones which tends to bias a L-M difference signal in the L direction
for short wavelengths where S-cones are strongly activated. A point
of view described by Lennie and D'Zmura (1988) is that the L-M
mechanism receives S-cone input with the same sign as the L- cones.
This connection is seen in the simple opponent model represented
in Figure 7.1.

SOME METHODOLOGICAL NOTES

It is possible to impale single cone photoreceptors of fish and turtles
with very fine microelectrodes in order to measure the voltage differ-

ence between the inside of each such cell and its surrounding medium. This work cannot be done, *in vivo*, with human subjects. Nor has it proved possible as yet to do this class of research in a species more closely related to man than are turtles and fish. It would be particularly helpful to have such evidence from macaque monkeys, because they have a visual system much like that of the human, and there is ample behavioral evidence to document that they have a human form of trichromatic vision. But monkey cones, like our own, are much smaller than those of fish and turtles. Even the finest electrode, by penetrating the cell membrane of such a cone, would probably destroy the cell as a functional unit.[4] Retinal electrophysiology is therefore especially difficult to do when using warm-blooded animals. Recall, however, the suction electrophysiology we discussed in preceding chapters. This method allows for the electrophysiological recording of isolated single receptors, including those of human and monkey cones, and yields much the same kinds of information as intracellular recording. As with the intracellular recordings noted above, suction electrophysiology is performed on excised eyes whose retinas have been removed and whose outer segments have been separated from the pigment epithelium.

Electroretinogram (ERG)

Electrical records in response to light stimulation can be obtained from the human retina by placing an electrode-impregnated contact lens on the cornea of the eye. Although these records, known as electroretinograms (ERGs), are complex and much more difficult to analyze than are microelectrode recordings from single cells, they do have the important advantage of coming from intact human eyes.[5] The ERG is based on the activity of neurons in the retina, including the photoreceptors. Human ERGs have been obtained for more than 100 years, during which time there has been a gradual improvement in stimulating conditions, in recording procedures, and in the interpretation of data. ERG recording received a powerful assist in the form of procedures that permit the recording of a local electroretinogram (LERG) and fractional ERG from monkeys.[6] These improved records are not obtainable from humans because the technique requires the *in vivo* insertion into the eye of a microelectrode whose tip nestles among (not in) the receptors. Although records obtained in this way come from thousands of cells, the response is much more localized than the ordinary ERG, which comes from millions of them. Recall the research by Hood and Birch (1993) we discussed in Chapter 6 where they analyzed the onset of the ERG a-wave. Even though these responses arise from a population of cones, rather than from a single receptor, they reveal the onset of cone activity.

Local Electroretinogram (LERG)

K. T. Brown (1962) achieved the first recordings of receptor potentials from macaque monkeys. He did this by recording a special kind of local ERG (LERG) in an eye where the primary circulation of the retina was "clamped" by putting pressure on the optic disc, where the major vascular supply of the retina passes into the eye along with the optic nerve fibers. Because the receptors are selectively nourished by blood supplied to the choroid, only their responses survive this clamping procedure. Being a local ERG, and not an intracellular record, the response arises from many receptors, but probably from receptors alone. In Chapter 6, we discussed results from this technique in the research of Boynton & Whitten. Recall also Valeton's technique, which he called fractional LERG (Fr-LERG). By using a bipolar electrode Valeton and van Norren (1983) were able to record local potentials from outer segments of receptors without resorting to retinal blood vessel clamping.

Visually Evoked Cortical Potential (VECP)

The techniques for recording brain waves in humans (the electro-encephalogram, or EEG) have been available for a long time. In response to light flashes, a component of the recording specifically related to the stimulus, sometimes known as the visually evoked cortical potential (VECP), is elicited.[7] The magnitude of such evoked potentials is in the microvolt range, and because they are so small they are ordinarily not visible in the EEG; instead they are swamped by the background activity of the brain and unavoidable sources of noise in the recording. One trick that is used to observe the VECP is called response averaging. Although small, the potential fluctuations that comprise the VECP are reliably related to the timing of the light flash that produces them. In other words, the visually relevant potentials tend to follow the same time course in response to each repeated presentation of the stimulus. The background activity, on the other hand, bears a random relation to the timing of the flashes. If one adds together a large number of responses elicited by repetitions of the same stimulus, taking care to use the onset of the stimulus as a trigger to begin each recording period, the time-locked VECP is observed to rise majestically from the background in a spectacular triumph of digital electronic wizardry. Another device, called a lock-in amplifier, can accomplish much the same aim when a flickering input is used. By selectively amplifying only those response components whose frequency is close to that of the stimulus, signals are extracted from background activity. Signal-averaging procedures are also used to advantage in ERG recording.

HUMAN VISUAL ELECTROPHYSIOLOGY

Although the use of electrophysiological methods with humans shows considerable promise, they have had only limited success in revealing new information about color coding that was not already known from inferences based on psychophysical experiments. Nevertheless, the electrical experiments can serve to confirm and reify such conceptions. Moreover, when relatively gross electrical records recorded from humans are obtained from Old-World monkeys, which have color vision similar to humans, a comparison of such records with those obtained using microelectrodes inside the visual system can help clarify the exact meaning of human records, particularly with respect to the sources of the externally recorded potentials.

As examples of the sorts of electrophysiological experiments that can be done with humans, studies from four different laboratories will be mentioned briefly.

• Riggs, Johnson, and Schick (1966) studied electrical responses of the human eye to changes in wavelength of the stimulating light. Because the human ERG is strongly influenced by stray light falling outside the image proper (Boynton & Riggs, 1951), spatially alternating stripes were used that could be exchanged for one another at equal luminance. Fifteen wavelengths in 15-nm steps from 450 to 660 were compared in all 210 possible combinations; the magnitude of the average response to the shifting pattern, alternated at about 10 displacements per second, was recorded. The results were summarized, using three functions that resemble constant-luminance output curves for L-, M-, and S-cones. The results suggest that L-, M-, and S-cones contribute linearly to the recorded responses, and that response magnitude is predictable in terms of the total amount of change, for all three types of cones combined, that occurs for a particular wavelength shift at constant luminance.

• Using the visually evoked cortical potential (VECP), Estévez, Spekreijse, van den Berg, and Cavonius (1975) demonstrated that spectral sensitivities essentially identical to psychophysically obtained π-mechanisms could be measured. In order to study the electrophysiological analog of π_5 a longwave test stimulus was used that was alternated with a lesser amount of green light designed to eliminate the flickering component of M-cone stimulation. Because VECPs are much more vigorous when patterned rather than uniform stimuli are used (Harter & White, 1970), a checkerboard with elements 15' on each side was employed, and adjacent squares were exchanged six times per second to elicit what was termed a "contrast EP" (EP = evoked potential).

The experiment consisted of determining the intensity of adapting lights of various wavelengths required to drive the recorded response down to a criterion level of 2 µv, which was smaller than the response to the checkerboard would have been in the dark-adapted state. The same apparatus was also used to obtain π_5 with the same subjects using psychophysical methods. Similar procedures were also used to examine π_1 and π_4. The authors conclude that "the close agreement between our data and the π-mechanisms of Stiles suggests to us that the color coded channels as seen through the contrast EP are mediated through such mechanisms." This conclusion, which implies that signals from L-, M-, and S-cones are preserved in separate channels all the way to the cortex, is probably wrong. After all, because special techniques were used so that, for example, the entire L-M opponent-color variation resulted only from alterations in L-cone output, it is not surprising that only L-cone output was reflected. This point will be examined again in Chapter 9 in connection with a psychophysical experiment by Kelly and van Norren (p. 388).

• Above we made reference to comparing human and Old-World monkey electrophysiological data. Lee and colleagues have provided such information, mostly from monkey ganglion cells. Here, however, we are more interested in comparing human electrophysiological data with that of monkey. Regan and Lee (1993) provided just such a comparison. The human data were obtained both by psychophysics and from cortically evoked potentials. Regan and Lee compared spectral sensitivity functions obtained on humans both psychophysically and with visually evoked field potentials with records obtained from macaque retinal ganglion cells. The correspondence was gratifyingly similar for the human VECP, human heterochromatic flicker photometry, and magnocellular pathway macaque ganglion cell responses. These data led them to conclude that the VECP spectral sensitivity data collected at 40 Hz were processed by the magnocellular pathway in human subjects.

• Regan (1973) studied the effect of purely chromatic contours on the VECP by using checkerboards in which the adjacent squares were of different chromaticity. In a deuteranope presumably lacking M-cones (see Chapter 10), he found that a relative intensity of the adjacent red and green checks could be found that reduced the response to zero as expected, because two equally effective lights, for the remaining L-cones, would be exchanged. For normal subjects, on the other hand, a clear response was always recorded no matter what the relative intensities of the adjacent checks. Although Regan favored the idea that his results were due to long wavelength and middle wavelength signals transmitted over independent pathways to the cortex, his data are also consistent with the possibility (as he admits) that "the human visual system contains both chromatic contrast and luminance contrast channels (p. 2398)."

BRIEF TOUR OF COLOR-RELEVANT ANATOMY AND PHYSIOLOGY

The Retina

Color vision starts with the absorption of light by the outer segments of the photoreceptors, where the trichromacy of color vision begins. The signals generated in the photoreceptors are then delivered to the bipolar and horizontal cells. At one time it seemed certain that, in fish retinas, the transformation from trichromacy to spectral opponency depended upon an interaction between horizontal cells and the cone receptors. However, Wietsma et al. (1995) have published data that cast serious doubt on this conception. In addition, the source of this transformation has yet to be revealed in primates (see discussion of Baron, 1980 and Spileers et al., 1993 on page 269) and, indeed, recently has been seriously questioned (Dacey and Lee, 1995). From the bipolar cells the signal goes to ganglion cells either directly or indirectly via the amacrine cells. The axons of the ganglion cells carry the visual signal without any synapses to the lateral geniculate nucleus (LGN). From the LGN the visual signal goes via the optic radiations to the occipital cortex. The superior colliculus, a midbrain nucleus that receives retinal and cortical input, is concerned with eye movements. This structure plays no apparent role in color vision.

Now that we have provided an outline of the gross pathway, let us take a look at some of the details, particularly as they relate to color vision.

Receptors

As indicated in Chapter 5, there are four classes of photoreceptors: one kind of rod receptor and three classes of cone receptors (L, M, and S). We know this from a number of research techniques in addition to the original psychophysical studies. Research on these receptors still continues using the methods of microspectrophotometry, suction electrophysiology, anatomy, and molecular genetics research (see Chapter 10).

Many years ago the famed Swedish neurophysiologist and Nobel laureate, Ragnar Granit, concluded that the leading edge of the ERG had its origin in the photoreceptors, but the sign of the response was such as to imply a hyperpolarization of the receptors in response to light. This was not an appealing idea because all neurons then known were passively hyperpolarized, depolarizing only when stimulated.[8] Today we know that the receptors do indeed hyperpolarize when stimulated. Although complete details of receptor current flow still are not known, impressive headway has been made in recent years.[9]

In the dark-adapted state, each vertebrate photoreceptor actively generates an extracellular current that flows outward from the base of the cell toward the tip of the outer segment. To complete the circuit, a return current flows inside the cell from the outer segment toward the inner segment (Fig. 7.4). This current, which underlies the receptor component of the ERG, reflects the state of activity of the cell. In the absence of light, the flow of current in the circuit (in and around the cell) is believed to depend mainly on three variables: (1) the activity of a sodium/potassium pump (labeled "active transport" in Fig. 7.4) located somewhere in the inner segment, (2) the state of the cGMP gated channels, and (3) the state of the potassium selective nongated channels.[10]

The hyperpolarization of the receptors occurs as follows. There is a flow of current flux from the inner to the outer segment (Fig. 7.4A). As already noted in Chapter 5, the only direct action of light when it is absorbed by a photopigment in the outer segment of a receptor is to *isomerize* (cause a morphological change in) the pigment molecule. This isomerization starts a chain of activity in the receptor (Fig. 7.4B) that results in the cGMP gated channel closing, thereby preventing sodium ions from flowing into the outer segment. Potassium ions continuously leave the inner segment via the nongated K^+ channels. Because the cGMP gated channels close in the chain reaction to light being absorbed by the photopigment, the sodium ions (which are positive) can no longer enter the outer segment. The active transport mechanism continues to pump in K^+ and pump out Na^+. As a consequence the receptor hyperpolarizes when stimulated by light reaching a maximum negative potential of approximately 70 mvolts. In darkness, the cGMP gate channel is open permitting the influx of Na ions and the dark resting potential is about −40 mvolts.

We have here a picture of a most unusual receptor mechanism, one which is active even when totally unstimulated by light. In the light-adapted eye, decrements of light provide visual information just as increments do, because both modulate an intermediate level of activity that is in progress. In addition to acting as a detector and transmitter, the receptor also acts as an amplifier: the energy contained in an incident photon is trivial compared to the response

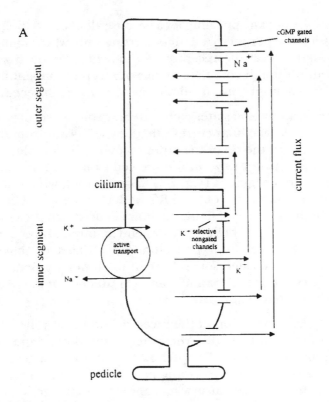

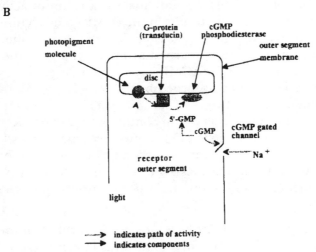

Figure 7.4 The mechanisms and current flow in the retinal receptor. A. Illustrates the flow of sodium and Postasium. The active transport is the so-called sodium/potasium pump. B. Illustrates the mechanism that causes the receptor to hyperpolarize when a photopigment molecule absorbs a quantum of light. (Adapted from Tessier–Lavigne, 1991.)

amplitude of the receptor. The action of a photon, when absorbed by a photopigment molecule, is to trigger, not to drive.

As we saw in Chapter 5, there are three classes of such cones, which differ according to the range of their spectral sensitivities. Suction electrophysiology has provided spectral sensitivities for human long wavelength and middle wavelength cones (see Chapter 5). Micropectrophotometric research has provided human spectral sensitivity functions for L-, M- and S-cones. The agreement between the electrophysiological sensitivities and those obtained by microspectrophotometry and psychophysics is gratifyingly good, constituting a further verification that three classes of cones with their photopigments provide the initial basis for trichromatic vision.

The hyperpolarization of cones in response to light occurs in the same way for all three types of cones. This means that without some external modulation there is no basis for spectral opponency in the behavior of individual receptors. As will be noted below, such modulation probably occurs with horizontal cell feedback onto the receptors. A variable degree of hyperpolarization can be accomplished with light of any wavelength, simply by using an intensity that is inversely proportional to the sensitivity of the cell. This provides an electrophysiological expression of response univariance at the receptor stage.

The degree of hyperpolarization depends upon light intensity, which in turn is related to the rate of photon absorption. (It is this fact that makes possible the examination of the spectral sensitivities of the cones.) To a first approximation, the response of the cell (degree of hyperpolarization) follows a modified Michaelis–Menten rule, which relates the relative response R to the stimulus intensity I:

$$R = \frac{I^n}{I^n + K^n} \tag{7.1}$$

This equation, with an exponent n of 0.7, is the basis for the response compression discussed on page 221 in Chapter 6. Theoretically, response compression can be related to the finite number of elements contributing to the increase of membrane impedance that controls the response. When the light intensity is low, only a trivial fraction of these elements is activated. If $n = 1$, the response rises almost in proportion to intensity (I is very small compared to K). When the light intensity is very high, I becomes very large relative to K and the value of the fraction approaches 1, which relates theoretically to the idea that all of the response elements have been exhausted. When this happens, the cell is then said to be "saturated" in a sense that is similar to the photographic analog discussed in the previous chapter.

Exponents of less than 1.0 were not observed in the suction electrode data of Schnapf, Nunn, Meister & Baylor (1990). An exponent of 0.7 was obtained by Boynton and Whitten (1970) when recording LRPs. Both experiments used monkey eyes. The LRP method records *in vivo* multi-receptor responses. The suction electrode method records *in vitro* single receptor responses. Future research will have to tease out the significant differences between these techniques and the related response differences. Nevertheless, it is worth pointing out that because human psychophysical responses are made using large numbers of intact receptors, the responses obtained *in vivo* using the LRPs probably yield data more closely related to human perception than would be expected from *in vitro* single receeport methods. That certainly is the implication of Figure 1A in Boynton and Whitten (1970). Yet, for those interested in the activity of individual receptors and how they combine to yield a conglomerate signal, the suction electrode approach is an appropriate investigative technique.

Receptors do not function independently of one another. This means that the response of any particular receptor depends not only upon the rate at which photons are being absorbed in its own outer segment, but also upon the activity of neighboring receptors. At the present time, more questions can be raised than answers definitely given about these interactions. Psychophysical evidence from humans has been brought to bear on these issues and some of it will be considered in Chapter 9. For now, the best we can do is state two of the most important questions, and provide some possible answers.

1. *What is the mechanism of cone–cone interaction?* Although the answer to this question for the human retina cannot be answered yet, considerable research on various other species has permitted informed speculation (Kolb & Lipetz, 1991; Kolb, 1991). Dowling (1987) tells us that most of the inter-receptor interactions are attributable to gap junctions (see Figs. 4.4 or 7.6), although he does allow that some inter-receptor contacts may be chemical. Kolb and Lipetz reported that submammalian photoreceptors exhibit telodendrial projections that end on other photoreceptors with chemical synapses. Mammals and man exhibit only electrical junctions between neighboring receptors. Boynton (1979) speculated that these inter-receptor gap junctions might be responsible for excitatory interactions. This hypothesis, although not confirmed, still appears to be viable and arguments can be made that their function is to provide physiological sharpening of the retinal image above that otherwise possible, given the nature of the receptor mosaic (Kolb & Lipetz, 1991).

At one time it seemed likely that the only function of the receptors was to transform an electromagnetic stimulus to an electrophysiological signal independently within each receptor. Such a simple view was called into question when Baron (1980) isolated a cone difference signal in monkey LERG. He found LERG evidence for both hyperpolarization and for negative-going potentials. Baron hypothesized a retinal subtractive process, suggesting in addition to the normal cone hyperpolarization that ". . . cone depolarization mediated by horizontal cell activity is a possible explanation of the negative-going component . . . (p. 1447)." More recent human ERG a-wave data also suggest a similar subtractive process in the L- and M-cones (Spileers, Falcao-Reis, Hogg & Arden, 1993). These investigators showed that it is possible to adjust the relative luminances of red and green stimuli to null the a-wave when going from a green to a red stimulus. But when switching from red to green using these same luminances, an a-wave response resulted. Neither of these investigations provides an idea of the magnitude of this receptor subtractive process. This information would be necessary to evaluate the importance of subtractive signals at the receptor level relative to the opponent processing signals evident in horizontal cells and beyond. On reviewing the synaptic feedback to cone photoreceptors Burkhardt (1993) concluded that "Feedback may impress some detectable wavelength dependency in some cones but the dominant mechanisms for color opponency probably reside beyond the photoreceptors" (p. 986). Dacey and colleagues very recently have generated direct electrophysiological evidence from *in vitro* electrophysiological data from monkey retinas showing that opponent responses must occur after the horizontal cells (personal communication).

2. *What differences are there, aside from the photopigments, among the three types of cones?* There are no anatomical distinctions known to exist between the L- and M-cones. The S-cones have been anatomically identified (Kolb, 1991; Ahnelt, Keri & Kolb, 1990; Ahnelt, Kolb & Pflug, 1987). However, there are many more L- and M-cones than S-cones, with the density of S-cones being especially low at the center of the fovea. L-, M-, and S-cones in the central fovea are distributed as polygonal subunits as seen in Figure 4.8 (Kolb & Lipetz, 1991; Ahnelt, Kolb & Pflug, 1987). There is a good deal of evidence that the L- and M-cones are highly similar to each other in all respects save for their photopigments and detailed connections. They have opportunities to contact cones of their own or different kinds.[11] L- and M-cones make major contributions to the achromatic channels and both are important for good acuity and contour perception. (These matters will be dealt with in more detail in Chapter 9.) The S-

cone system appears to not make a strong contribution to the perception of contour, and they adapt relatively slowly.

It has been shown that the receptor potential reacts to the effects of chromatic adaptation in a manner that indicates, not too surprisingly, that the overall response comes from cones of different types, and that these can be differentially adapted with chromatic light (Boynton & Whitten, 1972; Padmos & van Norren, 1975). Using a variation of this preparation, Boynton & Baron (1975) later found evidence that the temporal response properties of the L- and M-cones are identical, whereas the S-cones are more sluggish. These results agree to some extent with psychophysical observations to be discussed in Chapter 9.

Connections Between Receptors and Horizontal Cells

Receptors are connected to their postsynaptic elements, the horizontal and bipolar cells, by chemical synapses. The postsynaptic bipolar (or horizontal) cell therefore "knows" what the receptor is trying to tell it only in terms of the rate at which it receives packets of a chemical transmitter. Excitatory synapses are probably mediated by L-glutamate between receptors and bipolar cells. Acetycholine is believed to be an excitatory neurotransmitter for amacrine cells. γ-aminobutyric acid (GABA) acts as a inhibitory transmitter (Dowling, 1987, 1992). It is very unlikely that the postsynaptic cell knows anything directly about the current that flows in and around the receptor. Nevertheless, these currents play a direct role in vision because a message signaling that a single photon has been absorbed someplace in the outer segment must be transmitted to the cone pedicle. The modulation of extracellular current flow carries such information in amplified form, and plays a role in liberating the presynaptic transmitter substance (Baylor, 1987).

Horizontal Cells

The trichromacy of vision is clearly attributable to the cone receptors. Although, as we noted above, there is a possible indication of opponent responses in receptors, the earliest opponent responses were recorded in horizontal cells of goldfish when Svaetichin (1956), a Swedish investigator working in South America, published some landmark records using microelectrodes in fish retinas (Fig. 7.5). These were the first intracellular slow potentials ever recorded from the visual system, and some of these recordings also revealed, for the first time, direct electrophysiological evidence of opponent-color responses. Svaetichin used an apparatus in which interference fil-

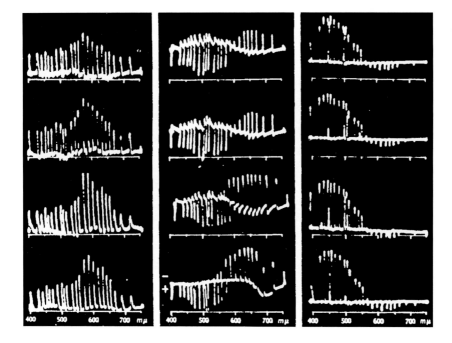

Figure 7.5   Sample recordings from horizontal cells of carp retina. The left column shows data analogous to an spectrally nonopponent, achromatic signal. The middle column represents a spectrally opponent red-green signal and the right column represents a blue-yellow signal. (From Svaetichin, 1956).

ters, used to supply nearly monochromatic light, were mounted in a bicycle wheel connected to a potentiometer that actuated the horizontal deflection of a spot on an oscilloscope. The responses that he recorded, which were actually sustained potentials lasting for the duration of the stimulus, appeared on the scope as spikes because of the very slow sweep speed of the oscilloscope. These sustained potentials were automatically plotted as a function of wavelength for an equal-energy spectrum.

Single unit electrophysiological recordings of an opponent-response in horizontal cells have been replicated many times since, but so far only in fish and turtles. The opponent-color units (called C-units), responded by hyperpolarizing over part of the spectrum and depolarizing over the remainder. Other units, called L (for luminosity) units, gave a consistent response of one type or the other across the entire visible spectrum. (Recordings of this kind from horizontal cells have since been called S-potentials, for Svaetichin.)

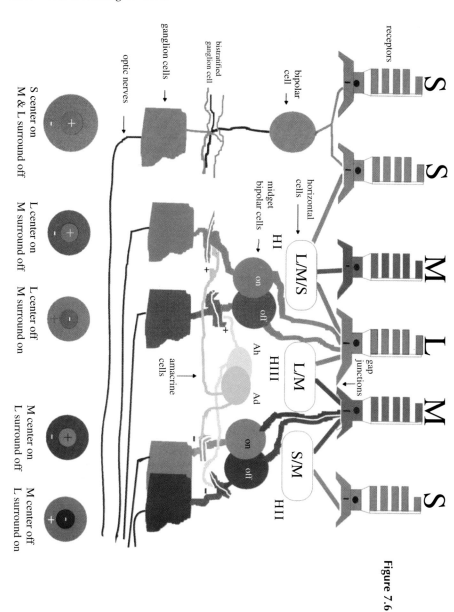

Figure 7.6

A diagram to help the reader follow the color vision signal path from receptors to optic nerve. HI, HII, and HIII are the three classes of horizontal cells discussed by Kolb and colleagues. The symbols Ah and Ad refer to hyperpolarizing and depolarizing amacrine cells. At the bottom are shown receptive fields associated with the ganglion cells above each receptive field. The colors are for informational purposes only; likewise the shapes of the neurons bear no relevance to real anatomy. This schematic was created from information obtained from Kolb and Lipetz (1991), Kolb (1994), Dowling (1987), Dacey and Lee (1994).

receptors

bipolar cell

ganglion cells

bistratified ganglion cell

optic nerves

horizontal cells

midget bipolar cells

HI

HIII

HII

L/M/S

L/M

S/M

on   off

Ah   Ad

on   off

amacrine cells

gap junctions

S   S   M   L   M   S

S center on
M & L surround off

L center on
M surround off

L center off
M surround on

M center on
L surround off

M center off
L surround on

Although Svaetichin thought at first that his recordings were from cones, the use of intracellular dye injection a couple of years later, in a study by MacNichol and Svaetichin, indicated that the recordings were in fact coming from horizontal cells.[12]

The C-potentials divided themselves statistically into two classes, which Svaetichin was quick to label r-g and y-b because he immediately perceived the relation of what he had discovered to opponent-color theory. It has now been established in cold-blooded vertebrates that horizontal cells of the C-type receive inputs from more than one type of cone. This has been shown by chromatic adaptation, which selectively eliminates almost all of the input to the cell excepting that from one of the two cone types.

It seems almost self-evident that the C-type horizontal cells must play an important role in creating opponent-color responses by somehow extracting the difference in the outputs of the two types of cones to which they apparently connect. But how? For the human retina the most recent answer we have so far comes from Ahnelt and Kolb (1994). As noted above, it is possible to anatomically distinguish between S-cones and the other two types. Using both electron microscopy and light microscopy, Ahnelt and Kolb recently distinguished among three types of human horizontal cells whose interactions with cone pedicles differ (Fig. 7.6). HI horizontal cells seem to be primarily connected to M- and L-cones. Only one or two contacts of S-cones with HI cells are reported. HII horizontal cells contacted all cone pedicles within their dendritic fields, but synapses with S-cones were made in disproportionately large numbers as compared with the M- and L-cones. Ahnelt and Kolb report that the 'axons' of HIII horizontal cells synapsed only with S-cones. The dendrites of the four HIII cells they studied contacted M- and L-cones exclusively.

Before considering an interpretation of these observations, it would be prudent to consider the following. Ahnelt and Kolb's data came from 3D reconstructions of serial sections laboriously constructed from electron micrographs and light micrographs. Only a total of 13 such reconstructions were made: three HI cells, six HII, cells and four HIII cells. All reconstructions were made outside of a 5 mm radius of the central area. Before it is possible to be confident of these findings it would be useful to learn how representative these 13 reconstructions are for other nearby horizontal cells. The research technique is provocative and has considerable heuristic value.

HI cells, because they receive input from L-, M-, and S-cones may be broad band. If so, then they could be responsible for achromatic responses. Dacheux and Raviola's (1990) electrophysiological record-ings from Macaca mulatta eyecup preparations of the retina support this hypothesis. HII horizontal cells seem to serve mostly the S-cones. The yellow-blue opponency then would come to the HII cell by di-rect M- and L-cone input and feedback signal reversals. Ahnelt and Kolb suggest that HIII cells are long and middle wavelength sensi-tive. However they do not know whether this sensitivity is manifested as a long wave/middle wave biphasic response or simply a luminosity response. Ahnelt and Kolb tell us that we must wait for better physi-ological recordings to clarify the functional significance between these horizontal cells and luminosity responses. We are told that feedback signals from HI and HIII cells that synapse with middle and long wavelength sensitive receptors could be the basis of opponent sur-rounds for the midget bipolar and ganglion cells.

The final story about horizontal cells clearly has not been writ-ten. Although Ahnelt and Kolb seem convinced that there are three types of these cells, others do not agree (e.g., Boycott, Hopkins & Sperling, 1987; Dacheux & Raviola, 1990; Wässle & Boycott, 1992). Ahnelt & Kolb (1994 p. 426) put it as follows (HC = horizontal cells; OPL = outer plexiform layer; IPL = inner plexiform layer):

> Whether or not these conjectures have any substance to them will ulti-mately be proved by more electrophysiology and dye-identification stud-ies. However, the finding of the present series of papers (Ahnelt & Kolb, 1994a; Kolb et al., 1994; this paper) provide evidence that the trichromatic human/primate retina has three distinct types of HC rather than the two types found in other mammals with dichromatic color vision. Each of these types appears to have differently weighted connectivity with the three spectral types of cone. This may have sig-nificance in the creation of color interactions. We submit that these specific HC connectivities will be found to underlie some modicum of color opponency at the OPL which is perhaps further enhanced by amacrine cell circuitry in the IPL (Kolb, 1991).

This section on horizontal cells can be viewed as much as a les-son in the progression of visual science as it is a description of what we know. In point of fact, even as this chapter is being revised, new information becomes available almost from week to week because of a new and interesting recording procedure being used in Dacey's laboratory at the University of Washington where electrophysiologi-cal recordings from monkey retinas are being made in a rather spe-cial way. The recordings are made *in vitro*, which means that the retina has been excised from the globe and placed in a recording chamber. Dacey and his group isolate ". . . the retina, together with the pig-ment epithelium and choroid, and mounted this preparation flat on a recording chamber" (Dacey & Lee, 1994, p.732). The chamber is set into a light microscope and with proper preparation of the specimen it is possible to identify various neurons from which they wish to record. This preparation allows them to record from a cell for many hours. The cells from which recordings are made are stained with a fluorescent dye called acridine orange that reveals the cell bodies.

Preliminary results from horizontal cells using this method suggest that cells that appear to be HI and HIII like seem to represent extreme ends of a single population of cells all of which are achromatic. HII cells, according to Dacey and Lee (1995), have strong S-cone input just as Ahnelt & Kolb suggest, but the M- and L-cone input to HII cells is of the same polarity as the S-cone input. The latest conclusions from Dacey's lab is that in monkey and man there are only two classes of horizontal cells and these do not support opponent processing (personal communication).

So here is an example of investigators performing exactly the kind of research needed, according to Ahnelt and Kolb, to test their anatomically-based conjectures. Also we must remember that Wietsma *et al.* (1995) were unable to confirm the horizontal cells of goldfish as the location of the transfer from trichromacy to opponent processing.

Bipolar Cells

Boycott & Wässle (1991) report six types of bipolar cells. These can be grouped into three general types (Wässle & Boycott, 1992; Wässle *et al.*, 1994), that are not represented in Figure 7.6, but to some extent are evident in Figure 4.4.

- 1. Diffuse bipolars are connected to as many as ten cones and are proposed to carry luminosity signals.

- 2. Midget bipolars are each connected to one cone.

- 3. S-cone bipolars are connected to S-cones.

The midget bipolars carry chromatic signals and are ". . . considered the first distinct step in the parvocellular (P-) pathway of the primate visual system . . ." (Wässle *et al.*, 1994, p. 561). Midget bipolars come in two varieties: invaginating and flat, so-called because each has a slightly different type of synapse with cone receptors. The invaginating midget bipolars are thought to be depolarizing neurons, which produce on-center ganglion cell, and the flat midget bipolars hyperpolarize, producing off-center ganglion cell responses (Kolb, 1994).

Amacrine Cells

Amacrine cells are neurons that send processes horizontally in a layer between the bipolar cells and the ganglion cells (the inner plexiform layer). As the schematic in Figure 7.6 suggests, some amacrine cells have excitatory or inhibitory synapses near the terminals of bipolar and ganglion cells (Kolb, 1991). There are in fact many types of amacrine cells but their relation to color vision, if any, is not understood. Gouras (1991) suggests that amacrine cells might play a role in spectral antagonism.

Ganglion Cells

Anatomically there are three major classes of ganglion cells. Polyak referred to two of them as midget and parasol. The midget and parasol cells are sometimes called parvocellular (the midget ganglion cells) and magnocellular (the parasol ganglion cells). These designations refer to the areas of the lateral geniculate nucleus where the axons of these ganglion cells synapse. A third type of ganglion cell that Kolb (1991) referred to as "wider-field ON center" carries information solely from short wavelength sensitive receptors. Dacey and Lee (1994) recently investigated such ganglion cells and found them to be a small bistratified cell from which axons project to the parvocellular layers of the LGN (see Fig. 7.6). Although this research was done on monkey, Dacey (1993) demonstrated anatomically that similar small field bistratified ganglion cells were evident in human retina. Midget (parvo) ganglion cells receive most of their input from midget bipolar cells. Dowling (1987) reports that a midget ganglion cell receives input from single or at most only a few midget bipolar cells. The midget ganglion cells carry chromatic signals to the LGN.

This brings us to the end of the retinal story. The above only represents an anatomical outline of this structure, which measures about 0.2 mm in thickness. The situation is much more complex than noted above. There are some structures about which there is agreement and others which require additional research before agreement is reached. Now it is time to leave the peripheral part of the visual system and move up into the more central parts of the brain.

PROJECTIONS TO THE BRAIN

Lateral Geniculate Nucleus (LGN)

The general outlines of organization of the visual brain have been known for a long time and are available in many standard texts. Very briefly, it goes like this. Optic nerve fibers, which are the axons of the

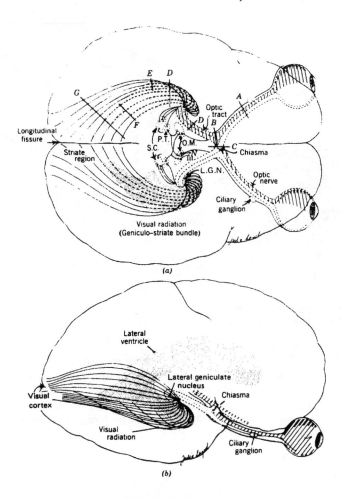

Figure 7.7   Top: Central visual pathways as seen from above (or below) with the outline of the brain also shown. L.G.N. represents the lateral geniculate nucleus. Pathways involving the pretectum (P.T.), superior colliculus (S.C.), and the oculomotor nuclei (O.M.) subserve visual functions believed to mediate control of the pupil and eye position. These are not discussed in this book. Bottom: side view of the sensory pathways. (From Brown, 1965, as modified from Fox and German, 1936.)

retinal ganglion cells, run to four major places in the brain before terminating at a synapse. About 80 percent of these fibers go to the lateral geniculate nucleus (LGN) of the thalamus (Fig. 7.7) This is an important site for color vision research because the nature of its structure and its accessibility via microelectrodes. It is the only terminus for ganglion cell axons that need concern us here.

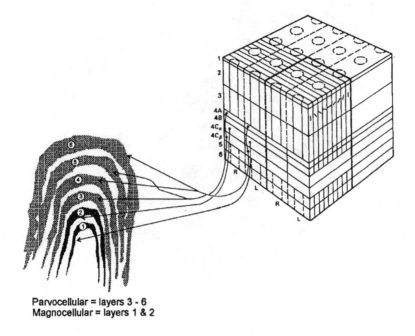

Parvocellular = layers 3 - 6
Magnocellular = layers 1 & 2

Figure 7.8   A schematic illustrating the connections between the lateral geniculate nucleus and the various layers of cortical V1. R and L represent the right and left eye ocular dominance columns. The slash marks on the right side represent orientation columns and the circular areas represent cross sections of columns forming the blobs. (Modified from Levine and Shefner, 1991.)

About half the optic nerve fibers from each eye cross the midline of the head at the optic chiasm, and each of the lateral geniculate nuclei (one on each side) receives input from both eyes. The LGN also receives signals from the reticular formation (an area extending from the midbrain to the brain stem) and visual cortex. Although these latter influences are not well understood, it seems clear that information sent to the LGN is modifiable by a variety of influences. It has a laminated structure, whose alternating layers contain cell bodies of the postsynaptic elements that receive input from optic nerve fibers (Fig. 7.8). There are six laminations, the top four of which contain smaller cells and are called *parvocellular*. The bottom two layers contain larger cells and are called *magnocellular*. These neurons that project to the LGN or emanate from it are frequently referred as belonging to the parvo or magno pathways. Visual scientists in recent years have taken considerable interest in these parallel pathways, which will be discussed in detail elsewhere. Messages from the two eyes are segregated into separate layers, and there appears to be little or no interocular interaction. The number of postsynaptic fibers emerging from each LGN (one in each hemisphere), heading for the visual cortex, is of the same order, a million or so, as are the number that enter the LGN from each eye.

The LGN is *topologically* organized, which means that it is possible to predict with some accuracy where messages initiated in a particular region of the retina will be received at the LGN. This high degree of organization of the LGN is surely a boon to the electrophysiologist who wishes to sink his electrode so as to encounter a cell receiving messages related to a particular region of visual space.

Most of the fibers from the LGN project to a region of the occipital cortex (outer layers of the brain at the back of the head) known variously as *V1, area 17, primary visual cortex, calcarine cortex,* or *striate cortex*[13] (Figs. 7.7 and 7.8). Although this area of the brain might seem to be very high up in the cerebral scheme of things, it probably is not. For example, our perception of a stable external visual world survives despite very complicated movements of our head and eyes. Yet a cell in the LGN cannot tell the difference between whether the eye or the external world has moved (Wurtz, 1969), although some cells in other areas of the brain can (Erickson & Thier, 1991). Similarly, the activity of units that carry a chromatic code in V1 seems unlikely to be directly related to the immediate precursors of consciousness. Nevertheless, V1 has a very specific topological relation to areas of the LGN and consequently also to the retina and the visual field. In particular, it seems to be the place where messages from the two eyes are brought together for comparison, because many of the cells there respond to stimuli to either eye delivered from the same location in visual space.

The visual cortex provides a kind of map of the retinal image, but a complex and greatly distorted one. For example, an enormous cortical area corresponds to the minuscule portion of the retina that constitutes the foveal region (recall from Chapter 4 that this is the region where cones are packed at a very high density, and which is most critical for detailed spatial vision). If a given distance across the surface of the primary visual cortex were related to a just discriminable distance in the lateral visual world, the existing arrangement is roughly what would be expected.

SINGLE UNIT ELECTROPHYSIOLOGY

We have seen that there is only modest (albeit significant) variability within the three subclasses of cone types whose slow potentials can be recorded with suction electrodes from monkey and human receptors. Ganglion cell responses, and those of the LGN and cortex, are quite a different matter. The diversity of firing patterns from cell to cell is astonishing. Little if any appreciation of how information is processed in any part of the visual nervous system can be obtained by looking at the behavior of just a few cells. Instead, hundreds of them are typically sampled, even to produce one publishable study. This permits the determination of a statistical distribution of cells of various types. The problem is complicated by the diversity of stimuli (sometimes called *trigger features*) that must be tried in order to obtain a maximum response from cell to cell, especially for cells in the cortex. For example, when a large field of light is delivered to the eye, a particular unit very well might fail to respond at all. In other words, its resting level of discharge (which is seldom zero) simply does not change when such a field is flashed on and off. But the cell is not unresponsive: it might, for example, respond vigorously to a green slit moving in a particular direction within a restricted region of the visual field. Because not all experimenters use the same criteria for classifying cells, the interpretation of single unit data is often very difficult. Yet some kind of classification scheme is desperately needed; otherwise the experimental reports would become an endless litany of individual records. In most publications, sample data and records are shown that are believed to be representative of cells of particular types. The numbers of such cells of this-and-that type are reported. There is no way that the reader of the literature can see the raw data. Where classification is concerned, the judgment of the experimenter must be relied upon, and the procedures used are seldom totally objective.

Fortunately for those who need to record from hundreds of cells in order to report a single experiment, it is not necessary for the microelectrode to penetrate such units in order to record the activity of only one of them. The spike-like discharge of such a cell can be recorded if the electrode tip is merely near to it (*extracellular recording*). Moreover, even if the electrode should pick up activity from two or more cells, the amplitude of the spikes as recorded from the particular position of the electrode is likely to be quite different, and the probability of exactly superimposed spikes fairly low. Either electronically or by eye, the responses of the constituent units can usually be picked out of such a record. A series of cells is often encountered on a single electrode penetration, as the electrode tip is advanced very slowly through the tissue.

One more caveat about single unit records must be mentioned. There is unquestionably a sampling problem to worry about. The larger a cell, the more likely it is to be found. Moreover, the complete analysis of a unit, for example, the determination of its spectral sensitivity and other properties, may take half an hour or even longer. Many units are lost before such procedures can be completed, and there may be a selective bias regarding which cell types can be held for long periods. It is therefore likely that more data have come from large rather than from small cells in the visual system. If the small cells have particularly unique roles to play in visual processing, those roles might not be well studied. Considering all of these problems, the agreement among various studies of chromatic units is more impressive than are the discrepancies. One reason, however, for the good agreement is that similar sampling biases have probably operated in all labs.

CHROMATIC MECHANISMS
IN THE GANGLION CELLS AND LGN

The essential feature of a chromatic mechanism is that it should display a capacity to react differently to two stimuli having unequal spectral distributions, regardless of their relative intensities. Figure 7.9 shows an excellent example of this, recorded many years ago from a single cell in the LGN of a macaque monkey. In this experiment, a standard wavelength of 593 nm was suddenly changed to one of four other test wavelengths. (Shifting from the standard to a test field of the same wavelength, delivered through a second optical channel, was also included as a control, because in the absence of substitution artifacts this procedure should be equivalent to steady presentation of the standard.) For this cell, substitution of a shorter wavelength caused an increase in the firing rate when the test light was present, whereas substitution of a longer wavelength caused a decrease. These effects survived a nine-fold range of relative intensities, without showing any significant change in the response pattern; equal luminance (as established behaviorally in the monkey) is near the middle of that range.

LGN cells responding in this manner to chromatic inputs probably play an important role in the monkey's color perception. Schiller and his colleagues have shown that when the parvocellular layers of a monkey's LGN are chemically lesioned the ability to discriminate colors is markedly reduced (e.g., Schiller, Logothetis & Charles, 1990a,b Logothetis, Schiller, Charles & Hurlbert, 1990; Schiller, Logothetis & Charles, 1991). Indeed, once the behavior of such a cell is established and correlated with the stimulus, the experimenter can tell, by looking at the spikes on his oscilloscope, in which direction the wavelength shift occurred. At the same time, however, there are other units that behave in just the reverse fashion, showing a decrease in response rate to a shift toward shorter wavelengths, and

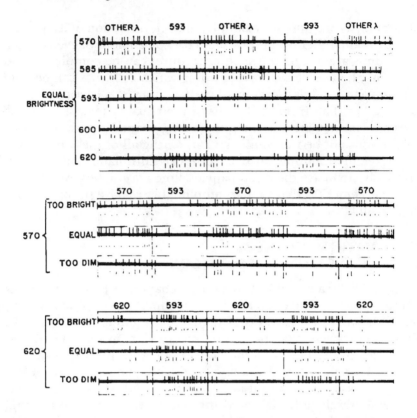

Figure 7.9 Firing pattern of a single cell in the LGN, probably of the r-g type, which reacts well to shifts in wavelength but is indifferent to shifts in luminance (From DeValois, Jacobs & Abramov, 1964.)

vice versa. Therefore, when experimenters encounter such a unit for the first time in a random penetration of the LGN, assuming that they knew nothing about the stimulating conditions, they would have no idea what the response might mean. Indeed, it could have come in response to an intensity change from a broadband, nonopponent cell (to be discussed below).

Most of the early work on chromatic cells was done in the LGN. Subsequent research has revealed no important differences between LGN and retinal ganglion cell responses to light (De Monasterio & Gouras, 1975; Marrocco, 1972; Kaplan & Shapley, 1984). Because no obvious alteration in the form of chromatic information occurs at the LGN, evidence from retinal ganglion cells and LGN can be considered collectively. Because evidence from macaque monkeys is both available and relevant, only this evidence will be considered here.

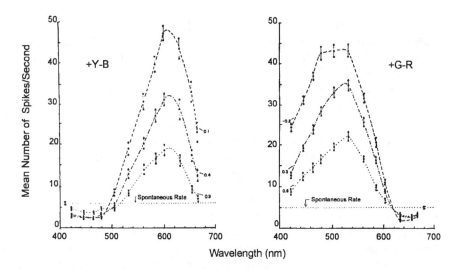

Figure 7.10   Firing patterns of +Y-B and +G-R units, based on average data for cells with crossover wavelengths of less than 559 nm (left) or 560 nm or greater (right). High, medium, and low are the relative radiance levels of the stimuli. The three functions shown in the bottom also relate to these three radiance levels (from DeValois, Abramov & Jacobs, 1966).

Pioneering Work of DeValois and Colleagues

The pioneering work in this field was done by R. L. De Valois and his collaborators.[14] Almost all of the early work from his laboratory was undertaken with large diffuse fields of monochromatic light, to which LGN single units were found to be responsive. It proved possible to fit most of the results into a scheme essentially like that of the model presented earlier in this chapter. Some cells were found that apparently carried a red-green hue code. By comparison with their level of activity in the dark, such a cell might, for example, discharge more vigorously in response to long wavelengths delivered to the eye and less so for short ones. DeValois called these +R −G cells. A plot of spike frequency vs. wavelength from such a cell exhibited a pattern like a single cycle of a distorted sine or cosine wave, with a crossover wavelength somewhere intermediate in the spectrum, where the stimulus was ineffective no matter what its intensity (Fig. 7.10). For the L-M cells (as we refer to them), this wavelength was most often in the neighborhood of 600 nm.

Figure 7.10 is from a major study based on diffuse field stimulation and recordings from the LGN of the macaque monkey; the legend gives the classification scheme. The procedure used was to irradiate the retina with spectral light for one-second intervals, separated by equal intervals of darkness. Counts were made of the firing rates in a number of such intervals and averages were taken. About two thirds of these LGN cells displayed opponent-color characteristics [(L-M, M-L, S-(L+M), and (L+M)-S) (using the nomenclature adopted in this text)]. The remainder of the LGN cells responded in the same way to all wavelengths — some cells by increasing, and some by decreasing their spontaneous discharge rate. These latter units were called broadband, nonopponent cells.

In order to produce the curves of Figure 7.10, it was first necessary to decide into which of six categories [(L-M, M-L, (L+M)-S, S-(L+M)] a particular cell belonged. For the spectrally opponent cells, there was never any ambiguity about deciding whether a cell was excitatory to long wavelengths or inhibitory to short ones. Both classes were in fact found, in about equal numbers. But a problem exists regarding the classification of such spectrally opponent cells into L-M vs. (L+M)-S categories.

What types of cones provide input to these cells? In a study in which the techniques of chromatic adaptation and silent substitution (see p. 391) were employed, Abramov (1968) concluded that the r-g units received their input from only L- and M-cones, and that the y-b units receive input from only L- and S-cones. Using a different approach, Derrington, Krauskopf and Lennie (1984) have verified these conclusions. Although there is little dispute about the nature of the r-g pathways, the physiological evidence for the y-b system is not as well established. However, recent evidence reported by Kolb (1991) suggests that the requisite anatomy exists to produce the interactions required of a y-b system (see Fig. 7.6).

The conclusions to be drawn from these studies are limited by an important complication to be discussed below, concerning the complex interactions between spatial and chromatic vision that are noticed only when stimuli smaller than those used in DeValois's early work are employed. Since the first edition *Human Color Vision* was published, De Valois and his colleagues have intensively investigated the interactions between spatial and chromatic vision. In 1988, De Valois and De Valois published a book entitled *Spatial Vision*. Chapter 7 of their book is entitled "Sensitivity to Color Variations" in which the authors explicitly consider the intersection between color and spatial vision. In Chapter 9 we will discuss, in more detail, the interaction of spatial and chromatic factors in vision.

Phasic vs. Tonic Cells

Gouras (1968) was the first to point out an important temporal difference between spectrally opponent and nonopponent cells. He noted (and this has been frequently reported since) that in addition to their receptive field organizations and responses to color, nonopponent cells produce responses that are phasic and that spectrally opponent cells produce responses that are tonic. For *phasic* cells (spectrally nonopponent) this means that the recorded spikes occur transiently after the onset or extinction of the test stimulus. *Tonic* cells (spectrally opponent), on the other hand, tend to respond continuously in the presence of an appropriate stimulus. Current wisdom is that L–M ganglion cells receive their input from cones by way of the midget-bipolar-cell system, whereas signals received by phasic ganglion cells are delivered through the diffuse bipolars, which receive input from a large number of receptors over a relatively large area. The tonic-phasic dichotomy should be kept in mind, for it helps to explain certain observations concerning temporal differences when achromatic and chromatic pathways are isolated psychophysically (Chapter 9).

TWO PATHWAYS

We have already discussed spectrally opponent and spectrally nonopponent pathways in the visual system. Let us now take a look at the correspondence of this dichotomy to that of phasic vs. tonic and magnocellular vs. parvocellular pathways.

Parvocellular vs. Magnocellular Pathways

In recent years, visual scientists have attempted to distinguish between the physiology associated with those signals that travel through the parvocellular and magnocellular layers of the LGN (Fig. 7.8). As it turns out there is evidence suggesting that signals transmitted via the magnocellular pathway are not significantly used for processing chromatic information. The parvocellular layers of the LGN conduct the signals that result in the perception of color.

The precise distinction between the kinds of visual signals mediated by each of these pathways is still under investigation. There are some (e.g., Lee *et al.*, 1988) who believe all luminance-related signals travel by way of the magnocellular pathways. Others (e.g., Ingling & Martinez–Uriegas, 1983; De Valois & De Valois, 1993; Martinez–Uriegas, 1994) believe that the parvocellular pathway also conducts luminance information.

Contemporary Work of Lee and Colleagues

One of the important tasks in applied color work is measuring the visual effectiveness of light emanating from a chromatic source, whether that source is a primary source such as a lamp or a reflecting stimulus. This activity is often referred to as heterochromatic photometry. In most applied conditions photometry is accomplished with a photoelectric photometer. For research purposes one often does not use such a photometer because the spectral sensitivity of these devices is based upon the CIE $V(\lambda)$ function. In research involving human observers it is often desirable to make photometric measurements using the spectral sensitivity of the particular human observer (sensation luminance) participating in the investigation because the CIE function represents only an average, from which individual subjects deviate significantly.

Two of the frequently used research techniques in visual photometry are heterochromatic flicker photometry and minimally distinct border photometry. The flicker photometric method uses two rapidly alternating fields. Frequently one field consists of a reference white and the other field is one of a series of chromatic lights. The frequency of alternation is such that the colors of the alternating fields fuse and the observer is instructed to adjust the amount of chromatic light in order to minimize the perceived flicker. The minimally distinct border method (MDB) uses two precisely abutted fields. When the spectral distributions and brightness of these fields are identical the two fields appear as one homogeneous field. However, when the colors between these two fields differ a border appears between them. The observer's task using the MDB method is to minimize the perceived strength or distinctness of the border by adjusting the brightness of the chromatic hemifield. As it turns out, similar results are obtained with both methods in spite of their procedural differences. (Photometric methods will be described in detail in Chapter 9, starting on page 361.)

Lee and his colleagues recorded from Old-World macaque ganglion cells to investigate the physiological bases of both heterochromatic flicker photometry and minimally distinct border photometry. Consistent with the similar results obtained by these two photometric techniques, Lee and his colleagues found that heterochromatic flicker photometry and minimally distinct border photometry share an underlying physiological basis (Lee, Martin, and Valberg, 1988; Kaiser, Lee, Martin, and Valberg, 1990). Recall that retinal ganglion cells come in two major varieties: magnocellular, which send their axons to the magnocellular layers of the LGN, and parvocellular, which send their axons to the parvocellular layers of the LGN. The stimulus conditions used for the electrophysiology with monkeys were virtually the same as that used psychophysically with human observers. Whereas the observer's task in flicker photometry was to minimize the perceived flicker, in the physiologically analogous experiments the relative luminance of the flickering fields were adjusted to minimize the electrophysiological response (Fig. 7.11). The interesting finding was that when recording from ganglion cells in the magnocellular pathway (phasic ganglion cells) a minimum response was obtained when the luminances of the alternating fields were nearly identical (i.e., luminance ratio of 1.0). Similar results were not obtained for tonic cells. For example, note the responses of the red on-center cells in Figure 7.11, showing data collected when a 500 nm stimulus was alternated with a white one. The experiment was conducted with a total of nine wavelengths, and by determining the luminance required at various wavelengths to obtain a minimum physiological response, it was possible to determine the spectral sensitivity of the phasic ganglion cells. As seen in Figure 7.11B, this spectral sensitivity agrees well with that obtained by human heterochromatic flicker photometry. The conclusion drawn from this research is that the phasic ganglion cells of the magnocellular pathway provide the underlying physiological basis for heterochromatic flicker photometry.

Similar physiological experiments were conducted using minimally distinct border paradigm and the same conclusions were reached by Kaiser *et al.* (1990).

RECEPTIVE FIELD ORGANIZATION

The concept of the *receptive field* has its origin in a paper published by Nobel laureate H. K. Hartline, in 1938. Recording from ganglion cells in the retina of the frog, Hartline discovered that such a cell was responsive to light over a wide region of the retina. For each cell, a location on the retina could be found for which the cell responded most vigorously. As a small light probe was moved away from the region of optimal response, the intensity required to maintain the response increased. For the most distant spots used, 1000 times as much light was required to elicit a given level of response. The nature of the preparation was such that stray light could not have caused such a result. The conclusion drawn was that a particular retinal ganglion cell was connected, via interneurons, to many receptors. Today we would call this an *excitatory receptive field*. It can be represented graphically as a bell-shaped curve of sensitivity (reciprocal of the radiance required to elicit a constant response) plotted as a function of location on the retina or in the visual field.

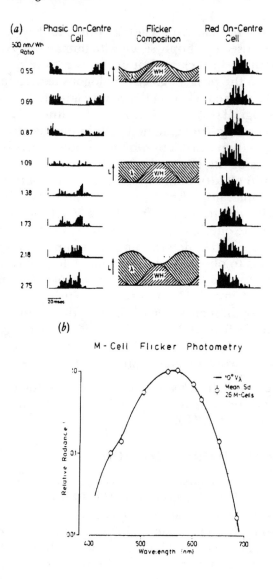

Figure 7.11 A. An electrophysiological test of heterochromatic flicker photometry. The test was performed on magnocellular-pathway ganglion cells (left histograms) and parvocellular-pathway ganglion cells (right histograms). "Flicker composition" shows the stimulus components and the histograms show the responses. When stimulus amplitude of the chromatic and white fields are equal magnocellular ganglion cells (phasic) have a minimum response, whereas parvo ganglion cells (red on-center) show no such minimum. B. Data from magnocellular pathway ganglion cells are superimposed on a 10° human V(λ) function, showing that these neurons probably provide the physiological basis for luminance. (From Lee, 1991.)

The discovery by Kuffler, and independently by Barlow, (both in 1953) that ganglion cell responses of the cat and frog could be either excitatory or inhibitory, depending upon the placement of the light in the visual field, constituted another landmark in the history of visual science. These findings have subsequently been extended to a wide variety of species, including the macaque monkey, and to recordings from the visual brain as well as the retina. The basic findings are ubiquitous, so much so that it has proved possible to work out the quantitative principles of receptive field organization on the lowly Limulus; this work (by Ratliff and Hartline) still stands as the most comprehensive quantitative treatment of the subject.[15]

Briefly, the story goes as follows: After a single cell is isolated (say a retinal ganglion cell) the experimenter moves a small flashing spot around in the visual field until he locates the region of maximum activity. For a train of light pulses of 1-s duration, separated by equal intervals of darkness (as used by DeValois in his early experiments just reviewed), this activity occurs either when the light comes on, or after it is turned off. If the first of these occurs, the unit is said to have an *excitatory on-center,* the second is called *an inhibitory off-center.* If, for an excitatory center, the stimulus spot is concentrically enlarged, the response at light onset grows more vigorous until some optimal spot size is reached, beyond which the vigor of the response decreases with further increases in spot size. In some cases it may cease altogether; in other instances very large spots may cause the response to occur to the onset of darkness, rather than to the onset of the light pulse itself. Another way to explore the receptive field organization is to maintain a small size of the test spot, while systematically moving it around in the visual field. Consider as an example a spot of optimal size for center excitation. Any movement of the spot reduces the response. A position can be found where the response disappears altogether. Then a relatively large surrounding area is discovered in which the *sign* of the response definitely reverses and the discharge is in response to darkness, rather than to light.

What has just been described is an example of a cell having an excitatory center and inhibitory surround. With about equal frequency, cells of the opposite sort are found that have inhibitory centers and excitatory surrounds. Implicit in much of the preceding description is the idea of *reciprocal overlap*: each receptor is functionally connected to many ganglion cells and each ganglion cell receives input that begins in the activity of many receptors.

The functional significance of these arrangements is illustrated schematically in Figure 7.12 where a cell with excitatory center is

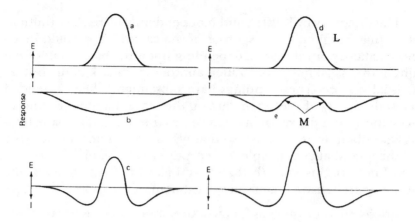

Figure 7.12 Two ways in which a receptive field with an excitatory center and inhibitory surround can be constructed. For a nonopponent unit, at the left, all wavelengths reveal an excitatory center (top), a broad inhibition that includes both center and surround (middle), and a resultant "Mexican hat" sensitivity (bottom) with the classical excitatory center and inhibitory surround. At the right an L-M cell shows an excitatory center (but only to longwave light) and an inhibitory surround (which does not include the center) only to middlewave light. A large long wavelength field of any size will produce excitation, due to the center, and large middle wavelength field of any size will produce inhibition, due to the surround.

used as an example. The figure shows two overlapping receptive fields—one (a) excitatory with a high central peak and narrow lateral extent, and a second inhibitory one (b) with a poorly defined central peak and broad lateral extent. These excitatory and inhibitory responses combine to produce what has been called a *Mexican hat function (c)*.

What is the purpose of this arrangement? One purpose is to provide a neural enhancement of contour. Suppose that, instead of a circular spot, we project a bipartite field on to the retina, with light on one side and darkness on the other. The response of an on-center ganglion cell to such a stimulus can be predicted as the edge dividing the left and right halves of the bipartite field is moved across the retina. When the edge is far away, the response of the cell is minimal, because both its excitatory center and inhibitory surround are equally unstimulated. As the bright half enters the inhibitory surround field of the cell, the resting level of activity of the unit will be reduced. As the bright half intrudes further into the cell's receptive field, so that a portion of it now stimulates the excitatory center, the inhibition will be canceled and the response rate will return to its resting level. Further incursion increases response rate as the central receptive field is progressively filled with light. This rate reaches a maximum as the bright half moves across the excitatory center to fill it completely and then, as it begins to irradiate the surround field on the other side, the response is reduced again. Finally, as both the center and surround fields are fully filled with light, the activity level will decrease further and may not differ appreciably from how the cell responds during darkness. The details would depend on the relative areas under curves of the sort shown in Figure 7.12.

Even if the edge of light dividing the bipartite field does not literally move, the consequence of this receptive field organization is to provide a neural enhancement of such an edge represented as a series of messages, each coded in terms of impulse frequency, in a lateral series of ganglion cells. (Each cell is assumed to have a more or less similar receptive field organization, although such fields are smallest for foveal stimuli and are larger in the periphery.) We know that edges fade from view if the retinal image is artificially stabilized, and we also know that the eye is normally always in motion, even during attempted fixation (Ditchburn, 1973). Therefore it appears probable that the edge enhancement provided by receptive field organization results in part from the increased activity of each cell as the image moves across it.

RECEPTIVE FIELDS AND THE CHROMATIC CODE

Although large white fields do not elicit much of a response from a retinal ganglion cell, large chromatic ones do, as we saw in the early work of DeValois, who used very large fields. Why is this? The answer, which to a first approximation at least turns out to be rather straightforward, was first suggested by the results of an important experiment by Wiesel and Hubel (1966). Many, probably most, of the opponent cells in the LGN (and retinal ganglion cells as well) have a spatially as well as a chromatically opponent organization. For example, suppose the basic experiment initially described above is repeated with a 640 nm rather than a white test spot. As the area of the long wavelength spot is increased, the vigor of the response increases until it reaches a maximum that defines the limit of the excitatory center for the cell being examined (Fig. 7.13). Unlike the case for white light, a further enlargement of the test spot has little or no additional effect. Probing the field with a spot exactly the size of the excitatory center would probably reveal that the surround is essen-

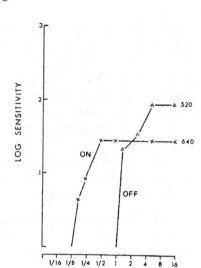

Figure 7.13   Behavior of an LGN cell exhibiting a red excitatory center and a green inhibitory surround. Curve at the left shows how an on response (excitatory) grows with spot diameter, leveling off after $\frac{1}{4}°$. The off response (inhibitory) to green light cannot be recorded until the spot is 1° in size; it then increases as the spot is further enlarged to 4°, stabilizing thereafter. (From Wiesel & Hubel, 1966.)

tially uninterested in such a spot; it fails to react to it one way or another. Recall that this situation is very different from that for a white spot, where probing the surround would cause an inhibitory response.

Now repeat the experiment, this time using a middle wavelength rather than a long wavelength spot. This time it is found that the central field, of a size that was defined by the long wave spot, is not interested in middle wave light. But as the spot is enlarged (or the smaller probe is moved into the surround field) the resting level of activity is reduced: this same unit is inhibited by middle wavelength light in the surround field.

Now we can understand DeValois's success with large stimulus fields, and why a particular unit responds in the way it does. The receptive field structure is shown in Fig. 7.12. If long wavelength light is used, an excitatory response is obtained that comes from the central field (Fig. 7.12d). This long wavelength light present in the surround field has no effect one way or another. However, as the wavelength is shifted and a large middle wavelength field is used, an inhibitory response is recorded. This response comes from the surround field only (Fig. 7.12e), because the central field is unresponsive to middle wavelength light. The resulting Mexican hat function (Fig. 7.12f) is not very different from that produced by white light from a nonopponent unit (Fig. 7.12c).

Suppose now that we have a contour formed by a chromatic, rather than a luminance, difference. Visualize a large field that appears red on one side and green on the other, with the relative radiances adjusted for equal luminance. (Electrophysiologically, this could in principle be confirmed by locating a spectrally nonopponent broadband cell, and showing that it has no response as the chromatic contour is moved through its receptive field.) How will the cell described above, with its excitatory long wave sensitive center and inhibitory middle wave surround, react to the movement of this contour through the field?

Consider that the long wave side of the bipartite field fills the entire receptive field of the cell and that the middle wave side of the field is still very far away (Fig. 7.14a). The result will be an excitatory response, mediated by the long wave center of the cell's receptive field. As the edge is moved, the middle wave region will eventually begin to encroach on the cell's surround field (Fig. 7.14b). Because the surround is inhibitory to middle wave light, the excitatory response, still mediated by long wave light on the central field, will be reduced somewhat. As the middle wave field moves farther and includes part of the central field (Fig. 7.14c), the response will be further reduced not only by added surround inhibition, but also because of excitatory loss as long wave input is removed from the center. As the middle wave half of the bipartite field moves still farther to include all of the central field (Fig. 7.14d), the net response will be inhibitory because the excitatory contribution from the center is completely eliminated. Finally, as the middle wave half moves to include the remainder of the inhibitory surround, the response becomes fully inhibitory (Fig. 7.14e).

The change just described will be smooth and gradual, with no basis for an edge enhancement of the sort described for white light. Nevertheless, this cell has accomplished something very important. It has signaled the presence of a border which in a color-blind system (or cell, as in the case of a broadband nonopponent unit), would not be visible. In addition, if the field is large, it carries a message about color: excitation for long wavelengths, and inhibition for short ones.

There is reason to believe that the most salient information about chromatic contour may be mediated by red-green opponent cells of

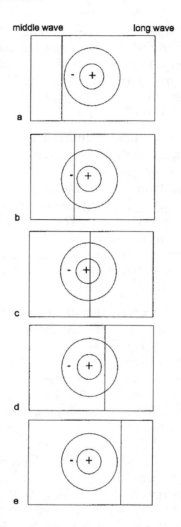

Figure 7.14 This diagram is to help visualize the isoluminant chromatic border moving across a receptive field example discussed in the text. The squares represent an isoluminant heterochromatic bipartite field; the left half being of middle wavelength and the right of long wavelength. In each successive part (a–e) the border between the two hemifields is placed at different locations with respect to the on center off surround receptive field.

the sort just described, if their counterparts with L-cone excitatory centers are also included. The evidence for this will be given in Chapter 9. For any reader who may have felt that in a book supposedly devoted to color too much emphasis has already been placed on spatial vision, it should be pointed out that we have now arrived at the clearest reason yet why it is absolutely necessary to do so. For what we are discussing here is a situation where cells apparently have the dual function of signaling contour as well as color.

A cell like the one just described can respond equally well to a small white spot or large red field. It will not respond well to a large white field. It will respond in an inhibitory fashion to a large green field, or a white (or green) annulus. And, as described above, it will respond to a chromatic edge with either excitation or inhibition, depending upon the location of a red-green contour that is presented anywhere in its visual field.

How can such a cell tell which of these various events has caused its response? It cannot. Although such a single cell can be regarded as a chromatic mechanism, in the same sense that the receptors are, a single cell is unable to discriminate among different wavelengths just as single type of cone is able to make these discriminations. The meaning of its message, for form and for color, must require a comparison of its activity with that of other cells. The simultaneous presence of broadband spectrally nonopponent cells gives us a clue as to how this might happen. Consider a comparison of the outputs of a red-green cell of the type just described and a broadband cell having an excitatory center and inhibitory surround. A small white spot will excite both cells. A large white spot will excite neither cell. A small red spot will excite both cells. A small green spot will excite only the broadband cell. A large red spot will excite the red-green cell and fail to activate the broadband cell. Just these two cells, if their outputs can be compared, can tell whether the spot is large or small. If the spot is large, it is now possible to deduce whether it is red or green. If the spot is small, it may be red, or white. These various possibilities are summarized in Table 7.1.

There are other kinds of cells besides those that have been described that are found both in LGN and the ganglion cell layer of the retina. Only a few of these complications will be discussed here because it is difficult to understand the function of most of them, except in the most general terms. By various techniques, especially through the use of chromatic adaptation, De Monasterio, Gouras, and Tolhurst (1975) have shown that many cells that might be classified as pure red-green opponent units actually receive an input from S-cones, usually operating in concert with an input from L- or M-cones in the surround field of the unit. Gouras (as well as Padmos and van Norren, 1975) questioned DeValois's original division of opponent cells into red-green and yellow-blue categories, suggesting instead that units receiving input from S-cones always receive input from both L- and M-

Table 7.1   Classification of responses from two cells. The red-green cell has an excitatory red center and an inhibitory green surround. The broadband cell has an excitatory center and an inhibitory surround to all wavelengths. Small spots are assumed just to fill the center of the excitatory fields. Large spots include the center and the surround as well. A + indicates that the cell will respond by increasing its firing rate to the stimulus indicated; a – indicates that the response will be inhibitory (decreased rate), and a 0 means that there will be no change in the resting level of response. Conjointly, the two cells can differentiate all of these, excepting small red vs. small white spots. But if these are allowed to move slightly (symbols in parentheses) even these conditions can be discriminated.

Size & Color of the spot	Response of a r-g cell	Response of a broadband cell
Small white	+(–)	+(–)
Small green	0(–)	+(–)
Small red	+(0)	+(–)
Large white	0(0)	0(0)
Large green	–(–)	0(+)
Large red	+(+)	0(0)

cones as well. Padmos and van Norren also show that, with chromatic adaptation, many of the so-called nonopponent cells in fact show clear opponent-color properties. Derrington *et al.* (1984), using stimuli that modulated from achromatic to chromatic colors, determined that parvocellular LGN neurons all showed chromatic opponency. This opponency was of two major types L-M and S-(L&M).[16]

Somehow, at some level of the brain, comparisons among the outputs of the various cell types must be made, and in these comparisons is contained the information whereby the spatial and chromatic codes, still entwined at the single cell level in the LGN, can be unraveled.

VISUAL CORTEX

The early study of cortical activity as it relates to color vision involved EEG investigations as noted earlier in this chapter. But perhaps the more interesting studies involved single unit recordings. These single unit electrophysiological recordings continue to be of value (see, for example Vautin & Dow, 1985). We have already mentioned Hubel and Wiesel's significant contributions in this area that earned them the Nobel Prize. Since 1979 when this book was first published, at

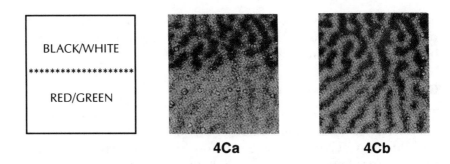

4Ca   **4Cb**

Figure 7.15   The right two figures are autoradiographs from layers 4Ca (magnocellular influence) and 4Cb (parvocellular influence) of the Macaque striate cortex. The figure at the left represents the stimulus presented to the visual system. The top half of the stimulus field was a luminance varying square wave grating and the bottom half was a chromatically varying square wave grating. The uptake of ¹⁴C-2-deoxy-d-glucose in the parvo pathway cortical cells (4Cb) were approximately equal for the luminance and chromatically varying stimuli. However, in the magno pathway cortical cell (4Ca) the luminance varying stimulus had greater ¹⁴C-2-deoxy-d-glucose uptake than did the chromatically varying square wave grating (Tootell, Silverman, Hamilton, De Valois & Switkes, 1988).

least two additional staining methods have played increasingly important roles in providing information about cortical neuroanatomy as it relates to visual function. These techniques use ¹⁴C-2-d-oxyglucose and cytochrome oxidase.

¹⁴C-2-d-oxyglucose

When the ¹⁴C-2-d-oxyglucose method is used, a radioactive chemical is injected into an animal just prior to the application of the visual stimulating conditions. Various visual stimuli, depending on the questions being asked, are then presented to the animal. Because stimulating conditions cause increased metabolic activity in those parts of the brain that actively process the visual information, there is differential uptake of this radioactive substance precisely in those parts of the brain affected by the visual stimulus. The animal is then sacrificed and the brain cut into very thin slices, which are placed on x-ray film for several weeks. The x-ray film is then developed and one obtains a picture of the brain activity that was caused by the stimulating conditions. Figure 7.15 provides an example of such a picture (Tootell, Silverman, Hamilton, De Valois, and Switkes, 1988). In this figure one can see that parvocellular pathway cortical cells stain heavily in response to both luminance and chromatic stimuli whereas magnocellular pathway cortical cells stain heavily only for luminance varying stimuli. This is precisely the difference one would expect between parvo and magno pathway neurons.

Cytochrome Oxidase

The mitochondria in all living cells except bone and hair contain an enzyme called cytochrome oxidase. The cells of the brain also contain this enzyme, and it has been possible to identify certain anatomical areas because of differential levels of staining. The original research that has gained considerable attention yielded the so-called *blobs* (as originally observed by Wong–Riley (1979) and named by Livingstone and Hubel (1984). These blobs are found in areas of high cytochrome oxidase concentration where, in macaque monkey, a great deal of color information is processed. Figure 7.16 shows sections V1 and V2 from the monkey cortex. In V1 the small round dots are blob areas of cells stained for cytochrome oxidase. In V2 one sees the thin, thick and pale stripes referred to in Figure 7.17.

It would appear that the regions identified as blobs exhibit very little, if any, orientation specificity. This finding has been confirmed by ^{14}C-2-d-oxyglucose marking, by retrograde marking achieved with horseradish peroxidase (see below), and by electrophysiological recording. It is important to understand that because most cells contain cytochrome oxidase this enzyme cannot be equated with cells that process color information. Another factor to consider is that retinas of nocturnal monkeys with very little color vision exhibit blobs indicating a richness of cytochrome oxidase (personal communication from R. Tootell).

It is of interest to know about the connections between various anatomical locations in the visual pathway. One of the frequently used methods is the application of a substance with the curious name *horseradish peroxidase*. When applied, for example to certain areas of the cortex, staining travels along the neuronal axon and can show the optic radiation paths back to the LGN. It is thereby possible to determine where the parvocellular and magnocellular neurons synapse in the cortex.

A SUMMARY DIAGRAM

Figure 7.17 is a schematic diagram to help understand the visual pathways from the retina through the LGN, through areas V1, V2, V4, V5 and to the inferotemporal complex. The upper left of Figure 7.17 was discussed previously. We will now take a look at the various

Squirrel Monkey

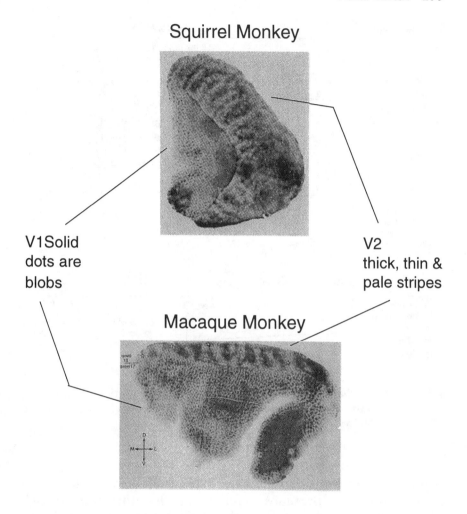

V1Solid
dots are
blobs

V2
thick, thin &
pale stripes

Macaque Monkey

Figure 7.16 Cytochrome oxidase records from squirrel monkey (Livingstone & Hubel, 1988) and from Macaque monkey (Livingstone & Hubel, 1984). Areas V1 show the blobs and V2 the thick, thin, and pale stripes.

other cortical areas and try to understand how they might contribute to color vision.

As already noted, the magnocellular pathway performs very poorly, if at all, with respect to differentiating on the basis of wavelength. Its major cortical input is via layer 4C. As seen in Figure 7.17, 4C sends information to 4B, which is concerned mainly with movement and also has an input to the blobs in layers 2 and 3. The role of this magno input to the blobs does not seem well understood, and it

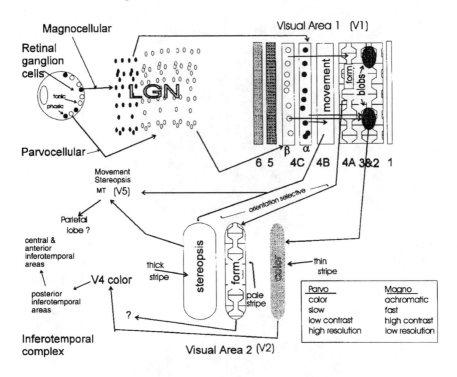

Figure 7.17   A schematic diagram showing proposed connections between the retina and the cortex. (Adapted from Livingstone & Hubel, 1988.) See text for explanation.

is puzzling when one considers the rather well documented wavelength sensitivity of the blobs. Layer 4B sends its information to thick stripes in V2 and also to V5 (an area also referred to as medial temporal area or MT). There is also speculation that the visual pathway from V5 goes to the parietal area (Livingstone and Hubel, 1988).

Referring to Figure 7.17 we can see that color information travels through the tonic ganglion cells, to the parvocellular layers of the LGN, and into layer 4C in striate cortex (V1). This pathway then goes to layers 4A, 3, and 2. In 4A it joins the inter blobs and in layers 3 and 2 connection is made with the blobs. The interblob area is not so much concerned with color as it is with orientation selectivity and form. The interblob neurons then send the information to the pale stripes in V2. As indicated by the question mark (?) in Figure 7.17, the issue has been raised whether the pale stripes also send information to V4. The blobs send the signal to the thin stripes of V2 and from there to V4. Livingstone and Hubel (1988) report that there is some evidence that V4 sends information to the temporal cortex. Although some intriguing information has appeared in the literature to suggest that V4 plays a major role in color vision, newer research has not supported this idea. For example, Heywood *et al.* (in press) have shown that abalation of V4 in monkey produced only mild impairment of color discrimination. Kulikowski *et al.* (1994) reported that monkeys with lesions in V4 exhibited deficits in color constancy but were able to discriminate hues and they segmented the spectrum in a categorical manner. Heywood *et al.* (1988) reported that "Whereas lateral striate or prestriate lesions centred on visual area V4 mildly impaired only the most difficult discriminations, inferotemporal abalation resulted in a severe impairment in the acquisition of colour discriminations" (p. 437).

The reader might wonder why there has been no mention of area V3. Until 1987 it was thought that there were no color selective cells in this area. However, Felleman & Van Essen (1987) found that about 21% of the neurons in V3 are color selective. The average chromatic tuning of 20 color selective V3 cells had a half-width at half-amplitude of about 50 nm.

Given that all cells except those of bone and hair contain cytochrome oxidase, how can we know that those cortical neurons that show up as blobs when stained for cytochrome oxidase necessarily process color information? Presumably, if most cells contain this enzyme we should see evidence of it everywhere when the appropriate staining procedure is conducted. One line of evidence comes from combining both the cytochrome oxidase and electrophysiological techniques. Tootell *et al.* (1988) conducted an interesting study that provides rather graphic evidence that the neurons which show up in blobs are responsible for at least transmitting, if not processing, color information. They used both the ^{14}C-2-d-oxyglucose marking method and the cytochrome oxidase method in the same cortical sections. They injected monkeys with the 2-d-oxyglucose and then presented them with chromatic stimuli. This method would stain those cortical neurons that were metabolically active as a result of the chromatic stimuli. These sections were also stained for cytochrome oxidase. If the blobs are responsible for chromatic information then those neurons that were marked by the 2-d-oxyglucose methods should coincide with the neurons stained for cytochrome oxidase. Tootell *et al.* reported that "For all hues each spotty region of high DG (2-d-oxyglucose) uptake coincides with a cytochrome oxidase blob" (p. 1577). There has been speculation that individual colors might be separately represented in different columns of the cortex. However, Tootell *et al.* reported that, given the limited level of resolution possible with the 2-d-oxyglucose marking method, there was no obvious evidence for hue columns.

For an observer to say that two fields are identical in color requires that sufficient information reach at least the cortical levels of the brain. We know this because those who have sustained injury to the occipital cortex can be blind, or even if not blind may experience achromatopsia, even though all neural paths leading to the cortex are intact. It is probably the case that the critical information processing related to color matching occurs in the most peripheral stages, perhaps even in the cone receptors. However, it seems reasonable to suppose that for an observer to say "I see a red light or I see green grass" requires not only important processing peripherally, but also additional processing at the highest cortical stages.

What kind of information would one like to see at the cortical level that would be consistent with the cognitive activity of color naming? The answer to this question must, of course, depend on the color-naming data. In Figure 7.18A we see an example of color-naming functions obtained by Boynton and Gordon (1965) from which the curves in Figure 7.2 were derived. Observers who generated these data were asked to name spectral stimuli using four color names: red, green, yellow, and blue. If a stimulus appeared to be a combination of two hues the observer responded with the dominant hue name first and the nondominant second. For example, suppose a yellowish red (orange) color was presented the observer would respond yellow red. If the color appeared to contain more red than yellow the observer would respond red yellow. A point value of 3 was assigned when a single color name was the response. When pairs of color names were used 2 points were assigned to the first name and 1 to the second one. As can be seen the resulting functions (Fig. 7.18A) appear similar to chromatic tuning curves (Fig. 7.18B) obtained by Vautin and Dow (1985), from single unit cortical cells in awake macaque monkeys. Between 400 and 650 nm they obtained four such tuning curves whose peaks occur in wavelength regions that human observers would call red, yellow, green, and blue. Evidence for this assertion is seen when one compares Figures 7.18A and 7.18B. Figure 7.18C shows data obtained by the hue cancellation method (Hurvich, 1981) discussed earlier. The figure plots hue coefficient as a function of wavelength, where hue coefficient is the ratio of each chromatic response to the sum of the total chromatic responses.

A closer look at what Vautin and Dow did will provide a better understanding of the electrophysiological data. Awake behaving macaque monkeys were trained to fixate a tangent screen on which

A   Human Color Naming

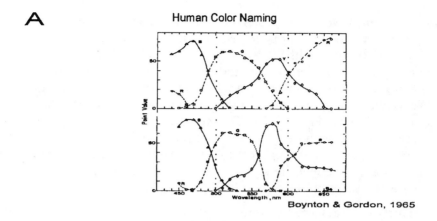

Boynton & Gordon, 1965

B   Macaque V1 Single Unit

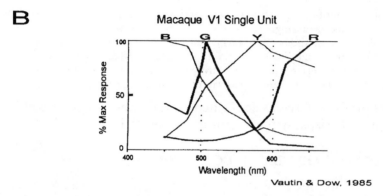

Vautin & Dow, 1985

C   Human Hue Cancellation

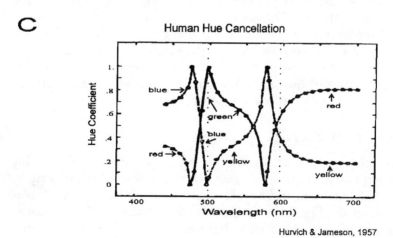

Hurvich & Jameson, 1957

Figure 7.18   A comparison of data collected by human color naming, macaque V1 single unit data presented as chromatic tuning functions, and human hue cancellation coefficients. See text for explanation.

spectral stimuli were rear projected. When a cell was found that was responsive, the investigators determined the optimal stimulus orientation, length and width. Once this was determined the centers of the receptive fields were stimulated with 500 ms flashes followed by 1,500-ms dark intervals in repeating cycles. A variety of wavelengths were used to determine the relative spectral tuning characteristics of the cortical cells (Fig. 7.18B). The coincidence of the single unit tuning functions with those of Boynton and Gordon's color naming functions and (to a lesser extent) with those of Hurvich's hue cancellation data may reflect the kinds of cortical activity that are responsible for the psychophysical results.

Thirty-six years ago Boynton (1960, p. 944) wrote:

> It should not be long before the electrophysiologists, already capable of recording from single cortical cells in mammals, will turn their attention to color and begin in earnest to gather this evidence. We know ahead of time that their findings will be confusing; that single cells in the cortex generate patterns of activity that are not readily interpretable except as they relate to patterns of neighboring cells. . . .

This prediction seems confirmed, as the nature of color coding in the primate visual system continues to be clarified.

PHYSIOLOGICALLY BASED COLOR SPACE

It may seem strange to discuss color spaces in a chapter on color coding. In fact the more general topic of color space is approached in Chapters 8 and 11. The topic is relevant here because it is now possible to plot stimuli in color spaces that have physiological significance. Specifically, it is possible to make inferences about cone excitation caused by chromatic stimuli. Below we describe two such related diagrams and in Appendix, Part IV a numerical example for the DKL cone excitation space is presented.[17]

Cone Excitation Diagram

Whereas the CIE chromaticity diagram is a good defining tool for color, it is inadequate for representing colors from a physiological perspective. In 1978 MacLeod and Boynton published a 2D isoluminant cone excitation space (Fig. 7.19).[18] This diagram is based on the excitation of cone receptors in response to light absorption. The assumption is made that S-cones make no contribution to luminance. In order to make this an isoluminant space the cone excitations are normalized to constant luminance as shown in Equations (7.3).

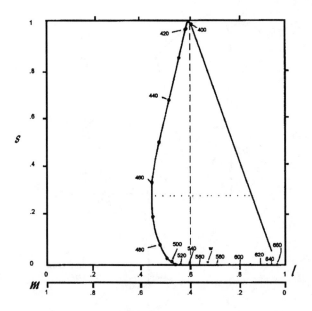

Figure 7.19   Cone excitation isoluminant chromaticity diagram. See Equation (7.3) for definition of the ordinate and abscissa. The W in the diagram is the equal energy white point. The numerical values represent the wavelengths on the spectrum locus. The vertical dashed line is a locus of constant L- and M-cone excitation. The horizontal dotted line is a locus of constant S-cone excitation. (Adapted from MacLeod & Boynton, 1979.)

$$l = \frac{L}{L+M}$$

$$m = \frac{M}{L+M} \tag{7.3}$$

$$s = \frac{S}{L+M}$$

The reader can easily see that the vertical dashed line in Figure 7.19 represents constant l and m and varying s, whereas the horizontal dots represent constant s and an exchange between l and m. For example, stimuli that plot in various places along the vertical dashed line will all be the result of the same level of L- (or M-) cone excitation but will have increasing S-cone excitation when going from the

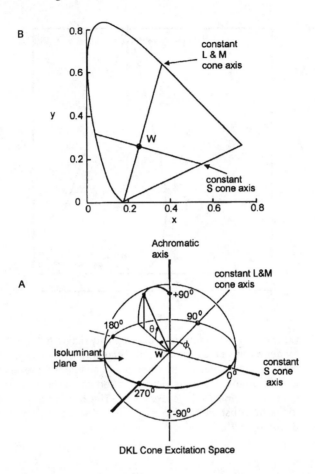

Figure 7.20   A. The Derrington, Krauskopf & Lennie (DKL) cone excitation space. B. 1931 CIE chromaticity diagram showing the constant axes represented in the DKL space. See text for detailed explanation. (Slightly modified from Derrington et al., 1984.)

bottom of the diagram to the top. An analogous but reversed situation exists for stimuli that plot along the horizontal dotted line.

Derrington, Krauskopf, and Lennie Chromaticity Space (DKL)

Figure 7.20A shows Derrington, Krauskopf, and Lennie's (1984) chromaticity space (DKL). Unlike the 2D spaces of the CIE diagram or the cone excitation diagram (MacLeod & Boynton, 1978) this space also contains an achromatic dimension. Derrington et al. took the cone excitation diagram as their point of departure ". . . because its axes were the same as the cardinal directions of the Krauskopf *et al.* (1982) color space . . ." (p. 243).

The DKL diagram assumes that receptive fields stem from two antagonistic mechanisms with different spectral sensitivities and that cone signals contributing to the mechanisms sum linearly. They further assume that if the adaptive state of the mechanism is not altered, its response to a stimulus of any spectral distribution and fixed intensity can be matched by the response to a stimulus of another spectral distribution if its intensity is appropriately adjusted (Derrington *et al.*, 1984). In other words, if the mechanism combines cone signals linearly it is capable of remaining undisturbed under conditions of silent substitution. Recall that silent substitution is a procedure in which a mechanism of a given spectral sensitivity can be stimulated by different wavelengths of suitably chosen intensities and the mechanism will respond in a constant manner. That is to say, for example, if two such wavelengths are alternately presented to the mechanism it will not respond differentially to the two wavelengths and its response will mimic that of an unchanging stimulus.

A pair of stimuli that causes silent substitution for a particular neuron gives it a distinctive *signature* that represents its spectral sensitivity. A neuron would have an infinite number of silent substitution pairs and Derrington *et al.* wanted a single means of representing the chromatic signature. Using the axes of the cone excitation diagram plus the achromatic axis permits a unique signature. To say this in another way, "For any cell, the 'null' set, which depends on the relative weights of the signals received from the different classes of cone, can be used as a chromatic 'signature' (Lennie & D'Zmura, 1988, p. 368)." As can be seen in Figure 7.20B there are three principal axes: $0°–180°$ (the constant S-cone axis), $90°–270°$ (constant L&M cone axis), and the vertical achromatic axis. When stimuli are modulated along the constant S-cone axis the S-cone excitation is nulled and only the L- and M-cones co-vary yielding a constant sum of excitation. When a stimulus is modulated along the constant L&M cone axis only the S-cones are excited. Figure 7.20A shows the major chromatic DKL axes plotted in the CIE, chromaticity space. Signals from the L-, M-, and S-cones vary proportionately along the achromatic axis.

The center of the DKL chromaticity sphere represents a stimulus perceived as white. Modulation from white up the achromatic axis toward $+90°$ represents increasing luminance (assuming that the achromatic axis has a $V(\lambda)$ spectral sensitivity. Modulating from white along the constant S-cone axis towards $0°$ represents a modulation towards stimuli that appear red. This is not necessarily a unique red –

unique green axis. But as Lennie and D'Zmura (1988) point out, this axis probably does a better job of isolating the putative red-green mechanism than one based upon color appearance. Modulating from white towards 90° or 270° along the constant L&M axis represents a movement from white toward a stimulus that appears yellow-green or violet. Another way of thinking about the constant L&M axis, and this is seen more easily in Figure 7.20B, is that this axis corresponds to a tritanopic confusion line. The constant L&M cones axes and the constant S-cone axis in DKL space are identical to the S and L (or M) axes of the constant luminance cone excitation diagram.

The horizontal plane in Figure 7.20A defines an isoluminance plane (again, assuming the achromatic axis with a V(λ) spectral sensitivity). Lennie and D'Zmura point out that the DKL space assumes a red-green mechanism that receives opposed inputs only from L- and M-cones and this mechanism responds best to lights modulated along the constant S-cone axis and not at all to lights modulated along a plane defined by the achromatic axis or the constant L&M cone axis. A yellow-blue mechanism[19] that receives opposing inputs from S-cones vs L-cones + M-cones would respond best to lights modulated along the constant L&M cone axis (the tritanopic confusion line) but it would not respond to lights modulated in a planes defined by the constant S-cone axis or the achromatic axis. (Lennie & D'Zmura, 1988).

To summarize, if a neuron is stimulated only by L- and M-cones, its null plane passes through the constant L&M axis. If a neuron receives signals from L- and M-cones that are in balanced opposition to each other (i.e., a red-green opponent neuron) the null plane passes vertically through constant L&M axis. Finally, if a neuron received signals from L- cones + M cones (a luminance unit) the null plane is the isoluminant plane. Lennie and D'Zmura remind us that the location of the null plane gives the chromatic signature of a cell and that if one knows the action spectra of the three cone classes it is possible to calculate from the position of the null plane the weights attached to a neuron to inputs from the three cone classes.

SUMMARY

This chapter discusses research that helps us to understand the basic processing of color information. We start by presenting a simple color model that helps guide the reader through the major color processing stages. Experiments are then described that employ a color naming technique and a hue cancellation technique as a means for providing a description of spectral colors.

Intracellular records from photoreceptors and other nerve cells of the retina have been obtained from cold-blooded animals, but so far only the spikes of ganglion cells have been recorded from single units in the eyes of intact primates having color vision similar to that of humans. The major kinds of electrical records that can be obtained from human subjects (electroretinograms and visually evoked cortical potentials) seem too crude, at least at present, to provide critical insights. Nevertheless, they help to reify and confirm concepts that have been developed via human psychophysics and animal single unit electrophysiology. Three-dimensional reconstructions of serial sections from electron micrographs and light micrographs have aided in the understanding of retinal anatomy and its probable functions.

Photoreceptors are unusual because they are continuously depolarized in the dark. Each receptor hyperpolarizes to a level related to the intensity of the light. Increments and decrements are signaled relative to that level. The three types of human cones do not differ very much from one another, although the S-cone system has response characteristics that differ somewhat from the luminance channels that are fed by L- and M-cones.

Based upon opponent-color responses that have been recorded from horizontal cells for a quarter of a century, these cells seem to have an important role to play in chromatic encoding, but the exact nature of their role is still obscure. The lateral geniculate nucleus (LGN) has been a favorite recording site in Old-World primates whose color vision, as established behaviorally, is virtually impossible to distinguish from that of humans. Single units in the LGN respond well to large, diffuse chromatic stimuli, whereas large white fields are relatively ineffective. This behavior reflects a center-surround receptive-field organization that is chromatically organized.

An attempt has been made to organize evidence derived from diffuse stimulation of the retina and spike responses from the LGN into a simple color model consistent with the opponent processing introduced earlier in the chapter. It is emphasized that no single cell of the LGN, or elsewhere in the brain, can carry a chromatic message unless the category to which that cell belongs is somehow specified. Many cells that appear to exhibit chromatic specificity may be as much, or even more, concerned with spatial vision. It is not known where cells are located whose activity might directly underlie chromatic sensations. The cells of the visual cortex, so far explored, many of which have chromatically specific properties, are far from certain candidates.

At the present time, the evidence concerning the chromatic code of the visual nervous system is incomplete and difficult to interpret. This is seen as an area of research with a bright and colorful future.

NOTES

[1] Good discussions of the effects of electrical stimulation of eye and brain are given by Brindley, in his monograph (1970) and his technical papers (Brindley, 1962; Brindley & Lewin, 1968).

[2] When discussing the hue cancellation experiment we describe light with reference to hue names. In so doing we mean that the light had the appearance described by the named hue.

[3] When referring to the opponent functions we sometimes continue to use hue names for two reasons. Opponent processes theory purports to explain color appearance and it is difficult to distinguish between G and Y using cone description except by referring to yellow as L+M. However, L+M also refers to luminance and we do not wish to equate luminance (L+M) with yellow.

[4] Predictions such as this one are always dangerous because the technical advances of the future are probably no more predictable than those that have surprised us in the past. For a summary of electrical recording techniques, see Thompson and Patterson (1973–1974).

[5] An excellent textbook by Armington (1974), describes the human ERG.

[6] For a summary of this work see K. T. Brown (1968).

[7] An outstanding book on evoked potentials is that of Regan (1989). For a briefer treatment, see MacKay and Jeffreys (1973).

[8] In referring to this issue, Granit (1947) stated, in reference to the "P-III" component of the ERG (which includes the leading edge): "Even if the retina is removed from the bulb and placed between the electrodes the direction of PIII remains the same; the inner surface of the retina becomes negative and the outer surface positive. This means, if the receptors are involved, that their free ends become positive relative to their bases when they are subjected to illumination. If we accept this conclusion we must believe that P-III differs from all the isolated receptor potentials hitherto discovered with respect to its electrical sign" (p. 112, in the 1963 reprinted edition).

[9] For a more complete description of receptor phototransduction see Tessier–Lavigne (1991) and Pugh & Cobbs (1986).

[10] The bleaching of one rhodopsin molecule causes the disappearance of 50,000 cyclic guanosine monophosphate (cGMP) molecules. cGMP acts as an internal transmitter substance from disk to surface membrane providing great amplification.

[11] The first direct evidence of the distribution of L-, M-, and S-cones in the primate retina was reported by Marc and Sperling (1977), based on a selective reaction of cones treated with nitro-blue tetrazolium chloride when stimulated with lights from various spectral regions. For the peripheral retina they found a rhomboidal pattern of S-cones, and very few of them, just as Walraven had speculated. L- and M-cones were, however, irregularly distributed, with about twice as many M- as L-cones, just the opposite of Walraven's prediction. However, there appear to be substantial individual differences in the ratio of M- and L-cones (Cicerone & Nerger, 1989a,b).

[12] MacNichol and Svaetichin (1958). Early dye markers were crude. Dyes are now available that serve as excellent conductors in micropipette electrodes, which can be injected electrophoretically into the impaled cell and then viewed by the fluorescence induced by ultraviolet radiation. For many cells, including horizontal cells, the dye migrates into even the smallest processes of the cell without penetrating adjacent cells.

[13] Brodman labeled this section of the cortex area 17 because it was the 17th area he studied. It is called the striate cortex because of the visible striations when stained (Zeki, 1993).

[14] The first report from DeValois's laboratory was that of DeValois, Smith, Kitai, and Karoly (1958). For summaries of the extensive work of this laboratory, which moved over the years from Michigan to Indiana to California, see DeValois (1965a, 1965b, 1973) and DeValois and DeValois (1975, 1993).

[15] In a volume put together to celebrate Hartline's seventieth birthday, the papers of Hartline and his collaborators have been assembled by Ratliff (1974). The material added by Ratliff helps to make this not only the most convenient, but also the best source for Hartline's important papers.

[16] We assume that Derrington, Krauskopf and Lennie referred to "L&M" rather than "L+M" to avoid the assumption of linear addition.

[17] As did Derrington, Krauskopf and Lennie, we refer to these diagrams as cone excitation spaces. Brainard (see Appendix, Part IV) treats the DKL space in terms of post-receptoral mechanisms.

[18] Boynton (1986) reported that a similar diagram was first proposed by R. Luther (1927). In 1986, Boynton referred to this diagram, based on cone excitations, as the "Luther Diagram," but this has not caught on. Most people call it the "MacLeod–Boynton chromaticity diagram."

[19] Although this axis of color discrimination has classically been called yellow-blue, the sensations elicited as the stimulus moves away from white are violet and yellow-green.

Chapter 8

Chromatic Discrimination

INTRODUCTION

This chapter will be concerned with three interrelated topics that can be expressed as questions:

- In order for two colors to be barely distinguishable as different, how different must they be?

- What is the physiological basis for such thresholds of color difference?

- Can large color differences be measured and, if so, how?

These concerns relate to problems with which many readers will have had personal experience. Anyone who has tried to replace a broken ceramic tile or match the color of a piece of fabric or paint will know that the task can be nearly impossible. Experienced painters will not permit a batch of paint to run out in the middle of a wall, even if it is a standard commercial mix, because the eye will probably see a difference between the two areas, even though the label on the replacement can reads identically to that of the original.

Another more detailed example may serve to remind readers of similar problems while pointing up the difficulty of defining a detectable color difference. Boynton once had some carpet installed in his home, most of which was of the same blue-green hue. But at a division between hallway and dining room, the installers switched to a new roll and there was an obvious color difference — greener in the hall, bluer in the dining room. When the areas being compared are very large, as in this instance, the eye is extremely sensitive to such color differences. Small fields are a different matter. When the dividing line was inspected through a paper towel roll, in order to reduce the field size, the difference was barely discernible. But it fairly leapt out when the tube was removed to expose the carpet in the normal way.

Suppose that Boynton had insisted that the match between the two carpeted areas be "made right." Who then would decide when the match was close enough to be acceptable? The matter might well have landed in a small claims court, where the following scenario can be imagined.

> **Boynton:** "Your honor, the carpet in my dining room does not match that in the rest of the house. I find this offensive and feel that it is my right to have it match properly."
>
> **Judge** (to installer): "How do you regard the match?"
>
> **Installer:** "It looks okay to me."
>
> **Boynton:** "Judge, would you be willing to come to my home and look for yourself?"
>
> **Judge:** "Your suggestion is impractical." (to installer): "Can you show me a sample of the two sections of the carpet?"
>
> **Installer:** "Not without tearing them off the floor. We threw the scraps away." (This is fortunate because very small scraps from the two sections might not have looked different enough to impress the judge.)
>
> **Judge:** "Can either of you give me some measurement of the amount of the color difference?"
>
> **Boynton:** "As a matter of fact, I can. I have run a spectrophotometric curve on each section and have computed the tristimulus values for each. From this I calculated their chromaticity values on the CIE chart."
>
> **Judge** (perplexed): "I must admit that I don't exactly follow what you are saying. Can you show me such a chart?"
>
> **Boynton:** "Yes, your honor. I just happen to have one with me. (Boynton hauls it out.) This is a standard chart, one certified by the International Commission on Illumination as the proper way to represent all possible colors."
>
> **Judge:** "Can you show me where the colors of the two sections of your carpet would be represented on this chart?"
>
> **Boynton:** "Yes. The measurements and calculations have been done. The two points plot here and here" (Boynton points to the chart and draws two X's on it).

Judge (astutely): "How far apart do your X's have to be, in order for the color difference to be noticeable?"

Boynton: "About this far" (Boynton holds his thumb and forefinger very slightly apart).

Installer (reddening): "I don't understand any of this mumbo-jumbo. Believe me, your honor, the difference isn't very great. It happens all the time when we're forced to switch to a new roll. We do the best we can, and besides the difference will fade out after a while."

Judge (to installer): "Apparently then, you admit that there is a color difference. How much would it cost to eliminate it?"

Installer: "We'd have to re-carpet the whole house because we'd never find another roll exactly like the first one! We thought we had enough to do the whole job, but it was hard to figure, with the crooked stairway and all. . . ."

In a case like this, even though the difference could be calculated and displayed on the CIE chromaticity chart, the judge would be in a very difficult position. We will see that, depending upon the region of the chart, equal differences are represented by very unequal distances. Moreover, if the judge were willing to inspect the difference for himself, how would he know whether his perception of the difference would be the same as that of the average individual?

Manufacturers of ceramics, fabrics, paints, yarn, food, cosmetics, and other products would much prefer that incidents like this one (which are by no means rare) never occurred. The fact that such problems frequently arise is only partly due to the lack of quality control of manufactured products. Because of the almost incredible sensitivity of the eye to color differences, and despite improvements in recent years, color-sensitive devices still cannot match human vision for detecting small differences. The problem is compounded by the fact that the only safe match is a physical one, and such matches are often not possible. Suppose, for example, that a manufacturer wishes to match the plastic of his automobile's dashboard with that of the fabric on the door. Differences between the substrates of the two materials, combined with the need to use different dyes and pigments, make it impossible to duplicate exactly the spectral reflectances of the two materials. This is why metameric matches are the only ones that can be sought. Such metamers often fail when the illuminant is changed, and different observers will not agree entirely about metameric matches even for materials viewed under the same illumination.

CHROMATIC VS. ACHROMATIC COLOR DIFFERENCES

We define chromatic color by paraphrasing Wyszecki and Stiles (1982, p. 487).[1]

Chromatic color is that aspect of visual perception by which observers distinguish differences between equally bright, structure-free, fields of view of identical size and shape.

A *chromatic color difference* occurs whenever the relative spectral distributions of two lights are sufficiently different that, no matter what their relative intensities, they always look different. One of the two lights may appear brighter than the other, or it may not. As an example, visualize two fields, one of which is distinctly green and the other red. Place them side by side so that they are perfectly aligned. Suppose that, to begin with, the green side is obviously very much brighter than the red one. By reducing the intensity of the green side (for example, by placing neutral filters in front of that side only), it becomes possible to make it look much dimmer than the red. Or by placing filters in front of the red side, the green could be made relatively brighter. Throughout the entire range of such adjustment, there will be no point where the fields look alike, nor will the border that separates them ever disappear.

When this experiment is repeated with two fields having the same relative spectral energy distribution, or that match metamerically, a different result will occur. For example, remove the red field and replace it with the same physical green (i.e., they are isomeric) that is on the other side. Make one side much brighter than the other; then gradually reduce its intensity so that it eventually becomes much dimmer than the other side. Somewhere between the two fields will match exactly. The dividing line between them will disappear at this point and only a single circular green field will be seen.[2] In this second example, we have a range of achromatic color differences; somewhere within this range the two fields have equal luminances that are based upon their physical identity.

Returning now to the red-green pair, repeat the experiment. This time pay strict attention to the border separating the fields, while trying to ignore the color difference. When the green side is much brighter than the red, the border separating them will be very distinct. As the intensity of the green side is reduced, the distinctness of the border between the two fields grows less. At some point it becomes *minimally distinct*, but it does not disappear. Further decreases in the intensity of the green field will again cause the border to appear more distinct. In this second example, the color differences are in general comprised of both chromatic and achromatic components; the difference that remains at the minimally distinct border setting is purely chromatic.

The observed sequence:

very distinct ⇒ distinct ⇒ minimally distinct ⇒ distinct ⇒ very distinct

is the same as that observed for an achromatic color difference, except that, in the chromatic case, some border is usually seen at the minimally distinct point, whereas in the achromatic case the border will disappear completely.

Now suppose we pick lights of two wavelengths that are only very slightly different, such as 650 nm and 651 nm; we would like to know whether or not they are visually different. If the 650-nm field is much brighter or dimmer than the 651-nm one, there will be an obvious brightness difference and the border between the two fields will be clear and sharp. The experimental question now becomes this: at the minimally distinct border setting, will any visible difference remain? We will see later (Fig. 8.1) that, for this particular example, the answer is "no." But if we were to repeat the experiment, using 589 nm and 590 nm as the stimulus components, the answer would probably be "yes." This tells us that chromatic discriminations based on wavelength differences are more acute in the neighborhood of 590 nm than around 650 nm. But this conclusion could not be drawn unless the relative intensities of the fields being compared were carefully controlled, as in the example given. Setting a minimally distinct border is one operation that can be used to define equal *sensation luminance* between any two fields.[3] To test for a chromatic difference between two fields it is necessary to ensure that they are equated for sensation luminance, because this is when they differ least. Only then is the difference between them a purely chromatic one.

A luminance or brightness difference occurs whenever there is a difference in the output of the achromatic pathways (magnocellular and parvocellular) associated with the two stimuli being compared. This difference might or might not be a discriminable one, depending upon its magnitude. A chromatic difference will occur whenever there is a difference in the outputs of at least one of the opponent-color pathways (parvocellular), and this becomes a purely chromatic difference in the special case where there is no difference between the outputs of the luminance channels. We define a *chromatic dis-*

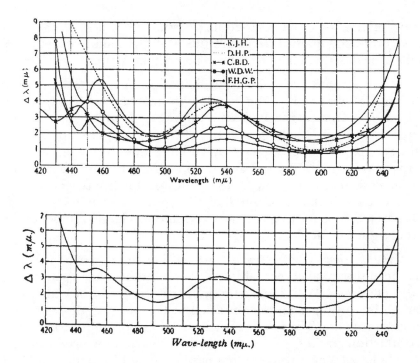

Figure 8.1   Wavelength discrimination functions obtained by Wright and Pitt (from Wright, 1946). The method of adjustment was used and the intensity of the spectrum was about 70 trolands but was somewhat less in the short wavelengths. The bottom curve, which is the mean of the five observers, has been frequently reproduced as a "typical" wavelength discrimination function.

crimination as depending upon purely chromatic differences; such differences will be the major concern of this chapter.

INTRODUCTION TO
WAVELENGTH DISCRIMINATION

Consideration of experimental data will be postponed until the second half of this chapter, to be preceded by a discussion of some fundamental theoretical issues. But theory cannot be discussed *in vacuo*. Therefore, as an aid to discussion, the basic experiment on wavelength discrimination will now be described. This is not intended as a description of any particular experiment, but it does indicate how such an experiment can be done, together with the expected result. Real experiments on wavelength discrimination have used many methods and have varied many parameters; accordingly they have produced many different results. But the main features of results to be described here have been noted in most such experiments.

Given a reference wavelength, λ, the problem is to determine the smallest variation in this wavelength that can just barely be detected. This amount is called $\Delta\lambda$. If this experiment is repeated for a large number of λs, a large number of $\Delta\lambda$s will be generated. When these are plotted, they appear to fall upon a smooth (if complicated) curve; a continuous curve drawn through these points describes the wavelength discrimination function. Results for five subjects taken from one particular experiment of this type are shown in Figure 8.1. However, before starting such an experiment, a large number of decisions must be made.

What psychophysical method will be used? The method of adjustment has been the usual choice, although other methods have sometimes been employed. With this method, the subject could vary the wavelength by turning a knob connected to the wavelength drum of a monochromator. The wavelength drum turns a prism (or sometimes a diffraction grating) so that a slit in the projected spectrum permits the choice of a narrow band that passes out and irradiates the field of view. In the ideal case, which can be closely approached though never actually achieved, the field will be strictly monochromatic and completely uniform over its entire extent. Two such fields are required. One is the reference field, in terms of which λ is defined; the other is the variable field, to be set so that it looks just barely different from λ. It is not easy to establish and maintain a criterion concerning what is just-noticeably different from λ. For this reason, an alternative procedure has sometimes been used, where the experimenter sets the variable field off from the reference by a substantial amount, and the subject attempts to make a match. On repeated trials, the matches he makes will vary slightly from one trial to another. A measure of dispersion of many such matches (for example, their standard deviation) can serve as an index of discriminability.

How will luminance be controlled? Ideally, when the method of adjustment is used, the luminance of the variable field should remain constant as its wavelength is changed throughout the full visible spectrum. The amount of light coming from the monochromator can be adjusted, at each wavelength, by connecting a moveable variable neutral filter (wedge) to the wavelength control in such a way as to keep the luminance constant. In an earlier era, this could only have been done mechanically, for example, by using specially devised cams and linkages. Today it is done by programming a digital computer and interfacing it with the neutral density wedge that is used to vary intensity. Most of the older experiments did not in fact control very well for luminance. The results of such flawed experiments are nevertheless of value because it turns out that the chromatic variation caused by changing the wavelength of light emerging from a monochromator is usually much more potent than the small luminance change that may accompany it.[4]

What values should be chosen for other parameters, such as field size, stimulus duration, relative position of the fields, and the basic luminance of the standard wavelengths? Most often, viewing has been continuous, the field size is small — on the order of a degree or two — the fields are close together, but some dividing line usually remains when the two parts are physically identical.

Many tests of chromatic discrimination are possible other than those that depend upon variations of the wavelength of monochromatic light. For example, *saturation discrimination* experiments have tested the amount of monochromatic light required, when added to white, in order to produce a just-noticeable tinge of color difference (see below). In general, *chromatic discrimination* can be investigated starting at any point in a chromaticity plane (recall the color triangles of Chapter 5), and chromaticity discrimination can be tested in any desired direction. Such experiments will be considered later in this chapter.

THEORETICAL DEVELOPMENT: PRELIMINARIES

As noted below, the following treatment is not a model representing the literal truth. Rather it is offered as a guide with which the reader can systematically follow through considerations we believe to be important.

Although there exists a general agreement that the initial basis for the perception of a color difference lies in the differential stimulation of three classes of cones, many ideas have been proposed about the exact manner in which a threshold difference is determined. Theoretical suggestions fall generally into two classes. In the first class are theories which assume that the brain has direct access to signals reflecting the outputs of each class of cone separately, or that the receptors themselves limit the discrimination. In order for two colors to look different, according to this view, cones of at least one of the three classes are required to produce differential signals that are above some kind of a threshold. Many specific versions of this class of theory are possible, depending upon how the changing outputs

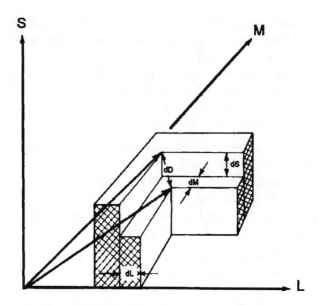

Figure 8.2   In this simplest possible line-element model, the threshold of the color discriminations is taken to be dD, regardless of its position or orientation in three-dimensional Euclidean space. If L, M, and S represent the outputs of the L-, M-, and S-cones respectively, then $(dD)^2 = (dL)^2 + (dM)^2 + (dS)^2$.

of the three types of cones are assumed to interact. Helmholtz favored this class of theory and gave it a geometrical form.[5] The outputs of three classes of receptors can be represented as points in three-dimensional space (Fig. 8.2). In the simplest possible model used to characterize the relation between two stimuli, discrimination threshold would be reached for any change in receptor activities caused by those stimuli that yield the same distance ΔD between the representations of their response loci in Euclidean three-dimensional space. Such a distance is called a *line element*, and it is the aim of discrimination theories of this type to determine a set of relations that will generate line elements of the same length between just-discriminable pairs of stimuli plotted anywhere in the space, oriented in any possible direction. (A complete treatment of line-element theory is given by Wyszecki and Stiles, 1982, p. 654.)

In attempting to bring the results of line-element theory into concordance with experimental data, the chief manipulations are concerned with (1) the assumed receptor input-output relations, (2) the kind of space (Euclidean, Riemannian, and so on) in which the sensory vectors are imagined to plot, and (3) the rules according to which the distances between vector ends may be measured.[6]

On the basis of the physiological evidence that was reviewed in Chapter 7, and psychophysical evidence to be covered in Chapter 9, purely trichromatic theories of color discrimination are highly implausible. Nevertheless, because of their historical interest, we will deal a bit further with them later in this chapter. Opponent-color theory, which will be emphasized here, does not deny the trichromacy of the first stage. As noted above, trichromatic theories of color discrimination assume either that (1) the higher visual centers have direct access to information about the responses of the three classes of cones — the Helmholtzian view — or (2) the level of processing that limits discriminability is that of the receptor — the view of Stiles. Alternatively, by the opponent-color view, higher centers have access only to what is delivered through the achromatic channels (reflecting the summed outputs of the L- and M-cones) and the spectrally opponent chromatic channels, r-g and y-b (see Fig. 7.1A).

CRITICAL QUESTIONS ABOUT CHROMATIC DISCRIMINATION

The topic of chromatic discrimination will now be further developed in the form of a series of questions, each to be followed by the kinds of answers that are suggested by the class of theory that includes an opponent-color stage.

1. *What excitation of the* L-, M-, *and* S-*cones is produced by an initial stimulus of spectral energy distribution* $E_{1\lambda}$ *(to be compared later with a second stimulus,* $E_{2\lambda}$*)?*

Let us temporarily assume that these pigments are uniquely isolated by cone type, so that, for example, L-cones contain a unique photopigment. We know that this assumption is not completely valid because a number of photopigments with slightly different peak absorptions have been found within each of the L- and M-cone classes (Neitz & Neitz, 1994). Moreover, we will ignore bleaching so that the relative action spectra of the three cone pigments can be assumed to be invariant. Granting these assumptions, cone absorption rates can be economically summarized by a set of three equations:

$$\rho = k_a \int E(\lambda) L(\lambda) d\lambda \qquad (8.1)$$

$$\gamma = k_b \int E(\lambda) M(\lambda) d\lambda \qquad (8.2)$$

$$\beta = k_c \int E(\lambda) S(\lambda) d\lambda \qquad (8.3)$$

where ρ, γ, and β are the rates of cone absorptions; k_a, k_b, and k_c are constants; and $L(\lambda)$, $M(\lambda)$, and $S(\lambda)$ are the cone fundamentals as a function of wavelength.

We know that receptors respond nonlinearly, and because it is only their response to which post-receptoral neurons have access, this nonlinearity should be taken into account. Although this fact should be kept in mind, we will ignore it for now. Instead, a simple proportionality will be assumed, one which is not too far from the truth, at least for modest levels of perturbation around a mean adaptation level for a receptor. On this basis, cone responses L*, M*, and S* are:

$$L^* = k_d \int E(\lambda)L(\lambda)\,d\lambda \tag{8.4}$$

$$M^* = k_e \int E(\lambda)M(\lambda)\,d\lambda \tag{8.5}$$

$$S^* = k_f \int E(\lambda)\,S(\lambda)\,d\lambda \tag{8.6}$$

The receptor potential would be a measurable aspect of this cone response. The rate at which a neurotransmitter is liberated at the cone pedicle would be another.

2. If $E(\lambda_1)$ is changed to $E(\lambda_2)$, by what amounts does this change alter the response of the L-, M-, and S-cones?

We will initially examine this question with respect to L- and M-cones only, and focus on long wavelengths where S-cones are not involved. (We will deal with S-cones later.) Because we have assumed a simple proportionality between absorption and cone response, we can treat the action spectra of L- and M-cones as if they were the response levels of these cones for an equal-energy spectrum. Because we wish to deal with wavelength shifts at equal luminance, each must be divided by luminance (L + M).[7]

$$L' = \frac{L}{L+M} \tag{8.7}$$

$$M' = \frac{M}{L+M} \tag{8.8}$$

$$S' = \frac{S}{L+M} \tag{8.9}$$

These values for Equation 8.7 have been calculated for monochromatic lights at 10-nm steps centered on wavelengths chosen at 10-nm inter-

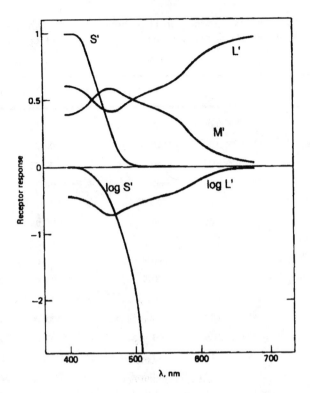

Figure 8.3   **Top:** Computed responses of the three classes of cones, at equal luminance (L + M), shown as a function of wavelength. Note, that the L'
and M' functions are mirror images of each other. **Bottom:** Log S' and
log L' plotted as a function of wavelength.

vals from 400 to 680 nm. They are given in Table 8.1 (column B), based
on the Smith–Pokorny fundamentals, and are plotted in Figure 8.3.

An example will help. Suppose we are concerned with the consequences of changing from 620 to 630 nm. The Smith–Pokorny sensitivity values for these wavelengths (see p. 558) are as follows:

	$\lambda = 620$	$\lambda = 630$
L	0.3377	0.2421
	0.0432	0.0229
L + M	0.3809	0.2650

Table 8.1 Calculations Pertaining to Hypothetical Wavelength Discrimination Mediated at Constant Luminance by Differential L-cone Responses

A	B	C_1	C_2	D	E	F
Wavelength	$L'=\dfrac{L}{L+M}$	$\dfrac{|\Delta L'|}{10nm}$	$\dfrac{|\Delta L'|}{1nm}$	$J=1+|L'-2M'|$	$\dfrac{|\Delta L'|}{J}$	$\Delta\lambda=0.004J/\Delta L'$
400	.600			1.20		
405		.009	.0009		.00074	5.41
410	.591			1.23		
415		.014	.0014		.0012	3.33
420	.577			1.27		
425		.032	.0032		.0024	1.67
430	.545			1.37		
435		.039	.0039		.0027	1.48
440	.506			1.48		
445		.038	.00038		.0025	1.60
450	.468			1.59		
455		.030	.0030		.0018	2.22
460	.438			1.68		
465		0	0		0	
470	.438			1.68		
475		.039	.0029		.0018	2.22
480	.467			1.60		
485		.029	.0029		.0018	2.22
490	.496			1.51		
495		.023	.0023		.0016	2.50
500	.519			1.44		
505		.017	.0015		.0011	3.63
510	.536			1.39		
515		.016	.0016		.0012	3.33
520	.552			1.34		
525		.019	.0019		.0014	2.86
530	.571			1.29		
535		.019	.0019		.0015	2.67
540	.590			1.23		
545		.021	.0021		.0018	2.22
550	.611			1.17		
555		.025	.0025		.0022	1.82
560	.636			1.09		
565		.032	.0032		.0031	1.29
570	.668			1.00		
575		.038	.0038		.0036	1.11
580	.706			1.12		
585		.047	.0047		.0040	1.00
590	.753			1.26		
595		.049	.0049		.0037	1.08
600	.802			1.41		
605		.047	.0047		.0032	1.24
610	.849			1.55		
615		.038	.0038		.0022	1.82
620	.887			1.66		
625		.027	.0027		.0016	2.50
630	.914			1.74		
635		.020	.0020		.0012	3.33
640	.934			1.80		
645		.014	.0014		.0008	5.00
650	.948			1.84		
655		.006	.0006		.00032	12.5
660	.954			1.86		
665		.005	.0005		.00027	14.8
670	.959			1.88		
675		.006	.0006		.00032	12.5
680	.965			1.90		

Column B: Computed L-cone output by Equation (8.7). Column C: Computed difference in L-cone output, specified for intermediate wavelengths. Column D: "J-factor," the relative output of the r-g opponent channel. Column E: Difference in L-cone output attenuated according to the J-factor appropriate to the intermediate wavelength. Column F: Proportional to the reciprocal of Column E, used to convert threshold cone output to threshold of wavelength. The scaling factor .004, by which it is multiplied, is arbitrary. Although initial 10 nm steps are used here for expository purposes, the continuous and differentiable functions derived by Boynton and Wisowaty (1983) are preferred for modeling continuous variations in cone excitations as wavelength changes.

For unit luminance, the values of L and M are in each case divided by their sum, L + M. This gives:

	$\lambda = 620$	$\lambda = 630$
L′	0.887	0.914
M′	0.113	0.086

To calculate $\Delta L'$, $0.914 - 0.887 = 0.027$. This value is shown in column C_1 of Table 8.1 and is referred to $\lambda = 625$ nm, the wavelength midway between, as a linear approximation of the appropriate wavelength to which this value of $\Delta L'$ should be associated. In column C_2, the values of column C_1 have been divided by 10 to provide an estimate of $\Delta L'$ for 1-nm wavelength shifts.

3. *If the response of S- and M-cones were held constant, how much change in response of the L-cones would be required for a just-noticeable chromatic difference?*

This is a "trick" question because it is not possible to vary only the stimulation of L-cones to cause a purely chromatic change. By definition a chromatic discrimination is one that occurs at constant luminance, and we assume that the signals in the luminance channels are fixed; therefore, L + M must be constant. But if L varies and M does not, then L + M will vary as a function of L, producing output changes in both the r-g and L_v channels. To avoid this "Catch 22" situation, Question 3 needs to be asked as follows.

4. *What is required to produce a change that occurs only in the r-g channels?*

One way to accomplish this objective is to vary wavelength over the longwave region of the spectrum (to which the S-cones are virtually insensitive) while holding luminance constant. This can be done experimentally by calibrating the spectrum for relative luminance at all wavelengths and then proceeding as discussed in the section on "Introduction to Wavelength Discrimination."

5. *Assuming that only the r-g signal varies, how much variation of it is required to produce a just barely noticeable change?*

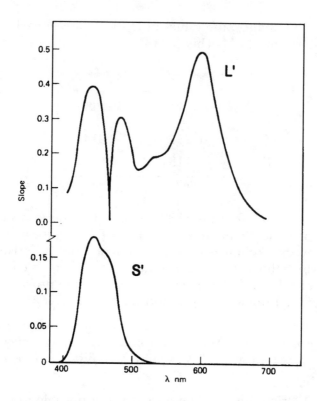

Figure 8.4 **Top:** Slope of the L′ (cone output) function depicted in Fig. 8.3. The calculations, which are shown in Table 8.1, are based on 10 nm segments straddling the points plotted in Fig. 8.3. The results are plotted at intermediate wavelengths. **Bottom:** Slope of the S′ function similarly calculated, based on calculations given in Table 8.2.

There is no simple answer to this question. Here, and in Chapter 9, we will see that the threshold for such r-g chromatic discriminations depends importantly on spatial and temporal parameters. But a simple analysis can give the general idea. One would expect discrimination to be good when, as wavelength varies, the rate of change in output of r-g channels is high, and that it would be poor when this rate of change is low. The slope of the L′ function of Figure 8.3 represents that change.[8] In Figure 8.4, the slope segments of Figure 8.3 are plotted (for a continuous function, this would correspond to the first derivative). Where this value is high, a relatively small change in wavelength should be required to produce a given change in the value of r-g. Where the slope value is low, a larger change is required to produce the same effect.

6. *Does the threshold signal of the r-g difference depend upon the value of luminance level?*

The answer to this question is definitely "yes." Recall that luminance depends upon the summed outputs of L- and M-cones. At moderate luminances, at least for long wavelengths, wavelength discrimination is virtually independent of luminance. In this part of the spectrum discrimination depends only upon $\Delta L'$ (or $\Delta M'$), which by assumption is directly proportional at any wavelength to the intensity of the stimulus. Therefore, if it is experimentally true that wavelength discrimination is independent of luminance, then the fraction $\Delta L'/(L' + M')$ must be a constant. Therefore the threshold signal for the r-g channels, which is directly proportional to $\Delta L'$, must depend upon luminance; indeed, it would be directly proportional to it in this example.

The idea that threshold values of $\Delta L'/(L' + M')$ are constant is similar to Weber's Law for achromatic discrimination (Chapter 5). It is to be expected, and indeed it is found, that this relation holds only for moderate intensities so that the value of $\Delta L'/(L' + M')$ required for a threshold of chromatic discrimination becomes larger as the intensity is reduced (and sometimes when it is increased). If it did not, then our ability to perceive color differences of reflecting samples would be independent of all variations of illumination. Instead, chromatic discrimination, like luminance discrimination, becomes relatively poor at low luminance levels. An exception that occurs at short wavelengths will be discussed later in this chapter.

7. *Does a threshold change in r-g differences depend upon the initial value of r-g?*

The experimental evidence is much less striking in this case, but it indicates a positive answer. As the activity level of the r-g opponent channels increases, they apparently become relatively insensitive to differential signals as wavelength is changed. The load on the r-g channels is minimal at 570 nm, where the signal is zero no matter how bright the light.

8. *What are the rules of operation for the y-b opponent channels?*

All of the questions that have been asked about the r-g channels can be repeated for the y-b case. For the most part there is no need to do this because the answers will be about the same. There is however one important exception because the "Catch 22" situation related to the third question does not arise for the y-b case.

9. If the response of the L- and M-cones were held constant, how much change in excitation of the S cones would be required for a just-noticeable chromatic difference?

"Catch 22" does not apply here because we assume that the S-cones make no contribution to luminance. Therefore, if some means can be discovered to vary the stimulation of S-cones without altering that of the L- and M-cones, an empirical answer can be found. From the standpoint of the y-b opponent channels, such a change manipulates the S input while holding constant the y input (which is proportional to luminance).[9]

Note in Figure 8.4 that the slope of the S' (S' is derived in a manner similar to L') function is highest for wavelengths near 445 nm. But wavelength discrimination in the shortwave end of the spectrum is keenest at about 490 nm,[10] and it is probable that S-cones mediate wavelength discrimination there. So ΔS' alone makes a very poor prediction. If log ΔS' were the controlling variable, the prediction would become even worse. Because the slope of this function increases as log S' decreases with increasing wavelength (see Fig. 8.3), the function implausibly and incorrectly predicts that the closer the S-cone response is to oblivion, the better is the discrimination mediated by such cones. The truth must lie somewhere between these assumptions.

One approach to solving this problem is to assume an expression of the form ΔS'/(S' + K) that is constant for a threshold discrimination mediated by S-cones. Such an equation has been used frequently in the history of the visual discrimination literature because it seems necessary also for a quantitative description of what is known about luminance discrimination. A quantity like K has been called the "self-light" of the retina (or "dark" light), because K has the same units as S', and behaves as a real light of K units would in a system where ΔS'/S' is strictly constant, but with all measurements made against a constant background of intensity K. The exact value of K in the denominator of the fraction S'/(S' + K) is critically important. (A similar model is described by LeGrand, 1968, p. 487.)

10. What are the rules of interaction between the two types of opponent-color channels?

As wavelength is changed at constant luminance a simultaneous change usually results in the signals of the r-g and y-b channels. The rates of these changes are shown by the slopes of the curve segments that are plotted in Figure 8.4. Because of the requirement of constant luminance, the y-b system contributes almost no information at long wavelengths: the y value is constant because the S-cones are insensitive to these long wavelengths. In the short wavelengths, it might seem likely that the varying y-b signals are so dominant that a smaller contribution from the r-g system could be ignored; but we will see that this prediction is false.

In regions where the rates of change of the two systems are nearly equal the interaction rules become important for an exact prediction of wavelength discrimination. These rules of combination are worth discussing theoretically. If there were total independence between the two channels so-called *probability summation* would result. At some later stage where such signals are detected, suppose that the detector will signal "yes" whenever either of the two contributing systems indicates that a threshold of wavelength change has occurred. For example, imagine that on any particular trial of the experiment, for some particular wavelength shift, the probability that either the r-g or the y-b system will detect the change is exactly 0.5. If so, the probability that neither system will detect it is $(0.5)^2 = 0.25$. This means that the probability that one or both of these systems will detect the change is $1 - 0.25 = 0.75$. Therefore, in order to reduce this combined probability to 0.5, a smaller wavelength shift would be needed, with both systems active, relative to that required for only one.

Another possibility is that the outputs of the two systems combine fully (complete summation). If this were the case, the wavelength shift with both systems operating would have to be small enough so that the total signal from both systems would be just large enough to detect. Partial summation is also possible. A general empirical rule for specifying such interactions is the following:

$$T = [(r - g)^n + (y - b)^n]^{1/n} \qquad (8.10)$$

Linear summation occurs when $n = 1$, because the total signal T in this case is equal to the linear sum of r-g and y-b. Although probability summation cannot be exactly expressed by this equation, a value of $n = 2$ is not too far from an adequate description. (This same value describes another related model, according to which the r-g and y-b values are treated as orthogonal vectors in a Euclidean plane.)

As the value of n in Eq. (8.10) approaches infinity, the *upper envelope* rule is described. According to this rule, sensitivity depends only upon changes in the most active system, regardless of changes in less active ones. In the present context the upper envelope rule predicts that wavelength changes are signaled either by the r-g or by the y-b system, depending upon which system shows the largest change with wavelength. Even if the other system is changing very nearly as much, it makes no contribution by this rule.

By any of these rules, the contribution of the less sensitive channel is for all practical purposes negligible if it is much less sensitive (about five times or more) than the more sensitive channel. This is probably the case for wavelength discrimination in most regions of the spectrum.

MODELING WAVELENGTH-DISCRIMINATION FUNCTIONS

The model described below is not offered as literal truth, but only as a tool to help guide the reader. The literature is full of discrimination models, and all of them can "predict" the wavelength discrimination curve, more or less. It is suggested that the model presented here be kept in mind in the following discussions.

Adjustment of the Smith–Pokorny M-Function

Unique yellow should be seen at a wavelength corresponding to the crosspoint of the L- and M-receptor sensitivity functions. These functions (called S_L and S_M in Appendix Part III) were instead positioned by Smith and Pokorny so that their sum would be proportional to the photopic luminous efficiency function. Doing so causes the curves to cross twice at short wavelengths (see Fig. 5.28, p. 190). An implication of the failure of these functions to account for luminance when they cross at 575 nm, near where unique yellow is seen, is that the relative contributions of L- and M-cones to the r-g opponent-color channels must differ when compared to their relative contributions to the luminance channels. In order to make the curves cross near 570 nm, all that is required is to double the relative weight of the M-cone input to the opponent channels. Physiologically this could mean that, relative to their contributions to luminance channels, (1) M-cone signals are amplified for purposes of chromatic balance, (2) L-cone signals are attenuated as they contribute to chromatic channels, or (3) only half the M cones contribute to luminance, whereas all of them contribute to color balance. In the calculations to follow, assumption (1) has been used. (The choice of assumption does not alter the relative vertical positioning of the two functions.)

The r-g System

From Figure 8.4, it will be seen that the predicted maximum of the $\Delta L'$ function is approximately at 600 nm (this can also be seen in Table 8.1, where the largest value of $\Delta L'$ occurs at 595 nm). Figure 8.1 shows this to be near the minimum of empirical wavelength discrimination functions but the experimental minimum is at wavelengths a bit less than this. (A weighted average of data from four more recent studies[11] suggests a minimum close to 580 nm.) Although discrimination in the long wavelengths seems mostly dependent on $\Delta L'$, an additional assumption is needed to resolve this small yet significant discrepancy.

The J-Factor

Suppose that the "base" against which a change is seen includes a component derived from the r-g channel. Specifically, assume that $(L' + M')$ is replaced by a value that we will call the J-Factor. For a unit value of $(L' + M')$, $J = 1 + |L' - 2M'|$. J has a unit value at the wavelength of minimum saturation near 570 nm, where $L' - 2M' = 0$. This wavelength should also correspond closely to unique yellow and to the intersection of the L- and M-cone sensitivity functions, as these contribute to chromatic balance.

In the context of some theories, the larger values of J at other wavelengths would be related to the extra brightness produced by L- and M-cones via the r-g channels.[12] Perhaps it is this extra brightness, added to that supplied by the luminance channels, that tends somehow to mask the perception of chromatic differences. Values of J have been tabulated in Column D of Table 8.1, where it will be seen that J is minimum at 570 nm and is maximum for short wavelengths near 460–470 nm and for the long wavelengths at the spectral extreme.

Procedure for Calculating Discrimination Due to L- and M-Cones

As noted earlier, values of $\Delta L'$ have been approximated for 1-nm wavelength changes in column C_2 of Table 8.1, by dividing the values of column C, (which are for 10-nm shifts) by 10. Scanning column E, where the values of column C_2 have been divided by J, reveals that wavelength discrimination is best at 585 nm, where the value of $\Delta L'/$ J is .004 for a 1-nm wavelength change. From Figure 8.1, it will be seen that $\Delta \lambda \approx 1$ nm in this region of the spectrum. Apparently, then, the r-g channels can discriminate .004 parts of increase or decrease in L' (with the aid of a concomitant converse change in M') per unit of J. If we assume that this same proportion of change is also just

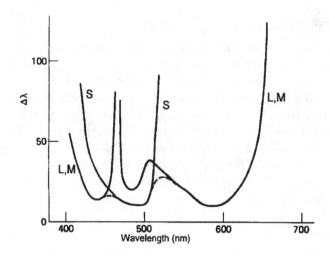

Figure 8.5   The values on the ordinate are the changes in wavelength required to cause a criterion response in the two hypothetical systems assumed to determine wavelength discrimination. The U-shaped curve represents discrimination mediated by S cones at constant luminance. The other function (LM), which crosses the S-cone function twice and is discontinuous at 465 nm, represents the discrimination mediated by the r-g opponent color system at constant luminance. The dotted portions of the curve are intended to represent probability summation between the two systems. The lower envelope, including the dotted portions, describes wavelength discrimination for the combined systems.

barely discriminable elsewhere in the spectrum, then we can determine, for various starting wavelengths, how much of a change in λ is required to generate the threshold value of 0.004 in $\Delta L'/J$. For example, at 535 nm, a 1-nm change produces a value for $\Delta L'/J$ of only 0.0015, which is below threshold. To achieve threshold, $\Delta\lambda$ must be increased by a factor of $(0.004)/(0.0015)$, which is 2.67 times the value for 580 nm. Therefore $\Delta\lambda = 2.67$ nm. In general, $\Delta\lambda = \frac{0.004J}{\Delta L'}$. These values are listed in Column F of Table 8.1, and are plotted in Figure 8.5 as the curve marked L,M.

Discontinuity at 465 nm?

At 465 nm, the L' vs. λ function (Fig. 8.3) has a zero slope, corresponding to the maximum separation of the log sensitivity curves of M- and L-cones that causes L' to reach a minimum at this wavelength. This in turn causes the function of Figure 8.5 to become discontinuous at 465 nm. At shorter wavelengths than this there is an indication that wavelength discrimination improves greatly and may once again be mediated by the r-g system. In Chapter 10, we will see that the form of this function is very similar to that observed experimentally in tritanopes, a class of color-defective individuals believed to lack S-cones while retaining normal red-green function.

A question has been raised by Knoblauch (1993) whether a discontinuity actually exists near 465 nm. He cites 10 studies of tritanopes, all of which had measurable $\Delta\lambda$'s near 460 nm. Two of the investigations report $\Delta\lambda$'s near 50 nm; others show various values as small as 10 nm. Knoblauch reminds the reader that attributing the size of $\Delta\lambda$ to the slope of the underlying response functions (e.g., Fig. 8.3) is only a first order approximation that depends on the assumption that jnds are small relative to the response. Whereas such an assumption is reasonable for trichromats under normal conditions, for tritanopes (and for normals, if they are made artificially tritanopic) this assumption is violated near 460 nm.

Discrimination of Short Wavelengths

In Chapter 7 (p. 252), it was suggested that there may be an S-cone contribution to the r-g opponent channels, which throws the r-g balance in the r direction. To be complete, the model just presented must be expanded to account for the possible improvement of wavelength discrimination caused by the reemergence of red, which gives the appearance of violet to the shortwave end of the spectrum.

In Figure 8.6, the theoretical wavelength discrimination curve of Figure 8.5 has been replotted as the dashed curve (1). Recall that this curve was calculated as $.004J/\Delta L'$, so that it represents the wavelength change required to produce a criterion change in L', the output of L cones at constant luminance. The solid curve (2) at the bottom of Figure 8.6 would have exactly the same shape as the dotted one except that, to account for the reemergence of shortwave red, $0.05S'$ has been added to $L' - 2M'$ in the denominator. That is, if the $0.05S'$ term were removed, curve 2 would be identical everywhere to curve 1.

With the $0.05S'$ term included, the predicted discrimination in the shortwave region of the spectrum (curve 2) is much better than that observed experimentally. A possible explanation for this discrepancy requires attention to the larger Weber fraction of S-cones, previously assumed to be 0.08 at high luminances, compared to 0.004 for the L- and M-cones — higher by a factor of 20. Probably this poor discrimination capacity applies also to the fraction of S-cone output that is diverted to the r-g channels. Physiologically this would imply,

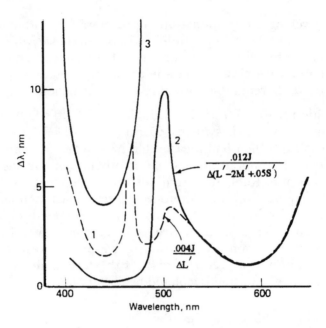

Figure 8.6 Curves 2 and 3 show the effects of assuming S-cone input to the r-g opponent system. See text for assumptions used.

quite plausibly, that the relatively poor intensity discrimination mediated by S-cones is due either to the S-cones themselves or to a limit imposed by their pathways prior to the point at which signals from S-cones enter into the r-g opponent process. A recalculation of the shortwave section of curve 2 has been made by multiplying each ordinate value by 20 and the result is shown as curve 3 in Figure 8.6. This branch is now so high as to suggest that, although S-cone input to the r-g opponent channel has an important effect upon color *appearance*, it nevertheless may not result in a sufficient rate of change of the S-cone signal to aid *discrimination* very much.

This conclusion is subject to at least a pair of provisos. In the first place, the assumption of a five percent contribution of S-cone output to the r-g opponent channel is arbitrary and in any event it is luminance-dependent, as experiments by McCree (1960) show. At very low photopic levels there is little appearance of violet at short wavelengths; the sensation grows to a maximum at intermediate levels, and then disappears again at very high levels. Similarly, McCree finds an optimal intensity for discrimination. In the second place, the 20:1

ratio of Weber fractions assumed for the calculations of this chapter is only approximate and is probably subject to change as a function of stimulus parameters such as area, duration, and intensity.

The y-b System

The calculations made so far have been intended to suggest only what the r-g opponent process contributes to the process of wavelength discrimination. We now turn our attention to the second opponent-color system.

Protanopes and deuteranopes, who are believed to lack L- and M-cones respectively (see Chapter 10), are able to make wavelength discriminations only in a narrow range of the spectrum near 500 nm. (In this region, they do about as well as normal subjects.) But they fail utterly at the shortest wavelengths and over the entire longwave region of the spectrum. This suggests that the y-b system mediates the discrimination that remains, and that such discrimination is best at about 500 nm.

From Figure 8.4 one can see that the slope of the S' function, which is tabulated in Table 8.2 at 10-nm intervals, is greatest at about 445 nm; this is also apparent in Figure 8.3. As previously noted, $\Delta S'$ is a very poor predictor of the wavelength discrimination that is mediated by the y-b system, even when y is held constant by the luminance criterion. The bottom graph of Figure 8.3 shows, as previously mentioned, that using the log response curve leads to an equally bad prediction, namely that wavelength discrimination should still be improving for the y-b system as wavelength is lengthened to 520 nm and even beyond.

Unlike the r-g system, the "base" against which changes in S' are perceived at constant luminance varies dramatically with wavelength, as shown by the thousand-fold range of S-cone output for constant luminance shown at the bottom of Figure 8.3. A "self-light" constant is needed, but it must be a small one with a value similar to that of S' at the wavelength of best discrimination, near 500 nm. Column D of Table 8.2 shows that the value of the expression $\Delta S'/(S' + 0.016)$, which reaches a maximum near 475 nm, remains high to 505 nm. The reciprocal of this function should be related to the change in wavelength required for a constant value of $\Delta S'$. The expression in Column E is the reciprocal value multiplied by 0.08, to make $\Delta\lambda$ equal to about 1 nm, (as empirical data suggest it should be) in the region of best discrimination. The U-shaped curve of Figure 8.5 is the function $\Delta\lambda = 0.08 \left[(S' + 0.016)/\Delta S' \right]$.

Table 8.2   Calculations Pertaining to Hypothetical Wavelength Discrimination Mediated by Differential S-cone Responses at Constant Luminance

A	B	C_1	C_2	D	E
Wavelength	$S' = \dfrac{S}{L+M}$	$\dfrac{\Delta S'}{10nm}$	$\dfrac{\|\Delta S'\|}{1nm}$	$\dfrac{\Delta S'}{S'+0.016}$	$.08 \left\| \dfrac{S'+0.016}{\Delta S'} \right\|$
400	1.000				
405		.009	.0009	.00088	90.9
410	1.009				
415		.033	.0033	.0033	24.2
420	.975				
425		.120	.0120	.0128	6.25
430	.855				
435		.173	.0173	.0225	3.56
440	.682				
445		.177	.0177	.0290	2.75
450	.505				
455		.155	.0155	.0350	2.29
460	.345				
465		.148	.0148	.0516	1.55
470	.197				
475		.109	.0109	.0688	1.16
480	.088				
485		.053	.0053	.0684	1.17
490	.035				
495		.021	.0021	.0523	1.53
500	.0132				
505		.011	.0011	.0468	1.17
510	.0018				
515		.001	.0001	.0057	14.03
520	.00076				

Columns B and C: Analogous to the same columns in Table 8.1. Column D: Weighting of differential S-cone output according to a modified Weber's law, including a "dark-light" factor. Column E: Proportional to the reciprocal of Column D, used to convert threshold S-cone output to threshold wavelength.

In a manner analogous to that already used for calculating r-g discrimination, this function is used to calculate wavelength changes, $\Delta\lambda$, required to produce the same value of $\Delta S'/(S'+0.016)$ as that required for a threshold discrimination of 1 nm at the wavelength of best wavelength sensitivity. The fact that $\Delta S'/(S'+0.016) = 0.08$ implies that a change in the rate of S-cone activation of eight percent is required, at high intensities, in order to cause a just-perceptible change of hue.

Interactions Between r-g and y-b Channels

If it is assumed that probability summation is the only interaction between the r-g and y-b systems, the dotted lines of Figure 8.5, shown near the regions of nearly equal sensitivities for the two opponent-color mechanisms, are suggestive of what this effect might be. The lower envelope, including the dashed portions, would characterize the predicted result for all wavelengths. All major features of a typical experimental wavelength discrimination function are accounted for qualitatively.

Looking again at the data of Figure 8.1, we are now in a position to speculate about sources of individual differences. Some of these could be caused by variations in the relative number of L- and M-cones, which are known to differ among subjects (Rushton & Baker, 1964; Cicerone, 1987; Cicerone and Nerger, 1989a,b). Observers might also vary in the degree to which the base of the r-g system is influenced by the brightness component implied by the J-factor variation. In spectral regions where the two curves of Figure 8.5 cross, subjects may vary according to how these two systems interact. The relative effectiveness of the r-g and y-b systems may also vary from subject to subject. Field size, exposure duration, retinal location, and stimulus intensity are known to affect these differentially for a given subject, and possibly also among subjects. Preretinal absorption, which differs in different subjects, has a minimal effect on r-g discriminations because it does not alter the crucial difference ratio between L- and M-cone outputs. But the S-cone system is highly luminance-dependent, so that preretinal reduction of light will affect it.

Wright and Pitt were not able to maintain their full values of retinal illuminance at the shortest wavelengths. It may be that subject C.B.D. (Fig. 8.1) suffered less preretinal absorption than the other subjects, permitting the shortwave limb of his r-g discrimination function to be sufficiently activated for him to maintain good discrimination there.

EXPERIMENTAL DATA: CHROMATICITY DISCRIMINATION

Prior to 1942, many experiments on wavelength discrimination (some of which have been mentioned in preceding sections) had been executed and reported. If described in chromaticity space (Chapter 5), such experiments constitute measures of just-discriminable steps along a curve that describes the locus of spectral colors.

Such experiments sample only a minuscule part of the total range of chromaticity variation for which one could ask the question: "Starting with point p_1, what distance change, dD, between p_1, and another point, p_2, is required in order to produce a significantly noticeable difference?" Viewed in this way, the enormity of the problem becomes immediately obvious. The question just posed must be expanded to include the following additional considerations.

Chromaticity space is continuous, being related to the ratios of cone outputs, each of which is in turn a continuous function of intensity. Accordingly, not all possible points in chromaticity space can be tested and only a few may be sampled. How might it be possible to generalize from such a sample to untested regions?

A similar problem exists with respect to an infinitude of possible directions of change that are testable around each point. How many directions should be tested? How does one extrapolate to predict results for untested directions?

By what method should the just-noticeable difference in chromaticity be tested, at each of the points and for each of the directions that have been decided upon?

MacAdam's Experiment

Although W. D. Wright (1941, 1946) had published relevant data even earlier, the year 1992 marked the 50th anniversary of the publication by David L. MacAdam, of the Eastman Kodak Company, of a landmark study that explicitly dealt with each of the problems just raised. One impetus for his study was to provide a scientific basis for obtaining a patent on "Kodak yellow" as a trademark for Eastman photographic products. The problem was similar to that described earlier in this chapter in the parable of the carpet. How can one say that two yellows are, or are not, sufficiently similar to be legally identical? Physical measures cannot tell because metameric matches are possible. It also would be unreasonable to require that, for the chromaticities of two colors to be called the same, they must be identical to seventeen decimal places. Where does one draw the line? The experiment that MacAdam chose to conduct examined the problem in a very general way and eventually led to the "MacAdam unit" of discrimination, in terms of which the amount of difference between the Kodak yellow and that of impostors can be stipulated.

MacAdam used more than 100 carefully calibrated color filters to provide his stimuli. His 2° colorimetric field was contained within a large uniform surround; MacAdam's apparatus had the important virtue that it maintained equal luminance automatically as chromaticity varied. The two halves of the colorimetric field could be set to a physical match. MacAdam elected to use the dispersion of repeated attempts at making matches as his index of discrimination.

Figure 8.7 shows the results of MacAdam's experiment for one of the 25 regions of chromaticity space that he tested. The symmetry of the figure may be somewhat misleading: only one independent test

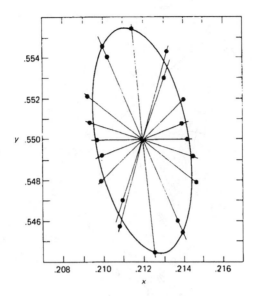

Figure 8.7   One of the 25 ellipses of chromatic discrimination measured by MacAdam (1942), plotted in CIE chromaticity space. Data points are shown.

was made along each axis because the results of repeated attempts to match the center point were symmetrically plotted as one standard deviation on either side. Therefore, only half an ellipse was independently measured. Given this caveat, the fit to an ellipse is remarkably good, and the figure selected for illustration here is in no way exceptional among the 25 that were obtained and reproduced in MacAdam's paper. Figure 8.8 shows all 25 ellipses, plotted (as MacAdam did it) at 10 times their actual size in the CIE chromaticity diagram.

Mathematical Considerations for Extending MacAdam's Results

As noted earlier, a color can be represented by the direction of a vector in a "color space," with the length of the vector representing the intensity of the color. Viewed in this way, the difference between two colors depends upon the distance between the ends of the vectors that represent them. In a Euclidean plane the measure is simply made along a straight line connecting two points. A kind of space that permits greater flexibility for the representation of local color differences is Riemannian space. In two-dimensional Euclidean space, the square of the distance between two points is calculated, by the

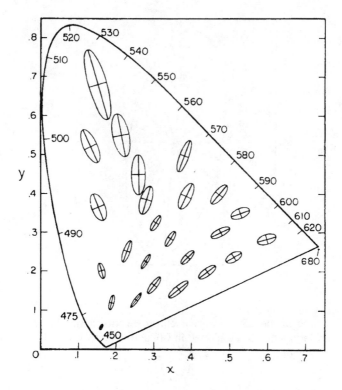

Figure 8.8   MacAdam's ellipses of chromatic discrimination, plotted at 10 times their actual size in the CIE chromaticity diagram, with data points omitted.

Pythagorean rule, as the sum of the squares of the component distances between them:

$$(dD)^2 = (dx)^2 + (dy)^2 \tag{8.11}$$

Here dD is the distance between the points, and dx and dy represent the component distances along the orthogonal axes of this ordinary plane. In Riemannian two-dimensional space, which can be used to represent colors at constant luminance,

$$(dD)^2 = m_{11}(dx)^2 + 2m_{12}(dx\,dy) + m_{22}(dy)^2. \tag{8.12}$$

The coefficients m_{11}, $2m_{12}$, and m_{22} are themselves functions of the values x and y, depending upon the region in space where discrimination is tested.[13]

MacAdam, having found that ellipses, when plotted on a chromaticity diagram, did in fact describe the thresholds of color difference in the 25 regions of measurement, quickly took it as his task to calculate from his data the Riemannian coefficients of Equation (8.12) and to determine smooth curves, looking much like those of contour maps, which described the course of coefficients of fixed values as they wiggled through the chromaticity plane. The *MacAdam unit* of color difference (M), which has been rather widely applied, is calculated by substituting, in the equation

$$M = [m_{11} \, (dx)^2 + 2m_{12} \, (dx \cdot dy) + m_{22} \, (dy)^2]^{1/2}, \qquad (8.13)$$

the values of m_{11}, $2m_{12}$ and m_{22} as interpolated from the contour lines plotted in the CIE chromaticity diagram (see Wyszecki & Stiles, 1982, pp. 306–313). The standard deviation of matching corresponds to a unit value of M, and something on the order of 3M is generally regarded as a just-noticeable difference.[14]

Additional Studies of Chromatic Discrimination

Since the pioneering work of MacAdam, a number of additional studies of chromatic discrimination were carried out in MacAdam's laboratory at the Eastman Kodak Company and in the laboratory of G. Wyszecki at the Canadian National Research Council laboratories in Ottawa. A significant change in methodology was adopted in both laboratories in order to permit the simultaneous evaluation, not only of chromaticity differences at constant luminance, but also of luminance differences at constant chromaticity. It will be recalled that, in MacAdam's original experiment, the observer varied chromaticity along only one dimension at a time, with luminance automatically being held constant. In the late 1940s, MacAdam built a new binocular colorimeter in which comparisons could be made between a reference field comprised of mixed light from three primaries and a comparison field based upon a second set of the same three primaries. The task of the observer was to attempt a complete color match, based upon the manipulation of three controls, each of which varied the intensity of one of the primaries. Later, Wyszecki constructed a

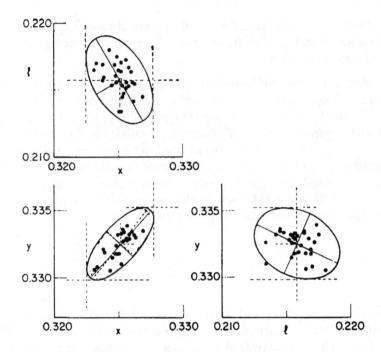

Figure 8.9   Some results from a color–matching experiment by Wyszecki and
Fielder (1971). Show here are projections of a cloud of points, each of
which represents an attempt to make an exact color match. Chromatic discrimination is gauged by the spread of data in a cross section
of the x-y plane shown at the lower left.

seven field colorimeter in his laboratory that permitted the same kinds
of measurements.

Results for one subject using one test color are shown from an
experiment by Wyszecki and Fielder (1971) in Figure 8.9. The basic
result of the experiment is a cloud of points that may be represented
in three-dimensional color space. (In this example, x and y refer to
the chromaticity coordinates of the CIE system, and l refers to luminance variation.) The ellipse fitted to the points in the y vs. x plot
corresponds to a criterion such that the ellipse contains, on the average, 95 percent of any random set of color matches.

Using similar procedures, Brown (1957) had earlier tested the
color discrimination of twelve observers; before that, Brown and
MacAdam (1949) compared two subjects (and occasionally three) in
a lengthy investigation. MacAdam (1959) investigated small field effects and Brown (1951) studied the effect of reducing luminance to

low photopic levels. In the Wyszecki and Fielder paper an attempt was made to compare their newer data with some of those already in the literature. Reductions in field size or luminance have the effect of (1) increasing the size of ellipses in all directions, and (2) selectively increasing them in a direction of discrimination that implies a selective loss of differential S-cone stimulation. Noorlander and Koenderink (1983) studied discrimination using a variety of spatial and temporal frequencies. Their results, for equiluminant slices though their discrimination ellipsoids, agreed with those of Brown & MacAdam only for low spatial and temporal frequencies.

Comparisons between different observers, whether in the same or a different experiment, present a discouraging picture. Although observers agree on certain major trends, individual differences are best described as enormous. Unfortunately, the methods used make it difficult if not impossible to understand these differences, which are doubtless due to an interplay of the kinds of factors discussed theoretically in this chapter. Moreover, as Wyszecki and Fielder note: "The question arises whether the use of three fixed primary colors in producing color matches inadvertently introduces a bias in the distribution of the color matches for a given test color. We notice the tendency of the color-matching ellipse to orient itself toward the chromaticity point of the nearest primary." (p. 1149). This finding casts a shadow upon many of the results that have been obtained subsequent to the original MacAdam studies.

Wavelength Discrimination

The data of Figure 8.1 reflect the serious extent of individual differences in wavelength discrimination functions measured under similar conditions. Over much of the spectrum the differences are more quantitative than qualitative, but below 480 nm the various curve shapes in the literature are so wildly discrepant that the shortwave segment of an average curve is of very dubious value. As illustrated in Figure 8.5, these short wavelengths encompass a region in which chromatic discrimination is probably controlled by variations both in L- and M-cone output as well as the S-cone output.

Figure 8.10 shows some selected results of a well-controlled study by Bedford and Wyszecki (1958), which included deliberate manipulations of stimulus size, configuration, and retinal illuminance. The form of the curves is reasonably similar to those of Wright and Pitt (Fig. 8.1). They confirm that, in addition to the two principal minima at about 580 and 480 nm, there is a third one around 440 nm. It is of interest to note that a 200 fold reduction in area (from a 1° half-

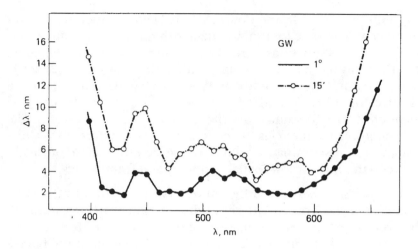

Figure 8.10 Wavelength discrimination data of Bedford and Wyszecki (1958). The solid points refer to a 1° field at 100 td; open points are for a 1.5' field of 2000 td. The larger field, which provides less total flux, nevertheless yields better discrimination.

circle to a 15' spot) is by no means compensated by a 200-fold increase in the illuminance of the small field relative to the large one. These results indicate that area and intensity have differential effects on the physiological substrates that mediate wavelength discrimination. Kaiser and Ayama (1985) showed that when all conditions were held constant save the visual angle, tritanopic-like wavelength discrimination functions were obtained using the criterion of a just noticeable border in a checkerboard pattern containing 8.6' elements. However, when 45' elements were used a normal function was obtained. A hint of this type of result is noticed in Bedford and Wyszecki's (1971) 15' data. These results are related to small field tritanopia. The scarcity of S-cones in the fovea is well understood and documented. It would also appear that wavelength discrimination is not immune to temporal factors of stimulus presentation. Uchikawa and Ikeda (1985), who studied wavelength discrimination with alternating stimuli, found that curves like these were obtained only for low temporal frequencies. Recently, Mollon *et al.*, (1992) showed that wavelength discrimination about a reference wavelength of 500 nm deteriorated monotonically as stimulus duration was decreased from 1 second to 1.4 milliseconds. Interestingly, when the reference wavelength was 460 nm, wavelength discrimination improved monotonically as stimulus duration was reduced by the same amount. Mollon *et al.*, also observed that observer SS in Uchikawa and Ikeda (1985) shows a similar variation in Δ as a function of duration near 460 nm.

Saturation Discrimination

Another special case of chromatic discrimination that has been extensively investigated is the first step from white. Figure 8.11 shows a selection of saturation discrimination investigation performed with a variety of techniques. Figure 8.12 is an example of the inter-subject variability that can be expected when determining the first just noticeable difference from white (Wright, 1946). The experimental measure is the luminance of the monochromatic component needed, when added to white, in order to produce a discriminable change in color at constant luminance. The fraction of the mixture that is comprised by the monochromatic component is calculated and in Figure 8.12 the reciprocal of this fraction is plotted. It will be seen that discrimination is poorest at 570 nm, which seems to make sense because the slightly greenish yellow seen by most observers at this wavelength is the least saturated hue in the spectrum, being most like white. Small luminances at the spectral extremes have a much higher coloring power. There are many other data on saturation discrimination in the literature, virtually all of which agree that 570 nm provides the least saturated spectral color.

It is also possible to measure the size of the first just noticeable step from the spectrum locus (Δ purity). Kaiser *et al.* (1976) performed such an investigation and were not able to replicate the results of previous investigations. Previous studies tended to find relatively flat Δ purity as a function of wavelength. Kaiser *et al.* found strong evidence that the shape of the saturation discrimination function of the first step from the spectrum locus was about the same as the shape of the function as the first step from white. However the difference between the maximum and minimum Δ purity was considerably less than that obtained when the first just noticeable step from white was measured.

Color Discrimination Work at UCSD

A program of research was undertaken by Boynton and his colleagues at the University of California, San Diego (UCSD), in which an attempt was made to examine some of these issues experimentally. The starting point for the work was a paper published in 1949 by Yves LeGrand, who performed a theoretically meaningful analysis of the ellipses of MacAdam.[15] LeGrand theorized that, corresponding to the two dimensions of the chromaticity plane, there are only

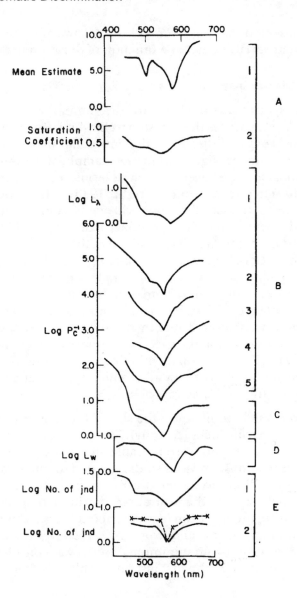

Figure 8.11 Saturation analyzed by a variety of methods. Group A- direct scaling of spectral lights: 1. Jacobs (1967); 2. Jameson and Hurvich (1959). Group B- saturation discrimination near white: 1. Purdy (1931); 2. Priest and Brickwedde (1938); 3. Wright and Pitt (1937); 4. Nelson (1937); 5. Martin, Warburton, and Morgan (1933). Group C- MacAdam's (1942) calculation from data on color matching near white. Group D- Troland's (1922) data using constant critical flicker frequency. Group E- Indirect scaling of spectral lights: 1. Jones and Lowry (1926); Martin, Warburton, and Morgan (1933). (Modified from Kaiser, Comerford, and Bodinger, 1976.)

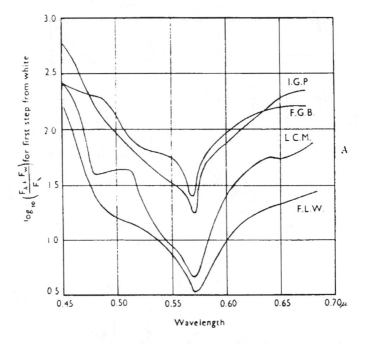

Figure 8.12   Saturation discrimination functions of four subjects (Wright, 1946). The first discrimination step from white is measured and its reciprocal is plotted to yield a sensitivity plot.

two physiological dimensions to be analyzed when purely chromatic color differences are measured, as by MacAdam, at fixed luminance. One of these is the level of excitation of the S-cones, which are assumed not to contribute to luminance. As we have seen, S-cone excitation level varies extensively as one shifts from the short wavelengths, where S-cones are heavily excited, to the long wavelengths where their response is essentially zero.

The second dimension relates to the activity of L- and M-cones. On the assumption that luminance depends on the sum of their excitation levels, it follows that any change in L-cone excitation must be mirrored by an equal and opposite change in that of M-cones (see Fig. 8.3). The L/M excitation ratio when L + M is constant provides a convenient way to express this dimension.

To deduce cone excitation levels from locations on the CIE chromaticity diagram requires knowledge of the actual action spectra of the three types of cones. Working with the best such estimates then available, LeGrand was able to deduce the functions displayed in

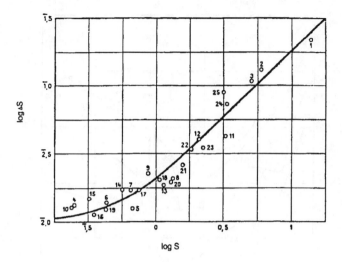

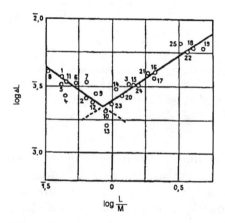

Figure 8.13 **Top**: A Weber type function for S cone excitation. S cone difference thresholds estimated from MacAdam's 25 ellipses, which appear to be independent of the L/M ratio. **Bottom**: Log L as a function of log L/M. (Modified from LeGrand, 1949.)

Figure 8.13. The upper panel shows a Weber-type function for S-cone excitation: The greater the initial level, the larger the increment or decrement required from that level to achieve a MacAdam unit of change. The S-cone thresholds, estimated in this manner from each of MacAdam's 25 ellipses, appear to be largely independent of the L/M ratio, which varies from point to point depending upon the starting chromaticity.

The curve shown in the lower panel tells the story for the L/M ratio. The two-branched curve exhibits a minimum when that ratio is approximately 1. For values greater or less than this, the discrimination threshold rises. This suggests (although LeGrand did not put it quite this way) that the base against which L/M changes are discerned does not depend directly upon the activity level of L- or M-cones, but is instead related to their difference, which would be registered at the opponent-color stage, corresponding to the J-factor that was introduced earlier to account for increased discrimination steps when the r-g opponent channels are unbalanced.

For the work at UCSD, larger discrimination steps were desired because when the standard deviation of repeated matches provide the primary data, experiments become almost unbelievably tedious and time-consuming. Furthermore, no color differences are actually seen at a match setting, which raises some concern about whether discrimination steps derived from the dispersion of matches are predictive of somewhat larger color differences that can actually be perceived. Testing was carried out deliberately and directly along the dimensions suggested by LeGrand, which later would become known as the "cardinal axes" of equiluminant color difference. Finally, a method was developed that helped to stabilize the subject's criterion by introducing the possibility of an incorrect response and associated feedback.

Apparatus was constructed that permitted fixed settings or continuous variations of either the level of S-cone excitation or of the L/M ratio. The subject viewed a split field, which, to start, was physically identical on the two sides. When thresholds that depended upon S-cone differences were being tested, the L/M ratio was fixed as desired by the experimenter. When changes in the L/M ratio were being tested, the level of S-cone excitation was set by the experimenter.

The subject was given a pair of preliminary trials that permitted substantial changes in the appearance of the variable field to be experienced, depending upon whether the level of S-cone excitation (or L/M ratio) was being increased or decreased. This also allowed preliminary experience with a pair of push-buttons that defined the two directions. On the experimental trials, an auditory signal was followed by a fore-period of unpredictable duration, following which a slow change in one of the fields was initiated. When confident that the direction of change had been correctly discerned, the subject depressed a third button that immediately terminated the change, which could then be recorded, and closed a shutter. The subject then indicated the direction of change by pressing one of the other two buttons.

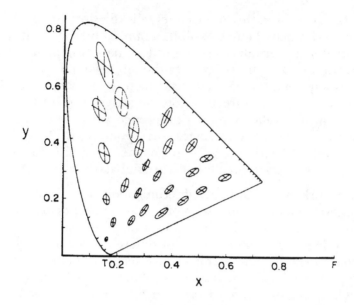

Figure 8.14 Just noticeable color difference thresholds. Starting chromaticities were the same as those used by MacAdam (1942). These data are plotted as 0.75 actual size where as MacAdam plotted his ellipses 10 larger than the actual size (Boynton and Kambe, 1980).

Two kinds of errors are possible with this method: (1) an antici-pation error, when a change is reported that has not yet occurred; (2) an incorrect indication of which type of change has occurred. Subjects received knowledge of results on every trial, and data were accepted only for blocks of trials that were error free. Tests were made at many starting chromaticities, from which simple formulas were developed to characterize the data.

Figure 8.14 from Boynton and Kambe (1980) shows the discrimi-nation steps calculated from these formulas, for the starting chromaticities used by MacAdam. MacAdam plotted his ellipses at ten times actual size; the newer data are plotted at 3/4 actual size. Although there are some discrepancies, the agreement is gratifyingly good. Thus, the new discrimination steps are about 13 times larger than MacAdam's, which is not surprising because there are not only perceptible differences, but ones that can be judged for direction of difference. The results also show that MacAdam's data are valid for predicting discrimination-step differences that can actually be seen.

Although LeGrand had analyzed MacAdam's data along the two cardinal axes, he could only offer speculative notions concerning why an ellipse should fit the data overall, including the majority of cases where differences occurred simultaneously along both dimensions. The next stage of the investigation at UCSD addressed this problem. For this purpose, an entirely new apparatus called the La Jolla Analytic Colorimeter was built, which permitted simultaneous changes along the two dimensions. The same experimental methodology was used. Although the resulting data could be reasonably well fit by ellipses, the directness of the approach led to some additional insights.

If one begins with a neutral white and then increases S-cone excitation while holding the L/M ratio fixed, the appearance of the field is toward purple, a simultaneous increase in redness and blueness. If L-cone excitation is increased (with a simultaneous decrease in that of M-cones as required to keep luminance constant), a not-unexpected increase in redness occurs. If both S- and M-cone excitations increase together, their effects summate and the resulting chromaticity step is smaller than that for either component alone. On the other hand, if one of the components increases and the other one decreases, their effects do not add. Not infrequently the threshold step is determined by whichever component reaches its used-alone threshold first. Sometimes there is inhibition and both components of the joint threshold are greater than when either is measured alone.

Figure 8.15 shows that these interactions, in the ideal case, lead to a six-sided figure, which, if rounded a bit, would not differ much at all from an ellipse. Either the hexagon or the ellipse provides an adequate description of the data. The hexagon provides a rationale for why the ellipse has the orientation that it does.

Further experiments suggested that in the general case, where discriminations depend upon simultaneous differences along both cardinal axes, the interaction rules are similar across subjects and for differing regions of chromaticity space. By contrast, individual differences in the size of discrimination steps along the cardinal axes were substantial, and the starting chromaticity had a large effect. These generalizations were confirmed by an analysis of published data by Nagy, Eskew & Boynton (1987), made possible by the transformation of 184 ellipses of 6 subjects from the CIE chromaticity diagram to cone-excitation space.

The exact nature of the chromatic discrimination data depends on how the experiment is performed. We noted above that MacAdam's observers performed color matches and the variability of these matches constituted the raw data from which discrimination ellipses were determined. Boynton and his colleagues in the San Di-

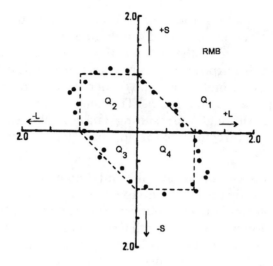

Figure 8.15 Chromatic discrimination steps in which opposite directions of chromatic change were sampled equally often. Data have been normalized by scaling the results relative to unit values assigned to threshold steps along the cardinal axes. Dashed lines describe perfect summation of component changes (1st and 3rd quadrants). (Boynton, Nagy, and Olson, 1983.)

ego studies asked observers to indicate the direction of color change. They obtained ellipses that had approximately the same orientation as MacAdam but which were larger, as would be expected from the task. Poirson and Wandell (1990) used two tasks: color matching and color detection in a set of briefly presented objects. They found that the ellipses for these two tasks differed both in size and orientation. Size differences were indicative of absolute sensitivity differences and orientation differences indicated relative sensitivity differences.

A Gap Effect

As we have seen, the r-g and y-b dimensions of chromatic discrimination differ in many ways. Differences in the r-g direction relate not only to color, but they also can support a contour between two fields of equal luminance. Differences in the y-b direction seem related only to hue. In Chapter 5 we reviewed evidence that S-cones are sparsely represented in the retina, which also contains, in addition to rods, L- and M-cone receptors. It is, therefore, to be expected that signals from S-cones must be averaged over extensive regions. Yet we do not see fuzzy blue edges around things, a fact which suggests that some kind of averaging mechanism works within regions that are defined by contours, even though the contours are exclusively defined by the activity of L- and M-cones.

With these thoughts as background, Boynton, Hayhoe & MacLeod (1977), conducted a study in which it was predicted that discriminations that depend only upon S-cones would be improved by slightly separating (and thus introducing a gap between) the two fields to be compared. The prediction depends upon the idea that if the fields are precisely juxtaposed there will be no contour dividing them despite their color difference — a fact that had already been established. The hypothetical averaging mechanism, not knowing where to stop, would therefore tend to derive its signal from the full field (both halves). By separating the two halves of the field, a clear luminance contour was provided between them so that the hypothesized averaging mechanism would be able to work independently for each half of the field. The prediction was confirmed. By contrast, it was found, in agreement with many other studies, that a slight field separation had a significantly deleterious effect upon discriminations that depended only upon luminance differences. Discriminations depending upon r-g differences were little affected by field separation over the range tested.

SUMMARY

Although the difference between two colors depends in the first instance upon differential stimulation of the three kinds of cones, their responses are transformed into two opponent-color signals and one kind of achromatic signal. It is these signals that probably should be examined in order to understand chromatic discrimination.

A model for wavelength discrimination is presented in which the outputs of r-g and y-b opponent systems are utilized. At constant luminance, the first of these reduces to L- (or M-) cone output alone, and the second to S-cone output only, provided that the probable influence of S-cones upon the r-g system at short wavelengths is ignored. In both cases, consideration is given to the "base" activity against which discrimination must be judged. In the r-g case, a "J-factor" is introduced to account for the worsening of discrimination as the red-green balance is upset. In the y-b case, a modified Weber-law relation, which includes a Helmholtzian "self-light" term in the denominator, seems necessary to account for the behavior of the S-cones at low intensity levels.

Experimental data on wavelength discrimination, purity discrimination, and generalized chromaticity discrimination were reviewed. Experiments conducted since the pioneering studies that generated the ellipses of MacAdam have added to our understanding of the subject by allowing analysis of the theoretical components as conceived physiologically.

NOTES

[1] Wyszecki and Stiles (1982) give the following definition, which is similar to that adopted by the International Commission on Illumination and the Optical Society of America: "*Color* is that aspect of visible radiant energy by which an observer may distinguish between two structure-free fields of view of the same size and shape, such as may be caused by differences in the spectral composition of the radiant energy concerned in the observation (p. 487)." This definition includes both the chromatic and achromatic aspects of the stimulus.

[2] It is not easy, except on a video monitor, to set up fields so precisely that the dividing line will disappear when the two halves of the field are of identical color. This observation relates to the fact that, in the world outside the laboratory, achromatic contours usually divide regions of different color. These may be caused by luminance differences, diffraction of light by edges of objects, or sometimes (as in the Sunday comics) by the deliberate introduction of dividing lines between otherwise adjacent regions of differing color.

[3] The term *luminance* has been used in two ways. The term was invented and defined by the CIE; it was briefly discussed on page 202 and will be further treated in Chapter 9. Consider first its strict use: Imagine a univariant detector with spectral sensitivity (V_λ). (This could be accomplished with a photocell receiving light through a suitably constructed filter, with the output of the photocell delivered to a digital voltmeter.) If such a photometer is pointed in turn at two fields that are different in color, and if each field elicits the same reading of the photometer, then the luminances of the two fields are equal.

The (V_λ) function, which applies to no particular individual, refers to a "standard observer," best regarded as being equivalent to the photometer just described. The (V_λ) curve is based on the data of many subjects, obtained mainly by the operation of flicker photometry, which is explained in the next chapter (p. 367). But for any real observer, two fields of equal luminance as defined by the photocell may not be equally effective. When two lights are equated for visual effectiveness for a particular observer, using flicker photometry or another method that yields the same result, these lights will generally be of slightly different luminance in the strict sense. It is, however, not unusual to refer to them as being equal in luminance *for that observer*.

Kaiser (1988) recommended that the term *sensation luminance* be used when the spectral sensitivity of an individual observer is taken into account. Although this suggestion does not enjoy official status, it used in the literature with increasing frequency. In the present context the term is used in this sense, and should be understood to refer to a particular human observer where it relates theoretically to an assessment of stimuli with respect to their effectiveness for the achromatic (luminance) channels of vision.

[4] An exception occurs at the spectral extremes, where discrimination based upon differences in hue and saturation becomes very poor. Alternatively, the *method of constant stimuli* could be used (see Siegel, 1962). Here the experimenter selects in advance, usually on the basis of some preliminary observations, a set of

five or six comparison wavelengths that have previously been equated for luminance relative to a fixed standard with which they are to be compared. For
example, the standard might be 580 nm and the comparison stimuli 578, 579,
580, 581, and 582 nm. The five comparison wavelengths are presented many
times in random order, and the subject is required to judge whether the comparison field appears greener or redder than the standard. When percent "redder" judgments are plotted as a function of a wavelength, a psychometric function results showing about 50 percent redder judgments at 580 nm and a smooth
curve passing through that point, rising from left (578 nm) to right (582 nm).
The more acute the wavelength discrimination, the steeper will be the slope of
such a curve. One way to gauge the threshold of wavelength discrimination
would be to determine the wavelength separation between wavelength values
corresponding to the 25 percent and 50 percent values of the curves. (See Engen,
1971, for a summary of classical psychophysical methods.)

[5] The English translation of Helmholtz's *Physiological Optics* (1924) does not contain the discussion of line elements that he developed in 1891 and 1892 and
that was included in the second edition. Discussions of Helmholtz's approach
are given by Stiles (1972, pp. 1–7), and Wyszecki and Stiles (1982, p. 654).

[6] For example, Bouman and Walraven (1972) employ a space in which the coordinates represent the square roots of L, M, and S. Discrimination is then imagined to take place according to distances measured on the surface of a spherical section whose radius depends upon luminance.

[7] The assumption that the outputs of the L- and M-cones combine linearly to produce luminance relates to the issue of additivity discussed in Chapter 5 (p. 169)
and Chapter 9 (p. 362). For convenience we also define S' in this section.

[8] In Figure 8.3, $L' + M' = 1$, so that $M' = 1 - L'$. Therefore any change in L' resulting
from a change in wavelength is exactly mirrored by an opposite change in M'.
Predictions about wavelength discrimination can therefore be based upon the
shape of either function. In this example, $\Delta M' = 0.113 - 0.086 = .027 = \Delta L'$.

[9] A reader of a preliminary draft of this chapter wanted to know why hue becomes
less yellowish for long wavelengths, if y-input is held constant. Although redness increases with wavelength, yellowness should, according to the model being used, be constant for all wavelengths presented at equal luminance. This
excellent question might seem to raise an embarrassment for the model, but
perhaps not. Consider that the amount of yellowness that can be achieved at a
given luminance is maximum around 570 nm, or perhaps at a wavelength a bit
longer than this. This is the least saturated region of the spectrum, where L
and M inputs cancel in the r-g opponent-color signal. Either (1) yellow is an
intrinsically desaturated sensation, (2) the ratio of activities of the chromatic
vs. achromatic channels is minimum in this region, or both. When aperture
colors are viewed, the yellowness of the wavelength that is maximally yellow is
in fact remarkably weak. As wavelength is increased at constant luminance, the
yellow signal should remain unchanged, but the r-g opponent system should
generate a progressively stronger redness signal. The judgment of hue is assumed to be essentially a judgment of the ratio of redness to yellowness. As
wavelength increases, redness predominates progressively more, and the field
becomes redder and more saturated. Provided that luminance is not too low, a
tinge of yellowness still remains at the longest wavelengths, assumed to be the
same as that seen at the wavelength of unique yellow. At low luminances, where

the spectrum appears nearly achromatic at the r-g balance point, the longest wavelengths would appear more nearly pure red, as they in fact do.

[10] We will see in Chapter 10 that red-green color-variant observers, whose wavelength discrimination depends upon S-cones, enjoy their most acute and essentially normal discrimination only in the region of 490 nm. It therefore seems safe to assume that wavelength discrimination in this region of the spectrum depends upon the differential activity of S-cones, rather than of L- and M-cones.

[11] For this purpose, data were weighted and averaged from the following experiments: Bedford and Wyszecki (1958) (data of subjects RE and GW from their Fig. 5, p. 134, for 1° data); Pokorny and Smith (1970); Siegel (1964); Siegel and Dimmick (1962).

[12] Additivity failure for brightness, to be discussed in the next chapter, indicates that when hue is canceled in a mixture of complementary colors, there occurs as well a partial cancellation of brightness. This finding is understandable if it is assumed that brightness depends upon a weighted sum of activity delivered through both the achromatic and opponent-color channels.

[13] Euclidean space will be recognized as a special case of Riemannian space where

$$m_{11} = m_{22} = 1 \text{ and } 2m_{12} = 0.$$

[14] This is controversial. For example, Friele (1972) indicates that "industrial tolerances are mainly well within 5 MacAdam units."

[15] As one of a series of translations of, and commentary on, classic articles in color science, LeGrand (1949) has been translated into English by K. Knoblauch with a commentary by R. M. Boynton (Color Research and Application, **19**, 296–39, 1994).

Chapter 9

Temporal and Spatial Factors in Color Vision

INTRODUCTION

A heavy snowfall, which visually obliterates all objects more than a few feet away, results in a phenomenon called *whiteout*. Whiteout is also experienced by pilots flying in heavy fog or clouds. Visually it can be considered a limiting case of spatial vision referred to as a *ganzfeld*, which is achieved by filling the entire visual field with light that is uniform in both luminance and chromaticity. Under these conditions, chromatic perception is very poor; colors fade markedly and often disappear entirely.[*1] Another limiting case occurs when a point of light is seen in an otherwise dark field; for example, when a signal light is viewed at night at a great distance. Here also color perception is poor — especially if the point of light is of low intensity. Optimal conditions for color perception lie between these extremes.

> A simple procedure for experiencing the effects of a ganzfeld makes use of a table tennis ball, which should be carefully cut in half. Place each half over your open eyes and illuminate the outside of the half spheres with uniform colored light. At first you will see the diffuse color of the transmitted light, but after a few seconds the color will fade. The color will return if you close and re-open your eyes.

If a flash of light is bright enough, there is no duration too short for it to be seen. Even complex scenes can be perceived in full color by the light of a photographic flash tube whose illumination lasts for only a few microseconds. This finding does not, however, imply that the physiological activity that is required to mediate such complex perceptions occurs with such lightning-like speed. When the stimulus is brief, both the physiological responses and the sensations that it produces far outlast the stimulus in time. Neural activity concerned with hue, such as color-specific waves of the human evoked cortical response, probably takes longer to travel than do the components associated with luminance changes (Regan, 1989 p. 348).

The perception of color depends importantly upon which region of the retina receives the image of the perceived object (Abramov, Gordon & Chan, 1991,1992; Hibino, 1992; Mullen, 1990). In general, color vision is primarily specialized in the fovea. Peripheral color vision is less well developed than that mediated by central vision, which goes hand in hand with the inferior spatial abilities of eccentric vision. Small peripheral targets appear desaturated and, except for red, of uncertain color. Large targets, especially if bright, can mediate good color perception similar to that of central vision. Especially as an aid to speed the search process, peripheral color vision is probably very important.[2]

Both the size of a colored patch, and the sharpness of the boundary that encloses it, can affect its perceived hue and saturation. We saw in Chapter 2 that colors are normally seen as inherent surface properties of objects. The color of an object appears much more uniform than would be expected from a detailed photometric examination of the substantial luminance variations across its surface that most lighting produces.

The perceived color in one part of the visual field can depend importantly upon the remainder of the field. Consider a small square that has a spectral reflectance with wavelengths entirely in the range from 570 to 580 nm. Such a square, seen in isolation, would appear yellow to most people. However, its hue can change dramatically depending on the color(s) of its surrounding elements. But, under controlled conditions, isolated fields yield color–naming behavior of astonishing predictability (Boynton, 1975; Boynton & Gordon, 1965; Boynton, Schafer & Neun, 1965; Abramov et al., 1991;1992). While the effects of context are undeniably important and will be considered in Chapter 11, their physiological bases are not yet well understood. In this chapter we will emphasize experiments concerned with spatial and temporal variables that help to elucidate the mechanisms of color vision. The stimuli used in these experiments are relatively simple and include a variety of arrangements that usually do not occur in our ordinary visual environment. Of special importance are lights that flicker.

At this point, the reader should refer once again to Figure 7.1, which depicts a simplified standard model of human color vision. Much of the present chapter is concerned with experiments and speculations related to the features of this genre of color vision model.

SPATIAL AND TEMPORAL BEHAVIOR RELATED TO L-, M-, & S-CONES

The visual literature is replete with experiments where color seems to have been tossed in as an afterthought. For example, an investigator who has studied visual acuity as a function of luminance may wonder what would happen if the color of the light was varied. Suppose this investigator first does an experiment by illuminating a Snellen acuity chart (of the sort that everyone has seen in doctors' offices or at the Motor Vehicle Bureau) with white light from a slide projector. By dropping neutral filters in front of the projector the luminance against which the black letters are seen can be controlled, and the results will show that acuity becomes poorer as luminance is reduced: letters on the 6/6 line, which formerly could be resolved, now drop below the threshold of recognition and only the larger letters above can be recognized.[3]

To investigate color, the experimenter drops a filter in front of the projector, which, say, passes only a narrow band of blue light centered at 450 nm. An observer, who formerly could read the 6/6 line, can now recognize only those letters corresponding to 6/18 acuity or worse. What can be legitimately concluded from this experiment? The answer is nothing at all, because luminance has been thoroughly confounded with the chromatic variable. By dropping in the blue filter the experimenter may have reduced the luminance of the chart to ten percent or less of what the unfiltered projector light had provided. A control experiment is needed where the same reduction in luminance is achieved using a neutral filter that does not alter the spectral distribution of the light.

When such controls are used, it is typically found that varying spectral distribution has remarkably little effect upon visual acuity[4] or spatial contrast sensitivity (Van Ness & Bouman, 1967). There may be a small loss in the short wavelengths, but even this probably could be avoided if the myopia of the normal eye for blue light were optically corrected. One cannot assume, just because a light appears blue, that S-cones are absorbing very much of the light captured by the photoreceptors. In other words, despite its blue appearance, it is probable that short wavelength light is mostly absorbed by the L-and M-cones, whose action spectra extend across the entire visible spectrum. L-and M-cones are by far the major contributors to luminance signals of the achromatic pathways concerned with detailed spatial vision. Light absorbed by S-cones is not very effective so far as critical spatial vision is concerned (Brindley, 1954; Eskew & Boynton, 1987; Williams, Collier & Thomson, 1983; Mullen, 1990). Yet apparently so little of it is lost that it is rather difficult to show that visual acuity is worse in shortwave than in the longwave light, where little is lost to the S-cones.

There are various ways to isolate the behavior of S-cones. When this is done they are found to be spatially inferior to the other two cone types. Although the density of S-cones is much less than that of the L- or M-cones, this is not necessarily the sole reason for their inferior spatial resolution. If receptor density were the determining factor for spatial resolution in the retina, one would expect a very high acuity just in those extra foveal regions where the density of the rods is the greatest. Clearly the retinal circuitry also plays a significant role. It was often reported that the temporal properties of the S-cones are also inferior to those of the L- and M-cones. However recent physiological evidence by Baylor *et al.* (1987) and Schnapf *et al.* (1990) together with psychophysical studies by Stockman *et al.* (1993) and Hess *et al.* (1989), show that this is not quite the whole story.

One procedure for isolating S-cones is the "test sensitivity" method that was discussed in Chapter 6. Recall that the L- and M-cones are strongly stimulated by a longwave adapting light. Therefore, one can strongly adapt the eye to longwave light, thereby increasing the fraction of visually effective shortwave test light that is absorbed by S-cones (Brindley, 1954; Green, 1969; Kelly, 1974; Stiles, 1949). Another technique, called "double silent substitution" (to be elaborated below), permits variations of the stimulus that are effective for S-cones but fail to produce any change in the steady absorption rate for either L- or M-cones (Boynton, Hayhoe & MacLeod, 1977). Stockman and his colleagues introduced a procedure called *beat sensitivity* and found that when a long wavelength sinusoidally modulated light, at 40 Hz, was presented together with short wavelength light at 40.5 Hz, a visible temporally modulated light was observed at a frequency of 0.5 Hz. If the S-cones were not able to generate a high frequency signal as previously believed, they would not be able to interact with L- or M-cones to produce these visible beats. Stockman, MacLeod &

Vivien (1993) showed that modulation transfer functions for L- or M-cone flicker sensitivity were virtually identical to S-cone beat sensitivity. A more direct test of S-cone temporal response is to perform the experiment on observers who have only one class of cones, namely the S-cones. Hess, Mullen & Zrenner (1989) studied two "blue mono-cone monochromats" and found that the S-cones and their postreceptoral pathways are capable of transmitting temporal frequencies of between 40 and 45 Hz when the retinal illuminance is about 10^4 trolands. Clearly, these results are consistent with those obtained by Stockman *et al.*

The L- and M-cones work intimately together in a fashion already discussed in Chapter 7. Their output is summed to produce an achromatic, or luminance, signal, and it is also subtracted to generate an opponent-color signal. Almost never is the visual brain permitted to see activity resulting from L or M-cones acting in isolation. L- and M-cones seem to have nearly identical spatial and temporal characteristics. But in order to generate signals for the opponent channels, the sign must be reversed for one of these. Possibly this relates in some way to temporal differences that have been noticed experimentally in connection with alternations between red and green lights at constant luminance.[5]

The temporal properties of the two classes of channels into which L- and M-cones feed seem to be very different; the spectrally opponent channels are more sluggish than the spectrally non-opponent channel. This point will be elaborated later in this chapter.

DIRECT HETEROCHROMATIC PHOTOMETRY

The practical importance of being able to specify which of two lights is visually more effective has long been recognized. When there is no spectral difference between two lights, the problem is merely one of physical measurement; whichever light discharges more photons per unit time in the direction of the eye will be the winner. But suppose the lights differ in color; then how can visual effectiveness be determined? If all vision were scotopic where only rods are operative the spectral radiance distributions of the two stimuli could simply be integrated with the scotopic luminous efficiency function $V'(\lambda)$ (Fig. 5.3), and the larger product would determine the more effective light. But for photopic vision, because there are three classes of cone receptors, serious problems arise.

Suppose, for example, we wish to compare two fields of light, one a middle wavelength 555 nm, the other a short wavelength 465 nm. If presented in equal physical amounts (whether specified in energy or in photon measurement) the 555 nm field would look so much brighter than the 465 nm one that there could be no doubt which was the more effective. Indeed, if equal radiometric amounts of these two lights were used for almost any purpose imaginable, ranging from reading lamps to the illumination of athletic fields, everyone would agree (and it could be shown experimentally) that visual performance[6] under the middle wavelength light would be better than under the short wavelength one.

A more subtle question is to ask by what factor the physical intensity of the 465 nm light must be raised in order to equate it for visual effectiveness with the original 555 nm light. By what criterion shall visual effectiveness be judged? One approach is to choose a dimension of subjective visual experience that correlates most closely with the physical intensity of the light. This dimension is *brightness*.

Brightness Matching

The procedure by which two fields are compared for brightness, when their colors differ, is called *direct heterochromatic brightness matching*. Consider again a 555 nm light on one side of a bipartite field, with a 465 nm field immediately adjacent to it. We ask an observer to adjust the intensity of the 465 nm field until it looks as equally bright as the 555 nm one. This turns out to be rather difficult. Although everyone has an intuitive idea of what brightness means, the task requires abstracting brightness from a complex sensation–one that may involve large hue and saturation differences in addition to the brightness component. It is found that observers can choose a criterion and hold it fairly well for a short series of measurements, but when they return later to repeat the experiment they tend to adopt different criteria (Walsh, 1958, p. 293). Thus they produce two sets of settings, each with a small variance, but where the mean of the first set differs significantly from that of the second.

Additivity Failures

These variability problems could be overcome with enough measurements, many subjects, and good experimental design. But another problem that cannot be so overcome led to the abandonment of direct heterochromatic brightness matching and to the search for other methods to visually equate the visual effectiveness of different hues. The problem is that of *additivity failure*.

Consider the following experiment. A white field in the left half of a bipartite stimulus is compared with a red one in the right half.

An observer adjusts the red field to appear equally as bright as the white one, and this is done enough times to ensure a stable measure. Now the red field is replaced by a green one and the subject makes a brightness match between the green and white. After this has been done, the red and green fields are optically superimposed. Next the white field at the left, whose intensity has been doubled, is compared on the right with this additive mixture of red and green (some kind of yellow or white, depending upon the specific spectral distributions of the red and green components). The surprise is that the right-hand field now appears appreciably dimmer than the white one at the left (Tessier & Blottiau, 1951; Guth, 1967; Boynton & Kaiser, 1968). To show that this is not some kind of an intensity artifact, these two fields can both be viewed through a 0.3 neutral density filter that absorbs half the light from each field. This returns the left field to the original luminance of each of its equal components. The yellow field at the right, being similarly dimmed, still looks much less bright than the white field at the left.

Such additivity failures are not trivial. To restore a brightness match, in a case like that just described, some observers will require that the luminance of the dimmer field at the right be increased by a factor of two or even more. This is a complicated situation upon which to base a photometric system. One would like instead to predict brightness matches by means of an equation having the following form:

$$L_v = k \int E_\lambda V(\lambda) d\lambda. \tag{9.1}$$

Here L_v is photopic luminance, E_λ represents the spectral energy distribution of a stimulus, $V(\lambda)$ is a photopic luminous efficiency function, and k is a constant.

Because the integral is inherently a summation operation an equation of this form could never account for additivity failure of the sort just described. Two options suggest themselves. One is to write a complicated equation that will predict relative brightnesses (e.g., Ware & Cowan, 1983). The other is to adopt some other criterion for the experiment, one that does not lead to additivity failure. *Heterochromatic flicker photometry*, to be discussed below, has approximated this criterion. This fact has been rather important for practical photometry, and its importance for understanding the properties of temporal vision is at least as great.

THE SENSATION OF FLICKER

The CIE has defined flicker as "Impression of unsteadiness of visual sensation induced by a light stimulus whose luminance or spectral distribution fluctuates with time" (CIE, 1987). The *Dictionary of Visual Science* (Cline, Hoffstetter & Griffin, 1980) defines flicker as "variation in brightness or hue perceived upon stimulation by intermittent or temporally non uniform light."

Operationally we can conceive of flicker as resulting from a spot of light placed behind a revolving sector disc. When rotated, the disc alternately exposes and occludes the light for equal periods. We will call this approach *single stimulus flicker*. If the rotation of the disc is slow enough, one sees the spot flashing on and off discretely. A further increase in the rate of rotation produces an ambiguous situation where subjectively the light fails to extinguish completely: in the waxing and waning of the subjective impression, the overall brightness of the pulsing light is greater than it would be if the disc were stopped in the open position, permitting the light to be viewed continuously (the so-called Brücke–Bartley effect: Bartley, 1938, 1941; Brücke, 1864). As the rotation rate is further increased, this enhancement of brightness is lost and eventually the field comes to appear almost, but not quite, steady. There remains a definite sensation of flicker, which is difficult to describe verbally. This sensation is poorly correlated with the physical flash rate; to the extent that it can be measured, the subjective rate of flicker is lower than the physical one (Forsyth & Chapanis, 1958). As the disc is spun still faster the sensation of flicker abruptly disappears. All that is seen then is a steady light. The perceived brightness of this steady light is exactly the same as if the interrupted light were viewed continuously at half intensity, as could be achieved by stopping the disc and placing a 50-percent-transmitting filter between the eye and the spot of light. Although spinning sector discs[7] were one of the original ways to temporally manipulate light, the description above is not dependent on this technology. Sinusoidal modulation can be obtained by using two polarizing filters. One filter is fixed and the other is rotated to achieve the desired flicker frequency. With the aid of computers it is possible to produce temporally modulated light of many waveforms on video monitors with short persistence phosphors.

The rate of presentation at which flicker disappears is called the *critical flicker frequency* (cff). The phenomenon of flicker disappearance at high presentation rates is called *flicker fusion*. The special case just described above can be extended to any rapidly repetitive stimulus, no matter how complex its luminance fluctuations in time. It will, if fused, have a brightness equal to a steady light having a luminance equal to the mean luminance of the complex stimulus, calculated for an integral number of cycles. This relationship is known as the *Talbot–Plateau law,* (Plateau, 1835; Talbot, 1834)

The Effect of Intensity

Critical flicker frequency (cff) is strongly dependent upon luminance. Suppose, for example, that cff has been established in an experiment like the one just described, at a fairly high luminance of the test spot. Decrease the frequency slightly so that flicker is clearly perceived. Next, place a 50-percent-transmitting filter in front of the eye, and the flicker disappears. Flicker can once more be recaptured by reducing the flicker rate. In systematic studies, cff is found to increase over a wide range approximately as a linear function of log intensity (the Ferry–Porter law).[8] This is a substantial effect: for every tenfold increase in stimulus intensity there is a 10- to 15-Hz increase in cff until very high intensities are reached, where cff stabilizes for large flashes somewhere above 60 Hz.[9]

Preliminary Theoretical Considerations

Why should an increase in intensity cause a change in cff? We should recall that the pathways of the visual system have time constants that make them unable to follow a square-wave input with a square-wave response. This fact also implies that, if an impulse stimulus is delivered to the eye (which can be physically approximated with a xenon flash), the resulting response will not be a spike, but will exhibit instead a rounded waveform of some kind.

Electrophysiological evidence indicates that some of this "rounding" of the response waveform takes place in the responses of the receptors themselves. Such rounding is evident in Figure 9.1 which shows monkey cone responses to a 10.7 ms flash. As seen by the succession of curves the slope and amplitude of the receptor responses are dependent on flash intensity.

The state of adaptation of the eye is controlled not only by steady fields; a flickering field will also adapt the eye, and the Talbot–Plateau law holds, in the limit, for adaptation also. Indeed, the precision with which the law holds under most conditions makes it likely that it is determined very early in visual processing, probably in the receptors. If so, a light that is flickering very fast leads to the summation of elemental receptor responses that cannot be distinguished from those produced by a steady light that generates the same mean rate of such responses.

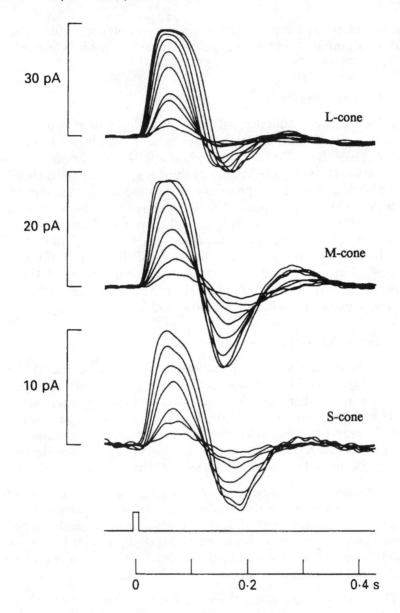

Figure 9.1 Responses of L-cones, M-cones, and S-cones of Macaca fasicularis monkeys. The curves for each cone type are the responses to a 10.7 ms flash of varying intensity at the wavelength of maximum sensitivity. The responses grow larger as flash intensities are increased by a nominal factor of 2: between 3.72×10^2 and 1.64×10^4 photons m^{-2} for the S-cone; 7.8×10^1 and 5.35×10^3 photons m^{-2} for the M-cone, and 1.78×10^2 and 3.86×10^4 photons m^{-2} for the L-cone. Each trace was averaged from 2 to 14 sweeps and digitally filtered (from Schnapf, Nunn, Meister & Baylor, 1990).

If a light is flickering at a frequency that is not too far below cff, it is convenient to consider it as being comprised of two components. One of these is the steady Talbot–Plateau equivalent, which may be regarded as determining the state of adaptation of the eye. The other is the modulation of light intensity, both above and below that level. For square-wave stimuli of the sort so far considered, the physical modulation is the maximum possible. But the modulation that is actually produced in the responses of photoreceptors is less than that of the stimulus. The response associated with the dark phase of each cycle will not fall all the way to the baseline as would be achieved if he light were extinguished for a long time. The higher the intensity of a fully modulated flickering light, the more light-adapted is the eye, the crisper are the elemental responses, and the greater is the physiological modulation that results.

HETEROCHROMATIC FLICKER PHOTOMETRY

Because we are now going to introduce a chromatic variable, it would be useful to elaborate our definition of flicker to include using pairs of lights, which we can call *dual-stimulus flicker*. We have already discussed at some length the concept of luminance flicker, the stimulus for which is represented in Figure 9.2a (single-stimulus flicker). Here we see a monochromatic light that is temporally modulated at frequency f and at modulation depth m (see Eq. (9.2) on p. 376). Figure 9.2b represents lights of two wavelengths modulated in counterphase so that the sum of the luminances does not vary. (This example is the sinusoidal equivalent to the square-wave example that will be discussed in Fig. 9.3c.) Another flicker paradigm that we will discuss below is represented in Figure 9.2c. This is the case where a single wavelength of frequency f is modulated at modulation depth m, superimposed on another wavelength at a certain constant average. The result is luminance and chromatic flicker. It is, of course, possible to take the stimulus situation in Figure 9.2b and present it superimposed on a stimulus of a wavelength at a constant average level. This situation is represented in Figure 9.2d and results in chromatic flicker. Finally, two stimuli at different wavelengths modulating at the same modulation depth but at a phase other than 0° or 180° results in chromatic and luminance flicker (Fig. 9.2e). If the phase difference of the two stimuli is 180° this is equivalent to Figure 9.2a. If the two stimuli are in phase this is equivalent to Figure 9.2a or c.

Above we introduced the expression heterochromatic flicker photometry and promised to expand on it as a solution to the additivity-failure problems of heterochromatic brightness matching. Because cff depends upon the energy of the light, one way to specify the rela-

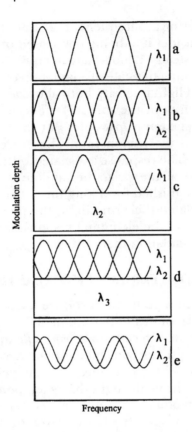

Figure 9.2 Five generic sinewave paradigms used in chromatic and achromatic flicker experiments (Kaiser, 1991).

tive effectiveness of lights of different colors is to determine the energy required for various wavelengths to appear just fused (or flickering) when the light is flickered against darkness at some fixed rate. This method has, for example, been used by DeValois and colleagues to determine the spectral sensitivity of macaque monkeys, and occasionally it has been employed in psychophysical experiments with humans as well (DeValois, Morgan, Polson, Mead & Hull, 1974; Heath, 1958; Marks & Bornstein, 1973). Because it is possible to work with one wavelength at a time with this method, difficult heterochromatic comparisons are eliminated, and the less ambiguous judgment of flicker or no flicker can be used instead.

Conventional heterochromatic flicker photometry, on the other hand, requires the use of two lights that are alternated with one an-

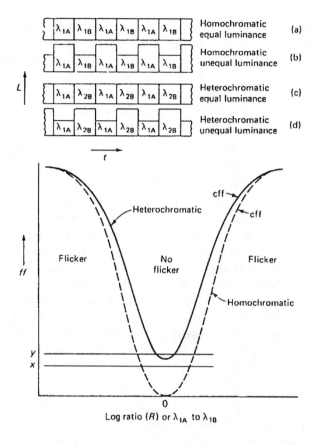

Figure 9.3   Regions of flicker and no-flicker for combinations of flicker frequency (ff) and luminance ratios of alternating homochromatic and heterochromatic components. (Adapted from Boynton and Kaiser, 1978.)

other (Ives & Kingsbury, 1914; Ives, 1917; 1922). Although technically more difficult than the single-stimulus procedure, this has proved to be an extremely sensitive method, exploited many years ago by engineers and physicists who recognized the need to develop a standard spectral sensitivity curve by means of which the *relative luminous efficiency* of any spectral light compared to a reference light could be calculated.

Figure 9.3 will help to explain this conventional method of heterochromatic flicker photometry. A means is required that allows two fields to be presented in the same place in rapid alternation. This can be accomplished with an appropriate optical system or a properly programmed computer display. It is very important that there be no physical artifact at the moment of substitution. As a control for this, consider the train of alternating light pulses represented by (a) in Figure 9.3. Lights of λ_1, delivered by field A, are substituted for those of the same wavelength from field B. If the fields are physically equated for radiance, a steady light will be seen, provided that the substitution is temporally and spatially precise. Conventional heterochromatic photometry cannot legitimately proceed until this condition is met.

If the intensity of one of the component fields is reduced, while that of the other is increased by a like amount, the situation represented in Figure 9.3(b) will result. This procedure differs from single stimulus flicker because light is now continuously present in the flicker train, whereas for single stimulus flicker, the luminance of component 1B would be zero, producing an alternation between light and darkness. As the luminance of component B is varied relative to A, the expected result is shown by the dashed curve at the bottom of Figure 9.3. When the two luminances are equal, no flicker will be seen at any frequency, and the function must reach the abscissa of the graph. When component A is reduced to zero, the single-stimulus cff for B will be established as the limit of the asymptotic left-hand branch of the function. At intermediate luminance ratios, the dashed curve is traced out, and there will be a second asymptote at the right, where the luminance of A is much higher than that of B.

Suppose now that the wavelengths of the two components are different. The expected result is depicted as the solid curve in Figure 9.3; the experimental condition that produces this function is depicted in Figure 9.3(d). In general, one would expect that the added chromatic difference would increase cff relative to the achromatic case (b). Of special interest is the minimum of the function (c). Provided that the flicker rate is not too fast, the spectral difference will make it impossible for any ratio of the two field intensities to eliminate the perceived flicker when one field is substituted for the other. Nevertheless, flicker will be minimized when the alternating stimuli are most similar in visual effectiveness. The location of the minimum of the curve on the abscissa may be used to define equal luminance of the two spectral components.[10]

Also of interest is the value of cff that is represented by the ordinate value corresponding to the minimum of the solid curve. Intuitively it would seem reasonable that the larger the color difference between the two components of the stimulus, the larger should be this minimum value. (At least we know this to be true for the limiting case of no spectral difference, where the ordinate value drops to zero.) Actually, functions of this sort have seldom been obtained because to do so for a large combination of stimulus wavelengths would comprise a very long and tedious experiment.[11] Instead, the typical procedure for conventional heterochromatic flicker photometry uses a short-cut. A flicker frequency is selected that is in the vicinity of those rates corresponding to the minimum of the solid curve of Figure 9.3, usually in the range from 10 to 15 Hz. The subject is given control of a knob that varies the intensity ratio of the two components of the field. By a method of adjustment, the subject determines the knob position which either (1) minimizes the sensation of flicker, or (2) bisects the range within which no flicker is seen. Which judgment is required depends upon the flicker rate chosen. For frequency x in Figure 9.3, flicker will always be seen and the task will be to minimize it. For frequency y, there is a range where no flicker is seen and this range must be bisected. Ideally, a frequency between x and y could be selected that would produce a condition where flicker just barely disappears at the ratio corresponding to the minimum of the solid curve.

Transitivity, Additivity, Proportionality, and Conventional Flicker Photometry

The results obtained by conventional flicker photometry are especially useful because the data conform, at least approximately, to the three linearity laws of color matching: transitivity, additivity, and proportionality. These three linear laws are three corollaries to Grassmann's principles or laws (Judd & Wyszecki, 1975). We will move directly to the corollaries that are more pertinent to the present discussion. *Transitivity* occurs when radiances of wavelengths A and B are adjusted for equal luminance by conventional flicker photometry, and when B and C are similarly equated, after which A and C produce minimum flicker when directly exchanged (LeGrand, 1968, p.75). Additivity experiments have already been described in another context (p.362). For flicker measurements, suppose that a red light is flickered with a white one, then a green light is flickered with a white one, and finally the additive combination of red and green lights is flickered with twice the intensity of the original white light. Provided that minimum flicker is perceived in each case, the additive combination still yields a condition of minimum flicker without the need for any further adjustment.[12] The *proportionality* corollary states that when the luminance of two different colors are set to produce minimum flicker they will continue to yield minimum flicker when both colors are increased or decreased by identical factors. So when light A yields minimum flicker when alternated with light B, then light αA will continue to yield minimum flicker when alternated with light αB. These linearity laws apply approximately, being most accurate in the middle luminance ranges. Deviations from the laws occur at very high luminance levels where response saturation takes place and at low luminance levels at or near threshold.

Important advantages accrue when these rules are obeyed. The choice of reference wavelength does not matter, in the sense that a relative luminous efficiency function can be derived by comparing many wavelengths with various fixed references, and the shape of the curve will not change from one reference to another. A further advantage results from the finding that flicker matches are independent of radiance over a wide photopic range. Therefore, because luminance is defined as being proportional to radiance, it becomes legitimate to calculate luminance for a mixture of lights simply by adding the luminances of the components of that mixture. For a continuous distribution of radiance, luminance can then be calculated by Equation (9.1) and any two fields having the same calculated value of L_v should be equal in luminance by the criterion of conventional heterochromatic flicker photometry. In a nutshell, this is the basis of our current photometric system.[13] When defined for a standard CIE observer, $V(\lambda)$ is the spectral luminous efficiency function for photopic vision. $V_M(\lambda)$ is this function as modified by Judd and Vos (CIE, 1990).

THEORETICAL BASIS OF FLICKER PHOTOMETRY

Behavior of the sort just described, where linearity laws are obeyed, is exactly what is expected from a univariant mechanism (Chapter 5, p. 136). But at least two classes of cones must supply input to whatever system is being examined by the operations of conventional photopic flicker photometry. If this were not so, the solid curve of Figure 9.3 would reach the x-axis, implying perfect substitution of effectively identical stimulus components, similar to what would be expected if the experiment were performed under scotopic conditions, where only rods are operative.

Examination of the shape of the photopic luminosity curve, $(V_M(\lambda))$ shown in Figure 9.4, indicates that it is too broad to be that of a single cone type, and moreover it shows that $V_M(\lambda)$ can be adequately fitted by assuming an additive contribution from only L- and M-cones.[14] If so, two fields will be of equal photopic luminance provided that the rate of photon absorption, spread across both L- and M-cones, is the same for each field, without regard to how the rates are distributed between the two types of cones.

Additional evidence in support of this concept of luminance will be considered later in this chapter. But now we must consider the

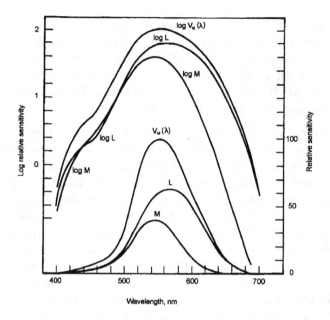

Figure 9.4   These graphs show how the Smith–Pokorny L- and M-cone fundamentals sum to produce $V_M(\lambda)$, the photopic luminosity function as
modified by Judd and Vos (CIE, 1990). The information is given on a
logarithmic ordinate (top curves, left scale) as well as on a linear one
(bottom curves, right scale).

issue of the apparent univariance of luminosity relationships. This
could be accounted for if the outputs of the L- and M-cones sum
linearly as they feed into the luminance channels. But we saw in Chapter 6 that the input-output relations of the photoreceptors are basically nonlinear. How then is it ever possible for their outputs to sum
in a linear fashion? The answer to this question is not known for
certain. One possibility is that, in a steady state of light adaptation,
receptor responses are nearly linear with intensity. Therefore, the
additivity failures may be too small to measure, and for all practical
purposes, linearity is therefore to be expected if the responses of the
L and M-cones are combined to produce the luminance signal.[15]

A Physiological Basis for Defining Luminance

It would seem desirable to define luminance as being related to
the linear sum of L- and M-cone sensitivities. What is required is an
agreed upon-pair of L- and M-receptor sensitivity curves. A decision
must be made about how their sensitivities should be set relative to

one another. The L- and M-curves of Figure 9.4 are adjusted vertically so that their sum is proportional to the modified photopic luminosity function, $V_M(\lambda)$. We will show here that two lights may be said to be of equal luminance when each causes the same rate of photon capture in the combined population of L- and M-cones, without regard to their relative distribution.

To obtain an experimental measure that correlates with luminance, an operation must be found that does not allow the opponent channels to interfere significantly with a comparison based on activity in the luminance channels. It is only the latter that receive summed inputs from L- and M-cones. Conventional flicker photometry apparently does this fairly well; the minimally distinct border procedure (p. 315, 404) may do so even better. Both procedures are little influenced by S-cone activity, as desired, because S-cones should deliver their signals to the brain only through y-b opponent channels and, therefore, make little contribution to luminance. As noted earlier in this chapter Stockman, MacLeod & Lebrun (1993) determined by beat sensitivity that S-cones can follow rather high temporal frequencies and that they do make an inverted contribution to luminance (Stockman, *et al.*, 1991). However, this seems to be a small effect realizable only by the beat sensitivity method. Therefore we will operate here with the working assumption that S-cones make no significant contribution to luminance.

With the foregoing as background, what remains as a theoretical explanation of the results of conventional flicker photometry is straightforward. The only additional assumption required is to suppose that psychophysically the opponent-color channels have a more sluggish temporal response than do the luminance channels, and for this reason cannot follow even the moderate rates of flicker that are used in flicker photometry. Ample evidence in support of this assumption now exists; some of it will be reviewed in subsequent sections of this chapter.

SINUSOIDAL FLICKER

The year 1952 separates the literature on flicker into two eras. In that year, Hendrik deLange, working with primitive equipment in a home laboratory in the Netherlands, produced the first of a series of papers that were to revolutionize the study of the response of the visual system to flickering light.[16] What deLange did was to investigate the feasibility of applying *linear systems analysis* to this class of visual phenomena. Among other things, linearity implies that the principle of *superposition* must be obeyed. For vision, this would mean that the size and shape of responses produced in the visual system must be the same regardless of the level of background luminance upon which the test stimuli are applied. As we saw in Chapter 6, where response compression and other mechanisms of adaptation were discussed, the visual system does not behave in such a linear fashion. How then is it possible to apply linear analysis to the nonlinear visual system?

The grossest nonlinearities in vision are those associated with changing adaptive states, produced by overloading the system with stimuli that are much too bright relative to the initial level of adaptation. The solution to the problem of linearity is straightforward; it is to deal with the eye in only one adaptive state at a time, and then to take care not to overload the system.

By allowing the eye to become completely adapted to the level being tested, the resulting response is nearly linear. This has already been discussed in the previous section in connection with the quasi-additivity of the signals from L- and M-cones. By using the threshold of flicker perception as a response criterion, the visual system is by definition perturbed to the smallest measurable extent, which further serves to negate any residual nonlinearities that might be a problem for stronger test probes. The idea here is that any nonlinear system, if examined over a narrow enough range will, over that range, approximate linearity.

To test the frequency response of a linear system, an appropriate stimulus to use is one having a sinusoidal modulation. Many readers will be familiar with the use of sinusoids in the evaluation of audio amplifiers and associated components. When the frequency response of such a system is plotted, it usually shows that the output becomes progressively more attenuated as input frequency increases, in which case the system is said to act as a *low-pass filter* because it transmits the low-frequency components of the signal better than higher ones. Often there may be a loss of response at low frequencies as well, and it is possible to build electronic filters that pass only a rather narrow band of input frequencies. Such filters are called *band pass.*

The mathematician Jean Baptiste Fourier had shown a century and a half before de Lange that any repetitive waveform could be replaced by the sum of a series of sinusoids having suitably chosen amplitudes, frequencies, and phases. Let's assume that the visual system behaves linearly at a fixed adaptation level and that superposition holds. If this assumption is granted and if the responses of the visual system to sinusoidally varying luminances of all frequencies can be established (including the phase lag between stimulus and response as a function of frequency), then linear systems analysis (Fourier analysis and synthesis) permits the calculation of responses to any arbitrary stimulus waveform. Because phase information is lacking in psychophysical data, it is important to measure the sensitivity of the eye to sinusoidal inputs directly, doing so at enough frequencies for a smooth function to be fitted to allow an interpolation of sensitivities to frequencies not actually tested. Such a curve is called a *modulation sensitivity function* or a *deLange curve*.

We will not go into detail about the calculations of Fourier analysis, or attempt to develop the formalisms of the method, which are second nature to physical science and engineering students, and to which many visual scientists have by now been exposed. Nor will any attempt be made here to cover the whole of the vast recent literature on visual flicker, most of which has relatively little to do with color vision. A chapter by Kaiser (1991) does cover some of the material especially as it related to color vision and heterochromatic flicker photometry.

In addition to the use of sine waves in recent years, an important difference between flicker studies of the two eras has been the decision to abandon the use of full modulation, which had been the standard practice. For sine-wave stimuli, *modulation, m,* (Michelson Contrast) is defined as

$$m = \frac{I_{max} - I_{min}}{I_{max} + I_{min}}. \qquad (9.2)$$

Modulation is thus a relative index, which, for reflecting surfaces, is independent of illumination. Modulation of 1.0, or 100 percent, is achieved when $I_{min} = 0$. Modulation of 0 occurs when the numerator, $I_{max} - I_{min}$, is zero.

In the older work, as noted above, pulses of light were almost always alternated with periods of complete darkness, as shown in Figure 9.5b. Figure 9.5a shows an example of a 100-percent modulated sinusoid. When full modulation was used, the dependent variable of the experiment was cff. Nowadays, in determining a modulation sensitivity function, the frequency is usually set at a fixed value and modulation is varied to find the smallest perturbation that will give rise to a sensation of flicker. Figure 9.5c and d provide examples of ten percent modulation for sinusoidal flicker and for a square wave stimulus, respectively, at the same adaptation level, having the same absolute amplitude as its sine wave counterpart.

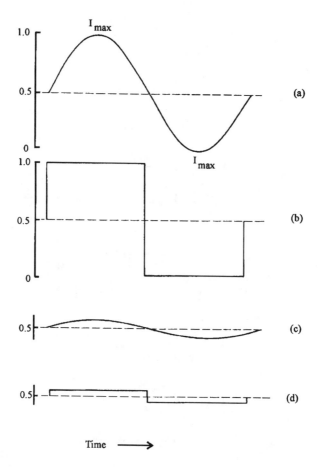

Figure 9.5   Examples of sinusoidal and square wave modulation. In (a) modulation is 100% and sinusoidal. In (b) a square wave of the same amplitude as the sinewave in (a) is shown. In (c) the sinusoidal modulation is reduced to 10 %. Panel (d) shows square wave modulation of the same amplitude as (c). For a linear system, the fundamental sinusoidal component corresponding to this square wave would have 127% contrast. To be as effective for the production of visual flicker as (a) the amplitude of (b) must be reduced to 78.5% of (a).

Many visual scientists today use spatially or temporally modulated sine waves. The reason is that a sine wave is the fundamental function underlying Fourier analysis. Square waves, for example, can be described by the appropriate summation of a series of sine waves at appropriate amplitudes and frequencies. Figure 9.6 illustrates the initial steps in the buildup of a square wave from component sine

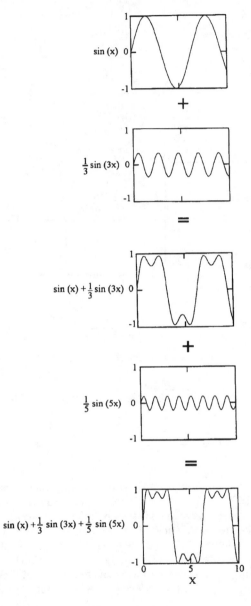

Figure 9.6 An illustration of how a square wave can be constructed by the appropriate summation of sine waves. The fundamental sine wave (top figure) is added to a sine wave of 1/3 amplitude and 3 times the frequency of the fundamental. The result is shown in the middle figure. Added to this composite is another sine wave which is 1/5 the amplitude and 5 times the frequency of the fundamental resulting in the bottom figure. For practical purposes, this procedure is followed with an odd series of modulations and frequencies until the ripples in the square wave are below visual threshold.

waves. As the progression continues, the ripples in the waveform become progressively smaller and in the limit approach a square wave.

Sensory vs. Adaptational Responses

It will be helpful at this point if we can separate our thinking about visual mechanisms into two classes — a *daptational* and *sensory*. As we saw in Chapter 6, mechanisms of adaptation determine sensitivity and certain other characteristics of the visual system. We do not ordinarily have direct sensory access to the behavior of adaptational systems. For example, a field that has completely faded from view under conditions of retinal image stabilization continues to exert its full adaptive effect.[17] By contrast, sensory signals should be regarded as directly responsible for the transmission of information from eye to brain, leading to visual sensations and perceptions.

For any modulation, the state of adaptation of the eye is determined by the mean luminance of the periodic stimulus. Recall that, in the limit where flicker is no longer seen, this value specifies exactly the intensity of a steady light that would be required to match the physically flickering one. To the extent the linear systems analysis is applicable, it suggests that the same law applies for the adaptive effects of stimuli that are perceived as barely flickering.

Steady state flicker is an expression that refers to the condition of equilibrium that a stable system achieves after it has been stimulated for a long time by any periodic input, whether or not a fluctuating response remains. For vision near the threshold for the perception of the flickering component of a stimulus, it is probable that the state of adaptation of the eye is literally steady. This is because the periodic effects of a flickering input are fully attenuated under conditions where the sensory component of the visual response can follow the flickering input somewhat more faithfully.

Measuring Temporal Modulation Sensitivity

If one had direct access to the responses of the visual system, the effects of flicker could be evaluated by measuring the response that results from an eye that is stimulated by 100-percent modulated flicker at various frequencies. Because this is not possible for the psychophysical examination of flicker, flicker frequency and modulation are manipulated in order to determine a just-perceptible flicker. Provided that the system is linear, this procedure is equivalent to the one where a 100-percent modulated input is always used, and a variable response is measured.

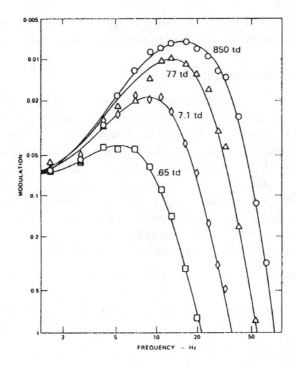

Figure 9.7   Threshold flicker modulation in a large achromatic field, with adaptation level held constant at values shown for each curve. (After Kelly, 1961.)

To produce curves that resemble those of purely physical measurement it has become conventional to define the modulation sensitivity function by plotting the reciprocal of the modulation threshold, which is a sensitivity measure, as a function of frequency. (When a logarithmic ordinate is used, the modulation sensitivity function is simply the modulation threshold curve plotted upside down.) One way to achieve modulations of less than 100 percent, is to add two stimulus components, one of which is steady while the other one flickers at full modulation (Fig. 9.2c).[18] To control adaptation level as modulation is decreased from 100 percent to lower levels, the intensity of the steady component must be increased so that the sum of the steady light and the Talbot equivalent of the flickering component is held constant.

Typical results are shown in Figure 9.7. The ordinate shows inverted threshold modulation, plotted as a function of frequency, with both scales logarithmic. The curves are for four different adaptation levels. At high frequencies, modulation sensitivity declines sharply at each adaptation level. In other words, as frequency is increased, progressively more modulation is required to keep the perception of flicker at a threshold level. When 100 percent modulation is reached (where the curves reach the abscissa of the graph) the experiment must cease because it is physically impossible to produce modulations greater than this. This limiting case is like the measurement of cff in the older studies, and confirms that cff increases with luminance. The remainder of the function provides new and important information.

The high-frequency behavior is not hard to understand in qualitative terms. As frequency increases, the response to each stimulus pulse overlaps progressively more with the one elicited by the next cycle of the stimulus; the responses smear together and if the frequency is high enough, there is insufficient response modulation remaining in the sensory channels for flicker to be perceived, even at full stimulus modulation. Intermediate and low-frequency behavior is more subtle.

It is clear from Figure 9.7 that there is an optimal frequency for the perception of flicker. For example, at an adaptation level of 850 td, less than 1 percent modulation depth is required to see flicker at a frequency of about 15 Hz. This modulation depth cannot be seen at 5 Hz, but 3 percent modulation can. In other words at 850 td observers are more sensitive to 15 than to 5 Hz. This result seems paradoxical because reducing frequency should allow the responses to be better separated in time at 5 Hz than at 15 Hz. What could be responsible for this inversion of a reasonably expected result?

Explaining the Low-frequency Sensitivity Loss

Sinusoidal variations of luminance in space, which have proved useful in modern vision research, are often called gratings. Gratings of low *spatial frequency* provide relatively few cycles showing relatively gradual changes of luminance across the visual field, whereas those of high spatial frequency exhibit many cycles of relatively rapid change. Spatial frequency, usually measured in cycles per degree (cpd) of visual angle, has the same formal property as temporal frequency except that space is substituted for time.

The loss of sensitivity at low temporal frequencies was originally established for a uniform field, which exhibits the lowest possible spatial frequency. Robson (1966) also observed such a loss for a low spatial frequency of 0.5 cpd. But for 4, 16, and 22 cpd the visual system behaved like a temporal low pass filter rather than band pass. One would suppose that with sufficiently high spatial frequencies a temporal low-frequency sensitivity loss would be observed. The value of this spatial frequency would be that which the visual system is unable to resolve. Kelly (1972) hypothesizes that a slower inhibitory process is the cause of the low frequency fall off. At low frequencies, inhibition tends to cancel the effectiveness of the flickering component, which otherwise could be seen. But the inhibitory process cannot follow rapid flicker, so high frequencies remain effective.

The exactness of the Talbot–Plateau law at very high frequencies suggests that neither the sensory nor the inhibitory machinery is able to react to the fact that the light is physically flickering at these rates. At intermediate frequencies, where flicker is more easily perceived, the inhibitory machinery may continue to respond only to the equivalent Talbot level without being able to follow the undulations of the stimulus. The sensory message, although generally attenuated by the effects of essentially steady adaptation, is therefore not selectively subject to inhibition within a cycle of the stimulus. As frequency is reduced still further, the inhibitory mechanisms begin to follow the flicker, only slightly at first, but progressively better as frequency is further reduced. At extremely low rates of flicker, the inhibitory mechanisms have time to follow almost perfectly, and their effect is to seriously attenuate the differential sensory response to variations in the stimulus.

In other words, inhibitory processes tend to reduce responses of varying magnitude to a common level. At high frequencies, where the inhibitory mechanism cannot follow at all, flicker is registered only to the extent that the excitatory pathways can follow the action. At low frequencies, where the excitatory channels could otherwise follow the flicker very well, inhibition reduces their response to flicker. As a consequence, flicker is easiest to see at intermediate frequencies, where the two factors are in optimum balance.

Effects of Different Luminance Levels

At low flicker rates, the curves of Figure 9.7 converge and the data obey Weber's law. This implies that, in order for Weber's law to apply, the stimulus must last long enough for inhibition to catch up with it, and thereby attenuate the response before the response has had time to run its course. At very high frequencies there is no inhibition at all; a surprising finding that is best visualized by plotting the same data, as Kelly did, in another way (Fig. 9.8). Here it is the absolute amplitude of modulation, in trolands, that is plotted on the or-

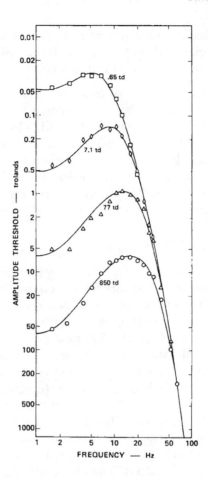

Figure 9.8 The data of Figure 9.7 replotted in terms of the absolute amplitude of modulation required for the threshold perception of flicker.

dinate instead of the relative modulation of Figure 9.7. The curves of Figure 9.8 are related to those of Figure 9.7 by a downward sliding of all of the functions, without change of shape, by amounts which are proportional to the adaptation level . [If A is amplitude, L_v is mean luminance, and m is modulation, $m = A/L_v$ by definition–this is equivalent to Eq. (9.2). Accordingly, $\log (L_v) = \log A - \log m$, and because $\log (L_v)^{-1}$ is plotted, $\log (L_v)^{-1} = \log m - \log A$. The second term, $-\log A$, causes the curves of Fig. 9.7 to be slid downward in Fig. 9.8.] The fact that the functions converge to a common high-frequency asymptote in Figure 9.8 implies that, no matter what the adaptation level, the inhibitory machinery is incapable of attenuating a threshold response to flicker that is modulated at 100 percent, or nearly so. (For example, in the neighborhood of 30 Hz, the amplitude of just-perceptible flicker is the same for adapting levels of 7 td and 77 td.)

Another important feature of these functions is their changing shape with adaptation level. The low-frequency sensitivity loss, which is very large at 850 td, is very slight at 0.65 td. This finding is consistent with the idea that the responsible processes of inhibition have temporal properties that are intensity-dependent, also showing a crisper response at high levels than at low ones. Therefore, as the level of adaptation increases, inhibition becomes more effective, which causes the optimum sensitivity to move toward higher frequencies.

FLICKER CURVES AND COLOR VISION

Instead of modulating a light by varying its luminance, it is possible instead to produce a chromaticity exchange at constant luminance. To simplify the experiment, one can keep the S-cones out of the way by choosing a pair of long wavelength monochromatic lights that are ineffective stimuli for the S-cones. The experiment of comparing chromatic modulation with achromatic was done by de Lange (1958). The classic results of de Lange's experiment re shown in Figure 9.9, where the monochromatic lights (labeled colour perception) are compared with an achromatic curve (labeled brightness perception) from the same study. Two features of the chromatic curve stand out in comparison to the achromatic one: (1) the high-frequency response is inferior; (2) there is no attenuation of sensitivity at the lowest frequencies tested. The chromatic curve describes behavior like that of a low-pass filter, rather than the tuned frequency response (band pass) of luminance flicker. Why should this tuning be absent for chromatic flicker?

We can begin to answer this question by first posing another. What sort of response is expected to a square-wave chromatic exchange? By such an exchange we mean, for example, the sudden substitution of a long wavelength light for a middle wavelength one, at constant luminance. From the L-cones we predict an increase in response level; from the M-cones, a decrease. There should also be a definite shift in the output of r-g channels in the r direction. There should be no change in either the luminance or the y-b channels.

The use of a sinusoidal flickering stimulus does not alter these basic relationships: it will still be the case that only the r-g channels will be active, along with the L- and M-cones that feed them. When compared to luminance flicker, the different behavior of the visual system in response to chromatic flicker cannot be explained by the behavior

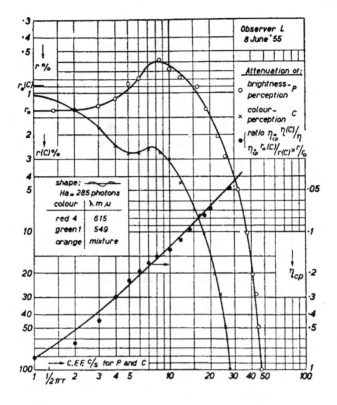

Figure 9.9   Results of the pioneering study of deLange (1958), as he displayed them. The ordinate values represent modulation in percent, either for luminance flicker (circles) or chromatic flicker (x's) obtained by shifting the phase of the stimulus components. The ascending curve at the bottom is based on an index of the ratio of flicker sensitivities represented by the two conditions of the experiment.

of the L- and M-cones themselves, because these receptors feed both kinds of channels. Therefore, we must look to the behavior of the r-g channels for an explanation of the chromatic flicker function.

Let us consider first the high-frequency difference between the luminance and chromatic flicker functions. At one level of analysis the explanation is simple: the luminance channels apparently have a high-frequency response that is higher than that of the r-g channels (under the assumption of independent channels). A fuller explanation would require a physiological demonstration of exactly why this is so; detailed evidence of this sort is still a matter of controversy (Gouras & Zrenner, 1979; Lennie & D'Zmura, 1988; Schiller & Logothetis, 1990; Lee, Martin & Valberg, 1988).[19] Whatever the de-

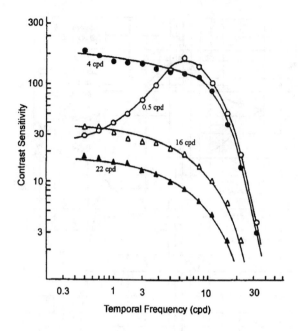

Figure 9.10 Contrast sensitivity as a function of temporal frequency, with spatial frequency as a parameter. All spatial frequencies except 0.5 cpd reveal low-pass characteristics. Band-pass characteristics are exhibited at 0.5 cpd. (From Robson, 1966.)

tailed physiological explanation may be, the general conclusion is clearly consistent with the results of conventional heterochromatic flicker photometry as discussed earlier.

INTERACTIONS BETWEEN L- AND M-CONES

The L- and M-cones feed into neural systems that exhibit spatial and temporal spectral opponent processing. The perception of a contour may depend upon a luminance difference alone, a chromatic difference alone, or both of these together. In all cases, L- and M-cones work together symbiotically in ways that are now beginning to be understood; the background physiology has already been examined in some detail in Chapter 7. An experiment by Kelly (1975) will help to illustrate this. But, before we look at Kelly's work, let's try to answer the question, do spatial frequency and temporal frequency both influence contrast sensitivity?

The answer to this question can be seen in Figure 9.10 from Robson (1966). It shows that the fall-off at high temporal frequen-

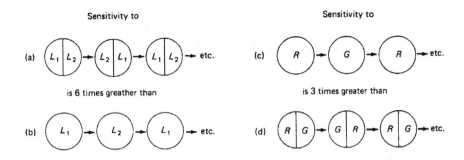

Figure 9.11 Summary of experimental conditions and main results of an experiment by Kelly (1975).

cies occurs for all spatial frequencies. But low frequencies are a different matter. It can be seen in Figure 9.10 that for 0.5 cpd there is a clear fall-off in sensitivity at low temporal frequencies, whereas for 4, 16, and 22 cpd there is not. In other words, the temporal contrast sensitivity function for achromatic low spatial frequency stimuli is band pass where as for higher spatial frequencies it is low pass.

Using low-frequency sinusoidal flicker (1 cpd), Kelly investigated modulation sensitivity to temporal variations in luminance and chromaticity, using fields that were either uniform, as shown in Figure 9.11(b) and (c), or vertically divided and modulated in counterphase, as shown in Figure 9.11(a) and (d). For 1-Hz flicker, he found that splitting the field greatly enhanced sensitivity for luminance modulation [Fig. 9.11(a)], but reduced it considerably for chromaticity modulation [Fig. 9.11(d)].

Let us now see what stimulus properties might affect the sensitivity to the 1 Hz temporally alternating stimuli depicted in Figure 9.11.[20] Because of the luminance difference between its two halves, the stimulus in Figure 9.11(a) has a higher spatial frequency than that of (b) which is uniform. Kelly's finding that sensitivity is greater for the divided field is understandable if we assume that the spatial frequencies in (b) that control sensitivity are less than 4 cpd, and those in (a) are at least 4 cpd. Because the chromatic spatial contrast sensitivity function has low-pass characteristics, the greatest chromatic sensitivity will be a low spatial frequencies. Hence, the uniform flickering field (c) is more visible than the bipartite field (d).

The function of lateral inhibition is to enhance contours. Most contours result from luminance differences. Therefore, so long as there exists a luminance difference to be enhanced (given that this same

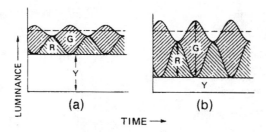

Figure 9.12   Examples of stimulus waveforms used by Kelly and van Norren (1977). Here the green/red ratio of two sinusoidal stimulus components is kept constant while the modulation depth is increased in (b) relative to (a). To keep the adaptation level of the eye constant, the luminance of a steady yellow component (Y) in (a) is reduced in (b), so that the sum of the steady Y component and the red-green flickering components produces the same mean luminance in each case. This is shown by the horizontal dashed lines.

machinery is also required for chromatic purposes to mediate lateral inhibition between receptors of different types) then why not use it also for this essentially achromatic purpose? A second question about this scheme relates to the behavior of dichromats (Chapter 10). For example, protanopes (who lack L-cone photopigment) show a lack of red-green discrimination as well. One may legitimately inquire: if L-cone photopigment is lacking in protanopes, what (if anything) takes its place? Is it possible that the protanopic retina is riddled with holes where L-cones and their photopigments normally would be? The anatomical evidence is to the contrary (Kalmus, 1965, p. 53), and such a situation would be a structural disaster. A very simple hypothesis is to assume that protanopic L-cones are still present, but that they are filled with middle wavelength photopigment normally found only in M-cones. If in addition these "L" cones of the protanope were otherwise normal, then "L" and M cones would mediate achromatic lateral inhibition in the usual way, although the r-g opponent signals would always be balanced at zero. Excepting a reduced sensitivity to long wavelengths and an inability to make color discriminations that depend upon r-g difference signals, protanopes would be expected to exhibit normal vision, and they do.

A study by Kelly and van Norren (1977) was designed as a further test of ideas similar to those just discussed. Their stimulus configuration is schematized in Figure 9.12. Three optical channels were used.[21] Two of these produced sinewave flicker, in this case of red and green appearing lights out of phase. Because the green (G) component in this illustration has a higher luminance than the red (R) one, there is an achromatic component of the stimulus whose amplitude is represented by fluctuations around the dashed lines at the top of each part of the figure. The contrast of the flickering component can be altered, without altering adaptation level, by manipulations depicted by the difference between the left-hand and right-hand diagrams. At the right, the R and G flicker components have been increased in proportion, resulting in a higher amplitude of chromatic and achromatic flicker. To keep adaptation level constant, a steady yellow-appearing (Y) field is used, whose intensity is manipulated so that the sum of Y and the average of the R + G flickering components of luminance remains fixed at the level shown by the dashed line.

The special case of purely chromatic flicker is shown in Figure 9.13(a). Here the G and R components have the same amplitude; because they are out of phase, there is no luminance fluctuation. Figure 9.13(b) shows an example of pure luminance modulation produced merely by altering the phase relationship without changing amplitude: now the R and G components are in phase. Because the total excitation of the R and G components of flicker is the same in each case, the level of photon absorption in L- and M-cones is also unchanged. In Figure 9.13(c), the G component of Figure 13(b) has been replaced by an equal luminance of R. If the chromatic component of the flickering stimulus is regarded as being proportional to the difference between R and G, then the chromatic flicker of Figure 13(c) is the same as that of Figure 12(a), except that it is now initiated only by activity of the R component. Because the luminance component of Figure 12(c) is the same as that of Figure 13(b), then Figure 13(c) can be regarded as combining both components of modulation in a single waveform.

The graph on the bottom left in Figure 9.13 shows the results of an experiment in which conditions seen in Figure 13(a) and (b) were tested. The chromatic flicker curve, shown by the filled symbols, is not completely flat at the lowest frequencies tested.[22] This result implies that not all inhibition occurs between L- and M-cones; there apparently is a certain amount that takes place also within cones of the same type. The achromatic flicker curve, shown by the open symbols, has an entirely different shape. It shows a marked low-frequency attenuation and a substantially better sensitivity to higher frequencies.

When stimulus in Figure 13(c) is used, it produces the result shown at the bottom right in Figure 9.13. Here the same two curves from the figure at the left have been drawn through the data points for condition (c) without any vertical or horizontal adjustment. The

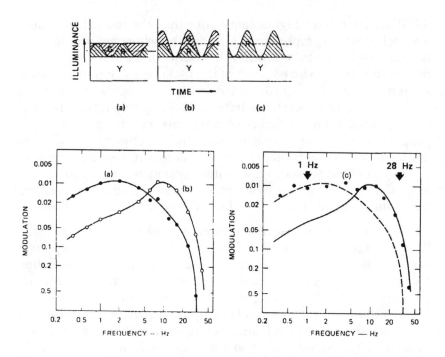

Figure 9.13 **Top**: Luminance profiles of stimulus waveforms used by Kelly and van Norren (1977). In (a) modulation is purely chromatic because a constant luminance is maintained as the red component replaces the green, and vice versa. By shifting the phase of one component relative to the other (b) pure luminance flicker is obtained. In (c) the green component of (b) has been replaced by an equal luminance of red, to produce a stimulus that includes both the chromatic component of (a) and the luminance component of (b). **Bottom**: Experimental results obtained for these three conditions. The results for condition (c) are accounted for by the upper envelope of the component functions derived from the other two conditions of the experiment.

conclusion seems clear: because the stimulus in Figure 9.13(c) contains both components of flicker (achromatic and chromatic) that the stimuli in Figure 9.13(a) and (b) contain individually, and at the same level of modulation for each, then sensitivity for the stimulus in Figure 9.13(c) is governed by the component having the greater sensitivity at each tested frequency. Below 5 Hz, this is the chromatic component; above 5 Hz, it is the achromatic one.

This experiment, and others from the same study, indicate that achromatic stimulation reveals different temporal characteristics than those obtained with chromatic stimulation.[23] Under most viewing

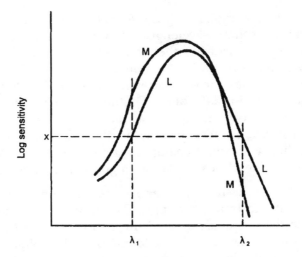

Figure 9.14   These hypothetical sensitivity curves are used to illustrate the principle of silent substitution. By choosing two wavelengths, λ_1 and λ_2, to which the L-cones are equally sensitive, alternation between them of equal radiance will silence the response to flicker in L-cones. Because the M-cones are much more sensitive to λ_1 than to λ_2, the same alternating stimulus will be an effective flickering stimulus for them.

conditions, chromatic signals passing from eye to brain are represented by the differences between cone outputs, so that activity related only to M-cones cannot generally be expected to reveal itself in single-unit responses (whether of ganglion cells, at the LGN or in visual cortex) any more than it does in psychophysical experiments. The only way to reveal the responses of L- or M-cones in isolation would be somehow to wholly negate the contribution of the other class of cone by some experimental technique. Stiles's field-sensitivity method (Chapter 6, p. 235) represents one attempt to do this, but it works only if one can safely assume that there is no transfer of adaptive effect from one type of cone to another. There is another method, to be described next.

Silent Substitution[24]

Consider the hypothetical spectral sensitivity curves of L- and M-cones that are shown in Figure 9.14. Choose an arbitrary sensitivity level x, and draw a horizontal line that intersects each curve twice. The intersection with the L-curve occurs at the wavelengths marked λ_1 and λ_2. Suppose that these two wavelengths are alternated with one another at equal radiance. Because we know that the L function has equal values at these wavelengths, then (by definition of what is meant by spectral sensitivity) they will have identical effects upon the L-cones. Therefore, an L-cone would not respond differentially to sudden switch from one of these wavelengths to the other. This is what is meant by a *silent substitution*. On the other hand, the M-cones are considerably more sensitive to λ_1 than to λ_2. The same equal-radiance substitution, therefore, that is silent for L-cones will produce a significant transient change in the stimulation of M-cones, with an increased level of stimulation in going from λ_2 to λ_1.

It must be emphasized that the L-cones are stimulated by this procedure, but only by a steady input. Therefore, if a flicker experiment is undertaken that uses a rapid alternation between these wavelengths at equal radiance, only the M-cones will be able to respond to the flicker. Actually there is no need to choose a pair of wavelengths to which cones of one type have exactly equal sensitivity. Sensitivity differences can easily be compensated by inverse adjustment of the radiances of the alternating components. The only requirements to be met are (1) that the two sensitivity curves be significantly different, and (2) that the spectral sensitivity of the class of cones to be silenced is known. In Chapter 5, the current status of our knowledge of cone action spectra was discussed with the conclusion that these are now fairly well established; recall that we needed to know these shapes in order to analyze chromatic discrimination in Chapter 8.

The result of Kelly and van Norren's application of the silent substitution procedure is shown in Figure 9.15. In this experiment a red light alternated with a green one. These investigators worked over a range of balances of their stimulus components designed to keep chromatic flicker constant as luminance flicker was varied. The abscissa of the figure refers to the fraction of the total luminance of their stimulus that is made up of the green component. A value of zero indicates that all of the sinusoidal flicker is in the red component; unity indicates that it is all in the green one. (Both L- and M-cones respond, though differentially so, to both components.)

The curve labeled "28 Hz" shows a sharp drop of temporal modulation sensitivity when the luminances of the two components are balanced. Because this is a condition of steady luminance, this curve would drop to zero if the 28-Hz stimulus were effective only upon the luminance channels. The fact that it does not do so indicates that the chromatic channels are capable of following at this frequency, but only rather poorly.

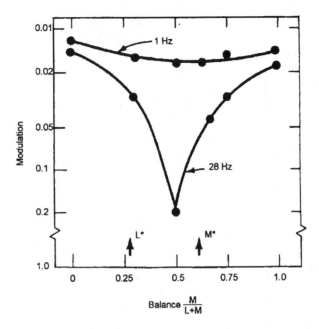

Figure 9.15   Results from Kelly and van Norren's (1977) experiment, in which the ratio of L and M components of a flickering stimulus was varied in such a way as to keep r-g chromatic flicker constant as luminance flicker was varied. At 1 Hz, where chromatic processes are most sensitive, the ratio of the two components has little effect. At 28 Hz, where achromatic processes are most sensitive, flicker sensitivity is minimized when the luminances of the counterphase components are equal. The arrows at the bottom represent the calculated ratios of the stimulus components for pure L-cone excitation (L*), with M-cones silenced, and for pure M-cone excitation (M*), with L-cones silenced.

The curve labeled "1 Hz" is for an identical stimulus condition at a lower temporal frequency. For the conditions of this part of the experiment, modulation sensitivity does not vary much across the entire range of ratios that were studied. If only the chromatic channels were capable of responding to l-Hz flicker, the curve would be horizontal. Perhaps there is a slight sag in the middle; if so, this may reveal that the achromatic channels are capable of following this frequency to a slight degree for the low levels of modulation to which the chromatic channels are mainly sensitive.

Recall that Kelly & van Norren (1977) found band-pass functions for luminance modulation and low-pass functions for chromatic modulation. Their chromatic modulation conditions did not allow

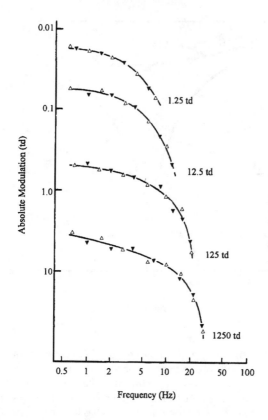

Figure 9.16 Absolute modulation as a function of temporal frequency of the L-cones (filled, inverted triangles) and the M-cones (open triangles). Cone responses were isolated by means of silent substitution The data were collected at four adaptation levels as indicated by the troland values next to each curve (from Estévez & Spekreijse, 1974).

them to distinguish between L- and M-cone responses. Estévez & Spekreijse (1974), using the silent substitution approach described above, reported modulation as a function of temporal frequency functions mediated separately for L- and M-cones (Fig. 9.16). They plotted their data as Kelly did in Figure 9.8, and found no differences as a function of cone types. Note that the open triangles (M-cones) and filled inverted triangles (L-cones) fall on common curves. Kelly's luminance functions in Figure 9.8 show clear low-frequency declines in sensitivity and the common high frequency fall-off meets the abscissa between 50 and 100 Hz. By contrast, the functions of Estévez & Spekreijse show no low-frequency fall-off. When Kelly & van Norren plotted their silent substitution data (their Figs. 8 and 9), they found similar high frequency fall-off as did Estévez & Spekreijse. The lowest temporal frequencies used by Estévez & Spekreijse were slightly higher than those of Kelly & van Norren; and the latter exhibit a slight low-frequency decline in sensitivity for temporal frequencies common to the two studies (their Figs. 8 and 9). The fact that no low frequency fall-off is evident when cones are isolated but is evident when they are not, suggests that the fall off at low frequencies is attributable to an opponent interaction between L- and M-cones that might be minimized when only one type is active.

TEMPORAL RESPONSES OF CONES AND THEIR PATHWAYS

When a temporal modulation sensitivity function is established by psychophysical procedures, the measurement will reveal the properties of photoreceptors only if it can safely be assumed that the pathways into which receptors feed have a much better frequency response curve than that of the receptors. Otherwise, the frequency response of the pathways will interact with that of the receptors in determining the overall ability of the system to follow a flickering input. Flicker photometry apparently succeeds because the r+g pathways, concerned with luminance, have a flicker response superior to that of the r-g pathways that are concerned with color. Because both pathways receive their inputs from the same L- and M-cones, it cannot be the receptors *per se* that determine the flicker response in both cases.

Figure 9.17 provides a further illustration of the effects of adaptation level on the response to flicker. The upper curve (solid circles) shows the threshold amplitude of a sinusoidal stimulus of 100 percent modulation, which of necessity is measured with no added background. The adaptation level for 100 percent modulation is therefore determined solely by the mean luminance of the sinusoidally varying field, which varies along the curve, increasing downward. For example, at a mean luminance of 10 td, the maximum frequency that can be resolved is about 18 Hz. The lower curve (open circles) is for a constant adaptation level of 25,000 td, produced mainly by a steady background upon which a smaller flickering component is superimposed (except at the highest frequency tested). To see 18 Hz flicker in this case, a larger amplitude of modulation is required than before–about 1500 td. But for an adaptation level of 25,000 td, this large amplitude of modulation nevertheless represents only about three percent relative modulation, which means that much greater modulation is yet possible. The limit is reached at the lower right-hand point on the graph, where flicker at nearly 50 Hz can be resolved for 100 percent modulation at 25,000 td.

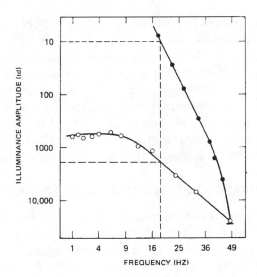

Figure 9.17 Results of an experiment by Kelly, Boynton and Baron, (1976). The solid points refer to a condition of 100% modulation and variable adaptation level; they specify the maximum frequencies of flicker that can be perceived at these levels. The open circles at the bottom represent flicker thresholds under a condition of 25,000 td adaptation level, which is held constant for all frequencies.

If the visual channels can handle nearly 50 Hz at a high adaptation level, it seems likely that they can also resolve better than 18 Hz at the lower adaptation level. The message probably fails to register at higher frequencies than this because of two effects associated with low adaptation levels: (1) the lower absolute amplitude of stimulation that physically can be provided by a fully modulated field, and (2) temporally less well defined responses of the receptors. Although light-adapting a receptor reduces its absolute sensitivity, it has the beneficial effect of crisping the temporal characteristics of responses having a given amplitude. Therefore, although a higher absolute amplitude of modulation is required for the light-adapted receptor to achieve a given amplitude of response, still higher modulations are available and these enable the flicker to be followed to very high frequencies.

The foregoing analysis does not rule out the possibility that some of the effects of adaptation are attributable to changes in the ability of the visual pathways to follow what the receptors deliver. It would, in fact, be extravagant to design a system in which the temporal resolution of the conducting pathways was much higher than that of the receptors themselves. At low adaptation levels, where there is very little light available, the primary task of the visual system is to provide vision that is as good as possible, given the shortage of photons. As an aid to this, the sensitivity of the eye can be improved by permitting the integration of light over longer time periods than might otherwise be optimal. As the adaptation level is increased, the intensity of an added stimulus must be made greater in order for it to be seen. The extra photons in the adapting field can be used to good advantage if they somehow lead to an improved temporal response of the eye. Such improvement occurs in the photoreceptors, as we have seen, but this would be of no use unless the pathways could take advantage of it. So the properties of the pathways are not only due to the receptors connecting to them, but arise also from the pathway structure.

This hypothesis about the temporal properties of pathways could be tested if the response of the entire visual system, as determined psychophysically, could be compared with that of receptors alone. When this is done by comparing monkey receptor potentials to human psychophysics, the high-frequency asymptote, but not the low frequency fall-off, of the psychophysical L- and M-modulation sensitivity functions are identical to each other and to those obtained electrophysiologically. A reasonable but not certain conclusion is that with high-intensity chromatic adaptation of the sort that is normally used to isolate L- and M-cones, the maximum temporal resolution of the visual pathways does not limit the psychophysical measurement, which therefore taps the high frequency limits of the receptors.

Frequency Response of L-, M-, and S-Cones

When 100 percent modulation is used to test the maximum frequency that monkey receptors can follow, the use of long and middle wavelength light yields essentially identical results, as shown by the solid and open circles of Figure 9.18. By use of longwave adapting stimuli of various intensities, it has proved possible to deduce the limits of the frequency resolution of the S-cones: this curve is also plotted in Figure 9.18. If the curves are adjusted to fit at low frequencies, the response of S-cones falls off more abruptly than that of the L- or M-cones as frequency increases. It may be concluded that, despite any known structural differences between the three kinds of cones in the primate eye, the temporal response of the S-cones at high frequencies is for some reason inferior to that of the other two types.[25]

At the lower frequencies normally used for flicker photometry, the L-, M-, and S-cones have more nearly comparable sensitivities to flicker. It therefore seems likely that the failure of S-cones to contrib-

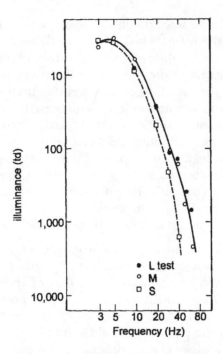

Figure 9.18 Retinal illuminance required to elicit a 10 microvolt criterion response to flickering lights under conditions designed to isolate responses of the L-, M-, and S-cones of Macaque monkeys (After Boynton & Baron, 1975.)

ute to luminance, as measured by flicker photometry, results largely from a limited frequency response of the y-b pathways. If so, both kinds of chromatic opponent pathways have a lower temporal resolution relative to that of the cone photoreceptors or the faster achromatic pathways.

COLOR AND MOTION

In 1965, R. L. Gregory prepared a patent application for a heterochromatic photometer (Gregory, 1974). The initial description reads as follow:

> This photometer might be a solution to an old problem: how to measure the visually effective intensity of lights of various colours. Normal comparison instruments cannot be used efficiently when the unknown light is of different colour from the internal standard, for it is then difficult to judge when the fields are of equal intensity.

> The idea arose from a chance observation: that if two sets
> of stripes move in opposite directions across each other, at
> the same speed, then if one set of moving stripes is illumi-
> nated at a higher intensity than the other, movement will
> be observed — *in the direction of the brighter stripes.* When
> the sets of stripes are of nearly equal brightness then no
> drift of movement is observed, but rather a strange and
> distinctive 'jazzing effect.' All of this is *independent* of the
> *colours* of the set of moving stripes; and so it would seem
> possible to use this as the basis of a visual photometer suit-
> able for coloured lights. (p. 475)

In the patent description Gregory provided detailed drawings of this heterochromatic photometer and tells the reader that the device, in fact, was never built. However, the idea has persisted. Wallman (1975) described an apparatus with two transparent, concentric, counter rotating chromatic and achromatic striped cylinders that he used to test the color vision of animals. Moreland (1982) also showed that "motion photometry," as he called it, yielded data consistent with heterochromatic photometry. In 1983, Anstis and Cavanagh implemented apparent motion on a color monitor to perform motion heterochromatic photometry. It has been demonstrated that their nulling of apparent motion criterion yields almost indistinguishable results from those obtained by flicker photometry (Anstis & Cavanagh, 1983; Cavanagh, Anstis & MacLeod, 1987).

It appears that a significant motion signal occurs via the magnocellular pathways. However, there is evidence from motion aftereffects that there may be a weak input to the motion via the parvocellular pathway, specifically attributable to the spectrally opponent neurons (Cavanagh & Favreau, 1985; Mullen & Baker, 1985.)

SPATIAL FACTORS

Interactions Among Receptors

If one creates a pure chromatic spatial counterphase grating made up of constant luminance long wavelength and middle wavelength sine waves, it will appear as a pattern of red/yellow/green stripes. The green stripes occur where the luminance of the green is maximum and the red is minimum. Likewise, red is seen where the red is maximum and green is minimum. When viewed at a close distance, yellow is seen where the luminance of the long and middle wavelength spatial sine waves are approximately equal.

When viewed at a distance, the dominant percept is a pattern of yellow and black stripes, perhaps with a reddish-yellow haze. As one moves way from a constant size object, the visual angle subtended by the object decreases and concomitantly the spatial frequency of this pattern increases. De Valois and De Valois (1988) describe the optical factors that cause this perceptual change. They are chromatic aberration and optical diffraction. Chromatic aberration of the human eye is a factor that does not have a great effect at low spatial frequencies, but has an increasing effect as spatial frequency increases. It shifts the red pattern with respect to the green pattern so they no longer are in exact counterphase. Therefore, it changes the modulation depth of the stimulus as it reaches the retina thereby transforming what in the stimulus plane is an equiluminous grating into a grating on the retina that varies in retinal illuminance.

Such a red/green grating illustrates a major difficulty in doing research with this type of spatial stimulus. One might think that this should not be such a big problem. Why not just use a very small artificial pupil that will greatly reduce problems associated with chromatic aberration? Unfortunately, this remedy will greatly increase the problems associated with diffraction (see Chapter 3). Another potential solution to the problem is to use an auxiliary lens, called an achromatizing lens (Bedford & Wyszecki, 1957: Powell, 1981.)[26] Unfortunately, achromatizing lenses do not correct for all three types of chromatic aberration; some may even increase the chromatic difference of magnification. The Powell lens does not increase it, but it also does not reduce the latter aberration. Regan (1973) has described a method of reducing all three type of chromatic aberration by placing the stimuli at appropriately different distances from the eyes and adjusting their sizes accordingly to insure that the different wavelengths are in focus on the retina.

Mullen (1985) measured the opponent chromatic contrast sensitivity as a function of spatial frequency. Simply put, she generated a pure chromatic grating by presenting two sinusoidal gratings of different wavelengths, 180° out of phase, and equated them for luminance. Then she determined the contrast sensitivity of this chromatic grating as a function of spatial frequency. She also measured the spatial contrast sensitivity for luminance sinusoidal gratings. To minimize the effects of chromatic aberration she used a different, but optically equivalent, procedure to that used by Regan. Appropriate positive or negative lenses were placed between the stimuli and a partially-silvered mirror that combined them before presentation to the visual system. Then the spatial frequency was adjusted so that perceptually the two sinewaves were equal. Wavelength dependent diffraction effects were avoided by using spatial frequencies no greater than 6 cpd.

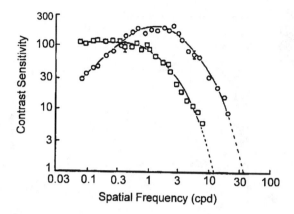

Figure 9.19   Contrast sensitivity as a function of spatial frequency for a red-green equiluminous grating (squares) and a green monochromatic grating (circles). Note the low pass nature of the red-green grating and the band pass nature of the monochromatic grating (from Mullen, 1985).

Mullen found that the chromatic spatial grating yielded a low pass function whereas the luminance grating yielded band pass functions. The peak contrast sensitivity for the luminance grating was at approximately 2 cpd (circles, Fig. 9.19). The chromatic grating showed no low- frequency fall-off (squares) at the lowest frequencies (approximately 0.1 cpd). The highest spatial frequencies for luminance gratings that the visual system could resolve was approximately 30 cpd, although for chromatic gratings these were not measured at spatial frequencies higher than 6 cpd. Extrapolations from the data suggest that the r-g grating has a high frequency cut off at just over 10 cpd (Fig. 9.19).

One of the major contributions in Mullen's research was her minimizing chromatic aberration. However, as Kelly (1989) noted, an uncontrolled factor remained in her data, namely eye movements. Unless special precautions are taken, involuntary eye movements are frequently uncontrolled in vision research. Kelly (1974) demonstrated the interaction between temporal and spatial frequency. He found that the degree of low frequency fall-off for spatial contrast sensitivity was reduced or eliminated by flickering the spatial grating. The temporal frequency on the retina of a steady grating is a function of the eye movement velocity times the spatial frequency of the grating. Therefore, normal involuntary eye movements, (even during fixation) add an uncontrolled temporal factor to the contrast sensitivity function (Kelly, 1989). It is possible to present stimuli using an appa-

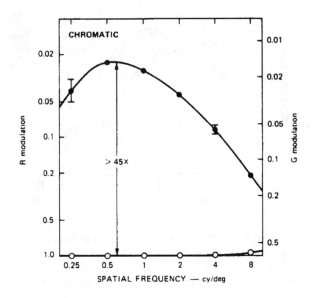

Figure 9.20 Modulation thresholds for a red-green grating at isoluminance. The curve for the solid circles was collected with natural eye movements. The curve with the open circles was collected under image stabilization conditions (Note that even 100% color contrast (1.0) is not enough to reach threshold because the grating disappears.) Left and right ordinates are the modulations of the red and green (respectively) components of the grating (from Kelly, 1983).

ratus that minimizes the effects of eye movements by stabilizing the stimulus image on the retina. Kelly (1983) showed that when a chromatic grating is presented as a stabilized image it was not possible to measure its purely spatial contrast sensitivity because the image faded too quickly under these conditions. Figure 9.20 compares the stabilized and unstabilized conditions for a spatial contrast threshold as a function of spatial frequency for an isoluminance red-green grating. Data for the stabilized condition (open circles) lie at the bottom of the figure.

It would be interesting to have an estimate of eye movement velocity when these chromatic contrast sensitivity functions are measured and image stabilization is not used. Kelly (1989) approximates just such an estimate in Figure 9.21. The filled circles are the data from Figure 9.20 and represent the unstabilized image function. The series of curves represent functions when eye movements are nulled and a red-green grating is continuously drifted across the retina at the velocities indicated. Kelly notes that "this creates the effect of an

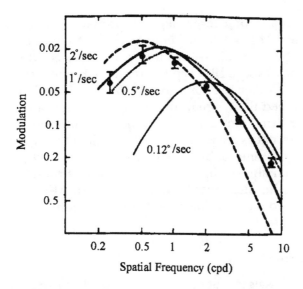

Figure 9.21   Modulation as a function of spatial frequency for a red-green grating moving at the velocities shown. The filled circles come from Fig. 9.20. The curves were determined by measuring the chromatic spatial contrast sensitivity under conditions where normal eye-movements were nulled and the chromatic grating drifted across the display at the velocities indicated (from Kelly, 1983).

'artificial eye-movement' (p. 84)." The reader can see that the contrast sensitivity with natural eye movements (filled circles) fits the 1°/s curve rather well, although the fit to the 0.5°/s is almost as good.

Mullen (personal communication) points out that her data are not affected by eye movements. Her argument is that Mullen & Boulton (1992) determined that a temporal frequency of drift of 0.4 Hz is the optimum frequency for vision at all spatial frequencies. Consequently, if eye movements introduce high temporal frequencies they would not improve the sensitivity. If one takes another look at Figure 9.21 it can be seen that the spatial contrast sensitivity function when using natural eye movements is, as noted above, nearly the same as that for stabilized vision with drift rates of 0.5 and 1 deg/sec. Therefore, it appears that the presence of natural eye movements in Mullen's experiment did not compromise her results.

Spatial Properties of the Three Classes of Cones

Evidence was presented in Chapter 7 to show that both chromatic and achromatic pathways mediate the perception of contour.

Spatial vision at photopic levels depends primarily on the activity of L- and M-cones. At low spatial frequencies the S-cones can make a contribution, but they almost assuredly make no contributions at spatial frequencies above 10–14 cpd (Stromeyer, Kranda & Sternheim, 1978; Williams, Collier & Thompson, 1983). The L- and M-cones, as we have seen, feed their signals into both luminance and r-g opponent channels. It is sometimes stated that the contours formed by luminance differences are necessarily more salient than those caused by chromatic differences, but this may be an incorrect generalization. It has been shown that the strength of a chromatic contour depends upon the differential amount of L- (or M-) cone activity related to the two parts of the visual field whose junction forms the contour.

Border Distinctness[27]

(Boynton & Kaiser, 1968) found it possible to determine the amount of luminance contrast needed to produce a contour of the same strength as that caused by any particular chromatic difference at constant luminance. The most distinct contour that a purely chromatic difference can produce is formed between fields of 465 and 700 nm. The first of these elicits the maximum possible ratio of M/L cone activity, whereas the second is optimal for L/M.[28] The amount of achromatic contrast required to mimic this maximum chromatic contour varies from one observer to another, but it is on the order of 30–40 percent. An achromatic contrast of this amount comes very close to what is needed to mediate the highest levels of spatial discrimination.

Three methods have been used to specify an equivalent achromatic contrast that produces the same strength of border as produced by a purely chromatic difference. In all three cases, the procedure is first to ask the subject to set a minimally distinct border between the two chromatically different fields being tested. For the subject under examination, we believe that this equates the activity of his achromatic pathways over the entire field.[29]

The first method for estimating border distinctness uses a direct comparison. Two juxtaposed fields of uniform chromaticity are presented slightly above, but clearly separated from, the chromatic fields that are being gauged. The observer adjusts the luminance of one side of the upper field in order to produce a contour which appears as distinct as the chromatic border seen below. A second method requires the use of only the chromatic pair: after having set the minimally distinct border, the subject simply rates its perceived strength along a 7-point scale, where zero means no border at all, 7 indicates a very strong contour, and 4 is intermediate (other integers are also used). A similar procedure can be used with borders formed by luminance differences only. The third method measures the tendency of steadily fixated borders to fade in terms of the percentage of time, during five minutes of intense staring, that a border is not seen. Results based upon the three methods agree well.

At a given luminance level, it proves possible to write an equation that relates the two kinds of contrast. But at low luminances, the achromatic contrast required to mimic a certain amount of chromatic border strength is greater than it is for high luminances. A plausible interpretation of this differential dependence upon luminance points up an essential difference between chromatic and achromatic borders that was discussed earlier in this chapter and also in Chapter 7. Border enhancement by lateral inhibition occurs only for achromatic borders (Fiorentini, 1972, p. 194). Assuming that the enhancement process is intensity dependent, being more effective at high intensities than low, then a higher achromatic contrast would be needed at low luminances than at high in order to mimic a border of fixed chromaticity difference. This hypothesis is consistent with the increased low-frequency inhibition that is found with increasing intensity in the experiments of Figure 9.8.

In experiments where borders divide small, centrally fixated fields, S-cones appear to play only a minor role. A curious situation exits where, for example, a 1° bipartite field, blue on one side and green on the other, provides a rather indistinct border between the hemifields, and the colors appear to melt together. If this field is masked down so that only an area of about 12' of width is seen, with the physical border dividing it, the field becomes homogeneous in appearance, with its hue depending upon the location of the physical border, which, as it moves, alters the percentage of the two components. When a similar border is formed by a luminance difference, or by a chromatic difference mediated by L- and M-cones, a clearly defined border is easily seen as moving within the masked area.

It was pointed out earlier in this chapter that visual acuity is not markedly dependent upon wavelength. However, if the activity of the S-cone system is isolated by the use of intense longwave adapting light, thereby selectively depressing the sensitivities of L- and M-cones, the true spatial inferiority of the S-cone system becomes evident. The physiological basis for this S-cone inferiority, where spatial vision is concerned, almost certainly relates to their sparse distribution in the retina, especially in the central foveal region, where they may be entirely absent in a region of 8' to 20' of arc or thereabouts.[30]

Why Is the S-cone System So Different?

It may be instructive to think teleologically and ask: why design the retina this way, rather than to use equal numbers of L-, M-, and S-cones? We may speculate that a principal job of the visual system is to localize regions of space, and then to provide sufficient spatial resolution within these smaller regions to permit a high level of visual acuity. The foveal region of the retina evolved to mediate high spatial resolution, as we saw in Chapter 4. In the fovea, the diffusing layers of the retina needed to process and carry visual messages are swept aside, and almost the entire thickness of the retina is made up of the receptors. Despite the thinness of the foveal retina, the outer segments of the receptors are longer and skinnier than elsewhere, achieving a peak density of at least 150,000 receptors per square millimeter. Rods are excluded from the select group of receptors that is found here and, in addition, S-cones are discouraged. There are some S-cones in the outer zones of the fovea, but probably few if any in the central bouquet with which we do our most critical seeing (Wald, 1967).

The L- and M-cones have a dual function, as has been repeatedly stressed: to mediate both spatial and chromatic vision. To do this properly, it is likely that they are functionally interrelated, as in the turtle, by way of horizontal cells and probably also by gap junctions (Chapter 7). The difference signals derived from them are simultaneously of two kinds, spatial and chromatic. It seems clear that these two kinds of cones must have very similar spatial and temporal properties in order to work together properly. They probably differ structurally in no way (Ahnelt, *et al.*, 1987; 1990). They differ only in the photopigments they contain, and the connections that they make (Calkins, Schein, Tsukamoto and Sterling, 1994).

S-cones, on the other hand, seem to have primarily a chromatic function. Although we once thought that S-cones did not process information having to do with the perception of borders, we now know that they do make a small contribution (Kaiser & Boynton, 1985; Boynton, Eskew and Olson, 1985). Mollon (1991) has written that, "It would, in fact, be careless to say that the information provided by the shortwave cones is *purely* chromatic." (p. 312). The S-cones have recently been distinguished structurally from other cones in the human retina (see pg. 269). Because there are so few of them, they capture relatively few photons and the intrinsic sensitivity of the S-cone system in central vision must be very low. To compensate for this, signals from S-cones summate over large regions. The purpose of this summation is to gain sensitivity, but this gain is achieved at a cost of low spatial resolving power. The maximum spatial frequency

S-cones can resolve is approximately 10 cpd and their maximum sensitivity is about 1 cpd (Mollon, 1991).

The hue that S-cones help to initiate appears to be well integrated within contours that the L- and M-cone are responsible for rendering. The process of integration seems to stop, or at least is severely discouraged, beyond these contours. Thus, the hue of an object appears to terminate at its edge and does not seem to spill into the space beyond. The gap effect, which was mentioned in the previous chapter (Boynton, Hayhoe & MacLeod, 1977), shows that discriminations which depend only upon differential activity of S-cones are improved by contours that serve to confine the averaging within each half of a split field.

Luminance/Color: A Function Of Spatial/Temporal Frequency?

Much remains to be learned about the functions of the separate chromatic and achromatic channels that seem to have evolved in human vision. The general outlines, however, seem already to be clear. Because spatial vision is its main assignment, the problem of design is to provide chromatic information without reducing spatial acuity or adding an excessive number of fibers to the million or so neurons of the optic nerve, which seems to be the principal bottleneck for information transmission from eye to brain. Most of these transmission lines probably are concerned with achromatic messages, fed by both L- and M-cones, the same ones that generate the chromatic difference signals. Fewer channels probably are devoted to these chromatic signals, which means that something must be sacrificed. Temporal resolution seems mainly to be what is lost, as we have seen by comparing chromatic and achromatic modulation transfer functions in time.

One of the more intriguing concepts with regard to the luminance and chromatic attributes of vision is the idea that these two functions require the use of the same neural pathways, namely the parvocellular pathway (Ingling & Martinez-Uriegas, 1983a,b; Lennie & D'Zmura, 1988). There are, however, two schools of thought. One, championed by Lee and his colleagues, is that luminance is primarily a function of the magnocellular pathway and the chromatic properties of the visual system are handled by the parvocellular pathways. There is a fair amount of physiological evidence to support this view (e.g., Lee, Martin & Valberg, 1988a,b; Kaiser, Lee, Martin & Valberg, 1990; Kaiser, 1991). On the other hand, strong arguments have been made that luminance can also be handled by the parvocellular pathway in addition to the signals carried by the magnocellular pathway.

The parvocellular pathway activity has been referred to as serving double duty: luminance and color.

One of the first pieces of physiological evidence in support of a so–called double duty hypothesis was by Gouras and Zrenner (1979). They recorded from monkey ganglion cells and found that when chromatic stimuli were flickered at a low frequencies ganglions cells responded in a typical spectrally opponent fashion. However, when excited by chromatic stimuli flickered at about 30 Hz the ganglion cells responded in a spectrally non-opponent way.

Ingling & Martinez–Uriegas (1983 a,b) as present an elegant analysis of L/M single opponent units and model a double duty mechanism using the idea of multiplexing of the luminance and chromatic signals. At low spatial and temporal frequencies L-cones are predicted to subtract M-cones and thereby behave in a spectrally opponent way. At high spatial and temporal frequencies L-cones are predicted to sum with M-cones and thereby be spectrally non-opponent. Therefore the same neural units would be expected to respond both to the chromatic and to the luminance contents of stimuli. These neural units are predicted to perform two functions but not at the same time. Whether they operate as a chromatic unit or a luminance unit depends on the spatial and temporal characteristics of the stimulus.

The y-b Opponent System

Little has been said here about the y-b opponent channels, which have so far been much less studied psychophysically. To the extent that the physiological dichotomy between r-g and y-b cells (Chapter 7) is accepted as convincing, these signals exist at the ganglion cell level in primates. Therefore, the y-b message, like the r-g, must be extracted in the retina. However, it seems less likely that the y-b signal is extracted in such intimate relation to receptor activity as is the case for the r-g signals. There are, in the first place, no Y-cones with which S-cones can subtractively interact. Rather, S-cones probably interact with signals representing the sum of L- and M-activity–the luminance signals. The S-cone spectral sensitivity is very different from the photopic luminosity function, so there is much less overlap between L+M and S signals than between L and M; this reduces the need for an immediate extraction of a difference signal. Finally, psychophysical evidence (Larimer, Krantz & Cicerone, 1975) that the r-g signal is much more linear than the y-b message is consistent with the idea that more stages of visual processing are completed, in the y-b case, prior to the extraction of a difference signal. The rivalrous perception of blue and yellow lights, when these are presented to opposite eyes, also tends to support this contention (deWeert & Levelt, 1975).

COLOR INFORMATION FROM EDGES

This chapter began with mention of the lack of color perception in a ganzfeld, which suggests that, without contour, there is no color. In Chapter 8 it was suggested that, if the S-cones are excepted, the distinctness of a chromatic border might serve as a valid index of the color difference between the fields being compared. Repeatedly it has been stressed that the same L- and M-cones that are responsible for initiating contour perception also feed the r-g opponent pathways. These ideas suggest that the perceived color of an area depends heavily upon messages associated with the contour that serves to define a region, and less upon signals coming from within the region so defined.

Contour is necessary for any kind of visual perception. When the retinal image is immobilized, thus eliminating even the smallest eye movements that are present in normal vision, all visual perception fades away after a few seconds.[31] It is possible to construct an optical apparatus so that both a central spot containing one hue and a surrounding region containing another hue are seen as a stabilized image (Krauskopf, 1963; Piantanida & Larimar, 1989; Nerger, Piantanida & Larimer, 1993). Krauskopf showed that when a central spot, and the region surrounding it are stabilized, the entire target faded from view. But when the central target was stabilized and the surround was not, the target once again could be seen. From the standpoint of color vision, the most interesting finding was that the hue of the entire field became that of the annulus, whereas without stabilization, they were different. When both the central spot and the annulus were stabilized, evidence of a hue discontinuity between annulus and central spot was apparently lost, along with information about the presence of the contour between spot and annulus. The hue of the central spot then became determined by the action of the unstabilized, and considerably remote, outer edge of the annulus. Nerger *et al.* (1993), using a similar apparatus, showed that under stabilized conditions the color appearance of the filled-in background has an effect on hue cancellation but not on detection thresholds. So it would seem that the filled-in hue affects some observers' tasks, but not others.

SUMMARY

Flicker photometry was developed as a procedure to equate the visual effectiveness of lights of different colors. It was used because direct procedures, such as those involving brightness matching, produced unreliable and nonlinear results. The theoretical basis of flicker photometry was originally obscure. The modern view, resting on theoretical conceptions rooted in psychophysical evidence, is that achromatic (luminance) channels of the visual system involved with flicker photometry tasks exhibit a temporal response superior to that of other non-opponent or opponent-color channels. Flicker photometry succeeds because, at intermediate frequencies, the luminance channels are more capable than the chromatic ones of following the flickering input. Luminance depends only upon signals from L- and M-cones. Their spectral sensitivities overlap sufficiently for departures from linearity to be very small, and additive achromatic channels exhibit nearly univariant properties despite their dual input.

The application of linear-systems theory to the study of the temporal response of the visual system has led to the view that the inhibitory activity associated with temporal inhibition tends to cancel the perception of low-frequency flicker, producing an optimal frequency for achromatic flicker perception. Chromatic signals exhibit little of this low-frequency attenuation of sensitivity. The overall evidence suggests that the inhibitory effect may stem more from interactions between L- and M-cone systems, than from within systems of the same type. Evidence is presented to show that the visual brain normally does not receive input from L- and M-cones individually, but instead sees only achromatic signals and chromatic signals that carry the red-green code. This is consistent with the opponent-color model first presented in Chapter 7.

The L- and M-cones play a critical role in all aspects of vision. Contours can be seen at equal luminance if differential L-M cone activation is present. S-cones, on the other hand, play a very secondary role in spatial vision in the foveal region, where they are sparsely represented. Their role is to mediate the shortwave input to the yellow-blue opponent channels.

NOTES

[1] See review by Avant (1965).
[2] Useful discussions of peripheral color vision can be found in Moreland (1972), Christ (1975), and Abramov, Gordon & Chan (1991; 1992).
[3] 6/6 is the metric equivalent of 20/20. It means that a person can see at 6 meters what the average person with normal visual acuity can see at 6 meters. 20/20 refers to feet.
[4] As will be explained later in this chapter, the concept of *luminance* depends mainly upon the procedures used in flicker photometry; these are not concerned with the spatial resolving power of the eye. Therefore it is not preordained that the relative weights of the contributions from L- and M-cones, as these are processed into sig-

nals that mediate acuity, will be the same as for those signals required by the perception of flicker. Nevertheless, when visual acuity is tested with gratings, the luminance required just to resolve a very fine grating is found to be independent of the spectral distribution of the light (Brown, Kuhns & Adler, 1957). Another approach to the problem, which obviates the need for an independent luminance scale, is to find a task where, unlike the case for gratings, acuity first improves with luminance and then becomes poorer again. Foxell and Stevens (1955) found this to be the case for Landolt Cs. Berbert (1955, 1958), using pairs of luminous dots, was able to determine the minimal separation of the dots required for them just barely to appear as double. He found small differences favoring optimal acuity for broad spectral distributions and narrow bands of light near the center of the visible spectrum, with some loss of resolution at the spectral extremes. Campbell and Gubisch (1967) found slightly better spatial resolution with monochromatic light at 578 nm in comparison with white light. For other references, see Riggs (1965), p. 331.

[5] deLange (1958) was the first to show that small phase adjustments are necessary to produce minimum flicker when there is a sinusoidal exchange of one wavelength for another. Walraven and Leebeek (1964 a, b) demonstrated that this effect is strongly dependent upon intensity, being clearly evident at 1 td but becoming absent at about 20 td and higher. In extending deLange's approach, their results were very complicated, particularly in regard to the influence of the frequency at which the phase shift was measured. A different approach is that of Weingarten (1972), who substituted red and green lights, each in an exposure of 1 s at 2 td, for parts of a white background field. The onset of a shift to 549 nm had to occur about 20–25 ms prior to a shift to 621 nm in order for the two events to be perceived as simultaneous. This difference disappeared when the luminance of the test fields was made three times greater than that of the background. The results can be explained by assuming that, when luminance does not change, the r-g opponent signals must carry the information. A change toward green for some reason takes longer to register than does one toward red. But when the same spectral changes are introduced together with a luminance change, the r + g nonopponent signals carry information that is probably registered centrally before that carried by the slower opponent signals.

[6] *Visual performance* is an expression used mainly in illuminating engineering to refer to any kind of human activity whose efficiency is importantly controlled by the quantity and distribution of illumination. An important example is reading.

[7] Think of a sector disk as a circular disk divided into an even number of pie shaped wedges. Alternate wedges are removed so that when the disk is spun in front of a light source it alternately passes and occludes the light.

[8] Ferry (1892); Porter (1902). This "law" is obeyed much more approximately than the Talbot–Plateau law.

[9] The limiting frequency for flicker perception depends importantly upon the area of the stimulus. Under some experimental conditions, for example those of Fig. 9.13, this value will be lower than 60 Hz.

[10] Although most of the data for CIE $V(\lambda)$ were collected by heterochromatic flicker photometry, other methods were also used. See Kaiser (1981) for a review of the origins of CIE $V(\lambda)$.

[11] Some such measurements were made for the special case where white and monochromatic lights were alternated, in the early days when the method of flicker photometry was being developed (Ives, 1917; Ives and Kingsbury, 1914; Troland, 1916). See also the more recent work of Truss (1957).

[12] But see Ingling *et al.* (1978) who show that as adaptation level increases, additivity failure also increases. However, even at high adaptation levels, if one takes one half of each component and compares their sum to the original reference field, a match is closely approximated. That is, additivity failures are greatest when unbalanced amounts of the components are added.

[13] The full story is more complicated than this. See Wright's comments in the Appendix, Part II, LeGrand (1968, Chapter 4) and Kaiser (1981). In determining the CIE photopic luminosity function, some data based on heterochromatic comparisons were used, and a good deal of smoothing was done. Judd (1951a) proposed a modified curve that differs from the original one mainly in showing an elevated sensitivity at short wavelengths. Wyszecki and Stiles (1982, p. 330) have summarized these data. A further modification was proposed by Vos (CIE, 1990).

[14] Very possibly (see the previous chapter) different weights must be attached to the effectiveness of photon absorptions in the L- vs. M-cones depending upon whether they contribute to luminance or to the red-green color balance. The present discussion assumes that the curves of Figure 9.4 represent the true relative ordinate positions of the L- and M-cone sensitivity curves; no adjustment of the Smith–Pokorny data is required to achieve this. To obtain a balance of L and M activity near 570 nm, as required for color balance, the log M-function in Figure 9.4 must be raised 0.3 log units relative to the position shown; equivalently, all values on the lower M-curve must be doubled.

[15] Sirovich and Abramov (1977) have shown how behavior indistinguishable from that for a univariant mechanism could result exactly despite the contributions of nonlinear components. For this to happen, each component must obey the same power law $R = kI^p$, then the sum of the two response components must be raised to the p^{-1} power.

[16] These papers were mainly published in the *Journal of the Optical Society of America*. References to this and other relevant literature may be found in a review chapter by Kelly (1972). In 1964, a collection of papers from a symposium on *Flicker*, which was held the previous year in honor of deLange, was published (Henkes & van der Tweel, eds.). The first chapter of that volume, by G. Sperling, provides an excellent introduction to the theory of linear systems analysis. A more extensive treatment is given by Cornsweet (1970).

[17] Sparrock (1969) showed that increment thresholds are the same, whether or not the adapting field is visible to the observer. He used the technique of image stabilization (Ditchburn, 1973) to render the adapting field invisible on some occasions.

[18] For example, to produce the 10 percent modulation of Figure 9.5 (c), with a steady component of the adapting field equal to 0.5 units, the maximum intensity of the fluctuating component must be 0.55 units and the minimum must be 0.45 units. Then, $I_{max} - I_{min} = (0.55 - 0.45) = 0.1$ and $I_{max} + I_{min} = (0.55 + 0.45) = 1.0$. The Michelson contrast equation is

$$\frac{I_{max} - I_{min}}{I_{max} + I_{min}} = \frac{0.1}{1.0} = 0.1.$$

[19] There is, however, clear evidence of separation of these two neural classes at the LGN, where nonopponent units are found in the magnocellular layers and opponent units are found in the parvocellular ones. The magnocellular units show a superior transient response (Dreher, Fukada & Rodieck, 1976).

[20] The spatial frequency of a uniform circular disk is not zero unless the peripheral edges are completely blurred.

[21] Kelly and van Norren also used a fourth field; to keep the discussion as simple as possible, its function is not described here.

[22] There is a general similarity between these functions and the ones originally obtained by deLange (Fig. 9.6). Two differences are that (1) Kelly and van Norren's stimuli were filtered lights of dominant wavelengths 632 and 535 nm, which would produce a higher chromatic contrast (L/M ratio) than deLange's monochromatic 615 nm and 549 nm components, and (2) Kelly and van Norren's data include measurements at three frequencies (1 Hz and below) not tested by deLange.

[23] See also King–Smith and Carden (1976).

[24] The procedures discussed in this section were developed independently by Rushton, Powell, and White (1973) and by Estévez and Spekreijse (1974). Such an exchange must be accomplished with excellent spatial and temporal precision. A control condition that is useful requires the exchange, through separate optical channels, of two fields that are spatially superimposed and of the same spectral distribution and radiance. If the apparatus is working adequately, nothing will be seen, other than a steady field.

[25] Krauskopf and Mollon (1971) tested and confirmed this indirectly by measuring the critical duration of flashes under conditions designed to isolate Stiles's π_1, π_4, and π_5 mechanisms.

[26] See Regan, Nakano & Kaiser (1993) for a succinct description and discussion of chromatic aberration.

[27] The work described in this section has been summarized in two reviews (Boynton, 1973, 1978), which may be consulted for additional references.

[28] For all practical purposes, the L/M ratio is constant beyond 700 nm. Actually, it reaches a maximum at about this wavelength and then declines, but only very slightly. See Brindley (1955), Stiles (1957), and Wyszecki and Stiles (1967, p. 561).

[29] It has been shown that there is good agreement between responses obtained by the minimally-distinct-border (MDB) technique and those measured on the same subjects using flicker photometry (Kaiser, 1971; Wagner & Boynton, 1972).

[30] Wald (1967). References to earlier work by König and Köttgen and by Willmer and Wright (1945) are given in this paper, which is based on Wald's Ives Medal address to the Optical Society of America. See also Brindley (1954), Green (1968), Kelly (1974), and Stiles (1949), and a paper by Marc and Sperling (1977) that provides the first direct evidence about cone distributions in primates (baboons).

[31] The literature of this field has been summarized in a book by Ditchburn (1973).

Chapter 10

Color Vision Variations

INTRODUCTION

In 1794, shortly after his election to the Manchester Literary and Philosophical Society, John Dalton presented the first of 116 papers that he would eventually deliver to that group. He spoke on "Extraordinary Facts Relating to the Vision of Colours," emphasizing his own variant color vision. Although Dalton's talk was not the first scientific communication about a variance in color vision, its influence was retroactively enhanced when Thomas Young chose to discuss Dalton's observations in *Lectures on Natural Philosophy* in 1807. Dalton's place in the history of color science was doubtless assured by the reputation that he later developed as the father of atomic theory.[1] In 1827, the term *Daltonism* was coined to describe red-green color deficiency, but this is only infrequently used in English-speaking countries today. However the term is preserved by the International Research Group on Color Vision Deficiencies (IRGCVD), which publishes a quarterly newsletter entitled *Daltoniana*.

It was assumed from descriptions Dalton gave of how he saw color that he was "red blind" or protanopic (see section of terminology below). If this were indeed true, then knowing what we know today, one would say that Dalton was missing the L-photopigment. (The reader will learn, in this chapter, that geneticists have identified the genes responsible for the production of the photopigments found in the outer segments of the receptors.) Dalton hypothesized that his color vision problems were due to a blue pigment in the vitreous humor in his eyes. He directed that upon his death the fluids of his eyes be examined to test his hypothesis. The vitreous was found to be entirely normal, as was his lens pigmentation, for a man of his age. Dalton's eyes have been retained to this day. DNA tests were recently performed on samples of Dalton's eye tissue and the genetic result indicates that he was actually missing his M-photopigment (Hunt, Kanwalijit, Bowmaker & Mollon, 1995). Hunt *et al.* also performed various colorimetric tests to show that the observations Dalton made were not inconsistent with the kinds of observations that would be expected of person missing the M-photopigment. With this interesting piece of historical reference, let us now look at various aspects of color variant vision that place the Dalton story into scientific perspective.

This chapter emphasizes the varieties of relatively common red-green color defects as these relate to their genetic and physiological underpinnings. This discussion will require frequent use of concepts developed in earlier chapters and will serve also to constitute a useful review of some of those ideas.

TERMINOLOGY

First, let us discuss some terminology. "Colorblind," a term that is often used to describe all abnormal color vision, is misleading. This term would seem to imply that one cannot see color. There are two classes of people who can properly be called colorblind. One group are those who do not have any functioning cone receptors. They see only with their rods. Such individuals, in addition to being colorblind, are photophobic, exhibit nystagmus, and have a severely reduced visual acuity. These observers are called *rod monochromats or achromats*. Another group of people who are truly colorblind are those that have rods and only one class of cone receptors. At photopic levels such observers would not be able to distinguish one color from another. These observers are called *cone monochromats*. Cone monochromats are distinguishable from rod monochromats by their normal visual acuity, and by a lack of nystagmus and photophobia that are characteristic of this condition (see p. 455).

Much more common are those who have two classes of functioning cones. They are called *dichromats*. Observers who have three classes of cones but don't see the world as so-called color normal observers are called *anomalous trichromats*. Dichromats and anomalous trichromats are not colorblind. Properly speaking they have color vision that is at variance with the so-called color normal observer. We shall refer to such observers as having color *variant vision*. Those classified as color normals are not carbon copies of one another as becomes evident later in this chapter. The reader can think of people with color variant vision as having color vision characteristics that place them outside of the normal range. We will refrain from using the term colorblind except for rod and cone monochromats. We will usually refer to people with defective color vision as having "color variant vision." This would be the proper terminology to use to describe the case of John Dalton, as well as to characterize the vast majority of people who do not have normal color vision.

The terms identifying people with various color vision capabilities were originally developed on the basis of color-matching experiments. Those who needed three primaries to match all spectral colors were called trichromats. Those who required only two primaries were called dichromats. Monochromats could match all spectral colors with one primary. In the current literature trichromacy, dichromacy, and monochromacy are also applied in reference to the numbers of functioning cone photopigments that an observer possesses.

There are three varieties of dichromats, depending on which one of the three normal photopigments (L, M, S) is missing: *Tritanopes* lack S; *deuteranopes* lack M; and *protanopes* lack L.

VARIATIONS IN NORMAL COLOR VISION

The reader undoubtedly knows about the normal "bell" curve distribution. Such a distribution has a central tendency (mean, mode, and median) and a width of distribution measured in standard deviations. When a group of color normals is tested, not all will give the same responses. If a sufficiently large sample is tested, one obtains, as expected, a normal distribution of responses. When we refer to "normal color vision," we refer to a range of responses that most people will give. By color variant (defective) vision we refer to those people whose color vision responses fall outside of this normal range. People who possess color variant vision can be defined by various color vision tests which are discussed below. First, however, we would like to provide an indication of the variations that comprise normal color vision.

Consider these two cases:

• There are certain shades of turquoise that one person may see as predominantly green, but which another insists are bluer than they are green. Who is correct?

• If many normal observers are asked to judge the spectral wavelength that appears as uniquely yellow, there will be a spread of estimates, each quite reliable, covering about 10 nm in the spectrum.[2] In this region of excellent wavelength discrimination, such a range implies that a distinctly greenish-yellow, as seen by one observer, may appear as definitely reddish when viewed by another. Who is right, and who is wrong?

To some extent, such disputes about color names might seem to reflect problems associated more with labels than with sensations. But this is surely not always so. Recall, for example, the exercise described on page 198 in Chapter 6. By selectively adapting only one eye, it is evident that the color sensations subsequently experienced by looking at objects with first one eye and then the other can be different. Such variation occurs in some people without the need for selective adaptation, occasionally in forms so extreme that one eye is essentially color-normal and the other color-defective. Leaving these special cases aside for later consideration, we may speculate about the possible causes of normal variations. Where blue-green is concerned, one's retina might contain a higher proportion of S-cones than another individual's retina. Where yellow is concerned, perhaps there are normal variations among humans in the proportions of their L- and M-cones or perhaps a variance in the peak spectral absorbance of the cone photopigments among observers (Dartnall, Bowmaker & Mollon, 1983). Even if all normal visual systems were otherwise identical, we would probably expect the reported results. From this point of view, both observers are correct in color naming, and there is no wavelength of the spectrum that should be expected to appear as unique yellow for all observers. As illustrated in Figure 10.1, if the sensation of yellow occurs when populations of L- and M-cones are stimulated about equally, the subject S_1 on the right would see unique yellow at λ_1. The subject S_2 represented on the left whose peak sensitivity of L-cones is less than that of the M-cones would see unique yellow at λ_2.

In Wald's study described on page 238 in Chapter 6, his star subject for isolating the short wavelength mechanism was R. H., whose sensitivity was about three times higher than the average observer for that mechanism. This could reflect the presence of more S-cones and/or more summation of S-cone signals in the eye of R. H. than for other subjects. We know that there are substantial variations in the proportions of L- and M-cones among normal observers (Rushton & Baker, 1964; Vimal, et al., 1989; Cicerone & Nerger, 1989a,b; Nerger & Cicerone, 1992). But the question of how color balance is affected by variations of cone populations in different people is a tricky one. Consider, for example, a case where an individual has twice as many L-cones, relative to M-cones, as the "normal" individual represented by a crossover of the L- and M-cone sensitivity curves at 570 nm as

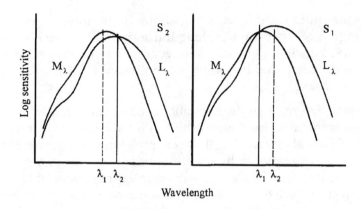

Wavelength

Figure 10.1 If a sensation of yellow arises when the numbers of L- and M-cones are equally stimulated, then the subject S_1 at the right, with relatively more L-cones than subject S_2 at the left, should see unique yellow at a somewhat shorter wavelength of the spectrum.

shown in Figure 7.1B on page 252. By the simplest view, this should cause the L-curve at 570 nm for this individual to be raised by a factor of 2 above the M-curve, causing 570 nm to appear decidedly orangish; the unique yellow wavelength would be decreased to about 490 nm. But reality may be more complicated than this. In the course of exposure to stimuli in the natural world, such an individual would, relative to the "normal" person, receive a steady excess excitation of L- over M-cones. This would be expected to cause selective adaptation at the cone level, and probably also in the r-g opponent pathways. Such adaptive mechanisms would probably serve to reduce the effects of excess L-cone stimulation in this individual. The adaptational adjustment might be short-term, based upon the immediately prior history of exposure of the eye to various parts of the visual field, as discussed in Chapter 6. However, there could also be a long-term component related to permanent changes in the visual system during critical stages of visual development caused by the relative excess of L- over M-cone stimulation (see endnote 11).

Sensations are private, so it is impossible to compare them directly among observers. All of us may agree that a 650 nm light appears red, but it is meaningless to ask whether one's sensation of red is the same as another's. What we can often agree upon is color names. For example, if one sees a red book on a shelf, one would undoubtedly be confident that a thousand observers, provided they have been screened as "color normal" by the sorts of tests to be described later in this chapter, would each call it "red" if limited to only a single color term. All of us have learned this name in association with objects that have been experienced in the presence of other people with whom we can communicate. Such objects reflect light and, by means of mechanisms and processes described in earlier chapters, certain patterns of activity arise in our brains. The association that we make between a color that we see and the name that we give to it is obviously learned, as are such color names themselves. Yet there is no reason to believe that the sensation caused by the activity of the brain has been acquired.[3]

All normal observers seem to agree that red, green, yellow, and blue are words that describe qualitatively different sensations. In Chapter 11 we will see that, despite their composite nature, similar agreement exists for purple, pink, brown, and orange. But there are certain blends of colors, including blue-green and yellow-green for which we must decide whether the balance between two hues of nearly equal strength is exact, or instead leans one way or the other.

In the context of the principles of human color vision that have been elucidated in this book, various physiological bases for individual differences in such judgments are easy to imagine. What is unimaginable is that such differences would not exist. After all, quantitative variations between individuals must occur at all stages of information processing throughout the complex chromatic visual system.

Large variations in the wavelength and chromatic discriminations of normal subjects were mentioned in earlier chapters. As we will see below, there is a range of responses obtained from color vision testing even among those who test as "normal." All observers show poorer discrimination as illumination is reduced, but some show this influence sooner and more precipitously than others.

A chief cause of variations among normal observers lies in prereceptoral absorption differences, beginning with a wide range of densities of macular pigment. Secondly, the yellowing of the eye lens with age leads to predictable changes in color vision that are associated with the selective absorption of shortwave light. As noted in Chapter 5 (see p. 183), most of the effect of this change can be eliminated by using Wright's system of normalizing mixture primaries, which boosts the intensity of the shortwave mixture component as much as may be required to keep the stimulus at the retina at normal levels.

Two additional kinds of variations among normal observers will be discussed: (1) those that apply to any particular observer as a result of changes in stimulating conditions other than spectral distribution, and (2) those that occur between observers under similar or identical stimulating conditions.

Effect of Field Size

Much of the emphasis in this book has been upon the perception of color in centrally fixated fields subtending about 2° or so of visual angle. A number of interesting changes occur when the field is made either larger or smaller than this.

As field size is reduced, the relative contribution of the y-b opponent system becomes progressively less important until, with very tiny centrally fixated fields, normal color vision becomes tritanopic. Only two primary stimuli are then required to make a color match, and lights are confused if they lie along tritan lines in the chromaticity plane (Willmer & Wright, 1945). The most likely interpretation of these results is that there are very few S-cones in the central fovea. Despite this lack, a very small shortwave light, when directly fixated, will often elicit a blue response (Ingling, Scheibner & Boynton, 1970). The explanation for this may relate to scattered light that excites some S-cones in the immediate surround. The stimulus is correctly localized at the foveal center because the light is seen there as a result of its action upon L- and M-cones, which are present there in high density. Perhaps the blueness becomes attached to the percept by mechanisms related to those discussed in connection with the "gap effect" on page 352.

As field size increases, red/green color discrimination improves (Nagy, 1994). With large fields at mesopic and moderate photopic levels, rods as well as cones are stimulated. Nevertheless, color matching does not become tetrachromatic. (The subject's task is made more ambiguous by the selective influence of the macular pigment, which affects only the central region but not the more peripheral parts of the field. In large-field matching studies, subjects are typically instructed to ignore the center, which they seem able to do; sometimes an annular field may be used instead.) Although the matches are trichromatic, the rods nevertheless can have an effect. The mathematical laws of color mixture (Chapter 5), which allow the transformation of color-matching data from one reference system to another, are not fully obeyed for large fields. Additivity often breaks down for such matches, and incompatible data may be generated depending upon details of experimental procedure (Crawford, 1965).

Fields larger than a degree or so of visual angle necessarily stimulate portions of the retina that become increasingly populated by rods (at least up to about 20° from the fovea centralis, see Fig. 4.9).

As noted in the preceding paragraph such large fields will stimulate rods as well as cones. However, it is possible to minimize the effect of rod intrusion by light adapting them. The retina is exposed to a bright bleaching light and then thrust into darkness and allowed to dark adapt. Initially the cones are more sensitive (see the dashed curve in Fig. 6.2). This cone curve reaches a plateau after a few minutes. At this cone-plateau level, cones are still more sensitive than the rods for a little while and then the rod sensitivity increases and take over. It is during this cone plateau period that it is possible to stimulate the retina and avoid the problem of rod intrusion (Nagy, 1980; Nagy & Doyal, 1993).

It is probable that the nonlinearities of large-field color matching are attributable to rod intrusion (Clarke, 1963). Because unique matches are made with only three variable reference stimuli, only by chance would the resulting match for cones also be a match for rods. When the rod activity generated by the two matching stimuli is different, it could have an effect on the relative appearance of the fields. If so, large-field trichromacy results from a limitation imposed by three pathways (luminance, r-g, and y-b) rather than one set by three pigments. No assurance remains that large-field color matches are physiologically identical at the cone stage. Implicit in this argument is the notion that the rods are not capable of generating any new sensations that differ from those mediated by the cone systems by themselves.

Trezona (1976) has reported a procedure whereby it is possible to obtain large-field color matches that are exact for rods as well as for the three types of cones. A fourth primary, chosen so as to be especially effective for rods, is added to the usual three. After a subject makes a trichromatic match with the usual three primaries at a photopic luminance level, and field radiances are reduced, (by inserting a neutral filter that does not change relative spectral distribution) the fields no longer match at scotopic luminances. By altering the fourth primary, the subject then makes an adjustment to permit a scotopic match. The intensities of the fields are then increased again, all in proportion, to photopic levels where the match again fails. By iterating between the two levels (a slow and tedious process) it proves possible finally to satisfy both the cones and rods. Therefore, when considered in terms of the numbers of reference stimuli required to cause such an overall physiological identity, four primaries are needed and human large-field color matching becomes tetrachromatic. Nevertheless, because the rods, lacking private pathways to the brain, cannot induce a novel scotopic quality of sensation, large-field color matching is trichromatic in the sense that three controls suffice to make color matches.[4]

These results have interesting implications for color-variant observers. For example, as we will see below, S-cone monochromats (observers with only S-cones and rods) exhibit a form of dichromatic vision over a mesopic range. This result implies that, in the case of these unusual observers, signals generated by rods lead to sensations that are qualitatively different from those attributable to what their cones alone can provide. A plausible interpretation is to suppose that rods are capable of generating signals that are transmitted through the r-g opponent pathways, and that this may happen also for normal subjects. At mesopic levels, this input would for normal observers alter only slightly the ongoing activity of the r-g pathways that is largely determined by input from the L- and M-cones — a minor effect and one that causes no new sensations. For the S-cone monochromat, on the other hand, such variable rod input might be sufficient to keep the r-g pathways functional, and to induce novel sensations (red and/or green) compared to what the S-cone monochromat would see without rod intrusion. Smith and Pokorny (1977) have made a strong case that at least some of the residual red-green vision that dichromats exhibit for large fields may have a similar cause.

Effect of Retinal Location

As the size of a centrally-fixated field increases, progressively more rods are recruited and the cone population simultaneously changes to include the fatter and more sparsely distributed peripheral cones. Therefore, the effect of field size *per se* is confounded with changes of central vs. peripheral retinal characteristics. To obviate this confounding it is better to compare fields of modest size in different retinal regions. When this is done, small changes in color mixture result that seem attributable to the different densities of cone pigments to be expected in foveal vs. peripheral cones (Pokorny, Smith & Starr, 1976). Much larger changes occur in color appearance, as shown by an excellent color-naming study reported by Gordon and Abramov (1977). These authors conclude that previous reports of color deficiency in the peripheral retina have been misleading: "The quality of color vision in the periphery depends critically on stimulus size. If the stimulus is sufficiently large, subjects see a full range of well saturated hues. . . ."

Now that we have briefly surveyed the varieties of normal color vision, and some of the variables that effect the manner in which observers respond to color, we are almost ready to take a close look at color variant observers. But before doing so let us look at the tests that help to identify color normals and the various types of color variant observers.

COLOR VISION TESTING

Color vision tests can be categorized in a number of different ways. One variety, with which many readers will have experience, consists of what we call *quick tests;* ones that in a few minutes are able to differentiate color normals from those who clearly have a color vision deficiency. One of the best known of such tests uses the Ishihara Plates, which belong to a category of tests called *pseudoisochromatic plates.* Another test that can be administered rather quickly is the anomaloscope test. The best known of this type of test is the Nagel Anomaloscope. It measures the ability of the observer to make a specific color match and differentiates between normal trichromats and anomalous trichromats. Some tests take considerably longer to administer. Many of these involve the kinds of psychophysical tests frequently done in a visual scientist's laboratory. These longer tests measure the spectral sensitivity of the observer, wavelength discrimination, saturation discrimination, threshold behavior, etc. The Farnsworth–Munsell 100 Hue test does not exactly fall in this latter category of a visual scientist's lab experiment, but its administration takes too long for it to be considered a quick test. This test measures the observer's ability to make very subtle color discrimination. With these introductory remarks, let us now take a close look at the various methods for screening people for color defective vision.

Quick Tests

It is remarkable that some people are able to reach adulthood without being aware that they have a serious red-green color deficiency. Pickford (1951), who personally tested the color vision of many hundreds of subjects using a wide variety of devices, relates the following anecdote concerning one such individual:

> A . . . subject was not aware of any difficulty with colours until he failed in a test for the R.A.F. [Royal Air Force]. In this test he once mistook fawn [a variable color averaging a light-grayish brown] for green, and was very annoyed at being rejected. In the laboratory he spent five minutes trying to make quite sure that a green and a fawn skein of wool were not the same colour. Losing patience a little, I asked him what his difficulty might be, but he replied that he had no difficulty and was merely trying to be very exact. I explained to him that if in five minutes he had been trying to be very exact over the colour of a green signal at night in a fog, he might have crashed his aircraft into a hangar and killed a number of people. He does not believe that he is colour blind, but has a marked difficulty in distinguishing reds and greens from each other and from yellows, when there are no brightness differences, though he has no weakness in blues or yellows. This is an example of moderate red-green blindness, and this sort of man is liable to call certain fawn or yellowish colour "reddish-green." He would not

be failed in a colour vision test with any injustice, however, because his sensitivity to the difference between red and green is at least ten times less than that of 90 per cent of men (p. 24).

People of this sort are rather sensitive about their color defect and do not wish to admit, even to themselves, that they are abnormal. Because there are many form and brightness cues that a clever person can use (wittingly or unconsciously) to make educated guesses about color names the condition may go undetected. This is of course especially true for anomalous color vision where good hue discrimination may remain.

For the screening of large masses of people, a quick test is an absolute necessity. Such tests are desirable not only for restraining people from entry into an Air Force or some other occupation where good color discrimination is necessary; they should be used also as a routine part of any optometric or ophthalmic examination in order to provide a full description of the patient's visual capacity. Moreover, such tests can have diagnostic value for ophthalmic disease. It would be desirable to have school children routinely tested for color defect, just as is commonly done for visual acuity deficit and hearing loss. Difficulty with colors can otherwise be embarrassing, whether the victim is a kindergartner who seems stupid to others because he does not learn his color names properly, or a high school chemistry student who fails in his qualitative analysis because he cannot tell red from yellow in a flame test.

Pseudoisochromatic Plates

The type of quick test in common use consists of a series of pseudoisochromatic plates. Many such plates have been made available (Table 10.1), however, the ones that seem to be used most frequently, at least for research purposes, are the Ishihara and the AO H-R-R plates. Each such plate is composed of a large number of small discs of various colors. The test takes advantage of one of the Gestalt laws of organization, the *law of similarity*.[5] According to this principle, elements having the same appearance tend to be apprehended as a pattern, as in the black-and-white example at the top of Figure 10.2. By manipulating the chromaticities of such elements at constant luminance, they can form a figure and a background. It is possible to develop a test plate in which figure and ground fall along a confusion line in chromaticity space for a certain dichromat, whereas they look very different for the color normal who will see the figure that the dichromat misses.

Such tests were originally developed mostly by trial and error. A number of them have been examined by Lakowski (1969a,b), whose

Table 10.1   Pseudoisochromatic plates for rapid color vision testing

Ishihara
American Optical Hardy, Rand & Ritter (AO H-R-R)
Velhagen Plates
Okuma Plates
F_2 Plate
Boström–Kugelberg Pseudoisochromatic Plates
Dvorine Pseudoisochromatics Plates
Tokyo Medical College Plates
American Optical Company Plates
The City University Color Vision Test
Standard Pseudoisochromatic Plates

From Pokorny *et al.*, 1979

papers on the theory and practice of colour-vision testing provide an excellent summary. A more recent description of these tests can be found in Birch *et al.* (1979).

An example of a particularly interesting and tricky kind of test is illustrated in Figure 10.3. This plot shows the chromaticities of the elements of a test plate where normals and dichromats usually see different numbers. In this plate the elements consist of four groups of colors labeled A B C D. The Gestalt number 74 is represented by dots formed by colors AC against a background of dots formed by colors BD, seen by normals as blue-green against orange-red. From inspection of the protan and deutan confusion lines that are shown in the figure, it is clear that neither class of dichromat can discriminate A from B or C from D, with any precision. Although they can tell B from C and A from D (because in each case these are differentially effective for S-cones) the coarse spacing of such dots contained within the number 74 seen by normals makes that configuration hard to discern relative to a number 21 provided when dots AB form the figure against CD as the background. But A and B do not look alike for the color normal, nor do C and D, and, therefore, the grouping that stands out for the dichromat exists at only half density for the normal. For the normal observer the number 74, based upon a substantial difference in L- vs. M-cone activation, is much more apparent. (Most plates are not this complicated.)

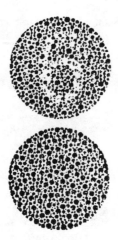

Figure 10.2 These pseudo-isochromatic plates, from the American Optical Company set, were originally reproduced in color where the number 12 stands out clearly in the lower plate. In this black and white reproduction, the camera had equal sensitivity to the orange dots that made up the number and the blue ones that formed the background. The red-green color differences forming the 6 at the top were translated into lightness differences. (From McConnell, 1977, p. 178.)

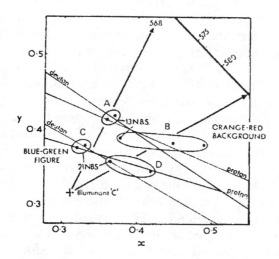

Figure 10.3 This diagram depicts the chromaticities in CIE space (see Appendix Part I) of the 9 colors used in a particularly complicated isochromatic plate where normals and dichromats see different numbers. (From Lakowski, 1969, p. 267; Ishihara plate from the fifth edition.)

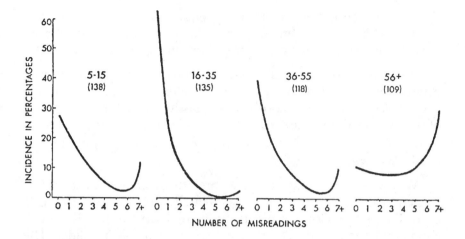

Figure 10.4 Frequency of "wrong numbers" seen on the Dvorine isochromatic test shown for groups of subjects divided according to ranges of age. (From Lakowski, 1969, p. 272.)

If properly administered, the best of such tests can discriminate normals from color-defective observers with reasonable accuracy. However, they are not dependable for discriminating protans from deutans. Nor is this a suitable type of test for separating dichromats from anomalous observers, because an anomalous subject may or may not pass the test, depending upon the severity of his defect. Nevertheless, there is a correlation between performance on the test and ability to perform other tasks that require red-green color discrimination.

Because the degree of defect is hard to quantify, such tests are better used as "go, no-go" screening devices to separate color normals from the red-green defectives. Because such a test consists of a number of plates of varying difficulty, one possible measure of degree of defect lies in the number of plates that are misread. But subjects who are color normal by more stringent tests also make some errors; for example the color normal usually can see the number 21 in the plate explained in Figure 10.3, if it is pointed out, and despite normal vision a normal observer might fail to read a number because of an inability to achieve the necessary Gestalt organization. In this context, the results of Figure 10.4 are of interest. It is probably not true, as the graphs seem to suggest, that subjects in the 5–15 year age group have poorer color vision than those in the 16–35 year age group. On the other hand, the increase in errors in the older age groups probably does represent, for the most part, a real deterioration of color vision. Apparently the higher-order requirement of Gestalt apperception, which may depend on age, intelligence, or perceptual aptitudes unrelated to color vision, may confound the result.

Pseudoisochromatic plates have also been developed for testing tritan deficiencies (the AO H-R-R plates contain such a test, for example). A tritanope would probably be classified as color-normal most of the time by pseudoisochromatic tests as currently administered.

D&H Color Rule

Why not then simply put two colors side by side? These could be chosen to look alike for the dichromat but different for the color normal. The D&H Color Rule is such an instrument (Kaiser & Hemmendinger, 1980) The device contains two colored slides. The observer is asked to move the two slides until both halves visible through an opening are identical or nearly so. One slide contains colors that change continuously from purple to green through neutral gray. The other slide changes from blue to brown through neutral gray. This interesting test has not received wide attention even though it is easy and convenient to use. Kalmus (1972) used it to test 195 color normal observers ranging in age from 5 to 90 yrs. He also tested 22 protans and 43 deutans with the Color Rule. Biersdorf (1977) tested 98 color normals, 4 protanomlous, and 4 deuteranomalous observes with the Rule. Kaiser and Hemmendinger (1980) collated these data into a common figure so it might be possible to use the scores on the D&H Color Rule, assuming appropriate illumination is used to classify color variant vision. As is obvious in Figure 5 of the Kaiser and Hemmendinger paper, at present the overlap between normal and near normal observers is considerable. However some protanomalous and deuteranomalous observers could be clearly distinguished.

Panel D-15

This test is similar to the 100 hue test (see below) except that it only contains 15 caps. The observer is presented with these caps arranged in random order and instructed to place them in a circle arranging them according to color. A reference cap is given as a starting point. Observers with normal color vision can usually complete the test in about one minute, so it qualifies as a quick test. However, it is designed to select color variant observers with moderate to severe losses in chromatic discrimination. Lanthony (1978) designed a desaturated version of this Panel D-15 test to be used specifically for the detection of acquired color vision defects.

Anomaloscopes

The undisputed queen of all color-vision testing instruments is the anomaloscope, the only device in common use (despite its high price) that is able to discriminate reliably between dichromats and anomalous trichromats. The best known is the Nagel anomaloscope; it is used to test only red-green variant vision. However, some anomaloscopes exist that test also for tritan defects (Moreland & Kerr, 1979).

The *Rayleigh equation* refers to color matching using nearly spectral colors. In the Nagel Model I anomaloscope, which is probably the most widely used, a semicircular yellow field is seen at the bottom. Its lateral subtense is about 1°–3° of visual angle, depending upon telescope focus. A red-green mixture (670 nm and 545 nm) is seen at the top, and the overall field is circular. The instrument is constructed so that one knob, when turned, varies the intensity of the yellow (589 nm) field while the other varies the ratio of red to green in the mixture field without altering its luminance. The color-normal individual, therefore, can make an exact match by (1) varying the red-green mixture to form a yellow and (2) also varying the intensity of the monochromatic yellow field to make the two fields match for brightness. Some iteration may be required, but for normal observers the match is easy and precise. Because longwave lights are used, the comparison does not involve the S-cones.

When deuteranopes attempt the match, they have one degree of freedom too many. The examiner can set the red-green knob to any position, and the subjects can make a match by means of the yellow knob alone. If given use of both controls, deuteranopes might by chance make a normal match, but on repeated occasions their matches will vary over a wide range of the red-green scale.

When protanopes attempt the match, they behave similarly to deuteranopes except that the brightness of the red-green field depends for them upon the ratio of the two components. In the Nagel Model I, for protanopes the full red looks very dim, while full green looks brightest. Therefore, if the red-green ratio is set toward red by the examiner, the protanope's setting of the yellow knob, as needed to produce a color match, will produce a field of lower luminance than if the red-green ratio is set toward green.

When protanomals attempt a match, they behave similarly to protanopes with respect to the yellow setting that they make, providing that their red-green setting, which they must also be allowed to make in order to produce a perfect match, is the same one used to

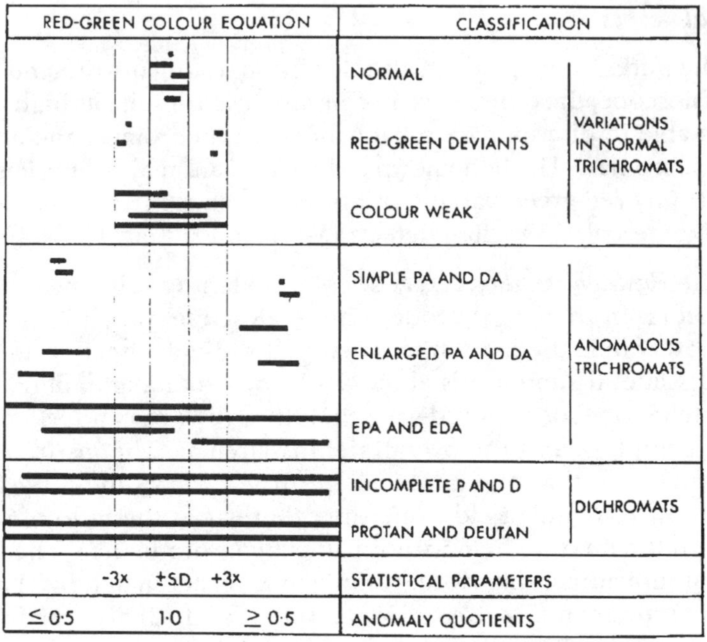

RED-GREEN COLOUR EQUATION	CLASSIFICATION	
	NORMAL	
	RED-GREEN DEVIANTS	VARIATIONS IN NORMAL TRICHROMATS
	COLOUR WEAK	
	SIMPLE PA AND DA	
	ENLARGED PA AND DA	ANOMALOUS TRICHROMATS
	EPA AND EDA	
	INCOMPLETE P AND D	DICHROMATS
	PROTAN AND DEUTAN	
-3x ±S.D. +3x	STATISTICAL PARAMETERS	
≤ 0·5 1·0 ≥ 0·5	ANOMALY QUOTIENTS	

Figure 10.5 Ranges of anomaloscope settings, when subjects are allowed to manipulate both the red-green and the yellow intensity controls, for normal and color defective observers. (Originally from Lakowski, 1969, p. 278; slightly modified and furnished by V. Smith and J. Pokorny.)

test protanopes. The settings of anomalous observers will be reasonably exact (as exact as those for normals in some cases), although on repeated matches most anomalous observers will show more variability of the red-green ratio, and their matches will not be acceptable to normals. An ordinary deuteranomal behaves like the ordinary (simple) protanomal except that his yellow setting is in the normal range. Extreme protanomals and deuteranomals have matching ranges so wide as to include both normal and anomalous matches. Figure 10.5 summarizes, in a graphical form, these generalizations about anomaloscope matches. Jameson & Hurvich (1956) would say that the mean position of the normal and anomalous responses in Figure 10.5 are a function of the photopigment peak spectral absorbances whereas the range of responses is due to post receptoral reduction of the red-green response process.

Longer Tests

Farnsworth–Munsell 100-Hue Test

This test was developed by a U.S. Navy captain, Dean Farnsworth. He got the idea for it from an Englishman named Pierce at the National Institute of Industrial Psychology (Pokorny & Smith, 1986). It is probably the best test of color discrimination available for general use. In its completed form, the test uses only 85 cylindrical objects. Because these resemble small bottle caps with pieces of Munsell-colored papers recessed into them, the test objects are usually called "caps."

The chromaticities of the 85 caps, shown in Figure 10.6, were chosen to form a continuous hue circle of about equal chroma relative to a white point ('C') shown in CIE chromaticity space (top). We also show these caps plotted in a cone excitation chromaticity space in the bottom diagram. Starting with color number 1, the hues shade from red through orange to yellow, then from yellow through green to blue-green, to blue, purple, and back to red. Colors numbered 1, 22, 43, and 64 are used as anchors at the ends of four wooden trays. The subject's task is to deal with one tray at a time. For example, the subject attempts to order caps 2 through 21 in the manner shown in the figure, "to form a continuous series of colors." The steps are very small and the task is not easy. A complete test requires the use of all four trays. Each cap contains its number on its reverse side; when the subject finishes arranging the caps of a tray, the cover of the tray is closed, the closed tray is inverted, and the bottom is lifted to expose the underside of the caps, showing their numbers. An error score for each cap is computed as the sum of the absolute differences between the number of that cap and the numbers of the adjacent caps. For example, if the ordering were 4-6-5, the error score for position 6 would be 3.

It is important that the error scores be localized in some way, rather than just averaged overall, because the pattern of such scores around the hue circle is of diagnostic value. The reason for this is clear from Figure 10.6, which shows confusion axes for various classes of color defect. When error scores are plotted on such a standardized polar diagram, the resulting lobes are characteristic of the major forms of color variance (Fig. 10.7). Because the discriminations require sensitivity to very small steps, few subjects obtain a perfect score and the test is useful also as a means to assess variations in color discrimination among color normals.

As with the pseudoisochromatic plates, the 100-hue test must be used with the appropriate illuminant. As the illumination level is re-

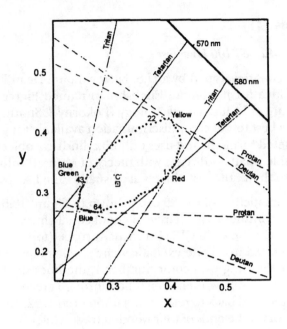

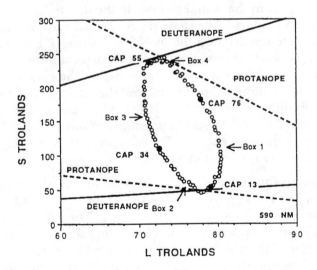

Figure 10.6 Top: Chromaticities of the 85 caps of the Fransworth–Munsell 100-hue test represented in CIE chromaticity space (see Appendix Part I). Confusion lines for 4 kinds of dichromats are shown. Because the elliptical configuration described by the chromaticities of the samples of the test is tangent to a dichromatic confusion line, poor discrimination is predicted (from Lakowski, 1969, p. 273). Bottom: Same as top but plotted in a cone excitation diagram (from Smith, Pokorny & Yeh, 1991).

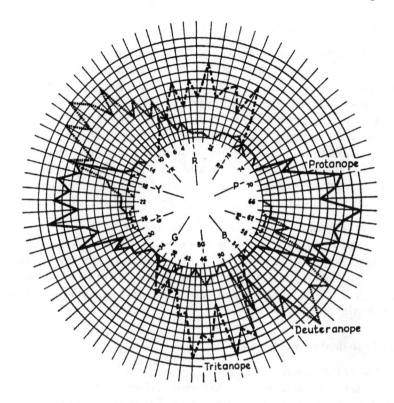

Figure 10.7 Illustrative data to show how the results for three kinds of dichromats are plotted on the polar diagram used for the Farnsworth–Munsell 100-hue test. No mistakes would be represented by the innermost circle; a normal observer does not produce an error score of more than two or three at any location, and sometimes will show no errors at all. (From Kalmus, 1965, p. 48.)

duced below the level that is recommended for the test, all normals make more errors, and in the limit, as scotopic levels are reached, a characteristic scotopic axis is achieved. Apparently most caps, of equal value (lightness) for cones but not for rods, can be ordered according to a scale of scotopic lightness, except for two regions around the circle where their scotopic lightnesses are nearly equal.

Because the 100-hue test takes about 15 to 30 minutes to administer, it is not a "quick test." It is considered too difficult to be used with young children, and the scores are influenced to some degree by psychological variables, such as the motivation of the subject.

Two Laboratory Tests

The analytical anomaloscope, discussed below, is not a conventional test for color blindness. Nor are measures of wavelength discrimination or spectral neutral points useful because these require apparatus too elaborate for general use. Many other tests have been suggested from time to time, but new tests are unlikely to be used unless they are diagnostically superior to those that have already become established. An example of such a procedure that remains unused is the HTRF test (see below) that was developed and tested over 30 years ago (Boynton & Wagner, 1961) and pursued also by Ikeda and Urakubo (1968), who developed a flicker version of it.

In addition, a variety of tests are designed for specific vocational purposes where color theory is not at issue, and the closer the test is to the actual task, the more valid it is likely to be. Examples include the sorting of skeins of wool and the naming of the colors of signal lights. A number of other tests are described by Burnham, Hanes, and Bartleson (1963).

The Analytical Anomaloscope

The color-matching behavior of normal, dichromatic, and anomalous observers can be neatly characterized by a device called an *analytical anomaloscope*, first described by Baker and Rushton (1963) and again by Mitchell and Rushton (1971). It is shown very schematically in Figure 10.8. The field at the left receives monochromatic light supplied by a variable wavelength filter, M_λ, which passes light whose wavelength depends upon the lateral position of the filter in a light beam that supplies the left field. The intensity of that field can be adjusted by means of a neutral density wedge W_λ.

The field at the right receives a mixture of red and green light supplied through the fixed filters F_G and F_R, which pass light of wavelengths 550 and 635 nm (wavelengths chosen so that they are not detected by S-cones). These beams are polarized orthogonally so that, when a polaroid analyzer, A, is turned, one component is gradually exchanged for the other as these are mixed in the right-hand field (red + green). The neutral wedge W_R is used to vary the amount of red light and thereby alter the relative strengths of the polarized beams *before* they enter the analyzer. This device is conceptually a modification of the simpler, commercially available Nagel anomaloscope, which is widely used for color-vision testing.[6]

To use the device as an analytical anomaloscope, a protanope is invited to adjust W_R so that, when A is turned, there is no change in

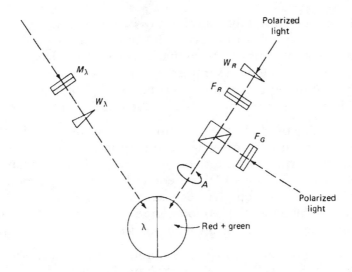

Figure 10.8   A schematic drawing to illustrate the principles of the analytical anomaloscope. Light in the left field is controlled for wavelength by a variable wavelength filter M_λ and for intensity by neutral density wedge W_λ. The right field contains a mixture of red and green light supplied through filters F_R and F_G. The polarized light transmitted by these filters is superimposed by the mixing cube (a beam splitting cube). The mixed beam passes through a polaroid analyzer A. As this polaroid analyzer A rotates, there is a continuous exchange of red for green light or vice versa. The instrument is used in two modes, depending on how protanopes and deuteranopes must set the neutral density wedge W_R in order that rotation of polaroid analyzer A does not vary the appearance of the right field for them.

the appearance of the right-hand field. The protanope can do this because the field is seen using only M-cones, and the appropriate setting of W_R will allow the two components of the mixture to produce a constant total absorption rate for the M-cones no matter what the position of the polaroid analyzer, A. Now, with M_λ set in turn for various wavelengths, the protanope makes settings of W_λ to control the brightness of the left field to match it with the right one. Because the two halves of the field match exactly at each wavelength used, the left field must also produce a constant absorption rate for the protanope's M-cones. Given the appropriate calibration data, the settings of W_λ can be converted into a spectral sensitivity curve, which should describe the action spectrum for M-photopigment (and of M-cones) in the protanope.

This method is suitable only for wavelengths of F_G, that are about 550 nm or longer, because S-cone intrusion otherwise vitiates the results. The part of the spectrum that can be measured extends from 550 nm to the wavelength supplied by filter F_R (635 nm). As far as it goes, the resulting curve resembles that of M-photopigment as deduced by various other methods described earlier in this book.

The setting of W_R, by the protanope, so that rotation of polaroid analyzer, A, produces no change in the right field, is called the *prot mode* of the instrument. When a deuteranope performs the same task, a much higher density of W_R is required in order to produce the desired result. The deuteranope's spectrum, as deduced from W_λ settings, resembles that of L-photopigment. The setting of W_R appropriate for the deuteranope is called the *deut mode* of the instrument.

When a normal observer uses the instrument there will be no setting of W_R that will cause the right-hand field to remain invariant for all positions of polaroid analyzer, A, because, as A is turned, the field changes in appearance — for example, from red through yellow to green. W_R could be set to maintain equal luminance, but it is much more instructive to set it either in the prot or deut mode.[7]

Consider the prot mode as an example. As A is turned, there should be no change in the degree to which photons are absorbed in M-photopigment, if the normal subject has the same M-photopigment as the protanope whose settings were uncontaminated by a second pigment.[8] Compared to a field at the left that matches the other one for a protanope when the right field is set fully for W_R, that field will look very bright to the normal observer because of the extra photons absorbed by the L-cones, which the protanope lacks. Nevertheless, a wavelength of M_λ can be found that will provide a match for hue, and an appropriate setting of W_λ, can be made that will increase the brightness of the left field to yield an exact match.

The experiment is more conveniently done the other way around; for each setting of M_λ selected by the experimenter, values of A and W_λ are set by the subject, who thereby makes a dichromatic match. When the W_λ values for various wavelengths are converted to a spectral sensitivity curve, it is found to be a similar M-photopigment curve as that of the protanope. This is because, no matter what the setting of A, the right field has a constant effect upon M-photopigment. In analogous fashion, using the deut mode, the spectral sensitivity defined by W_λ is found to agree with that of the deuteranope, revealing the action spectrum of L-photopigment. The obtained experimental agreement is very good.

The settings of polaroid analyzer that are reliably made by a normal observer cannot meaningfully be compared with those of dichromats because the analyzer settings are arbitrary for the dichromats. But color anomalous observers, like normals, require specific adjustment of A as well as W_λ in order to make matches. Consider a protanomalous subject with the instrument in the prot mode. We know that the protanomalous observer has some abnormal photopigment. If the M-photopigment of this observer differs from that of normal M-photopigment, then the spectral sensitivity, as determined by settings of W_λ, should also differ from that of normal and protanopic subjects. But this does not happen. Instead, the data of protanomalous observers are the same as for normals and protanopes. Similarly, in the deut mode, deuteranomalous observers produce results that agree with those of normals and deuteranopes. The almost inescapable conclusion is that only the L-photopigment in protanomalous observers is abnormal; the M-photopigment must be normal. Similarly, it is only the M-photopigment in deuteranomalous observers that is abnormal, so the L-photopigment for this observer must be of the normal variety.

Because anomalous observers must adjust polaroid analyzer, A, as well as W_λ to make a match, a comparison of A values between normal and anomalous subjects is possible. Figure 10.9A shows the result of such a comparison made by Pokorny, Smith, and Katz (1973) using data furnished by D. Mitchell on several anomals of each class. Circles represent the deut mode, squares, the prot mode. Filled symbols are for normal subjects, open squares represent protanomalous data, and open circles are for deuteranomalous observers. For intermediate wavelengths, the normal observer (black squares) needs little of the red component in the prot mode because W_R has been set by the protanope to admit a very high intensity of red light. For the deut mode, the normal curve is more nearly linear but bulges upward because the deuteranope lacks middle-wavelength sensitivity and must set W_R at a lower intensity than normal in order to match green. The curves for the two classes of anomalous observers lie between those of normals, differing only slightly from one another. This result suggests that their anomalous pigments may not differ very much from each other.

An assessment of the shapes and locations of the anomalous pigments has been made by Pokorny, Smith, and Katz (1973). In their analysis, they used the results of a study by Schmidt (1955), who had tested 883 recently drafted male recruits in the 17–23 year age range. In this population she found 5 protanopes (0.6 percent), 11 deuteranopes (1.2 percent), and 3 *extreme deuteranomals*. (The latter

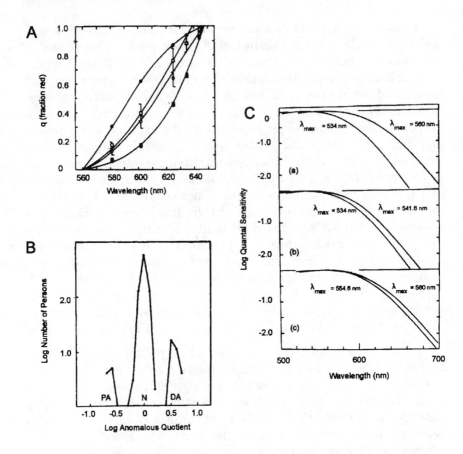

Figure 10.9   A. Settings of polaroid analyzer A (Fig. 10.3) for normal and anomalous subjects on the analytical anomaloscope of Mitchell and Rushton (1971). This figure is from Pokorny, Smith & Katz (1973); the solid rectangles represent the normal in prot mode and the solid circles represent the normal in deutan mode. The vertical extent of these symbols show 2 standard errors of the mean. The open squares represent the protanomal in protan mode and the open circles represent the deuteranomal in deutan mode. The vertical lines are standard errors of the mean. B. Distributions of anomalous quotients on the Nagel anomaloscope as found by Schmidt (1955). C. Results of an analysis by Pokorny, Smith & Katz (1973) showing (a) normal M- and L-spectral sesitivities, (b) protanomalous spectral sensitivities, and (c) deuteranomalous spectral sesitivities.

are nearly dichromatic, but will reject matches between the reference yellow and extreme red/green ratios on an anomaloscope.) There were no *extreme protanomals* in her sample, although these have often been observed (they show a reduction in longwave sensitivity similar to that of the protanope).

To compare normals with the remaining anomalous subjects of her sample, Schmidt used an *anomalous quotient,* which is the relative amount of green/red in the Nagel anomaloscope (see p. 429). Using this instrument, subjects matched a 589-nm field with a mixture of 670 nm (red) and 536 nm (green). A value of 1.0 was defined by the average setting of Schmidt's normal observers. She found 10 protanomalous, 822 normal, and 32 deuteranomalous subjects, with no overlap between the three distributions (see Fig. 10.9B).

Figure 10.9C shows the longwave portions of curves derived by Pokorny, Smith, and Katz. Starting with their L- and M-cone functions for normal observers, they assumed that only one of the normal curves is shifted for an anomalous observer, that the shifted curve has the same shape (on a frequency abscissa) as the normal, and that the concentration of pigment in the anomalous receptors is about the same as for normals. By a trial-and-error procedure, they determined the curve shifts required for a best fit of the Schmidt mean data; the resulting curves are shown in Figure 10.9C.

As a further test of the resulting functions, Pokorny, Smith, and Katz calculated the A-values to be expected for Schmidt's average anomalous observers on the analytical anomaloscope. The curves that are drawn through the Mitchell and Rushton data of Figure 10.9A constitute the results of these predictions, and the agreement is good.

Heterochromatic Threshold Reduction Factor

Studies of dichromats agree in showing that, unlike normals, there is no selective chromatic adaptation to pairs of longwave stimuli. A heterochromatic threshold-reduction factor (HTRF) test[9] was applied by Boynton and Wagner (1961) and Scheibner and Boynton (1968) with that result. Similar conclusions can be drawn for studies of Speelman and Krauskopf (1963) and Boynton, Kandel, and Onley (1959). This result is exactly what is predicted on the assumption that dichromats have only one longwave pigment. It would be expected that ordinary anomalous observers, with L- and M-curves separated by as much as 15 nm, would show a significant degree of selective chromatic adaptation. Watkins (1969a, 1969b) found such an effect, but the shortwave member of his HTRF pair was at 480 nm, too short a wavelength to exclude a contribution by the S-cones. In the study by Boynton and Wagner (1961) no such effect in normals was found either for flashed or steady background fields. Mean HTRF values, expressed as arithmetic factors, were as follows (for transient adapting conditions that produced the largest effect for normals):

Subject	Type of HTRF	Mean HTRF
Normal (N = 29)	RG	4.1
	RB	11.3
Protanope (N = 6)	RG	1.0
	RB	2.3
Deutranope (N = 5)	RG	1.0
	RB	8.1
Protanomalous (N = 2)	RG	0.9
	RB	2.7
Deuteranomalous (N = 5)	RG	1.1
	RB	9.1
Extreme Deuteranomalous (N = 2)	RG	1.1
	RB	11.3

In this study, red, green, and blue gelatin filters were used. That the red-green pair did not pass light that was effective on S-cones was indicated both by the physical characteristics of the light and the HTRF values of 1.0 for the RG pair, found both for protanopes and deuteranopes. The value of 4.1 for normal observers means that heterochromatic thresholds for the red-green filter pair are on average more than four times lower than their homochromatic counterparts. The results for 9 anomalous observers for the red-green filter pair do not differ from those of the dichromats. For the red-blue pairs, normals and all types of deutans agree that there is a substantial selective effect, averaging about tenfold, which must be due to the participation of S-cones and longwave cones that selectively adapt. The protans show a much smaller amount of red-blue selectivity, probably because of the reduced effective intensity of the longwave light for them (the same objective field intensities were used for all subjects). On the other hand, Piantanida and Sperling (1973a, b) found that, provided the exactly right adapting wavelengths were used, selective chromatic adaptation of anomalous observers could be demonstrated.

It may be concluded that the L- and M-cones of deuteranomalous and protanomalous observers, in addition to having spectral sensitivities whose peaks are closer together than those of normals, may not adapt as selectively as their relative sensitivities would predict. Or their spectral sensitivities may lie close enough together that the ratio of L/M cone stimulation is simply not sufficiently different to sustain the selective adaptation. Smith and Pokorny estimate this ratio, for anomalous observers, to be no greater than that elicited by stimuli of 570 and 600 nm for normals. The red-green HTRF for normal observers has not been tested for these wavelength pairs, although for some normals it is not significantly different from unity even for wavelengths more separated than this (Boynton, Scheibner, Yates & Rinalducci, 1965).

Other failures to achieve selective chromatic adaptation of anomalous observers have been reported by Wald (1964), using the two-color threshold techniques, and by Alpern and Torii (1968a, b), using brightness-matching procedures. Their failure to selectively adapt anomalous observers is particularly intriguing in that sufficiently high adapting levels were used to have achieved significant photopigment bleaching.

THE PROBLEMS OF PEOPLE WITH COLOR VARIANT VISION

Because they are far from rare, most of us have had experience with people who perceive color differently than we do. Some readers will themselves suffer from this condition, so for them the problem is firsthand and very personal. We may have been amused by their inability to name colors "correctly." Yet when they disagree with us, are they really wrong? This time the answer is both ''yes" and "no." They seem to err because there are too many color names in the normal vocabulary to suit their needs. Therefore, if people with color variant vision often name colors incorrectly it is only because we normals confuse them by giving them too many names to use. Color vocabulary evolved from the vast majority of people that possess "normal" color vision. They set the vocabulary and those with variant color vision are unable to fully use this vocabulary; at least not in the same way as those with so-called normal color vision.

It is perhaps more important that, quite apart from whatever color names are used, individuals with color variant vision make different color *discriminations* than normal observers by failing to discern differences that normals make without any difficulty. If an employee with color variant vision produces defective electrical equipment by connecting color-coded wires inappropriately, it seems certain that the employer will think that the employee is wrong and would feel justified not only in excluding that troublemaker from the assembly line, but also in attempting to screen out, in advance, others who might cause similar problems.[10]

Learning from Color Variant Vision

One can hope to learn something about how a system normally works by studying its behavior when it malfunctions. In this sense, the observer with color variant vision can be important for understanding normal color vision. Recall, for example, that the best estimates we have of the spectral sensitivities of the L- and M-cones, whose shapes must be precisely known in order to understand chromatic discrimination (Chapter 8), have depended heavily upon psychophysical studies of observers believed to possess just one of these cone types, while lacking the other. Later in this chapter we will see how protanopes (so-called red blind) and deuteranopes (so called green blind) helped to identify the genetic basis for the L- and M-photopigments. But not all color deficiencies have a genetic basis; some forms can result from insults to the body in the form of accident, disease, or drugs. By examining the nature of color variance inherited or acquired, information can sometimes be uncovered suggesting which parts of the visual pathways have probably been affected, thereby helping to diagnose disease or to assess theoretical ideas about the organization of the visual pathways. The study of color variant vision also raises subtle questions concerning the relation between perception and the neurochemical mechanisms of the brain whose activity underlies it. These concerns relate to what people with severe color variance really see and how their perceptions can best be gauged and understood.

HOW COLOR VISION CAN GO AWRY

Once again it is time to look at the opponent-color model of Figure 7.1A. This time we will consider the logical consequences of assuming that various components of that model have been altered in ways that would impair the normal system of chromatic information processing.

Dichromats

Suppose that the S-cones are missing and that the visual system is otherwise normal. Because there are few S-cones and they do not contribute importantly to the luminance channels, there should be no change in the spectral sensitivity of the eye as measured, for example, by flicker photometry (Chapter 9). There should also be negligible loss of contour perception, because S-cones are scarce and contribute little to contour. But the y-b chromatic channels would be perpetually biased in the y direction. Chromatic discrimination, therefore, would become dichromatic, mediated only by the r-g channels. The color triangle would be reduced to a line because only two components — one of long, the other of short wavelength — would be needed to match all possible colors. Dichromats with this type of vision are called tritanopes.

Protanopes who lack the L-photopigment have their L'-cones (we identify cones containing an inappropriate photopigment with a prime) inappropriately filled with the M-photopigment normally found in M-cones. Lateral inhibition between L'-and M-cones could then occur in the presence of luminance differences, and there would be no inactive or missing receptors in the retina. The luminance channel would reflect the action spectrum of the M-photopigment. The difference signal from L'- and M-cones would always be zero. The r-g opponent pathways would probably not develop normally,[11] but in any event there could be no discrimination mediated by them. The predicted color sensations would be yellow and blue.

Similarly, if M'-cones of deuteranopes were filled with L-photopigment, these subjects would exhibit essentially normal spatial vision. Their spectral sensitivity (i.e., of the M'-cones) would be that of L-cones, no color discrimination could be mediated by their r-g channels and, like protanopes, dichromatic color discrimination would be based only on the activity of y-b opponent channels. They also would see yellow and blue only, and sensitivity to midspectral wavelengths would be reduced, though only slightly.

Recall from Chapter 5 that color matches depend upon a physiological identity at the receptor level. One might expect therefore that observers who are missing one of the three photopigment classes would accept color matches made by normal observers who possess all three classes of normal photopigments. This prediction might follow because a match for all three types of receptors should remain a match for each member of the remaining pair if only one type is missing. This situation assumes that all normals have exactly the same three photopigments and the two remaining photopigments possessed by dichromats are identical to those of the normal.

Alpern & Pugh (1977) found that deuteranopes, indeed, had only one long wavelength photopigment. But they sometimes found clear differences in the action spectrum of this photopigment from that found in normal observers. The concluded that, "If each deuteranope is a reduced form of normal trichromacy, similar variability in the long wave sensitive cone visual pigment among trichromats can be expected to exist." (p. 642). Recent research supports this prediction (Neitz, Neitz & Jacobs, 1993; Neitz, Neitz, & Jacobs, 1991; Neitz & Jacobs, 1986).

Trichromats with Anomalous Photopigments

Suppose that all systems existed in their normal states except that some of the spectral absorption curves of cones were modified. Be-

Table 10.2   A 2 × 2 classification scheme for common types or red-green color
deficiency

		Dichromats	Anomalous trichromats
Deutans	Normal or nearly normal spectral sensitivity	Deuteranope (lacks M-photopigment	Deuteranomalous (abnormal M-photopigment)
Protans	Reduced sensitivity to long wavelengths	Protanope (lacks L-photopigment	Protanomalous (abnormal L-photopigment

Dichromats confuse all colors that are equally bright for them, and that stimulate S-cones identically,
whereas anomalous trichromats do not. Deutans have a spectral sensitivity that is nearly normal, whereas
protans exhibit a severely reduced sensitivity to long wavelengths.

cause all photopigments have action spectra of approximately the same
shape when plotted on a frequency basis (Dartnall 1962), the most
probable altered systems would feature one or more altered types of
cone photopigment, showing a shift of λ_{max}. Consider the relation between the L- and M-cone sensitivities. If the wavelength separation
between peak sensitivities were to be increased so that the overlap of
the two absorption curves became less than normal, sensitivity to wavelength changes might be improved somewhat in the middle region
where the curves cross, but the opposite would be true in the flanks.
In the limit, if two such curves were pulled apart until they failed completely to overlap, wavelength discrimination would be almost entirely
lost (recall Fig. 5.16). There is evidence that alteration by an abnormally great separation of L- and M-curves may occasionally occur (Smith
& Pokorny, 1978), but this is not among the common defects that appear to relate to the opposite case where the two curves have peaks
that are closer together than is normal. Here, too, it is predicted that
wavelength discrimination should get worse, and in the limit will be
lost as the two curves overlap completely.[12] Trichromatic color matches
are predicted, but with decreased precision of trichromatic settings as
the curves overlap more and more completely.[13]

Another interesting prediction results from such curve shifts,
namely that subjects so affected would not be expected to accept the
color matches of normal observers, and vice versa. These conditions
are met for subjects called *anomalous trichromats*, with the predicted
result. Anomalous trichromats fall into two classes as defined in Table
10.2, which summarizes the categories into which most color-defective observers fall. Additional criteria for classification will be described later in the chapter.

Jameson & Hurvich (1956; Hurvich, 1972, 1981) proposed that
the midpoint for normal and anomalous observers' color matches

on the anomaloscope is determined by the location of the photopigment peak spectral absorbance, and they hypothesized a multiple pigment shift for anomalous observers. Protanomalous observers, for example, who give narrow ranges of Rayleigh match responses do so because of a shift in the L-cone pigment. However, anomalous trichromatic observers who give a large range of color matches do so because of post-receptoral "neural efficiency losses" (1972, p. 597). These losses are psychophysically represented by ". . . graded reductions in the red-green response process" (Jameson & Hurvich, 1956).

Romeski (1978) performed a hue cancellation experiment on two deuteranomalous and three protanomalous observers. Her analyses of these data support the original Jameson & Hurvich (1956) hypothesis, which received additional discussion by Hurvich. Pokorny & Smith (1977), however, conclude, "that the single-pigment hypothesis can provide an adequate framework within which to view the color vision of X-chromosomal-linked anomalous trichromats" (p. 1208). Ruddock (1991) after providing a comprehensive review of bases underlying anomalous trichromacy recently concluded , ". . . the case for introducing changes in post-receptoral organization in addition to those which occur in the cone absorption spectra requires careful consideration" (p. 18).

DICHROMACY ON A CONE EXCITATION DIAGRAM

Figure 10.10 is reproduced from Figure 7.24. Recall that this is a chromaticity diagram in which the colors are specified in terms of cone receptor excitation. Because the abscissa represents both the L-cone and M-cone excitations we will refer to the axes in this diagram by the cone functions they represent. The origin ($l = 0$, $s = 0$) represents a color that would be produced by the unique excitation of the M-cones. We will call this the "M corner." The right-hand corner of the diagram, where $l = 1$ and $m = 0$ corresponds to a color that would be produced by the unique excitation of the L-cones (we call this the "L corner.") In this diagram there is no analogous "corner" representing a color produced by the unique activation of just the S-cones (MacLeod & Boynton, 1979).

If a protanope is lacking L-photopigment then any two stimuli that cannot be distinguished either by the S- or M-cones would be indiscriminable. Straight lines radiating from the L corner represent loci of such stimuli, for each of which the ratio of S- to M-cone activation is constant at some level. The solid line (labeled "P") that intersects the spectrum locus at 450 nm in Figure 10.10 represents

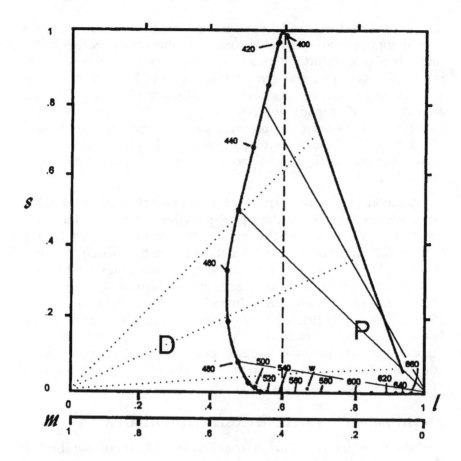

Figure 10.10 A chromaticity diagram based upon cone excitations derived from Smith & Pokorny (1975). Stimuli at $l = 1$, $s = 0$ and at $m = 1$, $s = 0$ if they physically existed would uniquely excite the L- and M-cones respectively. A protanope would confuse colors that lie along one of the lines radiating from $l = 1$, $s = 0$ (labeled P) and deuteranopes would confuse colors that lie along one of the lines radiating from $m = 1$, $s = 0$. Tritanopes would confuse colors that lie along vertical lines that are orthogonal to the abscissa.

one such locus representing colors that are confused by protanopes. The ability of normal observers to distinguish colors that plot along this line depends entirely on the differential capacity of such stimuli to excite L-cones. For protanopes who lack L-photopigment, all such stimuli, at equal luminance should appear alike. For a fan of lines (only three of which are shown in Figure 10.10) radiating from the L corner, each line describes a locus of such indistinguishable stimuli for a protanope. Similarly, a deuteranope, lacking M-photopigment, would confuse colors lying along lines fanning out from the M corner. Three such lines (dotted) labeled with a "D" are shown in Figure 10.10. As noted above, there is no unique corner related to S-cones, because vertical lines parallel to the ordinate represent confusion colors for tritanopes who are missing the S-photopigment. One of these lines is shown in Figure 10.10. All vertical lines parallel to the s-axis represent the tritanopic colors that observers, if missing their S-photopigment, would confuse.

It should be borne in mind that this representation is possible only to the extent that dichromatic vision is a reduced form of normal color vision, with the result that dichromats accept the trichromatic matches of normal observers. Monochromatic lights are located at points determined by the projection of vertical lines that pass through the locus of spectral colors for normal observers.

SOME CONTROVERSIAL ASPECTS OF RED-GREEN DEFICIENCY

Spectral Neutral Points

For the normal observer, all monochromatic lights are chromatic; that is, they differ in appearance from what would be judged as white. Recall (p. 345) that the least saturated spectral region is near 570 nm and appears as greenish-yellow. When asked to judge the appearance of the spectrum, protanopes and deuteranopes see it as chromatic except for a region near 500 nm that appears achromatic to them, although it appears as a highly saturated blue-green for the normal observer.

The existence of a neutral region in the part of the spectrum that looks blue-green to the normal observer is a generally accepted index of dichromatic red-green color defect. Much more controversial is the question of whether protanopes can actually be separated from deuteranopes on the basis of a mere 6-nm difference in their predicted neutral points. The controversy is worth reviewing in some detail.

The theoretical basis for the chromatically-neutral spectral colors of these dichromats is easily visualized on the cone-excitation chromaticity diagram (Fig. 10.11). For clarity, the vertical axis of the figure has been greatly expanded, and the spectrum locus for wavelengths shorter than 480 nm is not shown.

Consider the point W, one of the standard "whites" of the CIE system. Assuming that protanopia is a loss system, then all colors on a line

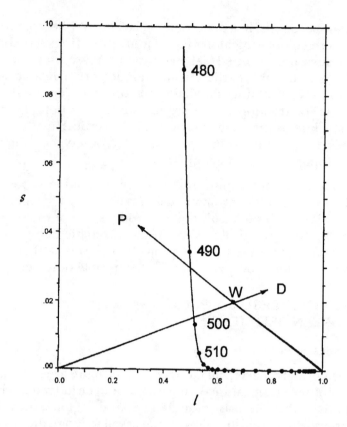

Figure 10.11 This construction, using the contant-luminance chromaticity diagram, shows the spectral stimuli that should be confused by protanopes (P) and deuteranopes (D) for a particular white (W). The full ranges of neutral points for 39 protanopes and 38 deuteranopes as determined by Walls and Heath (1956) fall between 490 and 500 nm, scattering around the lines shown, but with no overlap between the two groups.

from the L corner passing through W should be confused for the protanope. Because an extension of this line intersects the spectral locus at about 492 nm, that wavelength should match W and also appear achromatic, or nearly so.[14] Similarly for the deuteranope, all colors along a line drawn from the M corner through W should be confused; in this case the spectral light equivalent to W lies at about 498 nm.

Figure 10.12 shows the results of dichromatic neutral point determinations from five different laboratories. The procedure used in three of these (unfilled symbols and filled circles) was to compare a broadband white field with one supplied from a monochromator

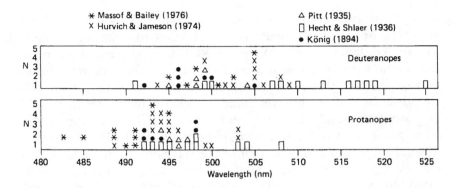

Figure 10.12 Spectral neutral points for protanopes and deuteranopes as determined by König (1894), by Pitt (1935), and by Hecht & Shlaer (1938), using a match with a broadband stimulus that appears achromatic to normal observers. Also shown are data from Hurvich & Jameson (1974) as well as Massof & Bailey (1976). The subjects of these studies set the wavelength drum of a monochromator to produce the "least amount of color" (Massof & Bailey) or "until the color in the test field is the transition between two hues that differ markedly from each other" (Hurvich & Jameson). (Adapted from Hurvich & Jameson, 1974, p. 208.)

whose wavelength was adjusted by the subject to match. The predicted result depends upon the chromaticity of the particular white chosen; because this differs between studies, perfect agreement cannot be expected. All three studies nevertheless agree fairly well, showing that protanopes and deuteranopes differ, on the average, in the theoretically expected direction. But there is substantial overlap between groups, even within studies, so it would not be possible to classify a subject as protanope or deuteranope on the basis of this kind of neutral point test.

Other possible sources of variability that could contribute to the overlap between the two populations include:

• Subjects might differ in the prereceptoral absorption of their ocular media.

• They might have a residual red-green discrimination based on a small number of cones of the putatively missing type.

• They may differ slightly with respect to their remaining longwave pigment, which could be slightly anomalous.

Also, if the remaining pigment of a dichromat were anomalous, this would invalidate the use of the chromaticity diagram based on normal observers for the purpose of predicting the wavelength that appears achromatic (the neutral point), leading to an uninterpretable spread of data if it were used anyway. Residual red-green discrimination would cause the match between white and the spectral color to become inexact, thus contributing to variance. Nevertheless, if sufficient numbers of settings were made, a reliable mean setting should be possible for each subject. With too much residual red-green discrimination, accurate settings would not be possible. (In the limit, a normal subject, if given control of the wavelength and intensity of the test light, would have a terrible time trying to "match" a saturated blue-green with a white). These three studies probably all suffer from the problem of differential prereceptoral absorption for the various subjects that were tested. Recall, from Chapter 5 (p. 183), that if the normalizing system developed by W. D. Wright is used, the location of a broadband stimulus (such as white) will shift in the chromaticity diagram relative to an invariant spectral locus as the ocular pigmentation is changed. A shifting white point, based on known variations in ocular pigmentation between human subjects, probably could account for much of the variation in the three original studies of Figure 10.12.

Walls and Mathews (1952) carried out experiments on dichromatic neutral points that largely circumvented the problem of individual differences in ocular pigmentation. Instead of using spectral colors to be compared with white, they used a color wheel similar to that originally introduced by Maxwell (see p. 22). Their 7° disc contained sectors of blue and green Munsell papers (of known tristimulus values) whose proportions could be varied. With this information they were able to determine the dominant wavelength of the blue-green mixture that matched their achromatic reference. The resulting mixture color was compared with an overlying mixture of black and white papers (the achromatic reference) of smaller radius, similarly adjustable. After a match was made, the junction of the chromatic and achromatic fields was viewed through a reduction screen that cut the field to about 3.5° with a slightly curved junction; the subject made his final match with this smaller field. The resulting protanopic and deuteranopic neutral-point distributions, though they differed by only about 5 nm in mean values for 19 protanopes and 14 deuteranopes, were so tight that they failed completely to overlap. This work was extended in a study by Walls and Heath (1956). For 39 protanopes the mean matching wavelength was 492.3 nm, with a standard deviation of only 0.70 nm; for 38 deuteranopes the corresponding values were 498.4 nm with a standard deviation of 1.21 nm.[15] Again there was no overlap despite the large populations used. The following is their comment about how they achieved such a clear separation where others had failed:

> Walls and Mathews did not understand why their protanopes and deuteranopes were grouped so closely that they pulled apart from each other and left a 1.6 nm no-man's land between them. This was later explained by D. B. Judd in a personal communication.

> . . . Judd pointed out that with this [Maxwell disk] method the effect of scattering the apparent neutral points is practically eliminated. The Munsell papers reflect such broad spectra that an interposed yellow filter shifts the chromaticity of the blue-green zone of the mixer about as much as it does the gray zone. If these shifts were exactly equal, a match made by a dichromat would remain a match even if his ocular pigmentation magically increased or magically disappeared (p. 641).

Another procedure for attempting to circumvent the problem of preretinal absorption has been to eliminate the use of a comparison stimulus altogether. Instead, observers are asked to adjust (or to judge) spectral wavelengths in an effort to find the center of the least saturated, most achromatic band. Hurvich and Jameson (1974) did this and their data are included in Figure 10.12. They report a difference of mean values in the expected direction between protanopes and deuteranopes, but with a much wider spread; 12 of 22 observers falling in an overlapping range. Because their standard deviations were about five times those of Walls and Mathews, it might seem that the absolute-judgement method is either less precise than the matching method, or taps other sources of variation between individuals of the same general type. However, Massof and Bailey (1976), using similar procedures but with extremely large numbers of settings by each subject, obtained essentially nonoverlapping distributions.

The imagined achromatic stimulus, with which the spectral light was being compared in the more recent studies, is not comparable to the physical white stimulus used by Walls and Mathews in their matching experiment. In the latter case there is no requirement (or even likelihood) that it arouses the same achromatic percept for protanopes and deuteranopes, or even that it should necessarily appear white to members of either group. Indeed, if white for the red-green dichromat results from the y-b opponent signals being set to zero, the mixtures of short and long wavelengths required to achieve this balance in the protanope would be expected to differ because of the serious loss of y input.

Varieties of Red-Green Anomaly

In an unusually thorough study of fairly large numbers of red-green anomalous observers, Wright (1946) measured wavelength dis-

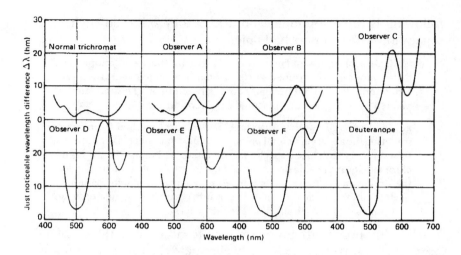

Figure 10.13 Wavelength discrimination curves of 6 deuteranomalous observers (from Wright, 1946, p. 313) shown with normal and deuteranopic functions as end points.

crimination curves and found that they covered a fairly continuous range from nearly normal to almost dichromatic. Figure 10.13 shows his results for six subjects classified as deuteranomalous. In addition, there are data for a normal trichromat and a deuteranope that serve to anchor the endpoints of the series. (Similar data were obtained for a sample of eleven protanomalous observers.)

WHAT DO RED-GREEN-DEFECTIVE OBSERVERS REALLY SEE?

The color perception of a red-green anomalous observer can most easily be understood by first calculating the L/M cone activation ratio for any particular stimulus, based on his (or much less likely, her) longwave cone sensitivities, which are too close together to be normal. Next, determine for a normal observer the wavelength that would be required to produce that same L/M ratio. Assume that S-cone activity is normal for both. Anomalous observers would be expected to see all of the hues that normal observers see, except for the most saturated reds and greens, which cannot be simulated because of the limited L/M cone ratios of the anomalous observer caused by the abnormal overlap of their cone absorption spectra. A protanomalous observer would in addition see the more saturated red colors as being much darker than they appear for the normal or deuteranomalous subject.

On the basis of the opponent-color model that has been presented, one can make reasonable predictions about what dichromats should see, assuming that the replacement hypothesis is correct and that the visual pathways are normal except for the r-g channels. For spectral colors, there is a division at the neutral wavelength that should cause shorter wavelengths to appear blue and longer ones yellow. For a short distance on either side of the neutral point, there is a rapid increase in saturation. This corresponds to the range within which the U-shaped wavelength discrimination functions of protanopes and deuteranopes can be measured. Outside this range, on each side of the zone of good discrimination, a dichromat should experience little or no difference in the appearance of equally bright spectral colors.

For the normal observer, spectral colors are the most saturated. For the deuteranope, spectral stimuli should have no such special quality. As plotted upon the chromaticity diagram of the normal observer, any nonspectral color can be matched by the protanope or deuteranope by a spectral color that lies on the protan or deutan confusion line passing through the point representing the chromaticity, for a normal observer, of the nonspectral stimulus. Therefore, if the appearance of spectral colors is known, that of any nonspectral color can readily be predicted.

The expected color perception of the protanope is essentially the same as that of the deuteranope, except that different spectral colors must be chosen to match non-spectral ones, and colors which are equivalent to long-wavelength spectral lights will appear very dim. Color names, for the dichromat, describe salient properties of objects other than hue. For example, a protanope learns that objects that would be described as "dark yellow" or "brown" by normal observers (if they could see them with a protanope's eyes) must be called "red" if the color identification is to be "correct" in the sense of agreeing with that of normal observers.

Few dichromats can be convinced that their color vision accords with the theoretical description just given. Moreover, there is no proof that the descriptions just given are accurate characterizations of what red-green defective observers actually do see. A major problem, as noted at the outset of the chapter, is that sensations are not logically comparable between different individuals. Therefore it is not really meaningful to state dogmatically that a deuteranope sees the long spectral wavelengths as yellow. Perhaps the closest that one can come to a solution of this dilemma is to study a *unilateral dichromat,* a person who is color defective in one eye and color normal in the other.

Some unilateral dichromats have been discovered. Judd (1948) stated that 37 cases had been reported by that time, but Hsia and Graham (1965) note that "only about 8 of these have proved useful for theory." Some unilateral subjects (for example, one studied intensively by Graham and his colleagues) seem to see colors in much the way that the opponent-color model predicts. But according to Walls (1958), no bona fide unilateral protanope has ever been discovered. This was a matter of great interest to him because he predicted, as a trichromatic theorist, that protanopes should see blue and green, not blue and yellow.

Walls pointed out that Graham's subject was not classically deuteranopic, probably being heterozygous for the deuteranopic gene so that the defect expressed itself in unusual ways. Besides the unusual asymmetry of the defect, it also seems likely that the deuteranopia was incomplete because wavelength discrimination in the supposedly dichromatic eye was not completely lacking in the longwave end of the spectrum.

MacLeod and Lennie (1974) discovered a man who was classically deuteranopic in one eye and deuteranomalous in the other. As previously noted, a deuteranomalous observer enjoys most of the normal color experiences; surely he has had sensations of red, green, yellow, and blue and should therefore be in a position to name the hue seen in the deuteranopic eye, using the relatively normal eye and his (presumably) normal brain as a gauge. It is embarrassing for opponent-color theory that the color he reported in response to long wavelengths, seen by his deuteranopic eye, was not yellow, but orange. These authors conclude:

> By providing such a clear exception to the rule that yellow and blue are the only colors perceived by the red-green blind, these observations of R. H. destroy the last remaining support for "opponent process" interpretations of color blindness and particularly of deuteranopia. But the support afforded to opponent process interpretations by the earlier unilateral cases was in any case flimsy. Binocular matches can lead to rigorous conclusions about retinal events only if a binocular match is a match at the retinal level, and this cannot be guaranteed unless the afferent pathways from left and right eyes are similar. The necessary assumption of afferent identity is difficult to justify in unilateral cases, for it is clear . . . that different "stimulus histories" for left and right eyes may bring about differences of organization in the afferent pathways at stages prior to binocular combination (pp. 132–133).

In other words, it is possible that a message from the deuteranopic eye that would have been interpreted as "yellow" if transmitted through normal pathways, and moreover received by a brain with normal, chromatically-rich, and binocularly-balanced input, might instead register as orange. Although this interpretation might seemingly help to save opponent theory (especially since some other unilateral color blinds do see the predicted colors) it logically implies that the issue of what dichromats "really" see probably can never be fully resolved.

OTHER FORMS OF COLOR VARIANCE

Rod Monochromacy

This form of color variance is properly called color blindness and is apparently caused by an absence (or near absence) of all cone function. It is considered to be congenital and autosomal recessive, that is, not sex-linked. Rod monochromats exhibit a foveal scotoma (blind spot) and frequently a related nystagmus (involuntary eye movements). Such subjects are often photophobic (dislike moderate to bright lights that do not bother normal observers very much) and they always show very low acuity, around 20/200. They have often proved useful as subjects for the study of rod vision at relatively high levels, where cone vision normally intrudes to make such investigation difficult. The rod monochromat has no color discrimination, as would be predicted on the basis of arguments advanced about rod vision in Chapter 5. A postmortem anatomical investigation by Glickstein and Heath (1975) has revealed the presence of cones in a "rod" monochromat, despite the lack of any such evidence based upon psychophysical testing.[16]

Tritanopia

Congenital tritanopia has been shown by Kalmus (1965) to be an autosomal dominant trait that is extremely rare (less than 1 in 10,000). In 1952, W. D. Wright reported on a substantial population of tritanopes, obtained following the publication in the widely circulated *Picture Post* magazine of pseudo-isochromatic plates that had been designed by Farnsworth. A similar plate is shown in Kalmus (1965) as Plate I. Tritanopic luminosity curves were found to be virtually identical to those of normals, color-mixture data were dichromatic, and the chromaticities that were confused tended to fall along lines radiating from a single tritanopic copunctal point. Their unusual wavelength discrimination functions were also measured. These are compared in Figure 10.14 (top panel) with data from a similar study by Fischer, Bouman, and ten Doesschate (1951) and a theoretical prediction by Walraven (1962) similar to that generated by the

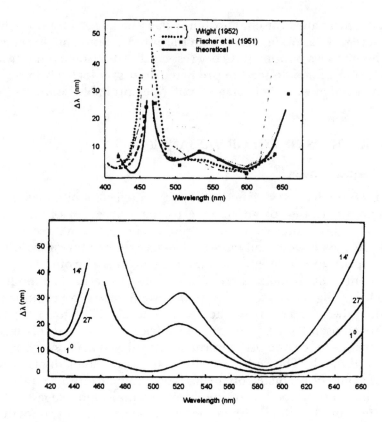

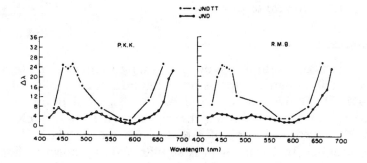

Figure 10.14 Top: Wavelength discrimination data of tritanopes (from Walraven, 1962, p. 63). Middle: Similar data from normal observers as a function of field size (data of C.R. Forshaw from Weale, 1960, p. 127). Bottom: Wavelength discrimination data with a 0.8 degree field open circles and with a 0.8 degree field but under transient tritanopic conditions (data from Kaiser & Boynton, 1985, p. 526). Note the similarity of the tritanopes data; the small field data of normal subjects and that of normal observers under conditions of transient tritanopia.

model of Chapter 8 (Fig. 8.5). For comparison, wavelength discrimination functions for normals as a function of stimulus area are shown (Fig. 10.14 middle panel); these show clearly that the normal subject tends toward tritanopia for the smallest field used. Another way to cause color normals to behave similarly to tritanopes is to induce *transient tritanopia* (Mollon & Polden, 1977). When a normal observer's eye is adapted to a yellow light and then this adaptation is removed, for a brief period of time the normal will respond like a tritanope. Kaiser & Boynton (1985) exploited transient tritanopia to perform a wavelength discrimination experiment. As can be seen in the bottom of Figure 10.14, the curve with filled circles has a sharp increase in $\Delta\lambda$ near 460 nm, just as is found with tritanopes or with normals when viewing very small fields (top and middle panels). For comparison, in the bottom panel (open circles) the reader can see a $\Delta\lambda$ function obtained when the eye was not chromatically adapted.

Cone Monochromacy

In his Friedenwald Award lecture to ARVO, Alpern (1974) reported the discovery of L-cone monochromacy.[17] His subject was capable of matching all spectral colors to a single standard, yielding a spectral sensitivity curve matching that of deuteranopes, except for wavelengths below 500 nm where the L-cone monochromat's sensitivity was higher. Curiously, his spectral sensitivity under conditions of strong yellow adaptation was that of π_3, one of Stiles's "blue" mechanisms. Apparently Alpern's subject has S-cones, but for some reason they are not useful for purposes of color discrimination; possibly his y-b opponent pathways are inoperative. M-cone monochromats were reported by Weale (1953b), who found that the spectral sensitivities of these subjects were a bit too high in the long wavelengths to match those of protanopes, so in his case there appeared to be some L cones contributing. Like Alpern's S-cones, these did not mediate chromatic discrimination; perhaps in Weale's subjects the r-g opponent pathways were nonfunctional.

S-cone monochromacy is relatively the most common type, although it is still exceedingly rare.[18] Such observers have about 20/60 acuity at best, roughly consistent with predictions based on normal subjects under conditions of S-cone "isolation" that may be achieved with strong yellow adapting lights and blue test stimuli (Brindley, 1954). Their photopic spectral sensitivity is essentially that of S-cones, as inferred from human color mixture and two-color threshold work. Their modulation sensitivity is close to what has been inferred for normals under conditions of S-cone isolation. Of special interest is the fact that, over a remarkably small range of luminance reduction, as judged from spectral sensitivity analysis, the basis of their vision switches from S-cone to rod. Many of these subjects have a rudimentary form of dichromatic color vision in the transition range, which indicates that the sensations mediated by the S-cone and rod systems must be qualitatively different.

Although it is difficult to be certain, it seems likely that the distribution of S-cones in S-cone monochromats is about the same as in the normal retina, and that their function is normal. They exhibit a normal Stiles–Crawford effect, which would not be likely if the remainder of the foveal cones were missing, and rod sensitivity can be obtained for small fixated stimuli. Although these facts suggest that the L- and M-cones may be present, and contain rhodopsin rather than cone pigments (a possibility which has also been entertained in the case of total rod monochromacy), rhodopsin-mediated vision is not found at intensities above rod saturation, and one cannot be certain that these subjects use their foveas in a normal way.

ACQUIRED COLOR VISION DEFICIENCIES[19]

Injury or diseases of the eye or neural pathways, which are frequently diagnosed by procedures not requiring color-vision testing, are often the cause of defects of color vision. That a condition is acquired rather than congenital is signaled, not only by the presence of other abnormalities, but by the awareness of the patient that there has been a change in color perception. Careful color vision testing can reveal losses in color discrimination that mimic the congenital forms, but which differ from these in detail.

Although relatively little has been learned about normal color vision by the study of acquired *dyschromatopsia,* a few brief remarks about this class of defect are needed to round out this section of the chapter. Of special interest are the ethambutol studies (Wietsma, Kamermans & Spekreijse, 1995). Humans who took this drug acquired a red-green color vision deficiency. Subsequent behavioral and physiological experiments on goldfish injected with this drug showed similar defects and suggested that ethambutol acts on the inner plexiform layer of the retina.

One of the first schemes to classify acquired color vision defects was proposed by Köllner (1912). The so-called Köllner's law attempts to classify the relation of acquired color vision deficiency to the location of pathology. It is clear from Marré's (1973) presentation that Köllner treats pathologies as progressive problems that can eventually lead to total color blindness. However, if one looks at the initial stages of visual pathology, Köllner's law suggests that blue deficien-

Table 10.3   Classification of Acquired Color Vision Defects

Verriest type	Discrimination Loss	Defect severity	Visual acuity loss	Wald–Marré type	Disorder
Type I	Red-Green	Mild	Moderate	IIb	Progressive cone
		Severe	Severe	III	degeneration
Type II	Red-Green + Blue	Mild	Mild	IIa	Optic nerve
		Moderate	Moderate	IIb	disorders
		Severe	Severe	III	(post optic disc)
Type III + Pseudo-PA	Blue	Mild	Mild	I	Choroidal disorders with sensory elevation
Type III	Blue + Red-Green	Mild	Mild	I	Pigmentary degeneration
		Moderate	Moderate	Ib	Vascular disease Glaucoma, papilledema Dominant optic atrophy Cataract

From Pokorny and Smith, 1986.

cies[20] develop in diseases of the retina whereas red-green deficiencies develop from diseases of the conduction pathways from the inner layers of the retina to the cortex. This rule remains valid even though there are occasional contradictions (Pokorny & Smith, 1986).

In Table 10.3 we reproduce the most recent classification proposed by Pokorny and Smith (1986). As is clear from the table, this classification is dependent on the previous efforts of Verriest and of Marré. We are cautioned by Pokorny & Smith that in this classification one can expect exceptions in individual cases.

The Verriest (1963) classification is based primarily on the Farnsworth–Munsell 100 Hue Test, the Panel D-15 Test and AO H-R-R tests color vision tests. "Wald–Marré" refers to Marré's use of Wald's method of chromatic adaptation (see Chapter 6, p. 238) to investigate a variety of visual pathologies for acquired color vision defects. After chromatically adapting the mechanisms to be suppressed, she obtained increment thresholds on the remaining active mechanism. Due to the restricted range of wavelengths that Marré tested for each mechanism, she probably avoided regions where isolation is the poorest and thereby avoided the criticism leveled against Wald's chromatic adaptation method for isolating cone mechanisms.

The most common form of acquired loss of color discrimination occurs as a natural part of the aging process, as the lens of the eye

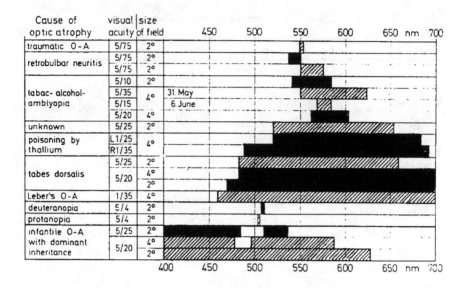

Figure 10.15 Wavelengths having a neutral appearance for patients with various diseases of the optic nerve. The much narrower bands of congenital dichromats are also shown (from Grützner, 1972, p. 654).

absorbs progressively more light at the short wavelengths (Lakowski, 1962; Weale, 1960, 1963). The effect is predominantly optical, as may be proved by tests using monochromatic lights that, if intense enough, can be made to reach the retina. Most of the changes with age in the chromaticity of the spectral locus can be eliminated by using the normalizing technique of Wright, described in Chapter 5. The loss of discrimination is therefore similar to what the young, normal observer would experience if looking through an attenuating filter that mimics the prereceptoral absorption of light in the older eye.

Most other acquired loss of color vision involves problems either with the retina or with the optic nerve. Figure 10.15, from Grützner (1972), shows that the spectral band that appears neutral is typically much wider and tends to be centered at longer wavelengths than for congenital protanopia or deuteranopia. Retinal disease is more likely to lead to tritan-like defects than to abnormal red-green discrimination; yet both occur and are specific to particular disease states. Acquired optic nerve dichromacies may resemble congenital ones, but there are important differences. Verriest (1963) puts it this way:

> ... the color discrimination is (as with congenital defects) reduced to a twofold function of wavelength and the confusions can be checked

in the chromaticity diagram by an infinity of confusion axes, which are parallel or are convergent to a point outside the spectrum locus. However, the acquired defectiveness is not quite as clear-cut as the congenital, because the direction of the neutral axis varies from case to case, because there is always some impairment of discrimination at right angles to the neutral axis, and because the discrimination often becomes much better when the visual angle is increased (p.191).

The latter is also true of congenital dichromacy, more so than is commonly realized (Pokorny & Smith, 1977). In any event, these complications make acquired color deficiencies, especially in their early stages, much harder to detect and to diagnose than the congenital form. It is probable that some disease states could be diagnosed earlier by color-vision testing than by any other procedure, if baseline data existed for the patient and sophisticated tests were used. But most ophthalmologists and optometrists rely only on the pseudoisochromatic plates, which are not adequate for detection and diagnosis of acquired defects, and baseline data using more sensitive tests seldom exist. Grützner (1972) provides a table indicating which tests constitute the preferred diagnostic tools as a function of retinal disease.

Although we touched on color vision testing above, a few words are appropriate as they relate to the testing of acquired color vision deficiencies. Summaries of the psychophysical methods used to assess acquired color vision defects have been provided by Marré (1973), Kinnear *et al.* (1979), and King–Smith (1991). Briefly, most of the tests usually used to evaluate normal color vision, e.g., spectral sensitivity, wavelength discrimination, saturation discrimination, detection thresholds, have also been used to assess these acquired defects. Of the color vision tests discussed above, Marré notes that the best ones for assessing the acquired defects are the Farnsworth Panel-D 15 Test and the Farnsworth–Munsell 100 Hue Test. Color–naming tests are reported to be well suited for diagnosing acquired defects, because such patients are often capable of naming colors as they remember them when their color vision was normal. One caveat that Marré gives is that these color names will be dependent on the observing conditions in addition to the acquired defect exhibited by the patient.

GENETIC BASIS OF COLOR VARIANCE

The tendency for color variant vision to "run in families" and skip generations had been noticed long before there was a science of genetics. Equally obvious was the fact that color deficiency is much more widespread among males than females. A family pedigree illustrating these characteristics, shown in Figure 10.16, was originally presented by an ophthalmologist named Horner in 1876. According to Kalmus

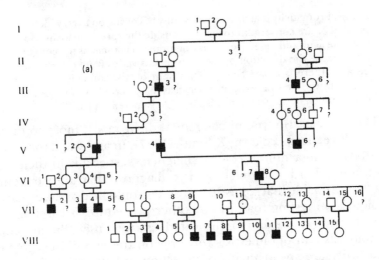

Figure 10.16 Horner's original pedigree of deuteranopes, first published in 1876. Squares: males; circles: females. Successive generations represented top to bottom. Filled symbols represent deuteranopes. Originally published by Bell (1926), this figure is reproduced from Kalmus (1965, p. 62).

(1965), Horner was the first to recognize the mode of inheritance. Note that all of the deuteranopes are male and that the condition skips generations, demonstrating "Horner's law of inheritance." Although Horner may have been the first to recognize the genetic relationship underlying defective color vision, there were earlier reports of people who have color vision problems. Piantanida (1991) reminds us of three such reports: Tubervile (1684); Huddart (1777); and Scott (1778). These latter two papers provide brief pedigrees but the are not really sufficient to provide an understanding of an inheritable basis.

The inheritable basis underlying defective color vision was nicely determined by mapping the family histories of these visual anomalies. This line of research, together with an understanding of basic genetics, prompted scientists to model the underlying genetics of color vision deficiency. Models became more factual when, starting in the early 1980s, genes responsible for human visual photopigments were identified. Before taking a brief look at this research, we need first to review some basic genetic principles.

Some Basic Genetics

Let us first review some basic genetic terminology. Cells of all living things are composed of several components, the most important of which is the nucleus. The nucleus is where all genetic information is stored, in structures called *chromosomes*. In humans, cells containing 23 pairs of chromosomes are called *somatic cells;* those possessing only 23 single chromosomes are called *gametes* (sperm or ova). In somatic cells, 22 of these pairs are referred to as *autosomes* and the remaining pair is called a *sex chromosome.* Autosomes are non-sex chromosomes that regulate all genetic characteristics common to both sexes. Sex chromosomes define gender. They also carry traits (e.g., defective color vision, hemophilia), which are dependent on the sex of the individual. Females have one pair of X chromosomes, while males possess one X chromosome and one Y chromosome (Fig. 10.17). Each chromosome is made up of small units called *genes,* which carry the information that characterizes the individual. The genetic information is referred to as the *genotype.* The various human characteristics "expressed" by the genes are called *phenotypes.*

Alleles are alternative forms of the same gene occupying the same location on the chromosome. For example the gene responsible for hair color has an allele for dark hair, one for blond hair, and yet another for red hair. Alleles can be either *dominant or recessive.* When the dominant form and the recessive form co-exist in an individual, this is known as a *heterozygous* state. When two identical alleles exist this is called the *homozygous state.* Recessive alleles are expressed phenotypically only when they are homozygous.

We can now begin to consider some basic principles of heredity as applied to human color vision. But before proceeding with our discussion of the genetics of color vision, the following paragraph from Suzuki *et al.* (1989) is worth noting.

> A gene does *not* determine a phenotype by acting alone; it does so only in conjunction with other genes and with the environment. Although geneticists do routinely ascribe a particular phenotype to an allele of a gene they have identified, we must remember that this is merely a convenient kind of jargon designed to facilitate genetic analysis. This jargon arises from the ability of geneticists to isolate individual components of a biological process and to study them as part of genetic dissection. Although this logical isolation is an essential aspect of genetics, the message of this chapter is that a gene cannot act by itself (p. 83).

Patterns of Inheritance in Color Vision

Let us now take a closer look at the genetic events take place after conception. When a cell divides (*mitosis*), chromosomes are duplicated and each member of the resulting pair carries an identical genetic message to the daughter cells. Ultimately, every one of the

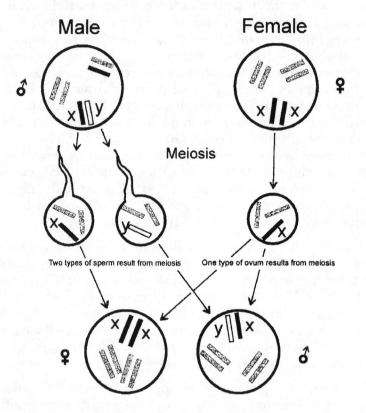

Diploid chromosome complement of

Sex determined by type of sperm entering the ovum

Figure 10.17 Prior to fertilization, meiotic division of germ cells results in two types of sperm, but only one type of ovum. Depending on which sperm is effective, the fertilized ovum will have two X cells and be female, or one X and one Y cell and be male. This diagram show why the X cell of the male offspring can come only from the mother. (From Watson, 1976, p. 14.)

60 trillion or so cells in a fully developed human contains the same genetic information. All 23 pairs of chromosomes in the human female are *homologous;* that is, the members of each of the pairs are identical. During *meiotic* division (formation of sex cells) these paired chromosomes divide to form ova of just one type, one of which is shown in Figure 10.17. Both ova, therefore, have the same morphology and contain genes that govern the same characteristics. This is

true of only 22 chromosomes in the male. The exception is the X chromosome, which has a morphologically disparate mate, the Y chromosome. Following meiotic division, these sperm are of two types, one containing an X chromosome, and the other a Y chromosome. At fertilization, when chromosomes derived from those of the parents are recombined into pairs, exactly half of the genetic material is received from each parent. If an X-chromosome-bearing sperm is effective in fertilizing the ovum (bottom left in Fig. 10.17), the offspring will be female and her twenty-third chromosome will be homologous. But if a Y-chromosome-bearing sperm is effective, the fertilized ovum will contain the X-Y chromosome pairing and the offspring will be male (bottom-right).

Just prior to the meiotic split, a recombination of genes occurs called *crossing over*. This is a pseudo-random process with contingent probabilities. Genes located close together along a chromosome are more likely to remain together (either be included or excluded together from the collection of genes in the new organism), whereas those located far apart along a chromosome behave more independently, with complete independence being the rule for genes located in separate chromosomes.

Genes controlling the same general trait exist at specific loci along the chromosome. From one organism to another, within a given species, genes at a specific locus exist in different types — the alleles. When the alleles differ at the same locus on each chromosome of a homologous pair (heterozygous gene pair), the tendency is for one allele to dominate the other in its phenotypical expression. Probably the most familiar example is eye color. By the simplest model, if both alleles were homozygous (brown-brown or blue-blue), then the phenotype would necessarily be brown or blue respectively. But the two heterozygous combinations of brown-blue and blue-brown would lead to brown eyes. By inference the allele for brown eyes is *dominant*, while that for blue eyes is said to be *recessive*. A person carrying the brown-blue gene combination is said to be a *carrier* of the blue-eyed gene. A quarter of the time, two brown-blue carriers, both of whom have brown eyes, would produce a blue-eyed offspring. This expression is probabilistic, so there would be a finite probability that two such blue-eyed carriers could produce, say, ten blue-eyed offspring in succession, although the odds against it would be about one in a million.

Regardless of our gender, we all inherit an X chromosome from our mother. The father contributes an X chromosome to his daughters and a Y chromosome to his sons. Y chromosomes contain no genes for photopigments. The X chromosomes, however, do carry genes that code for the L- and M-photopigments. The gene for the S-photopigment is on an autosomal chromosome. Males who inherit an X chromosome from the mother with a defective or missing photopigment gene become color deficient. Females, with two X chromosomes, will inherit one defective photopigment gene and one normal one. Because the normal gene is dominant, these females will exhibit normal color vision. Because they carry one gene for defective color vision these females are referred to as *carriers*. Females will have defective color vision only if the gene on each of the X chromosomes is missing or defective. From this analysis the reader can appreciate why males have a greater probability of inheriting defective color vision.

Chemical Basis of Heredity[21]

Genetic material is composed of very large molecules known as *nucleic acids*. These nucleic acids are classified as *deoxyribonucleic acid (DNA)* or *ribonucleic acid (RNA)*. DNA, present only in the nucleus of cells, is made up of nucleotides. Each *nucleotide* consists of a phosphate group, five carbon sugar, and one *nitrogenous base*. Nucleotides are connected by *phosphodiester bonds,* resulting in large molecules (Fig. 10.18). Watson and Crick (1953) showed that DNA consists of two separate strands interwound and held together by weak electrostatic *hydrogen bonds*. This DNA configuration is the well-known double helix (Fig. 10.19).

The nitrogenous base of the nucleotides contains the hereditary information, arranged in an order known as the *base sequence* of the gene. This arrangement of the nitrogenous base is highly specific, and any alternation of the initial base sequence causes a *mutation*. Because DNA cannot leave the nucleus, it transfers its genetic information by a complex process known as *RNA transcription;* a process that uses an RNA molecule called *messenger RNA* (mRNA). The mRNA molecule is also a nucleic acid and acts as the blueprint for DNA. Once DNA is copied into mRNA, it undergoes modification called *RNA splicing* (Fig. 10.20). The purpose of RNA splicing is not fully understood. The portions of genetic material that encode for protein are called *exons* and those portions which do not are called *introns*. We will see below that the number and position of these exons help to identify the genes responsible for the cone photopigments. The introns are removed from the mRNA and the exons are joined together, after which the RNA leaves the nucleus and enters the cell's *cytoplasm*. When the mRNA molecule enters the cytoplasm a process called *protein synthesis* begins which results in the formation of *polypeptides*.

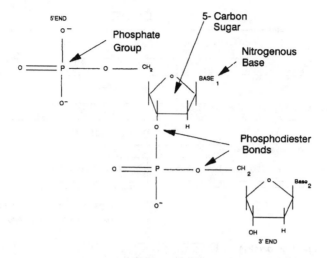

Figure 10.18 DNA is made up of a series of nucleotides each of which consists of a phosphate group, five carbon sugar, and one nitrogenous base. The nitrogenous base contains the hereditary information. Nucleotides are connected by phosphodiester bonds. Note the designation of the 5' end near the top and 3' end near the bottom, this designation will be seen again in Fig. 10.23.

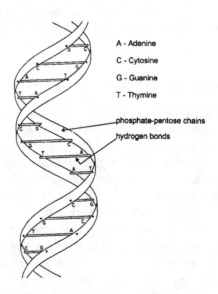

Figure 10.19 Schematic of the famous double helix. Each helix is held together by a series of hydrogen bonds. Denaturation refers to the breaking apart of these hydrogen bonds.

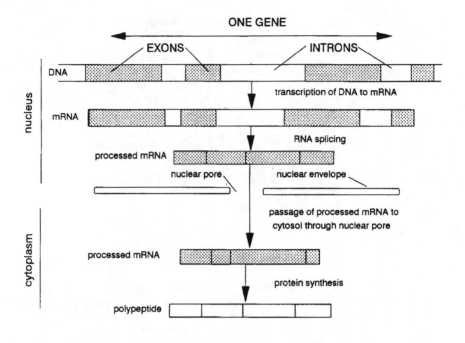

Figure 10.20 Because DNA cannot leave the nucleus of a cell it transfers its genetic information by a process known as RNA transcription. Genetic material, which encodes for protein, is called an exon, those which do not are called introns. Exons will become relevant again in Fig. 10.23. mRNA = messenger RNA. (See text.)

Hybridization of Nucleic Acids

The ability to use a known or manufactured piece of DNA to hybridize with the "target" DNA that one is studying utilizes one of the major principles in modern molecular genetics. Nucleic acids are long strands of nucleotides held together by hydrogen bonds (Fig. 10.19). These nucleic acids become *denatured* when exposed to an alkaline solution or high temperatures. This means that their hydrogen bonds break apart. Initially it was believed that *denaturation* was irreversible, but in 1961 it was discovered that two separate strands of DNA, which are complementary to each other, will reassemble the double helix by a process known as either *hybridization* or *renaturation*. The rate of hybridization depends on the concentration of nucleic acids and the collision rate of the complementary nucleotide sequence possessed by the nucleic acids. Hybridization is used in a number of genetic techniques (e.g., PCR and sequencing). Here we examine how hybridization is used to analyze nucleic acids in a technique called *Southern blotting*.

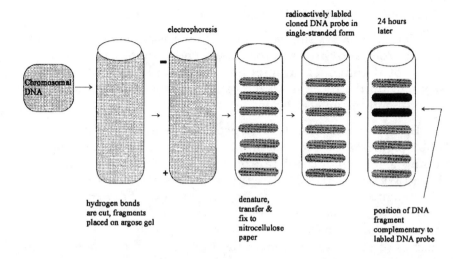

Figure 10.21 A schematic representation illustrating the Southern blotting procedure. The end result is a photograph of radioactive labeled DNA fragments. The smallest fragments move the furthest and the largest fragments move the least as a result of electrophoresis.

Southern Blotting

Southern blotting is a technique named after its inventor Edward Southern (1975). Figure 10.21 helps to guide the reader through a brief explanation of the Southern blotting technique. There are specific enzymes that cut DNA into small fragments. A small aliquot (sample) of solution containing the enzymatically cut DNA is loaded at one end of a slab (or strip) of gel. An electric current is applied to this gel (a process called gel electrophoresis). This electric current causes the DNA fragments to move down the gel, separating themselves according to their molecular size; the smallest fragments traveling the greater distances and the larger ones lagging behind them. Single-stranded DNA is transferred from the gel to a more stable support, namely a piece of nitrocellulose paper. The locations of the electrophoretically separated DNA fragments are preserved in the transfer, but at this point they all look alike. Then radioactive labeled DNA (a DNA *probe*) from a known source, (e.g., from bovine DNA) is added to the denatured DNA, which is incubated for 24 hours so that the DNA probe combines (*hybridizes*) with the denatured DNA and the position of DNA fragments are revealed. This technique is also valuable in showing on which chromosome a gene is located.

Genes and Their Related photopigments in Color Vision

Normal human vision depends on four classes of photopigments, one for rods and three sets for cones. These photopigments, as we have noted a number of times previously, are located in the outer segments of the receptors, each containing a chromophore (11-cis retinal) and the protein opsin.

Before recombinant DNA procedures were applied to the photopigments, bovine rhodopsin was analyzed by determining the amino acid sequence of the protein (Ovchinnikov *et al.*, 1983; Hargrave *et al.*, 1983). Bovine rhodopsin was also the first photopigment to be analyzed using the methods of modern molecular biology. Nathans and Hogness (1983, 1984) isolated and sequenced the bovine rhodopsin gene and quickly followed with an analysis of the gene for human rhodopsin, which they determined was on chromosome 3. Human and bovine rhodopsin genes consist of five exons and four introns. The difference that exists in the amino acid sequence between bovine and human rhodopsin molecule is very small. In fact, they differ in only 23 out of the 348 amino acids in their respective molecules (Fig. 10.22A).

An analogy might help the reader understand Figure 10.22. Suppose you have an overhead transparency of a map. However, because this transparency lacks names, you do not know the location that this map represents. So you find an atlas that is of the same scale as the transparency and start overlaying the transparency on various maps in the atlas. Finally, you find a map whose structure is similar to the structure represented on your transparency. You take a marker pen and note all of the discrepancies between the structure of your transparency and that on the map . When you finally find a map that has the fewest structural discrepancies it is not unreasonable to assume that your transparency is a copy of this map.

The circles in Figure 10.22 represent amino acids that are strung together like beads to make up the protein. The open circles represent perfect amino acid matches and the closed circles represent discrepancies. Remembering the analogy above, the reader can see that geneticists make comparisons of protein structures. Knowing the protein structure of bovine rhodopsin, they compare this structure with that obtained from a human. If they find a protein structure that looks like bovine rhodopsin then it is not unreasonable to assume that this is the human rhodopsin structure. That is the significance of Figure 10.22A. Because it is human rhodopsin that is being compared with the bovine variety, it is not expected that the two will be 100% identical.

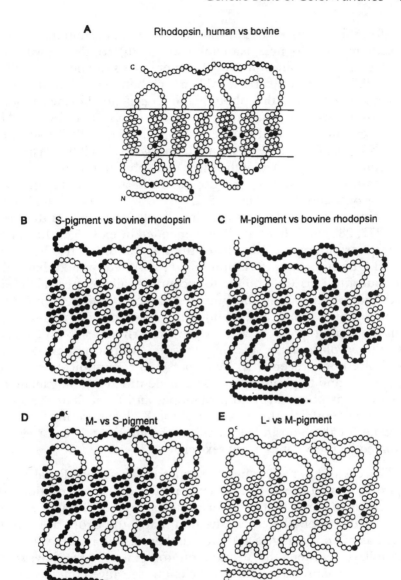

Figure 10.22 Representation of photopigment molecules. Each circle represents an amino acid. A. Comparison of human rhodopsin with bovine rhodopsin. Open circles represent identical amino acids, closed circles different amino acids. B. Comparison of human S-photopigment opsin with bovine rhodopsin. C. Comparison of human M-photopigment opsin with bovine rhodopsin. D. Comparison of human M-photopigment opsin with S-photopigment opsin. E. Comparison of L- and M-photopigment opsins (see text) (from Nathans *et al.*, 1986a).

After the successful identification of the human rhodopsin gene by Nathans and Hogness, Nathans *et al.* (1986) continued with research on human cone amino-acid sequences. As can be seen in Figure 10.22B, they found a reasonable match between the amino-acid sequence associated with S-photopigment opsin and bovine rhodopsin molecules. Comparisons were also made between M-photopigment opsin and bovine rhodopsin (Fig. 10.22C), and between human M- and S-photopigment opsins (Fig. 10.22D). Whereas the amino-acid sequences of the three cone photopigments are each only about 40–45% similar to rhodopsin, the M- and L-photopigments differ by only about 4% (Fig. 10.22E). Neitz *et al.* (1991) found only two amino acid substitutions that are closely separated on the protein (277, 285) and that these both, encoded by exon 5 of the gene, are responsible for the majority of the spectral difference between M- and L-photopigments. Asenjo *et al.* (1994) determined that only seven substitutions are required to account for all the spectral differences that occur among the human X-linked photopigments. On the other hand, the M- and L-photopigments are about as different from the S-photopigment as they are from rhodopsin, which suggests that, evolutionarily speaking, they were duplicated much later and evolved only recently (J. Neitz, personal communication). The genes for L- and M-photopigments were identified by doing analyses on specimens obtained from protanopes and from deuteranopes. Both genes reside on the long arm of the X chromosome. Because the gene for the S-opsin is located on chromosome 7, color vision mediated by the S-cones is not sex-related.

There is another way geneticists represent their data. Recall from Figure 10.20 and the associated text (p 466) that those portions of the genetic material that code for proteins are the exons. In Figure 10.23, at the level labeled "Restriction map," the exons are represented as open rectangles and are numbered. The reader will note the similarity between the M- and L-photopigments. As we have seen in previous chapters, the short wavelength sensitive cone system is quite different than the two longer wavelength sensitive cone systems (Mollon, 1982). It is, therefore, not surprising that the restriction map for the S-photopigment is quite different than that of the L- and M-photopigments, which probably, as noted above, is the result of a large separation in their evolutionary history.

Molecular Genetics and the Psychophysics of Color Vision

Males who exhibit no color vision deficiencies as indicated by, for example, tests involving pseudoisochromatic plates or the Farnsworth–

S-photopigment

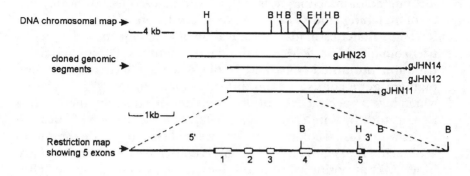

M-photopigment

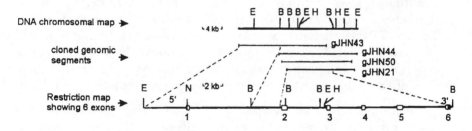

L-photopigment

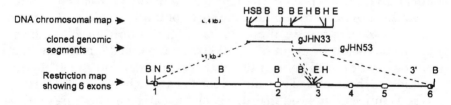

Figure 10.23 Three human opsin genes. The numbered boxes represent positions of the exons relative to the 5' and 3' ends. Note the similarity between the M-photopigment gene and the L-photopigment gene. The major difference between them is the location of exon #1. The S-photopigment gene, which resides on a different chromosome than the L- and M-photopigment genes, has 5 exons where as the former two genes each have 6 (see text) (From Nathans *et al.*, 1986a.)

Munsell 100 hue test, often demonstrate subtle variances when performing color-matching tests with an anomaloscope. Psychophysical color-matching studies done by Neitz and Jacobs (1986) found that Rayleigh matches made by Caucasian male subjects with normal trichromatic vision yielded a bimodal distribution. This bimodal distribution prompted Neitz and Jacobs to conclude that the L-cone pigment gene consists of two different allelic forms (*polymorphism*), which have a spectral absorption difference of a few nanometers. In a recent study by Winderickx *et al.* (1992), of a sample of 50 Caucasian males with normal color vision, 62% were observed to have the amino acid serine (Ser) and 38% were observed to have the amino acid alanine (Ala) at position 180 in the L-cone photopigment gene. They also found a bimodal distribution, just as Neitz and Jacobs did. From this bimodal distribution, Merbs and Nathans (1992) noticed that human L-cone pigments with either alanine or serine at position 180 absorb long wavelengths maximally at 552 nm or 557 nm respectively. Therefore, this polymorphism is correlated with the bimodal distribution of Rayleigh matches and remains consistent with that reported by Neitz and Jacobs. The relationship, therefore, between the genotype (Ser or Ala polymorphs) and the phenotype (spectral absorption difference) is observable by psychophysical experimentation.

Although females have a pair of X chromosomes, during the early embryonal development the somatic cells of the female embryo undergo a process called *X-inactivation;* where one of the X chromosomes is randomly inactivated. Due to the random inactivation of one of the X chromosomes, females who are heterozygous for an X-linked trait such as protan/deutan color deficiency are called *somatic mosaics,* whose expression take the form of both normal and abnormal photoreceptors in their retinae. This condition was shown psychophysically by Cohn *et al.* (1989). They studied female carriers of color vision deficiency who tested as normals on the Ishihara pseudoisochromatic plates and on the Farnsworth–Munsell 100 Hue Test. Cohn *et al.* showed that these female carriers, when presented with color spots of approximately 15' visual angle for 100 msec, made significantly larger numbers of color-naming errors than normal males who served as controls. This finding is consistent with that of Nagy *et al.* (1981), who found that the retinas of heterozygous women were found to contain more than three types of cones with different spectral sensitivities . Therefore, it is possible that females who are heterozygous for variant L- or M-cone pigments are functional tetrachromats. Nagy *et al.* (1981) found that women who possess more than three types of cones nevertheless accept trichromatic matches. Therefore their cones must feed into only three neural channels.

Table 10.4   Color vision of children in the six possible combinations of parental unions that are possible with respect to a particular near-recessive sex-linked color deficiency

Father	Offspring		Mother	
p, normal	sons	pp, normal	pp°, carrier usually normal	p°p°, color deficient
		p, normal	½p, normal ½p°, color deficient	p°, color deficient
	daughters	pp, normal	½pp, normal ½pp°, carriers, usually normal	pp°, carriers, mostly normal
p°, color deficient	sons	p, normal	½p, normal ½p°, color deficient	p°, color deficient
	daughters	p°p, carriers, usually normal	½pp°, carriers, usually normal ½p°p°, color deficient	p°p°, color deficient

After Kalmus, 1965, p. 61.

Males with normal color vision have been reported to have as many as four L-photopigment genes and as many as seven M-pigment genes (Neitz & Neitz, 1995). In a study of 27 color normal males Neitz and Neitz found some with only one L- and one M-photopigment gene. At the other end of the continuum, they found one subject with two L-photopigment genes and seven M-photopigment genes. These subjects each made Rayleigh color matches (red plus green equals monochromatic yellow) and it is difficult to see any relation between these matches and the genetic attributes of these subjects. However, Neitz & Neitz do report a statistical color match difference between those color normal males with one L-photopigment gene and those with multiple L-photopigment genes, which possibly may suggest that the "extra" genes in the array are expressed.

Color-deficient vision is of special interest to the human geneticist because it is *sex linked,* being, as noted above, carried on the X chromosome. As an example of what this implies, consider protanopia relative to the combinations of six parental unions of Table 10.4 (adapted from Kalmus, 1965). In each case the normal allele is dominant. The father has only one X chromosome, which is assumed to carry either the normal (p) or protanopic (p°) genotype at the protan color-vision locus. The mother has two X chromosomes, leading to three possible combinations (pp, pp°, and p°p°). In the female, when one of the alleles is for normal color vision (p) and the other is for protanopia (p°), the normal one dominates. For the male, the phenotype is determined by whatever allele is present, because there is no homologous second member that could dominate it.

Consider two examples from the table. If the father is p (normal) and the mother is pp° (a carrier), there are two possible combinations in the female offspring (pp and pp°) that should occur with equal probability. The pp° combination leads to normal color vision, but these females are carriers. So, on average, half the female offspring are fully normal, whereas the other half are phenotypically normal but are carriers.[22] For males, because their only X chromosome is of maternal origin, half will carry the p° allele and will be protanopes, whereas the other half will carry the p allele and be normal. As a second example, consider the color-deficient father (p°) and a mother who is a carrier (pp°). Here the two possible combinations for female offspring are pp° and p°p°; one is a carrier, the other herself a protanope. Again, half the male offspring will be protanopes.

An overall result is that there can be no protanope offspring of either sex without a mother who is either a carrier or a protanope. A father passes the defect along only through his daughters, most of whom are carriers with essentially normal color vision. For protanopic daughters there is the added requirement of a protanopic father, which severely reduces the probability of color deficiency in females relative to males. Finally, all offspring of parents who are both protanopes will also be protanopes, regardless of sex.

Dichromats' Residual Red-Green Discrimination

Although color matching may not be the most sensitive test of such residual function, Smith and Pokorny (1977) have found that dichromats become trichromats when large fields are used. They hypothesized that intervention of rod vision contributed to the color matches with large fields. Careful determinations of protanopic and deuteranopic copunctal points, using spectral lights that obviate the problem of pre-retinal absorption, do not reveal an ideal clustering of such estimates, as would be expected if dichromacy were complete. To the extent that a third pigment is present and functional, the prediction of converging confusion lines in trichromatic chromaticity space is violated; in practice the presence of a rod pigment may yield an influence so slight that the general scheme nearly works, but only with limited precision.

But rods may not present the full story. Scheibner and Boynton (1968) found that, with 3° fields flanked with a 1000 td surround, most dichromats could name equally bright spectral stimuli of wavelengths greater than 530 nm in a manner, which, though highly deficient, was nonrandom and revealed a surplus of "red" responses to the longer wavelengths. The possibility that differential rod stimulation was responsible for the residual discriminations could not be ruled out absolutely. It has been shown by color-naming and color-matching experiments, that dichromats make residual red-green discriminations, given large fields, even when stimuli are presented during the "cone plateau" phase of dark adaptation, from the fifth to ninth minute after exposure to a bright bleaching light (Nagy & Boynton, 1979; Nagy, 1979; 1982; Nagy, Purl & Houston, 1985, Nagy & Purl, 1987). During this period, cone sensitivity has recovered, but that of rods is still far above threshold. The stimuli used were virtually ineffective on S-cones; therefore the L- and M-cones appear capable of differential stimulation that translates into weak color differences. In one experiment (Nagy & Boynton, 1979), a color-naming technique was used in response to brief flashes that probably do not permit residual color differences to adapt out as they may during the steady examination of fields like those used during color matching.

This apparent trichromacy exhibited by dichromats when using large fields is frequently explained by proposing a residual third cone pigment. However, not all of the data can be so easily explained. Nagy & Purl (1987) note that variations in neural coding are implied by the situation where two observers differ markedly in their ability to discriminate color with small dim stimulus fields but who make very similar color matches with large bright fields. It is worth remembering Jameson and Hurvich's (1956) hypothesis that discrimination losses may be due to changes at the opponent processing stage.

Our visual experiences are mostly involved with looking at surfaces rather than lights. (An obvious exception is television.) Montag (1994) examined dichromats' color naming of surfaces by presenting them with color chips selected from the OSA Uniform Color Scales (see Chapter 11). He found, consistent with the results of Montag & Boynton (1987), that dichromats categorized colors similarly as did normals. To test the possible influence of rod contribution he employed a rod saturation method and also presented stimuli during the cone plateau (see Nagy and colleagues, above). Montag concluded that rods did not contribute to the dichromats color-naming behavior. He did, however, find that short duration (60 msec) and small (1°) stimuli had a detrimental effect on dichromat's color categorization, but these variables did not so affect normal observers. He concluded that dichromats may have cones that contain an anomalous photopigment requiring longer temporal and larger spatial summation to exhibit nearly the same color categorization abilities as normals.

A Genetic Model

In the early 1980s, Piantanida collaborated with geneticists and concluded that "the application of recombinant DNA technology to the analysis of normal and deficient colour vision has supplanted the replacement model by one based upon the known nucleotide sequences of the X-linked colour vision loci" (1991, p. 94). In his original model, Piantanida thought that spectral sensitivity shifts were due to a small number of point mutations in the normal L- and M-photopigments. However, experiments from molecular biology reveal that the structure of the M- and L- photopigment genes, and their arrangement on the X-chromosome, is completely different than what had been imagined from classical genetics. The high degree of similarity between the M- and L-pigment genes and their tandem arrangement in a repeated array allowed them to recombine. Recombination events can add and delete genes and they can produce hybrid genes that contain part M-pigment gene sequence and part L-pigment gene sequences. These kinds of mutational events appear to underlie many individual differences in color vision, including the spectral shifts in pigments that underlie anomalous trichromacy.

With the exception of acquired color vision deficiencies, normal and defective color vision are inheritable traits and it should theoretically be possible to locate the genes that are, at least, responsible for the production of the receptor photopigments. A landmark year was 1986 when two important *Science* papers were published; one by Nathans, Thomas, and Hogness and one by Nathans, Piantanida, Eddy, Shows, and Hogness. The first explains how they found the genes that encode the S-, M-, and L-photopigments. The second expanded on these discoveries to include the variations in these genes, which provides the beginning of an account of variations in human color vision. Utilizing genetic techniques, S-, M-, and L-photopigments have been "manufactured" and their absorption spectra measured (Merbs & Nathans, 1992; Asenjo, Rim, & Oprian, 1994). The mean λ_{max} are presented in Table 10.5. The differences between the two sets of longwave manufactured λ_{max} are due to the purer pigments obtained by Asenjo *et al.* The S-photopigment in the Asenjo *et al.* report was obtained from an unpublished study by Lee & Oprian. Recall that, whereas the genes for the L- and M-photopigments are on the X-chromosome, that of the S-photopigments is on chromosome 7. When the Southern blotting technique is applied to genetic materials of

Table 10.5   Comparison of genetically manufactured photopigment with invivo human photopigment

Photopigment	Mean λ_{max} (nm) manufactured		Human invivo λ_{max} (nm)	
S-photopigment	426[1]	410[2]		420[4]
M-photopigment	530[1]	532[2]	530[3]	534[4]
L-photopigment Ala[180]	552[1]	556[2]	560[3]	563[4]
L-photopigment Ser[180]	557[1]	563[2]		

1. Merbs & Nathans (1992); 2. Asenjo *et al.* (1994); 3. Schnapf *et al.* (1987) suction electrophysiology; 4. Bowmaker & Dartnall (1980) Microspectrophotometry;

protanopes and of deuteranopes, distinguishing differences are found. We saw in Figure 10.22 that the restriction maps associated with the L- and M-photopigments are nearly the same. Both of these contrast greatly with the S-photopigment, which is located on a different chromosome and features a very different restriction map with different numbers and locations of exons.

Although a start has been made at understanding anomalous trichromacy the results so far do not appear as dramatic and clear as for trichromacy and dichromacy.

As noted at the beginning of this discussion of color vision genetics, individual genes do not exercise their influence independently of other genes. The fact that a phenotype is ascribed to one particular allele of a gene is just a matter of convenience (Suzuki *et al.*, 1989). As we have seen, males have the genetic potential for as many as nine genes that determine receptor photopigments. However, it has not yet been possible to reliably ascribe the behavioral consequences of these multiple photopigment genes. It is important to remember that the science of genetics is less than 100 years old and that the DNA investigation of color vision only began in the early 1980s. We are experiencing the infancy of a fascinating area of color vision research and will have to wait to see how it matures to determine how, and if, this line of research can be related to our psychophysical understanding of color vision. Furthermore, we should remember that these genetic investigations have so far been concerned exclusively with receptor photopigments, which only represent the first stage of color vision. To understand human color vision we must also understand the genetic basis of the subsequent stages of the visual system to which signals from cones are delivered and transmitted.

SUMMARY

The chapter starts with a review of terminology and then a discussion of possible bases for variations in the color vision of normal observers.

Substantial variations in color perception exist among normal individuals, as exhibited by differences in unique yellow settings and disagreements about secondary color names, both of which probably have a physiological rather than a cultural basis. The frequently used term "colorblind", with a few exceptions, is inaccurate and inappropriate. Only people with no cone receptors or those with only one type of cone receptor are truly colorblind. Others are more properly called color deficient. We prefer the term color variant. Although color variant observers confuse many colors that normals would see as different, and mis-name some of them because the color vocabulary of the normal observer is for them needlessly rich, most color variant observers nevertheless are able to discriminate and name many colors.

Accurate conceptualization of the nature of variations of human color vision requires methods of classification that are fast and accurate. Pseudoisochromatic tests are fast, but inaccurate. The Farnsworth–Munsell 100-hue test is the best of those that use surface colors. The best of the screening devices, the anomaloscope, is fast, accurate, but relatively expensive.

Various possibilities exist for the alteration of the normal opponent-color model that was proposed in Chapter 7 and used in the last four chapters of this book. Only some of these possibilities seem to be expressed in color variant human observers. These include: (1) a missing photopigment, or — less certainly — a malfunctioning opponent pathway, (2) a reduction in the numbers of a particular cone type, and (3) shifts in the spectral location of one of the three types of cones. The latter seems required to account for anomalous color vision, which is trichromatic but of a different from (and usually inferior to) that of normal observers.

Because the remaining types of dichromatic cones appear to be those of normal observers, it becomes possible to represent the color confusions of dichromats in the chromaticity diagram of the normal observer. If a physiologically based diagram is used, these lines radiate from the "corners" of the diagram, which represent unique activation of normal L-, M-, and S-cones. The contribution of one type of cone to the color perception of each type of dichromat is apparently missing, although a weak residual capacity to discriminate colors along these "confusion lines" can be demonstrated in most such observers.

To further elucidate the relations among normal, dichromatic, and anomalous color vision, the analytical anomaloscope is discussed. This is followed by a brief consideration of the genetics of color deficiency. The most common forms, protanopia and deuteranopia, are most easily explained as sex-linked congenital losses of normal L- and M-cone function. The cones are not literally missing, but the abnormal cones may contain pigments of the other class, or ones very nearly like those. Anomalous observers probably have replacement pigments that differ from the normal ones by being shifted in the spectrum so as to overlap abnormally with the remaining, unaltered pigment.

Color defects actually exist in many varieties, most of them quite rare. Rod monochromacy, tritan defects, cone monochromacy, and acquired color deficiencies are discussed.

The genetic basis of color variations is presented. Genetic research since the early 1980s has discovered the genes responsible for the rod and cone photopigments. Based on this research it has been shown that various congenital color vision variations can be attributed to missing or hybridization of the two X-linked cone photopigment genes.

NOTES

[1] Parsons (1924, p. 170) and Boring (1942, pp. 183–184) cite Turbervil in 1684 as reporting a case of total color blindness, and Huddart in 1777 as reporting the first case of partial color blindness.

[2] A summary of such data is given by Judd (1951) and has been reprinted by Boynton (1975). An excellent study is that of Thomson (1954).

[3] Evidence supporting this assertion exists in cross-cultural studies by Berlin and Kay (1969) and in the use of hue categories by human infants (Bornstein, Kessen, and Weiskopf, 1976). See also Bornstein (1973) and Ratliff (1976). See Chapter 11.

[4] See Brindley (1970) for a discussion of a possible, though controversial, exception reported by Bongard, Smirnov and Friedrich (1957).

[5] See Hochberg and Silverstein (1956) for a rare experimental test of this law, which is often cited but seldom quantified.

[6] There are a number of differences between the instrument described here and the one actually developed by Mitchell and Rushton, but these are not fundamental to the theory of the instrument.

[7] To simulate the behavior of the Nagel device, W_R would be set so that the red and green fields are of equal luminance when the analyzer is rotated 90° to display first one component and then the other. Given this, the field changes, as A is turned, from red to green (or the reverse) without variation in luminance. A single wavelength in the yellow region of the spectrum is used in the left field. By varying W_λ, protanopes and deuteranopes can each match the right field no matter what the setting of A. Protanopes require less light in the left field to

make a match if the right field is fully red; normals and deuteranopes require approximately the same amount no matter how the analyzer is set. Normal subjects must be allowed to vary M_λ as well as A in order to make a color match.

[8] For this to work exactly, it is also necessary that the protanope's cones have the same optical density of photopigment, and the same prereceptoral absorptions, as those of the normal observer.

[9] The heterochromatic threshold-reduction factor (HTRF) is a measure of the degree to which two-color thresholds for heterochromatic pairs are lower than those for homochromatic ones (Boynton, Scheibner, Yates & Rinalducci, 1965). For a univariant mechanism, the factor will be 1; larger values imply selective chromatic adaptation of two or more chromatic mechanisms.

[10] It seems certain that people do not necessarily screen themselves from jobs requiring normal color discrimination. Often this is due to a lack of awareness that their color vision is at variance with the majority of people.

[11] A growing body of evidence suggests that, in order to develop normally, the neurons of the visual system must be exercised by reacting to the kinds of environmental inputs to which the eye is normally exposed. The literature on this subject has mainly been concerned with spatial vision (e.g., Hirsch & Spinelli, 1970). Pettigrew and Freeman (1973) report that kittens raised in a planetarium-like visual environment lacking straight-line contours develop cortical neurons that respond mostly to spots, rather than lines, quite in contrast to such cells in the normal cat. Anatomical changes may be associated with stimulus deprivation during development. It therefore seems unlikely that the r-g pathways, if they receive zero input during development (or one that is strongly biased in one or another direction) would exhibit normal activity if normal receptor function could somehow be restored to them as adults. However, it seems likely (see p. 259) that the r-g pathways receive input from S-cones in response to short wavelengths; the possibility that they may also receive excitation from rods is examined later in this chapter.

[12] Are the L- and M-cone-absorption spectra for normal human vision separated by an optimal amount? This question is much easier to state than to answer. The hypothesis cannot be tested without a full description of how the cone signals are utilized by the remainder of the visual system. Even if this were known — for example, if the simplified scheme of Chapter 8 were an accurate description of reality — a thorough ecological study would still be needed to determine what kinds of spectral differences are most important for us to discriminate colors in the real world. In addition to the degree of separation between them, the absolute placement of λ_{max} values for the two longwave cone photopigments would also be important. For example, discrimination between 700 and 750 nm is necessarily poor because the L/M cone activation ratio remains nearly constant as wavelength is varied over this range. By shifting the sensitivity curves of both classes of cones 150 nm toward longer wavelengths, discrimination might be improved in the neighborhood of 725 nm. But because of the high rate of spontaneous thermal decomposition and the low photon energy, it might be difficult to achieve reliable signals from receptors in response to such long wavelengths (recall the argument on p. 131). Shifting the S-cone sensitivity to shorter wavelengths would not be useful unless the high absorption of light by the optical media could be reduced, along with the fluorescence of the lens that occurs when it is stimulated with ultraviolet radiation. Although the problem of what is optimal is very complicated, it neverthe-

less seems likely that the action spectra of the cones actually possessed by normal human observers reflect an optimization of many factors, one that has been achieved through the process of evolution.

[13] The midpoint of the range, if enough settings are made to establish it reliably despite the variability of individual settings, is related to and serves as an index of the nature of the shift of λ_{max} of the anomalous pigment.

[14] Stimulus W presumably appears achromatic to the normal observer because it elicits a nearly zero output from both the r-g and y-b opponent systems. For protanopes and deuteranopes, the r-g system could be balanced because of photopigment replacement and therefore not biased in the g direction. But the y input to the y-b opponent system cannot be normal, if it depends upon the summed input from both L- and M- cones, one of which is missing in each class of red-green dichromat. Nevertheless, when some of Walls and Mathews' subjects were asked to name the hue of the mixture field that matched W, most of them said that it looked gray. Almost as many saw it as greenish, and 5 subjects (4 of 27 protanopes and 1 of 32 deuteranopes) called it pink. One subject said that it was "greenish with a little pink in it." For normal observers, there is a substantial region in chromaticity space that appears white, although if two colors were chosen from the extremes of this region they surely would not match, and hues would be reported. It seems probable that stimulus W falls within this region both for normals and dichromats. Because colors called "green" by normals look very desaturated to protanopes and deuteranopes, who probably lack the *sensation* of green entirely, little importance can be attached to the application of that name to the appearance of illuminant C. See Hurvich and Jameson (1951 a,b) and Jameson and Hurvich (1951) for a psychophysical study of white.

[15] Nonspectral colors, such as those provided by reflecting surfaces, do not have "a wavelength." The values provided by Walls and Heath are the so-called *dominant wavelengths*. In the CIE system (see Appendix Part I) these are determined by drawing a line from a white point in the CIE chromaticity diagram through the nonspectral color to be specified, in order to determine the wavelength of the spectral locus where an extension of that line intersects. Roughly speaking, the dominant wavelength is a spectral color that nearly matches the (usually less saturated) nonspectral color with which it is being compared.

[16] It is common for these subjects to show other evidence of cones in their retinas (Alpern, Falls & Lee , 1960; Falls, Wolter & Alpern, 1965); but it is possible that their cones contain rhodopsin.

[17] Alpern called this π_5 *cone monochromacy*; rod monochromacy was named π_0 and red and green cone monochromacies were designated as π_5 and π_4 types, respectively. Such a designation implies that the conditions are explicitly related to Stiles's π-mechanisms, which seems far from certain.

[18] Statements in this section about S-cone monochromacy are based on evidence from the following studies: Alpern, Lee, and Spivey (1965); Blackwell and Blackwell (1961); Daw and Enoch (1973); Green (1972); and Pokorny, Smith, and Swartley (1970). See also Alpern's Friedenwald Lecture to ARVO (1974).

[19] Space limitations do not permit the extensive discussion of acquired color vision variance that it deserves. However, there are a number of excellent reviews on the topic and our highlights of the topic were taken from these: Verriest (1963); Grützner (1972), Marré (1973); Birch *et al.* (1979); Pokorny & Smith (1986); King–Smith (1991); Krastel & Moreland (1991); Plant (1991).

[20] Köllner spoke of "blue-yellow blindness." However, Wright (1979) pointed out that "blue-yellow defect" is inaccurate because it is a tritan defect, which is a blue sensitivity loss resulting in blue-green and in yellow-violet confusions. Pokorny & Smith (1986) consequently refer to blue discrimination losses (see Table 10.3).

[21] We thank Peter Mente who assisted in the initial draft of this new section on genetics. We also thank Jay and Maureen Neitz who reviewed this chapter and made significant improvements to those sections that involve recent genetic research.

[22] Heterozygous females who are carriers of color defect are not normal in all respects. For example, carriers of protanopia have a somewhat decreased sensitivity in the long wavelengths, although they are trichromats (known as *Schmidt's sign*). Others exhibit patches of dichromatic retina, which is an aspect of the *Mary Lyon* Syndrome (see Wooten and Wald, 1973). Although these conditions are trivial from the standpoint of the color vision of the female carrier, they are important to the human geneticist working on family pedigrees, and for validating the idea that the color deficiency is transmitted to a male offspring from the mother.

Chapter 11

Naming, Ordering, and Recognizing Surface Colors

INTRODUCTION

For the most part, our discussion of human color vision has been concerned with principles that attempt to explain fundamental data obtained under artificial laboratory conditions designed to produce tight control of the variables being manipulated. Accordingly, except for some preliminary discussion in Chapter 2, there has been an emphasis upon such things as the matching of bipartite fields and the determination of increment thresholds, with relatively little concern about the appearance of objects under the complex conditions of the natural world. We wish now to step gingerly in that direction. But first, an analogy may help to explain why it is so difficult to do this.

The gravitational constant of acceleration can be used to predict the velocity of a falling object and the distance that it will have traveled at any time subsequent to its release. Contrary to common experience, theory and experiment agree that neither the shape nor the mass of an object will affect its rate of descent, provided that the experimental conditions are simplified by conducting tests in a vacuum. But as soon as one leaves the laboratory to compare, say, the flight of a brick with that of a feather, the brick will fall — well, like a brick, whereas a feather will rock back and forth and may take a thousand times longer to reach the ground.

Similarly, the relation between the spectral distribution of light reflected to the eye from an artificially isolated specimen and the color sensation that it elicits can be reasonably well understood, and it has been a major aim of this book to provide the basis for such insight. However, much as feathers outside the laboratory are not found in a vacuum, patches of color are seldom seen in isolation; and much as the atmosphere complicates the flight path of a feather, the surround in which a patch of color is seen will affect its appearance (recall the color plates of Chapter 2).

Changes in the spectral character of the illuminant cause the spectral distribution of the light reflected from any surface to change, so one might also expect its perceived color to change. Given this fact, and complications outside the laboratory related to the influence of real-world context, it seems paradoxical that the perceived colors of things do not ordinarily seem to change very much with alterations in background and illumination. We will deal with this topic of color constancy, already mentioned in Chapter 2 as being of evolutionary importance, in some detail in the last major section of this chapter.

The illusion that color is an inherent property of an object is enhanced by our remarkable ability to use language to communicate about the perceived colors of things. The fact that we seem to agree most of the time when we share the use of color terms tends to support our belief that the colors we see must be intrinsic to the objects to which they seem so intimately attached. We are not likely to be otherwise convinced even if we encounter a dichromat who uses names that seem obviously wrong to us. We are tempted instead to say to him, for example, "you are *wrong* — this object is green, not brown; its color does not change simply because *you* are looking at it." Strictly speaking, of course, we know from the previous chapters that this criticism is very unjust, because color is ultimately subjective, and if 99 percent of the population enjoyed a fourth class of cones and an extra pair of opponent-color sensations of a quality unimaginable to us, then *we* would be the ones subject to ridicule for our misuse of an expanded color vocabulary that would be of no help to us.

Nevertheless, for those of us with normal color vision, under many conditions of viewing, objects can be regarded as having intrinsic colors in the sense that they are fairly stable and we agree about the names that we assign to them [in Chapter 2 (p. 33) we defined these as objective colors]. When reference is made to the color of an object in this chapter, this is the intended meaning. The *perceived* color of an object, on the other hand, can be different — and sometimes very different — as the conditions of illumination and surrounds are varied. It will be helpful to have a standard condition in mind that would be likely to allow agreement about color names. For this purpose, we define a "standard viewing condition." Imagine a viewing booth painted a spectrally flat, 20-percent reflecting gray, indirectly illuminated by a tungsten source having a correlated color temperature of 3000 K. The color sample to be viewed, perceived, and described, has a matte finish and is viewed against this gray background.

Surfaces have many other properties, some of which will be discussed shortly, that might also be considered intrinsic to their perceived color. These include texture, gloss, and certain properties of metals. For example, it would be possible to find a gray surface that would match a silver one for chromaticity, and if both were suitably illuminated and viewed through a reduction screen, they could be indistinguishable. However, under normal viewing conditions they would never be confused. Although we will discuss these complications in the section to follow, we will not include their potential presence as part of what we mean by color. Other complications that will not be considered include polarization and fluorescence.[1]

This chapter will deal with surface colors with a heavy emphasis on their categorical nature. For this purpose, we will deal first with the nature of reflecting surfaces, then with the relations among colors, which involves the notions of color "space" and color ordering. Next we consider color naming and categorization, and conclude with a discussion of the extent to which we are able to recognize colors despite changes in illumination and surround conditions — the classical problem of color constancy.

THE NATURE OF SURFACE REFLECTANCE

How an object reacts to incident light depends upon various microscopic physical characteristics of its surface that determine the probability that an incident photon will be reflected in a particular direction depending upon its wavelength. In principle, one might be able to predict the spectral reflectance of a surface by knowing these characteristics, but this is a practical impossibility. This aspect of color is a complex subject concerning which Nassau (1983) has provided an excellent book-length summary.

It is important to distinguish clearly between two limiting aspects of surface reflection — diffuse, which mediates surface color perception, and specular, which usually does not (see Chapter 3). An example of specular reflectance is provided by a dust-free mirror. If an ideal mirror's edges are suitably disguised, its surface will be invisible. Light reflected from it does so at an angle equal to the angle of incidence, which is the geometric property that allows a plane mirror to provide perfect virtual images. As we all know, objects are seen by reflection "in the mirror" as if they were located behind it; this happens because the complex, three-dimensional flux of light reaching the eye is identical to what it would be if the perceived objects actually were located where they seem to be. If this phenomenon were not so commonplace, it probably would be regarded as the most spectacular of visual illusions.

Where reflection is concerned, the mirror anchors one end of a continuum that features the "perfectly diffuse" surface at the other. The latter is characterized by the polar diagram shown at the top in Figure 11.1, in which the varying vector lengths represent the relative intensities of reflected light as a function of the angle of reflection. A narrow beam of light is incident upon the surface at an angle of 45 degrees (this angle is not critical). For each element of a perfectly diffuse horizontal surface, reflection vectors are inscribed within a sphere that can be analyzed by the arbitrary vertical cross section shown. The intensity of the reflected light decreases as a cosine function of the reflection angle. Despite this fall-off, the luminance of the surface is independent of viewing angle because the area of the retinal image, relative to that of the region of the surface being viewed, also decreases with viewing angle, keeping the intensity per unit projected area constant.

Most surfaces exhibit reflectance components of both kinds. This situation is represented at the bottom in Figure 11.1. The intensities at most angles are characteristic of a diffuse reflector, but a lobe of much higher reflectance is represented at the specular angle. In very highly polished surfaces this lobe can be a spike, and the outermost smooth layer of a hard surface can act as a mirror. But unlike the mirror described above, such a surface is not totally reflecting. A significant fraction of the incident light penetrates the surface and is diffusely reflected by a substrate that contains dye and/or pigment particles collectively known as *colorants*. Diffuse reflection varies as a function of wavelength depending upon the nature of the colorants, and it is also affected to some extent by the type of binder that contains them. Diffuse reflectance provides the physical basis for the colors of most objects. For the most part, specular reflectance carries with it the wavelength composition of the source (metallic surfaces are the principal exceptions to this rule). An excellent introductory treatment of the interaction of light with matter, and of many other

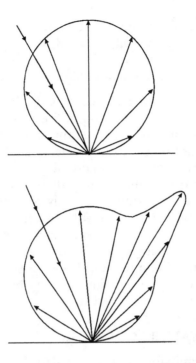

Figure 11.1 Varieties of reflection. Top: Perfectly diffuse surface. Arrows indicate the intensity of reflected light as a function of direction. Bottom: Reflectance from a diffuse surface that exhibits a specular lobe.

aspects of color (aimed at color technologists, but very useful for anyone) has been provided by Billmeyer and Saltzman (1981).

A colored surface, for example that of a new automobile, appears shiny if it exhibits a narrow specular lobe together with its diffuse component of reflectance. As the specular lobe broadens, the surface takes on a satin-like sheen, while surfaces without such a lobe appear matte. To judge the color of a shiny surface, it is necessary to position the eye or the material appropriately to avoid the specular component. For example, to appreciate the color of a car on a lot illuminated by strings of yellow lights, one must find a vantage point that does not permit an image of any of these lights to be seen in the area being scrutinized. Similarly, to discern the colors of illustrations in a "slick" magazine, it is necessary to adjust the angle at which the document is held so that the specular component, which forms a smeared virtual image of the reading lamp, misses the eyes. Smooth, convex surfaces, such as the marbles depicted in the color illustration of Chapter 2, produce specular highlights that retain the wavelength distribution of the illuminant. Outdoors under a cloudy sky, or in a room that is diffusely illuminated, specular and diffuse components of reflection mix, the color of an object can be discerned from almost any viewing angle, and highlights are minimized.

The interplay of lighting geometry with object surface properties is very important for perception in the natural world, as well as for representations of it by painting and photography, whether in color or black and white. For example, to optimally render the complex contours of the human face in two dimensions, portrait photographers typically use a combination of the two kinds of lighting: an indirect component (sometimes diffusely reflected from inside an open white umbrella), combined with concentrated flash illumination. Outside on a sunny day, the scene is similarly illuminated by the direct rays of the sun combined with the scattered light of the sky. The pleasant "sparkle" of a fine day is mediated, at least in part, by the specular component of reflections from objects.

THE CONTINUOUS YET CATEGORICAL NATURE OF COLOR

Based on discrimination data of the sort discussed in Chapter 8, one can calculate that there are at least a million possible color samples that could be created, no two of which would match if placed side by side and viewed by a person with normal color vision under the standard viewing condition described above. Most such pairs would, of course, differ greatly from one another. Yet no matter how great this difference might be, it is always possible — at least in principle — to arrange a series of color chips that very nearly match their flanking neighbors to form a series of gradually changing intermediate colors. These can eventually bridge between any two end colors, no matter how different they may be. From the earlier chapters of this book, it should be clear that the initial physiological basis for the ability to create such a chromatic series relates to very small changes in the ratios and levels of cone excitations that result when one's gaze is shifted from each sample to an adjacent one that differs only slightly in spectral reflectance. The path of such changes, as visualized on a chromaticity diagram or in tri-cone space, need not follow a straight line, meaning that any one of an infinite number of paths could connect any two end colors. (Going around the familiar hue circle provides an example showing that the final color can even be the same as the initial one.) When two colors differ by a large amount, then, how is it possible to specify, in a quantitative way, just how different they are? What might be the theoretical or practical importance of being able to do this?

Starting with the second question, it may be replied that, on a practical level, all people concerned with color — whether scientists or artists — seem to agree on the need for a system for the orderly representation of the domain of subjective color experience, more or less similar, at a given lightness level, to the psychological color plane that was described in Chapter 2 (Fig. 2.4). Colors lying close together in such a diagram are to be regarded as similar, whereas those that lie far apart should be judged as dissimilar. When judgments are confined to a single quadrant of the color plane, it is easy to imagine that a given distance on the diagram might represent a fixed sensory difference, regardless of the orientation or location of that distance within the quadrant. For short segments perpendicular to radii of the diagram, a change in hue at nearly constant saturation would be implied, one which we may presume is associated with a change in the ratios of opponent-color responses, but with their overall response magnitude unchanged. For radial segments of the same length, discrimination should depend instead upon a change in the magnitude of opponent-color responses, but with their ratios unchanged — a saturation difference.

It is when one crosses the boundaries from one quadrant to another that comparison become especially difficult. For example, is a unique red really more different from a unique green than from a unique blue (which is only 90° away and therefore closer to red)? In the sense that red and green are opposites that cancel and cannot be seen together, perhaps they are more different than red and blue, which can coexist. But in terms of judged sensory difference, is green actually seen as more different from red than is blue?

One possible approach to quantifying color difference would be to measure the number of discriminable steps from one color or another. There are two problems with this. In the first place, it is not obvious what path to take between the two colors. Long ago, Schrödinger (1920) argued that the shortest path from white to a spectral color should be along a path of constant hue. Loci of constant hue are generally curved on a chromaticity diagram, implying that discrimination steps should be measured along such a curve rather than along a straight line connecting the white point with the spectral color. Not even this hypothesis has been specifically tested, and for two stimuli that differ arbitrarily in both chromaticity and luminance, one would not have a clue concerning what path to take, and to establish such paths empirically would be a daunting task to say the least. The second problem is that there is no certain basis for making the claim that the sum of just-noticeable differences between two stimuli represents a valid index of sensory difference — a point that has been debated ad nauseam for the special case of luminance discrimination ever since Fechner claimed to measure sensation strength by this method.[2]

COLOR ORDER SYSTEMS

Color order systems, sometimes also called color appearance systems, have a long history dating back at least to 1611. Derefeldt (1991) has provided an excellent history and summary of these systems. Here we provide only a brief introduction to four of them that are in common use today. All of these color order systems have a physical manifestation in the form of atlases that can be purchased, and in which each color is appropriately labeled. Color samples in these systems are also specified in the CIE system of chromaticity and luminance, assuming an appropriate illuminant, so that, in theory at least, one can translate from one system to the other.

One may reasonably ask, why do we need such color order or appearance systems? An answer to such a question is offered by Hård and Sivik (1981, p. 129).

> It would seem important that architects, designers, color consultants and all those who participate in forming our environment should have access to a common color language by which to describe the color perceptions which the visual environment actually consists of. It would seem equally important that such a color-symbol language, or system of color measurements, should be founded on observations by subjects of how colors are related to each other and thus based on a model that describes color perceptions and their relationships. It should offer a means of describing colors using readily comprehensible terms, though with due consideration to the properties and restrictions of the human perceptual system.

Munsell Color System

Albert H. Munsell, an artist born in Boston in 1858, remarked in 1905 that he deplored "the incongruous and bizarre nature of our present color names." He noted that "music is equipped with a system by which it defines each sound in terms of its pitch, intensity, and duration. . . . So should color be supplied with an appropriate system, based on the hue, value, and chroma of our sensations, and not attempting to describe them by the infinite and varying colors of natural objects" (Nickerson, 1976). Munsell embarked upon an effort to arrange color chips along the three dimensions that he described. (Munsell's initial methods were rather subjective and intuitive, but the effort continued for many years, eventually being car-

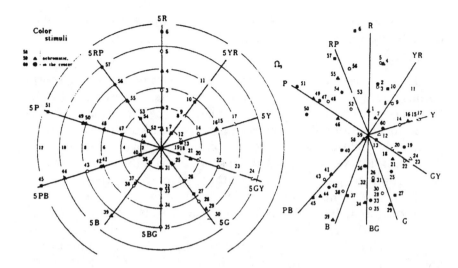

Figure 11.2   Results of an experiment on large color differences by Indow and Ohsumi (1976). See text for description.

ried forward in a more scientific fashion by his descendants and colleagues.) *Value*, in the Munsell system, is essentially the same as lightness and is correlated with the reflectance of a sample, which Munsell actually measured using a special visual photometer that he developed for the purpose. *Chroma* means about the same thing as saturation (see Chapter 2) and *hue* has its usual meaning. Eventually, through the development of the Munsell Color Company, and later the Munsell Foundation, a *Munsell Book of Color* was produced in which a huge gamut of reflecting samples is displayed and labeled. Munsell divided the color circle into ten segments as shown at the left in Figure 11.2. In this diagram, white is at the center, hue varies circumferentially, and chroma increases from the center outward. In addition to describing colors according to their hue, value, and chroma, Munsell wanted equal steps of these dimensions to correspond to equal perceptual spacing.

Indow and Ohsumi (1972) made an empirical test of Munsell spacing. They worked with a set of 60 reflecting colors, equal in lightness, or Munsell value, and 26 grays. Subjects were given from 5 to 8 color chips at a time. One of these was designated as a standard and subjects were instructed to order the remaining chips from most to least similar to the standard. Gray samples were then used in an attempt to represent the degree of perceived sensory difference that lay along the series of colors. In other words, the subjects were asked to match the perceived chromatic difference to a difference between gray chips.

This experiment thereby produced a series of difference scores among many combinations of pairs of colors, represented by the known reflectances of the series of grays. These differences were subjected to a multidimensional scaling procedure known as analysis of proximities. With this method, a computer algorithm attempts to arrange points in two-dimensional space so that the differences between sampled pairs of points in that space are in optimal correspondence with the experimentally-obtained difference scores. The result of this analysis of Indow and Ohsumi is shown at the right in Figure 11.2. There is a fair agreement between the outcome of this experiment and the arrangement evolved by Munsell and his associates. But there are also important differences; for example P and PB are too far apart. Indow and Ohsumi report that this anomaly in the region from B to P through PB has " . . . been repeatedly observed in previous studies with Japanese subjects (p.130)." It would be rash to assert (Indow and Ohsumi are careful not to do so) that the Munsell scaling is wrong because it does not agree with the outcome of their experiment; there simply is too much uncertainty concerning what the subjects are actually judging in so complex a task. Nevertheless, this study affords an interesting and instructive example of one attempt, among many, to scale large color differences.

Natural Color System

The Natural Color System (NCS), which was developed in Sweden, attempts to provide a common, easily understood language with which people are able to communicate their perceptions of color. The NCS system is based on the opponent processes theory put forth by Hering. It starts out with unique hues: red, green, yellow, and blue plus white and black. All colors are described in terms of these. The basic psychophysical ratings of colors were conducted as follows. Subjects rated the whiteness, blackness, yellowness, redness, blueness, and greenness of a color. The total rating of the color description summed to 100. The individual attributes just noted could range from 0 to 100 as long as the total rating did not exceed 100.

NCS colors are specified relative to 13 so-called "elementary scales" as shown in the NCS Color Hexagon (Fig. 11.3) by the lines connecting all possible pairs of six elementary colors, with the exceptions of R-G and Y-B. An elementary scale is the rating from one elementary color to another. An arbitrary color is defined according

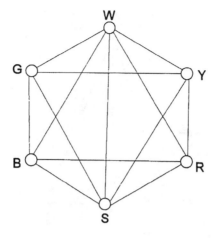

Figure 11.3 The Swedish National Color System (NCS) hexagon. Each of the connecting lines represents an elementary scale. The W-S dimension represents the lightness-darkness scale (Hård and Sivak, 1981).

to its location in the NCS color solid (Fig. 11.4), which in turn depends upon its resemblance to the nearest pair of chromatic colors and its judged location along the white-black (W-S) axis. A key idea underlying the system is that anyone with normal color vision can, with little training, learn to make the ratings, which constitute a practical, useful language for describing colors under any conditions. Hård and Sivak (1981) stress that the NCS system for describing color percepts is not based on the availability of an atlas, which is regarded as "a psychophysical correlate to the psychometrics of NCS notation under a restricted set of viewing conditions. The NCS Color Atlas can be seen as an aid for measuring colors by visual comparison much as a ruler is used for measuring length. But a meter ruler is not the meter system, and the NCS Color Atlas is not the NCS Notation System" (p. 138). One possible difficulty with this system is that the color brown cannot easily be described with the elementary scales provided.

OSA Color System

Whereas both the Munsell and NCS specifications relate to the categorical nature of color perception and the fact that names can be meaningfully attached to qualitatively different aspects of color experience, the aim in developing the Optical Society of America (OSA) color-order system was to determine a set of color samples which, under appropriate viewing conditions, defined an isotropic

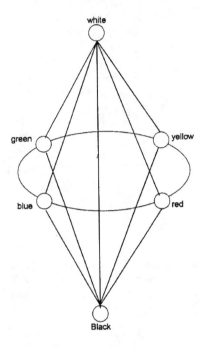

Figure 11.4   Swedish Natural Color System (NCS) color solid. Similar to Fig. 11.3 but plotted in the more familiar color-solid form (Hård and Sivak, 1981).

color space. An attempt was made to cause each color sample to be located an equal distance from each of its twelve nearest neighbors, with distance considered as related to numbers of discriminable color steps (about 20). The samples are arranged in an array along a vertical axis running from black to white, orthogonal to two chromatic axes, one of which runs roughly from red to green, the other from blue to yellow (Fig. 11.5). It is evident that the aim of the OSA committee that developed these samples has only been approximately met, and may be impossible to meet; most would agree that adjacent colors near white differ more from one another than do adjacent colors that are highly saturated. More details about the OSA system will be given below.

DIN Color System

The Deutsches Institut für Normung (DIN) developed a system that had a more uniform color space and was more practical than the Ostwald system, which Germany had been using (Derefeldt, 1991). The first draft of the DIN Color Chart used transparent gelatin fil-

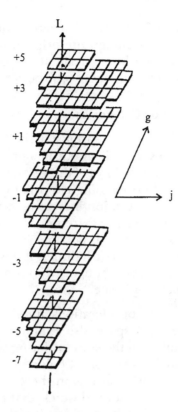

Figure 11.5 Arrangement of the OSA colors. The lightness axis L runs from near black at the bottom to near white at the top, with a neutral gray sample at each of the even-numbered lightness levels, which have been left off the diagram for clarity. At each lightness level, there are two chromatic axes, labeled j and g, which are perpendicular to each other and to the lightness axis. Each of the 424 color chips of the system is intended to be equidistant from its nearest neighbors, of which there are 12, except for the outermost shell of colors.

ters. Because these were not very practical, a final edition with easily cleanable matte color chips was produced in the years 1960–62 with less than 600 specimens (Richter and Witt, 1986, p. 143). A new edition using high gloss chips was added in the years 1978–1983.

The DIN system is similar to other systems with respect to its designation of hue and saturation. Hue varies from a value of T = 1 (yellow) via red, blue, and green to a green-yellow that has a value of T = 24. Saturation varies from a value of S = 0 (white) to S = 15. It differs on the lightness-darkness dimension. DIN calls it "darkness degree" and it ranges from a value of zero denoting white to a value of 10 denoting black. Although the original intent was to define a complete color space psychophysically, it was found that several compromises had to be made in order to produce a practical system.

Color Space and Color Categories

Color-order systems of the sort just described arrange colors in a "space" — one that exists only in our imaginations — within which colors change continuously. Most of these systems arrange colors shading from dark at the bottom to light at the top, with hues arranged circumferentially and saturation increasing outward from a central achromatic axis. At the vertical extremes, with white above and black below, no saturation variation is possible. The maximum chromatic variation occurs at intermediate lightness levels. The outermost shell of the space resembles, very roughly, two lopsided cones joined at their bases with apices opposite.

With the foregoing considerations in mind, it may seem surprising that subjective color space also exhibits categorical properties that are at least implicit in the color-ordering systems just described. Consider, for example, a region of color space to which the name green is assigned. Within that region there are many thousands of discriminably different shades to which that name will be applied. Similarly, there is another such region for blue. But as the spectral distribution changes and the perceived colors move from the green region toward the blue one, there is an intermediate region within which blue and green are simultaneously present and spatially co-extensive. In other words, when represented in three-dimensional subjective color space, color categories occupy overlapping regions. Moreover, their boundaries are fuzzy rather than sharp. For example, when moving away from the middle of the blue category toward the region called green, the degree of blueness very gradually diminishes and it is not easy to specify exactly where it disappears altogether to be fully replaced by green.

THE NAMING OF COLORS

Basic Color Terms

In 1969, the Berkeley anthropologists Berlin and Kay published a slim but influential monograph entitled *Basic Color Terms*. For their research, they used a subset of color samples selected from the Munsell color atlas, namely the most saturated ones at each lightness level. These color chips were laid out in a two-dimensional rectangular array and covered with clear plastic. The lightest specimens were arrayed at the top and the darkest ones at the bottom, with hue changing horizontally. Color names were provided for their subjects who, using a grease pencil, marked in turn the best example of each color, and followed this up by indicating the two-dimensional span of colors within which a name could to any extent apply.

Linguistic criteria helped these investigators decide which color names would be examined in the various languages they studied. Some of these criteria have been listed by Crawford (1982):

> A basic color term occurs in the ideolects [speech pattern] of all informants. It has stability of reference across informants and across occasions of use. Its signification is not included in that of any other color term. Its application is not restricted to a narrow class of objects (p.342).

In addition, basic color terms are *monolexemic* (single words) and they also tend to be those named first when people are ask to list, as quickly as they can, all color terms that come to mind.

Berlin and Kay studied the use of color terms in languages containing as few as two or as many as eleven basic color terms.[3] They concluded that, in going from languages with only two color terms to those with eleven, words are added in a fairly predictable order as subjective color space becomes progressively more finely partitioned. Partly on the basis of their research, it has been concluded by some — and we tend to agree — that all humans with normal vision probably see colors in the same way regardless of how many color names are used in a particular language. This assertion is distinctly contrary to a view that had been favored by most cultural anthropologists — and which is still favored by a few — namely that the partitioning of color space for purposes of naming is arbitrary and culturally dependent.[4]

The eleven basic color terms can be subdivided into three categories:

(1) *achromatic color terms* (white, gray, black); and two varieties of *chromatic color terms,*

(2) *primary* (red, yellow, green, blue) and

(3) *secondary* (orange, purple, pink, brown).

These eleven color names, given here in English, have exact equivalences in many other languages, including some (e.g., Japanese) which are believed to have entirely different origins.

The division between primary and secondary chromatic basic color terms reflects a distinction that seems to rest entirely upon subjective grounds. Most people, though not all, will agree that there are examples of red, green, yellow, and blue that are psychologically unique, in the sense that there is no trace of any other hue to be seen in optimal examples of them. The secondary chromatic terms refer to sensations that cannot meet this criterion because they seem to be blends of the primary ones: for example, we see orange as a blend of red and yellow and purple as a coalition of red and blue.

It may seem odd that a color name like orange which describes a sensation that contains both red and yellow as a blend should be considered to be a basic color term at all. Yet the experiment to be described in the next section confirms the basic color status of orange, and those of purple, pink, and brown as well.[5]

COLOR NAMING RESEARCH AT THE UNIVERSITY OF CALIFORNIA, SAN DIEGO

By providing names for their subjects to keep in mind when marking their colors, Berlin and Kay may have helped to determine the nature and number of basic color terms. To circumvent this, as well as to provide a better specification and control of the experimental conditions, a program of research was undertaken at the University of California, San Diego (UCSD) during the 1980s, in which color names were never introduced by the experimenter and linguistic criteria were irrelevant except that only monolexemic responses were permitted.

Choice of Stimuli: The OSA Set

Because it is obviously impossible to experiment with a million or more color samples, it is necessary to employ a severely restricted subset of the huge number of colors that potentially could be used. For the UCSD study,[6] a set of 424 commercially-available color specimens was chosen, called the OSA Uniform Color Scales samples. As mentioned above, the arrangement of these colors is intended to cause the perceptual distance between each color and its nearest neighbors to be constant throughout an ordered matrix of color samples.[7] To the extent that this aim was achieved, the system provides a set of equally-spaced color samples whose arrangement in physical space is intended to define a three-dimensional domain in which linear distances imply the same number of just-noticeable color steps regardless of the starting point or the direction traversed. Though imperfect, as already noted, the arrangement of the OSA color chips probably comes closer to meeting its objective than the other color-order systems that have been developed.

Experimental Procedures

Subjects sat in a diffusely illuminated booth, treated inside with a spectrally flat gray paint of about 20 percent reflectance (subjectively, this is about midway between black and white, corresponding to L = –2 and Munsell N5). They were instructed to be prepared on signal to expect a shutter to open, exposing a uniform square patch of color provided by exposure of an OSA color chip, which had been inserted from behind by the experimenter. They were also instructed to name the color using a single word, and to do so within five seconds, after which the shutter would close in preparation for the next trial. Responses seldom took more than two or three seconds to make, and there was no further mention of speed. Response times were recorded, not to measure hair-trigger reaction times, but rather to assess latencies that reflect decision processes in a natural way. Presented one at a time in random order, each of the 424 color samples was named twice. The data set for each subject therefore consisted of 848 color words — two for each of the 424 samples — and the response times for each.

Results

Any color name not included among the Berlin and Kay eleven was defined *a priori* as a nonbasic color term. All subjects used all eight basic chromatic color terms. Some nonbasic terms, among which olive, peach, lime, tan, violet, and maroon were the favorites, were used by many of the adult subjects, but none of these was universally employed. The frequency of nonbasic color term usage was wildly idiosyncratic: Of 27 subjects tested, some used as few as four, and others used nearly fifty.

In addition to mean response time, two additional measures were derived from the data:

• *Consistency* of color usage was defined as the probability that a color name, if used by a given subject on the first presentation, would be employed again on the second occasion;

• *Consensus* of color naming concerned the extent to which color terms were used similarly across subjects.

The results provided very strong support for the idea that basic color terms are in a class by themselves:

• All basic color terms were used more consistently than any nonbasic term.

• There was greater consensus for the use of all basic color terms than for any of the nonbasic ones.

• Mean response times were shorter for all basic color terms than for any of the nonbasic ones.

No significant differences were found, by any of these measures, between primary and secondary chromatic color term usage.

Centroids in the OSA Space

The middle of the three-dimensional space in which a color term is used is called the *centroid* location. Centroids are computed by averaging the L, j, and g values for all samples called by a particular name, weighted according to whether the name was used once or twice. Near the centroid location, the probability that another basic color term will be used approaches zero. The probability of using the centroid name decreases in most directions as colors are tested progressively farther from the centroid region, and other basic color names begin to creep in.[8] A given sample might, for example, be called yellow on one occasion and green on another. Approximately midway between the yellow and green centroid locations, the two basic color terms are used with roughly equal frequency to name samples that appear coextensively yellow and green, and the same sort of thing happens at other boundary regions. There also tends to be an increased use of nonbasic terms, so a chip might be called green one time and olive on the other presentation.

Building Bridges Between Colors

With only a few exceptions, it was found that the basic colors whose regions overlap, in the sense that both color terms are used at different times to name some of the intermediate samples, have centroids that plot less than 7.5 OSA units apart, whereas centroids for regions that do not overlap are separated by distances greater than this. A very interesting and unexpected observation, which held up for all subjects with normal color vision, was that the red and yellow regions did not overlap at all. That is, there were no samples that were called red on one occasion and yellow on another. But red and orange, and orange and yellow, were frequently "linked" in this sense. Orange therefore forms an essential connection, or bridge, on the route between red and yellow, just as yellow provides an essential bridge between orange and green. From a subjective viewpoint, these similar roles of orange and yellow are surprising. Colors intermediate between red and yellow are seen as shades of orange that most observers regard as containing components of both flanking colors. Yellow, on the other hand, which bridges between orange and green, does not in its pure form resemble green at all. A similar situation

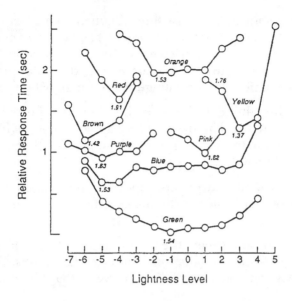

Figure 11.6   Lightness ranges (from Boynton and Olson, 1990). For each of the curves and at each lightness level, the shortest mean response time recorded (nine subjects combined) at that level is plotted. Where no points are plotted, the indicated color name was very seldom, if ever, employed. The plots show the range over which the basic color terms are used, and the minima of the plotted functions can be taken to indicate, by this criterion, the lightness levels for the best exemplars. The curves have been displaced arbitrarily in the vertical direction. Minimum response times are indicated for each color.

exists between red and blue, with purple providing the bridge. Despite their subjectively composite nature, all four of the secondary basic chromatic colors — orange, purple, pink, and brown — serve bridging functions and are just as essential for filling the color space as are the primary basic colors.

Overlapping regions named with basic colors fill most of the color space, with the exception of an odd region where color naming is extremely difficult. The non-basic terms applied most often to samples in this region, which were very inconsistently used, were peach, tan, and salmon. The centroids of basic colors flanking it are all more than 7.5 OSA units apart. It is almost as if a basic color were missing in this region, one that would serve a useful bridging function if it existed.

It is very important not to overlook the lightness dimension in the arrangement of the basic color centroids. In Figure 11.6, each curve shows the shortest response time obtained for any color sample used in each of the categories of chromatic basic color naming, plotted as a function of, and restricted to, the lightness level at which each term was used. These curves summarize the following important facts about basic color term usage as a function of lightness level:

- Unlike the other colors, green and blue are reported at virtually all lightness levels. The darker blues appear to be slightly more prototypic, yielding the shortest response times. The best greens are seen at the middle lightness levels.

- Red, brown, and purple are reported only at the lower lightness levels. Optimal brown is the darkest, followed by purple and then red.

- Next to blue and green, the use of orange covers the broadest range of lightnesses, and is optimum at intermediate levels. The lightness of the best pink is intermediate between that for orange and yellow.

- Yellow exists only at high lightness levels.

It is interesting to speculate about why the centroid locations of the basic colors should be located where they are. Viewing the array from the top (see Fig. 11.7, which also shows which chromatic pairs are linked) it is clear that each centroid occupies a unique location when projected onto a common chromatic plane. This is not surprising, because their locations reflect the relative excitations of the L-, M-, and S-cones of the retina that are fundamental to chromatic variation. However, the important proviso must be kept in mind that no chromatic plane at a single lightness level includes all of the basic colors. As already noted, yellow, orange, and pink simply do not exist at the lower levels, and purple, brown, and red are absent at the lightest ones.[9] Brown is unusual because it requires a lighter surround for its very existence.

COLOR SENSATIONS AND COLOR NAMING

Color sensations fade rapidly, whereas names — including those for color — can be retained indefinitely. Imagine that you have just been mugged on the street — robbed at gunpoint — and an officer is asking about the color of your assailant's clothing. Possibly, while being robbed, you could have said to yourself: "Because it will be important for me to testify later about the color of this robber's clothing, I will carefully note here and now that his jacket is blue." But this seems very unlikely, given that your attention will likely have been riveted upon other matters of more immediate significance, such as

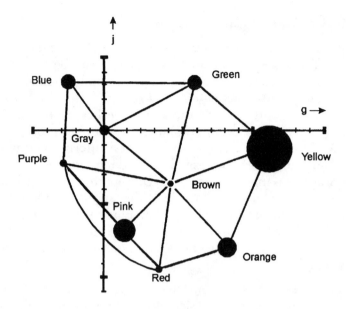

Figure 11.7   Location of centroids for the basic colors projected to a common chromatic plane of the OSA Uniform Color Scales system. The j and g axes are marked off in steps of unit OSA distance (from Boynton and Olson, 1987). The centroids of the colors are not actually located in the same plane; the size of the symbols has been varied to suggest their location in the third dimension (the higher the lightness level, the larger the symbol). Symbols for colors that are "linked" (see text) are connected.

the direction in which your assailant's pistol was pointed, and the pros and cons of trying to resist. Nevertheless, even if you had paid no attention to color during the commission of the crime, it might still be possible to dredge up some kind of an image that would enable a correct report to the effect that the jacket was blue. This kind of memory, which is rather mysterious, is neither vividly sensory nor probably verbal.

When names and colors are simultaneously present, their relation is so intimate that profound interactions can occur. The "Stroop effect," named after its discoverer (Stroop, 1935), results from asking subjects to view a list of color names that are printed with inks of various colors that differ from the meaning of the names, with instructions to name the colors while ignoring the words. Stroop (and many subsequent researchers) found that the meaning of the words could not be ignored and greatly interfered with the subjects' ability to name the colors of the inks in which the color names were printed.

Physiological Basis of Color Sensations

Despite the intimate association between color names and color sensations for those with normal vision, these can become remarkably dissociated in cases of brain damage. In some patients, while the ability to categorize or match colors is retained, the ability to name them is lost. A good entry to this literature has been supplied by Davidoff (1991), whose monograph describes and interprets clinical cases of various kinds. These cases and their interpretations are interesting and suggestive, but the most fundamental questions about color sensations remain unanswered. Despite the evidence reported in Chapter 7, we really have no clear idea about the nature of the neurochemical activity in the brain that generates a particular color sensation, and one can only speculate concerning the structure of the language areas that allows us to name colors. But some progress is being made.

Yoshioka *et al.* (1995) attempted to determine the physiological basis of the Berlin and Kay basic colors. Stimuli were presented to awake, behaving macaque monkeys and responses from V1, V2, and V4 were recorded. They explored dark colors as well as bright ones, which has rarely been done in electrophysiological studies of color vision. Their data support the idea that the basic colors are not only semantically grounded, but also have origins in cortical activity. It is not unreasonable to suppose that there could turn out to be eleven categorically-separate varieties of neurochemical activity in the brain, each corresponding to one of eleven kinds of color sensations that are identified by the eleven basic color terms.

It is also possible, although difficult to prove, that macaque monkeys have the same kinds of sensations that we enjoy, and this would be true also under conditions where surface colors remain relatively stable despite changes in illumination and surrounds, meaning that mechanisms of color constancy, the subject of the next section, would be operating. It is possible that the monkeys lack only the language centers required to name them. A behavioral study by Sandell, Gross, and Bornstein (1979), together with insights resulting from the anatomical and physiological work of Zeki (1993), suggest that our primate cousins probably categorize colors much as we do.

Zeki (1983, 1993) compared responses in cells of the monkey brain with the appearance of colors as they appeared to him under complex stimulus conditions. No matter what the context, one type seemed to respond according to its hue as if the color had been presented in isolation, whereas the other type responded according to the hue as affected by context. No cells of the second type were found in primary visual cortex. Zeki found cells of both types in area V4, which he had previously thought to play an important role in processing color. This experiment was not very well controlled, but the idea behind it, and the conclusion reached, will be of importance to us in the next section of this chapter. Supporting data have been reported by Wild, Butler, Carden, and Kulikowski (1985) in an article entitled "Primate cortical area V4 important for colour constancy [but] not wavelength discrimination". We agree with Maunsell and Newsome (1987), who conclude a brief section of a long review of visual processing in monkey extrastriate cortex with the following statement: "Although much remains to be learned about the cortical contributions to color constancy, the recognition of a distinction between the wavelength composition and perceived color is likely to prove important in interpreting the neural representation of color in the later stages of visual cortex" (p. 388).

The studies of Zeki and of Wild *et al.* are far from definitive. In a very thorough review of his own exemplary work, Schiller (1993) reports only mild impairment of visual function in Area V4, stating (p. 743) that it is "part of neural circuitry that makes an important contribution to the selection of crucial, physically less prominent stimuli in the environment which in the early parts of the visual system elicit less neural activity than do other stimuli that appear in the visual scene." Schiller deliberately did not attempt to study the role of color constancy in area V4 because (p. 726) "The validity of specific color-constancy effects would in fact seem to hinge on a total lack of deficit in color discrimination," and such deficits, although not large, were found in V4.

COLOR CONSTANCY

In choosing to deal with color constancy, we are taking a giant step into the "real world" mentioned at the outset in this chapter. Metaphorically, we are about to examine the chromatic feather to see how it might float in the atmosphere outside the laboratory. The long history of ideas and experiments about color constancy was extensively reviewed by Jameson and Hurvich (1989). Helmholtz and Hering both favored cognitive explanations that we would call "top down" today. The recent emphasis has been sensory, or "bottom up" interpretations, reflecting a revival of interest that can be attributed, to a considerable extent, to demonstrations by Land a few years after the two-color projection demonstration that was described in Chapter 1 (page 27).

Color Research of Land and Colleagues

In his two-color projections, Land had introduced the colorful but abstract "Mondrian" in response to the criticism that color memory probably had influenced the perceived colors of familiar objects that were depicted in his first demonstrations. Using the Mondrian and some other tricks, Land was able to show that the effects of color memory were relatively minor. In later lectures (1974) he illuminated a Mondrian with three projectors that provided narrow bands of short, medium, and longwave lights, individually adjustable for intensity, that could be mixed to illuminate the entire array of colors. With all projectors switched on to simulate a broadband white light, he pointed to one of the patches of color and got the audience to agree on its appearance, say blue. He brought with him a telephotometer whose output appeared on a large meter visible to the audience. The photometer was aimed at the blue-appearing patch, and readings were displayed in response to light reflected from that patch when illuminated by each of the projectors in turn, in each case with the other two switched off. Then he oriented the photometer to receive light from a different patch of an identical nearby Mondrian, and switched on the three projectors in turn. Because the spectral reflectance of the second patch did not match that of the first one (nor did its perceived color), each of the meter readings of course differed from the first ones. The next step was to adjust in turn the intensities of each of the three projectors, again with the other two switched off, to reproduce the original triad of readings. When all three projectors were switched on, and compared with the colors of the first Mondrian, the perceived color of the second patch appeared very different from that of the first one, perhaps appearing green instead of blue, despite the demonstration that exactly the same lights were delivered to the viewers' eyes in both instances. Land concluded that the local color of a surface in a complex array bore little or no relation to the local physical stimulus: otherwise, how could the same physical stimulus elicit two very different color sensations?

Land's "retinex" (for "retina" and "cortex") is not a physiologically based model, but is instead a computational scheme that attempts to account for the influence of the surrounding colors upon the appearance of a test color. First proposed in 1964, the retinex model was revised a number of times during Land's lifetime to correct a variety of deficiencies. In a 1984 paper, which also introduces the demonstration to be described in the next section, he gives credit to his colleague McCann for his contribution [see also McCann, McKee, and Taylor (1976)]. According to a detailed analysis by

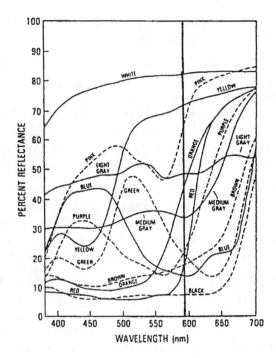

Figure 11.8   Spectral reflectance curves of ordinary construction papers used in an experiment by Stefurak and Boynton (1986). Percent diffuse reflectance is plotted as a function of wavelength. (Measured by the Hemmendinger Color Laboratory, Belvadere, N.J.). The names of the colors, as reported by the subjects, are indicated for each curve. The vertical line at 588 nm indicates that for a source having only a single wavelength, the color samples can differ only in their relative reflectances of that light, which will correlate with their relative lightnesses.

Brainard and Wandell (1986), the version of the retinex theory then extant (subsequently modified) showed poor predictive power.

General Considerations

Figure 11.8 shows spectral reflectance measurements for a collection of matte construction papers labeled with the basic color names that a group of observers all used when viewing them in an ordinary room situation. These curves are typical of reflecting surfaces, showing no discontinuities or rapid changes in slope. Every piece of paper reflects some light from all parts of the visible spectrum according to smooth functions that favor various spectral regions. (That the curves rise at very long wavelengths is insignificant because visual sensitivity is very low at this spectral extreme.)

Vision takes place under a wide variety of illuminants, some of which were discussed in Chapter 3. Sunlight varies markedly in its spectral distribution depending upon time of day, latitude, cloud cover, and air quality. In addition there are many artificial light sources in common use, of which tungsten incandescent and fluorescent are the most common, and these have spectral radiance distributions that differ from daylight as well as from one another.[10]

For a neutral gray surface, one that reflects all wavelengths equally, the light reaching the eye will change depending upon the spectral radiance of the source used to illuminate it. Offhand, one would expect the surface to take on the hue of the illuminant. To the extent that it does not, we have an example of the constancy phenomenon.

The light reflected from a surface is the product of functions that describe the spectral characteristics of both lights and surfaces. This product has been called the "color signal" by some authors, and we will adopt that expression. In Land's demonstration described above, identical color signals generated different color sensations from surfaces where no difference would occur without the influence of the surrounding colors. For a demonstration of perfect color constancy, one would want to show the converse, namely that no change in color sensation from a surface of fixed reflectance occurs despite the change in the color signal caused by altering the spectral quality of the illuminant.

If we lived in a world with only one kind of illumination, then variations in the color signal would depend only upon surface reflectances. When illuminants are allowed to vary, so that an infinite number of combinations of source spectral radiance and surface spectral reflectance are capable of producing exactly the same color signal, constancy implies that the perceived color is nevertheless determined only by surface reflectance. Inasmuch as the color signal is the only input that the visual system has to work with, the problem is to understand, if we can, how it might be possible for it to disentangle the two. In other words, the visual system must somehow discern the spectral character of the illuminant and, by taking this into account, compute that of the surface.

We will see that color constancy is never perfect, so there is no point in trying to account for something that never happens. In fact, there is a limiting condition for which no degree of color constancy is possible. This is the case where there is only one surface in the visual field, illuminated by a hidden source. Such a surface appears to "glow in the dark" as if it were itself a source of light. It is obvious that under these circumstances there is no conceivable way for the visual system, or any physical measuring device for that matter, to disentangle the spectral components of illumination and reflection. Therefore, for any degree of color constancy to occur, there must be more than one surface in the visual field. It is not intuitively obvious why this added context should help. But indeed it does, as a demonstration, patterned after one devised by David Brainard, shows dramatically.* (If the demonstration is not done, it should nevertheless be read for the message it imparts.)

Consider a collection of, say, 15 or 20 diffusely-reflecting color chips of various colors, mounted on a white background, slightly separated from one another and illuminated by ambient incandescent white light. Assume that one of the chips, designated as the test color, diffusely reflects about 20 percent of the incident light at all visible wavelengths and appears gray under the ambient room illumination. Alter a slide projector so that its lamp voltage can be controlled with a variable transformer, and place an aperture in the slide plane that restricts the projector beam to precisely illuminate only the gray rectangle. Increase the lamp voltage gradually and the test rectangle will become a lighter gray and then appear white. (It is important to stop at this point because further increases would cause the chip to appear fluorent and then self luminous.) If this recipe is followed properly, an observer freshly viewing the array will be entirely unaware that the test color is anything other than a truly white sample, ambiently illuminated along with the rest.

Next, with the aperture still in the slide plane, place a pale blue filter over the projector lens. This selectively alters the spectral distribution of the light incident upon the test chip and its appearance changes, becoming distinctly bluish as one would expect. Now, with the blue filter still positioned in front of the projector lens, quickly remove the restricting aperture from the film plane to allow the light from the projector to illuminate the entire array. The result is surprising: as the entire scene brightens, some overall change in the appearance of all of the colors will be noticed, but changes in hue are remarkably small except for the test chip, whose bluish appearance is suddenly restored to gray despite the fact that it is the only chip whose chromaticity was *not* changed by removing the aperture.[11]

The demonstration shows that a chip of color that appears initially gray, and which becomes bluish when spot illuminated, returns to gray when the spot illumination is extended to include surrounding colors. What is going on here?

"Gray World" Hypothesis

Suppose that the visual system averages color signals from all over the visual field and, regardless of what colors are represented there, regards this average as a neutral gray. This is an aspect of "adaptation level theory," pioneered by Helson (1934). In one of the earlier computational theories of object color perception, Buchsbaum (1980) promoted the view that

> The system arrives at the illuminant estimate assuming a certain standard common spatial average for the total field. It seems that arbitrary natural everyday scenes composed of dozens of colour subfields, usually none highly saturated, will have a certain, almost fixed spatial spectral reflectance average. It is reasonable that this average will be some medium gray, which comes back to Helson's principle (p. 24).

Other colors could then be scaled relative to the average, including the test color, which, being neutral in its reflectance, would be perceived as gray. This has been called the "gray world hypothesis." Definite limits to such a process are logically necessary: For example, if everything in a room were painted red, then red would be the "true" color of objects in that room and gray would be a false percept.

Selective Chromatic Adaptation

Color constancy should be enhanced by selective chromatic adaptation to an unbalanced illuminant of the sort discussed in conjunction with threshold experiments in Chapter 6. As it relates to the color constancy problem, this has been called the *von Kries adaptation* after the German investigator who proposed it in 1905. Such adaptation is usually considered to occur at an early stage of retinal processing and although it occurs selectively within receptor classes, it probably also involves cross talk among them. A second stage of chromatic adaptation, considered to be at the opponent-color stage, also seems likely (Jameson, Hurvich, and Varner, 1979). Chromatic adaptation does not help to solve the entanglement problem for isolated samples, and would therefore require that signals be averaged across larger areas of the visual field than that occupied by the test color. This influence of the surround on chromatic adaptation in the test area could be mediated by lateral pathways in the visual system, by huge cortical receptive fields (Zeki, 1993), or by temporal integration mediated by the kinds of eye movements that are habitually made when viewing complex scenes (D'Zmura and Lennie, 1986).

Fairchild and Reniff (1995) systematically studied the time course of chromaticity changes at constant luminance for the simulation of illuminants all of which were white-appearing, or nearly so. They did this by having the subject adjust test flashes, presented once per second, to maintain their gray appearance during a period of two minutes following the shift from one background chromaticity to another in a background field measuring 10 by 7.5 deg. The initial physical change required to maintain the appearance of gray was very rapid, followed by a slow change that had not yet become asymptotic after two minutes. These results suggest that, to the extent that color constancy is aided by chromatic adaptation, it should improve as adaptation becomes more complete. In the world of natural illuminants, changes occur slowly and the visual system has plenty of time to fully adapt. This work suggests that long-term adaptation should also benefit color constancy, and that rapid adaptation may play a role for color constancy obtained using brief flashes.

Uchikawa, Uchikawa, and Boynton (1989a) demonstrated the effectiveness of chromatic adaptation as a mechanism for color constancy by devising an experimental paradigm in which all other mechanisms were excluded. Subjects viewed isolated color samples illuminated by hidden projectors either by "white" or reddish light and named their colors. The same lights were independently seen by reflection for 5 min inside the viewing booth to set the observer's adaptation; this light was not allowed to fall on the color chips being viewed. Test colors were the OSA samples, and the effects of adaptation were assessed in terms of centroid shifts. The results verified that a partial color constancy can be mediated by selective chromatic adaptation alone.

White Reference

Most surfaces that reflect more than about 70 percent of the incident radiation appear either white or yellow, and most scenes tend to include white-appearing surfaces. Once white is established as the lightest of all areas in a scene, regardless of how it might appear in isolation under an unbalanced illuminant, this could provide the basis for an adjustment of the color signals for the remainder of the elements of the scene. However, this ploy would not work satisfactorily if there were nothing truly white in the scene. Gelb (1929) demonstrated the powerful influence of a white reference by showing that a neutral surface of low reflectance, one that would appear black under ordinary circumstances, appeared white when viewed in isolation by hidden illumination. It suddenly changed to black when a neutral surface of high reflectance was placed nearby so that it received illumination from the same hidden source.

Small surround elements can elicit large changes in test color appearance. Uchikawa, Uchikawa, and Boynton (1989b) found that, when seen entirely without context, isolated samples that normally would be called brown tended to be called orange. A contiguous white border less than one sixtieth the width of the sample was sufficient to restore brown. Jenness and Shevell (1995), whose subjects adjusted a test field to appear uniquely yellow, found that substituting random dots that replaced only 5 percent of a 5-degree surround strongly affected the perception of the test, whereas the dots had only a very small effect when presented alone.

Viewing the Illuminant

The schemes just described would fail for scenes that do not average to gray and fail to contain a white object. Therefore it would be useful if information about the illuminant could be provided by some more direct means. An obvious possibility would be to view the source of light directly. Although this is not always possible, it very often occurs in peripheral vision. Sometimes, even when the light source is not in the field of view, information about its color can be provided by specular reflections from objects in the environment, which, as already noted, retain the spectral distribution of the illuminant. A less obvious potential source of information about the illuminant is provided by excitation of the peripheral retina by light passing through the translucent sclera.

D'Zmura and Lennie (1986) consider the possible role of specular highlights, and point out that a considerable degree of constancy is maintained in scenes, such as Mondrians (real and simulated) that contain no highlights. However, the degree to which highlights might improve constancy is not well established. For that matter it is true in general that the interactions among the many possible cues and mechanisms that mediate color constancy are not well established.

Color Appearance Does Not Reveal Spectral Distribution

Even direct viewing of the source of light does not provide as much information about its spectral character as might at first be supposed. The reason for this should be clear from earlier chapters: two light sources that appear identical can be physically very different; if so, the appearance of a surface illuminated by one of them will usually change when the second illuminant is substituted. For example, it is possible to match a monochromatic yellow light with a broadband illuminant projected through a filter that selectively absorbs short wavelengths. A surface that selectively reflects long wavelengths would appear red only under the second illuminant. This example illustrates that color constancy can be expected to fail badly in extreme cases (as indeed it does). In other words, even if the chromaticity of an illuminant is known, one cannot compute its spectral distribution, and the latter is what must be known if the color rendering properties of arbitrary illuminants are to be taken into account.

Dimensionality of Natural Illuminants

It turns out that a reasonable inference about the spectral distribution of a light source can be made from its chromaticity if the spectral variations of the illuminant are suitably limited. For example, as its temperature varies, the chromaticity of a blackbody radiator (which an incandescent source approximates) traces out a unique locus. Therefore its chromaticity provides a specification of its temperature, from which its spectral distribution can be calculated. For isolated surfaces illuminated by incandescent light, chromaticity therefore can be estimated from color appearance.

In complex scenes, where chromaticity and color appearance are no longer related in any simple way, such estimates would be much more indirect unless information not influenced by the surrounds reached the brain. Zeki's observations suggest that parallel signals free of contextual influence may reach the brain, and these might be used for color calculations at a pre-conscious level. There is an analogy here to the perception of brightness, where large, diffuse fields tend to gravitate toward the same appearance after a period of adaptation. Nevertheless, the consensual pupillary response varies monotonically with the luminance level of the field, which proves that signals related to absolute luminance level — though not fully appreciated in perception — nevertheless reach the brain.

The spectral distribution of daylight (recall Fig. 3.3) varies considerably depending upon latitude, time of day, season of the year, and weather conditions. On a sunny day, it consists in the shade only of the bluish scattered light from the sky, and, in the open, of a mixture of skylight with the direct rays of the sun. Near sunset, as we all know, daylight can become very reddish as the sun's slanting rays must pass through an increasing thickness of atmosphere. Given that daylight conditions are those under which the visual system presumably has evolved, perhaps it is reasonable that daylight conditions are among those for which estimates of spectral distribution from chromaticity are to some extent possible.

The solution is expedited by an analysis of many phases of daylight by Judd, MacAdam, and Wyszecki (1964). They demonstrated that the many spectral variations of daylight could be reasonably well simulated as the sum of the three underlying functions depicted at

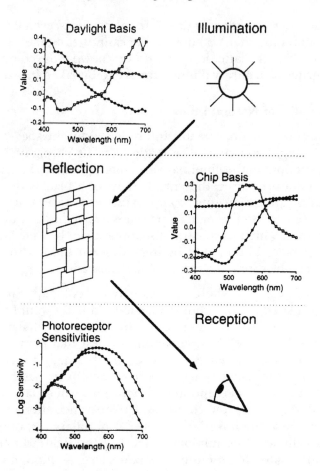

Figure 11.9 Sunlight, represented by three basis functions with variable weights (top) irradiates surfaces represented by three basis functions with variable weights (middle) to generate the color signal received by human photoreceptors having the spectral sensitivities shown at the bottom (from D'Zmura and Iverson, **in press**).

the upper left in Figure 11.9, assuming that all of the values on each curve can be scaled by a multiplicative factors that can differ for each curve.[12] (These are called *basis functions*.) The use of these basis functions reduces the continuous wavelength curve to only three values. These provide weights for the three basis functions, which, when summed, describe (within limits) the spectral distribution that is being simulated. This scheme provides a one-to-one relation between chromaticity and the spectral distribution of daylight, meaning that the color appearance of daylight can provide information about its spectral distribution, subject to the same provisos already mentioned for blackbody radiation.

Judging the Illuminant

Arend and Reeves (1986) presented simulated identical Mondrians side-by-side, as if illuminated by different light sources, and asked subjects to make matches under two conditions that differed only by the instructions given. In a "hue match" condition, the aim was to make a physical match between test and comparison patches and, if possible, to deliberately disregard all other colors in the Mondrian. In a "paper match" condition, subjects "were instructed to make the test patch 'look as if it were cut from the same piece of paper' as the corresponding patch in the standard" (p. 1745). In this study, as in most of those of recent years, the simulated illuminants varied only within the daylight range. Results were interpreted as shifts in the CIE chromaticity diagram (see Fig. 11.10). Matches differed greatly for the two conditions; within limits, subjects were able to make both kinds of matches.

Does this result imply that subjects can judge the illuminant directly? Perhaps they can in this situation, where the effects of the two simulated illuminants can be compared side-by-side, with the eye adapted to an average of the two as the observers looked back and forth. Craven and Foster (1992) tested this more directly by creating a situation in which equivalent amounts of chromatic change were approximated for two conditions in which Mondrians were presented successively. In one condition, the change was consistent with what a shift in illuminant would produce, in the other, not. Subjects made the discrimination between them easily and reliably, the more so the greater the amount of simulated illuminant change.

Simulations vs. Real Surface Colors

The study of Arend and Reeves was the first to attempt to simulate, on a video monitor, something as complex as the shifting chromaticities of an array of surface colors under differing illuminants. Other such experiments have followed, as part of an accelerating trend to replace other forms of visual stimuli by video displays. The advantages are substantial: Once the programming is complete, experiments can literally run themselves, beginning (if desired) with instructions to subjects and ending with the processing and plotting of data. Intertrial intervals are shortened, more data can be collected in less time, and various kinds of on-line interactions between the subjects and the consequences of their responses are possible that could not be handled the old-fashioned way.

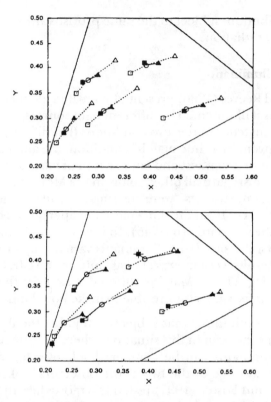

Figure 11.10 Sample results from Arend and Reeves (1986). The open circles represent the chromaticities of the standard illuminant of 6500 K. Open triangles represent chromaticities for 4000 K and open squares, for 10,000 K illuminants. The top x-y chromaticity diagram represents the subject's attempt to make hue matches. The bottom diagram shows data for matches made under instructions to imagine the Mondrian colors as pieces of paper under two different illuminants. Because the open symbols represent the actual chromaticities of the stimuli under the various simulated illuminants, they are identical in the top and bottom diagrams. The filled symbols represent the matches made for each illuminant. If color constancy held perfectly, open and filled symbols would be superimposed.

However, there are also disadvantages. Where color constancy is concerned, there are many aspects of viewing real, palpable chips of color that are not captured by the simulations. Real color samples can be viewed from various vantage points. They inevitably produce shadows near their edges. Actual color samples are much more stable in their spectral reflectances than are the phosphor ratios used to simulate them on a video monitor. They are illuminated, in natural settings, by the same sources that are illuminating a surround that fills far more of the visual field than that of a monitor. Only the chromaticity, and not the actual spectral distributions of light reflecting from real samples, can be simulated on a TV monitor, meaning that the retinal images are not identical to those being simulated. Because subjects differ in their color matches, no simulation is perfect for all of them. Smith & Pokorny (1995) have considered how individual variations in cone action spectra and pre-retinal absorption affect the accuracy of the representation of data in a cone excitation space like that of Figure 7.19. They pointed out that these effects are more serious for colors displayed on a video monitor than for real objects.

As this book is going to press, David Brainard has begun a program of research at the University of California, Santa Barbara, in which color constancy is being explored with real colors, using equipment that allows an unusual degree of flexibility and control. In a real room, illuminated by real light sources, an array of colors is displayed against the back wall. One of these, the test color, is illuminated by a hidden, computer-controlled trichromatic projector in a manner of which the subject is entirely unaware. By the method of adjustment, the subject can manipulate the appearance of the test color under instructions to produce a neutral gray appearance, and this can be done for whatever conditions of illumination and surround that Brainard chooses to investigate. The chromaticity of the test color is determined by, and is automatically calculated as, the additive sum of radiation provided by the room illumination and the hidden projector.

Brainard's preliminary work has shown that, to a remarkable degree, the appearance of the test color is only marginally influenced by the immediate surround, or even by a substantially larger one (as can be produced by surrounding the array as desired with colored papers). Surprisingly, even when a substantial portion of the back wall was draped with vivid red cloth, its influence on the test color was still minimal. Clearly, very peripheral parts of the visual field play a crucial role in color constancy, and this aspect of the problem is very difficult, if not impossible, to simulate.

Using a computer simulation, Bäuml (1994, 1995) obtained data that are not consistent with those of Brainard. Bäuml presented observers with a 5 × 5 matrix on a video monitor. Twenty four of the cells were simulated Munsell chips and one cell, the test, was adjustable by the observer. Observers were asked to adjust the test cell so that it either appeared achromatic (neither reddish nor greenish, neither yellowish nor bluish) or a memorized chromatic color. He found that the illuminant and the surrounding chips strongly affect the appearance of the test cell.

Dimensionality of Natural Surface Reflectances

We have seen that the constancy problem is simplified because of the limited nature of natural illuminants, which allows them to be simulated reasonably well with only a few basis functions. Maloney and Wandell (1986) have shown that such simplification would also be helpful where surface reflectance characteristics are concerned. Basis functions of this kind are possible, and are represented schematically at the middle right of Figure 11.9. This idea was first suggested by Cohen (1964), who analyzed the spectral reflectance characteristics of Munsell color chips and found that the sum of three properly-weighted basis functions could simulate their spectral reflectance distributions rather closely. Dannemiller (1992) has provided an analysis, based upon spectral reflectance functions originally published in 1947 by E. L. Krinov in the USSR, from which he concludes that "three basis functions are necessary and probably sufficient for representing the spectral reflectance functions of natural objects." (p. 507) R. O. Brown, who reads Russian (personal communication) takes strong issue with this, saying that Krinov did not study "natural objects," but rather the space-average of large terrains (e.g., forest, meadow). Furthermore, he swept his instrument across natural scenes while making his measurements, some of which were from airplanes.

Subsequent analysis by Vrehel, Gershon, and Iwan (1994) confirms that three basis functions are insufficient to simulate a larger range of materials. They investigated the reflectance spectra of 64 Munsell chips, a set of 120 paint chips, and "170 natural and man-made objects, including rocks, plants and vegetation, human skin and hair, and fabrics." For most of these items, substantial differences were found between chromaticities calculated from the actual spectral reflectances compared to those resulting from the use of an optimally-weighted triad of basis functions. Using a discrimination-distance error measure, their results indicate almost a twofold improvement of four functions over three, and nearly another twofold added improvement using five functions.

We emphasize once again that the simplifications provided by the use of basis functions to simulate illuminants and surfaces are of no avail in the limiting case where only one surface exists, spot illuminated in an otherwise dark field. An infinite number of weights attached to members of the two sets of three or more basis functions can produce exactly the same result. The chromatic context is vital, and the gray world assumption, a calculational scheme related to a reference white, viewing of the illuminant, or some other trick, is needed to take the illuminant into account. Probably all are used. And whatever scheme is imagined, the calculations are no better than the extent to which basis functions actually capture the characteristics of the lights and surfaces being considered.

Color Constancy Fails Completely in the Limit

Color constancy is not only imperfect, but in the limit, when the source of light is monochromatic, it fails completely regardless of context. This situation is approximated by low-pressure sodium street lighting, which is nearly monochromatic at a wavelength of about 588 nm. The only information about the color of a surface that this source can render is the extent of the surface's reflectance at that wavelength. In Figure 11.8, a vertical line drawn upward from the baseline at 588 nm intersects the various reflection functions at a variety of levels. These surfaces would differ perceptually only in lightness, depending upon their relative reflectances at that wavelength, without regard to the remainder of their spectral reflectance characteristics, in the order white, yellow, pink, light gray, orange, medium gray, purple, green, blue, brown, red, and black. Viewed under low-pressure sodium lighting, all surfaces are, in a sense, rendered in "black and white," although a definite yellowish cast pervades the scene, showing that chromatic adaptation is far from complete.

Measurement of Color Constancy

No consensus exists concerning how to measure the degree of color constancy that is maintained under various experimental conditions. Plotting shifts in a chromaticity diagram, as Arend and Reeves did, has been most commonly used. From these, various quantitative indices have been proposed. When the study of categorical color perception has been of interest, "errors" in color naming (compared to a reference condition) have been used as an index by Boynton and Purl (1989), Boynton, Fargo, and Collins (1990), and by Troost and de Weert (1991).

"Top Down" Considerations

As already noted, most of what we have considered in this book relates to "bottom-up" processing, or "pre-attentive vision," as it is sometimes called (Julesz, 1995). This is conceived to be a property of peripheral mechanisms not significantly influenced by higher mental processes. "Top-down" processing, on the other hand, includes the effects of past experience, complex judgments, and the influence of language; factors that probably play a role in color constancy. From past experience, because we are already familiar with the colors of many objects, there is a tendency to see their colors as shifting less than they otherwise would with changes in illumination. We learn to judge which regions of a scene are in shadow, and which are not, and this allows us to guess what the colors of shadowed objects would be if brought into full sunlight. We correctly judge uniformly-painted surfaces to be uniform in color, whereas a photometric analysis would show gross changes over its surface. The same is true for judged color; in a familiar scene we are unlikely to be critically aware of subtle changes of color that varying the illumination will provide.

It seems likely that, in a sense, color constancy is not as good as it seems to be. If colors do not shift between categories when lighting changes — which, for example, is the case for most surfaces when daylight varies — we are unlikely to notice considerable within-category variations from perfect constancy, especially because time usually will have passed and memory is required. The differences would be much more obvious if the comparisons could be made simultaneously. Though color constancy is only partial, we can still make use of the important categorical information about color that usually survives. For example, we have no trouble finding our red car in the parking lot. In such cases the exact color is not important, and when discrepancies are noticed, they are likely to be attributed, quite reasonably, to a change in illumination. The review of Jameson and Hurvich (1989) emphasizes this point, and provides further references.

SUMMARY

The idea of a color "space" — black at the bottom, white at the top, shaped like two cones stuck together with chromatic colors arranged circumferentially — is so natural that it reappears in almost all attempts to order colors systematically. The space is imagined as being filled with colors that change only gradually from one place to another. Thus it is always possible to move smoothly from one color to another, and the number of possible paths that may be taken between any two colors is unlimited. Despite this smooth and continuous nature of color order, which has its initial basis in the correspondingly gradual changes of excitation in the three kinds of cones, color space is also arranged categorically. This is revealed by color-naming experiments in which a given color name does not denote only one sensation, but embraces a considerable variety of them.

There appear to be eleven regions of color space that are denoted with basic color names, each of which refers to a fundamental sensation. These regions overlap and are fuzzy at the edges. Not all color regions overlap; those that do are defined as "linked," and these are found closer together in color space than those that are not. Regions denoted by basic color terms fill most of color space, but a curious region exists for which colors are very difficult to name.

The eleven basic color terms are white, gray, black, red, green, yellow, blue, orange, purple, pink, and brown. The first three of these refer to achromatic colors. The next four represent chromatic color sensations that can exist in pure form. The last four are chromatic colors that seem like blends of the others, but which, nevertheless, are shown to meet demanding experimental criteria for being full-fledged basic color terms.

Color constancy, which is the tendency for surface colors to resist changes in appearance under differing illuminants and surrounds, is an enduring and important problem for color theory to interpret. Somehow, the visual system must take the illuminant into account, a task that is impossible in the limit, but which is simplified to some extent by physical restrictions in the kinds of illuminants and surfaces that are usually encountered in the natural world. Color constancy is impossible for isolated surfaces and therefore depends on an assessment of chromatic context, for which a variety of possible mechanisms have been proposed.

Because names are used to remember colors categorically, they are much less precise in their denotation than are the original sensations. Consequently, many changes in color that would be readily observed if the sensations themselves could be remembered precisely will go unnoticed unless constancy fails sufficiently to shift the perceived color of an object into a different basic color category.

NOTES

[1] For a definition of fluorescence see Note 11, Chapter 3. Polarization relates to the fact that there are two orthogonal components to the vibration of light, called the electric and magnetic vectors. If light is unpolarized, these vectors assume random orientations. If light is plane polarized, the electric vector is constrained to assume only one orientation: in other words, the vibration of the photons are fixed in one direction. When light is circularly polarized, the angle of vibration changes as the photon moves, something like that of a turning screw. Some animals are sensitive to the angle of light polarization, but humans are not, except indirectly: light reflecting from surfaces having a specular component becomes partially polarized, and although this is not ordinarily detectable, the specular component can be selectively reduced by means of Polaroid glasses, making the diffuse component, and the object's color, more discernible.

[2] For more information on Fechner's law we recommend Falmagne, J. C. Psychophysical Measurement Theory, in *Handbook of Perception & Human Performance*, Vol. 1, Sensory Processes & Perception, Chap. 1, pp. 1–8 to 1–12, Boff, Kaufman & Thomas (eds.) New York, Wiley and Sons, 1986; and Boynton, R. M., Psychophysics, in *Optical Radiation Measurements*, Vol. 5, Visual Measurements, Bartleson & Grum (eds.) New York, Academic Press, Inc. 1984.

[3] Some languages may subdivide a large category and, unlike English, have a separate single-word name for each part of it. In the case of Russian, for example, there are two words for blue. There is dispute concerning whether both of these are basic color terms, or whether one denotes a region of color space that largely subsumes the other. More research is needed to settle this issue.

[4] Ratliff (1976) marshals strong evidence in favor of this viewpoint. For counter arguments, see Van Brakel (1993).

[5] Sternheim and Boynton (1966) published a study in which color naming of monochromatic lights was examined by a rating method. They concluded that the category orange was unnecessary for describing the appearance of long-wave spectral lights, although both red and yellow were shown to be essential for this purpose. Fuld, Wooten and Whalen (1981) asked the same kind of question about purple as it relates to red and blue, with the same result.

[6] Boynton and Olson (1990) provide an overall summary of this program of research with references to earlier papers.

[7] See Nickerson (1981). The OSA color samples have had little use for scientific purposes. Perhaps their only advantage is the nature of the stimulus spacing. The set does not contain an adequate example either of white or black. Also, the maximum saturation of the samples is less than in other color-order systems.

[8] A color plotting at the centroid (which no actual sample exactly matched) would be a very good example of that color, but the most saturated example of colors are found instead at the outer edges of the color space.

[9] The low-lightness centroid for red is dependent both on receptor physiology and the nature of reflecting pigments. To obtain a good red from a reflecting surface, all but the longest wavelengths of incident white light must be absorbed. The remaining long wavelengths are ones to which the eye is relatively insensitive, and it is for this reason that the red centroid plots at low lightness. Red can be seen without a surround (for example a red traffic signal retains its hue when seen in isolation at night). On the other hand, a brown signal light is an oxymoron, even though Smallman and Boynton (1990) have shown that brown is as useful as any other basic color for coding purposes in a reflecting display.

[10] See Boynton (1987 and 1990) for more detail and further references.

[11] It is important that the spot illumination does not spill over onto the background. It may help to put a black border around all of the color chips so that the "spill" light (and there is certain to be some) will strike the border of low reflectance. Richard O. Brown (personal communication) has created a similar demonstration for the Exploratorium in San Francisco (not yet installed at this writing). He offers the helpful advice that it is much easier to cut the aperture for the slide plane first, and then tailor the color patch to the shape of the projected aperture, rather than vice versa. It should also be noted that to vary the voltage supply to the projector lamp requires some special wiring because, to avoid overheating, the normal voltage to the projector fan should be maintained.

[12] The daylight basis functions in Figure 11.9 were derived from functions published by Judd *et al.* (1964). For details see D'Zmura and Iverson (1993).

Appendix

INTRODUCTION

The CIE system of colorimetry, mentioned in an historical context in Chapter 1 (p. 25) has been employed as little as possible in this book. The system has served a very valuable purpose, and will doubtless continue to be used into the indefinite future for practical work, but in this book — where emphasis has been upon physiological mechanisms of color vision — its use would not generally have been helpful. Nevertheless, the use of the CIE system is so widespread that the literature on human color vision (including some of the figures in this book) cannot be appreciated without knowing something about it. A major purpose of this Appendix is to furnish the needed information. As background, the concepts developed in Chapter 5 should be reviewed.

The Part I of this Appendix reproduces some material previously published as part of a chapter in a multiauthored textbook (Boynton, 1971). This will provide some needed background for Part II, which consists of remarks by W. David Wright that are "based on a tape recording of a very informal and highly personal account of the CIE system given to the Colour Group [of Great Britain] on 5th February 1969." Thanks are given to Dr. Wright, and to Mr. David J. McConnell (Secretary, The Colour Group) for permission to reproduce an abridged version of this material, which was originally transcribed for the *Colour Group Journal*, which has now ceased publication.

Dr. Y. Nakano contributed Part III, which is a tutorial on color vision mathematics. Herein the reader will find the Smith–Pokorny sensitivity curves in tabular form which was Part III of the Appendix in the first edition of this text. The reader is also shown various mathematical manipulations that are possible with the CIE colorimetric system including the calculations required to plot stimuli in CIE chromaticy space and the task of transforming from CIE XYZ system to other primaries. Since an acquaintance with matrix algebra is required, the reader can find a short summary of the operational rules in endnote #6 of Part III.

Dr. D. Brainard contributed Part IV, which is a tutorial on cone contrast and opponent modulation spaces and provides an example calculation using the DKL cone excitation space.

The references for Parts III and IV are listed in the consolidated Reference list. Because the bibliographic entries for Dr. Wright's presentation were identified by superscript we provide his Bibliography at the end of Part II.

PART I: CIE SYSTEM

Color Equations

The results of a color match using three spectral primaries may be described by an equation:

$$c(C) + r(R) \equiv g(G) + b(B) \tag{A.1}$$

Equation (A.1) should be read as follows: c units of the test color (C) plus r units of the red primary (R), additively mixed to one half of the field, exactly matches ($\equiv$) g units of the green primary (G) plus b units of the blue primary (B), additively mixed to the other half of the field.

For a test wavelength of 490 nm, the equation reads (from the curves of Figure A.1):

$$0.082 \, (C) + 0.058 \, (R) \equiv 0.057 \, (G) + 0.083 \, (B) \tag{A.2}$$

This is an empirical statement about an experimental operation, not a formal statement of mathematics. The plus sign is borrowed to indicate colorimetric addition by superposition of lights; the symbol "$\equiv$"

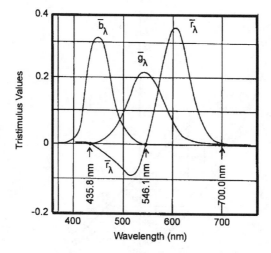

Figure A.1   Color-matching functions (tristimulus values for an equal energy spectrum) in the primary system where R = 700 nm, G = 546.1 nm, and B = 435.8 nm. (From Wyszecki & Stiles, 1967.)

is deliberately used to make it clear that an experimental match is implied, rather than a mathematical equality. Nevertheless, if the analogous mathematical statement is written and is manipulated in accordance with the rules of algebra, it is found experimentally (within fairly wide limits) that such calculations predict the results of new color matches when translated back into the experimental analog.

As an example, suppose we multiply Equation (A.2) by a constant factor of 2. It will then read

$$0.164 \ (C) + 0.116 \ (R) \equiv 0.114 \ (G) + 0.166 \ (B) \qquad (A.3)$$

After manipulating our wedges to produce these trichromatic amounts, we can then check to see whether there is still a match between the two halves of the field. There will be. Or we could add a given quantity to both sides of the match — let us call the quantity X. Then mathematically,

$$0.082 \ (C) + 0.058 \ (R) + X \equiv 0.057 \ (G) + 0.083 \ (B) + X \qquad (A.4)$$

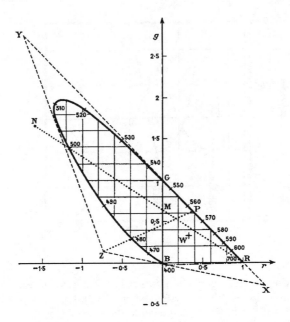

Figure A.2   Chromaticity diagram based on the spectral primaries of Figure A.1. X, Y, and Z represent the primaries of the CIE system, as represented in the RGB chromaticity space (LeGrand, 1957).

An easy way to check this out is to add a uniform light to the entire field — perhaps reflected off a glass plate in front of the colorimeter. The match will remain.

Generally, the additive, multiplicative, associative, and distributive laws of algebra all work, so that we can predict color-matching behavior using the powerful tool of algebra. This is consistent with the model of color vision that has been presented in this book, and in fact constitutes one of the primary reasons for believing that equal absorptions in photopigments are responsible for color matches.

There are some algebraic manipulations that cannot be exactly duplicated in the laboratory, namely those that require negative amounts of light. However if a positive quantity is added to the opposite side of the field, as previously explained, the predicted color match will hold.

The values r_λ, g_λ, and b_λ shown in Figure A.1 are known as *distribution coefficients* and the curves are called *color mixture functions*. The values have been adjusted so that the area under each of the three functions is 1.0.

In order to provide a colorimetric specification of any stimulus light, it is necessary to evaluate its effectiveness with respect to each of the three color mixture functions. (This is directly related to its effectiveness upon each of the three types of cone photopigment.) For this purpose, the concept of the *tristimulus value* is introduced. There are three of these defined as follows:

$$R = \int E_\lambda \, r_\lambda \, d_\lambda$$
$$G = \int E_\lambda \, g_\lambda \, d_\lambda \qquad\qquad (A.5)$$
$$B = \int E_\lambda \, b_\lambda \, d_\lambda$$

Here E_λ is the radiance distribution in the stimulus; E must be measured in physical energy units for every wavelength λ throughout the visible range of the spectrum. If we have two stimuli such that $R_1 = R_2$, $G_1 = G_2$, and $B_1 = B_2$, even though physically different values of E had to be used to produce them, they will match for the standard observer. Such matches are called *metameric* and the matching pairs are called *metamers*. (Physical matches are called *isomers*.)

The Chromaticity Diagram

Tristimulus values can have any magnitude, depending upon the radiance levels of the stimuli. Everyday experience tells us that if we double the amount of light (as for example by adding a second light bulb to a lamp) the color appearance of a surface illuminated by the lights changes very little. Because hue and saturation are approximately independent of luminance, it would be convenient to develop a two-variable scheme that deals with relations among trichromatic units, while at the same time factoring luminance out of the system. This is done by specifying *chromaticity coordinates*, defined as follows:

$$r = \frac{R}{R+G+B}$$
$$g = \frac{G}{R+G+B} \qquad\qquad (A.6)$$
$$b = \frac{B}{R+G+B}$$

Tristimulus values, R, G, and B, show the absolute amounts of the three primaries required to make the match being specified. The chromaticity coordinates tell us the ratio of each of the three trichromatic amounts to the sum of the three. (Their sum must total unity and therefore any two of them will provide a complete specification. In practice, a plot of g versus r is most often used.)

A *chromaticity diagram* for the set of primaries of Figure A.1 is shown in Figure A.2, in which each spectral stimulus plots as a point. For example if $\lambda = 490$ (for which the tristimulus values were specified in Equation [A.2]), the following chromaticity coordinates are produced:

$$r = \frac{-.058}{.082} = -0.707$$

$$g = \frac{.057}{.082} = +0.695 \qquad \text{(A.7)}$$

$$b = \frac{.083}{.082} = +1.012$$

Other spectral stimuli, calculated and plotted in the same way, form a *spectrum locus* connected by a continuous curve that includes all possible intermediate wavelengths.

System of Imaginary Primaries

The chromaticity system for specifying color, worked out by Maxwell (although in a triangular coordinate system) more than 100 years ago, proved so useful that an international standardizing organization, the Commission Internationale de l'Éclairage (CIE) in 1931 established an international system. A major point to be decided upon was the choice of primaries, for an infinity of chromaticity charts can be prepared, depending upon the colors that are taken as primaries. Whatever the choice, the red primary on an r versus g chart will plot at $r = 1.0$, $g = 0$, the green primary will plot at $r = 0$, $g = 1.0$, and the blue primary at $r = g = 0$ (note that this is the case in Figure A.2). It works out that the spectrum locus defined by one system of primaries is a projective transformation of that defined by any other system of primaries, a projection which places the three primaries in a relation that forms a right triangle with equal sides adjacent to the right angle (See Part III for the calculation involved).

A straight line in one chromaticity chart will transform into a straight line in another chart based on different primaries, but the lengths of such lines relative to one another will change from chart to chart, as will also their angular relations to one another.

In developing the CIE system, a decision was made to utilize a set of imaginary primaries. In essence, this amounts to an extrapolation in the mathematical domain beyond what can be realized physically. Probably the easiest way to visualize what was done is in terms of the chromaticity diagram of Figure A.2. This diagram, it will be recalled, is based upon a set of real primaries.

The imaginary primaries that were chosen are shown in Figure A.2 as the points X, Y, and Z. In this diagram, note that the angle YZX is not a right angle, X does not plot at an abscissa value of 1.0, Y does not plot at an ordinate value of 1.0, and Z is not at the origin. These positions are accomplished in the diagram of Figure A.3, which is the appropriate transformation to produce a chromaticity diagram specified in terms of the imaginary primaries X, Y, and Z indicated in the original chromaticity space of Figure A.2. In both projections, X, Y, and Z are well outside the spectrum locus; this is what makes them imaginary. They were deliberately chosen this way so that the chromaticity coordinates of all real stimuli would have positive values. In other words, the entire domain of real colors in the transformed diagram falls in the all-positive quadrant.

There are, of course, many sets of three points in the diagram of Figure A.2 that could accomplish this objective. The ones that were selected have several advantages. In the first place, the lines connecting them just barely graze the spectrum locus. This means that there is little waste space near the axes of the transformed diagram. The line XY, furthermore, is coincident with the locus of long-wave spectral stimuli from about 550 nm onward. Second, the line XZ was chosen to fall on the *alychne*, the zero-luminance line. A consequence of this is that both the X and Z primaries in this imaginary system have zero luminance. Calculations pertaining to luminance can therefore be based upon the Y primary alone. To finish the job, the line between Y and Z was drawn to be almost, but not quite, tangent to the spectral locus in the neighborhood of 500 nm.

It will be recalled that the chromaticity diagram in Figure A.2 was based upon the set of color-mixture curves of Figure A.1. It is possible to go the other way: Given the location of three primaries, such as X, Y, and Z in Figure A.2, and the luminance of each, a set of color mixture curves can be derived which correspond to these. This has been done for the CIE primaries, and these curves, called $\bar{x}$, $\bar{y}$, and $\bar{z}$ are shown in Figure A.4.[1] As would be expected, all values are positive. Values of $\bar{z}$ are zero beyond 560 nm. This corresponds to the fact that these stimuli fall on the line where $\bar{z} = 0$ in the chromaticity chart. Values of $\bar{x}$ form a double-humped curve as a function of wave-

length. It reaches close to zero near 500 nm, where the spectral locus of the chromaticity diagram nearly touches the ordinate. The
left-hand hump of $\bar{x}$ corresponds to the bending of the spectrum locus away from the ordinate in the chromaticity chart as the wavelength is shortened from 500 nm. The $\bar{y}$ function is exactly proportional to the V_λ function (the luminous efficiency function of the
standard observer in the CIE system). As previously noted, this results from a choice of X and Z primaries which puts both of them of
the alychne.

The curves of Figure A.4 are known as the distribution curves for
an equal-energy spectrum in the CIE system. These are widely used
in order to calculate chromaticities in a standard way, given that the
physical characteristics of a stimulus to be evaluated are known; and
to predict which stimuli will match other ones.

Suppose that we have two physical samples and we wish to know
whether they match. To find out, we determine the tristimulus values
X, Y, and Z in the CIE system, defined as follows [see Equation (A.5)]:

$$X_1 = \int E_\lambda \bar{x} \, d\lambda$$
$$Y_1 = \int E_\lambda \bar{y} \, d\lambda \qquad (A.8)$$
$$Z_1 = \int E_\lambda \bar{z} \, d\lambda$$

We do the same for the other sample to obtain X_2, Y_2, and Z_2. If $Y_1 = Y_2$, the two samples have the same luminance, but may not match for
hue and/or saturation. If additionally $X_1 = X_2$ and $Z_1 = Z_2$, the two
samples will match (for the "standard observer") in all respects.

To determine chromaticity in the CIE system, calculate

$$x = \frac{X}{X+Y+Z}$$
$$y = \frac{Y}{X+Y+Z} \qquad (A.9)$$

and plot the result in the standard diagram.

The development of the CIE system has been described here by
graphical means. [For a discussion of the corresponding algebra,
see LeGrand (1968), Graham (1965), or Wyszecki and Stiles (1982)
and the Appendix, Part III.]

An alternative scheme for specifying chromaticity does so in terms
of *dominant wavelength* and *excitation purity*. To determine the domi-

nant wavelength of a sample, draw a line from the white point through the point which represents the chromaticity of the sample, extending it until it intersects the spectrum locus. This intersection point defines the dominant wavelength. Excitation purity is defined (see Figure A.3) as the distance of the sample point from the white point, expressed as a percentage of the distance all the way from the white point through the sample point to the spectrum locus. For samples lying between the white point and the line of extraspectral purples (see above) excitation purity is similarly defined as a percentage of the distance from the white point to the purple line. The dominant wavelength of such a sample is specified by the complementary spectral wavelength, followed by a lower-case c; for example, $\lambda = 540$ c.

NOTE

[1] The CIE dropped the subscript $_\lambda$ on these symbols, which should be regarded as implicitly including them.

PART II: THE ORIGINS OF THE 1931 CIE SYSTEM

By W.D. Wright
Imperial College, London, England

I happened to be at the committee meeting when it was suggested that I might give this talk on the origins of the 1931 C.I.E. system. I was a little taken aback by this suggestion and I was not quite sure why I was asked to do this. I had half a feeling that they thought this dreadful C.I.E. business was all my fault! (laughter) I also got a distinct impression that they thought I was not looking too healthy and if they did not hurry up it might be too late. (laughter) Well, anyway, I have made it today, but how much longer I will last I do not know.

Now, the question is really where to start. The most active period was obviously in the 1920's but I thought it would be a good thing to go back a little further to pick out one or two historic landmarks, because, as you will see, some of the work done in the last century played quite an important part in the discussions. Now, the target we were aiming at in the 1931 system was the spectrum locus in the chromaticity chart, leading to a set of colour mixture curves (or colour matching functions). We had to derive standard data for an average observer and then establish a co-ordinate system for practical colour measurement and specification.

I think I should first make a brief reference to the pioneer work done by Maxwell. Among the various papers I have managed to collect, I am fortunate to have a reprint of Maxwell's 1860 paper[1] in which he describes his colour box and colour mixture curves which he produced. I was not around at that time, as you understand, but G. F. Thompson, Sir George Thompson, who was head of this Department, passed this reprint over to me when he left Imperial College. He himself had received it from his father, J. J. Thompson, so that it is really a sort of holy relic. Anyway, that was a beginning, and I think Maxwell's curves were the first set of colour mixture curves that were produced. The colour box itself consisted of a prism system, three entrance slits, the widths of which could be varied, and when they were illuminated they produced three overlapping spectra. Depending on the separation of the slits, you could choose the three particular wavelengths that were focused on the exit-pupil and entered the observer's eye. You made your colour match by varying the slit widths, and the curves he derived were in fact obtained from a series of matches on the white using various combinations of wavelengths.

The basic colour arithmetic had been established earlier by Grassmann's Laws and, to some extent, by Helmholtz.

The next experimental work I must refer to is the work of König and Dieterici. They measured the colour mixture curves using Helmholtz's colour mixing apparatus as described in his "Physiological Optics."[2]

This apparatus was used in the experiments by König and Dieterici in 1892. I have here my most precious possession, namely, König's collected works published in 1903.[3] It includes the paper in which he reports the colour mixture curves which they recorded and a number of others, including, of course, his paper on small field tritanopia.

At about the same time, Sir William Abney, using his colour patch apparatus at Imperial College, also measured the colour mixture curves. The results are included in Abney's "Research in Colour Vision," published in 1915.

Now I must move on to two papers by R. E. Ives, which I have here, published in the Journal of the Franklin Institute in 1915 and 1923.[4] In these papers he made some adjustments to the König mixture curves and produced what came to be known as the König–Ives colour-matching data. Then in 1920–21 another American, E. A. Weaver, combined König's and Abney's results to produce a set of mixture curves which were recommended by a colorimetry committee of the Optical Society of America for colour measurement work. There was also a report in 1921 by the O.S.A. Colorimetry Committee.[5] I think this really marks the beginning of modern colorimetry, and certainly led the way to the 1931 C.I.E. system. As you can see, it is quite a massive report and it covered a variety of topics. It included a long section on nomenclature, and other sections on standard psycho-physical data, physical standards, methods of colorimetry, and their inter-relations, and so on.

I would like to quote from the opening paragraph of this report. It says: "That the nomenclature and standards of Colour Science are in an extremely unsatisfactory condition is manifest to practically all workers in this field. It is the purpose of the present report to take an initial step towards remedying this state of affairs. That the result cannot be final as regards either nomenclature or standards is a natural consequence of the pioneer character of the effort."

This was the beginning of the very fruitful 1920–1930 period. Again in the section on the colour mixture problem, they said: "probably the most fundamental of all the psycho-physical data relating to colour are the three colour excitation curves" (which is what the colour mixture curves of colour matching functions were then called) "which represent the laws of three colour mixture. Extant data on these relationships are due to Maxwell, Abney, König and Dieterici."

This report had some really valuable information in it and it gives the tables and curves which Weaver derived by combining König's and Abney's results. And also, incidentally, it contains on one of its pages a diagram of the chromaticity chart or colour triangle. It is the first time, as far as I know, that the Maxwell triangle was produced on rectangular co-ordinates; it was also an all-positive system. So that was really quite a landmark.

This O.S.A. report and the two Ives' papers triggered off a series of quite outstanding papers by Guild published in the Transactions of the Optical Society in this country.[6] Ives' papers had shown that colour mixture data could be expressed in terms of any three stimuli. Usually they would be red, green and blue, but having recorded the results in terms of one set of stimuli you could transform them to another set if you wished. And there was no need to use the so-called fundamental sensation curves, representing the actual sensitivities of the processes in the eye, at least not for colorimetric purposes. Guild took up this theme of the transformation of data and produced simplified transformation formulae. He laid particular emphasis on the possibility of using a two dimensional chromaticity chart, although he did not call it that at that time. I have Guild's papers here and perhaps I could comment that these were my Colorimetric Bible when I started. You can see how tattered they are, and the most tattered numbers are the issues which have papers by Guild in them.

In addition to this theoretical work on transformations, Guild also carried out much experimental work. In the Transactions of the Optical Society there are important papers describing his visual spectrophotometer, his criticism of the monochromatic-plus-white method of colorimetry, his vector method of colorimetry and also, of course, his trichromatic colorimeter. In his colorimeter the red-green-blue mixture was produced by means of a prism rotating in front of segments of red, green and blue colour filters. You obtained a colour mixture as the rapid pulses of red, green and blue light were focused on the retina. You varied the amount of red, green and blue by changing the sector openings. This, of course, is the instrument which he used to measure his colour mixture curves.

All this was in the period 1924, 1925 and 1926, then came the very important survey which he gave at the Optical Convention of 1926, which was held in this College. This long paper of some 80 pages summarized the situation not only as far as colorimetry was concerned, but also photometry. He makes a reference to the conditions under which heterochromatic photometry should be carried out, because in 1924 (I shall come back to this) the C.I.E. had standardised the V_λ curve, then called the visibility curve, again partly on the basis of studies made by Ives, who established the conditions under which flicker photometry was additive.

I apologize that I must now be rather personal since this Optical Convention and the paper by Guild were very important events for me, as they led, through the influence of Sir John Parsons, the oph-thalmologist, to my being offered a grant from the Medical Research Council to undertake research on colour vision. I was at the convention as a student, and demonstrated some experiments there, although I did not go to hear Guild's paper. At that time I was just about to look for a job in the optical industry. However, the optical industry was then suffering from a severe depression and, although I was not at all interested in doing colour work, when the M.R.C. grant became available, it was offered to me and I was glad to take it up. So this was how I first came into colour research. I think it was very fortunate for me that I was around at that time looking for a job and that I was given the opportunity to work at such a critical moment in the subject. I would also say that I was very fortunate as far as the literature which I could consult. The books that I used as a research student were Helmholtz's *Physiological Optics*, König's *Collected Works*, Abney's *Colour Researches*,[7] Guild's *Survey*, the book on *Colour Vision* by Sir John Parsons,[8] Martin's own book on *Colour and Methods of Colour Reproduction*,[9] Walsh's *Photometry*,[10] the two Troland Reports, and, most of all, the papers that Guild had published in the Transactions of the Optical Society — the ones to which I have already referred. Because, although I had got the grant and I knew what the project was called, I really hadn't a clue what it was about except that my first job, I knew, was to build a colorimeter. This I set about doing, but the first thing I had to do was to dismantle Abney's colour patch apparatus. I pulled this to pieces, used some of the parts to build mine and I used also the same special room which Abney had built for his colour research. I decided in building my new colorimeter to stick to spectral matching stimuli, no doubt because Abney's colour patch apparatus used these (but I imagine also on the advice of Dr. Martin) whereas Guild of course had used filters in his colorimeter. I am embarrassed that I must once again describe my colorimeter because I have done it so many times before. As you know, it uses a prism to form two spectra. From one spectrum you pick out the red, green, and blue matching stimuli and from the other the monochromatic test colour. The selected wavebands are reflected back through the system and the dispersion which originally separated the light out into the spectrum is used in reverse to re-combine the red, green and blue stimuli. The amounts of red, green and blue are controlled with photometer wedges mounted in front of the matching stimuli. To add a little bit of human interest, in this first model I had to use a fairly narrow prism about ¾" thick with a face about 3" or so to select the strip of light which formed the test colour spectrum. Professor Conrady, who was on the staff then, suggested that I cut a slice from a larger prism which we had in the Department. I said, "Well, how do I go about doing that?" and he said "You get a hack saw, fit it with a copper wire and feed it with carborundum powder and saw away." And this, in the end, I did.

I really must have worked rather hard because I not only assembled the colorimeter and used it but I made the bits and pieces or a lot of them. I don't know how I managed to do it in the time, (October 1926 to March 1929) especially as I had to spend two and a half days sawing prisms!

In the meantime, Guild was carrying on with his programme using his colorimeter and I want to make it quite clear that he had probably almost completed his project before I had hardly started, certainly before I had got my colorimeter working. I remember visiting his laboratory with Professor Martin, probably in 1927, when I saw curves which Guild had already obtained of the spectrum locus in the colour triangle. He was using his filter colorimeter and obtained his monochromatic test light independently from two Hilger constant deviation spectrometers in series as a double monochromator. I was fortunate to be able to discuss the problem with Guild and must obviously have obtained some very valuable advice from him as well as from Professor Martin.

I described my colorimeter in 1927–28 and then in 1928–29 brought out a paper on the trichromatic coefficients and the spectrum locus, as well as a Medical Research Council Report which came out about the same time.[11]

I keep referring to Mr. Guild because I owe so much to him but not only did he write a number of very important papers, but he also took the trouble to discuss other people's papers at very considerable length. I benefited a lot from several pages of discussion on the papers which I gave — first of all on the one describing my colorimeter and then on my redetermination of the trichromatic coefficients.

I must apologise for all this personal history but it does have some bearing on the 1931 C.I.E. system. Having done this work I got a job in America with Westinghouse in Pittsburgh working on television. I was in fact only there for a year. For domestic reasons I had to come back after a year but while I was there and during my spare time in the evenings, I had a shot at working out the spectral mixture curves. So when I returned to England I presented another paper to the Optical Society, in which I reported this work. But in addition, I did something that Guild had previously asked me to do; I transformed my spectrum locus into the N.P.L. 700, 546.1, 435.8 primary system. Now this enabled Guild to make a comparison of my results with his and again I got about three or four pages of discussion from him which was terribly helpful. He appreciated that I had given the information in this way and went on to say: "I have compared these with my own figures at various critical parts of the chart, and am pleased to say that no discrepancies exceeding the colour limen in the neighbourhood were found at any of the points checked. This agreement adds enormously to the value of his data and mine because it must be remembered that the two determinations were made by two different groups of observers and using entirely dissimilar apparatus." I think I can fairly say that it was when he realised that his curves and mine were so close together that he was encouraged to press on with the idea of getting standard data adopted by the C.I.E. which was due to meet in England in 1931.

Guild then went ahead and presented a paper to the Royal Society called "The Colorimetric Properties of the Spectrum."[12] He read this in April 1931 giving his own curves which, as I have tried to make clear, he had measured a year or two before I had even got cracking but he had not published them. He then went on to compare his and my results. He also showed how the old König/Abney spectrum locus which Weaver had derived differed very significantly from our loci. He then made plans to submit our mean data for adoption by the C.I.E. at the meeting which was due to be held in Cambridge, England, in September 1931, only a few months after he produced this paper.

In 1931, colorimetry really burst on the C.I.E. and in the 1931 Proceedings we have several pages of discussion reported and, of course, the resolutions which determined the 1931 system. Two people were particularly involved in these discussions: Priest from America and Guild from this country. Priest was the official American delegate and I think it was quite clear that he had come briefed to delay the adoption of any standard observer, since he thought we were rushing things too much. He in fact raised a succession of objections — he had a week's visit to the N.P.L. before the C.I.E. meeting and during that time (I only know this from hearsay) he raised a succession of objections. Then overnight, T. Smith, who was Head of the Light Division and who involved himself in the subject, and Guild would recalculate a lot of data to meet Priest's criticisms,[13] and Priest would turn up next morning with something else to object to. In the end they wore Priest down and he accepted most of the proposals that Guild was going to put forward at the C.I.E. meeting. As you can imagine, there was quite a bit of discussion but they eventually approved the standard observer data. However, when you come to look at the resolutions you find that, whilst approval was given at the meeting, subsequently France reversed all its decisions and opposed all the resolutions — shades of de Gaulle! — and Germany reversed their vote, but as long as Britain and America agreed that was really all that mattered. (laughter) Having approved the standard observer data, they then approved the transformation of the data to the present all-positive X, Y, Z system.

In addition to adopting an all positive co-ordinate system, the decision was taken to follow a suggestion of Judd's in 1930 of locating X and Z on the alychne, that is the locus of colours in the chromaticity chart which have got zero luminance and which had been described by Schrödinger in 1925. This was done and the data were also combined with the 1924 V_λ curve. Interestingly enough, some fiddling had to be done with the actual relative luminances of the R, G, B stimuli in order to make the whole thing consistent. This was [a] procedure of mine that Guild had criticised. Also, I was rather pleased in looking through some of these papers recently to come across a paper of Judd's[14] in which he was prepared to support my approach and be critical of Guild. So we stood up to Guild from time to time but he was obviously the dominant person.

The C.I.E. produced their set of distribution curves in terms of x, y, z. The y curve was identical with the V_λ curve because of the particular choice of X and Z to have zero luminance. They also recommended the three illuminants, S_A, S_B and S_C, S_A a tungsten light, S_B tungsten light plus liquid filter to correspond to about 4800°K to simulate sunlight and S_C about 6500°K to correspond to north sky-light. The filters that were used were those recommended by the work that Davis and Gibson had reported.[15] They had made a big study on the reproduction of sunlight and daylight at various colour temperatures. At the N.P.L. itself, Guild had also produced some daylight liquid filters and he would no doubt have liked to have had those adopted, but he recognised that Davis and Gibson had done much more work on it, so he accepted the American filters. No doubt there was a bit of horse trading here so that, as Priest had yielded on the standard observer data, Guild could yield on these filters. In addition to the C.I.E. Proceedings, a full description of the system was given by Judd in the Journal of the Optical Society of America and by Smith and Guild in the Transactions of the Optical Society.

I must stop in a moment but I would like to look back and ask the question "Did we do a good job?" Well, one limitation, as you know, is that the 1931 C.I.E. observer refers to 2° field viewing conditions. This was quite inevitable because in the climate of the time the data had to fit in with the conditions under which the 1924 V_λ curve had been determined and this was under 2° viewing conditions. As far as Guild's and my data are concerned, I think that we can claim that the 2° spectral chromaticity co-ordinates have stood the test of time rather well and hardly differ at all from the results which Dr. Stiles obtained on his more elaborate instrument some twenty-five years or so later. There is in fact no major difference between the 1931 2° and Stiles' 10° spectral chromaticity co-ordinates. It is only when you incorporate the V_λ curve that you get the difference. Now I want to make it clear that in the distribution curves (or colour matching functions), there is a true difference between the 1931 C.I.E. 2° and 1964 C.I.E. 10° observers, especially in the blue-green.

I do not know whether everyone likes this alychne device with X and Z having zero luminance; I think it is hard to understand but it is a rather clever device and really rather convenient. Probably one of the biggest criticisms of the choice of co-ordinates is that they did not lead to a chromaticity chart with a more uniform distribution of discriminable colours across the chart. But the necessary discrimination studies had not been carried out in 1931.

We have come a long way from 1860 with Maxwell's paper and just to indicate how far we have got, we might compare the information in Maxwell's paper with the vast amount of information given, for example, in this very excellent book *Color Science* by Wyszecki and Stiles.[16] When you see all the data that has been accumulated over the years, you realise that quite a lot has happened. I hope my defence and description of the 1931 system has been adequate. If you do not like the actual X, Y, Z co-ordinate system, I would only say that, whilst I knew a good deal about the R, G, B system, when I attended the C.I.E. meeting in 1931, I had only the vaguest idea what the X, Y, Z system was. But personally I think that Guild and Priest, and I would want to include Judd for his influence behind the scenes, did a very good job indeed.

I would make one final comment before I stop. The C.I.E. Colorimetry Committee recently in their wisdom have been looking at the old 1931 observer and have been smoothing the data to obtain more consistent calculations with computers. This has also involved some extrapolation and, in smoothing, they have added some additional decimal places. When I look at the revised table of the $\bar{x}$, $\bar{y}$, $\bar{z}$, functions, I am rather surprised to say the least. You see, I know how inaccurate the actual measurements really were. (Laughter) Guild did not take any observations below 400 nm and neither did I, and neither did Gibson and Tyndall on the V_λ curve, and yet at a wavelength of 362 nm, for example, we find a value $\bar{y}$ of .000004929604! This, in spite of the fact that at 400 nm the value of $\bar{y}$ may be in error by a factor of 10. (Laughter) I can not help wondering what Mr. Guild thinks if he happens to see these tables. I know we can put the blame on the computer but we must not abdicate our common sense altogether.

I think on that note I had better stop!

Bibliography

The following is a list of books and journals referred to in the article and which were on display at the Colour Group meeting when the paper was presented.

[1] J. C. Maxwell, "On the theory of compound colours and the relations of the colours of the spectrum", Phil. Trans. Roy. Soc. Lond. v. 150, p. 57, 1860.

[2] H. V. Helmholtz, *Handbuch der Physiologischen Optik*. (Various parts of first edition appeared between 1856 and 1867). Translation of third edition published by Opt. Soc. Am., 1924.

[3] A. König, *Gesammelte Abhandlungen Zur Physiologischen Optik*, (Barth) 1903.

[4] H. E. Ives, "The transformation of color-mixture equations from one system to another". J. Franklin Inst., v. 180, p. 673, 1915. "The transformation of color-mixture equations from one system to another II. Graphical Aids". J. Franklin Inst., v. 195, p. 23, 1923.

[5] L. T. Troland, "Report of Committee on Colorimetry for 1920–21", J. Opt. Soc. Am., v. 6, p. 527, 1922. "The present status of visual science", Bull. Nat. Res. Counc., v. 5, Part 2, No. 27, 1922.

[6] J. Guild, "An equipment for visual spectrophotometry", Trans. Opt. Soc. Lond., v. 26, p. 74, 1924–25. "The transformation of trichromatic mixture data: algebraic methods", Trans. Opt. Soc. Lond., v. 26, p. 95, 1924–25. "The geometrical solution of colour mixture problems", Trans. Opt. Soc. Lond., v. 26, p. 139, 1924–25. "A trichromatic colorimeter suitable for standardisation work", Trans. Opt. Soc. Lond., v. 27, p. 106, 1925–26. "A criticism of the monochromatic-plus-white method of colorimetry", Trans. Opt. Soc. Lond., v. 27, p. 130, 1925–26. "On a new method of colorimetry", Trans. Opt. Soc. Lond., v. 27, p. 139, 1925–26. "A critical survey of modern developments in the theory and technique of colorimetry and allied sciences", Proc. Optical Convention 1926, Part 1, p. 61.

[7] W. de W. Abney, *Researches in Colour Vision*, (Longmans, Green) 1913.

[8] J. H. Parsons, *An Introduction to the Study of Colour Vision* (Cambridge University Press), 1st Ed. 1915, 2nd Ed. 1924.

[9] L. C. Martin and W. Gamble, *Colour and Methods of Colour Reproduction* (Blackie), 1926.

[10] J. W. T. Walsh, *Photometry* (Constable), 1926.

[11] W. D. Wright, "A trichromatic colorimeter with spectral primaries", Trans. Opt. Soc. Lond., v. 29, p. 225, 1927–28. "A re-determination of the trichromatic coefficients of the spectral colours", Trans. Opt. Soc. Lond., v. 30, p. 141, 1928–29. "A re-determination of the trichromatic mixture data", Medical Research Council Spectral Report Series No. 139, 1929. "A re-determination of the mixture curves of the spectrum", Trans. Opt. Soc. Lond., v. 31, p. 201, 1929–30.

[12] J. Guild, "The colorimetric properties of the spectrum", Phil. Trans. Roy. Soc. Lond., Ser. A., v. 230, p. 149, 1931. Proceedings, Commission Internationale de l'Éclairage, vols. for 1924, 1928, 1931.

[13] T. Smith and J. Guild, "The C.I.E. Colorimetric Standards and their use", Trans. Opt. Soc. Lond., v. 33, p. 73, 1931–32.

[14] D. B. Judd, "Reduction of data on mixture of colour stimuli", U.S. Bur. Standards J. of Research, v. 4, p. 513, 1930. "Comparison of Wright's data on equivalent colour stimuli with the O.S.A. data", J. Opt. Soc. Am., v. 21, p. 699, 1931. "The 1931 I.C.I. Standard Observer and co-ordinate system for colorimetry", J. Opt. Soc. Am., v. 23, p. 359, 1933.

[15] R. Davis and K. S. Gibson, "Filters for the reproduction of sunlight and daylight and the determinations of color temperature", U.S. Dept. Commerce Misc. Pub., Bur. Standards No. 114, 1931.

[16] G. Wyszecki and W. S. Stiles, *Color Science* (Wiley), 1967.

PART III: COLOR VISION MATHEMATICS: A TUTORIAL

By Yasuhisa Nakano
Hiroshima City University

In Part I of the Appendix, the CIE system of colorimetry was introduced, and details of the origins of that system were presented in Part II. The purpose of Part III is to provide a tutorial of how this colorimetric system is used and to show some calculations that are often used in vision research.

CIE XYZ System

A main purpose of the CIE system of colorimetry is to give a scientific notation of colors that is based on human vision. This notation provides communication among people who want to specify the color of objects precisely.[1] Color specification is hard to communicate because of the many varied and idiosyncratic uses of color names. Specifying the spectral power distribution of a color is much too abstract and removed from human vision. The CIE system stands somewhere in between. Figure A.3.1 illustrates relationship among perceptual, physical and psychophysical color representations.

Color perception arises from physical stimulation of light and this physical stimulus is represented as the spectral power distribution (i.e., the amount of light emitted by the object as a function of wavelength). However, such a physical description of color is not very informative to the average user of color information. Many animals, especially humans, have only a limited number of receptors sensitive to the visual spectrum. Humans have three main classes of receptors which we have been calling L-, M-, and S-cones. When the CIE system was established, spectral sensitivities of the cone photoreceptors were not known, though the principle that they can be derived from linear combinations of color matching functions was known. It is enough here to understand that the *tristimulus values X, Y* and *Z* indirectly relate to activities of cone photoreceptors. How they are related will be discussed in detail below.

Tristimulus values and other related values are called psychophysical quantities. They are based on the color matching functions derived from averaged data of multiple observers as described in Part I and result in the CIE standard observer. The tristimulus values are called psychophysical because they are derived from human observations and physical measurements of light energy. It is worth noting that the tristimulus representation of color does not correspond to perceptual

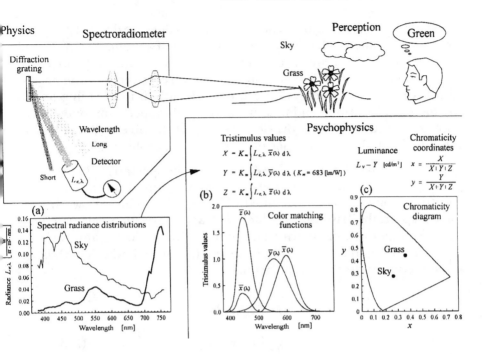

Figure A.3.1 Perceptual, physical and psychophysical color representations. Humans perceive colors as a consequence of physical stimulation, activity within the eye and brain. Such color specification is symbolized by color names. The physical entity of light stimulus is a spectral radiance distribution, (a), which is measured by a spectroradiometer. Psychophysical quantities such as tristimulus values are obtained by integrating products of the spectral radiance distribution, $L_{e,\lambda}$ and color matching functions, $\bar{x}(\lambda)$, $\bar{y}(\lambda)$ and $\bar{z}(\lambda)$, of a standard observer, (b), over the visible spectrum. They are plotted on the chromaticity diagram, (c), in which luminance factor is removed while factors of hue and saturation are preserved.

color because of the influence of varying preadaptation conditions, surround colors, brightnesses, retinal eccentricities, etc., all which can influence the color appearance of objects. In fact, the CIE system of specifying color has nothing to say about color appearance. In addition, plotting a color in chromaticity space only identifies a match at equal luminance for the standard observer. If two different spectral power distributions plot in the same place in chromaticity space then these two colors will match at equal luminance for the standard observer. In short, the CIE system is not for specifying color appearance but for specifying difference or equivalence of light stimuli.

Figure A.3.1 also illustrates how tristimulus values are derived using a spectroradiometer, that is a device composed of a monochromater and a detector. The monochromater, a diffraction grating in this case, disperses light emitted from an object into its spectrum and the detector converts light energy of specific wavelengths into a reading on the meter. By scanning and measuring the visible spectrum, one obtains the spectral radiance distribution, $L_{e,\lambda}$, of the object (Radiance is defined as radiant power per unit area per unit solid angle).

The second column of Table A.3.1 shows the spectral radiance of green grass under a blue sky measured by a commercially available spectroradiometer. The thick line in Figure A.3.1(a) also shows this data graphically. Tristimulus values X, Y and Z are then calculated using Equation (A.3.1) in which a product of the radiance and each color matching function, $\bar{x}(\lambda)$, $\bar{y}(\lambda)$ or $\bar{z}(\lambda)$, at each wavelength is integrated over the visible spectrum.

$$X = K_m \int L_{e,\lambda} \bar{x}(\lambda) d\lambda$$

$$Y = K_m \int L_{e,\lambda} \bar{y}(\lambda) d\lambda \qquad (A.3.1)$$

$$Z = K_m \int L_{e,\lambda} \bar{z}(\lambda) d\lambda$$

where K_m [lm/W] represents a constant called *maximum photopic luminous efficacy*. The rationale for this equation will be discussed later. The last three columns of Table A.3.1 show the products of the radiance and the color matching functions, $\bar{x}(\lambda)$, $\bar{y}(\lambda)$ and $\bar{z}(\lambda)$. These color matching functions are shown in Table A.3.2. In practical calculations, the summation sign (Σ) is substituted for the integral ($\int$) because it is impossible to get continuous data of the spectrum. The summation sign provides fairly accurate tristimulus values if one uses wavelength intervals of 10 nm or less. The sum is shown at the bottom of each column and the tristimulus values are obtained by multiplying the constant K_m and the wavelength interval to these sums as shown in Equation (A.3.2).

$$X = K_m \sum_{\lambda} L_{e,\lambda} \bar{x}(\lambda) \Delta\lambda$$

$$Y = K_m \sum_{\lambda} L_{e,\lambda} \bar{y}(\lambda) \Delta\lambda \qquad (A.3.2)$$

$$Z = K_m \sum_{\lambda} L_{e,\lambda} \bar{z}(\lambda) \Delta\lambda$$

Table A.3.1   Spectral radiance distribution and tristimulus values of green grass under a blue sky.

Wavelength [nm]	$L_{E,\lambda}\left[\dfrac{W}{sr \cdot m^2 \cdot nm}\right]$	$L_{E,\lambda}\bar{x}(\lambda)$	$L_{E,\lambda}\bar{y}(\lambda)$	$L_{E,\lambda}\bar{z}(\lambda)$
400	0.0077	0.0001	0.0000	0.0005
410	0.0090	0.0004	0.0000	0.0019
420	0.0097	0.0013	0.0000	0.0063
430	0.0093	0.0026	0.0001	0.0129
440	0.0114	0.0040	0.0003	0.0200
450	0.0146	0.0049	0.0006	0.0258
460	0.0178	0.0052	0.0011	0.0296
470	0.0174	0.0034	0.0016	0.0224
480	0.0160	0.0015	0.0022	0.0130
490	0.0146	0.0005	0.0030	0.0068
500	0.0154	0.0001	0.0050	0.0042
510	0.0195	0.0002	0.0098	0.0031
520	0.0266	0.0017	0.0189	0.0021
530	0.0369	0.0061	0.0318	0.0016
540	0.0403	0.0117	0.0385	0.0008
550	0.0430	0.0186	0.0428	0.0004
560	0.0410	0.0244	0.0408	0.0002
570	0.0351	0.0268	0.0335	0.0001
580	0.0312	0.0286	0.0271	0.0001
590	0.0264	0.0271	0.0200	0.0000
600	0.0264	0.0280	0.0167	0.0000
610	0.0246	0.0247	0.0124	0.0000
620	0.0220	0.0188	0.0084	0.0000
630	0.0205	0.0132	0.0054	0.0000
640	0.0192	0.0086	0.0034	0.0000
650	0.0158	0.0045	0.0017	0.0000
660	0.0140	0.0023	0.0009	0.0000
670	0.0118	0.0010	0.0004	0.0000
680	0.0113	0.0005	0.0002	0.0000
690	0.0135	0.0003	0.0001	0.0000
700	0.0306	0.0003	0.0001	0.0000
$\sum_{\lambda}$		0.2714	0.3266	0.1516

$K_m = 683\,[\text{lm/W}], \quad \Delta\lambda = 10\,\text{nm}$

$X = K_m \sum_{\lambda} L_{e,\lambda}\bar{x}(\lambda)\Delta\lambda = 1854$

$Y = K_m \sum_{\lambda} L_{e,\lambda}\bar{y}(\lambda)\Delta\lambda = 2231$

$Z = K_m \sum_{\lambda} L_{e,\lambda}\bar{z}(\lambda)\Delta\lambda = 1036$

$L_v = Y = 2231\,[\text{cd/m}^2]$

$x = \dfrac{X}{X+Y+Z} = 0.3621$

$y = \dfrac{Y}{X+Y+Z} = 0.4356$

Table A.3.2 The CIE 1931 Color matching functions.

Wavelength [nm]	$\bar{x}(\lambda)$	$\bar{y}(\lambda)$	$\bar{y}(\lambda)$
400	0.01431	0.00040	0.06785
410	0.04351	0.00121	0.20740
420	0.13438	0.00400	0.64560
430	0.28390	0.01160	1.38560
440	0.34828	0.02300	1.74706
450	0.33620	0.03800	1.77211
460	0.29080	0.06000	1.66920
470	0.19536	0.09098	1.28764
480	0.09564	0.13902	0.81295
490	0.03201	0.20802	0.46518
500	0.00490	0.32300	0.27200
510	0.00930	0.50300	0.15820
520	0.06327	0.71000	0.07825
530	0.16550	0.86200	0.04216
540	0.29040	0.95400	0.02030
550	0.43345	0.99495	0.00875
560	0.59450	0.99500	0.00390
570	0.76210	0.95200	0.00210
580	0.91630	0.87000	0.00165
590	1.02630	0.75700	0.00110
600	1.06220	0.63100	0.00080
610	1.00260	0.50300	0.00034
620	0.85445	0.38100	0.00019
630	0.64240	0.26500	0.00005
640	0.44790	0.17500	0.00002
650	0.28350	0.10700	0.00000
660	0.16490	0.06100	0.00000
670	0.08740	0.03200	0.00000
680	0.04677	0.01700	0.00000
690	0.02270	0.00821	0.00000
700	0.01136	0.00410	0.00000

The constant K_m transforms a physical unit of radiance, $W/sr/m^2$, into a psychophysical unit of luminance, cd/m^2. This transformation has significant meaning only for the value Y because only Y is calculated from $\bar{y}(\lambda)$, which is defined as equal to $V(\lambda)$, the CIE standard photopic luminous efficiency function. Therefore, Y is equal to L_v. The notation L_v is used to denote luminance and Y is used to denote the tristimulus value. The constant K_m is also multiplied to X and Z so that the ratios among X, Y and Z remain the same before after multiplying by this constant.[2]

As described in Part I, tristimulus values themselves are seldom used for specifying and communicating colors. Chromaticity coordinates x and y, instead, are used for this purpose. Chromaticity coordinates are defined in Equation (A.3.3).

$$x = \frac{X}{X+Y+Z}$$

$$y = \frac{Y}{X+Y+Z}$$

$$(A.3.3)$$

The xy-chromaticity coordinates of green grass are shown in the bottom of the Table A.3.1 and are shown in the chromaticity diagram (Figure A.3.1(c)) as the point labeled "Grass." Another point labeled "Sky" represents the chromaticity coordinates of the blue sky under which the green grass was observed, and its spectral radiance is shown in Figure A.3.1(a) as a thin line.

Are the tristimulus values, then, just intermediate values when deriving the chromaticity coordinates from spectral radiance? Are they ignored after the chromaticity coordinates are obtained? The answer is "no." They play important roles in various color calculations. The following examples show how the tristimulus values are helpful in calculating the luminance and chromaticity coordinates of a color composed of multiple components.

Combining Two Colors: An Exercise

Suppose one wants to mix two light stimuli whose CIE xy-chromaticity coordinates and luminances are known, and wants to know the new coordinates and luminance of a resulting light stimulus. One might think that the center of gravity principle described in Chapter 5 may help for this purpose, but this is not an easy way. Additivity of tristimulus values is a more basic principle for combining two colors and tristimulus values are handier than chromaticity coordinates for making this kind of calculation. Tristimulus values of the mixture are obtained just by separately adding tristimulus values of two light stimuli for each X, Y and Z. That is,

$$X_3 = X_1 + X_2,$$

$$Y_3 = Y_1 + Y_2, \qquad (A.3.4)$$

$$Z_3 = Z_1 + Z_2,$$

where X_3, Y_3, Z_3 are the tristimulus values of the mixture, and X_1, Y_1, Z_1 and X_2, Y_2, Z_2 are those of component stimuli 1 and 2. Then one can find the new xy-chromaticity coordinate using Equation (A.3.3).

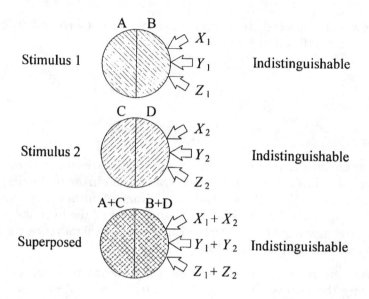

Figure A.3.2 Additivity of color matching. When two pairs of metamerically matched stimuli are physically superposed, the resulting pair of colors is still indistinguishable. This leads to additivity of tristimulus values.

Why are the tristimulus values of the mixture obtained just by adding those of the components? The answer to this question lies in the fact that color matching follows the *additivity law*. As described in Chapter 5, additivity of color matching is stated as "If stimulus A is indistinguishable from B, and C is indistinguishable from D, then A + C = B + D." This last equation means that the physical mixture of stimuli A and C is indistinguishable from that of stimuli B and D. Figure A.3.2 illustrates a relationship between the additivity law and Equation (A.3.4). Suppose stimulus A corresponds to stimulus 1 in the previous example, and this is indistinguishable from stimulus B that is composed of amounts X_1, Y_1 and Z_1 of three imaginary primaries.[3] This is self-evident from the definition of the tristimulus values. Similarly, suppose stimulus C is stimulus 2 and stimulus D is composed of X_2, Y_2 and Z_2 units of the primaries which are metamerically matched to stimulus C. Because of the relation A + C = B + D, the physical mixture of stimuli 1 and 2 is indistinguishable from the physical mixture of the stimuli metamerically matched with stimuli 1 and 2 using XYZ primaries. The latter mixture has $X_1 + X_2$, $Y_1 + Y_2$ and $Z_1 + Z_2$ amounts of XYZ primaries physically, and this means that the tristimulus values of the former mixture are $X_1 + X_2$, $Y_1 + Y_2$ and $Z_1 + Z_2$, as in Equation (A.3.4).

When one only knows the chromaticity coordinates and the luminance, L_v, of a stimulus, one can easily convert them into tristimulus values. That is,

$$X = \frac{x}{y}L_v,$$

$$Y = L_v, \tag{A.3.5}$$

$$Z = \frac{z}{y}L_v = \frac{1-x-y}{y}L_v.$$

This is derived from Equation (A.3.3) and the equation $z = Z/(X + Y + Z) = 1 - x - y$. So you can recover the tristimulus values even when you know only the chromaticity coordinates and the luminance of the stimulus. It is a good exercise to derive the center of gravity principle using Equations (A.3.3), (A.3.4) and (A.3.5). To do this, describe xy-chromaticity coordinates of the mixture using xy-chromaticity coordinates and luminances of the two component stimuli.[4]

Equation (A.3.4) is easily expanded to the mixture of more than two stimuli. When there are N stimuli with tristimulus values of X_i, Y_i and Z_i ($i = 1, \ldots, N$), the tristimulus values of the mixture of all the stimuli are calculated as

$$X = \sum_{i=1}^{N} X_i,$$

$$Y = \sum_{i=1}^{N} Y_i, \tag{A.3.6}$$

$$Z = \sum_{i=1}^{N} Z_i.$$

Again, after X, Y, and Z are determined, xy-chromaticity coordinates of the mixture are calculated by Equation (A.3.3). This is a much simpler way of calculating the chromaticity coordinates and the luminance of multi-color mixture than using the center of gravity principle.

You will find that Equation (A.3.6) is analogous to the Equation (A.3.2) if you account for the fact that the tristimulus values of monochromatic lights are defined as $X(\lambda) = K_m L_{e,\lambda} \bar{x}(\lambda)\Delta\lambda$, etc. and then the Equation (A.3.2) becomes $X = \sum_\lambda X(\lambda)$ etc. In Equation (A.3.2), a compound light is regarded as a mixture of monochromatic lights, and the tristimulus values of the mixture are obtained by summing the tristimulus values of every monochromatic light. The infinitesimal limit of wavelength intervals brings Equation (A.3.2) into the integral oriented definition of the tristimulus values as Equation (A.3.1). In other words, the rationale of Equation (A.3.1) is found in Equation (A.3.4).

Transform from XYZ To Other Primaries

Phosphor RGB System In Visual Display Units

Visual display units (color monitors) are extensively used to present visual stimuli in psychophysical and physiological experiments. To present exact colors on a color monitor, one has to control the luminances of red, green and blue (RGB)[5] phosphors. It is convenient to transform the primaries from the standard CIE XYZ system to the monitor's own RGB system. This is a good application of the information discussed in the previous section.

The chromaticity coordinates of the RGB phosphors provide the only information required. Suppose the red, green and blue phosphors are given as (x_R, y_R), (x_G, y_G) and (x_B, y_B), respectively, and suppose you want to present a color of chromaticity coordinates (x, y) and luminance L_v on the color monitor. To do this you need to know the luminances of the red, green and blue phosphors ($L_{v,R}$, $L_{v,G}$ and $L_{v,B}$) to produce the desired color when they are superimposed.

To understand the required calculations, it is easier to present the inverse problem first, i.e. the method of calculating L_v, x, y when the luminances of the phosphors are known. Suppose the luminances of phosphors are $L_{v,R}$, $L_{v,G}$ and $L_{v,B}$. Then, the tristimulus values of each phosphor are calculated using Equation (A.3.5).

$$X_R = \frac{x_R}{y_R} L_{v,R}, \quad X_G = \frac{x_G}{y_G} L_{v,G}, \quad X_B = \frac{x_B}{y_B} L_{v,B},$$

$$Y_R = L_{v,R}, \qquad Y_G = L_{v,G}, \qquad Y_B = L_{v,B}, \qquad \text{(A.3.7)}$$

$$Z_R = \frac{z_R}{y_R} L_{v,R}, \quad Z_G = \frac{z_G}{y_G} L_{v,G}, \quad Z_B = \frac{z_B}{y_B} L_{v,B},$$

where x_i, y_i and z_i, $(i = R, G, B)$, represent the chromaticity coordinates of each phosphor, and X_i, Y_i and Z_i, $(i = R, G, B)$, represent the tristimulus values of each phosphor.

The stimulus is produced by combining the emissions from the red, green and blue phosphors at luminances $L_{v,R}$, $L_{v,G}$ and $L_{v,B}$, and the tristimulus values of the mixture are calculated using Equation

(A.3.6), that is,

$$X = X_R + X_G + X_B = \frac{x_R}{y_R} L_{v,R} + \frac{x_G}{y_G} L_{v,G} + \frac{x_B}{y_B} L_{v,B} ,$$

$$Y = Y_R + Y_G + Y_B = 1 \cdot L_{v,R} + 1 \cdot L_{v,G} + 1 \cdot L_{v,B} , \qquad (A.3.8)$$

$$Z = Z_R + Z_G + Z_B = \frac{z_R}{y_R} L_{v,R} + \frac{z_G}{y_G} L_{v,G} + \frac{z_B}{y_B} L_{v,B} .$$

This equation is simply represented in a matrix as follows.[6]

$$\begin{pmatrix} X \\ Y \\ Z \end{pmatrix} = \begin{pmatrix} \frac{x_R}{y_R} & \frac{x_G}{y_G} & \frac{x_B}{y_B} \\ 1 & 1 & 1 \\ \frac{z_R}{y_R} & \frac{z_G}{y_G} & \frac{z_B}{y_B} \end{pmatrix} \begin{pmatrix} L_{v,R} \\ L_{v,G} \\ L_{v,B} \end{pmatrix} \qquad (A.3.9)$$

This is the equation to convert the primaries from RGB to XYZ. To convert them in the other direction, one has to solve the above linear equation. The solution is formally represented using the inverse matrix.

$$\begin{pmatrix} L_{v,R} \\ L_{v,G} \\ L_{v,B} \end{pmatrix} = \begin{pmatrix} \frac{x_R}{y_R} & \frac{x_G}{y_G} & \frac{x_B}{y_B} \\ 1 & 1 & 1 \\ \frac{z_R}{y_R} & \frac{z_G}{y_G} & \frac{z_B}{y_B} \end{pmatrix}^{-1} \begin{pmatrix} X \\ Y \\ Z \end{pmatrix} \qquad (A.3.10)$$

Figure A.3.3 illustrates an example of transformation from the XYZ system to an RGB system and *vice versa*. The *xy*-chromaticity coordinates of the red, green and blue phosphors are (0.620, 0.348), (0.291, 0.608) and (0.153, 0.079) respectively, and these coordinates are assumed to stay constant even when the luminance changes. This assumption is necessary in the above calculations. The conversion matrices in Equations (A.3.9) and (A.3.10) are numerically calculated as shown in the top right and top left equations in the figure respectively.[7]

To present a white stimulus having *xy*-chromaticity coordinates of (0.333, 0.333) and a luminance of 10 cd/m² on the color monitor, calculate tristimulus values X, Y and Z, first, using Equation (A.3.5), i.e., $X = Y = Z = 10$. Then convert them into $L_{v,R}$, $L_{v,G}$ and $L_{v,B}$ using Equation (A.3.10). $L_{v,R} = 2.999$ cd/m²: $L_{v,G} = 6.105$ cd/m² and $L_{v,B} = 0.896$ cd/m². The white stimulus is obtained by adjusting the volt-

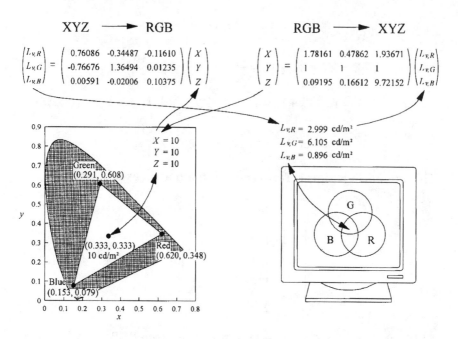

Figure A.3.3 Primary conversion from CIE XYZ to phosphor RGB and *vice versa*. The left top equation converts tristimulus values of *X*, *Y* and *Z* to luminances of RGB phosphors, $L_{v,R}$, $L_{v,G}$ and $L_{v,B}$. Superposition of RGB phosphors at these luminances produces a stimulus having luminance *Y* and chromaticity coordinates $x = X/(X+Y+Z)$ and $y = Y/(X+Y+Z)$. This conversion is valid within the triangle cornered by the coordinates of the three phosphors in the CIE *xy*-chromaticity diagram. The triangle is called the *color gamut* of the color monitor. The right top equation converts primaries the other way. Each matrix in the equations is the inverse matrix of the other.[7] The arrows in the figure indicate data flow in the conversion.

ages of the red, green and blue guns so that each phosphor has its required luminance. This process is reversible. When one knows only the luminances of the RGB phosphors, converting them into the XYZ system is done by using Equation (A.3.9).

Cone Primaries

Cone primaries (also called fundamentals) are extensively used in color vision studies. It is helpful if a visual stimulus is directly related to the activities of retinal cones especially when mechanisms and models of color vision are discussed.

Table A.3.3 Chromaticity coordinates of copunctal points for dichromats.

Protanope	Deuteranope	Tritanope
$x_{pc} = 0.7465$	$x_{dc} = 1.4000$	$x_{tc} = 0.1748$
$y_{pc} = 0.2535$	$y_{dc} = -0.4000$	$y_{tc} = 0.0000$
$z_{pc} = 0.0000$	$z_{dc} = 0.0000$	$z_{tc} = 0.8252$

The principle of how to determine conversion matrices for cone primaries is the same as in the case of the phosphor RGB system. All one needs to know are the xy-chromaticity coordinates of the three primaries that would each excite one and only one of the three cone systems. In the case of the cone primaries, however, there is no physical correspondence of these primaries. As described in Chapter 5, this happens because any physical stimulus excites two or three cone types whose spectral sensitivity curves overlap. In other words, these primaries are imaginary stimuli.

How can we determine the chromaticity coordinates of the cone primaries? As described in Chapter 10, data from color deficient observers gives us useful information. It has been shown that dichromats lack one of the three types of cone photopigments, and they can't distinguish certain colors that differ only in activity of the missing cone photopigment. Colors that are not discriminated by color variant observers form a line called a *confusion line.* By marking a number of indistinguishable pairs of colors for each type of dichromats, several confusion lines are drawn. Theoretically, they intersect at one point, called *the copunctal point* that is assumed to coincide with the coordinates of missing primary. Figure A.3.4 illustrates confusion lines and copunctal points for three types of dichromats.

Table A.3.3 shows the chromaticity coordinates of the cone primaries estimated by Smith and Pokorny (1975). The first column shows the estimated protanopic copunctal point which corresponds to the chromaticity coordinates of the L-cone primary. Similarly, the second and third columns show the deuteranopic and tritanopic copunctal points that correspond to the M- and S-cone primaries.

The conversion in principle follows the same equation as Equation (A.3.10), that is,

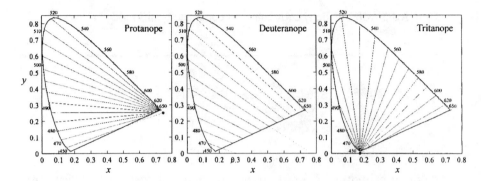

Figure A.3.4 Confusion lines and copunctal points for three types of dichromats. Confusion lines (thin lines) intersect at copunctal points (solid circle). The copunctal point for deuteranopes is located out of the range used here. The chromaticity coordinates of each copunctal point is shown in Table A.3.3 (Adapted from Wyszecki & Stiles, 1982.)

$$
\begin{pmatrix} L_{v,L} \\ L_{v,M} \\ L_{v,S} \end{pmatrix} = \begin{pmatrix} \dfrac{x_{pc}}{y_{pc}} & \dfrac{x_{dc}}{y_{dc}} & \dfrac{x_{tc}}{y_{tc}} \\ 1 & 1 & 1 \\ \dfrac{z_{pc}}{y_{pc}} & \dfrac{z_{dc}}{y_{dc}} & \dfrac{z_{tc}}{y_{tc}} \end{pmatrix}^{-1} \begin{pmatrix} X \\ Y \\ Z \end{pmatrix} , \tag{A.3.11}
$$

where x_{pc}, y_{pc} and z_{pc} represent the copunctal point of a protanope, x_{dc}, y_{dc} and z_{dc} represent that of a deuteranope and x_{tc}, y_{tc} and z_{tc} represent that of a tritanope. $L_{v,L}$, $L_{v,M}$ and $L_{v,S}$ represent luminances of the imaginary cone primaries. It is important to note that the Judd–Vos color-matching functions should be used as the XYZ system because problems exist in the CIE XYZ system in the short wavelength region. The Judd–Vos system is frequently used in vision research.

One can't apply this equation, however, to calculate numerical values using the values in Table A.3.3 because $y_{tc} = 0$ appears in denominators. There is a way to avoid this problem. Equation (A.3.11) can be changed to

$$
\begin{pmatrix} L_{v,L} \\ L_{v,M} \\ L_{v,S} \end{pmatrix} = \begin{pmatrix} y_{pc} & 0 & 0 \\ 0 & y_{dc} & 0 \\ 0 & 0 & y_{tc} \end{pmatrix} \begin{pmatrix} x_{pc} & x_{dc} & x_{tc} \\ y_{pc} & y_{dc} & y_{tc} \\ z_{pc} & z_{dc} & z_{tc} \end{pmatrix}^{-1} \begin{pmatrix} X \\ Y \\ Z \end{pmatrix} . \tag{A.3.12}
$$

Derivation of this equation from Equation (A.3.11) is described in endnote 8.

Denominators then disappear but there is still the problem that $L_{v,S} = 0$ if one uses the values of the Table A.3.3 in Equation (A.3.12). This happens because the unit of $L_{v,L}$, $L_{v,M}$ and $L_{v,S}$ is luminance for the same reason as the unit of RGB phosphors is luminance in Equation (A.3.9), but this constraint is not necessary in the case of the cone primaries. In effect the diagonal matrix in Equation (A.3.12) adjusts the units for $L_{v,L}$, $L_{v,M}$ and $L_{v,S}$.[9] By substituting this matrix by one containing three adjustable constants, the generalized conversion matrix is obtained as follows.

$$
\begin{pmatrix} P_L \\ P_M \\ P_S \end{pmatrix} = \begin{pmatrix} k_l & 0 & 0 \\ 0 & k_m & 0 \\ 0 & 0 & k_s \end{pmatrix} \begin{pmatrix} x_{pc} & x_{dc} & x_{tc} \\ y_{pc} & y_{dc} & y_{tc} \\ z_{pc} & z_{dc} & z_{tc} \end{pmatrix}^{-1} \begin{pmatrix} X \\ Y \\ Z \end{pmatrix}, \qquad (A.3.13)
$$

where k_l, k_m and k_s are called normalizing constants, which adjust the unit scale of each primary. The notations P_L, P_M and P_S are used instead of $L_{v,L}$, $L_{v,M}$ and $L_{v,S}$ because their units no longer specify the luminance. They are called fundamental tristimulus values. Let $k_l = y_{pc}$, $k_m = y_{dc}$ and $k_s = 0.01327$, then

$$
\begin{pmatrix} P_L \\ P_M \\ P_S \end{pmatrix} = \begin{pmatrix} 0.15516 & 0.54308 & -0.03287 \\ -0.15516 & 0.45692 & 0.03287 \\ 0.00000 & 0.00000 & 0.01608 \end{pmatrix} \begin{pmatrix} X \\ Y \\ Z \end{pmatrix} \qquad (A.3.14)
$$

is finally obtained using the values of the Table A.3.3.[10] The values of k_l and k_m were chosen so that $P_L + P_M$ represent the luminance of the stimulus. The value of k_s was arbitrarily chosen so that $PS/(PL + PM) = 1.0$ for the monochromatic stimulus $\lambda = 400$ nm.

The cone spectral sensitivity functions can be obtained using the same matrix, that is,

$$
\begin{pmatrix} L(\lambda) \\ M(\lambda) \\ S(\lambda) \end{pmatrix} = \begin{pmatrix} 0.15516 & 0.54308 & -0.03287 \\ -0.15516 & 0.45692 & 0.03287 \\ 0.00000 & 0.00000 & 0.01608 \end{pmatrix} \begin{pmatrix} \bar{x}'(\lambda) \\ \bar{y}'(\lambda) \\ \bar{z}'(\lambda) \end{pmatrix}, \qquad (A.3.15)
$$

where $L(\lambda)$, $M(\lambda)$ and $S(\lambda)$ represent the spectral sensitivity functions

Table A.3.4 Smith and Pokorny cone sensitivity functions. Smith and Pokorny (1975) used Judd (1951) color matching functions. Judd–Vos color matching functions (Vos, 1978) were used here instead, and it produces small differences at short wavelength region.

Wavelength [nm]	L(λ)	M(λ)	S(λ)
400	0.00169	0.00111	0.00280
410	0.00439	0.00301	0.00741
420	0.01008	0.00742	0.01714
430	0.01485	0.01245	0.02360
440	0.01917	0.01873	0.02600
450	0.02186	0.02494	0.02367
460	0.02624	0.03376	0.02078
470	0.03992	0.05106	0.01791
480	0.06492	0.07410	0.01216
490	0.10321	0.10481	0.00718
500	0.16748	0.15552	0.00425
510	0.26953	0.23347	0.00248
520	0.39296	0.31704	0.00123
530	0.49267	0.36933	0.00067
540	0.56285	0.39115	0.00032
550	0.60775	0.38720	0.00014
560	0.63293	0.36207	0.00007
570	0.63552	0.31648	0.00004
580	0.61460	0.25540	0.00003
590	0.56980	0.18720	0.00002
600	0.50635	0.12465	0.00001
610	0.42714	0.07586	0.00001
620	0.33778	0.04322	0.00000
630	0.24211	0.02289	0.00000
640	0.16341	0.01159	0.00000
650	0.10134	0.00566	0.00000
660	0.05820	0.00280	0.00000
670	0.03068	0.00132	0.00000
680	0.01634	0.00066	0.00000
690	0.00790	0.00031	0.00000
700	0.00395	0.00015	0.00000

of L-, M- and S-cones, and $\bar{x}'(\lambda)$, $\bar{y}'(\lambda)$ and $\bar{z}'(\lambda)$ represent the Judd–Vos color matching functions. Table A.3.4 shows numerical values for these spectral sensitivity functions.

The cone fundamentals derived here are merely one of several possible examples, as the search for better ones continues. Table A.3.5 summarizes a number of such investigations.

Table A.3.5   The list of the investigations deriving the cone fundamentals.

Year	Researcher(s)	Color matching functions	Normalization method
1971	Vos & Walraven	Judd modified CIE 1931	$L(\lambda) + M(\lambda) + S(\lambda) = V(\lambda)$
1975	Smith & Pokorny	Judd modified CIE 1931	$L(\lambda) + M(\lambda) = V(\lambda)$
1978	Vos	Judd–Vos modified CIE 1931	$L(\lambda) + M(\lambda) + S(\lambda) = V(\lambda)$
1979	Estévez*	Stiles–Burch 2°	$\int L(\lambda)d\lambda = \int M(\lambda)d\lambda = \int S(\lambda)d\lambda = 1$
1985	Hunt & Pointer	CIE 1931	$\int L(\lambda)C(\lambda)d\lambda = \int M(\lambda)C(\lambda)d\lambda$ $= \int S(\lambda)C(\lambda)d\lambda$ $C(\lambda)$:C illuminant
1990	Vos, Estévez & Walraven	Stiles–Burch 2°	$0.68L(\lambda) + 0.34M(\lambda)$ $+ 0.025S(\lambda) = V(\lambda)$
1992	DeMarco, Pokorny & Smith	Judd–Vos modified CIE 1931	Normalized to 1 at their peaks
1993	Stockman, MacLeod & Johnson	Stiles–Burch 2° and CIE 1964 10°	Normalized to 1 at their peaks

* Amended version of his cone fundamentals are described by Wsyzecki and Stiles (1982).

Notes

[1] Color is the result of human perception, but not a property of physical stimulus itself, as first noted by Newton (see also endnote 3 in Chapter 2). The CIE system does not specify color in that sense because it says nothing about perception. Instead, it specifies a group of physical stimuli that produce the same activity in three classes of cone photoreceptors. The word *color* will nevertheless be used to express physical stimuli in this Appendix. When it is necessary to distinguish perceived color from physical stimulus, the term perceptual color or color appearance will be used to stress human perception.

[2] The reason the constant K_m is missing in Equation (A.1.8) is that the tristimulus values are treated as intermediate values to calculate the chromaticity coordinates and their unit is not significant in this case. When you treat the tristimulus values by themselves, it is helpful to multiply by this constant because the value Y then coincides with luminance.

[3] Though you can't physically reproduce the matching experiment when you use imaginary primaries, the principle is the same as the case when you use real primaries such as the RGB system of the CIE. It is, therefore, reasonable to do the experiment in your mind using imaginary primaries.

[4] The answer is

$$x_3 = \frac{\dfrac{L_{v,1}}{y_1}}{\dfrac{L_{v,1}}{y_1} + \dfrac{L_{v,2}}{y_2}} x_1 + \frac{\dfrac{L_{v,2}}{y_2}}{\dfrac{L_{v,1}}{y_1} + \dfrac{L_{v,2}}{y_2}} x_2,$$

$$y_3 = \frac{\dfrac{L_{v,1}}{y_1}}{\dfrac{L_{v,1}}{y_1} + \dfrac{L_{v,2}}{y_2}} y_1 + \frac{\dfrac{L_{v,2}}{y_2}}{\dfrac{L_{v,1}}{y_1} + \dfrac{L_{v,2}}{y_2}} y_2,$$

where x_3 and y_3 are the xy-chromaticity coordinates of the mixture and x_1, y_1, Y_1 and x_2, y_2, Y_2 are the xy-chromaticity coordinates and luminances of the component stimuli 1 and 2.

[5] We use this notation to stand for the primaries of the phosphors because the perceived color of each phosphor when independently stimulated by its own gun correlates with the colors, red, green or blue. But keep in mind that we are not talking about perceptual color of the primaries but of physical stimuli when we say RGB. Although this is mistakable for the CIE RGB system, this notation is commonly used in engineering.

[6] Operational rules for matrix algebra are explained in many standard mathematical texts. The most important ones are summarized as follows.

Equality:
$$\begin{pmatrix} a_{11} & a_{12} & a_{13} \\ a_{21} & a_{22} & a_{23} \\ a_{31} & a_{32} & a_{33} \end{pmatrix} = \begin{pmatrix} b_{11} & b_{12} & b_{13} \\ b_{21} & b_{22} & b_{23} \\ b_{31} & b_{32} & b_{33} \end{pmatrix}$$

This means $a_{11} = b_{11}$, $a_{12} = b_{12}$, , etc. That is, $a_{ij} = b_{ij}$ $(i,j = 1, 2, 3)$, in general.

Addition:
$$\begin{pmatrix} a_{11} & a_{12} & a_{13} \\ a_{21} & a_{22} & a_{23} \\ a_{31} & a_{32} & a_{33} \end{pmatrix} + \begin{pmatrix} b_{11} & b_{12} & b_{13} \\ b_{21} & b_{22} & b_{23} \\ b_{31} & b_{32} & b_{33} \end{pmatrix} = \begin{pmatrix} a_{11}+b_{11} & a_{12}+b_{12} & a_{13}+b_{13} \\ a_{21}+b_{21} & a_{22}+b_{22} & a_{23}+b_{23} \\ a_{31}+b_{31} & a_{32}+b_{32} & a_{33}+b_{33} \end{pmatrix}$$

Each element of the resulting matrix is represented as $a_{ij} + b_{ij}$ $(i,j = 1, 2, 3)$.

Multiplication:
$$\begin{pmatrix} a_{11} & a_{12} & a_{13} \\ a_{21} & a_{22} & a_{23} \\ a_{31} & a_{32} & a_{33} \end{pmatrix} \begin{pmatrix} b_{11} & b_{12} & b_{13} \\ b_{21} & b_{22} & b_{23} \\ b_{31} & b_{32} & b_{33} \end{pmatrix} =$$

$$\begin{pmatrix} a_{11}b_{11}+a_{12}b_{21}+a_{13}b_{31} & a_{11}b_{12}+a_{12}b_{22}+a_{13}b_{32} & a_{11}b_{13}+a_{12}b_{23}+a_{13}b_{33} \\ a_{21}b_{11}+a_{22}b_{21}+a_{23}b_{31} & a_{21}b_{12}+a_{22}b_{22}+a_{23}b_{32} & a_{21}b_{13}+a_{22}b_{23}+a_{23}b_{33} \\ a_{31}b_{11}+a_{32}b_{21}+a_{33}b_{31} & a_{31}b_{12}+a_{32}b_{22}+a_{33}b_{32} & a_{31}b_{13}+a_{32}b_{23}+a_{33}b_{33} \end{pmatrix}.$$

Each element of the resulting matrix is represented as $\sum_{k=1}^{3} a_{ik}b_{kj}$ $(i, j = 1,2,3)$.

When the right-hand matrix has only one column,

$$\begin{pmatrix} a_{11} & a_{12} & a_{13} \\ a_{21} & a_{22} & a_{23} \\ a_{31} & a_{32} & a_{33} \end{pmatrix} \begin{pmatrix} b_1 \\ b_2 \\ b_2 \end{pmatrix} = \begin{pmatrix} a_{11}b_1+a_{12}b_2+a_{13}b_3 \\ a_{21}b_1+a_{22}b_2+a_{23}b_3 \\ a_{31}b_1+a_{32}b_2+a_{33}b_3 \end{pmatrix},$$

and each element is represented as $\sum_{k=1}^{3} a_{ik}b_k$ $(i = 1,2,3)$.

Unit matrix: $\begin{pmatrix} 1 & 0 & 0 \\ 0 & 1 & 0 \\ 0 & 0 & 1 \end{pmatrix}$

$$\begin{pmatrix} a_{11} & a_{12} & a_{13} \\ a_{21} & a_{22} & a_{23} \\ a_{31} & a_{32} & a_{33} \end{pmatrix} \begin{pmatrix} 1 & 0 & 0 \\ 0 & 1 & 0 \\ 0 & 0 & 1 \end{pmatrix} = \begin{pmatrix} 1 & 0 & 0 \\ 0 & 1 & 0 \\ 0 & 0 & 1 \end{pmatrix} \begin{pmatrix} a_{11} & a_{12} & a_{13} \\ a_{21} & a_{22} & a_{23} \\ a_{31} & a_{32} & a_{33} \end{pmatrix} = \begin{pmatrix} a_{11} & a_{12} & a_{13} \\ a_{21} & a_{22} & a_{23} \\ a_{31} & a_{32} & a_{33} \end{pmatrix}$$

Inverse matrix: $\begin{pmatrix} a_{11} & a_{12} & a_{13} \\ a_{21} & a_{22} & a_{23} \\ a_{31} & a_{32} & a_{33} \end{pmatrix}^{-1}$

$$\begin{pmatrix} a_{11} & a_{12} & a_{13} \\ a_{21} & a_{22} & a_{23} \\ a_{31} & a_{32} & a_{33} \end{pmatrix} \begin{pmatrix} a_{11} & a_{12} & a_{13} \\ a_{21} & a_{22} & a_{23} \\ a_{31} & a_{32} & a_{33} \end{pmatrix}^{-1} = \begin{pmatrix} a_{11} & a_{12} & a_{13} \\ a_{21} & a_{22} & a_{23} \\ a_{31} & a_{32} & a_{33} \end{pmatrix}^{-1} \begin{pmatrix} a_{11} & a_{12} & a_{13} \\ a_{21} & a_{22} & a_{23} \\ a_{31} & a_{32} & a_{33} \end{pmatrix} = \begin{pmatrix} 1 & 0 & 0 \\ 0 & 1 & 0 \\ 0 & 0 & 1 \end{pmatrix}$$

[7] Numerical methods, such as the Gauss–Jacobi elimination method, for calculating the inverse of a 3×3 matrix are explained in many standard mathematical texts and are available in many software packages.

[8] Derivation of the Equation (A.3.12) is as follows. Note that

$$\begin{pmatrix} \dfrac{x_{pc}}{y_{pc}} & \dfrac{x_{dc}}{y_{dc}} & \dfrac{x_{tc}}{y_{tc}} \\ 1 & 1 & 1 \\ \dfrac{z_{pc}}{y_{pc}} & \dfrac{z_{dc}}{y_{dc}} & \dfrac{z_{tc}}{y_{tc}} \end{pmatrix} = \begin{pmatrix} x_{pc} & x_{dc} & x_{tc} \\ y_{pc} & y_{dc} & y_{tc} \\ z_{pc} & z_{dc} & z_{tc} \end{pmatrix} \begin{pmatrix} 1/y_{pc} & 0 & 0 \\ 0 & 1/y_{dc} & 0 \\ 0 & 0 & 1/y_{tc} \end{pmatrix}.$$

Then the inverse matrix is represented as

$$\begin{pmatrix} \dfrac{x_{pc}}{y_{pc}} & \dfrac{x_{dc}}{y_{dc}} & \dfrac{x_{tc}}{y_{tc}} \\ 1 & 1 & 1 \\ \dfrac{z_{pc}}{y_{pc}} & \dfrac{z_{dc}}{y_{dc}} & \dfrac{z_{tc}}{y_{tc}} \end{pmatrix}^{-1} = \begin{pmatrix} y_{pc} & 0 & 0 \\ 0 & y_{dc} & 0 \\ 0 & 0 & y_{tc} \end{pmatrix} \begin{pmatrix} x_{pc} & x_{dc} & x_{tc} \\ y_{pc} & y_{dc} & y_{tc} \\ z_{pc} & z_{dc} & z_{tc} \end{pmatrix}^{-1}.$$

You can confirm this by multiplying this inverse matrix to original matrix, that is,

$$\begin{pmatrix} x_{pc} & x_{dc} & x_{tc} \\ y_{pc} & y_{dc} & y_{tc} \\ z_{pc} & z_{dc} & z_{tc} \end{pmatrix}\begin{pmatrix} 1/y_{pc} & 0 & 0 \\ 0 & 1/y_{dc} & 0 \\ 0 & 0 & 1/y_{tc} \end{pmatrix}\begin{pmatrix} y_{pc} & 0 & 0 \\ 0 & y_{dc} & 0 \\ 0 & 0 & y_{tc} \end{pmatrix}\begin{pmatrix} x_{pc} & x_{dc} & x_{tc} \\ y_{pc} & y_{dc} & y_{tc} \\ z_{pc} & z_{dc} & z_{tc} \end{pmatrix}^{-1} =$$

$$\begin{pmatrix} x_{pc} & x_{dc} & x_{tc} \\ y_{pc} & y_{dc} & y_{tc} \\ z_{pc} & z_{dc} & z_{tc} \end{pmatrix}\begin{pmatrix} 1 & 0 & 0 \\ 0 & 1 & 0 \\ 0 & 0 & 1 \end{pmatrix}\begin{pmatrix} x_{pc} & x_{dc} & x_{tc} \\ y_{pc} & y_{dc} & y_{tc} \\ z_{pc} & z_{dc} & z_{tc} \end{pmatrix}^{-1} = \begin{pmatrix} x_{pc} & x_{dc} & x_{tc} \\ y_{pc} & y_{dc} & y_{tc} \\ z_{pc} & z_{dc} & z_{tc} \end{pmatrix}\begin{pmatrix} x_{pc} & x_{dc} & x_{tc} \\ y_{pc} & y_{dc} & y_{tc} \\ z_{pc} & z_{dc} & z_{tc} \end{pmatrix}^{-1} =$$

$$\begin{pmatrix} 1 & 0 & 0 \\ 0 & 1 & 0 \\ 0 & 0 & 1 \end{pmatrix}.$$

[9] Note that the Equation (A.3.12) can also be written as

$$\begin{pmatrix} L/y_{pc} \\ M/y_{dc} \\ S/y_{tc} \end{pmatrix} = \begin{pmatrix} x_{pc} & x_{dc} & x_{tc} \\ y_{pc} & y_{dc} & y_{tc} \\ z_{pc} & z_{dc} & z_{tc} \end{pmatrix}^{-1}\begin{pmatrix} X \\ Y \\ Z \end{pmatrix}.$$

This is obtained by multiplying $\begin{pmatrix} 1/y_{pc} & 0 & 0 \\ 0 & 1/y_{dc} & 0 \\ 0 & 0 & 1/y_{tc} \end{pmatrix}$ to both sides of Equation

(A.3.12) from the left. Then it is obvious that y_{pc}, y_{dc} and y_{tc} in the diagonal matrix adjust the unit scale of L, M and S respectively.

[10] Values of the matrix in Equations (A.3.14) and (A.3.15) are slightly different from the original Smith and Pokorny (1975) values. This might be because of a calculation error in the original.

PART IV: CONE CONTRAST AND OPPONENT MODULATION COLOR SPACES

By David H. Brainard
University of California Santa Barbara, Santa Barbara, CA

Introduction

Cone excitation diagrams were introduced in Chapter 7. The advantage of using such a color space is that cones represent the initial encoding of light by the visual system. Because cone excitation is proportional to the quantal absorption rates of the three types of cone photopigments, it easier to think about how subsequent visual mechanisms combine and process cone signals. Fortunately there is consensus on the current estimates of cone spectral sensitivities (See Chapter 7).

The same logic that justifies the use of a cone excitation space can be applied to develop color spaces that represent explicitly the responses of subsequent visual mechanisms. Two ideas about the nature of retinal processing have been widely used in this fashion. The first is that photopigment excitations are recoded as contrast signals, so that the information available for further processing is provided in relative rather than absolute form. The second (as seen in Figure 7.1) is that signals from individual classes of cones are combined into three post-receptoral channels: one summative and two color-opponent. A color space based on the first idea alone is referred to as a cone *contrast space*. Color spaces based on both ideas are referred to as *opponent modulation spaces.*

One widely used opponent modulation color space was introduced explicitly by Derrington, Krauskopf, and Lennie (1984) based in part on ideas suggested by MacLeod and Boynton (1979) and by Krauskopf, Williams and Heeley (1982). This implementation of an opponent modulation space is here referred to as the DKL color space. (In Chapter 7 it is called the DKL cone excitation space.) Many of the ideas key to understanding the DKL space can be understood more simply in the context of cone contrast space. For this reason, we begin with a discussion of cone contrast space and then build on this material to develop the DKL space. We assume that the reader is familiar with the mathematics of color vision as presented in Part III of this Appendix.

Cone Contrast Space

The use of cone contrast space (or opponent modulation space) makes sense primarily when there is a background with respect to which contrast may be computed. Two typical stimulus configurations where this prerequisite holds are shown schematically in Figure A.4.1, where the stimuli being described are modulations of a large uniform background. Panel (a) shows a spot increment/decrement; panel (b) shows a sinusoidal modulation. We use the term increment/decrement to describe the spot stimulus because it is possible for a spot to be an increment for one cone type and a decrement for another. As shown in the figure, we let the vector $(P_{LO} P_{MO} P_{SO})^T$ represent the cone excitation coordinates of the background and the vector $(P_L P_M P_S)^T$ represent the cone coordinates of the stimulus region we wish to describe.[1] We define the differential cone excitation coordinates $(\Delta P_L \Delta P_M \Delta P_S)^T$ as the vector (entry-by-entry) difference between $(P_{LO} P_{MO} P_{SO})^T$ and $(P_L P_M P_S)^T$.

Transforming to Cone Contrast Coordinates

The transformation between cone excitation coordinates and cone contrast coordinates is given by equation A.4.1.

$$\left(C_L\, C_M\, C_S\right)^T = \left(\frac{\Delta P_L}{P_{LO}}\ \frac{\Delta P_M}{P_{MO}}\ \frac{\Delta P_S}{P_{SO}}\right)^T \tag{A.4.1}$$

where $(C_L\, C_M\, C_S)^T$ is simply a vector of the conventional contrasts seen by each class of cone. Panels (a) and (b) of Figure A.4.2 show how a stimulus of the sort shown in panel (a) of Figure A.4.1 can be represented graphically in cone excitation space and in cone contrast space. These sorts of geometric representations make natural the terminology in which colored stimuli are referred to as points in color space. The transformation from excitation to contrast space may be thought of as a shift in the origin followed by a rescaling of the axes.

The key feature of cone contrast space is that it incorporates a simple Von Kries/Weber normalization model of retinal processing into the stimulus representation. Von Kries (1905) suggested that signals were normalized independently in the three separate cone pathways. Weber's Law may be understood as stating that in each pathway the normalization takes the specific form of Equation A.4.1. This model has the effect of equating stimuli across different choices of background. An example is shown in panel (c) of Figure A.4.2. Because cone contrast coordinates depend on the background, a crucial component of using cone contrast coordinates is to specify the background. Without this additional information, it is not possible to determine the excitation coordinates of the stimulus from the contrast coordinates.

(a)

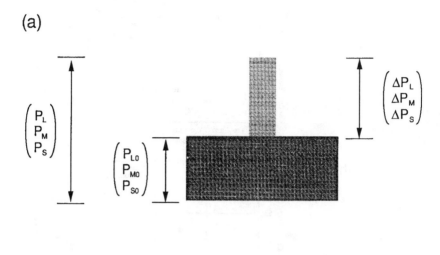

(b)

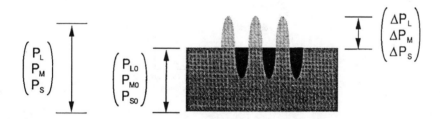

Figure A.4.1 Two stimulus configurations for which a cone contrast (or opponent modulation) stimulus description is appropriate. Panel (a) An increment/decrement is presented on a uniform background. The increment/decrement and the background do not necessarily have the same spectral composition, and the same stimulus may be an increment for one type of cone and a decrement for another. The cone excitation coordinates of the background are $(P_{L0} P_{M0} P_{S0})^T$. The cone excitation coordinates of increment/decrement plus the background are given by $(P_L P_M P_S)^T$. We define the differential cone excitation coordinates $(\Delta P_L \Delta P_M \Delta P_S)^T$ as the vector difference between $(P_{L0} P_{M0} P_{S0})^T$ and $(P_L P_M P_S)^T$. Panel (b) A uniform background is modulated sinusoidally. The cone excitation coordinates of the background are $(P_{L0} P_{M0} P_{S0})^T$, while the cone excitation coordinates at the peak of the modulation are $(P_L P_M P_S)^T$. The differential cone excitation coordinates $(\Delta P_L \Delta P_M \Delta P_S)^T$ are again the vector difference between $(P_{L0} P_{M0} P_{S0})^T$ and $(P_L P_M P_S)^T$. When the stimulus is a spatial or temporal modulation, it is conventional to use the differential cone excitation coordinates calculated for the modulation peak.

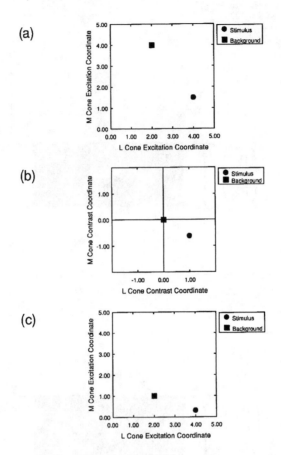

Figure A.4.2 Graphical representation of cone excitation and cone contrast coordinates for a spot increment/decrement. For graphical simplicity, only a two-dimensional plot of the L- and M-cone coordinates is shown. To visualize three-dimensional cone coordinates, one must either provide several two-dimensional views or use some other graphical technique which shows the full three-dimensional structure. Panel (a) Cone excitation coordinates. The closed square shows the L- and M-cone excitation coordinates of the uniform background (2.0,4.0). The closed circle shows the L- and M-cone excitation coordinates of the spot stimulus (4.0,1.5). Note that the spot is an L-cone increment and M-cone decrement. Panel (b) Cone contrast coordinates for the same stimulus. The background always plots at the origin in a cone contrast diagram, and it is often omitted from plots. The stimulus has positive L-cone contrast and negative M-cone contrast (1.0,–0.625). Panel (c) Cone excitation coordinates for a different spot stimulus (4.0,0.375) against a different background (2.0,1.0). The physical difference between this stimulus and the stimulus depicted in panel (a) is clear in the cone excitation space. The two stimuli have identical representations in cone contrast space.

Whether to represent stimuli in cone excitation or in cone contrast space depends in large measure on the extent to which the investigator wishes to accept the Von Kries/Weber normalization model as a starting point for further thinking. The representational decision may depend in large measure on which space best brings out the regularities of a particular data set.

The definition of cone contrast coordinates is straightforward when there is an unambiguous background. For complex stimuli (in particular for natural images) the definition is less clear. The difficulty arises in deciding what cone excitation coordinates $(P_{LO} P_{MO} P_{SO})^T$ to use for normalization. One possible choice is the spatial average of the cone excitation coordinates at each stimulus location (Buchsbaum, 1980; Brainard and Wandell, 1986; D'Zmura and Lennie, 1986; Land, 1986). Another is the cone excitation coordinates of the brightest location in the stimulus (Land and McCann, 1971). There is no guarantee, however, that either choice correctly models early visual processing. For this reason, investigators studying performance for complex stimuli have tended to use cone excitation coordinates.

A Metric for Contrast

Consider two stimulus modulations whose cone contrast coordinates differ only by a single scalar, that is modulations A and B such that $(C_L^A C_M^A C_S^A)^T = k(C_L^B C_M^B C_S^B)^T$ for some constant k. We say that two such modulations are in the same direction in color space and differ only in their signal strength. Cone contrast is a natural measure of signal strength for modulations that isolate a single class of cone. For stimuli that modulate multiple cone classes, it is not clear that there is a generalization of the concept of contrast that would allow us to summarize signal strength with a single number. There is a great temptation to define contrast for arbitrary modulations, however. For example, if we have measured the spatial contrast sensitivity functions (CSFs) for modulations in several different directions in cone contrast space, it would be convenient to compare the CSFs by plotting them all against a single contrast axis.[2] But how should this contrast axis be defined for modulations in different color directions? There is currently no agreed upon answer to this question.

One possible choice is to define contrast for any color direction to have unit value at the detection threshold for modulations in that direction. This principle has the attractive feature that it equates the visual responses based on direct measurements. But detection thresholds vary between observers, with the background, and with the spatial and temporal properties of the stimulus, so this method is not practical in general. A related possibility is to define contrast to have unit value at the detection threshold for an ideal observer (Geisler, 1989; Sekiguchi, Williams and Brainard, 1993). This eliminates observer variability from the definition, but requires instead standardization of parameters such as the relative number of L-, M-, and S-cones present in the retina. Both methods seem appropriate for particular studies but too unwieldy for general use. Neither method is likely to coincide with the natural definition of contrast for cone isolating stimuli.

One convenient convention for specifying the contrast of a modulation in an arbitrary color direction is to compute the pooled cone contrast as shown in Equation A.4.2 (Chaparro et al., 1993).

$$C = \sqrt{C_L^2 + C_M^2 + C_S^2} \qquad (A.4.2)$$

This quantity is the square-root of the cone contrast energy and is closely related to the vector-length model of color thresholds (Poirson, Wandell, Varner and Brainard, 1990). Using pooled cone contrast as a measure of signal strength has the attractive feature that it is independent of apparatus, observer, and stimulus configuration details. It has the slightly peculiar feature that the maximum physically achievable contrast for an isochromatic modulation (that is a modulation where the differential cone excitation coordinates have the same chromaticity as the background) is $C_{Max} = \sqrt{3}$ rather than the conventional $C_{Max} = 1$. This may be remedied by modifying Equation A.4.2 to define the pooled cone contrast as $C = \sqrt{(C_L^2 + C_M^2 + C_S^2)/3}$, but this leads to the similar oddity that the maximum physically achievable contrast for cone isolating stimuli is limited at $C_{Max} = 1/\sqrt{3}$.

The fact that it is difficult to define a single number measure of modulation stimulus strength across color directions serves to remind us that chromatic signal strength is unlikely to be univariate. At the very least, investigators should be cautious about experimental designs or conclusions that depend critically on how the contrast is scaled across color directions.

DKL Space

The DKL color space shares with cone contrast space the feature that it is based on a model of early visual processing (See p. 251 and Figure 7.1). The model starts with the assumption that early processing extracts differential cone signals. Once extracted, however, the differential cone signals are not simply rescaled but rather recoded by three post-receptoral mechanisms: a luminance mechanism and two opponent chromatic mechanisms. DKL coordinates represent the responses of these hypothesized mechanisms. To understand how to represent stimuli in DKL space, it is necessary to understand how the responses of these mechanisms are computed. Indeed, in this appendix, I define the DKL space by specifying the response properties of the underlying mechanisms. This development is atypical. Flitcroft (1989) provides a clear example of the more conventional development, which defines the space in terms of the stimuli that isolate the mechanisms. I emphasize the mechanism properties because I believe this approach makes explicit the model underlying the DKL space. The two developments are formally equivalent (see Knoblauch, 1995). As we will see below, we can derive the mechanism-isolating modulations once we specify the mechanism properties.

Luminance Mechanism

The luminance mechanism is defined so that its response is proportional to the photopic luminance of the differential stimulus. By inverting Equation A.3.14, we can derive the relation between differential cone excitation coordinates and differential tristimulus coordinates:[4]

$$
\begin{pmatrix} \Delta X \\ \Delta Y \\ \Delta Z \end{pmatrix} = \begin{pmatrix} 2.9448 & -35001 & 13.1745 \\ 1.0000 & 1.0000 & 0.0000 \\ 0.0000 & 0.0000 & 62.1891 \end{pmatrix} \begin{pmatrix} \Delta P_L \\ \Delta P_M \\ \Delta P_S \end{pmatrix}. \quad (A.4.3)
$$

The second row of this matrix equation tells us that the differential response of the luminance mechanism (denoted by ΔR_{Lum}) is given by

$$
\Delta R_{Lum} = k_{Lum} \, (W_{Lum,L} \, \Delta P_L + W_{Lum,M} \, \Delta P_M + W_{Lum,S} \, \Delta P_S) \quad (A.4.4)
$$

where $W_{Lum,L} = 1.000$, $W_{Lum,M} = 1.0000$, and $W_{Lum,S} = 0.0000$. The notational choice "R" is a mnemonic for "response" while the notational choice "W" is a mnemonic for "weight" as in "weighted sum." The actual values for the weights come from the second row of the matrix in Equation A.4.3. The constant k_{Lum} defines the units for the mechanism response.[3]

L-M Opponent Mechanism

The first chromatic mechanism is referred to as the L-M opponent mechanism. Unlike the luminance mechanism, which is defined directly in terms of its weights, the L-M opponent mechanism is defined by two properties it must satisfy. First, it is a chromatic mechanism, so that its response is zero when the differential signal has the same chromaticity as the background. That is, the response of the mechanism is zero when

$$(\Delta P_L \; \Delta P_M \; \Delta P_S)^T = k \; (P_{LO} \; P_{MO} \; P_{SO})^T \qquad (A.4.5)$$

for any constant k. Second, the mechanism response is not affected by the excitation of the S-cones. The general form for the response of the L-M opponent mechanism is

$$\Delta R_{L-M} = k_{L-M} \; (W_{L-M,L}\Delta P_L + W_{L-M,M}\Delta P_M + W_{L-M,S}\Delta P_S). \qquad (A.4.6)$$

To specify the L-M opponent mechanism, we must find weights $W_{L-M,L}$, $W_{L-M,M}$, and $W_{L-M,S}$ so that the two defining properties are satisfied. From the second defining condition we have $W_{L-M,S} = 0$. To satisfy the first condition, we plug in the values P_{L0}, P_{M0}, and P_{S0} for $\Delta P_L, \Delta P_M$, and ΔP_S in Equation A.4.6 and set the result to 0. By using the fact that $W_{L-M,S} = 0$ we obtain $W_{L-M,L} P_{L0} + W_{L-M,M} P_{M0} = 0$ and derive that $W_{L-M,M} = (-W_{L-M,L}P_{L0})/P_{MO}$. Note that the weights for the L-M opponent mechanism vary with the background. In this sense, the DKL space incorporates a very specific theory of adaptation. The constant defines the units for the mechanism response.

S-Lum Opponent Mechanism

The second chromatic mechanism is referred to as the S-Lum opponent mechanism. The S-Lum opponent mechanism is also defined by two properties it must satisfy. Like the L-M opponent mechanism, its response is zero when the differential signal has the same chromaticity as the background. The second property may be stated as follows. The response of the mechanism is zero when both the differential S-cone signal ΔP_S and the response of the luminance mechanism ΔR_{Lum} are zero. Together, these conditions give us that

$$\Delta R_{S-Lum} = k_{S-Lum} \; (W_{S-Lum,L}\Delta P_L + W_{S-Lum,M}\Delta P_M + W_{S-Lum,S}\Delta P_S) \qquad (A.4.7)$$

with $W_{S\text{-}Lum,L} = -W_{Lum,L}$, $W_{S\text{-}Lum,M} = -W_{Lum,M}$, and $W_{S\text{-}Lum,S} = -(W_{S\text{-}Lum,L}P_{L0} + W_{S\text{-}Lum,m}P_{M0})/P_{S0}$. As for the L-M opponent mechanism, the weights for the S-Lum opponent mechanism vary with the background. The constant $k_{S\text{-}Lum}$ defines the units for the mechanism response.

Conversion to DKL Space

The discussion above defines the weights for the three DKL mechanisms given any background. The weights let us calculate the mechanism responses $(\Delta R_{Lum}\ \Delta R_{L\text{-}M}\ \Delta R_{S\text{-}Lum})^T$ (up to the free unit constants k_{Lum}, $k_{L\text{-}M}$, and $k_{S\text{-}Lum}$) from the differential cone coordinates $(\Delta P_L\ \Delta P_M\ \Delta P_S)^T$. Matrix notation is used to express the calculation succinctly.[4] Each row of the matrix that relates $(\Delta P_L\ \Delta P_M\ \Delta P_S)^T$ to $(\Delta R_{Lum}\ \Delta R_{L\text{-}M}\ \Delta R_{S\text{-}Lum})^T$ should contain the weights for the corresponding mechanism. Collecting together the expressions for the weights derived above and bringing the free unit constants to the left-hand side, we obtain

$$
\begin{pmatrix} \dfrac{\Delta R_{Lum}}{k_{Lum}} \\[2.5ex] \dfrac{\Delta R_{L\text{-}M}}{k_{L\text{-}M}} \\[2.5ex] \dfrac{\Delta R_S}{k_{S\text{-}Lum}} \end{pmatrix}
=
\begin{pmatrix} 1 & 1 & 1 \\[2ex] 1 & \dfrac{-P_{L0}}{P_{M0}} & 0 \\[2.5ex] -1 & -1 & \dfrac{P_{L0}+P_{M0}}{P_{S0}} \end{pmatrix}
\begin{pmatrix} \Delta P_L \\[2.5ex] \Delta P_M \\[2.5ex] \Delta P_S \end{pmatrix}
\qquad (A.4.8)
$$

Equation A.4.8 lets us compute DKL coordinates up to three free multiplicative constants for each mechanism. Note again that the construction of the conversion matrix depends on the cone excitation coordinates of the background.

Setting the Unit Constants

To compute DKL coordinates for any specific background, we must choose values for the constants k_{Lum}, $k_{L\text{-}M}$, and $k_{S\text{-}Lum}$. Setting these constants is closely related to the issue of how to define a color contrast metric. A natural choice for k_{Lum} is to set it so that ΔR_{Lum} expresses luminance contrast. There is no such natural choice for $k_{L\text{-}M}$ and $k_{S\text{-}Lum}$. In their original paper Derrington et al. (1984) choose these constants so that the two chromatic mechanism responses took on the value 1.0 at the maximum modulation obtainable within the gamut of their monitor. Although this is a natural choice for any particular monitor, it has the disadvantage that it makes the definition of the color space apparatus dependent. Other possible strategies include normalizing to real or ideal observer detection thresholds, as discussed for cone contrast space above. A final possibility is to normalize each mechanism to have unit response when it is excited in isolation by a stimulus with unit pooled cone contrast. This has the attractive feature that it is independent of apparatus, observer, and stimulus configuration details. It is the choice we adopt for the example below.

A Conversion Example

This section provides a worked example for computing the DKL coordinates of a stimulus. Table A.4.1 provides a listing of a MATLAB program that performs the example calculations in their entirety.

Suppose we wish to convert a stimulus with differential cone excitation coordinates $(\Delta P_L \, \Delta P_M \, \Delta P_S)^T = (2.0000 \, -2.5000 \, 1.0000)^T$ seen against a background with cone excitation coordinates $(P_{L0} \, P_{M0} \, P_{S0})^T = (2.0000 \, 4.0000 \, 3.0000)^T$ into DKL coordinates. (The numbers for this example were chosen arbitrarily. There is no guarantee that these differential coordinates can be achieved within the gamut of a physically realizable device.) Inserting the values for the background cone coordinates into Equation A.4.8 we have

$$
\begin{pmatrix} \dfrac{\Delta R_{Lum}}{k_{Lum}} \\[2mm] \dfrac{\Delta R_{L\text{-}M}}{k_{L\text{-}M}} \\[2mm] \dfrac{\Delta R_S}{k_{S\text{-}Lum}} \end{pmatrix} = \begin{pmatrix} 1 & 1 & 0 \\[1mm] 1 & -\dfrac{1}{2} & 0 \\[1mm] -1 & -1 & 2 \end{pmatrix} \begin{pmatrix} \Delta P_L \\[1mm] \Delta P_M \\[1mm] \Delta P_S \end{pmatrix}. \tag{A.4.9}
$$

To set the normalization constants, we find the stimuli with unit pooled cone contrast that isolate each of the DKL mechanisms. The first step is to invert Equation A.4.9 to derive

$$
\begin{pmatrix} \Delta P_L \\[2mm] \Delta P_M \\[2mm] \Delta P_S \end{pmatrix} = \begin{pmatrix} \dfrac{1}{3} & \dfrac{2}{3} & 0 \\[1mm] \dfrac{2}{3} & -\dfrac{2}{3} & 0 \\[1mm] \dfrac{1}{2} & 0 & \dfrac{1}{2} \end{pmatrix} \begin{pmatrix} \dfrac{\Delta R_{Lum}}{k_{Lum}} \\[2mm] \dfrac{\Delta R_{L\text{-}M}}{k_{L\text{-}M}} \\[2mm] \dfrac{\Delta R_S}{k_{S\text{-}Lum}} \end{pmatrix}. \tag{A.4.10}
$$

The three columns of the matrix in Equation A.4.10 provide the differential cone coordinates of stimuli that isolate each of the DKL mechanisms. This is because in each column of the matrix are the differential cone coordinates obtained for substituting the three DKL vectors $(1.0000\ 0.0000\ 0.0000)^T$, $(0.0000\ 1.0000\ 0.0000)^T$, and $(0.0000\ 0.0000\ 1.0000)^T$ into the right-hand side of the equation. Thus the differential cone coordinates of stimuli that isolate the DKL mechanisms are $(0.3333\ 0.6667\ 0.5000)^T$, $(0.6667\ -0.6667\ 0.0000)^T$, and $(0.0000\ 0.0000\ 0.5000)^T$ for the luminance, L-M opponent, and S-Lum opponent mechanisms respectively. (This may be checked easily by plugging these three vectors into the right-hand side of Equation A.4.9 and verifying that each of the results has only one non-zero entry.) Derrington et al. (1984) referred to these stimuli as luminance, constant-B and constant R & G modulations. In Chapter 7 (Figure 7.20) they are referred to as the achromatic, constant-S, and constant L & M modulations. I prefer to call them isochromatic, red-green isoluminant, and S-cone isoluminant modulations. (The terminology and conventions for using the DKL color space are still evolving.)

The differential cone coordinates obtained from Equation A.4.10 do not have unit pooled cone contrast. In this example, we adopt the convention that the normalizing constants, k_{Lum}, k_{L-M}, k_{S-Lum}, be chosen so that mechanism-isolating stimuli with unit pooled cone contrast produce unit responses in the three DKL mechanisms. Normalizing each modulation obtained above, we get $(1.1547\ 2.3094\ 1.7321)^T$, $(1.7889\ -1.7889\ 0.0000)^T$, and $(0.0000\ 0.0000\ 3.0000)^T$ as the differential cone excitation coordinates of the stimuli that should generate unit response in each of the DKL mechanisms. (To compute pooled cone contrast, we divide differential cone excitation coordinates above by the cone excitation coordinates of the background and then apply Equation A.4.2.) We want to choose the scalars k_{Lum}, k_{L-M}, and k_{S-Lum} so that when these three vectors are multiplied by the matrix in Equation A.4.9, the three corresponding mechanism responses ΔR_{Lum}, ΔR_{L-M}, and ΔR_S are unity. The appropriate scalars are $k_{Lum} = 0.2887$, $k_{L-M} = 0.3727$, and $k_{S-Lum} = 0.1667$. Substituting the constants into Equation A.4.9 and simplifying gives us

$$\begin{pmatrix} \Delta R_{Lum} \\ \Delta R_{L-M} \\ \Delta R_S \end{pmatrix} = \begin{pmatrix} 0.2887 & 0.2887 & 0.0000 \\ 0.3727 & -0.1863 & 0.0000 \\ -0.1667 & -0.1667 & 0.3333 \end{pmatrix} \begin{pmatrix} \Delta P_L \\ \Delta P_M \\ \Delta P_S \end{pmatrix}. \quad (A.4.11)$$

Performing this matrix multiplication for the vector $(\Delta P_L \ \Delta P_M \ \Delta P_S)^T$ = $(2.0000 \ -2.5000 \ 1.0000)^T$ we obtain its DKL coordinates as $(\Delta R_{Lum} \ \Delta R_{L\text{-}M} \ \Delta R_S)^T = (-0.1443 \ 1.2112 \ 0.4167)^T$. To convert from DKL coordinates back to differential cone coordinates, we would use the inverse of Equation A.4.11:

$$
\begin{pmatrix} \Delta P_L \\ \Delta P_M \\ \Delta P_S \end{pmatrix} = \begin{pmatrix} 1.1547 & 1.7889 & 0.0000 \\ 2.3094 & -1.7889 & 0.0000 \\ 1.7321 & 0.0000 & 3.0000 \end{pmatrix} \begin{pmatrix} \Delta R_{Lum} \\ \Delta R_{L\text{-}M} \\ \Delta R_S \end{pmatrix}. \qquad (A.4.12)
$$

Graphical Representation and Spherical Coordinates

The DKL coordinates obtained above may be used to plot the stimulus modulation in the color space diagram shown in panel (A) of Figure 7.20. The first coordinate, −0.1443, would locate the stimulus below the isoluminant plane towards the −90° pole of the axis labeled achromatic; the second coordinate, 1.2112, would locate the stimulus towards the 0° pole of the axis labeled constant S-cone; the third coordinate, 0.4167, would locate the stimulus towards the 270° pole of the axis labeled constant L & M-cone. (The convention in Figure 7.20 is that the 270° pole represents the direction of increasing S-cone response.)

Modulations represented in this color space diagram are sometimes expressed in spherical coordinates. The angular azimuth and elevation are readily computed from the rectangular coordinates. With the sign conventions of Figure 7.20, we obtain $\phi = \arctan(-0.4167/1.2112) = -18.98°$ and $\theta = \arctan(-0.1443/\sqrt{(-0.4167)^2 + (1.2112)^2}) = -6.43$. It is important to note that these angular specifications depend on the normalization method used to define unit responses for the three DKL mechanisms. For this reason, angular specifications must be interpreted with great care.

Discussion

The DKL space is not simple to understand or to use. As with cone contrast space, its usefulness depends chiefly on whether it brings out regularities in experimental data. Indeed, most of the discussion of cone contrast space above applies to the DKL space as well. At a broad level, the model underlying the space clearly captures the opponent nature of color coding (Hurvich and Jameson, 1957). Understanding the exact nature of the opponent mechanisms (and whether there are only three) is a subject of much current interest (see for example Krauskopf, Williams and Heeley, 1982; Krauskopf, Williams, Mandler and Brown, 1986; Guth, 1991; Krauskopf and Gegenfurtner, 1992; Cole, Hine and McIlhagga, 1993; DeValois and DeValois, 1993; Poirson and Wandell, 1993; Chichilnisky, 1994; Webster and Mollon, 1995). The derivation of DKL space presented here may be generalized to define color spaces based on the responses of any three linear color mechanisms.

As with cone contrast space, proper interpretation of DKL coordinates requires an explicit specification of the cone excitation coordinates of the background. In addition, since there is no agreed upon standard for the normalization constants k_{Lum}, k_{L-M}, and k_{S-Lum}, these must be explicitly specified whenever the space is used.

The specification of the DKL mechanism weights used here (Equation A.4.3) depends on the relative scalings chosen for the L, M, and S-cone sensitivities. In particular, the scalings used in Equation A.3.14 are chosen so that photopic luminance of a stimulus is given by the sum of its L- and M-cone coordinates. Sometimes cone sensitivities are scaled so that the maximum sensitivity of each cone is equal to unity. Such scaling changes must be taken into account when deriving DKL coordinates. The space as conventionally defined also incorporates the simplifying assumption that S-cones do not contribute to photopic luminance. The Smith–Pokorny (Table A.3.4) estimates of the cone sensitivities are designed so that this assumption holds.

The Relation Between Mechanisms and Modulations

As mentioned above, the development here is atypical in that it defines the DKL space in terms of visual mechanism properties rather than in terms of the modulations that isolate the mechanisms. Advanced students may garner insight about the relation between the two approaches from Figure A.4.3, which shows graphically the relation between color mechanisms and the modulations which isolate them.

Notes

[1] The superscript "T" after a vector denotes vector transpose. It indicates that the vector should be treated as a column vector in any matrix operation. We use this notation for the inline expressions to conserve vertical space; we show column vectors explicitly in the matrix equations and figures where space permits.

[2] See Chapter 9 for more on spatial contrast sensitivity functions.

[3] To avoid the inconvenience of double subscripts in this appendix, we denote luminance with "Lum" rather than the CIE approved "L_v."

[4] See Endnote 6 in Appendix Part III for the operational rules of matrix algebra.

(a)

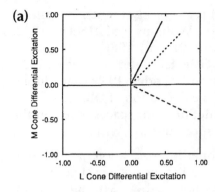

(b)

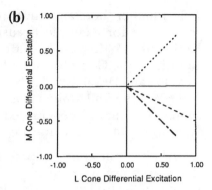

Figure A.4.3 Graphical representation of mechanisms and the modulations which isolate them. For graphical simplicity, only two-dimensional plots of the L- and M-cone coordinates are shown. For purposes of this figure, only color directions are of interest, therefore all vectors are shown normalized to unit length.

Panel (a) The color direction of an isochromatic modulation is shown by the solid line. Points on this line specify the differential L- and M-cone excitations that isolate the luminance mechanism. The direction of the line was obtained from the first column of the matrix in Equation A.4.12 and has the same relative cone coordinates as the background. The color direction of the L-M opponent mechanism is shown by the dashed line. Points on this line give the relative contribution of the differential L- and M-cone excitations to the mechanism response. The direction of this line was obtained from the second row of the matrix in Equation A.4.11. Note that the isochromatic stimulus is orthogonal to the L-M opponent mechanism. Readers familiar with analytic geometry will recognize that this orthogonality indicates that the mechanism response to the modulation is zero. If a full three dimensional plot were shown, the modulation would also be orthogonal to the direction of the S-Lum opponent mechanism. The color direction of the luminance mechanism is shown as the dotted line. The direction of this line was obtained from the first row of the matrix in Equation A.4.11. Note that the isochromatic stimulus does not line up with the luminance mechanism. The defining feature of the isochromatic modulation is its orthogonality to the chromatic mechanisms, not its relation to the luminance mechanism. The orthogonality is preserved under transformations of color space, whereas the angle between the modulation and the luminance mechanism is not.

Panel (b) The color direction of an isoluminant modulation that isolates the L-M opponent mechanism is shown by the dot-dash line. The direction of this line was obtained from the second column of the matrix in Equation A.4.12. As in panel (a) the color direction of the luminance mechanism is shown by the dotted line. Note that the isochromatic stimulus is orthogonal to the luminance mechanism. The color direction of the L-M opponent mechanism is again shown as the dashed line. Note that the isoluminant stimulus does not line up with the opponent mechanism it isolates.

Table A.4.1   The table provides a listing of a MATLAB program that computes the conversion example described in the appendix. MATLAB is a widely available numerical programming language. The interested reader may find this listing helpful in understanding the details of the color space conversion. Comments have been added to the listing in an attempt to make the program readable even for those unfamiliar with MATLAB syntax. MATLAB is a registered trademark of The MathWorks, Inc.

```
% DKL Example
%
% MATLAB program to compute the example
% used for the space in Appendix Part IV.
%
% MATLAB is a registered trademark of the
% MathWorks, Inc.
%
% 7/6/95 dhb Wrote it.

% STEP 1: Set the background vector for
% the conversion
bg = [2 4 3]';

% STEP 2: Set the vector we wish to convert
diffcone_coords = [2 -2.5 1]';

% STEP 3: Set M_raw as in equation A.4.9.
% This is found by inserting the background
% values into equation A.4.8. Different
% backgrounds produce different matrices.
% The MATLAB notation below just
% fills the desired 3-by-3 matrix.
M_raw = [ 1  1  0 ; ...
          1 -bg(1)/bg(2) 0 ; ...
         -1 -1 (bg(1)+bg(2))/bg(3) ];

% STEP 4: Compute the inverse of M for
% equation A.4.10. The MATLAB inv() function
% computes the matrix inverse of its argument.
M_raw_inv = inv(M_raw);

% STEP 5: Find the three isolating stimuli as
% the columns of M_inv_raw.  The MATLAB
% notation X(:,i) extracts the i-th column
% of the matrix X.
isochrom_raw = M_raw_inv(:,1);
rgisolum_raw = M_raw_inv(:,2);
sisolum_raw = M_raw_inv(:,3);

% STEP 6: Find the pooled cone contrast of each
% of these.  The MATLAB norm() function returns
% the vector length of its argument. The MATLAB
% ./ operation represents entry-by-entry division.
isochrom_raw_pooled = norm(isochrom_raw ./ bg);
rgisolum_raw_pooled = norm(rgisolum_raw ./ bg);
sisolum_raw_pooled = norm(sisolum_raw ./ bg);

% STEP 7: Scale each mechanism isolating
% modulation by its pooled contrast to obtain
% mechanism isolating modulations that have
```

(continued on next page)

Table A.4.1   *continued*

```
% unit length.
isochrom_unit = isochrom_raw / isochrom_raw_pooled;
rgisolum_unit = rgisolum_raw / rgisolum_raw_pooled;
sisolum_unit = sisolum_raw / sisolum_raw_pooled;

% STEP 8: Compute the values of the normalizing
% constants by plugging the unit isolating stimuli
% into A.4.9 and seeing what we get.  Each vector
% should have only one non-zero entry.  The size
% of the entry is the response of the unscaled
% mechanism to the stimulus that should give unit
% response.
lum_resp_raw = M_raw*isochrom_unit;
l_minus_m_resp_raw = M_raw*rgisolum_unit;
s_minus_lum_resp_raw = M_raw*sisolum_unit;

% STEP 9: We need to rescale the rows of M_raw
% so that we get unit response.  This means
% multiplying each row of M_raw by a constant.
% The easiest way to accomplish the multiplication
% is to form a diagonal matrix with the desired
% scalars on the diagonal. These scalars are just
% the multiplicative inverses of the non-zero
% entries of the vectors obtained in the previous
% step.  The resulting matrix M provides the
% entries of A.4.11.  The three _resp vectors
% computed should be the three unit vectors
% (and they are).
D_rescale = [1/lum_resp_raw(1) 0 0 ; ...
             0 1/l_minus_m_resp_raw(2) 0 ; ...
             0 0 1/s_minus_lum_resp_raw(3) ] ;
M = D_rescale*M_raw;
lum_resp = M*isochrom_unit;
l_minus_m_resp = M*rgisolum_unit;
s_minus_lum_resp = M*sisolum_unit;

% STEP 10: Compute the inverse of M to obtain
% the matrix in equation A.4.12.
M_inv = inv(M);

% STEP 11: Multiply the vector we wish to
% convert by M to obtain its DKL coordinates.
DKL_coords = M*diffcone_coords;

% STEP 12: convert to spherical coordinates.
% According to the conventions in the original DKL
% paper, azimuth of 0 is along our rgisolum axis,
% azimuth of 90 is along our negative sisolum
% axis.  The isochromatic axis has an elevation
% of 90 degrees.  To do the conversion, we flip the
% sign of the sisolum coordinate and then do a
% standard conversion to polar coordinates.
RADS_TO_DEGS = 360/(2*pi);
azimuth_rads = atan(-DKL_coords(3)/DKL_coords(2));
isolum_len = sqrt(DKL_coords(2)^2 + DKL_coords(3)^2);
elevation_rads = atan(DKL_coords(1)/isolum_len);
azimuth = RADS_TO_DEGS*azimuth_rads;
elevation = RADS_TO_DEGS*elevation_rads;
```

Acknowledgment

My understanding of the material presented here has developed through numerous discussions over the past several years. Particularly helpful have been conversations with R. Brown, C. Chen, M. D'Zmura, J. Foley, G. Jacobs, J. Krauskopf, P. Lennie, J. Palmer, A. Poirson, N. Sekiguchi, and B. Wandell. G. Boynton, P. K. Kaiser, A. Poirson, and J. Speigle provided critical comments on the chapter.

References

(* new to second edition)

Abramov, I. Further analysis of the responses of LGN cells. *Journal of the Optical Society of America* 58, 574–579 (1968).

*Abramov, I., Gordon, J. & Chan, H. Color appearance in the peripheral retina: Effects of stimulus size. *Journal of the Optical Society of America* 8, 404–414 (1991).

*Abramov, I., Gordon, J. & Chan, H. Color appearance across the retina: effects of white surround. *Journal of the Optical Society of America* 9, 195–202 (1992).

*Abramov, I. & Gordon, J. Color appearance: on seeing red or yellow, or green, or blue. *Annual Review of Psychology* 45, 451–485 (1994).

Aguilar, M. & Stiles, W. S. Saturation of the rod mechanism at high levels of stimulation. *Optica Acta* 1, 59–65 (1954).

*Ahnelt, P. K., Keri, C. & Kolb, H. Identification of pedicles of putative blue-sensitive cones in the human retina. *Journal of Comparative Neurology* 293, 39–53 (1990).

*Ahnelt, P. K., Kolb, G. & Pflug, R. Identification of a subtype of cone photoreceptor, likely to be blue sensitive in the human retina. *Journal of Comparative Neurology* 255, 18–34 (1987).

*Ahnelt, P. K. & Kolb, G. Horizontal cells and cone photoreceptors in human retina: A Golgi-Electron microscopic study of spectral connectivity. *Journal of Comparative Neurology* 343, 406–427 (1994).

Alpern, M. What is it that confines in a world without color? *Investigative Ophthalmology & Visual Science* 13, 648–674 (1974).

Alpern, M., Falls, H. F. & Lee, G. B. The enigma of typical total monochromacy. *American Journal of Ophthalmology* 50, 996–1011 (1960).

Alpern, M., Lee, G. B. & Spivey, B. E. π_1 cone monochromatism. *Archives of Ophthalmology* 74, 334–337 (1965).

Alpern, M. & Pugh, Jr. E.N. Variations in the action spectrum of erythrolabe among deuteranopes. *Journal of Physiology (London)* 266, 613–646 (1977).

Alpern, M. & Torri, S. The luminosity curve of the protanomalous fovea. *Journal of General Physiology,* 52, 717–737 (1968a).

Alpern, M. & Torri, S. The luminosity curve of the deuteranomalous fovea. *Journal of General Physiology,* 52, 738–749 (1968b).

*Ansitis, S.M. & Cavanagh, P. A minimum motion technique for judging equiluminance. In J.D. Mollon & L.T. Sharpe (Eds.) *Color Vision,* New York: Academic Press, 99. 155–166, 1983.

Arden, G. B. & Frumkes, T.E. Stimulation of rods can increase cone flicker ERGs in man. *Vision Research,* 26, 711–721 (1986).

Arden, G. B. The retina—neurophysiology. In: Davson, H. (Ed.), *The eye* (2nd ed.). New York: Academic Press, 1976.

*Arend, L. & Reeves, A. Simultaneous color constancy. *Journal of the Optical Society of America* A, 1743–1751 (1986).

Armington, J. C. *The electroretinogram.* New York: Academic Press, 1974.

*Asenjo, A.B., Rim, J. & Oprian, D.D. Molecular determinants of human red/green color discrimination. *Neuron,* 12, 1131–1138 (1994).

Avant, L. L. Vision in the Ganzfeld. *Psychological Bulletin* 64, 246–258 (1965).

Baker, H. D. & Rushton, W. A. H. An analytical anomaloscope. *Journal of Physiology* 168, 31P–33P (1963).

*Bailey, J. E. & Montag, E. Short-wavelength sensitive cone system function in hereditary tritanopia. *Investigative Ophthalmology & Visual Science,* 33, 701 (1992).

Barlow, H. B. Summation and inhibition in the frog's retina. *Journal of Physiology* 119, 69–88 (1953).

Barlow, H. B. Dark and light adaptation: Psychophysics. In: Jameson, D. & Hurvich, L. M. (Eds.), *Handbook of Sensory Physiology* VII/4. New York: Springer-Verlag, 1972.

*Baron, W. S. Cone difference signal in foveal local electroretinogram of primate. *Investigative Ophthalmology & Visual Science* 19, 1442–1448 (1980).

Bartleson, C. J. Brown. *Color Research and Application* 1, 181–191 (1976).

Bartley, S. H. Subjective brightness in relation to flash rate and the light-dark ratio. *Journal of Experimental Psychology* 23, 313–319 (1938).

Bartley, S. H. *Vision.* New York: Van Nostrand, 1941.

*Bäuml, K-H. Color appearance: effects of illuminant changes under different surface collections. *Journal of the Optical Society of America,* 11, 531–543 (1994).

*Bäuml, K-H. Illuminant changes under different surface collections: examining some principles of color appearance. *Journal of the Optical Society of America A*, 12, 261–271 (1995).

Baylor, D. A., Fuortes, M. G. F. & O'Bryan, P. M. Receptive fields of cones in the retina of the turtle. *Journal of Physiology* 214, 265–294 (1971).

*Baylor, D. A., Lamb, T. D. & Yau, K. -W. The membrane current of single rod outer segments. *Journal of Physiology* 288, 589–611 (1979).

*Baylor, D. A. Photoreceptor signals and vision. *Investigative Ophthalmology & Visual Science* 28, 34–49 (1987).

*Baylor, D. A., Nunn, B. J. & Schnapf, J. L. Spectral sensitivity of cones of the monkey Macaca fascicularis. *Journal of Physiology* 390, 145–160 (1987).

Beare, J. I. *Greek theories of elementary cognition from Alcmaeon to Aristotle.* Oxford:Clarendon Press, 1906.

*Bedford, R.E. & Wyszecki, G. Axial chromatic aberration of the human eye. *Journal of the Optical Society of America*, 47, 564–565 (1957).

Bedford, R. E. & Wyszecki, G. Wavelength discrimination for point sources. *Journal of the Optical Society of America* 48, 129–135 (1958).

Bell, J. Colour blindness. *Treasury of human inheritance*, v. II, part II, 125–268. Cambridge, England: Cambridge University Press, 1926.

Berbert, J. H. Visual acuity as a function of luminance for different hues. *Journal of the Optical Society of America* 45, 902 (1955).

Berbert, J. H. Visual acuity as a function of intensity for different hues. *NRL Report 5104*. Naval Research Laboratory, Washington, D.C. (1958).

Berlin, B. & Kay, P. *Basic color terms: Their universality and evolution.* Berkeley: University of California Press, 1969.

*Biersdorf, W. The Davidson and Hemmendinger Color Rule as a color vision screening test. *Archives of Ophthalmology*, 95, 134–138 (1977).

*Billmeyer, F.W. & Saltzman, M. *Principles of Color Technology* (2nd ed) New York: Wiley, 1981.

*Birch, J., Chisholm, I. A., Kinnear, P., Pinckers, A.J.L.G., Pokorny, J., Smith, V., & Verriest, G. Clinical testing methods. In J. Pokorny, V. Smith, G. Verriest, A.J.L.G. Pinckers (Eds.) *Congenital and Acquired Color Vision Defects*, New York: Grune & Stratton,1979.

Blackwell, H. R. Contrast thresholds of the human eye. *Journal of the Optical Society of America* 36, 624–643 (1946).

Blackwell, H. R. & Blackwell, O. M. Rod and cone mechanisms in typical and atypical congenital achromatopsia. *Vision Research* 1, 62–107 (1961).

Boll, F. On the anatomy and physiology of the retina. Translated by R. Hubbard. *Vision Research* 17, 1253–1265 (1977).

Bongard, M. M., Smirnov, M. S. & Friedrich, L. The four-dimensionality of the human eye. In: *Visual problems of colour* (pp. 325–330). Her Majesty's Stationery Office London, 1958.

Boring, E. G. *Sensation and perception in the history of experimental psychology.* New York: Appleton-Century-Crofts, 1942.

Bornstein, M. H. Color vision and color naming: A psychophysiological hypothesis of cultural difference. *Psychological Bulletin* 80, 257–285 (1973).

Bornstein, M. H., Kessen, W. & Weiskopf, S. Color vision and hue categorization in young human infants. *Journal of Experimental Psychology (Human Perception andPerformance)* 2, 115–129 (1976).

*Botstein, D. The molecular biology of color vision. *Science* 232, 142–143 (1986).

Bouman, M. A. & Walraven, P. L. Color discrimination data. In: Jameson, D. & Hurvich, L. M. (Eds.), *Handbook of Sensory Physiology* VII/4. New York: Springer-Verlag, 1972.

Bowmaker, J. K., Dartnall, H. J. A., Lythgoe, J. N. & Mollon, J. D. The visual pigments of rods and cones in the rhesus monkey, Macaca mulatta. *Journal of Physiology* 274, 329–348 (1978).

*Bowmaker, J. K., Dartnall, J. A. & Mollon, J. D. Microspectrophotometry demonstration of four classes of photoreceptor in an old world primate, Macaca fascicularis. *Journal of Physiology* 298, 131–143 (1980).

*Bowmaker, J. K. & Dartnall, H. J. A. Visual pigments of rods and cones in a human retina. *Journal of Physiology* 298, 501–511 (1980).

*Bowmaker, J. K., Astell, S., Hunt, D. M. & Mollon, J. D. Photosensitive and photostable pigments in the retinae of old world monkeys. *Journal of Experimental Biology* 156, 1–19 (1991).

Boycott, B. B. & Dowling, J. E. Organization of the primate retina: Light microscopy. *Philosophical Transactions of the Royal Society of London* 255B, 109–176 (1969).

*Boycott, B. B., Hopkins, J. M. & Sperling, H. G. Cone connections of the horizontal cells of the rhesus monkey's retina. *Proceedings of the Royal Society London B* 229, 345–379 (1987).

*Boycott, B. B. & Wässle, H. Morphological classification of bipolar cells of the primate retina. *European Journal of Neuroscience* 3, 1069–1088 (1991).

Boynton, R. M. Rapid chromatic adaptation and the sensitivity functions of human color vision. *Journal of the Optical Society of America* 46, 172–179 (1956).

Boynton, R. M. Theory of color vision. *Journal of the Optical Society of America* 50, 929–944 (1960).

Boynton, R. M. Contributions of threshold measurements to color-discrimination theory. *Journal of the Optical Society of America* 53, 165–178 (1963).

Boynton, R. M. Discussion: Competing theories of receptor excitation. *Psychological Bulletin* 61, 262–267 (1964).

Boynton, R. M. Vision. In: Sidowski, J. B. (Ed.), *Experimental methods and instrumentation in psychology.* New York: McGraw-Hill, 1966.

Boynton, R. M. Color vision. In: Kling, J. W. & Riggs, L. A. (Eds.), *Experimental Psychology.* New York: Holt, Rinehart and Winston, 1971.

Boynton. R. M. Implications of the minimally distinct border. *Journal of the Optical Society of America* 63, 1037–1043 (1973).

Boynton, R. M. The visual system: Environmental information. In: Carterette, E. C. & Friedman, M. P. (Eds.), *Handbook of Perception,* v. 1. New York: Academic Press, 1974.

Boynton, R. M. Color, hue, and wavelength. In: Carterette, E. C. & Friedman, M. P. (Eds.), *Handbook of Perception,* v. 5. New York:Academic Press, 1975.

Boynton, R. M. Ten years of research with the minimally distinct border. In: Armington, J. C., Krauskopf, J. & Wooten, B. (Eds.), *Visual psychophysics: Psychophysics and physiology.* New York: Academic Press, 1978.

Boynton, R. M. Color in contour and object perception. In: Carterette, E. C. & Friedman, M. P. (Eds.), *Handbook of Perception* v. 8. New York: Academic Press, 1978.

*Boynton, R. M. *Human Color Vision.* New York: Holt, Rinehart & Winston, 1979.

*Boynton, R. M. Psychophysics. In: Bartleson, C. J. & Grum, F. (Eds.), *Optical Radiation Measurements* Volume 5 (pp.335–366). London: Academic Press, 1984.

*Boynton, R.M. A system of photometry and colorimetry based on cone excitations. *Color Research and Application,* 11, 244–252 (1986).

*Boynton, R.M. Color, Science of. *Encyclopedia of Science and Technology.* New York: Academic Press, 187–210, (1987).

*Boynton, R. M. Color vision. *Annual Review of Psychology* 39, 69–100 (1988).

*Boynton, R.M. Human color perception. In Leibovic, K.N. (Ed), *The science of vision: A convergence of disciplines.* New York: Springer-Verlag, 211–253, 1990.

Boynton, R. M. & Baron, W. S. Sinusoidal flicker characteristics of primates cones in response to heterochromatic stimuli. *Journal of the Optical Society of America* 65, 1091–1100 (1975).

*Boynton, R.M., Fargo, L. & Collins, B.L. Categorical color rendering of four common light sources. *Color Research and Application,* 15, 222–230, (1990).

Boynton, R. M. & Gordon, J. Bezold–Brücke hue shift measured by color-naming technique. *Journal of the Optical Society of America* 55, 78–86 (1965).

Boynton, R. M., Hayhoe, M. M. & MacLeod, D. I. A. The gap effect: Chromatic and achromatic visual discrimination as affected by field separation. *Optica Acta* 24, 159–177 (1977).

Boynton, R. M., Ikeda, M. & Stiles, W. S. Interactions among chromatic mechanisms as inferred from positive and negative increment thresholds. *Vision Research* 4, 87–117 (1964).

Boynton, R. M. & Kaiser, P. K. Vision: The additivity law made to work for heterochromatic photometry with bipartite fields. *Science* 161, 366–368 (1968).

Boynton. R. M. & Kaiser, P. K. Temporal analog of the minimally-distinct border. *Vision Research* 18, 111–113 (1978).

*Boynton, R. M. & Kambe, N. Chromatic difference steps of moderate size measured along theoretically critical axes. *Color Research and Application* 5, 13–23 (1980).

Boynton, R. M., Kandel, G. & Onley, J. W. Rapid chromatic adaptation of normal and dichromatic observers. *Journal of the Optical Society of America* 49, 654–666 (1959).

*Boynton, R. M., Nagy, A. L. & Olson, C. X. A flaw in equations for predicting chromatic differences. *Color Research and Application* 8, 69–74 (1983).

*Boynton, R. M. & Olson, C.X. Salience of chromatic basic color terms confirmed by three measures. *Vision Research,* 30, 1311–1317 (1990).

*Boynton, R.M. & Purl, K. Categorical color perception under low-pressure sodium lighting with small amounts of added incandescent illumination. *Lighting Research and Technology,* 21, 23–27, (1989).

Boynton, R, M. & Riggs, L. A. The effect of stimulus area and intensity upon the human retinal response. *Journal of Experimental Psychology* 42, 217–226 (1951).

Boynton, R. M., Schafer, W. & Neun, M. E. Hue-wavelength relation measured by color-naming method for three retinal locations. *Science* 146, 666–668 (1964).

Boynton, R. M., Scheibner, H., Yates, T. & Rinalducci, E. Theory and experiments concerning the heterochromatic threshold-reduction factor (HTRF). *Journal of the Optical Society of America* 55, 1672–1685 (1965).

Boynton, R. M. & Wagner, M. Two-color threshold as test of color vision. *Journal of the Optical Society of America* 51, 429–440 (1961).

Boynton, R. M. & Whitten, D. N. Visual adaptation in monkey cones: Recordings of late receptor potentials. *Science* 170, 1423–1426 (1970).

Boynton, R. M. & Whitten, D. N. Selective chromatic adaptation in primate photoreceptors. *Vision Research* 12, 855–874 (1972).

*Boynton, R. M. & Wisowaty, J. J. Equations for chromatic discrimination models. *Journal of the Optical Society of America* 70, 1471–1476 (1980).

*Brainard, D. H. & Wandell, B. A. Analysis of the retinex theory of color vision. *Journal of the Optical Society of America* 3, 1651–1661 (1986).

Bridges, C. D. B. Visual pigments of the pigeon (Columba livia). *Vision Research* 2, 125–137 (1962).

Brindley, G. S. The summation areas of human colour-receptive mechanisms at increment threshold. *Journal of Physiology* 124, 400–408 (1954).

Brindley, G. S. The colour of light of very long wavelengths. *Journal of Physiology* 130, 35–44 (1955).

Brindley, G. S. *Physiology of the retina and the visual pathway*. London: Edward Arnold, 1960.

Brindley, G. S. Beats produced by simultaneous stimulation of the human eye with intermittent light and intermittent or alternating electric current. *Journal of Physiology* 164, 157–167 (1962).

Brindley, G. S. *Physiology of the retina and the visual pathway* (2nd ed.). Baltimore, MD: Williams & Wilkins, 1970.

Brindley, G. S. & Lewin, W. S. The sensations produced by electrical stimulation of the visual cortex. *Journal of Physiology* 196, 479–493 (1968).

Brindley, G. S. & Willmer, E. N. The reflexion of light from the macular and peripheral fundus oculi in man. *Journal of Physiology* 116, 350–356 (1952).

Brown, J. L. The structure of the visual system. In: Graham, C. H. (Ed.), *Vision and visual perception*. New York: Wiley, 1965.

Brown, J. L., Kuhns, M. P. & Adler, H. E. Relation of threshold criterion to the functional receptors of the eye. *Journal of the Optical Society of America* 47, 198–204 (1957).

Brown, K. T. The electroretinogram: Its components and their origins. *Vision Research* 8, 633–677 (1968).

*Brown, P. K. & Wald, G. Visual pigments in single rods and cones of human retina. *Science* 144, 45–52 (1964).

Brown, W. R. J. The influence of luminance level on visual sensitivity to color differences. *Journal of the Optical Society of America* 41, 684–688 (1951).

Brown, W. R. J. Color discrimination of twelve observers. *Journal of the Optical Society of America* 47, 137–143 (1957).

Brown, W. R. J. & MacAdam, D. L. Visual sensitivities to combined chromaticity and luminance differences. *Journal of the Optical Society of America* 39, 808–834 (1949).

*Buchsbaum, G. A spatial processor model for object colour perception. *Journal of the Franklin Institute* 310, 1–26 (1980).

*Buchsbaum, G. & Gottschalk, A. Trichromacy, opponent colours, coding and optimum colour information transmission in the retina. *Proceedings of the Royal Society B*, 220, 89–113 (1983).

Brücke, E. Über den Nutzeffekt intermittierender Netzhautreizungen. *Akadamie der Wissenschaften, Mathematisch-Naturwissenschaflichen classe*, Wien 49, Part 2, 128–153 (1864).

*Burkhardt, D.A. Synaptic feedback, depolarization, and color opponency in cone photoreceptors, *Visual Neuroscience*, 10, 981–989, (1993).

Burnham, R. W., Hanes, R. M. & Bartleson, C. J. *Color: A guide to basic facts and concepts*. New York: Wiley, 1963.

*Burns, S. A. & Elsner, A.E. Color matching at high illuminances: the color-match-area effect and photopigment bleaching, *Journal of the Optical Society of America A*, 2, 698–704, (1985).

Cajal, S. Ramon y. The vertebrate retina. Translated by R. W. Rodieck & D. Maguire. Appendix A in: Rodieck, R. W., *The vertebrate retina.*San Francisco:Freeman, 1973.

*Calkins, D.J., Shein, S.J., Tsukamoto, Y. & Sterling, P. M and L cones in macaque fovea connect to midget ganglion cells by different numbers of excitatory synapses. *Nature,* 371, 70–71 (1994).

Campbell, F. W. & Gregory, A. H. Effect of size of pupil on visual acuity. *Nature* 187, 1121–1123 (1960).

Campbell, F. W. & Gubisch, R. W. The effect of chromatic aberration on visual acuity. *Journal of Physiology* 192, 345–358 (1967).

*Campbell, F. W. & Rushton, W. A. H. Measurement of the scotopic pigment in the living human eye. *Journal of Physiology* 130, 131–147 (1955).

*Carpenter, R. H. S. *Movement of the Eyes.* London: Pion, 1988.

*Cavanagh, P. & Favreau, O.E. Color and luminance share a common motion pathway. *Vision Research* 25, 1595–1601 (1985).

*Cavanagh, P., Anstis, S.M. & MacLeod, D.I.A. Equiluminance: spatial and temporal factors and the contribution of blue-sensitive cones. *Journal of the Optical Society of America A* 4, 1428–1438 (1987).

*Chaparro, A., Stromeyer, III, C.F., Nuang, E.P., Kronauer, R.E. & Eskew, Jr., R.T. Colour is what the eye sees best. *Nature* 361, 348–350 (1993).

*Chichilnisky, E.J. Perceptual measurements of neural computations in color appearance. *Neuroscience Program*, Stanford, CA, Stanford University, 1994.

*Chevreul, M. E. *The Principles of Harmony and Contrast of Colors and their Applications to the Arts.* PA: Schiffer Publishers Ltd.,1824.

Christ, R. E. Review and analysis of color coding research for visual displays. *Human Factors* 7, 542–570 (1975).

*CIE (International Commission on Illumination). CIE Publication No. 17.4 *International Lighting Vocabulary.* Vienna, Austria: Bureau Central de la CIE, (1987).

*CIE (International Commission on Illumination). CIE 1988 2 degree spectral luminous efficiency function for photopic vision. Vienna, Austria: CIE Central Bureau, 1990.

*Cicerone, C. M. Constraints placed on color vision models by the relative numbers of different cone classes in human fovea centralis. *Farbe* 34, 59–66 (1987).

*Cicerone, C. M. & Nerger, J. L. The relative numbers of long-wavelength-sensitive to middle-wavelength-sensitive cones in the human fovea centralis. *Vision Research* 29, 115–128 (1989a).

*Cicerone, C. M. & Nerger, J. L. The density of cones in the fovea centralis of the human dichromat. *Vision Research* 29, 1587–1595 (1989b).

*Cicerone, C. M., Volbrecht, V. J., Donnelly, S. K. & Werner, J. S. Perception of blackness. *Journal of the Optical Society of America* 3, 432–436 (1986).

Clarke, F. J. J. Extra-foveal colour metrics. *Optica Acta* 7, 355–384 (1960).

Clarke, F. J. J. Further studies of extrafoveal colour metrics, *Optica Acta* 10, 257 (1963).

*Cline, D., Hofstetter, H. & Griffin, J.R. *Dictionary of Visual Science* 3rd Edition, Radnor, PA, Chilton Book Co. 1980.

*Cohen, J.B. Dependency of the spectral reflectance curves of the Munsell color chips. *Psychonomic Science*, 1, 369–370, (1964).

*Cohn, S. A., Emmerich, D. S. & Carlson, E. A. Differences in the responses of heterozygous carriers of color-blindness and normal controls to briefly presented stimuli. *Vision Research* 29, 255–262 (1989).

*Cole, G.R., Hine, T. & McIlhagga, W. Detection mechanisms in L-, M-, and S-cone contrast space. *Journal of the Optical Society of America A*, 10, 38–51 (1993)

*Commerford, J.P. Stereopsis with chromatic contours. *Vision Research* 14, 975–982 (1974).

Cooper, G. F. & Robson, J. G. The yellow colour of the lens of man and other primates. *Journal of Physiology* 203, 411–417 (1969).

Cornsweet, T. N. *Visual perception.* New York: Academic Press, 1970.

*Crane, H. D. & Piantanida, T. P. On seeing reddish green and yellowish blue. *Science* 221, 881–890 (1983).

*Craven, B.J. & Foster, D.H. An operational approach to color constancy. *Vision Research,* 32, 1359–1366 (1992).

Crawford, B. H. Visual adaptation in relation to brief conditioning stimuli. *Proceedings of the Royal Society London B* 134, 283–302 (1947).

Crawford, B. H. Colour matching and adaptation. *Vision Research* 5, 71–78 (1965).

*Crawford, T.D. Defining "basic color terms" *Anthroplogical Linguistics,* 24, 338–343 (1982).

Crombie. A. C. Helmholtz. *Scientific American* 198 (3), 94–102 (1958).

*Crescitelli, F. & Dartnall, H. J. A. Human visual purple. *Nature* 172, 195–197 (1953).

*Curcio, C. A., Sloan, K. R. Jr., Packer, O., Hendrickson, A. E. & Kalina, E. Distribution of cones in human and monkey retina: individual variability and radial asymmetry. *Science* 236, 579–582 (1987).

*Dacey, D.M. Morphology of a small-field bistratified ganglion cell type in the macaque and human retina. *Visual Neuroscience,* 10, 1081–1098 (1993).

*Dacey, D. M. & Lee, B. B. The blue-ON opponent pathway in primate retina originates from a distinct bistratified ganglion cell type. *Nature* 267, 731–735 (1994).

*Dacey, D.M. & Lee, B.B. Physiological identification of cone inputs to HI and HII horizontal cells in Macaque retina. *Investigative Ophthalmology & Visual Science,* 46, S3 (4) 1995.

*Dacheux, R. F. & Raviola, E. Physiology of H1 horizontal cells in the primate retina. *Proceedings of the Royal Society of London B* 239, 213–230 (1990).

Dalton, J. Extraordinary facts relating to the vision of colours: With observations (read in October, 1794). *Memoires of the Literary and Philosophical Society (Manchester)* 5, 28–45 (1798).

*Dannemiller, J.L. Spectral reflectance of natural objects: how many basis functions are necessary? *Journal of the Optical Society of America A,* 9, 507–515 (1992).

Dartnall, H. J. A. The interpretation of spectral sensitivity curves. *British Medical Bulletin* 9, 24–30 (1953).

Dartnall, H. J. A. Extraction, measurement, and analysis of visual photopigment. In: Davson, H. (Ed.), *The eye.* New York: Academic Press, 1962.

*Dartnall, H. J. A., Bowmaker, J. K. & Mollon, J. D. Human visual pigments: microspectrophotometric results from the eyes of seven persons. *Proceedings of the Royal Society of London B* 220, 115–130 (1983a).

*Dartnall, H.J.A., Bowmaker, J.K. & Mollon, J.D. Microspectrophotometry of human photoreceptors. In J.D. Mollon & L.T. Sharpe (Eds.) *Colour Vision, Physiology and Psychophysics,* London:Academic Press, 1983b

*Davidoff, J. *Cognition Through Color.* Cambridge, MA: MIT Press, 1991.

Daw, N. W. & Enoch, J. M. Contrast sensitivity, Westheimer function, and Stiles–Crawford effect in a blue cone monochromat. *Vision Research* 13, 1669–1680 (1973).

deLange, H. Experiments on flicker and some calculations on an electrical analogue of the foveal systems. *Physica* 18, 935–950 (1952).

deLange, H. Research into the dynamic nature of the human fovea cortex systems with intermittent and modulated light: II.Phase shift in brightness and delay in color perception. *Journal of the Optical Society of America* 48, 784–789 (1958).

De Monasterio, F. M. & Gouras, P. Functional properties of ganglion cells of the rhesus monkey retina. *Journal of Physiology* 251, 167–197 (1975).

De Monasterio, F. M., Gouras, P. & Tolhurst, D. J. Trichromatic colour opponency in ganglion cells of the rhesus monkey retina. *Journal of Physiology* 251, 197–216 (1975).

*Derefeldt, G. Colour appearance systems. In: Cronly–Dillon, J. R. (Ed.), *Vision and Visual Dysfunction Volume 6: The Perception of Color.* P. Gouras (Ed.). New York: Macmillan Press, 1991.

*Derrington, A.M., Krauskopf, J. & Lennie, P. Chromatic mechanisms in lateral geniculate nucleus of Macaque. *Journal of Physiology,* 357, 241–265 (1984).

DeValois, R. L. Behavioral and electrophysiological studies of primate vision. In: Neff, W. D. (Ed.), *Contributions to sensory physiology* v. 1. New York:Academic Press, 1965a.

DeValois, R. L. Analysis and coding of color vision in the primate visual system. *Cold Spring Harbor Symposia on Quantitative Biology* 30, 567–579 (1965b).

DeValois, R. L. Central mechanisms of color vision. In: Jung, R. (Ed.), *Handbook of sensory physiology* VII/3A, New York: Springer-Verlag, 1973.

DeValois. R. L., Abramov, I. & Jacobs, G. H. Analysis of response patterns of LGN cells. *Journal of the Optical Society of America* 56, 966–977 (1966).

DeValois, R. L. & DeValois, K. K. Neural coding of color. In: Carterette, E. C. & Friedman, M. P. (Eds.), *Handbook of Perception*, v. 5. New York: Academic Press, 1975.

*DeValois, R. L. & DeValois, K. K. *Spatial Vision*. New York, Oxford University Press, 212–238, 1988.

*DeValois, R. L. & DeValois, K. K. A multi-stage color model. *Vision Research* 33, 1053–1065 (1993).

DeValois, R. L., Jacobs, G. H. & Abramov, I. Responses of single cells in visual system to shifts in the wavelength of light. *Science* 146, 1184–1186 (1964).

*DeValois, R. L. & Jacobs, G. H. Primate color vision. *Science* 162, 533–540 (1968).

DeValois. R. L., Morgan, H. C., Polson, M. C., Mead, W. R. & Hull, E. M. Psychophysical studies of monkey vision: 1. Macaque luminosity and color vision tests. *Vision Research* 14, 53–67 (1974).

DeValois, R. L., Smith, C. J., Kitai, S. T. & Karoly, S. J. Responses of single cells in different layers of the primate lateral geniculate nucleus to monochromatic light. *Science* 127, 238–239 (1958).

deWeert, Ch. M. M. & Levelt, W. J. M. Comparison of normal and dichoptic colour mixing. *Vision Research* 16, 59–70 (1976).

Dirac, P. A. M. *The principles of quantum mechanics* (4th ed.). London: Oxford University Press, 1958.

Ditchburn, R. W. *Eye-movements and visual perception*. Oxford: Clarendon Press, 1973.

Ditchburn, R. W. *Light* (3rd ed.). New York: Academic Press, 1976.

Dow, B. M. & Gouras P. Color and spatial specificity of single units in Rhesus monkey foveal striate cortex. *Journal of Neurophysiology* 36, 79–100 (1973).

Dowling, J. E. Organization of vertebrate retinas. *Investigative Ophthalmology* 9, 655–680 (1970).

*Dowling, J. E. *The Retina: an approachable part of the brain*. Cambridge: The Belknap Press of Harvard University Press, 1987.

*Dowling, J. E. *Neurons and Networks: An introduction to Neuroscience*. Cambridge: The Belknap Press of Harvard University Press, 1992.

Dowling, J. E. & Boycott, B. B. Organization of the primate retina: Electron microscopy. *Proceedings of the Royal Society of London B* 166, 80–111 (1966).

Dowling, J. E. & Ehinger, B. Synaptic organization of the amine-containing interplexiform cells of the goldfish and Cebus monkey retina. *Science* 188, 270–273 (1975).

Dreher, B., Fukada, Y. & Rodieck, R. W. Identification, classification, and anatomical segregation of cells with X-like and Y-like properties in the lateral geniculate nucleus of old-world primates. *Journal of Physiology* 258, 433–452 (1976).

*D'Zmura, M. & Iverson, G. Color constancy. I. Basic theory of two-stage linear recovery of spectral descriptions for lights and surfaces. *Journal of the Optical Society of America A* 10, 2148–2165 (1993).

*D'Zmura, M. & Iverson, M. A formal approach to color constancy: The recovery of surface and light source spectral properties using bilinear models. In C. Dowling, F. Froberts, & P. Theuns (Eds) *Recent Progress in Mathematical Psychology*. Lawrence Earlbaum Associates, Hillsdale, N.J.: 1996 (in press).

Egan, J. P. *Signal detection theory and ROC Analysis*. New York: Academic Press, 1975.

*Eisner, A. & MacLeod, D. I. A. Flicker photometric study of chromatic adaptation: selective suppression of cone inputs by colored background. *Journal of the Optical Society of America* 71, 705–718 (1981).

Engen, T. Psychophysics: I. Discrimination and detection. In: Kling, J.W., & Riggs, L.A. (Eds.), *Experimental psychology*. New York : Holt, Rinehart, and Winston, 1971.

Enoch, J. M. Wave-guide modes in retinal receptors. *Science* 133, 1353–1354 (1961a).

Enoch, J. M. Nature of the transmission of energy in the retinal receptors. *Journal of the Optical Society of America* 51, 1122–1126 (1961b).

Enoch, J. M. Optical properties of the retinal receptors. *Journal of the Optical Society of America* 53, 71–85 (1963).

Enoch, J. M. Physical properties of the retinal receptor and response of retinal receptors. *Psychological Bulletin* 61, 242–251 (1964).

Enoch, J. M. The two-color threshold technique of Stiles and derived component color mechanisms. In: Jameson, D., & Hurvich, L. M. (Eds.), *Handbook of sensory physiology* VII/4. New York: Springer-Verlag, 1972.

*Erickson, R.G. & Thier, P. A neuronal correlate of spatial stability during periods of self-induced visual motion. *Experimental Brain Research*, 86, 608–616 (1991).

*Eskew, R.T. & Boynton, R.M. Effects of field area and configuration on chromatic and border discriminations. *Vision Research*, 27, 1835–1844 (1987).

*Estévez, O., On the fundamental data-base of normal and dichromatic color vision. Doctoral Dissertation, University of Amsterdam, 1979.

Estévez, O. & Cavonius, C. R. Human color perception and Stiles' π-mechanisms. *Vision Research* 17, 417–422 (1977).

Estévez, O. & Spekreijse, H. A spectral compensation method for determining the flicker characteristics of the human colour mechanisms. *Vision Research* 14, 823–830 (1974).

Estévez, O., Spekreijse, H., van den Berg, T. J. T. P. & Cavonius, C. R. The spectral sensitivities of isolated human color mechanisms determined from contrast evoked potential measurements. *Vision Research* 15, 1205–1212 (1975).

*Estévez, O. & Spekreijse, H. The "silent substitution" method in visual research. *Vision Research* 22, 681–691 (1982).

Evans. R. M. *An introduction to color.* New York: Wiley, 1948.

Evans. R. M. Variables of perceived color. *Journal of the Optical Society of America* 54, 1467–1474 (1964).

Evans, R. M. *The perception of color.* New York: Wiley, 1974.

Evans, R. M. & Swenholt, B. K. Chromatic strength of colors: Dominant wavelength and purity. *Journal of the Optical Society of America* 57, 1319–1324 (1967).

*Fairchild, M.D. & Reniff, L. Time course of chromatic adaptation for color-appearance judgments. *Journal of Optical Society of America, A,* 12, 824–833 (1995).

Falls, H. F., Wolter, J. R. & Alpern, M. Typical total monochromacy. *Archives of Ophthalmology* 74, 610–620 (1965).

*Falk, D., Brill, D. & Stork, D. *Seeing the Light.* New York: John Wiley & Sons, 1986.

*Falmagne, J.C. Psychophysical measurement and theory, in K.R. Boff, L. Kaufman & J. P. Thomas (Eds.) *Handbook of Perception and Human Performance,* vol. 1, Sensory Processes and Perception, New York: A Wiley-Interscience Publication, 1986.

Fechner, G. *Elements of psychophysics,* vol. 1. Translated by H. E. Adler, D. H. Howes & E. G. Boring. New York: Holt, Rinehart and Winston, 1966.

Feinberg, G. Light. *Scientific American* 219 (3), 50–59 (1968).

*Felleman, D.J. & Van Essen, D.C. Receptive field properties of neurons in Area V3 of Macaque monkey extrastriate cortex., *Journal of Neurophysiology* 57, 889–920 (1987).

Ferry, E. S. Persistence of vision. *American Journal of Science* 44, 192–207 (1892).

*Feynman, R. P. *The character of physical law.* Cambridge: M.I.T. Press, 1965.

Fiorentini, A. Mach band phenomena. In Jameson, D. & Hurvich, L. M. (Eds.), *Handbook of sensory physiology* VII/4. New York: Springer-Verlag, 1972.

Fischer, F. P., Bouman, M. A. & ten Doesschate, J. A case of tritanopy. *Documenta Ophthalmologica* 5, 73–87 (1951).

Forsyth, D. M. & Chapanis, A. Counting repeated light flashes as a function of their number, their rate of presentation, and retinal location stimulated. *Journal of Experimental Psychology* 56, 385–392 (1958).

Fox, J. C. & German, W. J. Macular vision following cerebral resection. *Archives of Neurology and Psychiatry* 35, 808–826 (1936).

Foxell, C. A. P. & Stevens, W. R. Measurements of visual acuity. *British Journal of Ophthalmology* 39, 513–533 (1955).

Friele, L. F. C. FMC-metrics: What next? In: Vos, J. J., Friele, L. F. C., & Walraven, P. L. (Eds.) *Color metrics*. Soesterberg, The Netherlands: Institute for Perception TNO, 1972.

*Frumkes, T. E. & Wu, S. M. Independent influences of rod adaptation on cone-mediated responses to light onset and offset in distal retinal neurons. *Journal of Neurophysiology* 64, 1043–1054 (1990).

*Fuld, K., Werner, J. S. & Wooten, B. R. The possible elemental nature of brown. *Vision Research* 23, 631–637 (1983).

*Fuld, K., Wooten, B.R. & Whalen, J.J. The elemental hues of shortwave and extra-spectral lights, *Perception and Psychophysics,* 29, 317–322 (1981).

*Gelb, A. Die "Farbenkonstanz" den Sehndinge. In A. Bethe (Ed.) *Handbuch der normalen und pathologischen Physiologie*, 12, Berlin:Springer, 1929.

*Geisler, W.S. Sequential ideal-observer analysis of visual discriminations. *Psychological Review* 96, 267–314 (1989).

Glickstein, M. & Heath. G. G. Receptors in the monochromat eye. *Vision Research* 15, 633–636 (1975).

Gordon, J. & Abramov, I. Color vision in the peripheral retina. II. Hue and saturation. *Journal of the Optical Society of America* 67, 202–207 (1977).

Gouras, P. Identification of cone mechanisms in monkey ganglion cells. *Journal of Physiology* 199, 533–547 (1968).

Gouras, P. Opponent-colour cells in different layers of foveal striate cortex. *Journal of Physiology* 238, 583–602 (1974).

*Gouras, P. Precortical physiology of colour vision. In: Cronly-Dillon, J. R. (Ed.) *Vision and Visual Dysfunction: The Perception of Color Volume 6*. Edited by P. Gouras. New York: Macmillan Press, 1991.

*Gouras, P. & Zrenner, E. Enhancement of luminance flicker by color-opponent mechanisms. *Science,* 205, 587–589 (1979).

Graham, C. H. (Ed.) *Vision and visual perception*. New York: Wiley, 1965.

Graham, R. E. Communication theory as applied to television coding. *Acta Electronica* 2, 333–343 (1957–1958).

*Graham, N. & Hood, D. C. Modeling the dynamics of light adaptation: the merging of two traditions. *Vision Research* 32, 1373–1393 (1992).

Granit, R. *Sensory mechanisms of the retina.* London: Cambridge University Press, 1947.(Reprinted in 1963 by Hafner Publishing Co., New York.)

Green, D. G. Sinusoidal flicker characteristics of the color-sensitive mechanisms of the eye. *Vision Research* 9, 591–601 (1969).

Green, D. G. Visual acuity in the blue cone monochromat. *Journal of Physiology* 222, 419–426 (1972).

Gregory, R. L. & Wallace, J. G. Recovery from early blindness. *Experimental Psychology Society* (England) Monograph No. 2, 1963.

*Gregory, R.L. Patent specification of a heterochromatic photometer. In R. L. Gregory (Ed.) *Concepts and Mechanisms of Perception,* London: Duckworth, pp.475–481, 1974

Griffin, D. R., Hubbard, R. & Wald, G. The sensitivity of the human eye to infra-red radiation. *Journal of the Optical Society of America* 37, 546–554 (1947).

Grützner, P. Acquired color vision defects. In: Jameson, D. & Hurvich, L. M. (Eds.), *Handbook of sensory physiology,* VII/4. New York: Springer-Verlag, 1972.

Guild, J. The colorimetric properties of the spectrum. *Philosophical Transactions of the Royal Society of London* 230A, 149–187 (1931).

Guild, J. Discussion in Report of a joint discussion on vision held on June 3, 1932, at the *Imperial College of Science by the Physical and Optical Societies,* p. 157. London: Physical Society, 1932.

*Guild, J. The colorimetric properties of the spectrum. *Philosophical Transactions of the Royal Society of London* 230A, 149–187 (1925–1926).

Guth, S. L. Nonadditivity and inhibition among chromatic luminances at threshold. *Vision Research* 7, 319–328 (1967).

*Guth, S. L. Model for color vision and light adaptation. *Journal of the Optical Society of America* 8 976–993 (1991).

*Guth, S. L., Massof, R. W. & Benzschwel, T. Vector model for normal and dichromatic color vision. *Journal of the Optical Society of America* 70, 197–211 (1980).

*Hård, A. & Sivak, L. NCS-Natural Color System: A Swedish standard for color notation. *Color Research and Application* 6, 129–138 (1981).

*Hargrave, P. A., McDowell, J. H., Curtis, D. R., Wang, J. K., Juszczak, E., Fong, S. -L., Rao, J. K. M. & Argos, P. The structure of bovine rhodopsin. *Biophysics of Structure and Mechanism* 9, 235–244 (1983).

Harter, M. R. & White, C. T. Evoked cortical responses to checkerboard patterns: Effect of check-size as a function of visual acuity. *Electroencephalography and Clinical Neurophysiology* 28, 48–54 (1970).

Hartline, H. K. The response of single optic nerve fibers of the vertebrate eye to illumination of the retina. *American Journal of Physiology* 121, 400–415 (1938).

Harwerth, R. S. & Sperling, H. G. Prolonged color blindness induced by intense spectral lights in Rhesus monkeys. *Science* 174, 520–523 (1971).

*Hayhoe, M. M., Benimoff, N. I. & Hood, D. C. The time course of multiplicative and subtractive adaptation process. *Vision Research* 27, 1981–1996 (1987).

Heath, G. Luminosity curves of normal and dichromatic observers. *Science* 128, 775–776 (1958).

Hecht, S. A quantitative formulation of colour-vision. In Report of a joint discussion on vision held on June 3, 1932, at the *Imperial College of Science by the Physical and Optical Societies*. London: Physical Society, 1932.

Hecht, S. Brightness, visual acuity and colour blindness. *Documenta Ophthalmologica* 3, 289–306 (1949).

Hecht, S., Ross, S. & Mueller, C. G. The visibility of lines and squares at high brightness. *Journal of the Optical Society of America* 37, 500–507 (1947).

Hecht, S. & Shlaer, S. The color vision of dichromats: I. Wavelength discrimination, brightness distribution, and color mixture. II. Saturation as the basis for wavelength discrimination and color mixture. *Journal of General Physiology* 20, 57–82; 83–93 (1936).

Hecht, S., Shlaer, S. & Pirenne, M. H. Energy, quanta, and vision. *Journal of General Physiology* 25, 819–840 (1942).

Helmholtz, H. *Physiological optics* (edited by J. P. C. Southall; 3 volumes). Rochester, New York: Optical Society of America, 1924.

*Helmholtz, H. In: Southall, J. P. C. (Ed.) *Helmholtz's Treatise on Psychological Optics*. Volume III. New York: Dover, 1962.

*Helson, H. Some factors and implications of color constancy. *Journal of the Optical Society of America*, 33, 555–567 (1934).

Helson, H. Fundamental problems in color vision: 1. The principle governing changes in hue, saturation, and lightness of non-selective samples in chromatic illumination. *Journal of Experimental Psychology* 23, 439–476 (1938).

Helson, H. Studies of anomalous contrast and assimilation. *Journal of the Optical Society of America* 53, 179–184 (1963).

Helson, H. & Michels, W. C. The effect of chromatic adaptation on achromaticity. *Journal of the Optical Society of America* 38, 1025–1032 (1948).

Henderson, S. T. *Daylight and its spectrum* (2d ed.). Bristol, England: Adam Hilger, 1977.

Henkes, H. E. & van der Tweel, L. H. (Eds.) *Flicker.* The Hague: W. Junk, 1964. [Also published as *Documenta Ophthalmologia* 18 (1964.)]

Hering, E. *Outlines of a theory of the light sense.* Translated by L. M. Hurvich & D. Jameson. Cambridge, Massachusetts: Harvard University Press, 1964.

Herrnstein, R. J. & Boring, E. G. (Eds.), *A source book in the history of psychology.* Cambridge, Mass.: Harvard University Press, 1965.

*Hess, R.F., Mullen, K.T. & Zrenner, E. Human photopic vision with only short wavelength cones: Post-receptoral properties. *Journal of Physiology, 417, 151–172 (1989)*.

*Heywood, C.A. , Shields, C. & Cowey, A. The involvement of the temporal lobes in colour discrimination. *Experimental Brain Research, 71, 437–441 (1988)*.

*Heywood, C.A., Gaffan, D. and Cowey, A. Cerebral achromatopsia in monkeys (in press).

*Hibino, H. R-G and Y-B opponent-color responses a function of retinal eccentricity, *Vision Research, 32, 1955–1964 (1992)*.

Hirsch, H. V. B. & Spinelli, D. Visual experience modifies distribution of horizontally and vertically oriented receptive fields in cats. *Science* 168, 869–871 (1970).

Hochberg, J. & Silverstein, A. A quantitative index of stimulus similarity: Proximity vs. differences in brightness. *American Journal of Psychology* 69, 456–458 (1956).

*Hood, D. C., Ilves, T., Maurer, E., Wandell, B. & Buckingham, E. Human cone saturation as a function of ambient intensity: a test of models of shifts in the dynamic range. *Vision Research* 18, 983–993 (1978).

*Hood, D. C. & Finkelstein, M. A. Sensitivity to Light (Chapter 5) In: Boff, K. R., Kaufman, L. & Thomas, J. P. (Eds.), *Handbook of Perception and Human Performance: Volume I.* New York: John Wiley and Sons, 1986.

*Hood, D. C. & Birch, D. G. Human cone receptor activity: The leading edge of the a-wave and models of receptor activity. *Visual Neuroscience* 10, 1–15 (1993).

Horner, F. Die Erblichkeit des Daltonismus: Ein Beitrag zum Vererbungsgesetz. *Amtl. Ber. Verwaltung d. Medizinalwesens Kanton Zürich*, 208–211, 1876.

Hsia, Y. & Graham, C. H. Color blindness. In: Graham, E. H. (Ed.), *Vision and visual perception.* New York: Wiley, 1965.

Hubbard, R. Preface to the English translations of Boll's On the anatomy and physiology of the retina and Kühne's Chemical processes in the retina. *Vision Research* 17, 1247–1248 (1977).

Hubel, D. H. & Wiesel, T. N. Receptive fields and functional architecture of monkey striate cortex. *Journal of Physiology* 195, 215–243 (1968).

Hull, E. Corticofugal influence in the macaque lateral geniculate nucleus. *Vision Research* 8, 1285–1298 (1968).

*Hunt, D.M., Kanwaljit, S. D., Bowmaker, J.K. & Mollon, J.D. The chemistry of John Dalton's color blindness. *Science*, 267, 984–988 (1995).

Hunt, R. W. G. *The reproduction of colour* (3rd ed.). New York: Wiley, 1975.

*Hunt, R. W. G. Revised colour-appearance model for related and unrelated colours. *Color Research and Application* 16, 146–165 (1991).

*Hunt, T. The initiation of protein synthesis. *Trends in Biochemical Sciences* 5, 178–181 (1980).

Hurvich, L. M. Color vision deficiencies. In: Jameson, D. & Hurvich, L. M. (Eds.), *Handbook of sensory physiology* VII/4. New York: Springer-Verlag, 1972.

*Hurvich, L. M. *Color Vision*. Sunderland, MA: Sinauer Assoc. Inc., 1981.

*Hurvich, L. M. & Jameson, D. Helmholtz and the three-color theory: An historical note. *American Journal of Psychology* LXII, 111–114 (1949).

Hurvich, L. M. & Jameson, D. A psychophysical study of white: I. Neutral adaptation. *Journal of the Optical Society of America* 41, 521–527 (1951a).

Hurvich, L. M. & Jameson, D. A psychophysical study of white: III. Adaptation as variant. *Journal of the Optical Society of America* 41, 787–801 (1951b).

Hurvich, L. M. & Jameson, D. Some quantitative aspects of an opponent-colors theory: II. Brightness, saturation, and hue in normal and dichromatic vision. *Journal of the Optical Society of America* 45, 602–616 (1955).

*Hurvich, L.M. & Jameson, D. An opponent-process theory of color vision. *Psychological Review*, 64, 384–404 (1957).

*Hurvich, L.M. & Jameson, D. Translation of *Outlines of a Theory of the Light Sense*, by Ewald Hering. Cambridge, MA: Harvard University Press, 1964.

*Hurvich, L. M. & Jameson, D. Human color perception: An essay review. *American Scientist* 57, 143–166 (1969).

Hurvich, L. M. & Jameson, D. On the measurement of dichromatic neutral points. *Acta Chromatica* 2, 207–216 (1974).

Ikeda, M. & Boynton, R. M. Effect of test-flash duration upon the spectral sensitivity of the eye. *Journal of the Optical Society of America* 52, 697–699 (1962).

Ikeda, M. & Urakubo, M. Flicker HTRF as test of color vision. *Journal of the Optical Society of America* 58, 27–31 (1968).

Indow, T. & Ohsumi, K. Multidimensional mapping of sixty Munsell colors by nonmetric procedure. In: Vos, J. J., Friele, L. F. C. & Walraven, P. L. (Eds.), *Color metrics.* Soesterberg, The Netherlands: Institute for Perception TNO, 1972.

Ingling, C. R., Jr. The spectral sensitivity of the opponent-color channels. *Vision Research* 17, 1083–1089 (1977).

*Ingling, C.R. Jr. Color naming of small foveal fields. *Vision Research,* 10, 501–511 (1970).

*Ingling, C.R., Tsou, B. H-P., Gast, T.J., Burns, S.A., Emerick, J.O. & Riesenberg, L. The achromatic channel—I. The non-linearity of minimum border and flicker matches. *Vision Research,*18, 379–390 (1978).

*Ingling, C. R., Jr. & Martinez-Uriegas, E. The relationship between spectral sensitivity and spatial sensitivity for the primate r-g X-channel. *Vision Research* 23, 1495–1500 (1983).

Ingling, C. R., Jr. & Tsou, B. H-P. Orthogonal combinations of three visual channels. *Vision Research* 17, 1075–1082 (1977).

Ives, H. E. A polarization flicker photometer and some data of theoretical bearing obtained with it. *Philosophical Magazine* 33, 360–380 (1917).

Ives. H. E. A theory of intermittent vision. *Journal of the Optical Society of America and Review of Scientific Instruments* 6, 343–361 (1922).

Ives, H. E. & Kingsbury, E. F. The theory of the flicker photometer. *Philosophical Magazine* 28, 708–728 (1914).

*Jacobs, G. H. Saturation estimates and chromatic adaptation. *Perception and Psychophysics* 2, 271–274 (1967).

*Jameson, D. Color in the hands of the artist and in the eyes of the beholder. *Color Research and Application* 14, 284–292 (1989).

Jameson, D. & Hurvich, L. M. A psychophysical study of white: II. Neutral adaptation: Area and duration as variants. *Journal of the Optical Society of America* 41, 528–536 (1951).

Jameson, D. & Hurvich. L. M. Some quantitative aspects of an opponent-colors theory: I. Chromatic responses and spectral saturation. *Journal of the Optical Society of America* 45, 546–552 (1955).

*Jameson, D. & Hurvich, L.M. Theoretical analysis of anomalous trichromatic color vision,. *Journal of the Optical Society of America,* 46, 1075–1089, (1956).

*Jameson, D. & Hurvich, L. M. Perceived color and its dependence on focal, surrounding, and preceding stimulus variables. *Journal of the Optical Society of America* 49, 890–898 (1959).

Jameson, D. & Hurvich, L. M. Color adaptation: Sensitivity, contrast, after-images. In: Jameson, D. & Hurvich, L. M. (Eds.), *Handbook of sensory physiology* VII/4. New York: Springer-Verlag, 1972.

*Jameson, D. & Hurvich, L.M. Essay concerning color constancy. *Annual Review of Psychology*, 40, 1–22 (1989).

*Jameson, D., Hurvich, L.M & Varner, F.D. Receptoral and postreceptoral processes in recovery from chromatic adaptation. *Proceedings of the National Academy of Sciences (USA)*, 76, 3034–3038 (1979).

*Jenkins, F. A. & White, H. E. *Fundamentals of Optics*. New York: McGraw-Hill, 1957.

*Jenness, J.W. & Shevell, S.K. Color appearance with sparse chromatic context. *Vision Research*, 35, 797–805 (1995)

*Jones, L. A. & Lowry, E. M. Retinal sensibility to saturation differences. *Journal of the Optical Society of America and Review of Scientific Instruments* 13, 25–34 (1926).

Judd. D. B. The 1931 I.C.I. standard observer and coordinate system for colorimetry. *Journal of the Optical Society of America* 23, 359–374 (1933).

Judd, D. B. Hue, saturation, and lightness of surface colors with chromatic illumination. *Journal of the Optical Society of America* 30, 3–32 (1940).

Judd, D. B. Color perceptions of deuteranopic and protanopic observers. *Journal of Research of the National Bureau of Standards* 41, 247–271 (1948).

Judd, D. B. Report of U. S. Secretariat, Committee on Colorimetry and Artificial Daylight. Proc. CIE 1, part 7, p. 11 (Stockholm, 1951a). Paris: Bureau Central CIE.

Judd, D. B. Basic correlates of the visual stimulus. In: Stevens, S. S. (Ed.), *Handbook of experimental psychology*. New York: Wiley, 1951b.

Judd. D. B. Some color demonstrations I have shown. *Journal of the Optical Society of America* 49, 322–328 (1959).

Judd, D. B. Appraisal of Land's work on two-primary color projections. *Journal of the Optical Society of America* 50, 254–268 (1960).

*Judd, D.B., MacAdam, D.L. & Wyszecki, G. Spectral distribution of typical daylight as a function of correlated color temperature. *Journal of the Optical Society of America*, 54, 1031–1040 (1964).

*Judd, D.B. & Wyszecki, G. *Color in Business, Science, and Industry, 3rd edition*, New York: John Wiley & Sons, 1975.

Julesz, B. *Foundations of cyclopean perception.* Chicago: University of Chicago Press, 1971.

*Julesz, B. *Dialogues on Perception.* Cambridge, MA: MIT Press, 1995.

*Kaiser, P.K. Minimally distinct border as a preferred psychophysical criterion in visual heterochromatic photometry. *Journal of the Optical Society of America,* 61, 966–971(1971)

*Kaiser, P. K. Nonvisual color perception: a critical review. *Color Research and Application* 8, 137–144, 1983.

*Kaiser, P.K. Photometric Measurements, in C.J. Bartleson and F. Grum (Eds.), *Optical Radiation Measurements,* Volume 5, *Visual Measurements,* Toronto: Academic Press, 563–614, 1984.

*Kaiser, P. K. Sensation luminance: A new name to distinguish CIE luminance from luminance dependent on an individual's spectral sensitivity. *Vision Research* 28, 455–456 (1988).

*Kaiser, P.K. Flicker as a function of wavelength and heterochromatic flicker photometry, in J. J. Kulikowski, V. Walsh and I.J. Murray (Eds.) *Vision and Visual Dysfunction,* Volume 5, *Limits of Vision,* Boca Raton, FL: CRC Press, 171–190, 1991.

*Kaiser, P.K. & Hemmendinger, H. The color rule: A device for color-vision testing. *Color Research and Application,* 5, 65–71, (1980).

*Kaiser, P. K. & Ayama, M. Just noticeable inhomogeneity criterion for determining wavelength discrimination functions. *Vision Research* 25, 1327–1330 (1985).

*Kaiser, P. K., Comerford, J. P. & Bodinger, D. M. Saturation of spectral lights. *Journal of the Optical Society of America* 66, 818–826 (1976).

*Kaiser, P. K., Lee, B. B., Martin, P. R. & Valberg, A. The physiological basis of the minimally distinct border demonstrated in the ganglion cells of the macaque retina. *Journal of Physiology* 422, 153–183 (1990).

*Kaneko, A. Physiological and morphological identification of horizontal, bipolar and amacrine cells in goldfish retina. *Journal of Physiology* 207, 623–633 (1970).

Kalmus, H. *Diagnosis and genetics of defective colour vision.* New York: Pergamon Press, 1965.

*Kalmus, H. Metameric color rule matches of normal, color deficient cataractic and aphakic observers, *Annals of Human Genetics,* 36, 109–118 (1972).

*Kaplan, E. & Shapley, R. The origin of the S (Slow) potential in the mammalian lateral geniculate nucleus. *Experimental Brain Research* 55, 111–116 (1984).

Katz, D. *The world of color.* Translated in abridged form from the second German edition (1930) by R. B. MacLeod & C. W. Fox. London: Kegan, Paul, 1935.

602   References

Kaufman, J. E. (Ed.) *IES Lighting Handbook* (5th ed.), New York: Illuminating Engineering Society, 1993.

Kelly, D. H. Visual responses to time-dependent stimuli: 1. Amplitude sensitivity measurements. *Journal of the Optical Society of America* 51, 422–429 (1961).

Kelly, D. H. Sine waves and flicker fusion. *Documenta Ophthalmologica* 18, 16–35 (1964).

Kelly, D. H. Diffusion model of linear flicker responses. *Journal of the Optical Society of America* 59, 1665–1670 (1969).

Kelly. D. H. Theory of flicker and transient responses: I. Uniform fields. *Journal of the Optical Society of America* 61, 537–546 (1971).

Kelly, D. H. Flicker. In: Jameson, D. & Hurvich, L. M. (Eds.), *Handbook of sensory physiology* VII/4. New York: Springer-Verlag, 1972.

Kelly, D. H. Lateral inhibition in human colour mechanisms. *Journal of Physiology* 228, 55–72 (1973).

Kelly. D. H. Spatio-temporal frequency characteristics of color-vision mechanisms. *Journal of the Optical Society of America* 64, 983–990 (1974).

Kelly, D. H. Luminous and chromatic flickering patterns have opposite effects. *Science* 188, 371–372 (1975).

*Kelly, D. H. Spatiotemporal variation of chromatic and achromatic contrast thresholds. *Journal of the Optical Society of America*, 73, 742–750 (1983).

*Kelly, D. H. Spatial and temporal interactions in color vision. *Journal of Imaging Technology*, 15(2) 82–89 (1989).

Kelly, D. H., Boynton, R. M. & Baron, W. S. Primate flicker sensitivity: Psychophysics and electrophysiology. *Science* 194, 1077–1079 (1976).

Kelly, D. H. & van Norren, D. Two-band model of heterochromatic flicker. *Journal of the Optical Society of America* 67, 1081–1091 (1977).

Kingslake, R. Refraction. In: Bensançon, R. M. (Ed.), *The Encyclopedia of Physics* (2nd ed.). New York: Van Nostrand Reinhold, 1974.

King-Smith, P. E. & Carden, D. Luminance and opponent-color contributions to visual detection and adaptation and to temporal and spatial integration. *Journal of the Optical Society of America* 66, 709–717 (1976).

*King-Smith, P.E. Psychophysical methods for the investigation of acquired colour vision deficiencies. In: J.R. Cronly-Dillon (Ed) *Vision and Visual Dysfunction*, Vol 7, *Inherited and Acquired Colour Vision Deficiencies: Fundamental Aspects and Clinical Studies*, D.H. Foster (Ed.) Macmillan Press, 1991.

*Kinnear, P., Marreé, M., Pokorny, J., Smith, V., & Verriest, G. Specialized methods of evaluating color vision defects. In J. Pokorny, V. Smith, G. Verriest, A.J.L.G. Pinckers (Eds.) *Congenital and Acquired Color Vision Defects,* New York: Grune & Stratton, 1979.

Kling, J. W. & Riggs, L. A. *Woodworth and Schlosberg's Experimental Psychology* (3rd ed.). New York: Holt, Rinehart, and Winston, 1971.

Köllner, H. *Die Störungen des Farbensinnes ihre klinsche Bedeutung und ihre Diagnose,* Berlin Karger, 1912.

*Knoblauch, K. Theory of wavelength discrimination in tritanopia. *Journal of the Optical Society of America* 10, 378–381 (1993).

*Knoblauch, K. Dual bases in dichromatic color space. *Colour Deficiency XII,* B. Drum (Ed.) Boston, Kluwer Academic Pub., 165–176, 1995

Kohler, I. Experiments with goggles. *Scientific American* 206 (5), 62–84 (1962).

Kolb, H. Organization of the outer plexiform layer of the primate retina: Electron microscopy of Golgi-impregnated cells. *Philosophical Transactions of the Royal Society of London B,* 258, 261–283 (1970).

*Kolb, H. Anatomical pathway for color vision in the human retina. *Visual Neuroscience* 7, 61–74 (1991).

*Kolb, H. The architecture of functional neural circuits in the vertebrate retina, *Investigative Ophthalmology & Visual Science,* 35, 2385–2404, 1994.

*Kolb, H. & Lipetz, L. E. The anatomical basis for colour vision in the vertebrate retina. In: Cronly-Dillon, J. R. (Ed.), *Vision and Visual Dysfunction: The Perception of Color Volume 6.* Edited by P. Gouras. New York: Macmillan Press, 1991.

Köllner, H. *Die Störungen des Farbensinnes ihre klinsche Bedeutung und ihre Diagnose,* Berlin Karger, 1912.

König. A. Über den menschlichen Sehpurpur und seine Bedeutung für das Sehen. *Acadamie der Wissenschaften (Berlin) Sitzungsberichte,* 577–598 (1894).

König, A. & Dieterici, C. Die Grunempfindungen in normalen und anomalen Farbensystemen und ihre Intensitätsverteilung im Spektrum. *Zeitschrift für Psychologie und Physiologie der Sinnesorgane* 4, 241–347 (1893).

*Kraft, T. W., Makino, C. L., Mathies, R. A., Lugtenburg, J., Schnapf, J. L. & Baylor, D. A. Cone excitations and color vision, *Cold Harbor Symposium on Quantitative Biology LV,* 635–641 (1990).

*Krastal, H. & Moreland, J.D. Colour vision deficiencies in ophthalmic diseases. In J.R. Cronly-Dillon (Ed) *Vision and Visual Dysfunction,* [vol 7, D. H. Foster (Ed.) *Inherited and Acquired Colour Vision Deficiencies,*] Boca Raton, FL: CRC Press, 1991.

Krauskopf, J. Effect of retinal image stabilization on the appearance of heterochromatic targets. *Journal of the Optical Society of America* 53, 741–744 (1963).

Krauskopf, J. & Mollon, J. D. The independence of the temporal integration properties of individual chromatic mechanisms in the human eye. *Journal of Physiology* 219, 611–623 (1971).

*Krauskopf, J., Williams, D. R. & Heeley, D. W. Cardinal directions of color space. *Vision Research* 22, 1123–1131 (1982).

*Krauskopf, J., Williams, D.R., Mandler, M.B. & Brown, A.M. Higher order color mechanisms, *Vision Research,* 26, 23–32 (1986).

*Krauskopf, J. & Gegenfurtner, K. Color discrimination and adaptation, *Vision Research,* 32, 23–32 (1992)

Kuffler. S. W. Discharge patterns and functional organization of mammalian retina. *Journal of Neurophysiology* 16, 37–68 (1953).

*Kulikowski, J.J., Walsh, V., McKeefry, D., Butler, S. & Carden, D. The electrophysiological basis of colour processing in Macaques with V4 lesions. *Behavioral Brain Research,* 60, 73–78 (1994).

Lakowski, R. Is the deterioration of colour discrimination with age due to lens or retinal changes? *Farbe* 11, 69–86 (1962).

Lakowski, R. Theory and practice of colour vision testing: A review. Part 1. *British Journal of Industrial Medicine* 26, 173–189 (1969a).

Lakowski, R. Theory and practice of colour vision testing: A review. Part 2. *British Journal of Industrial Medicine* 26, 265–288 (1969b).

*Lamb, T. D. & Pugh Jr., E. N. G-protein cascades: gain and kinetics. *Trends in Neuroscience* 15, 291–297 (1992).

Land, E. H. Color vision and the natural image: Part 1. *Proceedings of the National Academy of Sciences USA* 45, 115–129 (1959a).

Land, E. H. Color vision and the natural image: Part II. *Proceedings of the National Academy of Sciences USA* 45, 636–644 (1959b).

Land, E. H. Experiments in color vision. *Scientific American* 200 (5),84–99 (1959c).

*Land, E.H. The retinex, *American Scientist,* 52, 247–264 (1964).

*Land, E.H. The retinex theory of colour vision. Proceedings of the Royal Institute of Great Britian, 47, 23–58 (1974)

Land, E. H. The retinex theory of color vision. *Scientific American* 218 (6), 108–128 (1977).

*Land, E.H. Recent advances in retinex theory. *Vision Research,* 26, 7–21 (1986).

Land, E. H. & McCann, J. J. Lightness and retinex theory. *Journal of the Optical Society of America* 61, 1–11 (1971).

*Lanthony, P. The desaturated Panel D15. *Documenta Ophalmologica,* 46, 191–199, 1978.

Larimer, J., Krantz, D. H. & Cicerone, C. M. Opponent-process additivity. I: Red/green equilibria. *Vision Research* 14, 1127–1140 (1974).

Larimer, J., Krantz, D. H. & Cicerone, C. M. Opponent-process additivity: II. Yellow/ blue equilibria and nonlinear models. *Vision Research* 15, 723–731 (1975).

Lawson, R. B., Goldstein, S. G. & Musty, R. E. *Principles and methods of psychology.* New York: Oxford University Press, 1975.

*Lee, B. B. Die Universität Göttingen und die entstehung der farbenlehre. *MPG-Spiegel*, B20396 F, 3/91, 11–15, (1991).

*Lee, B.B. Macaque ganglion cells and spatial vision, *Progress in Brain Research*, 95, 33–43, (1993)

*Lee, B. B., Martin, P. & Valberg, A. The physiological basis of heterochromatic flicker photometry demonstrated in the ganglion cells of the macaque retina. *Journal of Physiology* 404, 323–347 (1988).

*LeGrand, Y. Les seuils différentiels de couleurs dans la théorie de Young. *Revue d'Optique* 28, 261–278 (1949). See also, translation by K. Knoblauch and Commentary by R.M. Boynton and K. Knoblauch, in *Color Research and Application* 19, 296–309 (1994).

LeGrand. Y. *Light, colour, and vision* (2nd ed.). Translated by R. W. G. Hunt, J. W. T. Walsh & F. R. W. Hunt. Somerset, NJ: Halsted Press, 1968.

LeGrand, Y. Unsolved problems in vision. In: Pierce, J. R. & Levine, J. R. (Eds.), *Visual Science.* Bloomington, IN: University Press, 1971.

*Lennie, P. & D'Zmura, M. Mechanisms of color vision. *CRC Critical Review in Neurobiology* 3, 333–400 (1988).

*Levine, M.W. & Shefner, J.M. *Fundamentals of Sensation and Perception,* second edition, Brooks/Cole Pub. Co. Pacific Grove, CA. 1991.

*Liebman, P. A. & Entine, G. Sensitive low-light-level microspectrophotometer: detection of photosensitive pigments of retinal cones. *Journal of the Optical Society of America* 54, 1451–1459 (1964).

Liebman, P. Microspectrophotometry of photoreceptors. In: Dartnall, H. J. A. (Ed.), *Handbook of sensory physiology* VII/1. New York: Springer-Verlag, 1972.

*Livingstone, M. S. & Hubel, D. H. Anatomy and physiology of a color system in the primate visual cortex. *Society for Neuroscience* 4, 309–356 (1984).

*Livingstone, M. S. & Hubel, D. H. Segregation of form, color, movement, and depth: Anatomy, physiology, and perception. *Science* 240, 740–749 (1988).

*Logothetis, N.K., Schiller, P.H., Charles, E.R. & Hurlbert, A.C. Perceptual deficits and the activity of the color-opponent and broadband pathways at isoluminance. *Science,* 247, 214–217 (1990).

*Luther, R. Aus dem Gebiet der Farbreizmetrik, *Z. Tech. Phys.* 8, 540–558 (1927).

MacAdam, D. L. Visual sensitivities to color differences in daylight. *Journal of the Optical Society of America* 32, 247–274 (1942).

MacAdam, D. L. Small-field chromaticity discrimination. *Journal of the Optical Society of America* 49, 1143–1146 (1959).

MacAdam, D. L. (Ed.), *Sources of color science.* Cambridge, MA: M.I.T. Press (1970).

MacKay, D. M. & Jeffreys, D. A. Visually evoked potentials and visual perception in man. In: Jung, R. (Ed.), *Handbook of sensory physiology* VII/3B. New York: Springer-Verlag, 1973.

MacLeod, D. I. A. Visual sensitivity. *Annual Review of Psychology* 29, 613–645 (1978).

*MacLeod, D.I.A. & Boynton, R.M. A chromaticity diagram showing cone excitation by stimuli of equal luminance, *Journal of the Optical Society of America,* 69, 1183–1186 (1979).

MacLeod, D. I. A. & Hayhoe, M. Three pigments in normal and anomalous color vision. *Journal of the Optical Society of America* 64, 92–96 (1974).

MacLeod, D. I. A. & Lennie, P. A unilateral defect resembling deuteranopia. *Modern Problems in Ophthalmology* 13, 130–134 (1974).

MacNichol, E. J. & Svaetichin, G. Electric responses from the isolated retinas of fishes. *American Journal of Ophthalmology* 46, No. 3 Part II, 26–46 (1958).

Magnus, R. Goethe as a scientist. Translated by Heinz Norden from *Goethe als Naturforscher,* Leipzig, Germany, 1906. New York: Henry Schuman, Inc.; Reprint: Collier Books, 1949.

Makous, W. L. Cutaneous color sensitivity: Explanation and demonstration. *Psychological Review* 73, 280–294 (1966).

*Maloney, L.T. & Wandell, B.A. Color constancy: A method for recording surface spectral reflectance. *Journal of the Optical Society of America A,* 3, 29–33, (1986).

Marc, R. E. & Sperling, H. G. Chromatic organization of primate cones. *Science* 196, 454–456 (1977).

*Marks, W. B., Dobelle, W. H. & MacNichol, M. F. Jr. Visual pigments of single primate cones. *Science* 143, 1181–1183 (1964).

Marks, L. E. & Bornstein, M. H. Spectral sensitivity by constant CFF: Effect of chromatic adaptation. *Journal of the Optical Society of America* 63, 220–226 (1973).

*Marré, M. The investigation of acquired colour vision deficiencies. In *Colour 73,* Adam Hilger, London, 1973.

Marriott, F. H. C. Colour vision: The two-colour threshold technique of Stiles. In: Davson, H. (Ed.), *The eye.* New York: Academic Press, 1962.

Marrocco, R. T. Responses of monkey optic tract fibers to monochromatic lights. *Vision Research* 12, 1167–1174 (1972).

*Martin, L. C., Warburton, F. L. & Morgan, W. J. Determination of the sensitivities of the eye to differences in the saturation of colors. *Medical Research Council: Special Report* 188, London, 1933.

Massof, R. W. & Bailey, J. E. Achromatic points in protanopes and deuteranopes. *Vision Research* 16, 53–57 (1976).

*Maunsell, J.H.R. and Newsome, W.T. Visual processing in monkey extrastriate cortex. *Annual Review of Neuroscience,* 10, 363–401 (1987).

Maxwell, J. C. Experiments on colour, as perceived by the eye, with remarks on colour blindness. *Transactions of the Royal Society, Edinburgh* 21, 275–298 (1855).

McCamy, C. S. Colors perceived with abridged color projection systems. *Journal of the Optical Society of America* 50, 510 (1960).

McCann, J. J., McKee, S. P. & Taylor, T. H. Quantitative studies in retinex theory: A comparison between theoretical predictions and observer responses to the 'Color Mondrian' experiments. *Vision Research* 16, 445–458 (1976).

*McCollough, C. Color adaptation of edge detectors in the human visual system. *Science* 149, 1115–1116 (1965).

McConnell, J. V. *Understanding human behavior* (2nd ed.). New York: Holt, Rinehart and Winston, 1977.

McCree, K. J. Small-field tritanopia and the effects of voluntary fixation. *Optica Acta* 7, 317–323 (1960).

*Merbs, S. L. & Nathans, J. Absorption spectra of human cone pigments. *Nature* 356, 433–435 (1992).

*Merton, R. K. *On the shoulders of giants.* New York: Harcourt, Brace & World, Inc., 1965.

*Michaelis, L. & Menten, M. L. Die Kinetik der Invertinwirkung. *Biochemische Zeitschrift* 49, 333–369 (1913).

Miller, S. S. Psychophysical estimates of visual pigment densities in red-green dichromats. *Journal of Physiology* 223, 89–107 (1972).

*Mitchell, D. E. & Rushton, W. A. H. Visual pigments in dichromats. *Vision Research* 11, 1033–1043 (1971a).

Mitchell, D. E. & Rushton, W. A. H. The red/green pigments of normal vision. *Vision Research* 11, 1045–1056 (1971b).

*Mollon, J. D. The theory of colour vision. In: Connolly, K. (Ed.), *Psychology Survey No. 2*. London: George Allen & Unwind Ltd., 1979.

*Mollon, J.D. What is odd about the short-wavelength mechanism and why is it disproportionately vulnerable to acquired damage? Report of a Discussion. G. Verriest (Ed.) *Documenta Ophalmologica Proceedings Series*, 33, 145–149. The Hague: Dr. W. Junk Publ. 1982.

*Mollon, J. D. Colour vision and colour blindness. In: Barlow, H. B. & Mollon, J. D. (Eds.), *The Senses*. Cambridge, U. K.: Cambridge University Press, 1982.

*Mollon, J. D. L'auteur énigmatique de la théorie trichromatique. *Mondial couleur 85* Proc. Assoc. Int. de la Couleur Monte-Carlo, (1985).

*Mollon, J. D. John Elliot MD (1747–1787). *Nature* 329, 19–20 (1987).

*Mollon, J.D. Uses and evolutionary origins of primate colour vision, In J.R. Cronly-Dillon (Ed.) [*Vision and Visual Dysfunction, Vol 2, Evolution of the Eye and Visual System.* J.R. Cronly-Dillon and R.L. Gregory (Eds.)] Boca Raton, FL: CRC Press, Inc., 306–319, 1991a.

*Mollon, J. D. Palmer, George (1740–1795). In: Nicholls, C.S. (Ed.), *Dictionary of National Biography, Supplementary Volume.* Oxford: Oxford University Press, 1991b.

*Mollon, J. D., Astell, S. & Cavonius, C. R. A reduction in stimulus duration can improve wavelength discriminations mediated by short-wave cones. *Vision Research* 32, 745–755 (1992).

*Mollon, J.D. & Polden, P.G. An anomaly in the response of the eye to light of short wavelengths. *Physiological Transactions, Royal Society of London Series B*, 278, 207–240 (1977).

*Montag, E.D. Surface color naming in dichromats. *Vision Research,* 34, 2137–2151 (1994).

*Montag, E.D. & Boynton, R.M. Rod influence in dichromatic surface color perception. *Vision Research*, 27, 2153–2162 (1987).

Monty, R. A. & Senders, J. W. (Eds.), *Eye movements and psychological processes.* New York: Lawrence Erlbaum Associates, 1976.

Moreland, J. D. Threshold measurements of the blue arcs phenomenon. *Vision Research* 8, 1093–1106 (1968a).

Moreland, J. D. On demonstrating the blue arcs phenomenon. *Vision Research* 8, 99–107 (1968b).

Moreland, J. D. Retinal topography and the blue-arcs phenomenon. *Vision Research* 9, 965–976 (1969).

Moreland, J. D. Peripheral color vision. In: Jameson, D., & Hurvich, L. M. (Eds.), *Handbook of sensory physiology* VII/4. New York: Springer-Verlag, 1972.

*Moreland, J. D. & Kerr, J. Optimization of a Rayleigh-type equation for the detection of tritanomaly. *Vision Research,* 19, 1369–1375 (1979).

*Moreland, J. D. Spectral sensitivity measured by motion phtometry. *Documenta Ophtholmologia Proceedings Series,* 33, 61–66 (1982).

Moscowitz, H. R., Scharf, B. & Stevens, J. C. *Sensation and measurement: Papers in honor of S. S. Stevens.* Boston: Reidel Publishing Co., 1974.

*Motulsky, A. G. Invited Editorial: Normal and abnormal color-vision genes. *American Journal of Human Genetics* 42, 405–407 (1988).

*Mullen, K.T. The contrast sensitivity of human colour vision to red-green and blue-yellow chromatic gratings, *Journal of Physiology,* 359, 381–400 (1985).

*Mullen, K.T. The chromatic coding of space. In C.B. Blakemore (Ed.) *Vision: Coding and Efficiency.* Cambridge University Press, N.Y., 1990.

*Mullen, K.T. & Baker, C.L. A motion aftereffect from isoluminant stumulus. *Vision Research,* 25, 685–688 (1985).

*Mullen, K.T. & Boulton, J.C. Absences of smooth motion perception in color vision. *Vision Research,* 32, 483–488 (1992)

Müller, G. E. Zur Psychophysik der Gesichtsemfindungen. *Zeitschrift für Psychologie und Physiologie der Sinnesorgane* 10, 1–82, 321–413 (1896).

*Nagy, A.L. Large-field substitution Rayleigh matches of dichromats, *Journal of the Optical Society of America,* 70, 778–784 (1980).

*Nagy, A. L. Red/green color discrimination and stimulus size. *Color Research and Application,* 19, 99–104, (1994).

Nagy, A. L. & Zacks, J. L. The effects of psychophysical procedure and stimulus duration in the measurement of Bezold–Brücke hue shifts. *Vision Research* 17, 193–200 (1977).

*Nagy, A.L. Large-field substitution Rayleigh matches of dichromats. *Journal of the Optical Society of America,* 70, 778–784, (1980).

*Nagy, A.L. & Boynton, R.M. Large-field color naming of dichromats with rods bleached. *Journal of the Optical Society of America,* 1259–1265 (1979).

*Nagy, A. L., MacLeod, D. I. A., Heyneman, N. E. & Eisner, A. Four cone pigments in women heterozygous for color deficiency. *Journal of the Optical Society of America* 71, 719–722 (1981).

*Nagy, A.L. & Doyal, J.A. Red-green color discrimination as a function of stimulus field size in peripheral vision. *Journal of the Optical Society of America A,* 10, 1147–1156 (1993)

*Nagy, A.L., Purl, K.F. & Houston, J.S. Cone mechanisms underlying the color discrimination of deutan color deficients. *Vision Research*, 25, 661–669, (1985).

*Nagy, A.L. & Purl, K.F. Color discrimination and neural coding in color deficients. *Vision Research*, 483–489 (1987).

*Naka, K. I. & Rushton, W. A. H. An attempt to analyse color reception by electrophysiology. *Journal of Physiology* 185, 556–586 (1966).

*Nassau, K. *The Physics and Chemistry of Color.* New York: Wiley, 1983.

*Nathans, J. The genes for color vision. *Scientific American* 260, No. 2 42–49 (1989).

*Nathans, J. & Hogness, D.S. Isolation, sequence analysis, and intron-exon arrangement of the gene encoding bovine rhodopsin. *Cell* 34, 807–814 (1983).

*Nathans, J., Thomas, D. & Hogness, D. S. Molecular genetics of human color vision: The genes encoding blue, green, and red pigments. *Science* 232, 193–202 (1986a).

* Nathans, J., Piantanida, T. P., Eddy, R. L., Shows, T. B. & Hogness, D. S. Molecular genetics of inherited variation in human color vision. *Science* 232, 203–210 (1986b).

*Neitz, J. & Jacobs, G. H. Polymorphism of the long-wavelength cone in normal human color vision. *Nature* 323, 623–625 (1986).

*Neitz, M., Neitz, J. & Jacobs, G. H. Spectral tuning of pigments underlying red-green color vision. *Science* 252, 971–974 (1991).

*Neitz, J. & Neitz, M. & Jacobs, G.H. More than three different cone pigments among people with normal color vision. *Vision Research*, 33, 117–122 (1993).

*Neitz, J. & Neitz, M. Color vision defects. In: Wright, A. F. & Jay, B. (Eds.), *Molecular Genetics of Inherited Eye Disorders, Modern Genetics Book Series,* Chur Switzerland: Harwood Academic Publishers. 1994

*Neitz, M. & Neitz, J. Numbers and ratios of visual pigment genes for normal red-green color vision. *Science*, 267, 1013–1016 (1995).

Nelson, J.H. The colour-vision characteristics of a trichromat, Part 2. *Proceedings of the Physical Society*, 49, 332 (1937).

*Nerger, J.L. & Cicerone, C.M. The ratio of L cones to M cones in the human parafoveal retina, *Vision Research*, 32, 879–888 (1992).

*Nerger, J.L., Piantanida, T.P. & Larimer, J. Color appearance of filled-in backgrounds affects hue cancellation but not detection thresholds. *Vision Research*, 33, 165–172 (1993).

Newton, I. New theory about light and colors. *Philosophical Transactions of the Royal Society* 6, 3075–3085 (1671).

Newton, I. *Opticks* (4th ed.). London: William Innys, 1730. Reprint New York: Dover, 1952.

Nickerson, D. History of the Munsell color system, Company, and Foundation: Parts 1, II., and III. *Color Research and Application* 1, 7–10; 69–77; 121–130 (1976).

*Noorlander, C. & Koenderink, J. J. Spatial and temporal discrimination ellipsoids in color space. *Journal of the Optical Society of America* 73, 1533–1543 (1983).

Normann, R. A. & Werblin, F. S. Control of retinal sensitivity: I. Light and dark adaptation of vertebrate rods and cones. *Journal of General Physiology* 63, 37–61 (1974).

*Nunn, B. J. Influence of spatial structure of adaptation fields on parafoveal colour matches. *Color Research and Application* 2, 171 (1977).

Optical Society of America. *The Science of Color.* New York: Crowell, 1953.

*Optical Society of America. *OSA Uniform Color Scales.* 2010 Massachusetts Ave., NW, Washington, DC 20036.

*Østerberg, G. A. *Acta Ophthalmologica* (Suppl. 6) 1 (1935).

*Ovchinnikov, Y. A., Abduaev, N. G., Feigeia, M. Y., Artomonov, I. D., Zolotarev, A. S., Moroshnikov, A. I., Martinow, V. I., Kostina, M. B., Kudelin, A. G. & Bogachuk, A. S. The complete amino acid sequence of visual rhodopsin. *Biorganichekaia Khimiia* 8, 1424–1427 (1983).

Padmos, P. & van Norren, D. Cone spectral sensitivity and chromatic adaptation as revealed by human flicker-electroretinography. *Vision Research* 11, 27–42 (1971).

Padmos, P. & van Norren, D. Cone systems interaction in single neurons of the lateral geniculate nucleus of the macaque. *Vision Research* 15, 617–619 (1975).

Palmer, G. *Theory of colours and vision.* London: S. Leacroft, 1777.

Parsons, J. H. *An introduction to the study of colour vision.* Cambridge, U. K.: Cambridge University Press, 1924.

Pettigrew, J. D. & Freeman, R. D. Visual experience without lines: Effect on developing cortical neurons. *Science* 182, 599–601 (1973).

Pfleegor, R. L. & Mandel, L. Interference of independent photon beams. *Physical Review* 159, 1084–1088 (1967).

Piantanida, T. P. A replacement model of X-linked recessive colour vision defects. *Annals of Human Genetics London* 37, 393–404 (1974).

Piantanida, T. P. Polymorphism of human color vision. *American Journal of Optometry and Physiological Optics* 53, 647–657 (1976).

*Piantanida, T. P. Molecular genetics of human color vision and color blindness. *Trends in Genetics* 4, 319–322 (1988).

*Piantanida, T. P. Molecular genetics in color vision. In: Drum, B. & Verriest, G. (Eds.), *Colour Vision Deficiencies IX.* Dordrecht, The Netherlands: Kluwer Academic Publishers, 1989. *Piantanida, T. P. Molecular biology of color vision. In:J. R. Cronly-Dillon, (Ed.), *Vision and Visual Dysfunction* Vol 6, *The Perception of Color.* P. Gouras. (Ed.), Macmillan Press, 1991.

*Piantanida, T.P. Genetics of inherited colour vision deficiencies, In: J.R. Cronly-Dillon (Ed) *Vision and Visual Dysfunction,* Vol 7, *Inherited and Acquired Colour Vision Deficiencies,* D.H. Foster (Ed), Macmillan Press, 1991.

Piantanida, T. P. & Sperling, H. G. Isolation of a third chromatic mechanism in the protanomalous observer. *Vision Research* 13, 2033–2047 (1973a).

Piantanida, T. P. & Sperling, H. G. Isolation of a third chromatic mechanism in the deuteranomalous observer. *Vision Research* 13, 2049–2058 (1973b).

Pickford, R. W. *Individual differences in colour vision.* London: Routledge and Kegan Paul, 1951.

Pickford, R. W. A practical anomaloscope for testing colour vision and colour blindness. *British Journal of Physiological Optics* 14, 2–26 (1957).

Pickford, R. W. Some heterozygous manifestations of colour blindness. *British Journal of Physiological Optics* 16, 83–95 (1959).

Pickford, R. W. & Lakowski, R. The Pickford–Nicolson anomaloscope. *British Journal of Physiological Optics* 17, 131–150 (1960).

Pirenne, M. H. *Vision and the eye.* London: Chapman and Hall, 1948.

Pirenne, M. H. *Optics, painting, and photography.* London: Cambridge University Press, 1970.

Pitt, F. H. G. Characteristics of dichromatic vision, with an appendix on anomalous trichromatic vision. *Great Britain Medical Research Council, Special Report Series,* No. 200 (1935).

Pitt, F. H. G. The nature of normal trichromatic and dichromatic vision. *Proceedings of the Royal Society of London B* 132, 101–117 (1944).

*Plant, G.T. Disorders of colour vision in diseases of the nervous system. In J.R. Cronly-Dillon (Ed) *Vision and Visual Dysfunction,* vol 7, D. H. Foster (Ed.) *Inherited and Acquired Colour Vision Deficiencies,* Boca Raton,FL: CRC Press, Inc., 1991.

Plateau, J. Sur un principe de photométrie. *Bull. Acad. Roy. Sci. Belllet. Bruxelles* 2, 52–59 (1835).

*Poirson, A.B. & Wandell, B.A. Task-dependent color discrimination. *Journal of the Optical Society of America A,* 7, 776–782, 1990.

*Poirson, A.B., Wandell, B.A., Varner, D.C. & Brainard, D.H. Surface characterizations of color threshold. *Journal of the Optical Society of America A*, 7, 783–789 (1990)

*Poirson, A.B. & Wandell, B.A. Appearance of colored patterns: Pattern-color separability. *Journal of the Optical Society of America A*, 10, 2458–2470 (1993).

Pokorny, J. & Smith, V. C. Wavelength discrimination in the presence of added chromatic fields. *Journal of the Optical Society of America* 60, 562–569 (1970).

Pokorny, J. & Smith, V. C. Luminosity and CFF in deuteranopes and protanopes. *Journal of the Optical Society of America* 62, 111–117 (1972).

Pokorny, J. & Smith, V. C. Effect of field size on red-green color mixture equations. *Journal of the Optical Society of America* 66, 705–708 (1976).

Pokorny, J. & Smith, V. C. Evaluation of single-pigment shift model of anomalous trichromacy. *Journal of the Optical Society of America* 67, 1196–1209 (1977).

Pokorny, J., Smith, V.C. & Starr, S.J. Variability of color mixture data: II The effect of viewing field size on the unit coordinates. *Vision Research* 16, 1095–1098 (1976).

*Pokorny, J. & Smith, V.C., Verriest, G. & Pinckers. A.J.L.G. *Congenital and Acquired Color Vision Defects*. New York: Grune & Stratton, 1979.

*Pokorny, J. & Smith, V.C. Eye disease and color defects. *Vision Research*, 26, 1573–1584, (1986).

Pokorny, J., Smith, V. C. & Katz, I. Derivation of the photopigment absorption spectra in anomalous trichromats. *Journal of the Optical Society of America* 63, 232–237 (1973).

Pokorny, J., Smith, V. C. & Swartley, R. Threshold measurements of spectral sensitivity in a blue monocone monochromat. *Investigative Ophthalmology* 9, 807–813 (1970).

Polyak, S. L. *The retina*. Chicago: University of Chicago Press, 1941.

Polyak, S. L. *The vertebrate visual system* (edited by Heinrich Klüver). Chicago: University of Chicago Press, 1957.

Porter, T. C. Contributions to the study of flicker: II. *Proceedings of the Royal Society of London B* 70, 313–329 (1902).

*Powell, I., Lenses correcting for chromatic aberration of the human eye, *Applied Optics*, 20, 4152–4155 (1981).

Priest, I. G. & Brickwedde, F. G. The minimum perceptible colorimetric purity as a function of dominant wavelength. *Journal of the Optical Society of America* 28, 133–139 (1938).

*Pugh Jr., E. N. The nature of the colour mechanism of W. S. Stiles. *Journal of Physiology* 257, 713–747 (1976).

Pugh Jr., E. N. & Sigel, C. Evaluation of the candidacy of the π-mechanisms of Stiles for color-matching fundamentals. *Vision Research* 18, 317–330 (1978).

*Pugh Jr., E. N. & Cobbs, W. H. Visual transduction in vertebrate rods and cones: A tale of two transmitters, calcium and cyclic GMP. *Vision Research* 26, 1613–1643 (1986).

*Pugh Jr., E. N. & Kirk, D. B. The π-mechanisms of W. S. Stiles: an historical review. *Perception* 15, 705–728 (1986).

*Purdy, D. M. On the saturations and chromatic thresholds of the spectral colours. *British Journal of Psychology* 21, 283–313 (1931).

Purkinje, J. *Beobochtungen und Versuche zur Physiologie der Sinne.* Prague: J. G. Calve, 1823.

Rainwater, J. *Vision: How, why, and what we see.* New York: Golden Press, 1962.

Ratliff, F. (Ed.) *Studies on excitation and inhibition in the retina.* New York: Rockefeller University Press, 1974.

*Ratliff, F. On the psychophysiological bases of universal color terms. *Proceedigs of the American Philosophical Society.* 120, 311–330 (1976).

*Ratliff, F. *Paul Signac and color in neo-impressionism.* New York: Rockefeller University Press, 1992.

Regan, D. M. *Evoked potentials in psychology, sensory physiology, and clinical medicine.* London: Chapman and Hall, 1972.

Regan, D. M. Evoked potentials specific to spatial patterns of luminance and colour. *Vision Research* 13, 2381–2402 (1973).

*Regan, D. *Human Brain Electrophysiology: Evoked Potentials and Evoked Magnetic Fields in Science and Medicine.* New York: Elsevier Science Publishing Co. Inc., 1989.

*Regan, D. & Lee, B. B. A comparison of the 40-Hz. response in man, and the properties of macaque ganglion cells. *Visual Neuroscience* 10, 439–445 (1993).

*Regan, D., Nakano, Y. & Kaiser, P.K. Dissociation of achromatic and chromatic processing of spatial form and temporal modulation by the titration method. *Journal of the Optical Society of America A,* 10, 1314–1323 (1993).

Richards, W. Visual suppression during passive eye movement. *Journal of the Optical Society of America* 58, 1159–1160 (1968).

*Richter, M. & Witt, K. The story of the DIN Color System. *Color Research and Application* 11, 138–145 (1986).

Riggs. L. A. Visual acuity. In: Graham, C. H. (Ed.), *Vision and visual perception.* New York: Wiley, 1965.

Riggs, L. A., Johnson, E. P. & Schick, A. M. L. Electrical responses of the human eye to changes in wavelength of the stimulating light. *Journal of the Optical Society of America* 56, 1621–1627 (1966).

Robinson, D. A. Eye movement control in primates. *Science* 161, 1219–1224 (1968).

*Robson, J.G. Spatial and temporal contrast sensitivity functions of the visual system. *Journal of the Optical Society of America,* 56, 1141–1142 (1966)

Rock, I. *An introduction to perception.* New York: Macmillan, 1975.

Rodieck, R. W. *The vertebrate retina.* San Francisco: Freeman, 1973.

*Rodieck, R. W. The primate retina. *Comparative Primate Biology,* Volume 4: *Neurosciences,* 203–278 (1988).

Ronchi, V. *The nature of light* (translated by V. Barocas from *Storia della Luce,* 1939). Cambridge, MA: Harvard University Press, 1970.

Ruddock, K. H. Light transmission through the ocular media and macular pigment and its significance for psychophysical investigation. In Jameson, D. & Hurvich, L. M. (Eds.), *Handbook of sensory physiology,* VII/4. New York: Springer-Verlag, 1972.

*Ruddock, K.H. Psychophysics of inherited colour vision deficiencies, In: J.R. Cronly-Dillon (Ed.) *Vision and Visual Dysfunction,* Vol 7, *Inherited and Acquired Colour Vision Deficiencies: Fundamental Aspects and Clinical Studies.* D.H. Foster (Ed.), Macmillan Press, 1991.

Rushton, W. A. H. A cone pigment in the protanope. *Journal of Physiology* 168, 345–359 (1963).

Rushton, W. A. H. Color blindness and cone pigments. *American Journal of Optometry* 41, 265–282 (1964).

Rushton, W. A. H. The Ferrier lecture 1962: Visual adaptation. *Proceedings of the Royal Society of London B* 162, 20–46 (1965a).

Rushton, W. A. H. A foveal pigment in the deuteranope. *Journal of Physiology* 176, 24–37 (1965b).

Rushton, W. A. H. Visual pigments in man. In: Dartnall, H. J. A. (Ed.), *Handbook of sensory physiology* VII/1. New York: Springer-Verlag, (1972).

Rushton, W. A. H. Visual pigments and color blindness. *Scientific American* 232 (3), 64–74 (1975).

Rushton, W. A. H. A highly speculative eye model. *Proceedings of the Institute of Electrical and Electronic Engineers,* 1130 (1966).

Rushton, W. A. H. & Baker, H. D. Red/green sensitivity in normal vision. *Vision Research* 4, 75–85 (1964).

Rushton, W. A. H., Campbell, F. W., Hagins, W. A. & Brindley, G. S. The bleaching and regeneration of rhodopsin the living eye of the albino rabbit and of man. *Optica Acta* 1, 183–190 (1955).

Rushton, W. A. H., Powell, D. S. & White, K. D. The spectral sensitivity of "red" and "green" cones in the normal eye. *Vision Research* 13, 2003–2015 (1973a).

Rushton, W. A. H., Powell, D. S. & White, K. D. Pigments in anomalous trichromats. *Vision Research* 13, 2017–2031 (1973b).

Rushton, W. A. H., Powell, D. S. & White, K. D. Exchange thresholds in dichromats. *Vision Research* 13, 1993–2002 (1973c).

Sabra, I. *Theories of Light from Descartes to Newton.* London: Oldbourne Book Co., 1967.

Salzmann, M. *The anatomy and physiology of the human eyeball in the normal state* Translated by E. V. L. Brown. Chicago: University of Chicago Press, 1912.

*Sandell, J.H., Gross, C.G., & Bornstein, M.H. Color categories in macaques. *Journal of Comparative & Physiological Psychology*, 93, 626–635 (1979).

Scheibner, H. M. Adaptive color shifts. *Journal of the Optical Society of America* 56, 938–942 (1966).

Scheibner, H. M. O. & Boynton, R. M. Residual red-green discrimination in dichromats. *Journal of the Optical Society of America* 58, 1151–1158 (1968).

Schmidt, I. Some problems related to testing color vision with the Nagel anomaloscope. *Journal of the Optical Society of America* 45, 514–522 (1955).

*Schnapf, J. L., Kraft, T. W. & Baylor, D. A. Spectral sensitivity of human cone photoreceptors. *Nature* 325, 439–441 (1987).

*Schnapf, J. L., Nunn, B. J., Meister, M. & Baylor, D. A. Visual transduction in cones of the monkey Macaca fascicularis. *Journal of Physiology* 427, 681–713 (1990).

*Schiller, P.H., Logothetis, N.K. & Charles, E.R. Role of the color-opponent and broadband opponent channels in vision. *Visual Neurosciences*, 5, 321–346 (1990).

*Schiller, P.H., Logothetis, N.K. & Charles, E.R. Functions of the color-opponent and the broad-band channels of the visual system. *Nature*, 68–70 (1990).

*Schiller, P.H., Logothetis, N.K. & Charles, E.R. Parallel pathways in the visual system: their role in perception. *Neuropsychologia*, 29 433–441 (1991).

Schrödinger, E. Grundlinien einer Theorie der Farbenmetrik im Tagessehen. *Annalen der Physik und Chemie* (iv) 63, 481–520 (1920).

Scully, M. O. & Sargent, M. The concept of the photon. *Physics Today* 25, 38–47 (1972).

*Sekiguchi, N.,Williams, D.R. & Brainard, D.H. Efficiency for detecting isoluminant and isochromatic interference fringes, *Journal of the Optical Society of America A*, 10, 2118–2133 (1993).

*Sharpe, L.T. A landslide for colour science? *Color Research and Application* 12, 81–84, 1987.

*Sherman, P. D. *Colour vision in the nineteenth century.* Bristol: Adam Hilger Ltd., 1981.

*Shevell, S. K. The dual role of chromatic backgrounds in color perception. *Vision Research* 18, 1649–1661 (1978).

*Shevell, S. K. Color perception under chromatic adaptation: Equilibrium yellow and long wavelength adaptation. *Vision Research* 22, 279–292 (1982).

*Shevell, S. K. & Humanski, R. A. Color perception under chromatic adaptation: Red-green equilibria with adapted short-wavelength-sensitive cones. *Vision Research* 28, 1345–1356 (1988).

*Shevell, S. K. On neural signals that mediate induced blackness. *Vision Research* 29, 891–900 (1989).

*Shute, C. C. D. Subjective colours and brain function. *Endeavour, New Series* 5, 141–146 (1981).

Siegel, M. H. Discrimination of color: I. Comparison of three psychophysical methods. *Journal of the Optical Society of America* 52, 1067–1070 (1962).

Siegel, M. H. Discrimination of color: IV. Sensitivity as a function of spectral wavelength, 410 through 500 nm. *Journal of the Optical Society of America* 54, 821–823 (1964).

Siegel, M. H. & Dimmick, F. L. Discrimination of color: II. Sensitivity as a function of spectral wavelength, 510–630 nm. *Journal of the Optical Society of America* 52, 1071–1074 (1962).

Sigel, C. & Pugh, E. N. Evaluation of candidate cone action spectra by a new minimization technique. *Investigative Ophthalmology & Visual Science* 16 (Suppl.), 161 (1977).

Sirovich, L. & Abramov, I. Photopigments and pseudo-pigments. *Vision Research* 17, 5–16 (1977).

Sjöstrand, F. S. The ultrastructure of the outer segments of rods and cones of the eye as revealed by the electron microscope. *Journal of Cellular and Comparative Physiology* 42, 15–44 (1953).

*Smallman, H.S. & Boynton, R.M. Segregation of basic colors in an information display. *Journal of the Optical Society of America* A, 7, 1985–1994 (1990).

Smith, V. C. & Pokorny, J. Spectral sensitivity of color-blind observers and the cone photopigments. *Vision Research* 12, 2059–2071 (1972).

Smith, V. C. & Pokorny, J. Spectral sensitivity of the foveal cone photopigments between 400 and 500 nm. *Vision Research* 15, 161–171 (1975).

Smith, V. C. & Pokorny, J. Large-field trichromacy in protanopes and deuteranopes. *Journal of the Optical Society of America* 67, 213–220 (1977).

Smith, V. C. & Pokorny, J. An unusual color vision defect. *Investigative Ophthalmology & Visual Science* 17 (Suppl.) 198 (1978).

*Smith, V.C., Pokorny, J. & Yeh, T. The Farnsworth-Munsell 100-hue test in cone excitation space. *Colour Vision Deficiencies XI*, Boston, MA: Kluwer Academic Publ. 281–291, 1993.

*Smith, V.C. & Pokorny, J. Chromatic-discrimination axes, CRT phosphor spectra, and individual variation in color vision. *Journal of the Optical Society of America A*, 12, 27–35 (1995).

Sparrock, J. M. B. Stabilized images: Increment thresholds and subjective brightness. *Journal of the Optical Society of America* 59, 872–874 (1969).

Speelman. R. G. & Krauskopf, J. Effects of chromatic adaptation on normal and dichromatic red-green brightness matches. *Journal of the Optical Society of America* 53, 1103–1107 (1963).

Sperling, H. G. Linear theory and the psychophysics of flicker. *Documenta Ophtholmologica* 18, 3–15 (1964).

Sperling, H. G. & Harwerth, R. S. Red-green cone interactions in the increment threshold spectral sensitivity of primates. *Science* 172, 180–184 (1971).

Sperling, H. G. & Lewis, W. G. Some comparisons between foveal spectral sensitivity data obtained at high brightness and absolute threshold. *Journal of the Optical Society of America* 49, 983–989 (1959).

*Sperling, H. G. & Mills, S. L. Red-green interactions in the spectral sensitivity of primates as derived from ERG and behavioural data. *Visual Neuroscience* 7, 75–86 (1991).

*Spileers, W., Falcao-Reis, F., Hogg, C. & Arden, G. B. Evidence from human electroretinogram. A and off responses that color processing occurs in the cones. *Investigative Ophthalmology & Visual Science* 34, 2079–2091 (1993).

*Sternheim, C.S. & Boynton, R.M. Uniqueness of perceived hues investigated with a continuous judgemental technique. *Journal of Experimental Psychology*, 72, 770–776 (1966).

Stell, W. K. & Lightfoot, D. O. Color-specific interconnections of cones to horizontal cells in the retina of the goldfish. *Journal of Comparative Neurology* 159, 473–501 (1975).

Stell, W. K., Lightfoot, D. O., Wheeler, T. G. & Leeper, H. F. Goldfish retina: Functional polarization of cone horizontal cell dendrites and synapses. *Science* 190, 989–990 (1975).

Stiles, W. S. The directional sensitivity of the retina and the spectral sensitivities of the rods and cones. *Proceedings of the Royal Society of London B* 127, 64–105 (1939).

Stiles, W. S. Increment thresholds and the mechanisms of colour vision. *Documenta Ophthalmologica* 3, 138–163 (1949).

Stiles, W. S. Further studies of visual mechanisms by the two-colour threshold method. *Coloquio sobre Problemas Opticos de la Vision* 1, 65–103. Madrid: Union Internationale de Physique pure et appliquée (1953).

Stiles, W. S. 18th Thomas Young oration: The basic data of color-matching. In: *Physical Society Year Book,* pp. 44–45. London: Physical Society, 1955.

Stiles, W. S. Color vision: The approach through increment-threshold sensitivity. *Proceedings of the National Academy of Sciences* 45, 100–114 (1959).

Stiles, W. S. Appendix: Foveal threshold sensitivity of fields of different colors. *Science* 145, 1016–1017 (1964).

Stiles, W. S. The line element in colour theory: A historical review. In: Vos, J. J., Friele, L. F. C. & Walraven, P. L. (Eds.), *Color metrics.* Soesterberg, Netherlands: Institute for Perception TNO (1972).

Stiles, W. S. *Mechanisms of colour vision.* New York: Academic Press, 1978.

*Stiles, W. S. & Burch, J. M. N.P.L. Colour-matching investigation: final report. *Optica Acta* 6, 1–26 (1959).

Stiles, W. S. & Crawford, B. H. The luminous efficiency of rays entering the pupil at different points. *Proceedings of the Royal Society of London B* 112, 428–450 (1933a).

Stiles, W. S. & Crawford, B. H. The liminal brightness increment as a function of wave-length for different conditions of the foveal and parafoveal retina. *Proceedings of the Royal Society of London B* 113, 496–530 (1933b).

Stiles, W. S. & Wyszecki, G. Colour-matching data and the spectral absorption curves of visual pigments. *Vision Research* 14, 195–207 (1974).

*Stockman, A., MacLeod, D. I. A. & DePriest, D. D. The temporal properties of the human short-wave photoreceptors and their associated pathways. *Vision Research* 31, 189–208 (1991).

*Stockman, A., MacLeod, D. I. A. & Vivien, J. A. Isolation of middle- and long-wavelength-sensitive cones in normal trichromats. *Journal of the Optical Society of America* 10, 2471–2490 (1993).

*Stockman, A., MacLeod, D.I.A. & Lebrun, S.J. Faster than the eye can see: blue cones respond to rapid flicker. *Journal of the Optical Society of America* A, 10, 1396–1402 (1993).

*Stockman, A., MacLeod, D. I. A. & Johnson, N. E. Spectral sensitivities of the human cones. *Journal of the Optical Society of America A* 10, 2491–2521 (1993).

*Stratton, G. M. *Theophrastus and the Greek physiological psychology before Aristotle,* Amsterdam: E.J. Bonset, P. Schippers N.V. (1964).

*Stromeyer, C.F., Kranda, K. & Sternheim, C.E. Selective chromatic adaptation at different spatial frequencies, *Vision Research,*18, 427–438 (1978).

Strong, J. *Concepts of classical optics.* San Francisco: Freeman, 1958.

*Stroop, J.R. Studies of interference in serial verbal reactions. *Journal of Experimental Psychology,* 18, 643–662 (1935).

*Suzuki, D.T., Griffiths, A.J.F., Miller, J.H. & Lewontin, R.C. *An Introduction to Genetic Analysis,* W.H. Freeman & Co. N.Y. , 1989.

Svaetichin, G. Spectral response curves from single cones. *Acta Physiologica Scandinavica* 39 (Suppl. 134), 17–46 (1956).

Talbot, H. F. Experiments on light. *Philosophical Magazine* (3rd series) 5, 321–334 (1834).

Taylor, E. & Jennings, A. Calculation of total retinal area. *British Journal of Ophthalmology* 55, 262–265 (1971).

Tessier, M. & Blottiau, F. Variations des caractéristiques photométriques de l'oeil aux luminances photopiques. *Revue d'Optique* 30, 309–322 (1951).

*Tessier-Lavigne, M. Phototransduction and information processing in the retina. In: Kandel, E. R. & Schwartz, J. N. (Eds.), *Principles of Neural Science* (3rd Edition). Norwalk, CT: Appleton & Lange, 1991.

Thomson, L. C. Sensations aroused by monochromatic stimuli and their prediction. *Optica Acta* 1, 93–101 (1954).

Thompson, R. F. & Patterson, M. M. (Eds.), *Bioelectric recording techniques* (3 volumes). New York: Academic Press; Vol. 1: 1973; Vols. 2 and 3: 1974.

*Tootell, R. B. H., Silverman, M. S., Hamilton, S. L. DeValois, R. L. & Switkes, E. Functional anatomy of macaque striate cortex. III. Color. *Journal of Neuroscience* 8, 1569–1593 (1988).

Trezona, P. W. Aspects of peripheral color vision. *Modern Problems in Ophthalmology* 17, 52–70 (1976).

*Trezona, P. W. Individual observer data for the 1955 Stiles-Birch 2 degree pilot investigation. *Journal of the Optical Society of America A* 4, 769–782 (1987).

Troland, L. T. Notes on flicker photometry: Flicker-photometry frequency as a function of light intensity. *Journal of the Franklin Institute* 182, 261–262 (1916).

*Troland, L. T. Report on committee on colorimetry for 1920–1921. *Journal of the Optical Society of America* 6, 527–596 (1922).

*Troost, J. Empirical studies in color constancy. In: Walsh, V. & Kulikowsky, J. (Eds.), *Visual Constancies: Why things look as they do.* Cambridge, UK: Cambridge University Press (in press).

*Troost, J. & De Weert, C.M.M. Naming versus matching in color constancy, *Perception & Psychophysics,* 50, 591–602 (1991).

Truss, C. V. Chromatic flicker fusion frequency as a function of chromaticity difference. *Journal of the Optical Society of America* 47, 1130–1134 (1957).

*Uchikawa, K., Uchikawa, H. & Boynton, R.M. Partial color constancy of isolated surface colors examined by a color naming method. *Perception,* 18, 83–92 (1989a).

*Uchikawa, H., Uchikawa, K. & Boynton, R. Influence of achromatic surrounds on categorical perception of surface colors. *Vision Research* 29, 204–209 (1985b).

*Uchikawa, K. & Ikeda, M. Wavelength discrimination with a chromatically alternating stimulus. *Color Research and Application* 10, 204–209 (1985).

*Valberg, A., Seim, T., Lee, B.B. & Tryti, J. Reconstruction of equidistant color space from responses of visual neurons of macaques. *Journal of the Optical Society of America A,* 3, 1726–1734 (1986).

*Valeton, J. M. & van Norren, D. Light adaptation of primate cones: An analysis based on extracellular data. *Vision Research* 23, 1539–1547 (1983).

*Van Brakel, J. the plasticity of categories: The case of colour. *British Journal of the Philosophy of Science,* 44, 103–135, (1993).

*Van Essen, D.C. Neural Mechanisms of form and motion processing in the primate visual system. *Neuron,* 13, 1–10 (1994).

*Van Helden, A. *Sidereus Nuncius, Galileo Galilei.* Translated with introduction, conclusion, and notes by A. Van Helden. Chicago, IL: University of Chicago Press, 1989.

van Norren, D. & Padmos, P. Human and macaque blue cones studied with electroretinography. *Vision Research* 13, 1241–1254 (1973).

*van Ness, F.L. & Bouman, M.A. Spatial modulation transfer in the human eye. *Journal of the Optical Society of America,* 57, 401–406 (1967).

*Vautin, R. G. & Dow, B. M. Color cell groups in foveal striate cortex of the behaving macaque. *Journal of Neurophysiology* 54, 273–292 (1985).

Verriest, G. Further studies on acquired deficiency of color discrimination. *Journal of the Optical Society of America* 53, 185–195 (1963).

*Vimal, R.L.P., Pokorny, J. Smith, V. & Shevell, S.K. Foveal cone thresholds. *Vision Research,* 29, 61–78, (1989).

*Volbrecht, V. J., Werner, J. S. & Cicerone, C. M. Additivity of spatially induced blackness. *Journal of the Optical Society of America A* 7, 106–112 (1989).

*von Kries, J. Die Gesichtsempfindungen. In: Nagel, W. (Ed.) *Handbuch de Physiologies des Menschen,* Vol. 3 (pp. 109–282). Braunschweig, 1905.

von Kries, J. Theories of vision. In: Southall, J. P. C. (Ed.), *Helmholtz's treatise on physiological optics.* Rochester, NY: Optical Society of America, 1924.

*von Kries, J. Influence of adaptation on the effects produced by luminous stimuli. In D.L MacAdam (Ed.) *Mechanisms of Color Vision.* Cambridge, MA: MIT Press, 1970.

*Vos, J. J. Colorimetric and photometric properties of a 2° fundamental observer. *Color Research and Application,* 3, 125–128 (1978).

Vos, J. J. & Walraven, P. L. On the derivation of the foveal receptor primaries. *Vision Research* 11, 799–818 (1971).

Vos, J. J. & Walraven, P. L. An analytical description of the line element in the zone fluctuation model of colour vision: I. Basic concepts. *Vision Research* 12, 1327–1344 (1972).

*Vos, J. J., Estévez, O. & Walraven, P.L. Improved color fundamentals offer a new view on photometric additivity. *Vision Research,* 30, 937–943 (1990).

*Vrehel, M.J., Gershon, R. & Iwan, L.S. Measurement and analysis of object reflectance spectra. *Color Research and Application,* 19, 4–9, (1994).

Wagner, G. & Boynton, R. M. Comparison of four methods of heterochromatic photometry. *Journal of the Optical Society of America* 62, 1508–1515 (1972).

Wald, G. Photo-labile pigments of the chicken retina. *Nature* 140, 545–546 (1937).

Wald, G. Human vision and the spectrum. *Science* 101, 653–658 (1945).

Wald, G. The receptors of human color vision. *Science* 145, 1007–1016 (1964).

Wald, G. Blue-blindness in the normal fovea. *Journal of the Optical Society of America* 57, 1289–1301 (1967).

Wald, G. Molecular basis of visual excitation. *Science* 162, 230–239 (1968).

Wald. G., Brown, P. K. & Gibbons, I. R. The problem of visual excitation. *Journal of the Optical Society of America* 53, 20–35 (1963).

*Wallman, J. A simple technique using an optomotor response for visual psychophysical measurements in animals. *Vision Research* 15, 3–8 (1975).

*Walls, G. L. The G. Palmer story. *Journal of the History of Medicine Allied Science* 11/1, 66–96 (1956).

Walls, G. L. Graham's theory of color blindness. *American Journal of Optometry and Archives of the Academy of Optometry* 35, 449–460 (1958).

Walls, G. L.. Land! Land! *Psychological Bulletin* 57, 29–48 (1960).

Walls, G. L. & Heath, G. G. Neutral points in 138 protanopes and deuteranopes. *Journal of the Optical Society of America* 46, 640–649, (1956).

Walls, G. L. & Mathews, R. New means of studying color blindness and normal foveal color vision. *University of California Publications in Psychology* 7, 1–172 (1952).

*Walraven, J. Discounting the background-the missing link in the explanation of chromatic induction. *Vision Research* 16, 289–295 (1976).

*Walraven, J. Chromatic induction. Soesterberg, The Netherlands: Ph.D. Thesis, Institute for Perception, 1981.

Walraven, P. L. On the mechanisms of colour vision. Soesterberg, The Netherlands: Thesis, Institute for Perception RVO-TNO, 1962.

Walraven, P. L. A closer look at the tritanopic convergence point. *Vision Research* 14, 1339–1343 (1974).

Walraven, P. L. & Leebeek, H. J. Phase shift of sinusoidally alternating colored stimuli. *Journal of the Optical Society of America* 54, 78–82 (1964a).

Walraven, P. L. & Leebeek, H. J. Phase shift of alternating coloured stimuli. *Documenta Ophthalmologica* 18, 56–71 (1964b).

Walsh, J. W. T. *Photometry* (3rd ed.) London: Constable, 1958. Reprinted, New York: Dover. 1958.

*Ware, C. & Cowan, W.B. Specification of heterochromatic brightness matches: A conversion factor for calculating luminance stimuli that are equal in brightness, *National Research Council Publication* No. 26055, National Research Council of Canada, Ottawa (1983).

*Wässle, H. & Boycott, B. B. Functional architecture of the mammalian retina. *Physiological Reviews* 71, 447–479 (1991).

*Wässle, H. & Boycott, B. B. Colour coding in the primate retina: predictions from anatomy. *Perception* 21, 9 (1992).

*Wässle, H., Grünert, U., Martin, P. R. & Boycott, B. B. Immunocytochemical characterization and spatial distribution of midget bipolar cells in the macaque monkey retina. *Vision Research* 34, 561–579 (1994).

Watkins, R. D. Foveal increment thresholds in normal and deutan observers. *Vision Research* 9, 1185–1196 (1969a).

Watkins, R. D. Foveal increment thresholds in protan observers. *Vision Research* 9, 1197–1204 (1969b).

Watson, J. D. *Molecular Biology of the Gene* (3rd ed.). Menlo Park, CA: Benjamin, 1976.

*Watson, J. D. & Crick, F. H. C. A structure for deoxyribose nucleic acids. *Nature* 171, 737–738 (1953a).

*Watson, J. D. & Crick, F. H. C. The structure of DNA. *Cold Spring Harbor Symposia on Quantitative Biology Proceedings* 18, 123–131 (1953).

Weale, R. A. Photochemical reactions in the living cat's retina. *Journal of Physiology* 122, 322–331 (1953a).

Weale, R. A. Cone-monochromatism. *Journal of Physiology* 121, 548–569 (1953b).

*Weale, R. A. Trichromatic ideas in the seventeenth and eighteenth centuries. *Nature* 179, 648–651 (1957).

Weale. R. A. *The eye and its function*. London: Hatton Press, 1960.

Weale, R. A. *The aging eye*. London: Lewis, 1963.

Weale, R. A. Vision and fundus reflectometry: a review. *Photochemistry and Photobiology* 4, 67–87 (1965).

*Webster, M.A. & Mollon, J.D. Colour constancy influenced by contrast adaptation, *Nature,* 356, 431–433 (1992)

Weingarten, F. S. Wavelength effect on visual latency. *Science* 176, 692–694 (1972).

Weisskopf, V. How light interacts with matter. *Scientific American* 219 (3), 60–71 (1968).

Werblin, F. S. Control of retinal sensitivity: II. Lateral interactions at the outer plexiform layer. *Journal of General Physiology* 63, 62–87(1974).

Werblin, F. S. & Copenhagen, D. R. Control of retinal sensitivity: III. Lateral interactions at the inner plexiform layer. *Journal of General Physiology* 63, 88–110 (1974).

Werblin, F. S. & Dowling, J. E. Organization of the retina of the mudpuppy, Necturus maculosus: II. Intracellular recording. *Journal of Neurophysiology* 32, 339–355 (1969).

*Werner, J. S., Cicerone, C. M., Kliegl, R. & De La Rosa, D. Spectral efficiency of blackness induction. *Journal of the Optical Society of America A* 1, 981–985 (1984).

Westheimer, G. The Maxwellian view. *Vision Research* 6, 669–682 (1966).

Westheimer, G. Visual acuity and spatial modulation thresholds. In Jameson, D. & Hurvich, L. M. (Eds.), *Handbook of sensory physiology* VII/4. New York: Springer-Verlag, 1972.

*Wild, H.M., Butler, S.R., Carden, D. & Kulikowski, J.J. Primate cortical area V4 important for colour constancy not wavelength discrimination. *Nature*, 313, 133–135 (1985).

Wiesel, T. N. & Hubel, D. H. Spatial and chromatic interactions in the lateral geniculate body of the rhesus monkey. *Journal of Neurophysiology* 29, 1115–1156 (1966).

*Wietsma, J.J., Kamermans, M. & Spekreijse, H. Horizontal cells function normally in ethambutol-treated goldfish. *Vision Research*, 12, 1667–1674 (1995).

*Williams, D.R., Collier, R.J. & Thomson, B.J. Spatial resolution of the short wavelength mechanism. In *Colour Vision: Physiology & Psychophysics*, J.D. Mollon & J.T. Sharpe, (Eds.) London: Academic Press, 487–504, 1983.

Willmer, E. N. & Wright, W. D. Colour sensitivity of the fovea centralis. *Nature* 156, 119–121 (1945).

*Winderickx, J., Lindsey, D. T., Sanocki, E., Teller, D. Y., Motulsky, A. G. & Deebs, S. S. Polymorphism in red photopigment underlies variation in color matching. *Nature* 356, 431–433 (1992).

*Wong-Riley, M.T. Changes in the visual system of monocularly sutured or enucleated cats demonstrable with cytochrome oxidase histochemistry. *Brain Res.* 171, 11–28 (1979).

Wooten, B. R. & Wald, G. Color-vision mechanisms in the peripheral retinas of normal and dichromatic observers. *Journal of General Physiology* 61, 125–145 (1973).

Wright, W. D. A re-determination of the mixture curves of the spectrum. *Transactions of the Optical Society London* 30, 141–164 (1928–29).

Wright. W. D. The sensitivity of the eye to small colour differences. *Proceedings of the Physiological Society of London B* 53, 93–112 (1941).

Wright, W. D. *Researches on normal and defective colour vision*. London: Henry Kimpton, 1946.

Wright, W. D. Characteristics of tritanopia. *Journal of the Optical Society of America* 42, 509–521 (1952).

*Wright, W. D. The measurement of color. In: Cronly-Dillon, J. R. (Ed.), *Vision and Visual Dysfunction Volume 6: The Perception of Color*. Edited by P. Gouras. New York: Macmillan Press, 1991.

*Wright, W. D. & Pitt, F. H. G. The saturation-discrimination of two trichromats. *Proceedings of the Physical Society* 49, 329–331 (1937).

Wurtz, R. W. Comparison of effects of eye movements and stimulus movements on striate cortex neurons of the monkey. *Journal of Neurophysiology* 32, 987–994 (1969).

Wyszecki G. & Fielder, G. H. New color-matching ellipses. *Journal of the Optical Society of America* 61, 1135–1152 (1971).

Wyszecki, G. & Stiles, W. S. *Color science*. New York: Wiley, 1967.

*Wyszecki, G. & Stiles, W. S. *Color science* (2nd ed.). New York: Wiley, 1982.

*Wyszecki, G. & Stiles, W. S. High-level trichromatic color matching and the pigment-bleaching hypothesis. *Vision Research* 20, 23–37 (1980).

*Yoshioka, T., Dow, B.M. & Vautin, R.G. Neural mechanisms of color categorization in areas V1, V2, and V4 of Macaque monkey cortex. *Brain & Behavioral Science*, in press

Yates, J. T. Chromatic information processing in the foveal projection (area striata) of unanesthetized primate. *Vision Research* 14, 163–173 (1974).

Young, R. W. Visual cells. *Scientific American* 223 (4), 80–91 (1970).

Young, R. W. The renewal of rod and cone outer segments in the rhesus monkey. *Journal of Cellular Biology* 49, 303–318 (1971).

Young, R. W. Visual cells and the concept of renewal. *Investigative Ophthalmology* 15, 700–725 (1976).

Young, R. W. Visual cells, daily rhythms, and vision research. *Vision Research* 18, 573–578 (1978).

Young, T. On the theory of light and colours. *Philosophical Transactions* 12–48 (1802).

*Young, T. A course of lectures on natural philosophy and the mechanical arts. Joseph Johnson, St. Paul's church yard, Bedfordbury, 1807.

Zeki, S. The mosaic organization of the visual cortex in the monkey. In: Bellairs, R. & Gray, E. G. (Eds.), *Essays on the nervous system*. Oxford: Clarendon Press, 1974.

*Zeki, S. The representation of colours in the cerebral cortex. *Nature* 284, 412–418 (1980).

*Zeki, S. Color coding in the cerebral cortex: The responses of wavelength-selective and colour-coded cells in monkey visual cortex to changes in wavelength composition. *Neuroscience*, 9, 767–781 (1983).

*Zeki, S. Color vision and functional specialization in the visual cortex. *Discussions in Neuroscience* VI, 1–64, (1990).

*Zeki, S. The visual image in mind and brain. *Scientific American* 267, 68–76 (1992).

*Zeki, S. *A Vision of the Brain.* Oxford: Blackwell Scientific Publications, 1993.

Zoethout, W. D. *Physiological optics* (4th ed.). Chicago: Professional Press, 1947.

Index of Names

Index of Subjects